ANTIMICROBIAL AGENTS AND CHEMOTHERAPY—1969

ANTIMICROBIAL AGENTS AND CHEMOTHERAPY–1969

Proceedings of the Ninth Interscience Conference on
Antimicrobial Agents and Chemotherapy,
Washington, D.C., 27–29 October 1969

Editor

GLADYS L. HOBBY

American Society for Microbiology

Bethesda, Maryland

Library of Congress Catalog Card Number: 62–12476

PREFACE

This volume, like its predecessors in this series, represents the proceedings of the annual Interscience Conference on Antimicrobial Agents and Chemotherapy. This present volume contains the papers presented at the Ninth Interscience Conference, held in Washington, D.C., 27–29 October 1969.

It was in Washington just nine years ago that the American Society for Microbiology was asked to assume sponsorship of this meeting. At that time I was Secretary of ASM and an interdisciplinary conference of this sort was a new venture for the Society. Nevertheless, we soon recognized the need for a mechanism through which microbiologists, chemists, geneticists, physiologists, clinicians, and, in fact, all scientists with an interest in antimicrobial agents and chemotherapy could meet to exchange information. Therefore, we agreed to sponsor the meeting as a service both to our members and to the entire scientific community.

Those of you who regularly attend this Conference are in a better position than I to evaluate the results of that decision. During the past nine years, average attendance has more than doubled. Persons interested in infection have formed a new and thriving organization, the Infectious Diseases Society of America, which conducts its meetings in conjunction with this conference. The proceedings of the Conference provide a valuable repository of information on antimicrobial agents. For these and other reasons I am convinced that the conference serves a valuable purpose, which is the main consideration of the ASM.

This is not to suggest that everyone is satisfied. Questions are being asked about the content of the program, about the method of publishing the proceedings, about the scheduling of the meeting, and even about the need for the Conference itself. In my view this is a healthy sign. It is often too easy to keep doing things the same old way. Improvement comes only when someone asks if this is the best way to do them. Change does not necessarily mean improvement, but improvement certainly will not come unless someone proposes an alternative for consideration.

The committee that organizes this Conference is broadly representative of many interests. I know that the members of this committee are constantly looking for ways to improve the program. The chairman of the committee is a member *ex officio* of the ASM Meetings Board and of the Council of the Society. Thus, he is in position to convey the interests of Conference participants to the governing board of ASM.

Dr. C. W. Pettinga, the Chairman, the Vice-Chairmen Drs. E. H. Kass and G. B. Whitfield, and the other members of the committee deserve thanks for making the Ninth Conference one of our most successful yet. On behalf of ASM, I also thank Dr. Albert Sabin, President, and the other officers and members of the Infectious Diseases Society of America whose generous cooperation and participation insured the success of the Ninth Conference. Finally, I express sincere gratitude to Dr. Gladys L. Hobby and her hard-working band of Editorial Board members whose efforts have insured the success of this volume.

E. M. Foster, *President*
American Society for Microbiology

Publisher's Statement

Antimicrobial Agents and Chemotherapy is a serial publication, published annually by the American Society for Microbiology. Volumes in the series contain reports presented at the Interscience Conference on Antimicrobial Agents and Chemotherapy, held in the fall of each year; the volumes are published during the spring of the following year. The present publication is the ninth in the series.

All volumes in the series are available from the Society and from the Society's agent, The Williams & Wilkins Co. (428 E. Preston St., Baltimore, Md. 21202). The price is $15 per copy (with 50% discount to members of ASM).

Reprints of the papers in each volume were made available to authors, and readers should request reprints by writing directly to authors.

Papers in *Antimicrobial Agents and Chemotherapy* are indexed in *Index Medicus,* and are abstracted in *Biological Abstracts* and in *Chemical Abstracts.*

References to articles in these volumes should be cited in the following manner:

Smith, J. 1970. Properties of a new antitumor antibiotic. Antimicrob. Agents Chemother.–1969, p. 167–171.

Acknowledgments

The Society extends its thanks to the following, who served as Moderators of scientific sessions:

R. Austrian	I. Hooper	F. Schabel, Jr.
W. Celmer	G. Jackson	G. Stewart
L. Cluff	J. Johnson	G. Stollerman
L. Freedman	J. Lein	M. Turck
W. Hewitt	C. Martin	M. Weinstein
E. Hook	L. Sabath	W. Wright

The following served as invited, special reviewers for some of the contributions in this volume, and their help is greatly appreciated.

John Bennett	Jay Sanford	Wheedon Sutliff
Jean Hawkins	Arthur Saz	John Utz
Leon Sabath	Leon H. Schmidt	Ruth Wichelhausen

Table of Contents

Antibiotics as Probes to Elucidate Cell Biochemistry

Pharmacological Action of Antimicrobial Agents

Mechanism of Action and Antimicrobial Resistance

Chemical Studies on Antimicrobial Agents and Semisynthetic Antibiotics

Viral Studies

New Antibiotics and Antimicrobial Agents

Studies of Phosphonomycin, a New Antibiotic

Chemotherapy and the Control of Infections in Humans

In Vitro Antimicrobial Action and Experimental Studies in Animals

Antimicrobial Agents and Chemotherapy—1969

Control of Infectious Diseases

ALBERT B. SABIN[1]

The Children's Hospital Research Foundation, University of Cincinnati College of Medicine, Cincinnati, Ohio 45229

The discoveries of antibiotics, insecticides, and vaccines during the past 25 years have brought great advances in the control of the major infectious diseases that have plagued mankind for centuries. This progress has led many people to believe that infectious diseases are now a problem chiefly in the economically developing countries in which the utilization of existing knowledge is greatly impeded by never-ending, and in some instances continually increasing, poverty.

With the aid of statistics gathered by the 1963–1964 U.S. National Health Survey, I should like to demonstrate to you how serious a health problem the infectious diseases still are, even in so affluent a country as the USA. Although statistics on mortality are not an adequate indicator of the continuing problem of infectious diseases, it is important to note that in 1963 these diseases ranked as the number three killer, after heart disease plus stroke and cancer. A total of 108,795 Americans died of infectious diseases in that year. Clinically diagnosed influenza and pneumonia alone accounted for 70,761, tuberculosis for 9,311, kidney infections for 8,952, bronchitis for 5,462, and syphilis plus sequelae for 2,666. Aside from mortality, there were 259,589,000 episodes of infectious disease, of which 144,541,000 required medical attention. The common childhood diseases accounted for 24,666,000 and various respiratory infections for 204,301,000. Despite the existence of influenza vaccines for the past 25 years, clinically diagnosed cases of influenza amounted to about 62,000,000 in 1963. Acute respiratory illness in 1963 accounted for about half of all recorded sickness. The "average" American had four, and his child six, nose, throat, or lung infections that year. The total incidence of acute respiratory illness is estimated to be much higher than the figures just cited because much of it is unrecorded.

Medical expenditures for infectious diseases in the USA in 1963 amounted to a total of about 2.4 billion dollars, of which 1,000 million went for medical treatment, 753 million for anti-infective drugs, 400 million for so-called respiratory pharmaceuticals, and 290 million for preventive immunizations.

I should like to stress that, while the proper application of existing knowledge in the economically developed countries could lead to further improvement in the control of infectious diseases, the major problem is still insufficient scientific knowledge. I shall attempt now to call attention to at least some of the research goals in the field of infectious diseases caused by viruses, bacteria, and protozoa, and to consider the strategy by which the achievement of these goals may be accelerated.

DISEASES CAUSED BY VIRUSES

The currently available vaccines for smallpox, poliomyelitis, measles, and mumps can control these diseases of the human heritage wherever the health services are sufficiently well developed and financed. Current research on an improved smallpox vaccine is directed toward the elimination of some of the undesirable complications that occur in a small number of persons. The main objective of the recently developed rubella vaccines is not to protect against the mild illness this virus produces but rather to prevent the devastating and tragic consequences of congenital infection. Whether or not mass vaccination of preadolescent children will actually break the chain of transmission of this virus and thereby protect susceptible pregnant women, and, if it does, how many years it may take to achieve this goal, only time will tell. One can only hope that ongoing research will provide the knowledge required for

[1] President, Infectious Diseases Society of America. Address given at joint meeting of Infectious Diseases Society of America and Ninth Interscience Conference on Antimicrobial Agents and Chemotherapy sponsored by American Society for Microbiology. Present address: The Weizmann Institute of Science.

the safe vaccination of women of child-bearing age.

From the point of view of numbers, infections of the respiratory tract present the most important problem. It is reliably estimated that about 95% of respiratory illnesses in the United States are not caused by bacteria, and it is highly probable that viruses of different kinds are responsible for most of them. Primary viral infections of the respiratory tract, usually in early childhood, are more severe, taking the form of croup, bronchiolitis, and pneumonia. Unfortunately, these primary infections often do not result in immunity to reinfection with the same type of virus. However, when reinfection does occur, the disease is frequently, but by no means always, a mild upper respiratory illness or a so-called "common cold" syndrome without fever. It is noteworthy that, of the very large number of viruses identified in recent years in the human respiratory tract, only four—respiratory syncytial virus and parainfluenza virus types 1, 2, and 3—have been found to play a major role in the more severe manifestations of pneumonia, bronchiolitis, bronchitis, and croup. Of the 31 different types of adenovirus, only 2 (types 1 and 2) usually produce illness during early infancy, and 3 (types 3, 5 and 7) cause illness during childhood. The influenza viruses (especially types A and B) assume importance in respiratory illness in infancy and childhood only during epidemics, which recur every 2 to 4 years. It is important to note, however, that up to the present time only about 50% of the respiratory diseases of early childhood have been accounted for by viruses identifiable by current technology.

In adults, the proportion of respiratory illness that can be accounted for by viruses identifiable by current technology is even smaller. It appears that about 40% of the afebrile upper respiratory ("common cold") episodes can be attributed to the rhinoviruses, to the recently identified human coronaviruses, which are morphologically similar to the avian infectious bronchitis and mouse hepatitis viruses, and less frequently to influenza A and B, parainfluenza types 1, 2, and 3, respiratory syncytial virus, and adenoviruses. In the febrile upper respiratory tract illnesses of adults, the influenza viruses play the most important role, but this occurs chiefly when major new variants emerge for which the population has little or no immunity. In the lower respiratory tract illnesses of adults, only about 20% of the nonbacterial infections are accounted for by myxoviruses, adenoviruses, and mycoplasma. *Mycoplasma pneumoniae* is an infrequent cause of respiratory illness in early childhood and assumes importance as a cause of pneumonia chiefly in the second and third decades of life. A recent study on acute pneumonia in 427 civilian adults admitted to a large municipal hospital in Washington, D.C., showed that the overall rate of virus infection, excluding herpesvirus, was approximately 16% as compared with 7% in individuals without respiratory tract illness. *M. pneumoniae* infection was found in only 4%. Only 17% of this group of pneumonia patients had pneumococcal bacteremia, and the role of pneumococci in the absence of bacteremia could not be accurately assessed. It was clear, however, that in a large proportion of adult patients with pneumonia no etiological agent could be incriminated by current technology.

The point of this review of our current knowledge of the etiological agents associated with infectious diseases of the human respiratory tract is that we still do not know the cause of approximately half of this most important segment of all human infectious diseases. Although much work is currently in progress in this field, in my judgment the effort is not commensurate with the need nor is it as well planned and coordinated as it ought to be.

One hopes that the ongoing research on influenza vaccines may bring us better tools for the prevention of this important recurring epidemic disease. I am frankly pessimistic that current research on other vaccines will bring us any that will be capable of preventing a significant proportion of respiratory disease in early childhood or later life. This leaves us with two other approaches that currently are being intensively investigated, i.e., specific antiviral chemotherapy and nonspecific stimulants of host resistance. It is not my purpose here to review or evaluate the many interesting findings already on record, but I am again impelled to express my judgment that the effort is not commensurate with the need.

In the meantime, I wish to call attention once again to the misuse of antibacterial antibiotics in the treatment of nonbacterial infections of the respiratory tract. These antibiotics are used by physicians all over the world in an attempt to prevent the complications caused by secondary bacterial infections. It is highly probable that a large proportion of the more than 750 million dollars spent annually in the United States on anti-infective drugs is spent for this purpose. Several well-controlled studies showed that the use of antibiotics for this purpose is contraindicated not only because they fail to diminish the incidence of secondary bacterial complications but also because the secondary infections that do occur are frequently caused by antibiotic-resistant bacteria that are very difficult to treat. Antibiotics should be used only after a secondary bacterial infection has been identified.

The infectious diseases caused by viruses that have their portal of entry in the enteric tract are also responsible for a great deal of illness, especially during the summer months of the year. The illnesses caused by the more than 60 coxsackie and echo viruses are, with only rare exceptions, without serious sequelae. The ultimate control and prevention of the diseases caused by these viruses cannot practically be attempted by vaccination and will have to await the development of suitable broad-spectrum antiviral drugs or other types of inhibitors. The most important unsolved problem among the enteric viruses is that of the viruses responsible for hepatitis. Thus far, all attempts to propagate the viruses of this serious disease, which is of world-wide importance, have met with failure. When and if these viruses can be easily cultivated, prevention of the disease by vaccination will become a most important research goal. Hepatitis is a prime example of a disease that calls for a greater concerted effort to provide the infrastructure of knowledge that is required for the control of an important infectious disease.

Chickenpox (varicella) and its recrudescent form of exceedingly painful herpes zoster are systemic virus diseases of the human heritage that deserve as much consideration for elimination by vaccination as mumps. The main obstacle here has been the failure of the virus to grow in sufficient concentration in any cell culture that would be acceptable for vaccine production. A desirable research goal would be the development of a suitably attenuated strain that could be used as a live-virus vaccine that would immunize without localizing in the sensory ganglia, whose involvement appears to be the cause of subsequent attacks of herpes zoster.

The diseases caused by arboviruses, unlike the virus diseases of the human heritage, occur only in certain regions. The most important arbovirus disease, yellow fever, is already under excellent control by means of a very good attenuated live-virus vaccine. Although killed-virus vaccines are currently in use against Japanese B encephalitis and tick-borne encephalitis, a more concentrated and concerted effort is desirable for the development of effective and acceptable live-virus vaccines that would give long-lasting immunity. Similar live-virus vaccines that could produce immunity quickly enough to be used in the face of epidemics should be developed for the St. Louis, Western equine, Eastern equine, and the Venezuelan encephalitis viruses, and for the Argentinian hemorrhagic fever virus (the latter most likely not an arbovirus), and studies should be pursued to a point that would establish the practical usefulness of the vaccines. The dengue viruses periodically produce epidemics of large size, and in recent years have been shown to be the cause of severe hemorrhagic disease in children in the Phillipines and Thailand. Although experimental live-virus vaccines for two of the four or more types have been available for many years, sufficient work has never been done to develop such vaccines to a point where they would be available for use during epidemics.

Trachoma, the greatest single cause for progressive loss of sight in the world, is estimated to affect about 400 million persons in countries with poor sanitation and hygiene. The causative agents, formerly regarded as viruses and now classified in the Bedsonia group, are susceptible to sulfonamides and certain other antibiotics. Relapses have, however, been frequent after treatment with these antibiotics. The recent discovery that a new type of antibiotic, rifampicin, is highly effective in tissue culture, and in preliminary tests in vivo, provides an opportunity for important new studies. Not enough work has as yet been done on vaccination to rule out this approach as a potential means of prevention. A vaccine that would produce immunity without hypersensitivity is the goal.

DISEASES CAUSED BY BACTERIA AND PROTOZOA

Although the discovery and continued development of new antibiotics and chemotherapeutic agents have provided the tools for the most spectacular control of infectious diseases caused by bacteria and certain protozoa, there is still a need for immunization procedures for some of these diseases and a need for a continuing search for new antibiotics and drugs to meet the challenge of emerging resistant strains and of other special problems.

The appearance of tubercle bacilli with increasing resistance to isoniazid, even in previously untreated patients, emphasizes the continuing race between the development of new drugs and the emergence of resistant microorganisms. For this reason, competent workers in this field believe that there is a great need for the development of a better method of vaccination than by the currently used BCG vaccine.

Recent experiences of American Forces in Vietnam have emphasized the fact that we still do not have a good preventative for bacterial dysentery, and a continued effort is indicated for the development of an effective vaccine against this disease. Cholera is another bacterial disease for which an improved method of vaccination is highly desirable.

Despite the great successes that have been achieved by the use of residual insecticides and of highly effective drugs in the control of malaria, this disease continues to present challenges which call both for the development of new drugs for the emerging resistant parasites and for those basic studies on the immunology and cultivation of the parasites that might lead to the ultimate prevention of malaria by immunization.

STRATEGY FOR ACCELERATING ACHIEVEMENT OF THE INDICATED GOALS

This "shopping list" of goals in research on infectious diseases is far from complete. In almost every case, I indicated that the current effort was not commensurate with the need. In my judgment, practically all of the research goals that I mentioned would benefit from a well-planned, coordinated, and cooperative effort. There is so much work to be done that it seems wasteful to leave it to chance that someone will choose to do all that is necessary. It seems to me that each major goal should have a general staff made up of competent scientists whose job should be not only clearly to define the problems but also, with the aid of suitable administrative support, to recruit other competent scientists to work on these problems. The art of seducing investigators to work in a cooperative manner on research goals of immediate importance to human health needs to be cultivated to a high level and cannot be left entirely in the hands of administrative personnel. Frequent meetings of the working scientists are essential for critical evaluation of work in progress and for decisions regarding changes in tactics as new information is accumulated. A general staff undertaking responsibility for a specific research goal may do well to heed Sir Francis Drake, who said: "Grant us to know that it is not the beginning, but the continuing of the same until it is thoroughly finished, which yieldeth the true glory."

There is good reason to believe that increased recruiting of competent scientists to work on urgent problems of immediate importance to human health can be carried on in proper balance with the equally important pursuit of non-mission-oriented research whose main goal is to give us ever greater understanding of natural phenomena. Our growing population and resources should be able to provide enough people and facilities for both types of activity. And scientists may well ponder Kant's statement in "Dreams of a Ghost Seer": "To yield to every whim of curiosity, and to allow our passion for inquiry to be restrained by nothing but the limits of our ability shows an eagerness of mind not unbecoming to scholarship. But it is *wisdom* that has the merit of selecting from among the innumerable problems which present themselves, those whose solution is important to mankind."

Antimicrobial Agents and Chemotherapy—1969

Antibiotics as Elucidators of Nucleic Acid Structure, Replication, and Transfer

VERNON BRYSON, RUTH M. LIBERFARB,[1] and PATRICIA S. DANIELSON

Institute of Microbiology, Rutgers, The State University, New Brunswick, New Jersey 08903

The selective action of actinomycin D has enabled biochemists to use this antibiotic for the analysis of polynucleotides and the determination of operon substructure in deoxyribonucleic acid (DNA). Inhibition of protein synthesis by chloramphenicol continues to be employed in identifying mechanisms of nucleic acid synthesis, replication, or repair. Mitomycin C shares with ultraviolet radiation the ability to selectively inhibit some strains of bacteria characterized by high mutation rates (mutator strains). Presumably, DNA synthesis, replication, or repair is abnormal in these strains. Genetically effective transfer of DNA in bacterial transformation or conjugation, as measured by efficiency of recombination, can be greatly diminished or abolished by the development of bacterial resistance to polymyxin B or colistin.

Antibiotics are structurally improbable substances of doubtful value to the organisms producing them. It is tempting to believe that they exist to aid physicians or to amuse biochemists. In either case, a feature of their activity is extreme specificity. By this we mean the ability to act on particular cellular structures, interfere uniquely with metabolic pathways, and uncouple coordinated biochemical systems by selective effect on one component. Intensive studies of deoxyribonucleic acid (DNA) and ribonucleic acid (RNA)—which characterize the past 20 years of genetic and biochemical research—refer repeatedly to antibiotics as inhibitors of RNA metabolism, DNA metabolism, purine and pyrimidine synthesis, and membrane structure or function. In this review, we will be concerned with DNA and RNA, the template molecules that carry genetic information and that may interact with antibiotics directly, or with enzymes and cell structures that have already been modified by antibiotics. Rather than cite the vast literature in this field, already well summarized by Gottlieb and Shaw (11), we will select a few examples provided by antibiotics as elucidators of nucleic acid structure, replication, and transfer.

[1] Present address: Department of Molecular Biology and Microbiology, Tufts University School of Medicine, Boston, Mass. 02111.

ANTIBIOTICS AND NUCLEIC ACID STRUCTURE

With the advent of in vitro systems for protein synthesis and the isolation of synthetic or purified natural polynucleotides for use in these systems, it is now possible to question the relation between polynucleotide structure and interaction with antibiotics. A recent example of the subtleties encountered has been provided by Wells (34), who began with the widely accepted view that actinomycin binding is specific for polynucleotides containing guanine. What Wells found was that actinomycin could be used to distinguish the structure of two different sequence isomers of double-stranded DNA. Poly d(A-T-C)· poly d(G-A-T), containing a deoxyadenylyldeoxythymidylyldeoxycytidylyl sequence in one strand and a deoxyguanylyldeoxyadenylyldeoxythymidylyl sequence in the complementary strand, was prepared at high molecular weight (approximately 0.3 million daltons). Although the double-stranded DNA contained one-third guanine plus cytosine (G + C), little or no actinomycin D was bound as judged by methods capable of detecting one actinomycin D molecule per 100 DNA nucleotides. In contrast, the sequence isomer poly d(T-A-C)·poly d(G-T-A) did bind actinomycin D as expected. Apparently in most cases, but not in all, the presence of guanine induces a structural configuration in DNA conducive to actinomycin D binding. The relevant structural differences between the two sequence isomers that would explain their reaction to actinomycin D have not yet been found.

Two further examples of structural insight into polynucleotides or nucleic acids made possible by antibiotics are provided by experiments recently reported. Because of its affinity for DNA, actinomycin D is able to shield polynucleotides against degradation by nucleases. It has been suggested that variations in the extent of micrococcal nuclease degradation of crab poly d(A-T) could be used as an analytical test for structural purity (30).

The natural message for ribosomal translation is RNA, but McCarthy and Holland have made the interesting observation that single-stranded DNA can be translated directly in vitro in the presence of neomycin B (20). One model for translation suggests that ribosomes may require a non-circular messenger, i.e., one that can be threaded on from the 5′ end. Such a scheme is consistent with the known events in protein synthesis wherein enzymes appear in a sequence related to the order of genetic messages in the chromosome. Since a nonpermuted linear message is the usual in vivo molecule to be translated, is a circular message with no obvious entrance for "threading" necessarily excluded in an experimental situation? The problem is structural, with an antibiotic elucidating the answer. Bretscher (3) found that formylmethonyl-transfer RNA (tRNA) is bound to ribosomes by single-stranded circular DNA of phage fd. In the presence of neomycin B, the circular DNA was able to function as a messenger for protein synthesis.

The structure of DNA presents a linear representation of a sequence of genes. The use of antibiotics in the mapping of genes is therefore a way of looking at DNA structure. The usefulness of so-called "transcriptional mapping" is particularly evident where genetic recombination cannot be obtained, where the genes are redundant, and where gene products are elusive (e.g., tRNA). The method is best suited to magnify small lengths of genome; that is, to look at a few contiguous genes within a single operon. Bleyman and his colleagues (1) reasoned the actinomycin D could be used to interrupt transcription in an informative manner. By means of random actinomycin-induced blocks to polymerase travel along an operon, large cistrons or operons (as bigger targets) could be distinguished from small by the former's greater probability of being "hit." Also, rare random blocks would insure, statistically, that the further away from an operator locus a cistron was located, the more likely it would be that an intervening actinomycin block would interrupt transcription of the cistron. Operator-proximal cistrons could thereby be recognized. As an elucidator of the structure of *Bacillus subtilis* DNA, actinomycin D-induced interruptions of transcription have revealed that the 16*S* and 23*S* ribosomal RNA cistrons are, in all probability, independent units. Also, 23*S* ribosomal RNA (rRNA) and 5*S* rRNA are components of the same operons. Finally, the tRNA cistrons in *B. subtilis* are aggregated in either one or a small number of polycistrons (1).

REPLICATION OF NUCLEIC ACID

Major features of the replication and transcription of nucleic acids are now well understood, although the exact enzymes involved have not, for DNA replication, been identified with certainty as replicative versus reparative. The problem of transcription (DNA → RNA) is beyond the scope of our discussion, but it should be mentioned in passing that selection for rifampicin resistance results in the isolation of bacterial strains with altered RNA polymerase (33). Selection of mutants with modified enzymes, providing that the enzymes are associated with replication or transcription, may provide a better eventual understanding of how these processes occur. Unfortunately, the knowledge of how enzymes work is, with few exceptions, entirely inadequate.

Mitomycin C is a radiomimetic and mutagenic antibiotic that interferes with DNA replication, probably by several mechanisms. Szybalski and Iyer (31) reviewed the evidence for mitomycin-induced cross-linking of complementary DNA, a process which facilitates renaturation after heat treatment but which tends to block progress of the replicative enzyme in vivo. For several years, we have been interested in mutator genes (18, 28, 29) and have incorporated preliminary studies on mitomycin into the research. DNA replication may be implicated because mutator genes, now isolated from *Escherichia coli* to a total number of about two dozen (Liberfarb and Bryson, Bacteriol. Proc., p. 53, 1969), have several possible modes of action, including production of enzymes that carry out defective copying or repair of DNA. The numerous resulting "errors" in the replicated strands are manifested as accelerated rates of mutation involving random loci, including sites governing auxotrophy, phage resistance, drug resistance, and carbohydrate utilization (17, 18, 29).

Some bacterial mutants are ultrasensitive to both mitomycin C and ultraviolet radiation. In some instances the abnormal sensitivity may represent the effect of a mutator gene (Table 1). On this basis, increased sensitivity to mitomycin C can be used to select strains prone to mutation (2). We do not yet know whether incorporation errors, repair errors, or faulty replication is linked to deficient processes of recovery exhibited by certain mutants in reproducing DNA molecules after mitomycin injury. Selection of ultrasensitive mutants has not usually been employed to isolate mutator strains, simply because the procedure would be more laborious than alternatives depending on the increased number of antibiotic-resistant clones that appear during the growth of mutator cultures.

What turns off the replication of DNA in bacteria infected with certain phages, and what later turns off phage replication itself? Both kinds of shut-off for bacteriophage S13 and ϕX174 had been assumed to result from phage-coded information, but Ishiwa and Tessman (15) demonstrated by the use of chloramphenicol that postinfection synthesis of protein was not required for the stopping of host DNA synthesis. Corroborating evidence for the noninvolvement

Table 1. *Sensitivity to mitomycin C and to ultraviolet radiation of E. coli mutants defective in synthesis, repair, or replication of DNA as indicated by increased mutability*

Strain	Mutant	Genotypic stability	Per cent survival (600 ergs/mm^2 ultraviolet)	Level of resistance (μg of mitomycin/ml)[a]
K-12	AXA49	Mutator	78	2.6
K-12	AZA28	Mutator	12	1.9
K-12	JC355	Nonmutator	11	0.9
K-12	EMS34	Mutator	30	0.5
K-12	NTG208	Mutator	0.008	–
B	UV	Nonmutator	3.6	0.5
B	EMS107	Mutator	0.00005	0.4
B	EMS109	Mutator	0.009	0.3
B	4-112	Mutator	7.2	0.1
B	102	Mutator	5.2	0.1

[a] Streak limit on gradient plate.

of phage gene-products was obtained by using mutants blocked in the function of any of seven known phage genes.

Genetic evidence of a sequence in gene reproduction (21) and the remarkable electron photomicrographs of Cairns (6) have provided a generally satisfactory account of chromosome replication in *E. coli.* The circular double-stranded unit, about 1 mm in length, divides by the orderly progression of a Y-shaped growing point that travels around the entire circle, duplicating the structure. For determining the point of origin and direction of replication of bacterial chromosomes, chloramphenicol has proved very useful. By one technique, the progress of gene duplication was followed by determining the inducibility of several enzymes in synchronized culture. As each gene was duplicated, it permitted, via messenger RNA (mRNA), a step-jump in enzyme product. To provide a clean experiment, chloramphenicol was used to turn off the synthesis of enzyme protein at measured intervals (24).

The replication of the *E. coli* chromosome is considered to begin with synthesis of a specific protein, the "initiator protein." Clark and Maalϕe (7) followed the onset and course of replication in synchronously dividing cultures of *E. coli* B/r. Time of synthesis of the mutator protein was marked by a sudden increase in the cell's ability to synthesize DNA in the presence of chloramphenicol. Originally it had been thought that the beginning of a new round of bacterial DNA replication was coincidental with division of the cell. Clark and Maalϕe confirmed the alternative view: DNA replication starts about mid-point in the division cycle in response to a chloramphenicol-sensitive system. Once replication of DNA has begun, the initiator protein is not required. Yoshikawa (36) has extended the views of Clark and Maalϕe by reporting that the germination of spores in *B. subtilis* follows a related pattern: cells that have initiated replication when chloramphenicol is added complete the replication cycle, but cannot initiate a subsequent one. Minor differences between strains or species, and in response to different kinds of growth media, preclude a really satisfying generalization about initiator proteins and other proteins presumably required to trigger bacterial DNA chromosomal divisions; there may be alternatives for the point of origin of replication (24).

Brown and Dowell have compared the replication of filamentous phage M-13 with that of the well-studied φX174 (4). M-13 is released from host bacteria without cell lysis; phage-infected cells continue to grow and divide. To study the replication of M-13 DNA it was necessary to turn off nucleic acid synthesis of the *E. coli* bacterial host with the aid of mitomycin C before infection occurred. The method allows radioactive labeling of phage-specific DNA with ^{3}H-thymine. Later, characterization of DNA components provided some insight into the ratios of two replicative forms, RF I and RF II. In contrast to φX174, net RF synthesis took place in M-13 during single-strand DNA production.

New details of RNA phage replication are forthcoming with the use of rifampicin. Fromageot and Zinder (9) found that RNA phage growth was almost normal in rifampicin-treated *E. coli* cells, even though cellular RNA and protein synthesis were virtually shut off. If the drug was added before phage infection, synthesis was partially inhibited. This finding impelled Fromageot and Zinder to a tentative conclusion that, if rifampicin acts, as believed, on DNA-dependent RNA polymerase but not on DNA-dependent DNA polymerase, then the host-cell RNA polymerase may be implicated in viral RNA replication. Similar conclusions have been drawn for phage T4 and the *B. subtilis* phage SPO1 (10, 13).

Not only replication, but transcription as well, is often elucidated by antibiotics. Kumar and co-workers (19) have analyzed transcription in *E. coli* phage λ by means of chloramphenicol. In λ, transcription occurs in some operons on one strand of the DNA duplex, whereas other operons are transcribed off the complementary antiparallel strand. Both chloramphenicol and an amber mutation in cistron N of λ differentially depress transcription, depending on the location of the operons on the genetic map. The results suggest that a polymerase system coded by the bacterial host permits initiation and transcription of cistron N, but a protein coded by cistron N, and not formed in the presence of chloramphenicol, is necessary for continued transcription to the left of N. Interruptions of protein synthesis by antibiotics thus permit separation of preexistent and de novo enzyme requirements. Rouviere and co-workers (27) used phage T4 to investigate similar problems. They asked whether an inhibitor selectively blocking host DNA transcription could be responsible for the shut-off of mRNA synthesis for β-galactosidase. Their work confirmed earlier reports of an inhibitor, but showed with chloramphenicol that the inhibitor displayed, paradoxically, greater specificity for phage DNA itself. Furthermore, chloramphenicol prevented the appearance of the inhibitor without changing the shut-off of the *E. coli* mRNA.

TRANSFER OF NUCLEIC ACID

The effect of antibiotics on nucleic acid transfer has been studied in bacterial transformation and bacterial conjugation systems. In the analysis of transformation, Ranhand and Lichstein (26) reported that chloramphenicol, novobiocin, erythromycin, and streptomycin at appropriate concentrations are able to inhibit competence for transformation, with relatively little effect on cell viability. Presumably the uptake of transforming DNA into *Haemophilus influenzae* was inhibited in these experiments, but alternative explanations are possible. Contrary to the results of Ranhard and Lichstein, a preferential killing of noncompetent cells by penicillin has been observed with *B. subtilis* (22). Experiments on competence development with antibiotics have not shown any relation between (i) agents acting on cell walls or membranes, and (ii) interference with competence, a phenomenon though to involve the cell surface.

E. coli can rarely or never be transformed. No competent strains are known. However, treatment of these bacteria with agents that diminish the integrity of the cell wall allows the treated cells to exhibit "transfection." Here, infectious nucleic acid of phage origin is employed to transfer genetic information into structurally modified bacteria. Penicillin spheroplasts are among the kinds of bacteria cells able to take up viral DNA or RNA. In transfection experiments with φX174 DNA or MS2 RNA, Taketo and Kuno found penicillin less effective than lysozyme, probably because of a "less profound alteration" of cell structure (32).

Wlodarczyk et al. (35) selected Hfr strains of *E. coli* for resistance to the antibiotic edeine, an agent that interferes with DNA synthesis. The technique of zyotic induction shows that the edeine-resistant bacteria transfer their chromosomes, but that genetic recombination is reduced 1,000 times in the F^- recipient. Further work on the problem by Piekarowicz et al. (25) led to the discovery that edeine causes a 25-fold increase in F factor (sex factor) integration, producing Hfr strains from F^+ strains preincubated in the presence of this drug. An F^+ semiresistant to edeine showed increased recombination. In the midst of these contradictions, the investigators concluded that edeine causes some change in the "secondary or tertiary structure" of DNA and as a consequence recombination frequencies are abnormal (25). Obviously, some molecular evidence is needed to clarify the assumptions.

It is generally conceded that the transfer of DNA from Hfr *E. coli* donors to F^- recipients requires DNA synthesis. Antibiotics that interfere with synthesis might, therefore, reduce transfer.

Another antibiotic that interferes with the transmission of bacterial genetic information is polymyxin B. If a male (F^+) strain of *E. coli* is made resistant to this antibiotic, it no longer serves as an effective donor in $F^+ \times F^-$ crosses (5). The F factor, or sex factor, is thought to be physically associated with membrane at the cell surface (16); it follows that antibiotics with surface-active properties might cause loss or modification of F factor function, thus sterilizing the drug-resistant donor strains. Polymyxin B and colistin are surface-active cyclic polypeptide antibiotics that damage cell membranes (23). One of us (P.S.D.) has undertaken a further study on the fertility of polymyxin-resistant (PB/R) and colistin resistant (CO/R) derivatives of *E. coli* strain 58-278 containing the Treffers mutator gene (Table 2). Since polymyxin resistance and colistin resistance are difficult to obtain in *E. coli,* the mutator gene was used to increase the number of resistant colonies obtainable in the presence of the drugs. Recombination frequencies of the F^+ CO/R (colistin-resistant) strain crossed with F^- averaged about one-twentieth those of the drug-sensitive strain 59-278. Recombination in matings of PB/R was virtually abolished. The most direct hypothesis would be that PB/R and CO/R strains resemble acridine-treated Hfr; elimination of the F factor would perhaps be expected, and immunity to superinfection would disappear (14). In fact, superinfection immunity remains in most of the drug-resistant derivatives of the sensitive parent strain. Exposure to the surface-active drugs, polymyxin B and colistin, apparently selects F mutants which are sexually inhibited in drug-resistant, but not in drug-sensitive, parent strains. The experimental details of this work are described elsewhere (P. S. Danielson, Ph.D. Thesis, Rutgers University, New Brunswick, N.J., 1969).

Many of the reactions of antibiotics with nucleic acids exhibit some degree of template specificity. Hartmann and his colleagues (12) have considered actinomycin, chromomycin, and streptomycin as within such a category. They concluded that template-specific antibiotics are comparable to repressor proteins which control the amount of mRNA synthesized in the cell. The goal is to find antibiotics, or low molecular weight agents, that are able to selectively suppress information-controlled syntheses such as viral replication.

The attainment of the necessary specificity at particular regions of DNA or RNA seems improbable on the basis of our present knowledge.

Table 2. *Comparison of characteristics of a mutator strain and derived polymyxin B- and colistin-resistant strains of E. coli*

Strain	Drug resistance[a]		f2 susceptibility[b]			Bacteriophage production/ml	F superinfectibility[c]	F passage[d]	Recombination[e]
	Polymyxin B	Colistin	Cultures	Clones	Cells				
	units	*μg*					%	%	
Mutator . . .	0.01	0.001	S	100% S	43% S	6.6×10^{12}	–	70-75	3×10^{-5}
PB/R	10	1	R	100% R	100% R	3.9×10^{9}	5-10	0	Undetected
CO/R	100	90	R	100% R	100% R	7×10^{9}	0	30-55	1.4×10^{-6}

[a] Highest drug concentration at which growth occurred.

[b] The f2 susceptibility of cultures, derived cells, and clones, as indicated by lysis on agar; bacteriophage production in broth cultures of strains. S = sensitive; R = resistant.

[c] Percentage of F factor-converted recipients in matings with two different male strains, as indicated by f2 susceptibility (lysis) in the bacteriophage cross-streak test.

[d] Percentage of F factor-converted recipients in matings with two different female strains, as indicated by f2 susceptibility (lysis) in the bacteriophage cross-streak test.

[e] Average frequency of *thr-leu* recombinants per male per milliliter in matings with four different female strains.

However, the goal of specific effect is worth intensive search, whether the substances examined be antibiotics or other kinds of molecules. Highly specific regional inhibitors of nucleic acid activity such as those active in host-controlled restriction (8) would not only prove of great interest to medicine but would, in our opinion, provide a possible step to the more precise control of differentiation.

ACKNOWLEDGMENTS

This work was aided by a Public Health Service Training Grant from the Institute of General Medical Sciences to the two junior authors.

LITERATURE CITED

1. Bleyman, M., M. Kondo, N. Hecht, and C. Woese. 1969. Transcriptional mapping: functional organization of the ribosomal and transfer ribonucleic acid cistrons in the *Bacillus subtilis* genome. J. Bacteriol. **99**:535–543.
2. Böhme, H. 1967. Genetic instability of an ultraviolet sensitive mutant of *Proteus mirabilis*. Biochem. Biophys. Res. Commun. **28**:191–196.
3. Bretscher, M. S. 1968. Direct translation of a circular messenger DNA. Nature (London) **220**:1088–1091.
4. Brown, L. R., and C. E. Dowell. 1968. Replication of coliphage M-13. II. Intracellular deoxyribonucleic acid forms associated with M-13 infection of mitomycin C-treated cells. J. Virol. **2**:1296–1307.
5. Bryson, V. 1962. Antibiotics: practical and experimental aspects, p. 345–440. *In* B. Glass (ed.), Survey of biological progress, vol. 4. Academic Press Inc., New York.
6. Cairns, J. 1963. The bacterial chromosome and its manner of replication as seen by autoradiography. J. Mol. Biol. **6**:208–213.
7. Clark, D. J., and O. Maaløe. 1967. DNA replication and the division cycle in *Escherichia coli*. J. Mol. Biol. **23**:99–112.
8. Colson, A. M., C. Colson, and A. van Piel. 1969. Host-controlled restriction mutants of *Salmonella typhimurium*. J. Gen. Microbiol. **58**:57–64.
9. Fromageot, H. P. M., and N. Zinder. 1968. Growth of bacteriophage f2 in *E. coli* treated with rifampicin. Proc. Nat. Acad. Sci. U.S.A. **61**:184–191.
10. Geiduschek, E. P., and J. Sklar. 1969. Continual requirement for a host RNA polymerase component in a bacteriophage development. Nature (London) **221**:833–836.
11. Gottlieb, D., and P. D. Shaw (ed.) 1967. Antibiotics, vol. 1 and 2. Springer Verlag, Inc., New York.
12. Hartmann, G., W. Behr, K-A. Beissner, K. Honikel, and A. Sippel. 1968. Antibiotics as inhibitors of nucleic acid and protein synthesis. Angew. Chem. Int. Ed. Engl. **7**:693–701.
13. Haselkorn, R., M. Vogel, and R. D. Brown. 1969. Conservation of the rifampicin sensitivity of transcription during T4 development. Nature (London) **221**:836–838.
14. Hirota, Y. 1960. The effect of acridine dyes on mating type factors in *Escherichia coli*. Proc. Nat. Acad. Sci. U.S.A. **46**:57–64.
15. Ishiwa, H., and I. Tessman. 1968. Control of host DNA synthesis after infection with bacteriophages S13 and φX174. J. Mol. Biol. **37**:467–474.
16. Jacob, F., S. Brenner, and F. Cuzin. 1963. On the regulation of DNA replication in bacteria. Cold Spring Harbor Symp. Quant. Biol. **28**:329–348.
17. Jyssum, K. 1968. Mutator factor in *Neisseria meningitidis* associated with increased sensitivity to ultraviolet light and defective transformation. J. Bacteriol. **96**:165–172.
18. Koch, H.-J., and V. Bryson. 1964. Comparative mutability of normal and mutator strains of *Escherichia coli* and *Salmonella typhimurium* exposed to streptomycin, penicillin, polymyxin, colistin, and tetracycline. Antimicrob. Agents Chemother.–1963, p. 430–433.
19. Kumar, S., K. Bovre, A. Guha, Z. Hradecna, Sister Veronica M. Maher, and W. Szybalski. 1969. Orientation and control of transcription in *E. coli* phage 2. Nature (London) **221**:823–825.
20. McCarthy, B. J., and J. J. Holland. 1965. Denatured DNA as a direct template for *in vitro* protein synthesis. Proc. Nat. Acad. Sci. U.S.A. **54**:880–886.
21. Nagata, T. 1963. The molecular synchrony and sequential replication of DNA in *Escherichia coli*. Proc. Nat. Acad. Sci. U.S.A. **49**:551–559.
22. Nester, E. W. 1964. Penicillin resistance of competent cells in deoxyribonucleic acid transformation of *Bacillus subtilis*. J. Bacteriol. **87**:867–875.
23. Newton, B. A. 1956. The properties and mode of action of the polymyxins. Bacteriol. Rev. **20**:14–27.
24. Pato, M. L., and D. A. Glaser. 1968. The origin and direction of replication of the chromosome of *Escherichia coli* B/r. Proc. Nat. Acad. Sci. U.S.A. **60**:1268–1274.
25. Piekarowicz, A., E. Groniowska, and W. J. H. Kunicki-Goldfinger. 1969. Mechanism of conjugation and recombination in bacteria. V. Effect of edeine on F^+ cells. Acta Microbiol. Pol. (Ser. A) **1**:15–22.
26. Ranhand, J. M., and H. C. Lichstein. 1969. Effect of antibiotics and other inhibitors on competence development in *Haemophilus influenzae*. J. Gen. Microbiol. **55**:37–43.
27. Rouvière, J., J. Wyngaarden, J. Contoni, F. Gros, and A. Kepes. 1968. Effect of T4 infection on messenger RNA synthesis in *Escherichia coli*. Biochim. Biophys. Acta **166**:94–114.
28. Siegel, E. C., and V. Bryson. 1964. Selection of resistant strains of *Escherichia coli* by antibiotics and antibacterial agents: role of normal and mutator strains. Antimicrob. Agents Chemother.–1963, p. 629–634.
29. Siegel, E. C., and V. Bryson. 1967. Mutator gene of *Escherichia coli* B. J. Bacteriol. **94**:38–47.
30. Sulkowski, E., and M. Laskowski. 1968. Degradation of thymus DNA and crab poly d (A-T) by micrococcal nuclease in the presence of actinomycin D. Biochim. Biophys. Acta **157**:207–209.
31. Szybalski, W., and V. N. Iyer. 1967. The mitomycins and porfiromycins, p. 211–245. *In* D. Gottlieb and P. D. Shaw (ed.), Antibiotics, vol. 1. Springer Verlag, Inc., New York.
32. Taketo, A., and S. Kuno. 1969. Sensitivity of *Escherichia coli* to viral nucleic acid. I. Effect of lysozyme, EDTA, penicillin and osmotic shock treatment. J. Biochem. **65**:361–368.
33. Tocchini-Valentini. G. P., P. Marino, and A. J. Colvill. 1968. Mutant of *E. coli* containing an altered DNA-dependent RNA polymerase. Nature (London) **220**:275–276.
34. Wells, R. D. 1969. Actinomycin binding to DNA: inability of a DNA containing guanine to bind actinomycin D. Science (Washington) **165**:75–76.
35. Wlodarczyk, M., A. Piekarowicz, E. Borowski, and W. Kunicki-Goldfinger. 1968. Mechanism of conjugation and recombination in bacteria. II. Recombination deficiency in edeine-resistant Hfr cells. Acta Microbiol. Pol. **17**:121–128.
36. Yoshikawa, H. 1965. DNA synthesis during germination of *Bacillus subtilis* spores. Proc. Nat. Acad. Sci. U.S.A. **53**:1476–1483.

Antimicrobial Agents and Chemotherapy—1969

Use of Antibiotics in the Study of Ribosome Action

BERNARD D. DAVIS

Bacterial Physiology Unit, Harvard Medical School, Boston, Massachusetts 02115

Analysis of the action of the ribosome has been aided by the use of a number of antibiotics, which have been shown to interfere with that action in distinct ways. Recently our understanding of these mechanisms of interference has been considerably advanced by the use of viral ribonucleic acid as messenger, since its translation in extracts resembles protein synthesis in the cell much more closely than does the translation of synthetic polynucleotides. This paper will summarize the current picture of the mechanism of ribosome action and of its various types of inhibition by antibiotics, and will then discuss in greater detail recent studies on the action of streptomycin.

For quite a few years, antibiotics that act on the ribosomes, such as chloramphenicol, have been a most valuable tool in studying a variety of fundamental problems in cell physiology. Their use to inhibit protein synthesis selectively has contributed to the demonstration, for example, that enzyme induction involves synthesis of new protein rather than activation of a precursor, that new protein must be synthesized to initiate but not to complete a round of deoxyribonucleic acid (DNA) replication, that the regulation of net ribonucleic acid (RNA) synthesis is somehow related to the charging of transfer RNA (tRNA) (perhaps through its effect on the level of free ribosomes), and that in the physiological process of turnover of messenger RNA a region is protected from destruction while it is attached to ribosomes. More recently, antibiotics have both contributed to and benefited from an increasingly detailed analysis of the action of the ribosome itself, and we can now recognize a number of distinct modes of interference with ribosome function (35). I would like to review a number of these briefly, and then show how several antibiotics with these well-defined actions have contributed to our understanding of the action of streptomycin—of all the antibiotics known to act on the ribosome, the first to be discovered, and still one of the most obscure in its lethal action. Much of this material has been presented recently at the Sixth International Congress of Chemotherapy, in Japan.

As a background, let us first consider briefly the current view of the mechanism of ribosome action (18, 19).

RIBOSOME ACTION

The ribosome is undoubtedly the most complex biochemical machine known. In the course of protein synthesis, this gigantic assemblage of about 50 different macromolecules, with a total molecular weight of 3×10^6, goes through an elaborate process in which it passes along a messenger RNA (mRNA) molecule, translating the sequence of genetic information in the nucleic acid into a corresponding sequence of amino acids in the growing protein chain (Fig. 1). In this translation, each succesive set of three adjacent nucleotides constitutes a unit of information, or codon, which calls for a specific molecule of tRNA, 80 nucleotides long. That molecule serves as an adapter with two regions of specificity which account for the specificity of translation: at one end, three of its nucleotides (the anticodon) match a particular codon, and another region calls for a particular activating enzyme which charges the tRNA with a particular amino acid to form an aminoacyl-tRNA (aa-tRNA).

In describing the current model for this process (Fig. 1), it is convenient to start with a ribosome carrying a growing polypeptide chain. This chain is covalently linked to a tRNA molecule, which in turn is noncovalently bound to the ribosome in one of two binding sites, the

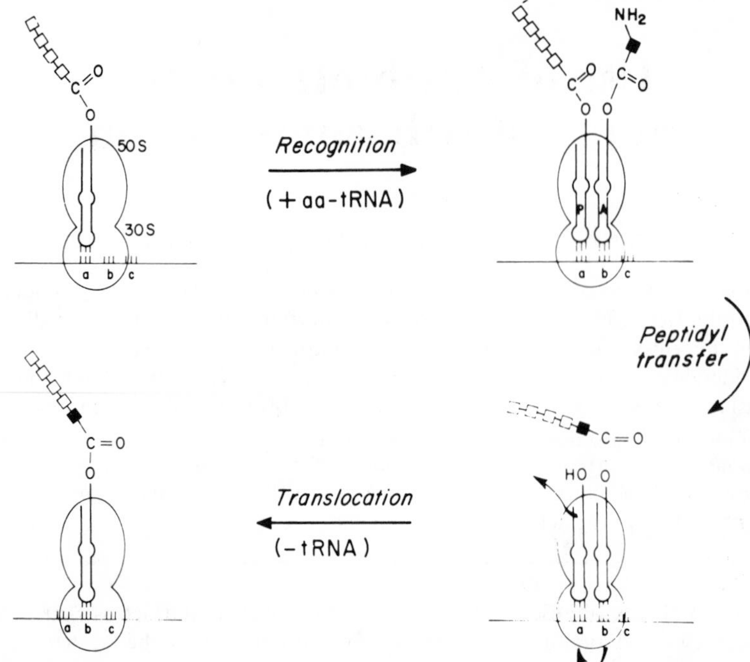

Fig. 1. *The three major steps in the "microcycle" of chain extension on the ribosome. Symbols a, b, and c designate successive trinucleotide codons in the messenger RNA.*

P (= polypeptide) site. In the process of adding an amino acid to this chain, three steps have been distinguished. In the first, or *recognition,* step the next codon to be translated specifies a particular aa-tRNA, which is taken up by the second binding site, called the A (= amino acid) site. (The region of codon-anticodon pairing at an end of the A site is also called the recognition region of the ribosome.) In the next step, *peptidyl transfer,* the polypeptide, attached by ester linkage to tRNA in the P site, is transferred to the -NH_2 group of the newly arrived amino acid residue attached to a tRNA in the A site. The polypeptide has thus become one residue longer, and it is still attached to the ribosome by a tRNA molecule (but not the one it has just left). In the third step, *translocation,* the peptidyl-tRNA moves from the A to the P site and ejects the free tRNA there, while an accompanying movement of the mRNA brings the next codon up to the recognition region.

All three steps are enzymatic (18, 19). Thus, peptidyl transfer substitutes a peptide for an ester bond, the enzyme being part of the 50*S* subunit. In recognition, the aa-tRNA is first loosely bound, along with a protein cofactor (T factor) and guanosine triphosphate (GTP); then, before the aa-tRNA can receive peptidyl transfer, it is firmly locked in at the expense of energy derived from hydrolysis of the GTP, and the T factor is released. It is not known whether the T factor is itself an enzyme or activates an enzymatic center on the ribosome. Similarly, in translocation energy is supplied by hydrolysis of another molecule of GTP, which involves the transient attachment of another protein cofactor (G factor).

The microcycle of chain extension was discovered largely through the use of synthetic polynucleotides (such as polyuridylic acid), which have also thrown much light on the action of various antiribosomal antibiotics. Nevertheless, this system reflects quite imperfectly the process of protein synthesis as it occurs in the cell. With the recent introduction of viral RNA as a natural messenger, however, protein synthesis in vitro has come to resemble much more closely that in the cell. In particular, this system has revealed a complex initiation process (Fig. 2) involving several new steps: (i) dissociation of the free ribosomes, released after completion of the reading of a messenger, into subunits;

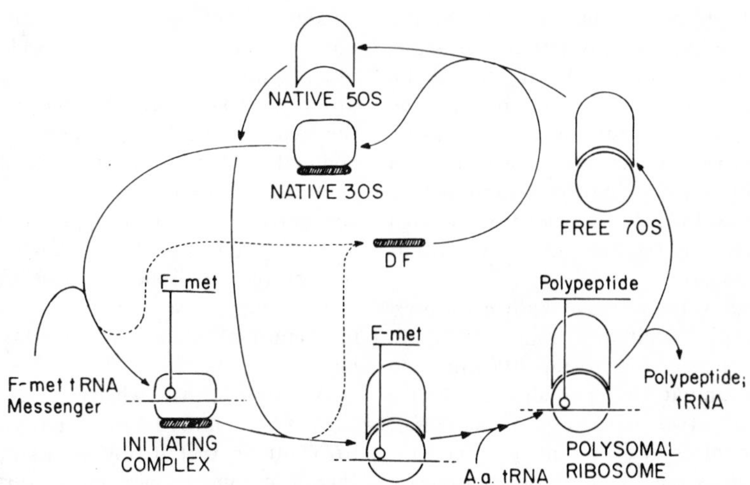

Fig. 2. *Proposed role of dissociation factor (DF) in the "macrocycle" of ribosome runoff, dissociation, and initiation (30). DF appears to be identical with initiation factor F3 (29), and there is evidence (12a) that the other initiation factors are also complexed with the native 30S subunit and are released when the addition of the 50S subunit converts it into a polysomal ribosome, complexed with messenger and with charged tRNA.*

Table 1. *Differences in function of synthetic and natural messengers*

Messenger	Mg^{++} optimum	Initiating particle	Initiation factors F-1, 2, 3	Initiating ligands	Inhibition by antibiotics[a]
	mM				%
Synthetic polynucleotides	10-20	70*S* ribosome	Not required	Any codon-aa-tRNA pair	0-60
Viral RNA	5	30*S* subunit	Required	AUG–f-met-tRNA	>95

[a] For example, chloramphenicol and streptomycin.

(ii) binding of the 30*S* subunit alone to a special initiation region of the mRNA; (iii) coding by this region for the binding of a special initiating tRNA, formyl-methionyl-tRNA (f-met-tRNA); and in (iv) addition of a 50*S* subunit to this initiation complex to form a polysomal ribosome. The completed ribosome then engages in chain extension, as already described, and moves along the messenger. When this ribosome has moved far enough, another ribosome is assembled on the initiation region, until eventually a whole string of ribosomes, constituting a polysome, are simultaneously reading the same messenger.

This elaborate initiation process, like the microcyle of chain extension, also involves GTP as well as certain protein factors (initiation factors) that cycle on and off the ribosome. One of these factors, F_3 (also called B), causes dissociation of the runoff ribosome (29, 30), while F_2 (C) promotes binding of mRNA and the subsequent binding of f-met-tRNA (15), and F_1 (A) stabilizes the binding of the f-met-tRNA (6).

For present purposes, it is particularly interesting that in the physiological in vitro system with natural messenger, just as in the cell, various antibiotics cause essentially complete inhibition, although previously, when tested with various polynucleotides, they caused only partial inhibition or even none (Table 1). The use of natural messengers has represented a major step forward in the study of antibiotic action.

Let us now consider the more detailed localization of the action of certain antibiotics.

Puromycin. This antibiotic has been understood longer, and with more certainty, than any other antiribosomal agent. It serves as an analogue of the aminoacylated terminal adenosine of aa-tRNA (36), accepting peptidyl transfer; but, since it does not provide nearly as strong a bridge to the ribosome as does tRNA, the growing chain is prematurely terminated and is rapidly released as polypeptidylpuromycin (1).

Puromycin can apparently accept polypeptide transfer from the P site but not from the A site; hence, it has been a most valuable reagent in determining the state of ribosomes inhibited by other antibiotics. Indeed, it provided the original basis for recognizing the presence of two different sites (24, 34).

Tetracycline. Tetracycline is known to interfere with the specific binding of an aa-tRNA, in the presence of its codon, to the 70*S* ribosome or to the 30*S* subunit. Under conditions where a ribosome binds two molecules of aa-tRNA, tetracycline reduces the binding by one-half; and, since it does not block puromycin release of what remains bound, it appears to block the A site but not the P site (27). The action of tetracycline thus strongly supports the two-site model for the ribosome.

Chloramphenicol and sparsomycin. These antibiotics block peptidyl transfer, as shown by the puromycin reaction (8, 13, 25, 34). Though this effect could conceivably be indirect, if the drug fixed the peptidyl-tRNA in the A site (i.e., blocked translocation), there is ample evidence, which cannot be detailed here, that the block in peptidyl transfer is direct.

Fusidic acid. Fusidic acid specifically blocks translocation. This conclusion was initially suggested by the inhibitory effect of this drug on GPT hydrolysis, and on G factor-promoted transfer of peptidyl-tRNA to a puromycin-releasable position (31). More recently, mutants resistant to fusidic acid have been isolated, and they have been found to be altered in the G factor rather than in the ribosome (16, 23).

Streptomycin. This drug has undoubtedly been investigated more extensively, and in more laboratories, than any other antibiotic. Substantial contributions to cell physiology have resulted: streptomycin resistance provided the first means of isolating mutants with altered ribosomes (7, 9); and the stimulation of misreading by streptomycin (11) revealed the ability of the ribosome (and of drugs acting on it) to influence the precision of translation, and also provided a plausible explanation for streptomycin dependence (i.e., distortion by streptomycin compensating for genetic restriction of the recognition region). Nevertheless, the misreading effect of streptomycin, which was observed in vitro with polyuridylic acid and other synthetic polynucleotides as messengers, differs conspicuously from the response seen in the cell: in the latter inhibition is rapid and complete, whereas in vitro the stimulation of incorrect synthesis can exceed, even at high concentrations of the drug, the inhibition of the correct synthesis (11). Hence, when the preparation of viral RNA became feasible, J. Modolell and I thought it worthwhile to reinvestigate the mechanism of inhibition, using this more physiological messenger.

We found that when an *Escherichia coli* extract was allowed to translate viral RNA for 5 to 6 min so that it reached a steady state, and then streptomycin was added, further synthesis was almost completely inhibited within a few seconds (Fig. 3). Moreover, by estimating the fraction of the ribosomes that were engaged in protein synthesis, we could calculate that the addition of streptomycin inhibited the average ribosome immediately, i.e., before it added two amino acids to its growing chain (22). It is therefore clear that streptomycin rapidly blocks chain extension.

Although this result was not unexpected, streptomycin had a surprising further effect on

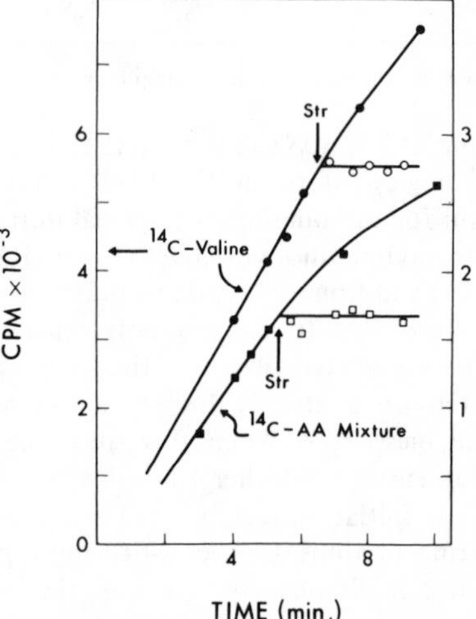

Fig. 3. *Kinetics of inhibition by streptomycin (Str) of incorporation of ^{14}C-amino acids (22). After synthesis was well under way, in an E. coli extract incubated at 34 C with phage MS2 RNA as messenger, streptomycin (20 µg/ml) was added to a portion of each reaction mixture. Samples taken at intervals were analyzed for radioactivity precipitated by hot 5% trichloracetic acid.*

this system: it caused a slow, progressive breakdown of the polysomes, which was half complete in about 4 min at 34 C (Fig. 4). This effect seemed particularly interesting because of its contrast with the action of other inhibitory antibiotics, including chloramphenicol, tetracycline, sparsomycin, and fusidic acid, which stabilized the polysomes. The breakdown by streptomycin was associated with loss of the attached polypeptide and messenger (23). It thus seems clear that streptomycin releases nascent chains, presumably as peptidyl-tRNA, well before their normal termination. The physiological significance of the Str-induced polysome breakdown is emphasized by its demonstration, by Luzzatto et al. (20, 21), in cells of *E. coli.*

In analyzing this effect, we first attempted to determine the location of the peptidyl-tRNA in the streptomycin-inhibited ribosome by adding puromycin after the streptomycin-induced release was well under way. The polysomes disappeared just as rapidly as when puromycin was added alone (Fig. 4). The peptidyl-tRNA thus appears to be blocked predominantly or entirely in the P site.

We could then ask whether the eventual release occurred from the P site or whether it required peptidyl transfer (or attempted transfer). This question was answered by testing the effect of inhibitors of peptidyl transfer (23). The results showed that either chloramphenicol (Fig. 4) or sparsomycin, added after the streptomycin-induced breakdown of polysomes was under way, strongly impeded further breakdown; chlortetracycline, which blocks aa-tRNA binding, was also effective. It thus appears that aa-tRNA binding and subsequent peptidyl transfer (or attempted transfer) are essential for the streptomycin-induced breakdown of the ribosomal complex.

In interpreting these results, we would suggest that both the effect of streptomycin on chain extension and its effect on polysome stability can be explained by a single action of the drug on the ribosome: distortion of the A site, in a manner that impairs its effective binding of any acylated tRNA. Thus, impaired binding of aa-tRNA would account for the almost complete inhibition of chain extension, with the peptidyl-tRNA blocked in the P site. However, from time to time the aa-tRNA must be bound effectively and engage in peptidyl transfer, since drugs that

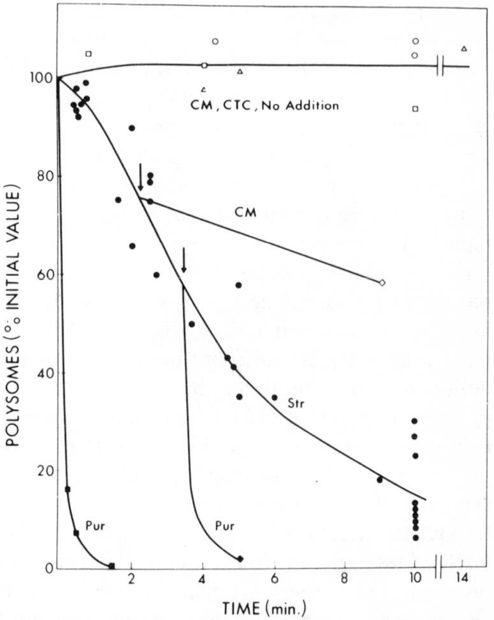

Fig. 4. *Effect of various ribosome inhibitors on polysomes formed in vitro (23). Zero time represents time of addition of antibiotics after 5 min of preliminary synthesis of polypeptide as in Fig. 3. At arrows chloramphenicol (CM) or puromycin (Pur) was added to samples in which polysome breakdown by streptomycin (Str) was already under way.*

block peptidyl transfer prevent the subsequent release of the polypeptide by streptomycin; hence, we infer that this release involves transfer of the polypeptide to the distorted A site. The stage at which the release occurs is not certain: it might conceivably be either during entry into the A site or during residence in that site, if the streptomycin caused the accepting tRNA to be unstably held; or it might be later, during abortive translocation from the distorted A site. An involvement of translocation is favored by the further observation that fusidic acid also blocks streptomycin-induced polysome breakdown.

Distortion of the A site thus appears to be responsible for both inhibition of protein synthesis and the subsequent polysome breakdown. But the A site of the ribosome overlaps, by definition, with the recognition region, whose distortion is undoubtedly responsible for the extensive misreading effect of streptomycin observed with homopolynucleotide messengers (11, 12). Hence *distortion of the recognition region* provides a unitary basis for all these actions of streptomycin.

Whereas the mechanism of inhibition of protein synthesis by streptomycin thus seems reasonably clear, the mechanisms responsible for its lethal action and for its production of phenotypic suppression now become less certain. Thus, in heterozygous cells of *E. coli,* which contain both sensitive and resistant ribosomes (28), we have found that streptomycin is rapidly bactericidal (P. F. Sparling and B. D. Davis, *unpublished data*), despite the report of a purely bacteriostatic action in similar cells (5). Since streptomycin-inhibited ribosomes fall off from polysomes, it is difficult to account for the dominance of sensitivity by a blockade, as previously suggested (17), of resistant ribosomes behind streptomycin-inhibited sensitive ribosomes. Thus, the mechanism of killing by streptomycin remains unsettled. Similarly, though the misreading observed with homopolynucleotides appeared to explain phenotypic suppression (14), we now see that this misreading is an artificial response: with a physiological messenger, streptomycin in the same concentrations causes virtually instant and complete inhibition, which allows no opportunity for misreading. The mechanism of phenotypic suppression is thus also not definitely settled.

MORPHOGENESIS OF RIBOSOMES

A dramatic development in the study of the ribosome has been Nomura's recent success in reconstituting active 30*S* subunits from their separated components: one RNA molecule and 19 different proteins (33). With this technique, he has been able to demonstrate that streptomycin resistance is associated with a particular protein, P10 (26). J. Davies, collaborating with the same group, has shown that spectinomycin resistance is associated with a different, more easily extracted protein (4). This work represents a very important step toward correlating structure and function in this complex organelle.

The in vitro reconstitution of ribosomes suggests that in the cell they are similarly formed by spontaneous aggregation from a pool of precursor molecules. However, since the striking insolubility of mixtures of ribosomal proteins has required the use of drastic solubilizing conditions (a high KCl concentration) in the reconstitution experiments, it has not been evident that the cell could maintain the required protein pool in solution. An alternative possibility would be that the ribosomal proteins are made along a polygenic messenger and the "growing" ribosome sequentially incorporates each protein as it is made. We have tested this possibility with doubly heterozygous strains of *E. coli,* carrying both a resistant and a sensitive allele of the *str* locus and a similar pair for the closely linked *spc* locus (2, 3, 10). About the same proportion of doubly resistant ribosomes was found (28) whether the allele for streptomycin resistance and that for spectinomycin resistance were both on the episome (*cis* position) or whether one was on the episome and the other on the chromosome (*trans* position). It thus appears that the products of these linked genes are not phenotypically linked but are incorporated from a common pool, to which both the chromosome and the episome contribute.

CONCLUSIONS

Our confidence in the current model of ribosome action is very much strengthened by the coherence of the results obtained by two separate approaches: biochemical fractionation of the system, and the use of drugs and of drug-resistant mutants. As the ribosome, interacting with various initiation factors and elongation factors, dissociates, forms an initiation complex, completes the polysomal ribosome, and then engages in a cycle of several steps in each unit of chain extension, it must undergo extensive and varied conformational changes. A major question today is the definition of these conformational changes, and also of the various functional regions of the ribosome, in terms of specific ribosomal proteins; another is a determination of the topographical relation of these proteins to each other and to specific regions of the ribosomal RNA. At present, there is little connection between what we know of ribosomal structure and what we know of its function. In the efforts to close this gap, antibiotics will surely continue to prove useful—for example, in selecting for an increasing variety of mutant ribosomes altered in one or another protein, and in fixing the ribosome in various conformations. Indeed, recent studies of the latter type already offer promise of analyzing the three known stages of chain extension (Fig. 1) into component parts.

ACKNOWLEDGMENT

This investigation was supported by grants from the National Science Foundation, U.S. Public Health Service, and American Cancer Society.

LITERATURE CITED

1. Allen, D. E., and P. C. Zamecnik. 1962. The effect of puromycin on rabbit reticulocyte ribosomes. Biochim. Biophys. Acta **55**:865–874.
2. Anderson, P., Jr. 1969. Sensitivity and resistance to spectinomycin in *Escherichia coli.* J. Bacteriol. **100**:939–947.
3. Anderson, P., J. Davies, and B. D. Davis. 1967. Effect of spectinomycin on polypeptide synthesis in extracts of *Escherichia Coli.* J. Mol. Biol. **29**:203–215.
4. Bollen, A., J. Davies, M. Ozaki, and S. Mizushima. 1969. Ribosomal protein conferring sensitivity to the antibiotic spectinomycin in *Escherichia coli.* Science (Washington) **165**:85–86.
5. Breckenridge, L., and L. Gorini. 1969. The dominance of streptomycin sensitivity re-examined. Proc. Nat. Acad. Sci. U.S.A. **62**:979–985.
6. Chae, Y. B., R. Mazumder, and S. Ochoa. 1969. Polypeptide chain initiation in *E. coli*: isolation of homogeneous initiation factor F_2 and its relation to ribosomal proteins. Proc. Nat. Acad. Sci. U.S.A. **62**:1181–1188.
7. Cox, E. C., J. R. White, and J. G. Flaks. 1964. Streptomycin action and the ribosome. Proc. Nat. Acad. Sci. U.S.A. **51**:703–709.
8. Cundliffe, E., and K. McQuillen. 1967. Bacterial protein synthesis: the effects of antibiotics. J. Mol. Biol. **30**:137–146.
9. Davies, J. 1964. Studies on the ribosomes of streptomycin-sensitive and resistant strains of *Escherichia coli.* Proc. Nat. Acad. Sci. U.S.A. **51**:659–664.
10. Davies, J., P. F. Anderson, and B. D. Davis. 1965. Inhibition of protein synthesis by spectinomycin. Science (Washington) **149**:1096–1098.
11. Davies, J., W. Gilbert, and L. Gorini. 1964. Streptomycin suppression and the code. Proc. Nat. Acad. Sci. U.S.A. **51**:883–890.
12. Davies, J., L. Gorini, and B. D. Davis. 1965. Misreading of RNA codewords induced by aminoglycoside antibiotics. Mol. Pharmacol. **1**:93–106.

12*a*. Eisenstadt, J. M., and G. Brawerman. 1967. The role of the native subribosomal particles of *Escherichia coli* in polypeptide chain initiation. Proc. Nat. Acad. Sci. U.S.A. **58**:1560–1565.

13. Goldberg, I. H., and K. Mitsugi. 1967. Inhibition by sparsomycin and other antibiotics of the puromycin-induced release of polypeptides from ribosomes. Biochemistry **6**:383–391.
14. Gorini, L., and E. Kataja. 1964. Phenotypic repair by streptomycin of defective genotypes in *E. coli.* Proc. Nat. Acad. Sci. U.S.A. **51**:487–493.
15. Greensphan, H., and M. Revel. 1969. Inhibitor protein dependent binding of messenger RNA to ribosomes. Nature (London) **224**:331–335.
16. Kinoshita, T., G. Kawano, and N. Tanaka. 1968. Association of fusidic acid sensitivity with G factor in a protein-synthesizing system. Biochem. Biophys. Res. Commun. **33**:769–773.
17. Lederberg, E. M., L. Cavalli-Sforza, and J. Lederberg. 1964. Interaction of streptomycin and a suppressor for galactose fermentation in *E. coli* K-12. Proc. Nat. Acad. Sci. U.S.A. **51**:678–682.
18. Lengyel, P., and D. Soll. 1969. Mechanism of protein biosynthesis. Bacteriol. Rev. **33**:264–301.
19. Lipmann, F. 1969. Polypeptide chain elongation in protein biosynthesis. Science (Washington) **164**:1024–1031.
20. Luzzato, L., D. Apirion, and D. Schlessinger. 1968. Mechanism of action of streptomycin in *E. coli*: interruption of the ribosome cycle at the initiation of protein synthesis. Proc. Nat. Acad. Sci. U.S.A. **60**:873–880.
21. Luzzato, L., D. Apirion, and D. Schlessinger. 1969. Polyribosome depletion and blockage of the ribosome cycle by streptomycin in *Escherichia coli.* J. Mol. Biol. **42**:315–335.
22. Modolell, J., and B. D. Davis. 1968. Rapid inhibition of polypeptide chain extension by streptomycin. Proc. Nat. Acad. Sci. U.S.A. **61**:1279–1286.
23. Modolell, J., and B. D. Davis. 1969. Mechanism of inhibition of ribosomes by streptomycin. Nature (London) **224**:345–348.
24. Monro, R. E. 1967. Catalysis of peptide bond formation by 50S ribosomal subunits from *Escherichia coli.* J. Mol. Biol. **26**:147–151.
25. Monro, R. E., M. L. Celma, and D. Vazquez. 1969. Action of sparsomycin on ribosome-catalysed peptidyl transfer. Nature (London) **22**:356–358.
26. Ozaki, M., S. Mizushima, and M. Nomura. 1969. Identification and functional characterization of the protein controlled by the streptomycin-resistant locus in *E. coli.* Nature (London) **222**:333–339.
27. Sarkar, S., and R. E. Thach. 1968. Inhibition of formylmethionyl-transfer RNA binding to ribosomes by tetracycline. Proc. Nat. Acad. Sci. U.S.A. **60**:1479–1486.
28. Sparling, P. F., J. Modolell, Y. Takeda, and B. D. Davis. 1968. Ribosomes from *Escherichia coli* merodiploids heterozygous for resistance to streptomycin and to spectinomycin. J. Mol. Biol. **37**:407–421.
29. Subramanian, A. R., B. D. Davis, and R. Beller. 1969. The ribosome dissociation factor and the ribosome-polysome cycle. Cold Spring Harbor Symp. Quant. Biol. **34**:223–230.
30. Subramanian, A. R., E. Z. Ron, and B. D. Davis. 1968. A factor required for ribosome dissociation in *Escherichia coli.* Proc. Nat. Acad. Sci. U.S.A. **61**:761–767.
31. Tanaka, N., T. Kinoshita, and H. Masukawa. 1968. Mechanism of protein synthesis inhibition by fusidic acid and related antibiotics. Biochim. Biophys. Res. Commun. **30**:278–283.
32. Tocchini-Valentini, G. P., and E. Mattocia. 1968. A mutant of *E. coli* with an altered supernatant factor. Proc. Nat. Acad. Sci. U.S.A. **61**:146–151.
33. Traub, P., and M. Nomura. 1968. Structure and function of *E. coli* ribosomes. V. Reconstitution of functionally active 30S ribosomal particles from RNA and proteins. Proc. Nat. Acad. Sci. U.S.A. **59**:777–784.
34. Traut, R. R., and R. E. Monro. 1964. The puromycin reaction and its relation to protein synthesis. J. Mol. Biol. **10**:63–72.
35. Weisblum, B., and J. Davies. 1968. Antibiotic inhibitors of the bacterial ribosome. Bacteriol. Rev. **32**:493–528.
36. Yarmolinsky, M., and G. de la Haba. 1959. Inhibition by puromycin of amino acid incorporation into protein. Proc. Nat. Acad. Sci. U.S.A. **45**:1721–1729.

Antimicrobial Agents and Chemotherapy—1969

Antibiotic Inhibition of Mitochondrial Energy-Transfer Reactions

PETER J. F. HENDERSON and HENRY A. LARDY

Institute for Enzyme Research, University of Wisconsin, Madison, Wisconsin 53706

The oligomycins and aurovertin have contributed greatly to our present understanding of energy conservation in mitochondria. Their role is reviewed, and recent results which further identify their receptor sites are presented. By comparing their inhibition of energy transfer with that of atractylate and bongkrekic acid, rapid screening methods for evaluating new inhibitors of the energy-transfer reactions may be derived. All of these antibiotics are currently providing information on the metabolic control and allosteric nature of the enzymes catalyzing phosphorylation and translocation of adenine nucleotides in mitochondria. This is discussed in terms of the integration of these processes, which is a central feature of a novel theory for oxidative phosphorylation and energy-driven ion transport recently described by Selwyn and Dawson.

In general terms, mitochondrial oxidative phosphorylation is susceptible to various inhibitors at three levels of structural and functional organization. The citric acid cycle enzymes of mitochondria (40) are inhibited at the α-oxoglutarate dehydrogenase step by lewisite oxide (13), at aconitase by fluorocitrate (46), and at succinic dehydrogenase by malonate (13). Secondly, the respiratory chain is located in the cristae membranes and reoxidizes the reduced nicotinamide adenine dinucleotide (NADH), reduced nicotinamide adenine dinucleotide phosphate (NADPH), or reduced cytochrome *b* produced by the activity of the citric acid cycle (40); the resulting electron transport along the respiratory enzymes–flavoprotein and cytochromes–may be inhibited by rotenone or piericidin between the flavoprotein of NADH dehydrogenase and cytochrome *b*, by antimycin at the cytochrome *b* level, and by cyanide and azide at cytochrome oxidase (for reviews, see 18, 34, 53, 56). The third level is the process by which energy available from the electron transport process is conserved and utilized for the endergonic phosphorylation of adenosine diphosphate (ADP) to adenosine triphosphate (ATP), a process susceptible to the compounds listed in Table 1; there is evidence that this "energy-transfer" process is morphologically situated in the inner membrane spheres (29, 54) and the stalks attaching the spheres to the cristae membranes (32, 42). Those inhibitors of oxidative phosphorylation acting on the citric acid cycle and respiratory enzymes which are not antibiotics are obviously outside the scope of this review. Also, the inhibition of electron transport by the antibiotics antimycin and piericidin, and by the plant-produced fish poison rotenone, have been sufficiently described elsewhere (17, 19, 20, 34, 56). Accordingly, we shall concentrate on the energy-transfer inhibitors of Table 1. A few of the experiments which reveal their similarity will first be described, together with a scheme for the mechanism of oxidative phosphorylation that accommodates their inhibitory properties. Examples of more recent studies that emphasized points of difference between these inhibitors will then be quoted, to lead to the identification of individual enzymes as the inhibitory sites.

The antibiotics have served as valuable tools in defining mechanistic theories of oxidative phosphorylation, as well as in the purification and elucidation of the metabolic properties of energy-transfer and nucleotide-translocation enzymes. They may also indicate an integration of these enzyme systems which is envisaged in a new theory of oxidative phosphorylation proposed by Selwyn and Dawson (59).

Table 1. *Inhibitors of energy-transfer reactions*

Inhibitor	Formula	Formula wt.	Concn for 50% inhibition (nmoles/mg of protein)	Comments
Oligomycin B	$C_{45}H_{72}O_{12}$	804	0.17	Equally effective on ATPase
Rutamycin	–	776	0.08	Equally effective on ATPase
Peliomycin	$C_{46}H_{76}O_{14}$	852	0.08	Equally effective on ATPase
Ossamycin	$C_{50}H_{87}O_{14}N$	925	0.29	Equally effective on ATPase
Venturicidin	$C_{43}H_{71}O_{12}N$	793	0.31	Much higher concentrations required for maximal inhibition of oxidative phosphorylation or ATPase
Aurovertin	$C_{25}H_{32}O_9$	476	0.26	Ineffective on ATPase
Atractylate	$C_{30}H_{44}O_{16}S_2K_2$	802	0.25 at 0.05 mM ADP	Inhibition overcome by ADP, or by ATP in ATPase assay
Bongkrekic acid	$C_{28}H_{38}O_7$	486	0.3–1.0	Some competition by ADP; approximately 5X required to inhibit ATPase

MATERIALS AND METHODS

Rat liver mitochondria were prepared according to the method of Johnson and Lardy (27). References to the techniques used for measuring oxygen consumption, cation transport, and volume changes of mitochondria will be given in the text. Adenosine triphosphatase activity was assayed by the inorganic orthosphosphate (P_i) released during 10-min incubations at 30 C (36), and in some experiments phosphoenolpyruvate and pyruvate kinase were included to regenerate ATP from the ADP product. A detailed description of the technique for measuring ADP or ATP uptake has been submitted for publication (Henderson and Lardy, J. Biol. Chem. **245**:1319, 1970).

Antibiotics were kindly donated by the following: rutamycin by Robert Thompson, Eli Lilly & Co.; aurovertin by H. Nash and C. Baldwin, Pitman-Moore Division, Dow Chemical Co.; bongkrekic acid by W. Berends and G. W. M. Lijmback; and atractylate by P. V. Vignais and A. Bruni.

PROPERTIES OF THE INHIBITORS

The compounds listed in Table 1 are all antibiotics except for potassium atractyloside (atractylate) which is derived from the roots of the thistle *Atractylis gummifera* (58). Oligomycins A to C (rutamycin is also a member of the oligomycin group), peliomycin, ossamycin, and venturicidin are produced by *Streptomyces* species (15, 62, 69). Aurovertin is from *Calcarisporium arbuscula* (2) and bongkrekic acid is from *Pseudomonas cocovenenans* (65).

The molecular weights of the oligomycins are taken from the recent reports of Strong and his co-workers (51) and Chamberlin et al. (10). Earlier figures were much lower (44, 55, 62), probably because of disintegration of the molecules in the analytical procedure. Oligomycin A has been omitted because of its relative instability in solution (37), and oligomycin C because it is less potent (37). Aurovertin may have a slightly different formula and higher formula weight than that given (2, 55); the figures for bongkrekic acid and atractyloside are exact, because their molecular structures have been elucidated (7; G. W. M. Lijmbach, Ph. D. Thesis, University of Delft, Delft, The Netherlands, 1969).

Assays for inhibition of mitochondrial metabolism. The dose for half-maximal inhibition in Table 1 refers to oxidation of glutamate by rat liver mitochondria in the presence of ADP, P_i, and glucose plus hexokinase as P_i acceptor system, monitoring oxygen uptake by Warburg manometry (64, 69). This assay measures the rate of oxidative phosphorylation in the direction of ATP synthesis. When the reverse reaction, i.e., the net release of P_i from ATP in the presence of uncoupling agents (36), is measured, the oligomycins, peliomycin, ossamycin, and venturicidin are as effective as in the forward direction, although very much higher concentrations of aurovertin are required to reach a maximum of about 55% inhibition (19, 33, 55). Atractyloside is unique in that it requires Mg^{++} for maximal potency (6, 70), and ADP or ATP competitively overcomes its inhibition (6, 8, 66, 67). The figure in Table 1 represents a maximally inhibitory amount at low ADP concentrations. To a much lower degree, adenine nucleotides also alleviate inhibition by bongkrekic acid (Henderson and Lardy, J. Biol. Chem., *in press*).

A comparison with inhibitory concentrations

derived from reports by other workers for both rat liver and beef heart mitochondria may be made by correcting to the molecular weights of Table 1. The following values, expressed as nanomoles per milligram of protein, required for 50% inhibition have been obtained: for oligomycin, 0.4 (20), 0.13 (7), and 0.2 (55); for aurovertin, 0.22 (55) and 0.21 (19); and for atractyloside, 0.2 (7) and 0.2 to 0.5 (70). Thus, all appear to act at similar levels with respect to total mitochondrial protein, a fact which will be referred to again below.

Phosphorus to oxygen (P/O) ratios may be measured in the Warburg manometry system by assaying total P_i consumption as well as oxygen uptake (64). With α-oxoglutarate as mitochondrial substrate and malonate to prevent further oxidation of the succinate produced, P/O ratios approaching a value of 4 may be obtained, representing 3 ATP molecules synthesized in the oxidation of NADH by the respiratory chain, and 1 ATP synthesized in the succinic thiokinase reaction—a "substrate-level" phosphorylation. Table 2 gives two examples demonstrating that antibiotics of Table 1 cause a decline in both oxygen and P_i consumption. This distinguishes them from uncoupling agents, which reduce P_i uptake without affecting the rapid respiration induced by the phosphate acceptor system (12). Table 2 also shows that oligomycin fails to inhibit substrate-level phosphorylation accompanying α-ketoglutarate oxidation, although this is susceptible to bongkrekic acid (and also to atractyloside).

In the presence of substrate and phosphate, the rate of mitochondrial respiration is limited by the supply of ADP (12). Thus, addition of ADP causes an increase of oxygen uptake, which ceases when all the ADP is converted to ATP (Fig. 1). This increase may be measured with a vibrating or Clark-type platinum electrode (Gilson Medical Electronics, Inc., Middleton, Wis., and Yellow Springs Instrument Co., Yellow Springs, Ohio, respectively) operated with the precautions given by Hagihara (24) and Chappell (13). Addition of any of the antibiotics in Table 1 before the ADP prevents the respiratory acceleration; their addition after the ADP prevents further respiratory "jumps" (Fig. 1). An uncoupling agent is then added to test whether maximal respiratory rates are still possible; a positive result indicates that the antibiotic does not inhibit electron transfer but only energy transfer to ADP. The P/O ratio in this experiment can be measured by the construction of Chance and Williams (12).

Thus, it may be deduced that the inhibitors listed in Table 1 prevent utilization of energy for phosphorlyation of ADP, or the release of energy from ATP. They do not prevent electron-transfer reactions. It also appears that uncoupling agents act at a point in the energy-transfer system which is nearer to the respira-

Table 2. *Antibiotic inhibition of oxidative phosphorylation*[a]

Antibiotic	Phospate uptake (μmoles)	Oxygen uptake (μatoms)	P/O ratio
None	24.12	6.67	3.6
Rutamycin	1.26	2.13	0.6
Bongkrekic acid . . .	0.00	0.70	0

[a] α-Ketoglutarate substrate, with malonate to prevent oxidation of succinate.

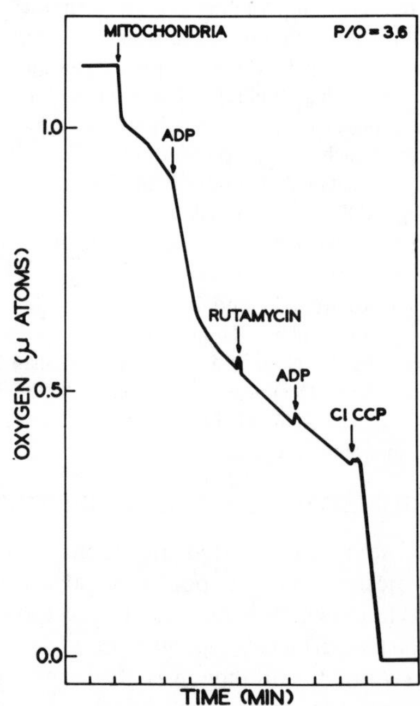

Fig. 1. *Inhibition of oxidative phosphorylation by rutamycin. Reaction mixture contained 4 mM oxoglutarate, 4 mM phosphate, 20 mM malonate as tris(hydroxymethyl)aminomethane (Tris) salts, and 100 mM potassium chloride, as osmotic supporting medium. Total volume was 2.5 ml, pH was 7.4, and temperature was 30 C. Additions were 4.3 mg of rat liver mitochondrial protein, 1 µmole of Tris ADP, 10 µg of rutamycin in 10 µliters of 96% ethyl alcohol, and 5 × 10⁻⁴ µmole of m-chlorocyanocarbonylphenylhydrazone (ClCCP).*

tory chain than the locus susceptible to Table 1 compounds.

Largely as a result of the studies of Pressman and co-workers (50), it has been established that the "high-energy intermediate" of mitochondria may be utilized for uptake of K^+ and other monovalent cations (against the concentration gradient). This will be discussed further in the next section. The activity is enormously enhanced by the "ionophorous" antibiotics, e.g., valinomycin, and may be measured with ion-selective electrodes (49). In Fig. 2, energy for K^+ uptake induced by valinomycin was provided by ATP hydrolysis, as indicated by the rapid H^+ output (47) occurring after addition of the valinomycin. ATP hydrolysis could also be assayed by measuring the P_i content of small samples withdrawn from the medium. Any antibiotic from Table 1 reversed the ATP hydrolysis, swelling, and K^+ uptake. However, subsequent addition of respiratory substrate (to generate energy through electron transport) reinitiated K^+ uptake and swelling, which was then abolished by the respiratory chain inhibitor antimycin.

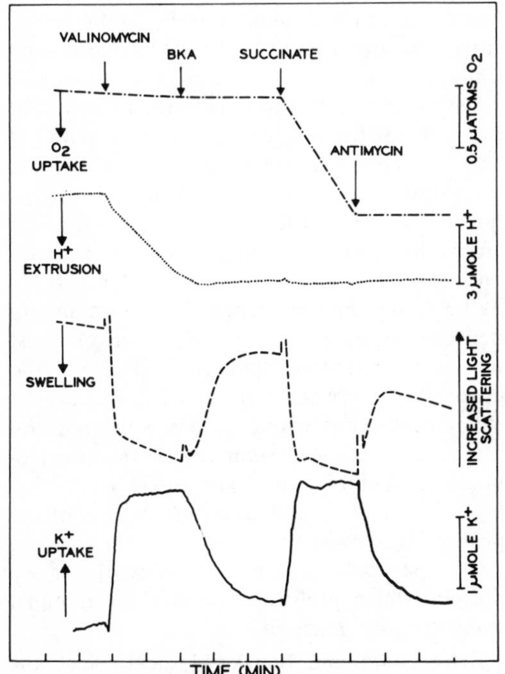

Fig. 2. *Inhibition of ATP-supported but not respiration-supported, cation uptake in rat liver mitochondria. Additions were* 10^{-7} *M valinomycin,* 6×10^{-6} *M bongkrekic acid,* 6×10^{-4} *M succinate, and 0.1 μg of antimycin. The 5.0-ml suspension (temperature 30 C, pH 7.4) contained 9 mM Tris ATP, 7.5 mM KCl, 3.75 mM triethanolamine* P_i*, 1 mM* $MgCl_2$*,* 6×10^{-8} *M rotenone, 200 mM sucrose, and 8.4 mg of mitochondrial protein.*

It can readily be seen that, by varying the order of additions in this experiment, an uncharacterized antibiotic may be tested for the following activities: (i) induction of cation uptake, e.g., valinomycin; (ii) prevention of cation uptake even though both substrate and ATP are present to generate the required energy, e.g., nigericin (35, 50); (iii) prevention of utilization of ATP-generated, but not respiration-generated, energy, e.g., oligomycin; (iv) inhibition of respiratory chain, but not of ATP-supported, energy utilization—an electron-transfer inhibitor, e.g., antimycin or rotenone (18); (v) prevention of utilization of energy from either source while inducing maximal rates of respiration or adenosine triphosphatase—an uncoupling agent, e.g., dinitrophenol, carbonyl cyanide *m*-chloro phenylhydrazone. With suitable controls, monitoring of fewer than the four parameters of Fig. 2 can be used for reasonably exact localization of an antibiotic's inhibitory site.

DEDUCTIONS CONCERNING THE ENERGY-TRANSFER REACTIONS

The inhibitors of Table 1 prevent transfer of energy from electron transport to the terminal ATP-synthesizing enzyme, or from ATP to the energized intermediate utilized for cation transport, but not the generation of intermediate from the electron transport chain. Experiments of the type presented above, and many other approaches, yield results that are consistant with the following scheme of energy transfer, based on the original proposals of Slater (60, cf. 61):

$$\text{electron carrier}^1_{\text{red}} + \text{carrier}^2_{\text{ox}} + I + X \longleftrightarrow \text{carrier}^1_{\text{ox}} + \text{carrier}^2_{\text{red}} + \mathrm{I{\sim}X} \quad (1)$$

$$I{\sim}X + P_i \longleftrightarrow X{\sim}P + I \quad (2)$$

$$X{\sim}P + ADP \longleftrightarrow ATP + X \quad (3)$$

$I{\sim}X$ may be considered to represent a high-energy intermediate identified by its susceptibility to uncoupling agents, but not Table 1 antibiotics, and by its utilization for cation transport and reversed electron transport. Reaction 2, and possibly 3, are susceptible to oligomycin, and reaction 3, and possibly 2, to aurovertin. The development of this scheme is best derived from the reviews of Ernster and co-workers (18, 19), and Lehninger (40). We will not discuss the nature of the "primary high-energy intermediate" $X{\sim}I$ generated by the respiratory chain, which may be an electrochemical potential (45), a protein conformational change (3), or even a hitherto nonconceptualized state, rather than the chemical compound depicted here. This has been recently reviewed by Lardy and Ferguson (34). It is also noteworthy that Jones and Boyer (28) have interpreted P_i-$H_2{}^{18}O$ experiments as evidence that phosphate does not form a convalent bond during its "activation" for combination with ADP, which is a requirement of this scheme.

Deductions on the validity of this model would obviously be improved if the exact nature of the sites reacting with the inhibitors were further identified. The experiments so far have emphasized the similarity of Table 1 antibiotics. Other studies have probed their differences and have resulted in identification of individual enzymes or proteins as the receptor sites.

IDENTIFICATION OF THE SUSCEPTIBLE SITES IN MITOCHRONDRIA

Oligomycins. Racker and co-workers fractionated mitochondrial extracts in a search for cofactors of the energy-transfer system. Their studies led to the purification of two proteins which appear to be involved in the synthesis of ATP.

The first of these is factor 1 (F_1), an oligomycin-insensitive, Mg^{++}-dependent adenosine triphosphatase (52). It has a molecular weight of 284,000 probably made up of about 10 subunits (48), and there is very good evidence (29, 54) that it is identical with the "inner membrane spheres" already referred to.

Racker et al. also obtained "factor 0" (F_0). This they further purified to "CF_0" (34) from which McLellan and Tzagaloff derived "oligomycin-sensitivity conferring protein" (OSCP), with a molecular weight of about 18,000 (43). OSCP lacks enzyme activity itself; yet, when combined with purified F_1 in the presence of a lipid-containing component, it confers oligomycin sensitivity on the F_1 adenosine triphosphatase. It is probable that oligomycin binds to OSCP, and there is inferential evidence that OSCP occurs in the stalk attaching the inner membrane spheres (F_1) to the cristae membranes (32, 42). Oligomycin has been an important tool in the characterization of these proteins of the mitochondrial energy-transfer system.

It is intriguing that oligomycin also inhibits the $(Na^+ + K^+)$-requiring adenosine triphosphatase extracted from erythrocytes (21), brain (1, 26), or the eel electric organ (21). The sites on these enzymes sensitive to oligomycin may be similar to that on the mitochondrial phosphorylating system, allowing the possibility of a common enzymatic mechanism.

Aurovertin. Thorough comparisons of the effects of aurovertin with those of oligomycin have revealed several differences. The adenosine triphosphatase of mitochondria and submitochondrial particles is much less susceptible to aurovertin than oligomycin (*see below*); aurovertin does not enhance phosphorylation in submitochondrial particles (19, 39); and, lastly, aurovertin directly inhibits the adenosine triphosphatase activity of isolated F_1 from either heart or liver mitochondria (33, 34). The inference that aurovertin binds to F_1 has been confirmed by the discovery of Chance, Lardy, and Chiu-Lin (*data to be published*) that aurovertin when added to mitochondria forms a fluorescent product, with an excitation maximum at 380 nm and an emission maximum at 474 nm.

In this laboratory, it has been found that purified F_1 forms the fluorescent complex with aurovertin. The combining weight of F_1 with one molecule of aurovertin is 250,000 to 350,000 daltons, indicating 1:1 stiochiometry between enzyme and this inhibitor. A most interesting result is that ATP (Fig. 3) and especially phosphate, but not ADP, depress the fluorescence, but without altering the position of the fluorescence maximum, or the stoichiometry of combination. The inference is that both ATP and P_i alter the conformation of the protein. It appears that aurovertin will prove an invaluable tool for kinetic studies of the F_1 protein, which probably catalyzes the terminal energy transfer reaction.

Atractylate and bongkrekic acid. Since the initial experiments of Vignais (68) and Bruni (6) and their co-workers on the inhibition of oxidative phosphorylation by atractyloside, many differences between the inhibitory effects of atractyloside and the oligomycins have been uncovered (e.g., 4, 5, 30). Recent work in our laboratory has shown that the effects of bongkrekic acid parallel those of atractyloside,

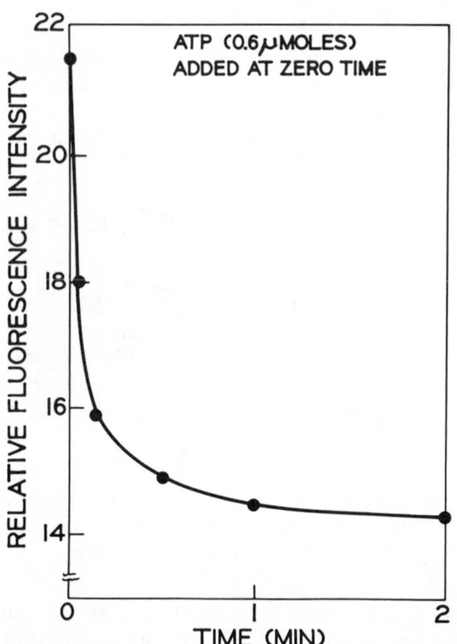

Fig. 3. *ATP depression of the fluorescence of aurovertin + F_1 complex. Aurovertin (4 μg) and F_1 (16 μg) were suspended in 0.25 M mannitol, 0.027 M sucrose, 0.012 M Tris SO_4 (pH 7.4; final volume, 1.0 ml). ATP was added after maximal fluorescence had been achieved as measured with an Aminco Bowman spectrophotofluorometer. From an experiment conducted by Chien-Ho Chiu-Lin.*

and two types of experiment revealing their differences from oligomycins and aurovertin are depicted in Fig. 4 and 5. Figure 4 shows that bongkrekic acid, atractylate, rutamycin, and aurovertin inhibited the uncoupler-accelerated adenosine triphosphatase of intact mitochondria. Atractyloside and bongkrekic acid were completely ineffective on the Mg^{++}-requiring adenosine triphosphatase of submitochondrial particles, prepared with a detergent (deoxycholate) or by sonic treatment, whereas rutamycin and aurovertin were as effective as with intact mitochondria. It may be deduced from this, and many other experiments reported elsewhere, that bongkrekic acid and atractyloside do not affect the energy-transfer system per se. Also, since the particles are probably "inside out" with respect to the intact mitochondria (38, 71), bongkrekic acid and atractyloside may be preventing translocation of ADP or ATP to the enzymatic sites *inside* intact mitochondria.

This has been confirmed by the demonstration that mitochondria possess an adenine nucle-

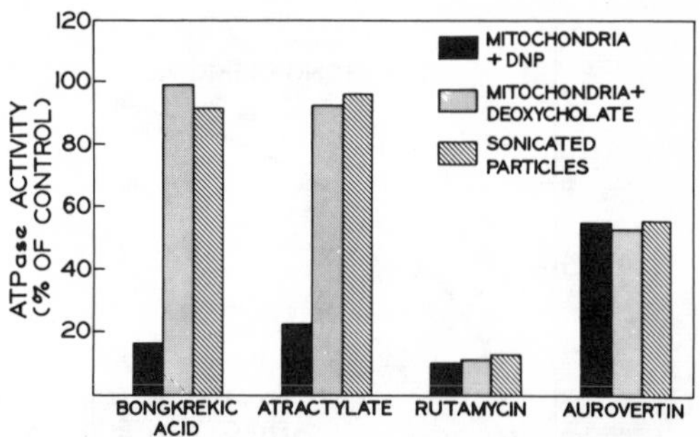

Fig. 4. *Efficiency of each antibiotic's inhibition of the adenosine triphosphatase of intact and particulate mitochondria. Portions of the particles prepared by sonic treatment or by treatment of the whole mitochondria with 1 mM deoxycholate were incubated at 30 C in tubes containing 6 mM Tris ATP, 20 mM triethanolamine Cl, 60 mM KCl, 70 mM sucrose, and 1.5 mM $MgCl_2$. Dinitrophenol 0.1 mM was included in all of the tubes containing the intact mitochondria. P_i released in tubes containing saturating amounts of each antibiotic is expressed as a percentage of that in the controls.*

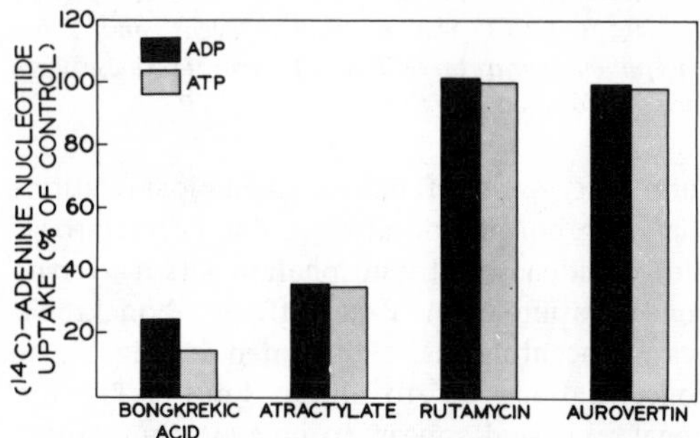

Fig. 5. *Efficiency of each antibiotic's inhibition of the adenine nucleotide translocase of rat liver mitochondria. Uptake of (^{14}C)-ADP or -ATP (0.33 mM) was measured in the presence of 12 nmoles of bongkrekic acid/mg of protein, 100 nmoles of atractylate/mg, 4 nmoles of rutamycin/mg, or 6 nmoles of aurovertin/mg, and in controls.*

otide translocase which is inhibited by atractyloside (4, 25, 31, 66) and also by bongkrekic acid. A typical experiment revealing this is shown in Fig. 5. The uptake of ADP or ATP, labeled with ^{14}C, into mitochondria in exchange for endogenous nucleotide was measured. Bongkrekic acid and atractyloside inhibited by 60 to 80%, whereas rutamycin and aurovertin were completely inactive.

Dose-response curves (16) for the antibiotics' inhibition of the uncoupler-accelerated adenosine triphosphatase of intact mitochondria are shown in Fig. 6. A linear relationship is obtained

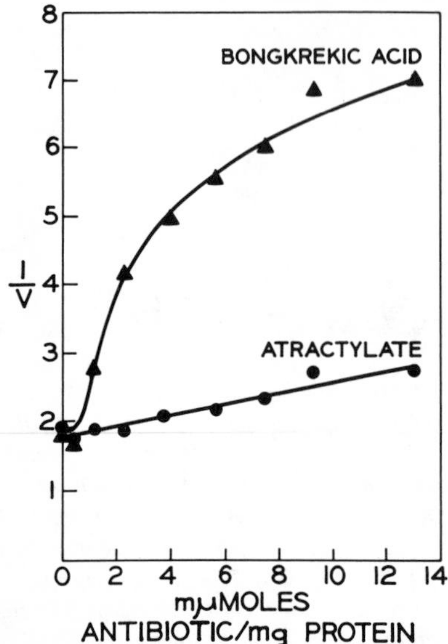

Fig. 6. *Dixon plot of bongkrekic acid and atractylate inhibition of adenosine triphosphatase of rat liver mitochondria. Conditions similar to Fig. 4 except that 7 × 10^{-7} M ClCCP was uncoupling agent, and 5 mM phosphoenolpyruvate + 50 μg of pyruvate kinase were included to regenerate the hydrolyzed ATP.*

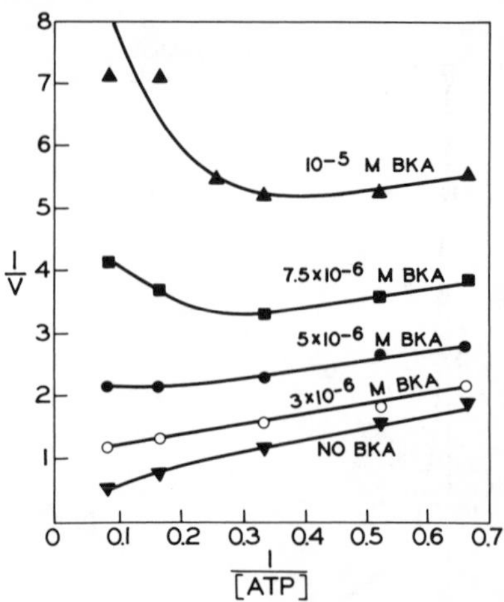

Fig. 7. *Double reciprocal plot of bongkrekic acid inhibition of adenosine triphosphatase. Conditions of Figure 6, but without the regeneration system.*

for atractyloside (cf. 6, 66); a sigmoidal relationship, for bongkrekic acid. A double reciprocal plot of adenosine triphosphatase activity versus concentration of ATP at different bongkrekic acid concentrations is presented in Fig. 7; at concentrations up to about 3 mM ATP, the bongkrekic acid appears to be an uncompetitive inhibitor. The curvature appearing above 3 mM ATP may be due to inhibition of the adenosine triphosphatase enzyme by the ADP product, a point which is under further investigation. Under similar conditions, different atractyloside levels produce converging straight lines indicative of competitive inhibition (8). Winkler and Lehninger (71) have deduced that the translocase has separate sites for atractyloside and adenine nucleotide, which is the best available support for Vignais' suggestion (66) that it is an allosteric enzyme. It reveals a paradox, however, in that competitive-type kinetics are supposed to demonstrate competition between inhibitor and substrate for the same site.

Other energy-transfer inhibitors. The antibiotic Dio-9 has been shown to inhibit energy transfer in rat liver mitochondria (23). However, in the absence of phosphate, it also appeared to be an uncoupling agent, a property which may have been related to an induction of mitochondrial swelling (23). It caused a mild inhibition of beef-heart F_1 adenosine triphosphatase activity, but was much more effective on yeast F_1 (53, 57). Like phloridzin and Atabrine, it is a potent inhibitor of energy transfer in chloroplasts, a system not susceptible to oligomycin (9, 41). It should also be mentioned that *NN'*-dicyclohexylcarbodiimide (DCCD) imitated the effects of oligomycin on beef heart mitochondria and submitochondrial particles (54, 55). However, its usefulness is limited by the long preincubation time necessary to observe its effects. In our hands, concentrations necessary to inhibit energy transfer in short-term experiments on rat liver mitochondria also caused some uncoupling.

DISCUSSION

Study of individual enzymes. Antibiotic experiments have revealed that the enzymatic activity of F_1 may be modified by aurovertin, or by oligomycin in the presence of a specific protein (OSCP) and an insoluble fraction. Conformational changes of F_1 are indicated by the induction of polarized fluorescence by aurovertin, and suppression of this fluorescence by ATP and P_i. Further studies to elucidate the metabolic control of this enzyme may be essential to our understanding of the energy-transfer process. Similarly, the physiological function of OSCP is far from clear.

Adenine nucleotide concentrations in cytoplasm and mitochondria affect the activity of many regulatory enzymes (22). Transport of nucleotides between the compartments is effected by the translocase enzyme, which may therefore have a fundamental regulatory role (31). The probably allosteric modification of the enzyme by bongkrekic acid and atractyloside may point to the existence of a physiological effector (cf. 66); at present, these antibiotics are revealing the potential (in terms of kinetics) of this enzyme, and may provide a means toward its purification.

Significance of stiochiometry. From Table 1, it is apparent that 0.2 to 0.6 nmoles of the antibiotics per mg of protein causes inhibition of oxidative phosphorylation even though there are at least three different susceptible sites. These figures are in close agreement with the concentrations of cytochromes (11, 61) and also of the F_1 protein (5 to 10% of mitochondrial protein or 0.18 to 0.36 nmoles/mg of protein) in both rat liver and beef heart mitochondria. It may be tentatively concluded that respiration, energy transfer, and adenine nucleotide translocase enzymes are present in similar amounts. This may indicate an integration of the functions of phosphorylation and translocation components.

Development of concepts. It has already been shown how the oligomycins have contributed to the formulation of a hypothetical mechanism of oxidative phosphorylation, although experimental evidence has since indicated some shortcomings of this theory. Selwyn and Dawson (59) have proposed some new views of older theories that emphasize the integration of translocation, respiration, and energy-transfer enzymes, which was inferred in the previous section. They also circumvented a definition of the nature of the high-energy intermediates. Our interpretation of their proposals is depicted in Fig. 8. They suggest that the charge separation caused by ADP uptake in exchange for ATP (31), and the *p*H gradient established by P_i uptake in exchange for OH^- ions (14), are compensated by the electron transport generation of one negative charge internally (as hydroxyl ion), as well as the production of a hydroxyl ion in the internal phosphorylation of ADP. We do not wish to discuss the detailed evidence for and against this scheme (for example, it seems to ignore the probably electrogenic nature of Ca^{++} transport), but perhaps experiments combining the inhibitory properties of oligomycin and aurovertin on energy-transfer reactions, atractylate and bongkrekic acid on nucleotide translocation, and

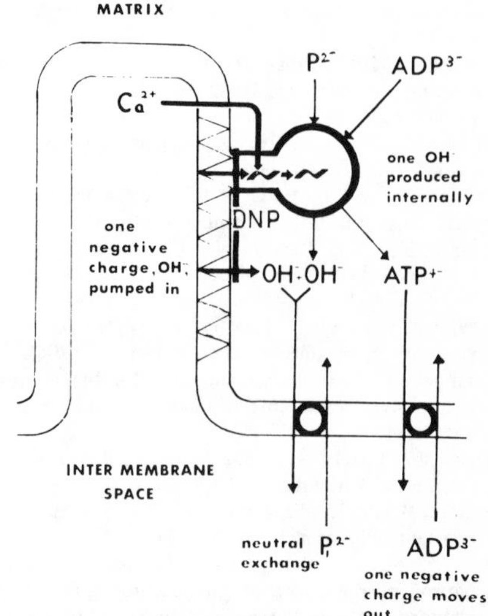

Fig. 8. *Scheme for mechanism of mitochondrial oxidative phosphorylation. A single invagination of the inner mitochondrial membrane is shown. Adapted from Selwyn and Dawson (59).*

sulfhydryl reagents on phosphate translocation (63) will shed some light on its validity.

ACKNOWLEDGMENTS

This investigation was supported by grants from the National Institutes of Health, the National Science Foundation, and the Life Insurance Medical Research Fund.

We greatly appreciated the opportunity to discuss current ideas on oxidative phosphorylation with Peter Reed and Shelagh Ferguson.

P.J.F.H. is the recipient of a Fulbright Travel Award.

LITERATURE CITED

1. Askari, A., and D. Koyal. 1968. Different oligomycin sensitivities of the $Na^+ + K^+$-activated ATPase and its partial reactions. Biochem. Biophys. Res. Commun. 32:227–232.
2. Baldwin, C. L., L. C. Weaver, R. M. Brooker, T. N. Jacobsen, C. E. Osborne, and M. A. Nash. 1964. Biological and chemical properties of aurovertin: a metabolic product of calcarisporium arbuscula. Lloydia (Cincinnati) **27**:88–95.
3. Boyer, P. D. 1965. Carboxyl activation and phosphorylation, p. 994–1008. *In* T. E. King, H. S. Mason, and M. Morrison (ed.), Oxidases and related redox systems, vol. 2. John Wiley and Sons, Inc., New York.
4. Bruni, A. 1966. Mechanism of action of atractyloside. BBA (Biochim. Biophys. Acta) Libr. 7:275–291.
5. Bruni, A., and G. F. Azzone. 1964. The sites of action of atractyloside and oligomycin in the mitochondrial energy-transfer system. Biochim. Biophys. Acta **93**:462–474.
6. Bruni, A., A. R. Contessa, and S. Luciani. 1962. Atractyloside as inhibitor of energy transfer reactions in liver mitochondria. Biochim. Biophys. Acta **60**:301–311.
7. Bruni, A., A. R. Contessa, and P. Scalella. 1965. The binding of atractyloside and oligomycin to liver mitochondria. Biochim. Biophys. Acta **100**:1–12.
8. Bruni, A., S. Luciani, and C. Bortignan. 1965. Competitive reversal by adenine nucleotides of atractyloside effect on

mitochondrial energy transfer. Biochim. Biophys. Acta **97**:434–441.
9. Carmeli, C. 1969. Properties of ATPase in choloroplasts. Biochim. Biophys. Acta **189**:256–266.
10. Chamberlin, J. W., M. Gorman, and A. Agtarap. 1969. Characterization of the oligomycins and related antibiotics. Biochem. Biophys. Res. Commun. **34**:448–453.
11. Chance, B., and B. Hess. 1959. Electron transfer in the mammalian cell. J. Biol. Chem. **234**:2404–2412.
12. Chance, B., and G. R. Williams. 1956. The respiratory chain and oxidative phosphorylation. Advan. Enzymol. **17**:65–134.
13. Chappell, J. B. 1964. Oxidation of citrate, isocitrate, and cis-aconitate by mitochondria. Biochem. J. **90**:225–237.
14. Chappell, J. B. 1968. Systems used for the transport of substrates into mitochondria. Brit. Med. Bull. **24**:150–157.
15. Delcambe, L. (ed.) 1966-68. International Centre of Information on Antibiotics Bulletin, Liege, Belgium, vol. 4–6.
16. Dixon, M. 1953. The determination of enzyme inhibitor constants. Biochem. J. **55**:170–171.
17. Ernster, L., G. Dallner, and G. F. Azzone. 1963. Comparison of the effects of rotenone and amytal on mitochondrial electron and energy transfer and titration of the respiratory chain with rotenone. Biochem. Biophys. Res. Commun. **10**:23–27.
18. Ernster, L., and C-P. Lee. 1964. Biological oxidoreductions. Ann. Rev. Biochem. **33**:729–788.
19. Ernster, L., C-P. Lee, and S. Janda. 1967. The reaction sequence in oxidative phosphorylation, p. 29–51. *In* E. C. Slater, E. C. Kaniuga, and L. Wojtczak (ed.), Biochemistry of mitochondria. Academic Press Inc., New York.
20. Estabrook, R. W. 1962. Observations on the antimycin A inhibition of biological oxidations. Biochim. Biophys. Acta **60**:236–248.
21. Glynn, I. M. 1963. Transport ATPase in electric organ. The relation between ion transport and oxidative phosphorylation. J. Physiol. **169**:452–465.
22. Goodwin, T. W. 1968. Metabolic roles of citrate. Biochem. Soc. Symp. **27**:1–133.
23. Guillory, R. J. 1964. The action of dio-9: an inhibitor and uncoupler of oxidative phosphorylation. Biochim. Biophys. Acta **89**:197–207.
24. Hagihara, B. 1961. Techniques for the application of polarography to mitochondrial respiration. Biochim. Biophys. Acta **46**:134–142.
25. Heldt, H. W., H. Jacobs, and M. Klingenberg. 1965. Endogenous ADP of mitochondria, an early acceptor of oxidative phosphorylation as disclosed by kinetic studies with ^{14}C labelled ADP or ATP, and with atractyloside. Biochem. Biophys. Res. Commun. **18**:174–179.
26. Jarnefelt, J. 1962. Properties and possible mechanism of the Na^{+} + K^{+}-stimulated microsomal ATPase. Biochim. Biophys. Acta **59**:643–654.
27. Johnson, D., and H. Lardy. 1967. Isolation of liver or kidney mitochondria, p. 94–96. *In* S. P. Colowick and N. O. Kaplan (ed.), Methods in enzymology, vol. 10. Academic Press Inc., New York.
28. Jones, D. H., and P. D. Boyer. 1969. The apparent absolute requirement of ADP for the P_iH_2O exchange of oxidative phosphorylation. J. Biol. Chem. **244**:5767–5772.
29. Kagawa, Y., and E. Racker. 1966. Correlation of morphology and function in submitochondrial particles. J. Bio. Chem. **241**:2475–2482.
30. Kemp, A., and E. C. Slater. 1964. The site of action of atractyloside. Biochim. Biophys. Acta **92**:178–180.
31. Klingenberg, M., and E. Pfaff. 1968. Metabolic control in mitochondria by adenine nucleotide translocation. Biochem. Soc. Symp. **27**:105–122.
32. Kopaczyk, K., J. Asai, D. W. Allmann, T. Oda, and D. E. Green. 1968. Resolution of the repeating unit of the inner mitochondrial membrane. Arch. Biochem. Biophys. **123**:602–621.
33. Lardy, H. A., J. L. Connelly, and D. Johnson. 1964. Inhibition of phosphoryl transfer in mitochondria by oligomycin and aurovertin. Biochemistry **3**:1961–1968.
34. Lardy, H. A., and S. M. Ferguson. 1969. Oxidative phosphorylation in mitochondria. Annu. Rev. Biochem. **38**:991–1034.
35. Lardy, H. A., S. N. Graven, and S. Estrada-O. 1967. Specific induction and inhibition of cation and anion transport in mitochondria. Fed. Proc. **26**:1355–1360.
36. Lardy, H. A., and H. Wellman. 1953. The catalytic effect of 2,4-dinitrophenol on ATP hydrolysis by celi particles and soluble enzymes. J. Biol. Chem. **201**:357–370.
37. Lardy, H. A., P. Witonsky, and D. Johnson. 1965. Comparative effectiveness of oligomycins A, B, C, and rutamycin as inhibitors of phosphoryl transfer reactions in mitochondria. Biochemistry **4**:552.
38. Lee, C. P., and L. Ernster. 1966. The energy-linked nicotinamide nucleotide transhydrogenase reaction. BBA Biochim. Biophys. Acta Libr. **7**:218–234.
39. Lee, C. P., L. Ernster, and B. Chance. 1969. Studies of the energy-transfer system of submitochondrial particles. Kinetic studies of the effect of oligomycin on the respiratory chain of EDTA particles. Eur. J. Biochem. **8**:153–163.
40. Lehninger, A. L. 1965. The mitochondrion. W. A. Benjamin, Inc., New York.
41. McCarty, R. E., R. J. Guillory, and E. Racker. 1965. Dio-9, an inhibitor of coupled electron transport and phosphorylation in chloroplasts. J. Biol. Chem. **240**:4822–4823.
42. McLennan, D. H., and J. Asai. 1968. Localization of the oligomycin sensitivity conferring protein. Biochem. Biophys. Res. Commun. **33**:441–447.
43. McLennan, D. H., and Tzagoloff, A. 1968. Purification and characterization of the oligomycin sensitivity conferring protein. Biochemistry **7**:1603–1610.
44. Masamune, S., J. M. Sehgal, E. E. Van Tamelen, F. M. Strong, and W. H. Peterson. 1958. Separation and characterization of oligomycins A, B, and C. J. Amer. Chem. Soc. **80**:6092–6095.
45. Mitchell, P. 1966. Chemiosmotic coupling in oxidative and photosynthetic phosphorylation. Glynn Research Ltd., Bodmin, England (condensed version in Biol. Rev. **41**:445).
46. Morrison, J. F., and R. A. Peters. 1954. Biochemistry of fluoroacetate poisoning: the effect of fluorocitrate on purified aconitase. Biochem. J. **58**:473–479.
47. Nishimura, M., T. Ito, and B. Chance. 1962. A sensitive and rapid method of determination of photophosphorylation. Biochim. Biophys. Acta **59**:177–182.
48. Penefsky, H. S., and R. C. Warner. 1965. Studies on the mechanism of cold inactivation of mitochondrial ATPase. J. Biol. Chem. **240**:4694–4702.
49. Pressman, B. C. 1967. Biological applications of ion-specific glass electrodes, p. 714–726. *In* S. P. Colowick and N. O. Kaplan (ed.), Methods in enzymology, vol. 10. Academic Press Inc., New York.
50. Pressman, B. C. 1968. Inophorous antibiotics as models for biological transport. Fed. Proc. **27**:1283–1288.
51. Prouty, W. F., H. K. Schnoes, and F. M. Strong. 1969. A molecular weight revision for compounds of the oligomycin complex. Biochem. Biophys. Res. Commun. **34**:511–516.
52. Pullman, M. E., H. S. Penefsky, A. Datta, and E. Racker. 1960. I. Purification and properties of soluble, dinitrophenol-stimulated ATPase. J. Biol. Chem. **235**:3322–3328.
53. Pullman, M. E., and G. Schatz. 1967. Mitochondrial

oxidations and energy coupling. Annu. Rev. Biochem. **36**:539–610.

54. Racker, E., and L. L. Horstman. 1967. Structure and function of submitochondrial particles completely resolved with respect to coupling factor. J. Biol. Chem. **242**:2547–2551.
55. Roberton, A. M., C. T. Holloway, I. G. Knight, and R. B. Beechey. 1968. A comparison of the effects of NN′-dicyclohexylcarbodiimide, oligomycin A and aurovertin on energy-linked reactions in mitochondria and submitochondrial particles. Biochem. J. **108**:445–456.
56. Sanadi, D. R. 1965. Energy-linked reactions in mitochondria. Annu. Rev. Biochem. **34**:21–48.
57. Schatz, G., H. F. Penefsky, and E. Racker. 1967. Interaction of purified mitochondrial adenosine triphosphatase from baker's yeast with submitochondrial particles from beef heart. J. Biol. Chem. **242**:2552–2560.
58. Santi, R. 1958. Potassium atractylate, a new inhibitor of the tricarboxylic acid cycle. Nature (London) **182**:257.
59. Selwyn, M. J., and A. P. Dawson. 1969. Proton transport in mitochondrial oxidative phosphorylation. Biochem. J. **114**:90P.
60. Slater, E. C. 1953. Mechanism of phosphorylation in the respiratory chain. Nature (London) **172**:975–978.
61. Slater, E. C. 1966. The respiratory chain and oxidative phosphorylation: some of the unsolved problems, p. 1–10. *In* E. C. Slater, Z. Kaniuga, and L. Wocjtzak (ed.), Biochemistry of mitochondria. Academic Press Inc., New York.
62. Smith, R. M., W. H. Peterson, and E. McCoy. 1954. Oligomycin, a new antifungal antibiotic. Antibiot. Chemother.–1953, p. 962–970.
63. Tyler, D. D. 1969. Evidence of a phosphate-transporter system in the inner membrane of isolated mitochondria. Biochem. J. **111**:665–678.
64. Umbreit, W. W., R. H. Burris, and J. F. Stauffer. 1964. Manometric techniques, p. 169–170. Burgess Publishing Co., Minneapolis, Minn.
65. van Veen, A. G. 2966. Toxic properties of some unusual foods. Nat. Acad. Sci. Nat. Res. Counc. Publ. 1354, p. 174–179.
66. Vignais, P. V., E. D. Duee, P. Vignais, and J. Huet. 1966. Effects of atractyligenin and its structural analogues on oxidative phosphorylation and on the translocation of adenine nucleotides in mitochondria. Biochim. Biophys. Acta **118**:465–483.
67. Vignais, P. V., and P. M. Vignais. 1964. Effect of ADP on the inhibition of oxidative phosphorylation by potassium atractylate. Biochem. Biophys. Res. Commun. **14**:559–564.
68. Vignais, P. V., P. M. Vignais, and E. Stanislas. 1962. Action of potassium atractylate on oxidative phosphorylation in mitochondria and submitochondrial particles. Biochim. Biophys. Acta **60**:284–300.
69. Walter, P., H. A. Lardy, and D. Johnson. 1967. Inhibition of phosphoryl transfer reactions in mitochondria by peliomycin, ossamycin and venturicidin. J. Biol. Chem. **242**:5014–5018.
70. Winkler, H. H., F. L. Bygrave, and A. L. Lehninger. 1968. Characterization of the atractyloside-sensitive adenine nucleotide transport system in rat liver mitochondria. J. Biol. Chem. **243**:20–28.
71. Winkler, H. H., and A. L. Lehninger. 1968. The atractyloside-sensitive nucleotide binding site in a membrane preparation from rat liver mitochondria. J. Biol. Chem. **243**:3000-3008.

Antimicrobial Agents and Chemotherapy—1969

Antibiotic Models for Carrier-Mediated Transport Through Membranes

BERTON C. PRESSMAN

Papanicolaou Cancer Research Institute and University of Miami, Miami, Florida 33136

A group of microbial metabolites generically termed "ionophores" are described which form lipid soluble complexes with alkali ions. By a sequence of complexation-decomplexation reactions, ionophores can transport alkali ions across biological membranes, thereby mimicking the action of naturally occurring membrane-bound carriers. Ionophores also resemble natural carriers in their striking ion selectivity, valinomycin complexing K^+ 10,000 times more effectively than Na^+. The complexing behavior and ionic discrimination of ionophores can be related to their structure and conformation as revealed by various physical techniques. Some of the dramatic metabolic effects of ionophore-induced membrane transport on mitochondria in particular are discussed.

This paper will survey some of the more interesting aspects of the interaction of the family of ion-bearing, or "ionophorous" (12), antibiotics with biological systems. The data obtained in this laboratory will be supplemented with selected data reported by other investigators.

Figure 1 presents the structures of several representative ionophorous antibiotics. Since their antibiotic properties are often feeble and they are extremely toxic to animals, it might be more appropriate to refer to them as microbial metabolites rather than antibiotics.

The first ionophore recognized as such is valinomycin (8), a cyclic depsipeptide (13) consisting of 12 alternating amino acid and hydroxy acid residues. Enniatin B is a closely related depsipeptide; it is somewhat less potent and its ring is only half the size of valinomycin. The family of macrotetralide actins, cyclic polyesters containing heterocyclic ether oxygen atoms, are quite different chemically. In nonactin, the R groups of the structure are all methyls; in monactin, dinactin, and trinactin, they are replaced progressively with one, two, or three ethyl groups. All of the compounds described thus far are chemically inert, are devoid of ionizable groups, and are inherently electrically neutral in solution. The salient structural features they share in common are a periodic array of electronegative oxygens and extensive lipophylic regions. Chemically, these compounds all have the ability to form charged lipid-soluble complexes with alkali cations which can diffuse across membranous or bulk-phase lipid barriers, either spontaneously or else at accelerated rates under the influence of an electric potential (12).

Monensin shares many of the properties of the above compounds—periodically spaced oxygen atoms, lipophylic regions, and alkali cation complexing capacity; however, it differs in possessing a terminal carboxyl group. It forms cation complexes in the deprotonated form, i.e., at neutral and higher *p*H so that its complexes are electrically neutral dipolar ions, the charge of the ionized carboxyl offsetting the charge of the complexed cation. In this particular ionophore, the distance between the carboxyl and complexed cation, as determined by X-ray crystallography, precludes any appreciable ionic character of the complexing bonds (1); however, in the case of a related ionophore, nigericin, the carboxyl-cation distance is smaller and the resulting ionic bond makes the complex considerably stronger (14).

The salient topological features of the valinomycin- and monensin-type ionophores are shown in Fig. 2. The valinomycin-type ionophores are electrically neutral molecules which form complexes by engulfing alkali ions by means of ion-dipole ligands to electronegative

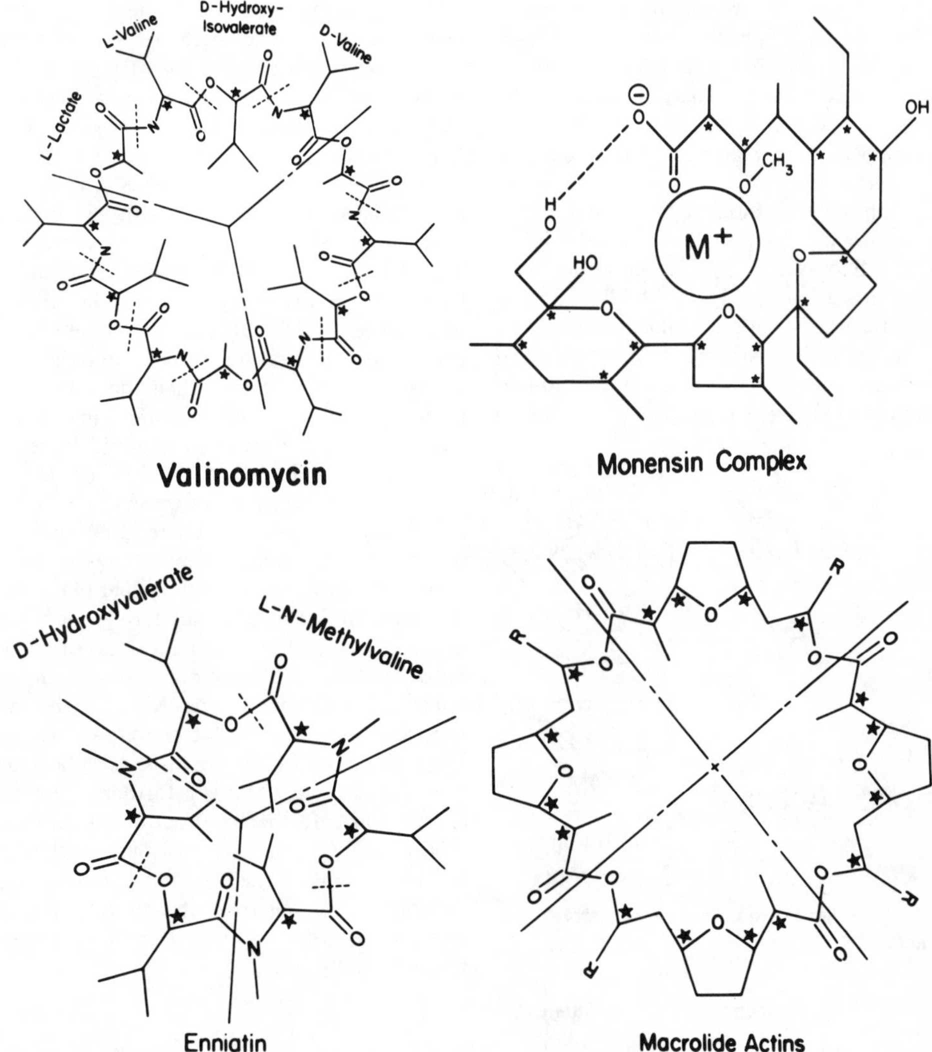

Fig. 1. *Structure of representative ionophores.*

oxygen atoms critically deployed in space. The lipophylic groups orient towards the exterior of the complex, thereby conferring overall lipophylicity. The monensin-type ionophores are linear rather than cyclic in the uncomplexed, protonated state. At an appropriately high *p*H, they are capable of wrapping themselves about cations by a structure strengthened by head-to-tail intramolecular hydrogen bonding (1), forming complexes analogous to the valinomycin-type ionophores save for their dipolar ionic character.

Although the ionophores were originally investigated as antibiotic agents, insight into their mechanism of action came through studies of their effects on animal mitochondria. If valinomycin is added to a suspension of mitochondria isolated from animal cells (Fig. 3) by means of a K^+ selective glass electrode, the energy-dependent transfer of K^+ from the medium into the mitochondria can be monitored on a continual basis (8, 11, 12). A concomitant expulsion of protons (i.e., extramitochondrial *p*H drop) occurs, along with a decrease of light scattering of the suspension signifying an increase in mitochondrial volume (i.e., water uptake). The subsequent addition of nigericin reverses all these changes. Time does not permit going into the details of why the two ionophores appear to have diametrically opposite effects on mitochondrial transport, but the opposing effects appear to derive from the charged nature of the valinomycin-type complexes as opposed to the neutral dipolar ionic character of the nigericin-type complexes (11).

These physical methods of information retrieval are even capable of following the interaction of valinomycin with mitochondria within a living cell suspension. Figure 4 illustrates an immediate marked light-scattering decrease from whole ascites cells analogous to that obtained from isolated mitochondria on the addition of valinomycin (15). Light is particularly prone to scattering from particles of the same approximate size as its wavelength. Hence, despite the abundance of potential light-scattering material within and on the surface of these cells, the scattering function measured appears to be selective for mitochondria. The increase of scattering due to the uptake of K^+ and water by mitochondria is associated with an increased respiratory rate indicative of the energy load imposed on the cell by valinomycin-induced transport. In these experiments, the predominant element in the *p*H trace is the net chemical production of acid through glycolysis of the substrate glucose, rather than the transport of protons across the cell membrane in a manner analogous to the cause of the *p*H trace with isolated mitochondria. Addition of the uncoupler *m*-chlorocyanocarbonylphenylhydrazone, which depletes mitochondrial energy reserves in the same manner described for dinitrophenol in the previous paper (4), reverses the mitochondrial light scattering, i.e., water uptake. Presumably, as in the case of isolated mitochondria, this is associated with intracellular redistribution of the K^+, but the latter process in this case cannot be followed directly. Upon the onset of anaerobiosis, as indicated by the oxygen trace, there is a further depletion of energy and a further contraction of mitochondria, resulting in the return of their scattering to the initial value. Thus, by appropriate physical techniques, we can track the relocation of ions and water within a living cell in response to physiologically active agents.

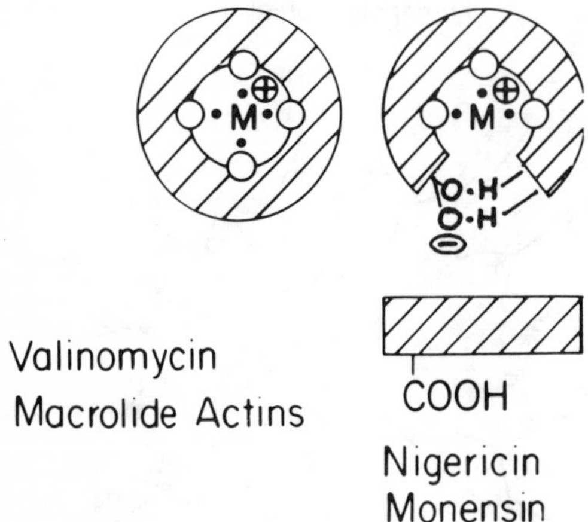

Fig. 2. *Symbolic representation of ionophore complex structures.*

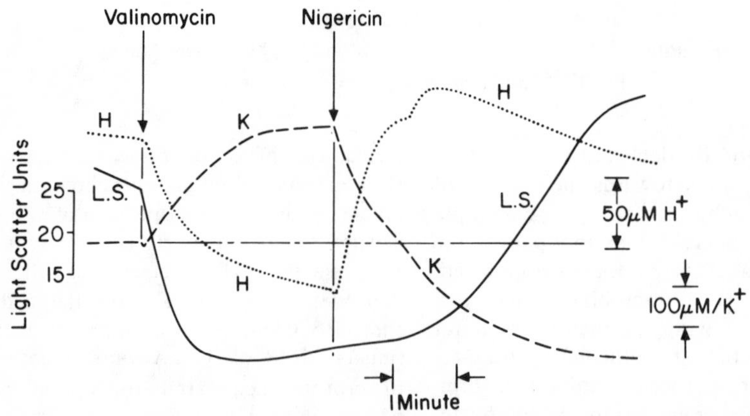

Fig. 3. *Three parameter recording of the interaction of valinomycin and nigericin with mitochondria (rat liver). K^+ and H^+ transport were measured with specific ion glass electrodes, upward deflection indicating entry into the mitochondria. Downward deflection of light scattering (L.S.) denotes uptake of water by mitochondria. The system was energized by the oxidation of glutamate and malate as substrates.*

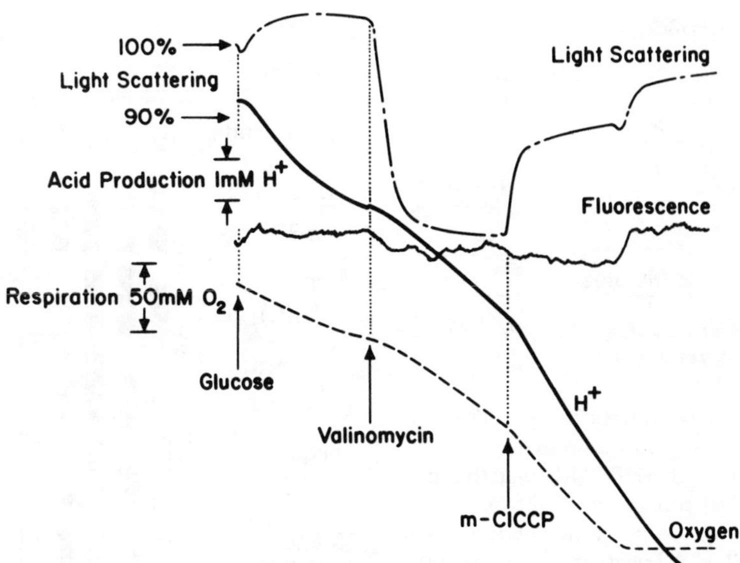

Fig. 4. *Effect of valinomycin on the transport properties of mitochondria within intact ascites cells. In addition to the parameters measured in Fig. 3, oxygen was measured polarographically. m-ClCCP = m-chlorocyanocarbonylphenylhydrazone.*

Information of a different category can be obtained by quantitating the valinomycin-induced uptake of K^+ by mitochondria and the corresponding amount of energy expended. In Fig. 5, the hydrolysis of adenosine triphosphate (ATP) has been used as an energy source for transport (cf. Fig. 3, where the energy source is oxidation of substrate), while the gradient against which the K^+ moves is varied by progressively altering the extramitochondrial K^+ concentration. At optimal K^+ concentrations, as many as seven equivalents of K^+ are transported for each ATP hydrolyzed (2). One use of such stoichiometries is to evaluate mechanisms proposed for oxidative phosphorylation in mitochondria. For instance the chemiosmotic hypothesis of Mitchell (7) predicts a fixed stoichiometry of two K^+ transported per equivalent ATP hydrolyzed. The experimental observation by us of seven K^+ per ATP constitutes a formidable obstacle to this hypothesis. Regretfully, while our experimental observations can rule out proposed mechanisms for mitochondrial energy transduction, they do not yet of themselves suggest alternative mechanisms.

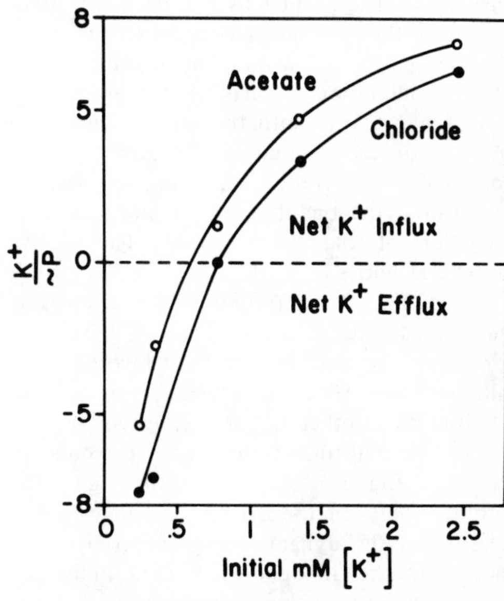

Fig. 5. *Efficiency of mitochondrial K^+ transport as function of K^+ gradient. The system was energized by the hydrolysis of ATP.*

The action of ionophores is not confined to mitochondria. In Fig. 6, we see the discharge of K^+ from human erythrocytes suspended in buffered sucrose by nigericin (12), and, as in the case of mitochondria, a counterion must move for preservation of electrostatic balance across the membrane; in this case, there is a compensatory uptake of protons from the medium. In actual fact, the ionophores transport ions across any form of lipid barrier, including a wide variety of biological membranes, artificial membranes, and bulk organic phases.

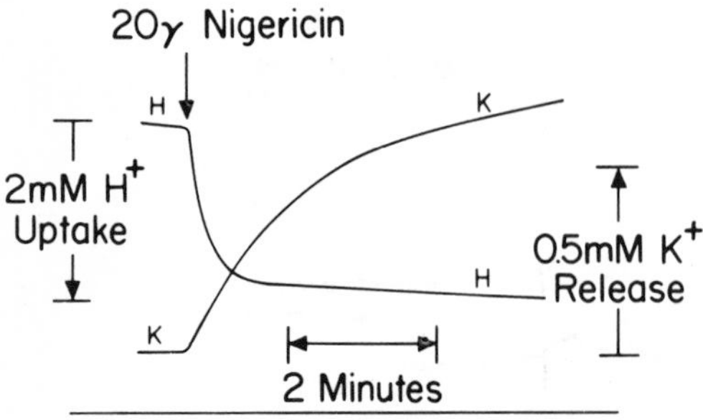

Fig. 6. *Release of K^+ and uptake of H^+ by human erythrocytes in buffered sucrose.*

One of the most interesting properties of ionophores is the extreme cation selectivity of their complexing behavior. Although this phenomenon was first recognized in the interaction between valinomycin and mitochondria where the apparent K^+–Na^+ selectivity is ca. 10,000:1 (8), the intrinsic ion selectivity of ionophores is most objectively measured in model solvent systems (11). Thus, in two-phase water-organic solvent systems, alkali ions will normally partition into the aqueous phase while the ionophores concentrate within the organic phase. Upon equilibration by shaking, the amount of alkali ion migrating into the organic phase is a measure of cation-ionophore complex formation. The concentration of cation required to half saturate the ionophore (K_D) can be taken as a measure of complexing affinity. The relative cationic affinities of a selection of ionophores is given in Fig. 7 as a function of decreasing unhydrated cationic radius. The bars have been normalized by assigning the most favored ion a value of two (i.e., 100%), and the relative affinities of all other ions are expressed logarithmically so that one scale unit represents an affinity difference of 10. On the right, the absolute values of the K_D for K^+ are given as a measure of the dynamic range of complexing ability of the ionophores tested. Individual ionophores display ionic preferences for Cs^+ through Na^+ with various degrees of ionic selectivity. Thus, we now have experimental means of mimicking the extreme ionic selectivity patterns encountered in biological systems by means of rather small molecules which lend themselves to detailed conformational study. This had provided considerable insight into the molecular basis of ionic discrimination of membrane-bound carriers in biological systems.

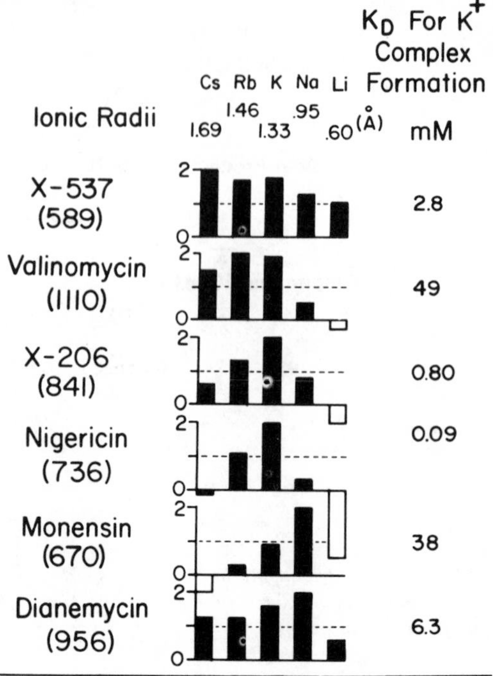

Fig. 7. *Cation selectivity of various ionophores. Complexing was measured by the migration of isotopically labeled cations ($^{13}Cs^+$, $^{86}Rb^+$, $^{42}K^+$, $^{22}Na^+$) from buffered water (pH 10.0) into 30% n-butyl alcohol, 70% toluene.*

One of the simplest types of ionophores known is the synthetic "crown" cyclic polyethers (9). The best known of this group is dicyclohexyl-18-crown-6 (Fig. 8), which contains six ether oxygen atoms. Two points become evident upon the construction of space-filling models of this compound. Firstly, the ring fits the dehydrated K^+ ion rather precisely with all six of the electronegative oxygens coming into close Van der Waals contact with the complexed cation (9). In general, the cations of all ionophores complexes are dehydrated, with the normal water of hydration being replaced by the oxygen system of the ionophore. Secondly, the ionic selectivity of this ionophore (K^+-Na^+>10:1) appears to be related to the poorer fit of the smaller Na^+ with the ring structure.

Random manipulation of molecular models does not readily explain why the 18-ring atom enniatin B and 40-ring atom macrolide actins (Fig. 1) show similar ionic discrimination patterns (K^+-Na^+, ca. 10:1). The explanation of this has come out of X-ray crystallography, which

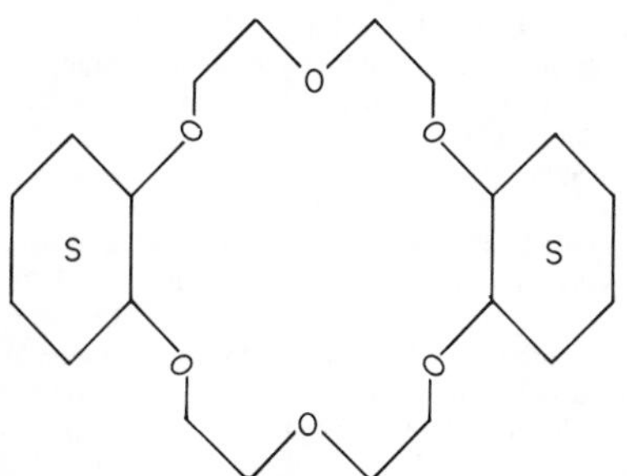

Fig. 8. *Structure of the crown polyether dicyclohexyl-18-crown-6.*

reveals that the large ring of the actins folds over the complexed ion in a conformation resembling "the seam of a tennis ball," with eight oxygen atoms forming ion-dipole ligands in a symmetrical cubic array (6).

The extreme K^+-Na^+ selectivity of valinomycin suggests that there might be something unique in the structure of its complexes. Although the data of Fig. 7 indicate a K^+-Na^+ discrimination ratio of only 60:1, the affinity for Na^+ was here measured indirectly by its ability to displace K^+ from its valinomycin complex. Other direct saturation measurements of valinomycin with Na^+ indicate a K^+-Na^+ discrimination ratio of 10,000:1, more nearly in line with the discrimination ratios encountered in mitochondrial systems (11). Independent studies by nuclear magnetic resonance (5) and X-ray crystallography (10) agree that the 36-atom ring of valinomycin is held in a rigid cylinder conformation by a system of hydrogen bonds between the amide protons and the carbonyl oxygens of the hydroxy acids. The six carbonyls of the amino acid residues, three above and three below the cylinder, ligand to the complexed cation, forming a rigid cage about it. The extreme inflexibility conferred by the secondary structure stabilized by hydrogen bonding makes it understandable that the molecule is too rigid to accommodate a cation of less than optimal radius, such as Na^+, effectively.

Three possible mechanisms have been proposed for the transport of ions across lipid barriers by ionophores; the first is that the ionophore confers a pore at the lipid interphase through which ions enter the hydrophobic phase. This is rendered unlikely by the ability of ionophores to promote cation transport across bulk phases of any thickness and the difficulty of getting ionophores to release their complexed cations in an environment of low dialectric constant (3), such as the interior of a lipid membrane. A second mechanism, stacking to form channels across the lipid barrier, is also rendered unlikely by the same considerations. This tends to support the third mechanism, by which the antibiotic serves as a mobile carrier for cations across the lipid barriers in a manner analogous to the role of natural carriers in biological membranes (3, 11, 12).

In summary, ionophores form highly selective lipid-soluble complexes with cations capable of carrying the latter across virtually any type of lipid barrier. At the small distances involved in biological membranes, they can transport ions extremely effectively; in the case of mitochondria, valinomycin and nigericin exhibit turnover numbers as high as 200 and 500/sec, respectively, rates fully comparable with those of enzymes. They serve as experimental models for natural membrane-bound carrier systems and help predict what attributes to expect in natural carriers which may be isolated in the future. They offer a means of experimentally altering the permeability of membranes which might ultimately prove useful pharmacologically. Finally, their structure is so simple that ionophores can be synthesized, along with analogues, and the conformational details of their mechanism of action can be studied with considerable precision by means of physical techniques.

LITERATURE CITED

1. Agtarap, A., J. W. Chamberlain, M. Pinkerton, and L. Steinrauf. 1967. The structure of monensic acid, a new biologically active compound. J. Amer. Chem. Soc. 89:5737–5738.
2. Cockrell, R. E., E. J. Harris, and B. C. Pressman. 1966. Energetics of potassium transport in mitochondria induced by valinomycin. Biochemistry **5**:2326–2335.
3. Haynes, D. H., A. Kowalsky, and B. C. Pressman. 1969. Application of nuclear magnetic resonance to the conformational changes in valinomycin during complexation. J. Biol. Chem. **244**:502–505.
4. Henderson, P. J. F., and H. A. Lardy. 1970. Antibiotic inhibition of mitochondrial energy-transfer reactions. Antimicrob. Agents Chemother.–1969. p. 18–27.
5. Ivanov, V. T., I. A. Laine, N. D. Abdullaev, L. B. Senuavina, E. M. Popov, Y. A. Ovchennikov, and M. M. Shemyakin. 1969. The physicochemical basis of the functioning of biological membranes: the conformation of valinomycin and its K^+ complex in solution. Biochem. Biophys. Res. Commun. **34**:803–811.
6. Kilbourn, B. T., J. D. Dunitz, L. A. R. Pioda, and W. Simon. 1967. A macrotetrolide antibiotic possessing highly specific K^+ transport properties. J. Mol. Biol. **30**:559–563.
7. Mitchell, P. 1966. Chemiosmotic coupling in oxidative and photosynthetic phosphorylation. Biol. Rev. **41**:445–502.

8. Moore, C., and B. C. Pressman. 1964. Mechanism of action of valinomycin on mitochondria. Biochem. Biophys. Res. Commun. **15**:562–567.

9. Pederson, C. J. 1967. Sylic polyethers and their complexes with metal salts. J. Amer. Chem. Soc. **89**:7017–7036.

10. Pinkerton, M., K. L. Steinrauf, and P. Dawkins. 1969. The molecular structure and some transport properties of valinomycin. Biochem. Biophys. Res. Commun. **35**:512–518.

11. Pressman, B. C. 1968. Ionophorous antibiotics as models for biological transport. Fed. Proc. **27**:1283–1288.

12. Pressman, B. C., E. J. Harris, W. S. Jagger, and J. H. Johnson. 1967. Antibiotic-mediated transport of alkali ions across lipid barriers. Proc. Nat. Acad. Sci. U.S.A. **58**:1949–1956.

13. Shemyakin, M. M. 1960. Die Chemie der Depsipeptide. Angew. Chem. **72**:342–345.

14. Steinrauf, L. K., and M. Pinkerton. 1968. The structure of nigericin. Biochem. Biophys. Res. Commun. **33**:29–31.

15. Wenner, C. E., E. J. Harris, and B. C. Pressman. 1967. Relationship of the light scattering properties of mitochondria to the metabolic state in intact ascites cells. J. Biol. Chem. **242**:3454–3459.

Antimicrobial Agents and Chemotherapy—1969

Pharmacokinetic Evaluation of the Oral Absorption of Different Ampicillin Preparations in Beagle Dogs

B. E. CABANA, L. E. WILLHITE, and M. E. BIERWAGEN

Research Division, Bristol Laboratories, Division of Bristol Myers Co., Syracuse, New York 13201

A pharmacokinetic model was used to describe the absorption, distribution, and elimination characteristics of sodium ampicillin, potassium ampicillin, and ampicillin trihydrate in beagle dogs. Drug concentrations in serum after intravenous administration of sodium ampicillin served as a basis for the kinetic model. The absorption of these compounds was compared in a crossover design after administration of a single oral dose in a loosely packed soft gelatin capsule. The parameters evaluated were maximal concentration (C_{max}), time of maximal concentration (T_{max}), area under the serum level curves, and the rate constant for drug absorption (k_a). The k_a for potassium and sodium ampicillin was significantly greater than that obtained for ampicillin trihydrate, thereby resulting in a shortening of the T_{max}, a higher C_{max}, and two- to threefold higher serum concentration during the first hour. Although the physiological availability of potassium and sodium ampicillin was 16 and 19% more, respectively, than that obtained with ampicillin trihydrate, these differences were not statistically significant. Similar results were obtained after oral administration of sodium ampicillin and ampicillin trihydrate in solution and as a suspension, respectively. Dissolution was not rate-limiting in the oral absorption of sodium ampicillin. Dissolution of ampicillin trihydrate was rate-limiting in terms of absorption rate, but had no significant effect on its physiological availability.

Since its discovery in 1961, ampicillin has been used successfully in the treatment of a wide variety of infections. These include respiratory, intestinal, and urinary tract infections, as well as bacterial meningitis and endocarditis (2, 5, 8, 13). Its popularity is due to the fact that ampicillin is the first semisynthetic, acid-stable penicillin with significant activity against both gram-positive and gram-negative organisms (1, 18).

Despite its wide usage, very little information is available concerning the physiological availability of ampicillin after administration to laboratory animals and humans. A few early publications on the oral absorption of ampicillin can be cited (1, 3). Comparative data on the concentrations of hetacillin, ampicillin, and penicillin G in the blood have also been published (20). Recently, Poole et al. (14) reported on the physiochemical factors influencing the absorption of ampicillin. However, the physiological availability of ampicillin and the pharmacokinetic aspects of its absorption, distribution, and elimination have not been reported.

This report presents a pharmacokinetic analysis of the absorption, distribution, and elimination of sodium ampicillin in beagle dogs after both oral and intravenous administration. In addition, the absorption of two other ampicillin preparations was compared in beagle dogs after oral administration. The parameters evaluated after oral doses were maximal concentration (C_{max}), time of maximal concentration (T_{max}), area under the serum level curves, and the rate constant for drug absorption (k_a). The physiological availability of each preparation was also determined.

MATERIALS AND METHODS

Sodium ampicillin was administered intravenously in isotonic saline at a dose of 300 mg. Sodium ampicillin, potassium ampicillin, and ampicillin trihydrate were administered orally in loosely packed solf-gelatin capsules. Sodium ampicillin and ampicillin trihydrate were also administered orally as a solution and as a fine suspension, respectively. All doses contained bioactivity equivalent to 300 mg of the amphoteric material.

Five beagle dogs weighing 9.0 to 11.0 kg (mean weight 9.8 kg) were used throughout this study in a crossover design. Unless otherwise specified, all dogs were starved overnight (22 to 24 hr). Blood samples were taken from an intravenous catheter (Bardic Intracath) implanted into the saphenous vein. Urine was collected over a 6-hr period by means of lucite-coated stainless-steel cannulae surgically implanted within the bladder of the dogs. Serum and urine specimens were kept in an ice bath or under refrigeration until bioassayed. Bioassays were performed by the cup-plate method (4), with *Sarcina lutea* as the test organism. Ampicillin concentrations were expressed in terms of the free acid.

Drug concentrations in serum were analyzed kinetically by means of a Fortran 4 computer program (12) on an IBM 360/30 digital computer. Nonlinear regression analysis of the serum concentration-time curves and the least squares estimation of the nonlinear parameters were determined according to the method of Marquardt (11). The kinetic equations and the model describing the drug concentrations in serum after intravenous and oral administration were those recently published (15, 16, 22 23). Calculation of the intrinsic absorption rate was determined according to the method of Loo and Riegelman (10). The cumulative amount of ampicillin absorbed (A_t) at any given time t is given by

$$A_t = V_P C_s + k_2 V_P \int_0^t C_s dt + V_P C_T \qquad (1)$$

and the percentage of absorbed ampicillin is given by

$$\frac{A_t}{A_\infty} \cdot 100 = \frac{C_s + k_2 \int_0^t C_s dt + C_T}{k_2 \int_0^\infty C_s dt} \cdot 100 \qquad (2)$$

where C_s is the concentration in serum and C_T is the corresponding concentration in tissue (expressed relative to the concentration in serum) at time t, $\int_0^t C_s dt$ and $\int_0^\infty C_s dt$ are the areas under the serum concentration-time curve at time t and at infinity, respectively, k_2 is the rate constant for total drug elimination from the body, and V_P is the volume of the central compartment (described herein). The intrinsic rate constant (k_a) for the oral absorption of ampicillin was determined by using the following equation

$$\log \frac{A_\infty - A_t}{A_\infty} = -k_a/2.303 \cdot t \qquad (3)$$

and subsequently plotting the log $(A_\infty - A_t)/A_\infty$ versus time t. The slope of such a plot is $-k_{a/2.303}$. The physiological availability of each ampicillin preparation was determined by comparing the area under the serum concentration-time curves after oral administration with that obtained after intravenous administration of sodium ampicillin by the following equation

$$\text{per cent availability} = \frac{\int_0^\infty C_s dt \text{ (oral)}}{\int_0^\infty C_s dt \text{ (iv)}} \cdot 100 \qquad (4)$$

The areas under the serum concentration-time curves were determined by integration of the appropriate equations describing such curves.

The time at which the peak concentration in serum (T_{max}) was achieved after oral administration of ampicillin was determined by means of an interative computer program with the use of the Newton-Raphson method (19). This method was utilized because the serum concentration-time curves were best described by tri-exponential equations which had no mathematical solution in terms of T_{max} after differentiation. The maximal concentration in serum (C_{max}) was determined by substitution of the T_{max} value in the appropriate equations describing the serum concentration-time curves.

The total serum clearances and renal serum clearances of ampicillin were determined from the concentrations in serum obtained from a single intravenous dose, by use of the following equations

$$\text{total serum clearance} = \frac{\text{dose}}{\int_0^\infty C_s dt} = \frac{\text{dose}}{\text{area}} \qquad (5)$$

$$\text{renal serum clearance} = f_e \cdot \text{serum clearance} \qquad (6)$$

where f_e is the fraction of administered ampicillin excreted unchanged.

RESULTS

Intravenous study. Before the absorption kinetics of any drug can be adequately described, the distribution and elimination kinetics must be defined for that drug after administration of an intravenous dose. The mean concentrations in serum obtained with sodium ampicillin in beagle dogs after intravenous administration (300 mg) are illustrated in Fig. 1 with its corresponding least squares nonlinear regression line.

The serum concentration-time curve (Fig. 1) could best be described by the bi-exponential equation

$$C_s = 78.06e^{-8.27t} + 64.83e^{-1.38t} \qquad (7)$$

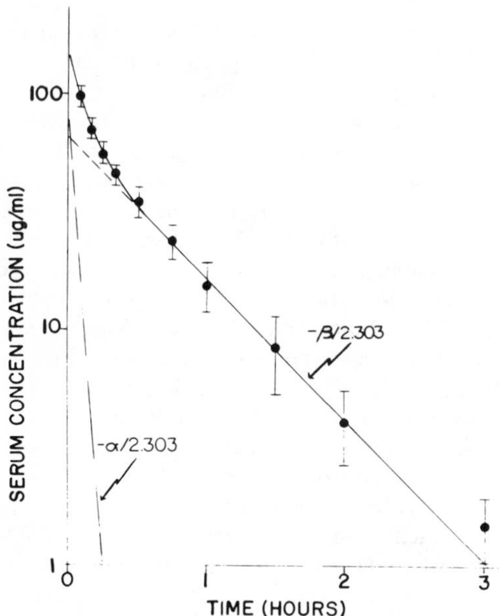

Fig. 1. *Semilogarithmic plots of serum concentrations of ampicillin in beagle dogs describing a two-compartmental open system model.*

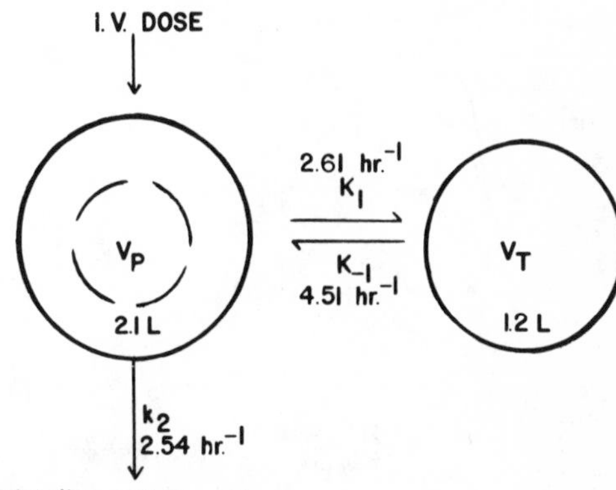

Fig. 2. *Two-compartmental open model describing the distribution and elimination of ampicillin in beagle dogs. Key:* V_P, *central compartment;* V_T, *peripheral tissue compartment.*

where C_s is the concentration in serum (in micrograms per milliliter), and t is the time (in hours). The distribution phase had a half-life of approximately 0.08 hr ($\alpha = 8.27\ hr^{-1}$), whereas the elimination phase had a serum half-life of approximately 0.50 hr ($\beta = 1.38\ hr^{-1}$).

The bi-exponential equation, 7, can best be interpreted in terms of a two-compartmental open system model (15, 16, 21, 22) as depicted in Fig. 2. The model consists of a central compartment (V_P) and a peripheral tissue compartment (V_T) between which ampicillin is a state of complete equilibrium only under steady-state conditions (17). Summarized in Table 1 are the distribution rate constants, K_1 and K_{-1}; the elimination rate constant k_2, evaluated from the bi-exponential equation for the two compartment open model (15, 22); and the sizes of the central (V_P) and tissue compartments (V_T). Also included in Table 1 is the total area under the serum concentration-time curve and the apparent volume of drug distribution (V_D). Thus, after intravenous administration to beagle dogs, ampicillin appears to be rapidly distributed within the extracellular fluids ($V_P \simeq 21\%$ body volume) and to a lesser extent within the peripheral tissue compartment ($V_T \simeq 12\%$ body volume). The biological half-life calculated from the rate constant k_2 is approximately 0.3 hr.

Table 1. *Parameters for the two-compartment open system model estimated from concentrations of sodium ampicillin in serum after intravenous administration of a 300-mg dose to beagle dogs*

Parameter	Value
K_1 (hr^{-1})	2.61
K_{-1} (hr^{-1})	4.51
k_2 (hr^{-1})	2.54
V_P (liters)	2.10
V_T (liters)	1.21
V_D (liters)	3.31
Area (μg-hr per ml)	56.31

The total serum clearance of ampicillin (calculated from equation 5) in the beagles was approximately 88.8 ml/min. Since approximately 73% of the administered dose of ampicillin was excreted unchanged in the 6-hr period, the renal clearance of ampicillin was approximately 64.4 ml/min.

Oral study. The results of a crossover study in beagle dogs in which 300-mg amounts of potassium ampicillin, sodium ampicillin, and ampicillin trihydrate were administered in loosely packed soft-gelatin capsules are shown in Fig. 3 with their respective least squares nonlinear regression lines. Kinetic analysis of the data on concentrations in serum revealed that the individual sets of data were best described by tri-exponential equations (23) having the general form

$$C_s = -Pe^{-\alpha t} + Qe^{-\beta t} + Re^{-kt} \quad (8)$$

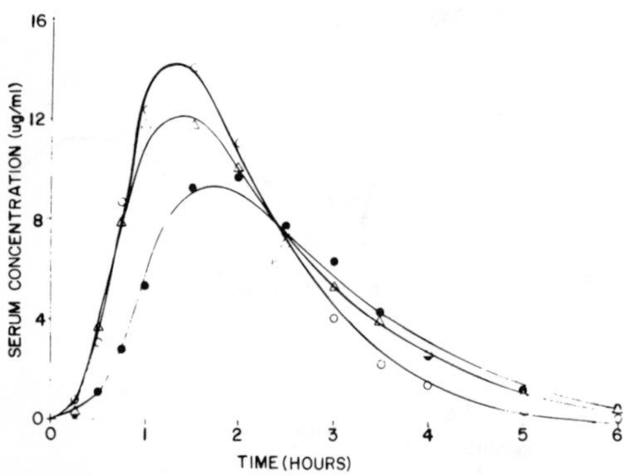

Fig. 3. *Mean concentrations of ampicillin in the serum of beagle dogs after oral administration of 300 mg of sodium ampicillin (○), potassium ampicillin (△), or ampicillin trihydrate (●) in loosely packed soft-gelatin capsules.*

where P is equal to the sum of Q and R; and the constants α, β, and k are hybrid rate constants dependent on the absorption, distribution, and elimination of ampicillin.

Summarized in Table 2 are the parameters T_{max}, C_{max}, k_a, and area, determined for potassium ampicillin, sodium ampicillin, and ampicillin trihydrate after oral administration. The rate of absorption for potassium and sodium ampicillin was significantly greater than that obtained with ampicillin trihydrate (Fig. 4). This enhanced rate resulted in earlier peak concentrations (T_{max}) and higher C_{max} values for both potassium and sodium ampicillin. The peak serum concentrations of potassium and sodium ampicillin were 12.04 and 14.95 μg/ml, respectively, whereas the peak serum concentration of ampicillin trihydrate was 9.1 μg/ml. The extent of oral absorption of potassium ampicillin, sodium ampicillin, and ampicillin trihydrate calculated from equation 4 was 55.7, 57.4, and 46.7%, respectively. These differences were not statistically significant.

The results of a similar study in which the oral absorption of sodium ampicillin and ampicillin trihydrate were compared when administered in solution and as a suspension, respectively, are shown in Fig. 5 with the corresponding nonlinear regression lines. Summarized in Table 3 are the kinetic parameters determined. Although no significant difference in physiological availability (area) was noted between these two preparations (Table 3), the k_a for sodium ampicillin was significantly greater (Fig. 6), thereby resulting in a shortening of T_{max}, higher C_{max}, and higher concentrations in serum during the first 90 min (Fig. 5).

The influence of food intake on the oral absorption of sodium ampicillin (in solution) was evaluated by comparing the concentrations of ampicillin in the serum of the same beagle dogs when fasted or allowed food *ad libitum*

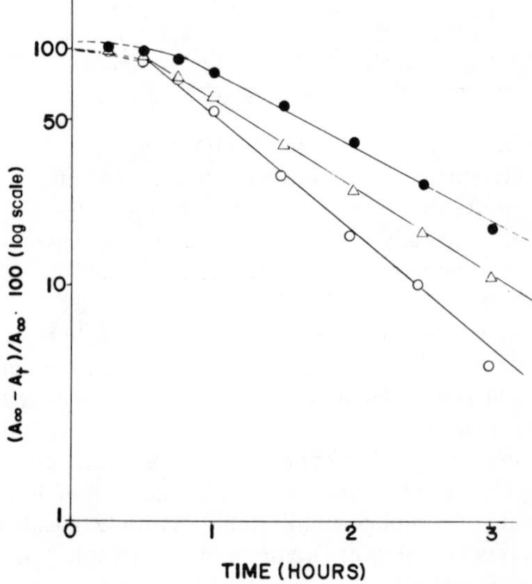

Fig. 4. *Rate of absorption of sodium ampicillin (○), potassium ampicillin (△), and ampicillin trihydrate (●) in beagle dogs after oral administration in loosely packed soft-gelatin capsules.*

Table 2. *Parameters for the two-compartment model estimated from concentrations of ampicillin in serum after oral administration in gelatin capsules*

Agent	Equation	T_{max} (hr)	C_{max} (μg/ml)	k_a (hr^{-1})	Area (μg-hr) per ml)
Potassium ampicillin	$-142.3e^{-1.89t} + 62.6e^{-0.78t} + 79.7e^{-3.06t}$	1.35	12.04	0.87	31.14
Sodium ampicillin	$-394.4e^{-1.88t} + 186.6e^{-1.12t} + 207.8e^{-2.72t}$	1.27	14.95	1.12	32.30
Ampicillin trihydrate	$-336.4e^{-1.31t} + 174.3e^{-0.89t} + 162.1e^{-1.84t}$	1.75	9.1	0.71	26.31

Table 3. *Parameters for the two-compartment model estimated from concentration of ampicillin in serum after oral administration of sodium ampicillin and ampicillin trihydrate in solution and suspension, respectively*

Agent	Equation	T_{max} (hr)	C_{max} (μg/ml)	k_a (hr^{-1})	Area (μg-hr) per ml)
Sodium ampicillin	$-173.35e^{-2.26t} + 79.48e^{-1.01t} + 93.87e^{-3.62t}$	1.09	13.4	1.11	27.76
Ampicillin trihydrate	$-257.17e^{-1.56t} + 117.9e^{-0.91t} + 139.3e^{-2.17t}$	1.45	10.88	0.77	29.31
Sodium ampicillin + food	$-13.15e^{-3.79t} + 5.97e^{-0.50t} + 7.18e^{-6.9t}$	0.83	3.39	0.67	9.45

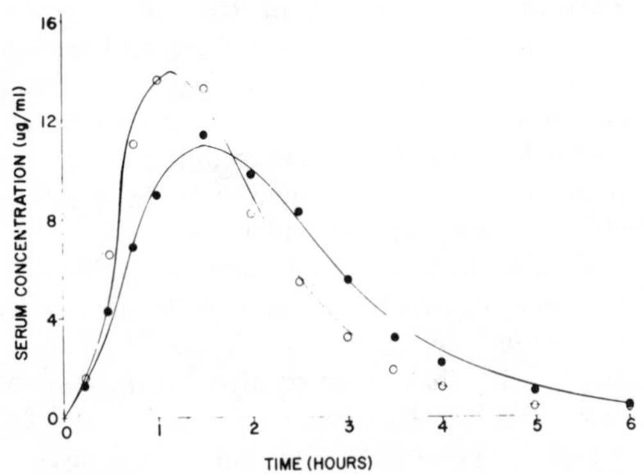

Fig. 5 *Mean concentrations of ampicillin in the serum of beagle dogs after oral administration of sodium ampicillin (○) and ampicillin trihydrate (●) in solution and suspension, respectively.*

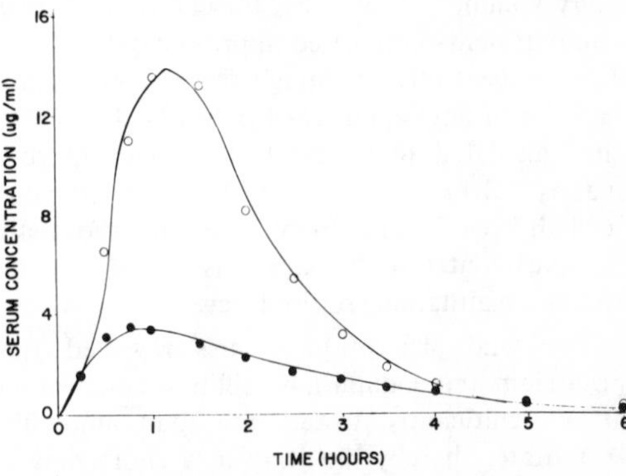

Fig. 7. *Effect of food intake on the oral absorption of sodium ampicillin in beagle dogs. Symbols: ○, sodium ampicillin concentrations in the absence of food; ●, sodium ampicillin concentrations after food intake.*

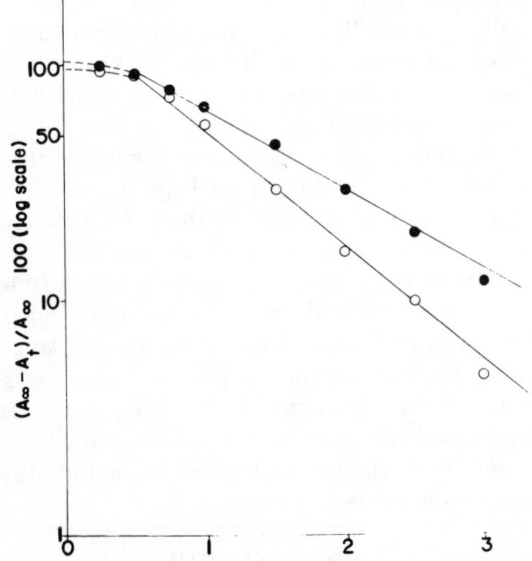

Fig. 6. *Rate of absorption of sodium ampicillin (○) and ampicillin trihydrate (●) in beagle dogs after oral administration in solution and suspension, respectively.*

overnight. The intake of food resulted in a significant reduction in the concentrations in serum (Fig. 7).

After food intake, the rate and extent of oral absorption of sodium ampicillin were reduced approximately 40 and 66%, respectively (Table 3).

DISCUSSION

The distribution and elimination characteristics of sodium ampicillin were determined in beagle dogs after administration of a single intravenous dose. Although the drug distribution phase appeared to be very rapid in the dogs ($t\frac{1}{2} = 0.08$ hr), the concentrations in serum could not be adequately fitted by a single exponential term, but rather were best described by a bi-exponential equation. Such an equation can best be interpreted in terms of a two-compartmental open-system model (15, 16, 22).

The model consists of a central compartment (V_P) and a peripheral tissue compartment (V_T). Ampicillin is in a state of equilibrium between these compartments only under homeostatic conditions (17). Although blood is an essential component of the central compartment, this compartment also includes the extracellular fluids. The peripheral tissue compartment includes intracellular fluids or tissue(s), or both (e.g., liver), in which ampicillin may be selectively distributed (1). Kinetic analysis of the data on concentrations in serum revealed that the apparent volume of ampicillin distribution in the beagles was approximately 33% of the total body volume. Of this 33%, the central and tissue compartments comprised approximately 21 and 12%, respectively. Although the apparent serum half-life of ampicillin was 0.5 hr ($\beta = 1.38\ hr^{-1}$), the calculated biological half-life was approximately 0.3 hr ($k_2 = 2.54\ hr^{-1}$). This discrepancy in half-lives is presumably due to the tissue compartment (V_T) behaving as a reservoir and thereby maintaining serum levels.

The oral absorption studies revealed that potassium and sodium ampicillin were absorbed at a significantly faster rate than ampicillin trihydrate, thereby resulting in a shortening of the T_{max}, a higher C_{max}, and two- to threefold higher serum concentrations during the first hour. However, the concentrations of ampicillin trihydrate in serum at later time periods (3 to 6 hr) were higher than those obtained with sodium ampicillin, presumably owing to delayed absorption. Consequently, the physiological availability, as indicated by the area under the serum concentration-time curves, for potassium and sodium ampicillin was only 16 and 19% more, respectively, than that for ampicillin trihydrate. These differences were not statistically significant.

Similar findings with regard to k_a, T_{max}, and C_{max} were also observed after oral administration of sodium ampicillin and ampicillin trihydrate in solution and as a suspension, respectively. No difference in physiological availability was noted with these two preparations.

The slower rate of absorption for ampicillin trihydrate can only be attributed to a slower dissolution rate of the hydrated form of ampicillin. This hypothesis is consistent with the recent dissolution rate studies of Poole et al. (14). A similar dissolution rate-limited absorption has been reported in man for aspirin by Levy and Hollister (9). The dissolution rate of sodium ampicillin does not appear to be rate-limiting, as evidenced by the fact that the k_a was the same (1.1 hr^{-1}) regardless of whether it was administered in a capsule or as a solution.

A lag time in the oral absorption of these preparations was indicated by the lack of linearity in the initial absorptive phase. The lag phase can best ascribed to gastric emptying (6), since ampicillin is poorly absorbed from the stomach (*unpublished results*). A shorter lag phase was observed with potassium and sodium ampicillin. The difference in lag time between ampicillin trihydrate and the salts may be ascribed to the effect of cations on gastric emptying (7). The longer lag phase with ampicillin trihydrate would tend to move the serum concentration-time curve for this preparation to the right, resulting in lower initial concentrations in serum, but would have little if any effect on physiological availability.

With respect to physiological availability, it is not always possible to compare the area under the serum concentration-time curves for oral dosing with that obtained after an intravenous dose (i.e., water-insoluble drugs). For that reason, physiological availability of a drug is often defined (21) in terms of that amount (or per cent) absorbed after administration of the most readily available form by the same route. In this study, sodium ampicillin in solution was considered to be the most readily available oral form. Comparison of the area under the serum concentration-time curves revealed that the extent of absorption of potassium ampicillin, sodium ampicillin, and ampicillin trihydrate, when administered in loosely packed gelatin capsules, was no less than that obtained with sodium ampicillin in solution. Therefore, the dissolution of these preparations is not a limiting factor in the extent of oral absorption. The major differences between these preparations appear to be their rates of oral absorption.

Finally, these studies have shown that the rate and extent of oral absorption of sodium ampicillin was significantly reduced by the intake of food. These latter findings point out that assessment of the physiological availability of a drug in fed animals may be unreliable, as food can hinder both the rate and extent of oral absorption in a haphazard manner.

LITERATURE CITED

1. Acred, P., D. M. Brown, D. H. Turner, and M. J. Wilson. 1962. Pharmacology and chemotherapy of ampicillin—a new broad-spectrum penicillin. Brit. J. Pharmacol. 18:356–369.

2. Beaty, H. N., M. T. Turck, and R. G. Petersdorf. 1966. Ampicillin in the treatment of enterococcal endocarditis. Ann. Intern. Med. **65**:701–707.
3. Brown, D. M., and P. Acred. 1961. "Penbritin"–a new broad-spectrum antibiotic. Brit. Med. J. **2**:197–206.
4. Grove, D. C., and W. A. Randall. 1955. Assay methods of antibiotics–a laboratory manual. Medical Encyclopedia, Inc., New York.
5. Holloway, W. J., C. D. Peters, and E. G. Scott. 1964. Clinical experience with oral and parenteral ampicillin. Antimicrob. Agents Chemother.–1963, p. 314–317.
6. Hunt, J. N. 1963. Gastric emptying in relation to drug absorption. Amer. J. Dig. Dis. **8**:885–894.
7. Hunt, J. N., and M. T. Knox. 1962. The regulation of gastric emptying of meals containing citric acid and salts of citric acid. J. Physiol. **163**:34–45.
8. Kirby, W. M. M. 1967. Summary of the conference on comparative assessment of the borad-spectrum penicillins and other antibiotics. Ann. N.Y. Acad. Sci. **145**:516–521.
9. Levy, G., and L. E. Hollister. 1965. Dissolution rate limited absorption in man. J. Pharm. Sci. **54**:1121–1125.
10. Loo, J. C. K., and S. Riegelman. 1968. New method for calculating the intrinsic absorption rate of drugs. J. Pharm. Sci. **57**:918–927.
11. Marquardt, D. W. 1963. A logarithm for least-squares estimation of nonlinear parameters. J. Soc. Ind. Appl. Math. **11**:431.
12. Marquardt, D. W. 1966. Least squares estimation of nonlinear parameters. IBM Share Program Library, No. 3094.
13. Parker, R. H., and P. D. Hoeprich. 1966. Parenteral sodium ampicillin therapy of endocarditis, salmonellosis, and other bacterial infections. Antimicrob. Agents Chemother.–1965, p. 618–626.
14. Poole, J. W., G. Owen, J. Silverio, J. N. Freyhof, and S. P. Rosenman. 1968. Physiochemical factors influencing the absorption of the anhydrous and trihydrate forms of ampicillin. Curr. Ther. Res. **10**:292–303.
15. Riegelman, S., J. Loo, and M. Rowland. 1968. Shortcomings in pharmacokinetic analysis by conceiving the body to exhibit properties of a single compartment. J. Pharm. Sci. **57**:117–127.
16. Riegelman, S., J. Loo, and M. Rowland. 1968. Concept of a volume of distribution and possible errors in evaluation of this parameter. J. Pharm. Sci. **57**:128–133.
17. Riggs, D. S. 1963. Mathematical approach to physiological problems, p. 203–209. The Williams & Wilkins Co., Baltimore.
18. Rolinson, G. N., and S. Stevens. 1961. Microbiological studies on a new broad-spectrum penicillin "Penbritin." Brit. Med. J. **2**:191–196.
19. Scarborough, J. B. 1958. Numerical mathematical analysis, 4th ed., p. 192. Johns Hopkins Press, Baltimore.
20. Tuano, S. B., L. D. Johnsen, J. I. Brodie, and W. M. M. Kirby. 1966. Comparative blood levels of hetacillin, ampicillin and penicillin G. N. Engl. J. Med. **275**:635–639.
21. Wagner, J. G., and E. Nelson. 1964. Kinetic analysis of blood levels and urinary excretion in the absorption after single doses of drug. J. Pharm. Sci. **53**:1392–1403.
22. Wagner, J. G., and J. I. Northam. 1967. Estimation of volume of distribution and half-life of a compound after rapid intravenous injection. J. Pharm. Sci. **56**:529–531.
23. Wagner, J. G., E. Novak, L. G. Leslie, and C. M. Metzler. 1968. Absorption, distribution and elimination of spectinomycin dihydrochloride in man. Int. J. Clin. Pharmacol. **1**:261–285.

Antimicrobial Agents and Chemotherapy—1969

Pharmacokinetic Interpretation of Penicillin Levels in Serum and Urine After Intravenous Administration

LEWIS W. DITTERT, WARD O. GRIFFEN, JR., JOHN C. LaPIANA, FREDERICK J. SHAINFELD, and JAMES T. DOLUISIO

University of Kentucky Medical School, Lexington, Kentucky 40506

The levels of penicillin activity in serum and urine were determined after intravenous administration of 250-mg doses of dicloxacillin, oxacillin, ampicillin, penicillin G, and methicillin to healthy adult male subjects. The results suggested that these drugs are distributed in at least two kinetically distinct body compartments: a central, or "serum," compartment and a peripheral, or "tissue," compartment. By use of established mathematical techniques, values were assigned to the rate constants controlling distribution between the central and peripheral compartments and to the rate constant controlling overall elimination of each drug from the body. The apparent volumes of the two compartments were also calculated. These pharmacokinetic parameters were used to calculate the fraction of the administered doses in the central and peripheral compartments as a function of time. The fractions of the administered doses excreted in the urine were also determined, and clearance rates were calculated.

Much useful information can be derived from a kinetic analysis of the levels of drugs in tissues. Such parameters as the biological half-life, the apparent volumes of distribution, and the rates of metabolic and urinary clearance can be calculated from serum and urine data. These parameters are useful in determining proper dosage regimens, avoiding adverse drug reactions, evaluating drug efficacy, quantitating drug-drug interactions, and comparing drugs of the same therapeutic class with respect to their time course in the body.

In the past, pharmacokinetic analysis of drug levels in blood was often accomplished by assuming that the body acted as a single homogenous compartment and that the concentrations of the drug in blood or serum were representative of drug concentrations throughout the entire body compartment. Thus, the kinetic model describing the elimination of a drug following an intravenous dose would be

drug in body ⟶ eliminated drug

If drug elimination from the serum is a first-order process, the decrease in serum levels after intravenous administration should be monoexponential throughout the entire postadministration phase.

The one-compartment model has found great utility in conceptualizing and describing in quantitative terms the in vivo dynamics of many drugs. But, with most drugs, the levels in serum after intravenous administration do not decrease in a monoexponential fashion. Very often the decrease is biexponential; that is, the semilogarithmic plots exhibit a curved segment ("α phase") followed by a straight line segment ("β phase"). This behavior suggests that the body consists of at least two kinetically distinct compartments, and a kinetic model which includes an extravascular tissue compartment should be of great value in describing the in vivo dynamics of these drugs. Such a model is shown below:

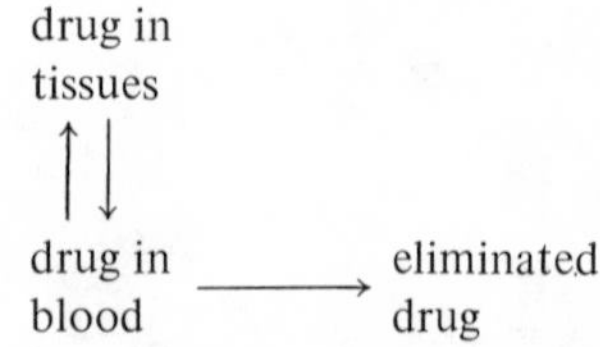

In this model, "tissue" is regarded as a single homogenous extravascular compartment, and it must be recognized that this is an oversimplification. But the model is more consistent with data on drug levels in serum after intravenous administration than the simpler one-compartment model. Also, with the antibiotics it is desirable to quantitate the dynamics of the drug in extravascular tissue, and interpretation of penicillin levels in serum in terms of a two-compartment model yields useful information concerning the drug's extravascular behavior.

Pharmacokinetic parameters of the antibiotics are commonly used as guides for their clinical usage. Kunin (6) reviewed the influence of factors such as rates of absorption and elimination and volumes of distribution on the delivery of drugs to body areas involved in infection. He mentioned, for example, that renal and hepatic blood flow are increased by fever; this response may result in an increased rate of drug clearance, making increased or more frequent dosing necessary. On the other hand, in patients with renal disease, reduced amounts of certain antibiotics may be required to avoid toxicity (9); creatinine clearance rates have been used to establish kanamycin dosage regimens in such patients (11). Progressively decreasing serum half-lives have been associated with progressively increasing urinary clearance of the penicillins and neomycin during the first month of life (1), and significant changes in the volumes of distribution of penicillins with bed rest (10) have been reported.

An understanding of certain drug interactions can be developed in pharmacokinetic terms. For example, Kunin (8) reported that salicylate and certain sulfonamides displaced penicillins bound to human serum protein in vivo, resulting in higher levels of free drug in the serum. In some instances, this effect was accompanied by a fall in the levels of total penicillin in the serum. He suggested that these results may have been due to changes in volumes of distribution, interference by sulfonamide with oral absorption of the penicillins, changes in liver metabolism of the penicillins in the presence of sulfonamide, or combinations of these effects. The pharmacological actions of probenecid have long been assumed to be largely confined to the inhibition of renal tubular secretion of organic acids (2). However, Gibaldi and Schwartz (3) showed that probenecid also reduced the apparent volume of distribution of penicillins, and this effect is largely responsible for the enhanced penicillin levels noted in serum in the presence of probenecid. Thus, pharmacokinetic parameters may interact, may be mutually dependent, or may do both. Most published studies deal with only one or two of these parameters. Studies in which a great number of parameters are determined for a homogeneous population of subjects would quantitate the differences among drugs as well as provide data against which other subject populations could be compared.

The purpose of the investigations reported here was to determine the parameters of a two-compartment model describing the dynamics of penicillin G, dicloxacillin, ampicillin, oxacillin, and methicillin after intravenous injection in normal healthy adult males. These base-line parameters can be used (i) to study the pharmacokinetic differences among the penicillins, for example, with regard to the apparent volumes of the two compartments, the rates of exchange of drug between the compartments, and the relative rates of metabolic and renal clearance; and (ii) to study the influence of such factors as bed rest, disease state, sex, age, route of administration, dosage form, drug interactions, etc. on the in vivo dynamics of the penicillins.

MATERIALS AND METHODS

Six healthy adult male volunteers ranging in age from 21 to 34 years and weighing between 150 and 200 lb (68 to 91 kg) were studied. Each subject received all penicillins, but the subjects were rested at least 1 month between drugs. The penicillins (250 mg of penicillin activity as the sodium salts in 2 ml of water) were administered intravenously in the back of the right hand over a 2-min period by means of a constant-rate infusion pump. Experimental timing was begun exactly in the middle of the infusion period.

Blood specimens were drawn from the left arm through an indwelling venous catheter equipped with a three-way stopcock. Dextrose (5%) was infused through the stopcock (about 0.5 liter/hr) to prevent clotting between collections. Blood specimens were collected at 3, 6, 9, 15, 20, 30, 45, and 60 min, and then every 0.5 hr for up to 6 hr. In the case of methicillin, blood specimens were collected every 15 min after the first hour, and the experiments were terminated after 4 hr.

The blood was allowed to clot, and the serum was separated by centrifugation and frozen until assayed (within 2 weeks of collection). Total urine was collected every 0.5 hr for 6 hr and then at random times up to 24 hr. (The subjects forced fluids to keep the urine flowing.) The volume of each urine specimen was recorded and a portion was frozen until assayed. The serum and urine specimens were assayed for penicillin activity by a standard cup-plate method (5).

RESULTS

A plot of the average levels of dicloxacillin activity in the serum of the six subjects (log scale) versus time is shown in Fig. 1. The dicloxacillin data are typical of the data obtained with all of the penicillins, and dicloxacillin will be used as a model drug for the purposes of this discussion. Normally, pharmacokinetic analysis should be carried out by using data on individual subjects and averaging the pharmacokinetic parameters, but in all experiments the average parameters calculated in this manner were very close to the parameters calculated from plots of averaged drug levels in serum.

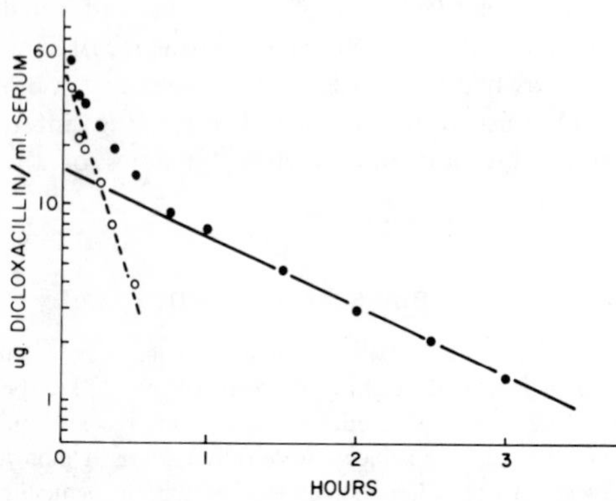

Fig. 1. *Average levels of dicloxacillin activity in the serum of six subjects (●; log scale) after 2-min intravenous infusion of 250 mg of dicloxacillin. The open circles are the differences between the "β-phase" line and the serum levels at early times.*

Thus, the parameters discussed in this report will be those calculated from plots of the average drug level in serum.

The plot in Fig. 1 consists of two segments: (i) a curved segment, or "α-phase" (sometimes called the "distribution phase"), resulting primarily from rapid distribution of the drug between serum and the extravascular tissue compartment; and (ii) a straight segment or "β-phase," the slope of which is related to the biological half-life of the drug. This serum level-time plot is described by the following biexponential equation:

$$C_P = Ae^{-\alpha t} + Be^{-\beta t} \qquad (1)$$

where C_P is the level of drug activity in the serum. The parameters of this equation can be determined as follows. The data are plotted on semilogarithmic paper, as shown in Fig. 1, and the β-phase line is extrapolated under the α-phase curve. The differences between the two lines are plotted on a logarithmic scale against time, giving the lower (residual) line shown in Fig. 1. A and α are the intercept and slope, respectively, of the residual line; and B and β are the intercept and slope, respectively, of the β-phase line. Values of A, B, α, and β for the five penicillins are shown in Table 1.

The area under a curve described by equation 1 is given by the following equation:

$$\text{area} = \frac{A}{\alpha} + \frac{B}{\beta} \qquad (2)$$

These areas for the five penicillins are shown in Table 1, along with areas under the serum level-time plots determined graphically by means of the trapezoidal rule. The agreement between these two areas suggests that the graphical method of determining the parameters of equation 1 is reliable within the limits of this data. Table 1 also shows values for $C_p{}^0$, the extrap-

Table 1. *Parameters of equation 1 (biexponential)*

Drug	U_∞/dose	A	B	α	β	$C_p{}^0$	Area[a]	Area[b]
Dicloxacillin	.56	42.0	14.8	5.3	0.79	56.8	26.6	27.9
Oxacillin	.43	25.0	3.4	5.0	1.0	28.4	8.4	9.70
Ampicillin	.89	20.0	6.2	4.6	0.69	26.2	13.3	13.3
Penicillin G	.79	22.1	3.7	5.8	0.99	25.8	7.56	7.70
Methicillin	.62	18.5	8.5	8.7	1.7	27.0	7.41	7.43

[a] By $(A/\alpha) + (B/\beta)$.
[b] By trapezoidal rule.

olated concentration of drug activity in serum at zero time. These values are best calculated by summing the two intercepts, A and B.

A, B, α, and β are hybrids of the volume and rate parameters of the two-compartment model shown below:

$$\begin{array}{ccc} \text{drug in tissues} & & \\ k_{21}\downarrow\ \uparrow k_{12} & & \\ \text{drug in serum} & \xrightarrow{k_{el}} & \text{eliminated drug} \end{array} \quad (3)$$

The individual rate constants in this model can be calculated from the hybrid factors by the following equations (12, 13):

$$k_{el} = \frac{C_p{}^0}{\frac{A}{\alpha} + \frac{B}{\beta}} \quad (4)$$

$$k_{21} = \frac{\alpha \cdot \beta}{k_{el}} \quad (5)$$

$$k_{12} = \alpha + \beta - k_{21} - k_{el} \quad (6)$$

A summary of these individual rate constants for the five penicillins is shown in Table 2, along with the β-phase half-lives of the drugs, which are commonly termed "biological" half-lives. For methicillin, all three rate constants are larger than the corresponding rate constants for the other penicillins, and the effect is manifested in the faster elimination of methicillin compared with the other penicillins. For all of the penicillins except methicillin, the rate constant k_{12}, controlling diffusion of the drug from serum to tissues, and the rate constant k_{21}, controlling return of drug from tissues to serum, are nearly equal.

Table 2. *Individual rate constants for the two-compartment open model (equation 3)*

Drug	k_{12} (hr^{-1})	k_{21} (hr^{-1})	k_{el} (hr^{-1})	t½ (hr) Serum$_{(\beta)}$	t½ (hr) Urine
Dicloxacillin	2.0	2.0	2.1	0.88	0.95
Oxacillin	1.1	1.5	3.4	0.70	1.0
Ampicillin	1.7	1.6	2.0	1.0	1.1
Penicillin G	1.7	1.7	3.4	0.70	0.80
Methicillin	2.8	3.8	3.6	0.43	0.50

The serum-tissue distribution of the penicillins can be visualized by calculating the fraction of the administered dose in the extravascular tissue compartment (T/D) and the fraction in the central or serum compartment (P/D) at various times. For intravenous administration, the fraction in the extravascular compartment is given by (13):

$$\frac{T}{D} = 1 - \frac{\int_0^t Cpdt}{\int_0^\infty Cpdt} - \frac{C_p}{C_p{}^0} \quad (7)$$

where $\int_0^t Cpdt$ is the area under the serum level-time curve up to time t, and C_p is the serum level at time t. The fraction of the dose in the serum compartment is given by:

$$\frac{P}{D} = \frac{C_p}{C_p{}^0} \quad (8)$$

Plots of T/D and P/D calculated from averaged serum level-time data for dicloxacillin are shown in Fig. 2; similar plots were obtained for the other penicillins. In all cases, the amount of penicillin in the extravascular tissue compartment peaked at between 21 and 27% of the administered doses, and, as might be expected, drug levels in serum and "tissue" then decreased in parallel. These results suggest that differences in the binding of these penicillins to human serum protein do not appear to have a great influence on their extravascular distributions.

Since total urine was collected every 0.5 hr for 6 hr and then at various times throughout

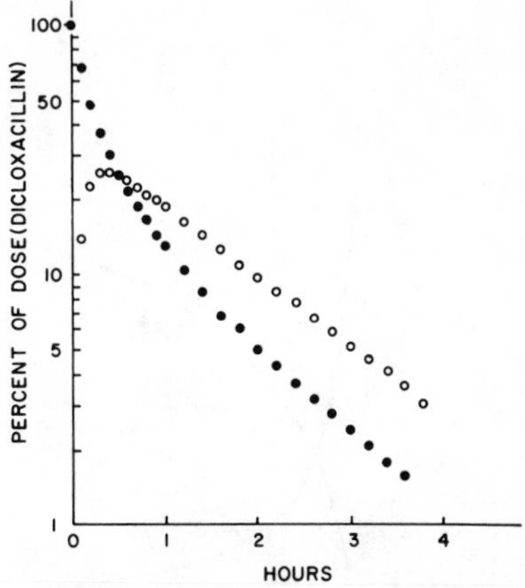

Fig. 2. *Percentage of the dose of dicloxacillin (log scale) in the peripheral compartment (○; equation 7) and in the central compartment (●, equation 8) after a 2-min intravenous infusion of 250 mg of dicloxacillin. (Average of six subjects.)*

the remainder of the 24-hr postdrug period, essentially all of the penicillin activity that was excreted was recovered, and it was possible to calculate a biological half-life from urine data (Table 2). The penicillin activity recovered is designated U_∞; and the fraction of the dose excreted in the urine, f, is then equal to U_∞ divided by the intravenous dose (see Table 1). Also, the agreement between the serum levels and urinary output of dicloxacillin activity can be compared as illustrated in Fig. 3. In this figure, the points are experimentally observed values, and the lines were generated by an analogue computer programmed with the two-compartment model and the rate constants shown in Table 2. The agreement between the experimental and theoretical values is good, and it should be emphasized that the rate constants utilized were those determined graphically.

The results shown in Fig. 3 suggest that a two-compartment open model and the graphical technique for estimating its parameters are adequate to interpret the pharmacokinetic behavior of the penicillins after intravenous administration. However, the present data on drug levels in serum and urine are being subjected to a more rigorous analysis by use of a digital computer; the results will be reported in a subsequent publication.

There are several ways of estimating "volumes of distribution." One of the more commonly used calculations employs the following equation:

$$V_D = \frac{\text{dose} - U_t/f}{C_p} \qquad (9)$$

where U_t is cumulative penicillin activity in urine to time t. V_D calculated by use of equation 9 is sometimes called "$V_{D\,\mathrm{clearance}}$" (14), and is the amount of drug in the body divided by the drug concentration in serum. Use of equation 9 involves the assumption that the concentration of the drug in the entire body is equal to its concentration in the serum. Because this is seldom true, V_D may be unrealistically large or small, but a constant value of V_D over a period of time indicates that the blood and tissue compartments have achieved distribution equilibrium. In the intravenous studies reported here, a V_D can be calculated for each urine specimen collected, and the V_D values were used as a test for distribution equilibrium. For all of the penicillins, the V_D values were constant during the β-phases, indicating that blood-tissue distribution equilibrium was established by the end of the α-phases.

V_D can also be calculated from the parameters (rate constants and volumes) of the two-compartment model by the following equation (14):

$$V_D \; \frac{k_{el} \cdot V_p}{\beta} \qquad (10)$$

Table 3 shows that V_D values calculated with this equation (listed under "serum") are in good agreement with those calculated with equation 9 (listed under "urine").

In equation 10, V_p is the volume of the central compartment which consists of the blood and certain high vascular tissues into which the drug distributes so rapidly that the

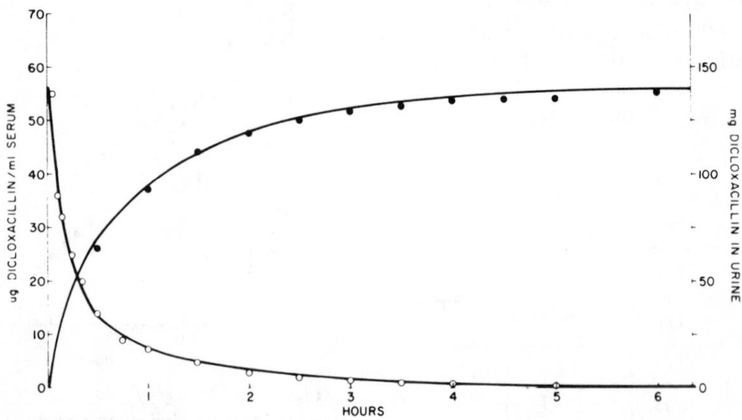

Fig. 3. *Average levels of dicloxacillin activity in the serum (○) and urine (●) of six subjects after 2-min intravenous infusion of 250 mg of dicloxacillin. The points are experimental data, and the lines were generated by an analogue computer programmed with equation 3 and the constants shown in Tables 2 and 3.*

Table 3. *Volumes of distribution*

Drug	V_p (liters)	V_D (liters)		V_T	V_T/V_p
		A[a]	B[a]		
Dicloxacillin	4.4	13	12	7.6	1.7
Oxacillin	8.8	27	30	21	2.4
Ampicillin	9.5	22	27	18	1.8
Penicillin G	9.7	26	33	23	2.4
Methicillin	9.3	22	21	12	1.3

[a] A, calculated with equation 9; B, calculated with equation 10.

distribution cannot be distinguished kinetically. Since initially the entire dose was injected into the central compartment, values for V_p can be calculated by dividing the dose by $C_p{}^0$, the serum level at zero time (extrapolated). Values of V_p calculated in this manner for the five penicillins are given in Table 3.

If V_D is the apparent volume of the entire body compartment and V_p is the volume of the central compartment, then the difference, $V_D - V_p$, is the apparent volume of the extravascular tissue compartment, V_T. Values for this parameter are also given in Table 3. Since estimation of V_D involves the assumption that the concentration of drug in the entire body compartment is the same as that in serum (equation 9), the ratio V_T/V_p is equivalent to the ratio of the amount of drug in the extravascular tissue compartment to the amount of drug in the central compartment. The data in Table 3 show that penicillins which have relatively small V_p values also have relatively small V_D and V_T values, and the V_T/V_p ratios range from 1.3 (for methicillin) to 2.4 (for penicillin G and oxacillin). The conclusion might be drawn that, for these penicillins, more than half the amount of drug in the body during the β-phase is in the extravascular tissue compartment.

Clearance rates are convenient parameters for expressing the elimination behavior of drugs because they can be calculated without estimating a volume of distribution or an elimination constant. Thus, the total clearance rate (TCR) of an intravenously administered drug may be estimated by dividing the dose by the area under the serum level-time curve. In addition, the TCR can be calculated from pharmacokinetic parameters as follows (14):

$$\text{TCR} = k_{el} \cdot Vp = \beta \cdot V_D \qquad (11)$$

The renal clearance rate (RCR) is that fraction of the TCR attributable to renal clearance of unchanged drug, and is calculated by multiplying the TCR by *f*, where $f = U_\infty/\text{dose}$, that is, the fraction of the dose excreted in the urine. Thus:

$$\text{RCR} = f \cdot (\text{TCR}) = f \cdot k_{el} \cdot Vp = f \cdot \beta \cdot V_D \qquad (12)$$

Table 4 shows values for the TCR and RCR of the five penicillins calculated by use of equations 11 and 12. The TCR values are identical to values calculated by the dose/area method.

DISCUSSION

Some authors (7) have emphasized the potentially deleterious effects of extensive binding to serum proteins on the antimicrobial activity of the penicillins, whereas others (15) have challenged the prognostic significance of protein binding in clinical medicine. The penicillins employed in this study have been reported to be bound to human serum protein to the following degrees: ampicillin, 10 to 21%; methicillin, 28 to 49%; penicillin G, 48 to 68%; oxacillin, 86 to 93%; and dicloxacillin, 89 to 96% (15). With the exception of dicloxacillin, the overall volumes of distribution (V_D) determined for the five penicillins in this study (Table 3) do not seem to reflect their degrees of intravascular protein binding. That is, all of the penicillins except dicloxacillin have V_D values of about 20 to 30 liters regardless of their reported degrees of binding to human serum proteins. In addition, the comparative volumes of the central and peripheral compartments for each drug and the results of the *T/D* (fraction of the dose in the peripheral compartment) calculations suggest that similar fractions of the doses of all five drugs (including dicloxacillin) reach the peri-

Table 4. *Clearance rates*

Drug	*f*	Clearance rates (liters/hr)	
		Total	Renal
Dicloxacillin	.56	9.4	5.3
Oxacillin	.43	30	13
Ampicillin	.89	19	17
Penicillin G	.79	33	26
Methicillin	.62	34	21

pheral tissue compartment. As Goldstein et al. pointed out (4), drug distribution is dependent upon storage (binding) in peripheral compartments as well as in the central compartment. Studies dealing with the influence of a therapeutic dose of a competitive protein-binding inhibitor for penicillins (sulfaethidole) on the pharmacokinetic parameters of the penicillins in the subjects employed in this study are presently being completed, and the influence of protein binding on these parameters will be discussed in a future publication.

Quantifiable pharmacokinetic parameters represent important processes which characterize a drug's movements through the body. By use of these parameters along with other knowledge, such as the drug levels in tissue needed for desirable activity and the levels in tissue that may cause toxicity, it is possible to design dosage regimens based on sound quantitative information. Such information would take into account the influences of dosage formulation and route and method of administration on drug availability. If the influences of disease state, bed rest, sex, concomitant drug therapy, etc. on the pharmacokinetic parameters are also understood, it should ultimately be possible to design individualized dosage regimens.

LITERATURE CITED

1. Axline, S. G., S. J. Yaffe, and H. J. Simon. 1967. Clinical pharmacology of antimicrobials in premature infants. II. Ampicillin, methicillin. oxacillin, neomycin, and colistin. Pediatrics **39**:97–107.
2. Brazeau, P. 1965. Agents affecting the renal conservation of water, p. 873–875. *In* L. S. Goodman and A. Gilman (ed.), The pharmacological basis of therapeutics, 3rd ed. The Macmillan Co., New York.
3. Gibaldi, M., and M. A. Schwartz. 1968. Apparent effect of probenecid on the distribution of penicillins in man. Clin. Pharmacol. Ther. **9**:345–349.
4. Goldstein, A., L. Aronow, and S. M. Kalman. 1968. Principles of drug action: The basis of pharmacology, p. 134. Hoeber Medical Division, Harper & Row Publishers, New York.
5. Grove, D. C., and W. A. Randall. 1955. Assay methods of antibiotics: A laboratory manual, p. 31. Medical Encyclopedia, Inc., New York.
6. Kunin, C. M. 1964. Pharmacology of the antimicrobials. Mod. Treat. **1**:829–848.
7. Kunin, C. M. 1966. Clinical pharmacology of the new penicillins. I. The importance of serum protein binding in determining antimicrobial activity and concentration in serum. Clin. Pharmacol. Ther. **7**:166–179.
8. Kunin, C. M. 1966. Clinical pharmacology of the new penicillins. II. Effect of drugs which interfere with binding to serum proteins. Clin. Pharmacol. Ther. **7**:180–188.
9. Kunin, C. M. 1967. A guide to use of antibiotics in patients with renal disease. Ann. Intern. Med. **67**:151–158.
10. Levy, G. 1967. Effect of bed rest on distribution and elimination of drugs. J. Pharm. Sci. **56**:928–929.
11. Orme, B. M., and R. E. Cutler. 1969. The relationship between kanamycin pharmacokinetics: Distribution and renal function. Clin. Pharmacol. Ther. **10**:543–550.
12. Rescigno, A., and G. Segre. 1966. Drug and tracer kinetics. Blaisdell Publishing Co., Waltham, Mass.
13. Riegelman, S., J. C. K. Loo, and M. Rowland. 1968. Shortcomings in pharmacokinetic analysis by conceiving the body to exhibit properties of a single compartment. J. Pharm. Sci. **57**:117–123.
14. Riegelman, S., J. Loo, and M. Rowland. 1968. Concept of a volume of distribution and possible errors in evaluation of this parameter. J. Pharm. Sci. **57**:128–133.
15. Warren, G. H. 1966. The prognostic significance of penicillin serum levels and protein binding in clinical medicine: A review of current studies. Chemotherapia **10**:339–358.

Antimicrobial Agents and Chemotherapy—1969

Pharmacokinetic Interpretation of Dicloxacillin Levels in Serum After Extravascular Administration

JAMES T. DOLUISIO, JOHN C. LaPIANA, GRANT R. WILKINSON, and LEWIS W. DITTERT

University of Kentucky Medical Center, College of Pharmacy, Lexington, Kentucky 40506

The rate and extent of dicloxacillin availability after intramuscular injection of a 250-mg dose and oral administration of various doses in capsule and suspension form were calculated by the method of Loo and Riegelman. This method is based upon a two-compartment open mathematical model and depends upon parameters calculated from intravenous data. The results suggest that dicloxacillin, in oral doses of 62.5 to 500 mg, obeys dose-independent kinetics and that, in fasted subjects, the biological availability is between 65 and 80% for both capsule and suspension dosage forms. A biological availability of approximately 71% was calculated from drug levels in serum after intramuscular administration, but the rate of absorption was found to be much slower than that following oral administration. Oral dicloxacillin was most available when it was administered on a fasting stomach. When it was administered 1 hr before a meal, the rate of absorption did not change, but the amount of drug absorbed decreased 14%. When dicloxacillin was administered with a meal, both the rate and extent of availability decreased, but the availability was the same as when the administration preceded the meal by 1 hr. These results suggest that the absorption of dicloxacillin is probably most affected by stomach emptying, and that the stability of dicloxacillin toward acid-catalyzed hydrolysis apparently contributes greatly to its gastrointestinal absorption characteristics.

Pharmacokinetic parameters calculated from drug levels in blood or plasma after intravenous administration can be utilized to determine the rate and extent of bioavailability of a drug when it is administered by extravascular routes or in various dosage formulations (7). This paper reports on the bioavailability of dicloxacillin when administered to human subjects (i) orally as a suspension and as a capsule and (ii) intramuscularly as a solution. The blood and urine data are analyzed by use of a two-compartment open mathematical model that is consistent with levels of dicloxacillin in serum after intravenous administration (2).

MATERIALS AND METHODS

The drug products employed in this study were experimental formulations prepared by Bristol Laboratories, Syracuse, N.Y. In the case of the capsules and oral suspensions, the formulations were identical to products currently sold under the name Dynapen. The intramuscular solution was prepared with dicloxacillin monohydrate (250 mg) and lidocaine hydrochloride. Each vial was reconstituted with 2 ml of water for injection, USP, and was used or discarded within 4 hr.

Procedure for bioavailability studies. The subjects were healthy adult volunteers ranging in age from 21 to 63 years and weighing 125 to 215 lb (56 to 97 kg). The majority were males; no females capable of childbearing were included. The oral dosage forms of the drug were administered to subjects in the morning, after an overnight fast. Subjects receiving the drug orally were permitted water and black coffee *ad libitum* but no solid food for 1 hr after drug administration. The subjects receiving the drug intramuscularly were not fasted and were permitted food and water *ad libitum.* Specimens of venous blood and urine were collected at appropriate time intervals after drug administration.

Procedure for studies on the effect of food. Subjects were divided into three groups and dosed according to a Latin Square experimental design. A group of subjects who were in a fasting state were given one capsule of dicloxacillin and were not allowed to eat until after the 4-hr blood sample had been drawn. Another group of subjects, also in a fasting state, were given one capsule and were fed a standard breakfast after the 1-hr blood sample had been drawn. The remaining subjects were given one capsule with a standard breakfast. The standard breakfast consisted of orange juice, bacon and eggs, toast, and coffee. This procedure was repeated on the third and fifth days after the initial study day. The subjects were dosed by a different method each time so that by the end of the study each subject had received the dicloxacillin under the three different conditions. Venous blood samples were taken from each subject at 0.5, 1, 2, 3, and 4 hr after drug administration.

Analytical procedure. The serum and urine specimens were frozen and shipped to the Microbiology Control Department of Bristol Laboratories where they were assayed for dicloxacillin activity by the standard cup-plate method (4).

RESULTS AND DISCUSSION

For purposes of this discussion, the term bioavailability is used to describe the amount of drug that appears in the blood after an extravascular dose compared with the amount following an intravenous dose. This parameter is used primarily to describe the ability of an extravascular dosage form to deliver the drug to the blood. The extent of dicloxacillin bioavailability can be estimated by (i) comparing the area under the serum level-time curve after extravascular administration with that following intravenous administration or (ii) comparing total urine output of dicloxacillin activity after extravascular administration with that following intravenous administration. In both of these methods, intravenous administration represents 100% bioavailability. The average dicloxacillin activity present in serum and recovered in urine after administration of 250-mg doses to fasted subjects as an oral suspension (1), an oral capsule (1), and an intramuscular solution is shown in Table 1 and Fig. 1. The areas under the serum level-time plots were determined by trapezoidal rule, and were found to be approximately equal even though the peak heights and durations of the drug concentrations in blood are different. As shown in Table 2, the estimates of availability obtained by the comparative area and urine output methods were in good agreement, and the results suggest that orally administered 250-mg doses of dicloxacillin are about 56 to 65% available compared with intravenously administered drug. This is high for a penicillin derivative and can be attributed, at least in part, to the stability of dicloxacillin in the acidic gastric environment (2).

It is interesting to note that only 71% of dicloxacillin appeared in the blood after intramuscular administration. Kunin (6) discussed the availability of dicloxacillin and other penicil-

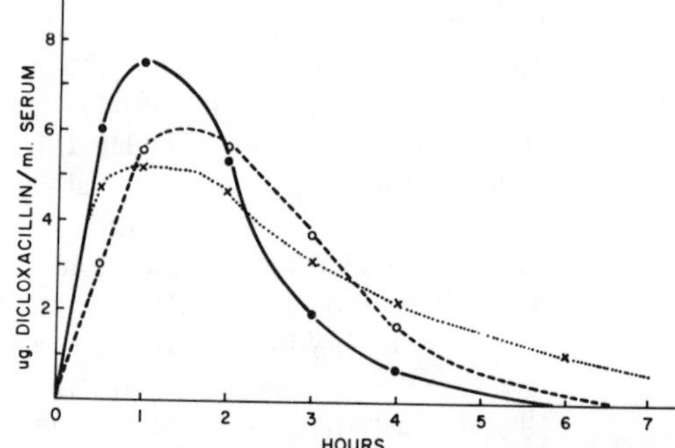

Fig. 1. *Average levels of dicloxacillin activity in serum of fasted adult subjects receiving a 250-mg dose as an oral suspension (●), an oral capsule (0), and an intramuscular solution (X).*

Table 2. *Dicloxacillin availability determined by comparative area and urinary output methods (250-mg dose)*

Dosage form	No. of subjects	$\frac{U\infty}{(U\infty)_{iv}} \times 100$	$\frac{\text{Area}}{\text{Area}_{iv}} \times 100$
Oral suspension	20	56	64
Oral capsule	123	64	65
Intramuscular	20	–	71

Table 1. *Average level of dicloxacillin in serum and recovery in urine after a 250-mg dose*

Dosage form	No. of subjects	Drug concn in serum (μg/ml)[a] after drug administration						Activity recovered in urine (mg)[a]	Time interval of urine collection (hr)
		0.5 hr	1 hr	2 hr	3 hr	4 hr	6 hr		
Oral suspension[b]	20	6.0 ±1.6	7.4 ±0.7	5.3 ±0.6	–	0.7 ±0.7	0.0	77.5 ±7.5	0–6
Oral capsule[b]	123	3.0 ±0.4	5.5 ±0.4	5.6 ±0.3	3.7 ±0.3	1.7 ±0.2	–	90 ±10	0–4
Intramuscular	20	4.7 ±0.2	5.1 ±0.2	4.6 ±0.1	3.1 ±0.9	2.2 ±0.1	1.1 ±0.1	80 ±6	0–4

[a] Mean ± standard error.
[b] Data published by DeFelice (1).

lins after oral administration by comparing outputs of penicillin activity in urine after oral and intramuscular administration; he came to the conclusion that dicloxacillin was 93% absorbed orally based on the assumption that the intramuscular dose was 100% available. Comparison of Kunin's recoveries of dicloxacillin in urine with those obtained after intravenous administration (2) suggests that his intramuscular dose was 70% available (rather than 100%) and his oral dose was 65% available (rather than 93%). Similarly, Kunin's urine data suggest that intramuscular doses of oxacillin and ampicillin are 92 and 70% available, respectively, and that oral doses of these drugs are 48 and 22% available, respectively. Comparison of recovery of drug in the urine after oral and parenteral administration is based on the assumption that the drug is handled by the body in the same manner regardless of route of administration. These results suggest that the metabolism or the distribution, or both, of dicloxacillin, oxacillin, ampicillin, and perhaps other penicillins after intramuscular administration is somewhat different from that following intravenous administration. One possible explanation is that the penicillins may be partially degraded at the intramuscular injection site. Future studies are planned in which intramuscular injection of oxacillin and ampicillin will be compared with slow intravenous infusion.

By use of the pharmacokinetic parameters for dicloxacillin obtained after intravenous administration (2), the rate and extent of bioavailability from extravascular dosage forms can be calculated by the method developed by Loo and Riegelman (7). This method is based on the model shown in Fig. 2 with values for k_{12}, k_{21}, and k_{el} of 2.0, 2.0, and 2.1 hr^{-1}, respectively, and a value for V_p of 4.4 liters (2). The results of the calculations in terms of the fraction of the extravascular dose that is physiologically available and the half-life for the process controlling its availability are shown in Table 3. The bioavailability values (per cent absorbed) in Table 3 are in good agreement with the estimates of availability based on areas under the curves or urine output of drug shown in Table 2. Figure 3 illustrates the method used to determine the half-life for dicloxacillin availability after administration of a 250-mg capsule. The amount of dicloxacillin remaining unabsorbed was calculated from serum data (Fig. 1) by the Loo-Riegelman method (7). For the 250-mg capsule, a lag time of approximately 0.4 hr preceded the first-order drug absorption phase, and the half-life of the absorption process was 0.8 hr. Lag times and absorption half-lives were also determined in this manner for the other serum data in Fig. 1, and the results are summarized in Table 3.

An analogue computer was used to test the agreement between the absorption data (i.e., lag times and rates and extents of absorption) and the pharmacokinetic parameters of the model (Fig. 2) which were determined previously in intravenous studies (2). An EAI TR-48 computer was programmed with the model shown in

```
                       Drug in
                       Tissues

                    k12↑   ↓k21

Unabsorbed   ka      Drug in   kel     Eliminated
   Drug    ----->     Blood   ----->      Drug
                      (Vp)
```

Fig. 2. *Mathematical model employed in the calculation of the rate and extent of dicloxacillin absorption.*

Table 3. *Dicloxacillin availability in terms of its half-life (250-mg dose)*[a]

Dosage form	Per cent absorbed	Absorption		Absorption period (hr)
		Lag time (hr)	t½ (hr)	
Oral suspension	66	0.2	0.6	2
Oral capsule	68	0.4	0.8	3
Intramuscular	74	0	1.3	8

[a] Calculated by the Loo-Riegelman Method (7).

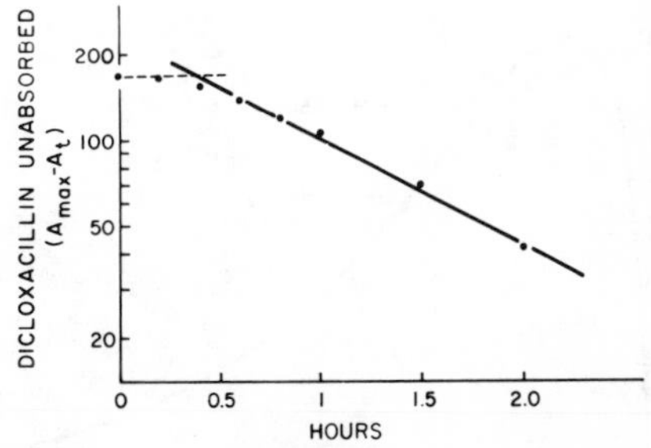

Fig. 3. *Plot of the amount of drug unabsorbed after administration of a 250-mg capsule. From this plot, a lag time preceding absorption (0.4 hr) and an absorption half-life (0.8 hr) can be determined.*

Fig. 2, and with the values for k_{12}, k_{21}, k_{el}, and V_p indicated above. Values for the lag times and rates and extents of absorption were those shown in Table 3 (determined by the method illustrated in Fig. 3). Typical results for this type of simulation are shown in Fig. 4, in which the points are experimentally determined drug levels in serum and the lines were generated by the computer. Similar good fits were obtained with the other doses and dosage forms. A particularly good fit was obtained with the intramuscular data (Fig. 5). The results in Table 3 suggest that dicloxacillin was absorbed slightly faster from the oral suspensions than from the oral capsules, but the difference in rates is probably not significant, and the fraction of the dose absorbed was about the same for the two dosage forms. On the other hand, slightly more dicloxacillin seemed to be available from the intramuscular dosage form; however, the rate of availability was slower than from the oral dosage forms.

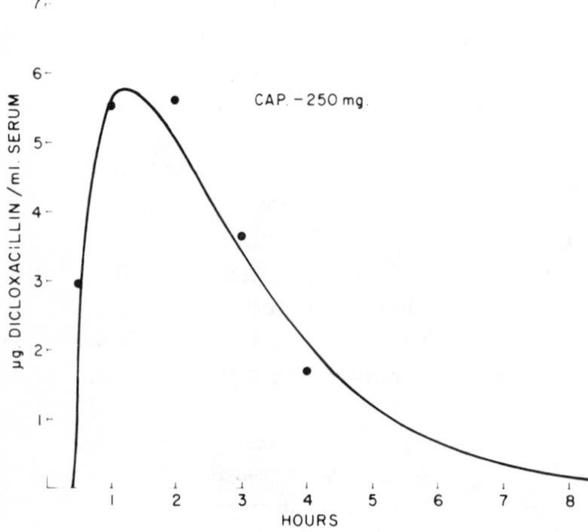

Fig. 4. *Comparison between an analogue computer generated curve and serum data points after administration of a 250-mg capsule of dicloxacillin. The analogue computer was programmed with the mathematical model in Fig. 2 and with values for the rate constants and V_p calculated after intravenous and oral capsule dicloxacillin administration.*

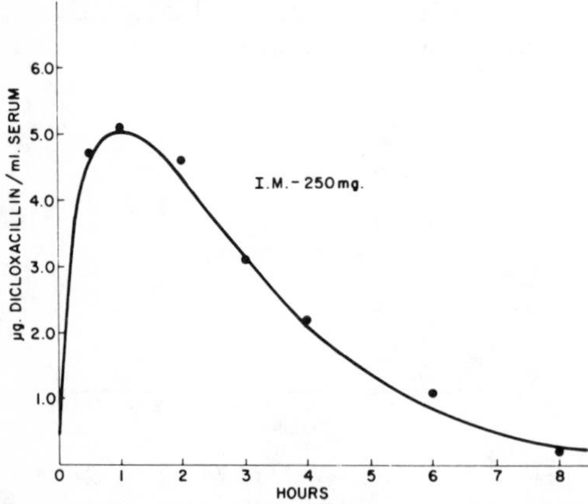

Fig. 5. *Plot similar to that shown in Fig. 4 for a 250-mg intramuscular dose of dicloxacillin.*

Estimations of the bioavailability of the oral dicloxacillin dosage forms from urine data (Table 2) were based on urine output of drug activity over the 4-hr period following drug administration. In retrospect, it would have been desirable to collect urine for a longer period, but estimates for the oral suspension and capsules were in good agreement with bioavailability estimates based on areas under the serum level-time curves (Table 2) and with those calculated by the Loo-Reigelmann method (Table 3). However, because of its slow rate of availability, a 4-hr urine collection was not adequate to estimate the bioavailability of the intramuscular dosage form. To reconcile the data on drug concentrations in serum and urine after intramuscular administration, an analogue computer programmed with the model of Fig. 2 was again used. In this case, the computer displayed, as a function of time, the overall elimination of dicloxacillin, the elimination via urinary excretion (drug activity), and the elimination via metabolism. The simulate overall elimination, k_{el} as shown in the model was used. To simulate urinary excretion $k_{el} \cdot f$ (where f represents the fraction excreted unchanged after intravenous administration) was used. To simulate metabolic elimination, $k_{el} \cdot (1-f)$ was used. The other pharmacokinetic parameters were those determined in the intravenous studies and those calculated from absorption data (Table 3). Figure 6 shows that the 4-hr urinary excretion of dicloxacillin activity after intramuscular administration is consistent with estimations of drug availability based on serum data and with the distribution and elimination behavior of dicloxacillin after intravenous administration Table 4 summarizes the availability data for dicloxacillin administered at various dosage levels and in various dosage forms. There is good agreement between availability estimates based on urine output of drug activity and those based on comparisons of areas under the serum level-

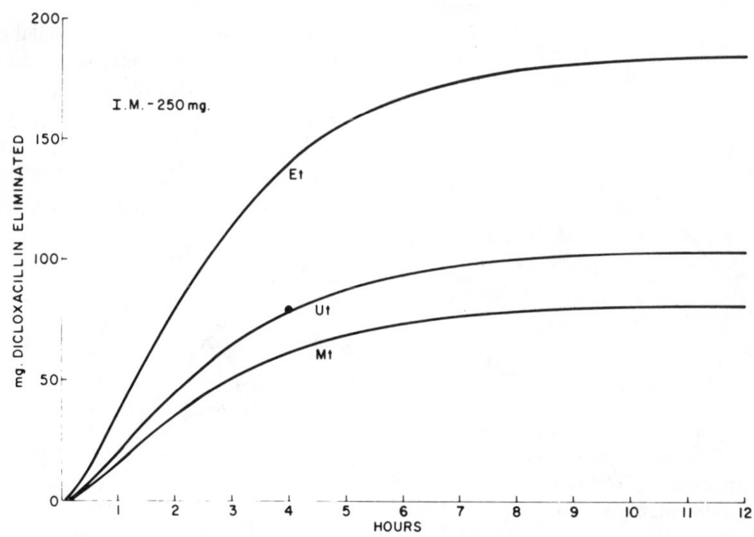

Fig. 6. *Analogue computer display of the amount of drug eliminated: overall (top curve), via the urine (middle curve), and via processes other than urinary excretion (bottom curve), after intramuscular injection of a 250-mg dose. The single point (●) is the cumulative amount of dicloxacillin activity excreted in the urine over the 4-hr postadministration period and shows excellent agreement with the computer-generated urinary excretion of the drug.*

Table 4. *Percentage availability of dicloxacillin after administration of various doses*

Dosage form	Dose (mg)	No. of subjects	$\frac{f}{f_{iv}} \times 100$	$\frac{\text{Area/mg}}{(\text{Area/mg})_{iv}} \times 100$
Intramuscular	250	20	(74)[a]	71
Oral capsule	62.5	20	72	86
	125[b]	22	50	66
	250[b]	123	64	65
	500[b]	28	66	63
Oral suspension	62.5[b]	12	86	73
	125[b]	52	80	84
	250[b]	20	56	64

[a] Parentheses indicate approximate value obtained by extrapolation. See Fig. 5.
[b] Calculated from data published by DeFelice (1).

time curves. The conclusion may be drawn that dicloxacillin is well absorbed orally from both capsules and suspensions.

The relationships among the areas under serum level-time curves, the urine output of drug activity, and the bioavailability of various dosage forms of a drug are only valid if the drug obeys dose-independent kinetics. That is, there must be a linear relationship between the area under the serum level-time curve and the dose of drug absorbed, or between the area and the total amount of drug eliminated (U_∞/f). Figure 7 illustrates a plot of area versus U_∞/f for dicloxacillin administered intravenously, intramuscularly, orally in capsules, and orally in suspension. The plot shows that dicloxacillin obeys dose-independent kinetics for all doses and all dosage forms. Consequently, the bioavailability of extravascular dosage forms of dicloxacillin may be evaluated by comparing the area under the serum level-time curve per milligram of extravascular dose with the area per milligram of intravenous dose if the doses are within the range of 62.5 to 500 mg. When dose-independent kinetics is obeyed, the slope of a plot such as that shown in Fig. 7 is equal to the

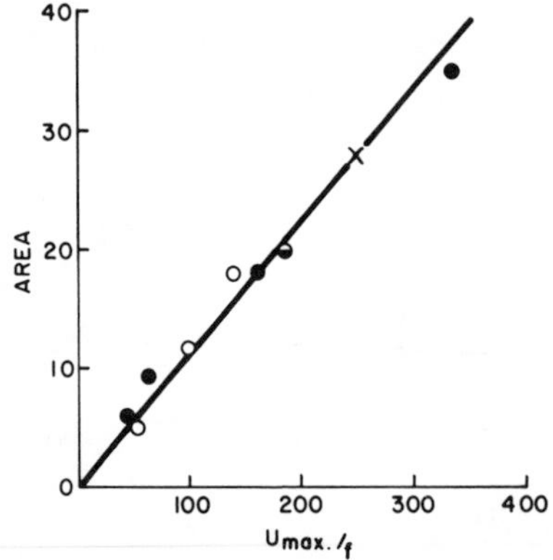

Fig. 7. *Plot illustrating dose-independent kinetics for dicloxacillin over the dosage range studied. The slope of this line is the reciprocal of the total clearance rate of dicloxacillin (X, intravenous; ●, intramuscular; •, capsule; 0, oral suspension).*

reciprocal of the total clearance rate (TCR) of the drug from the body. A total clearance rate of 8.9 liters/hr, which may be calculated from the slope of Fig. 7, compares favorably with a TCR of 9.4 liters/hr, calculated from pharmacokinetic parameters for dicloxacillin determined in intravenous studies (2).

The gastrointestinal absorption of many drugs is affected by the presence of food. The reduction in the rates and extents of absorption of penicillin G and various salts of penicillin V in nonfasted subjects has been particularly well documented (5). Since dicloxacillin appeared to be very well absorbed orally compared with the other penicillins (6), a study of the influence of a standard meal (*see* Materials and Methods) on the gastrointestinal absorption of dicloxacillin from the 250-mg capsules was conducted. Table 5 shows average levels in serum and recoveries in urine after administration of the dicloxacillin capsules (i) on a fasting stomach, (ii) 1 hr before the meal, and (iii) with the meal. These results are also plotted in Fig. 8. Table 6 shows the results of calculations of availabilities by the Loo-Riegelman method (7), lag times preceding first-order drug absorption, and absorption half-lives for the three dosage regimens. The lag times and half-lives were calculated from the plots shown in Fig. 9. Dicloxacillin showed the greatest extent of availability (76%) when it was

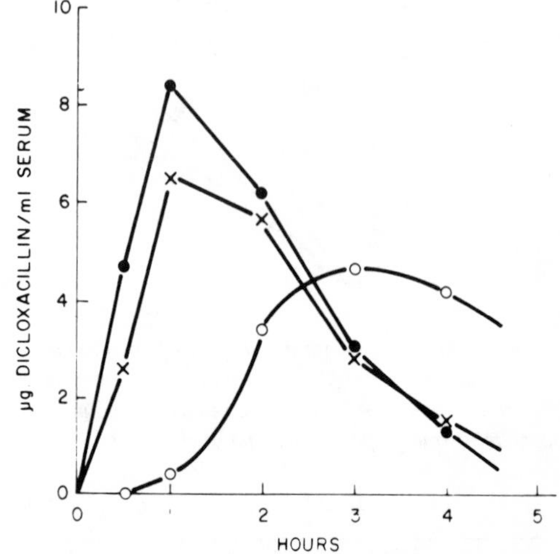

Fig. 8. *Average levels of dicloxacillin activity in serum of adults receiving a 250-mg capsule after an overnight fast (•), 1 hr preceding a standard breakfast (X), and with breakfast (0).*

Table 6. *Effect of food on dicloxacillin availability (250-mg capsule)*

Time of dosing[a]	Per cent absorbed	Absorption	
		Lag time (hr)	t½ (hr)
Fasting	76	0.4	0.5
Before breakfast, 1 hr	62	0.5	0.5
With breakfast	62	1.7	0.9

[a] Each time of drug administration was tested in 17 subjects.

Table 5. *Concentrations of dicloxacillin in serum after oral administration with and without food (250-mg capsule)*

Time of dosing	Drug concn in serum (µg/ml)[a] after drug administration				
	0.5 hr	1 hr	2 hr	3 hr	4 hr
Fasting	4.6 ± 1.0	8.4 ± 0.9	6.2 ± 0.6	3.0 ± 0.6	1.3 ± 0.3
Before meal, 1 hr	2.6 ± 0.6	6.5 ± 1.1	5.6 ± 0.6	2.8 ± 0.5	1.5 ± 0.4
With meal	0.0	1.1 ± 0.4	3.4 ± 0.6	4.4 ± 0.5	4.2 ± 0.4

[a] Mean ± standard error. Each time of drug administration was tested in 17 subjects.

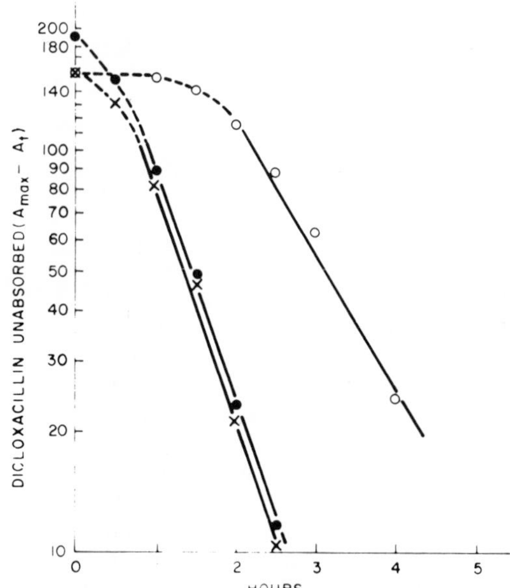

Fig. 9. *Plot of the amount of dicloxacillin unabsorbed after administration of a 250-mg capsule following an overnight fast (●), 1 hr preceding a standard breakfast (X), and with breakfast (0).*

administered on a fasting stomach. When it was administered 1 hr before a meal, the lag time and rate of absorption were not altered, but the extent of absorption was decreased significantly (62% compared with 76%). When dicloxacillin was administered with a meal, both the rate and extent of availability were decreased, but the availability was the same (62%) as when the administration preceded the meal by 1 hr. These results suggest that the absorption of dicloxacillin is probably most affected by stomach emptying. After a meal, mixing is poor and stomach emptying is slow. However, it should be noted that even when stomach emptying is slowed and the drug is exposed for long periods to the gastric environnment, the extent of availability is not greatly affected. Thus, the stability of dicloxacillin toward acid-catalyzed hydrolysis apparently contributes greatly to its gastrointestinal absorption characteristics and, consequently, to its efficacy via the oral route.

LITERATURE CITED

1. DeFelice, E. A. 1967. Serum levels, urinary recovery, and safety of dicloxacillin, a new semisynthetic penicillin, in normal volunteers. J. Clin. Pharmacol. 7:275–277.
2. Dittert, L. W., W. O. Griffen, Jr., J. C. LaPiana, F. J. Shainfeld, and J. T. Doluisio. 1970. Pharmacokinetic interpretation of penicillin levels in serum and urine after intravenous administration. Antimicrob. Agents Chemother.–1969, p. 42–48.
3. Gloxhuber, V. C., H. A. Offe, E. Rauenbusch, W. Scholtan, and J. Schmid. 1965. Dicloxacillin: chemistry, biochemistry, and toxicology, Arzneimittel-Forschung 15:322–330.
4. Grove, D. C., and W. A. Randall. 1955. Assay methods of antibiotics: a laboratory manual, p. 31. Medical Encyclopedia, Inc., New York.
5. Juncher, H., and F. Raaschou. 1957. The solubility of oral preparations of penicillin V. Antibiot. Med. Clin. Ther. 4:497–507.
6. Kunin, C. M. 1967. Clinical significance of protein binding of the penicillins. Ann. N.Y. Acad. Sci. Article 2 145:282–290.
7. Loo, J. C. K., and S. Riegelman. 1968. New methods for calculating intrinsic absorption rate of drugs. J. Pharm. Sci. 57:918–928.

Antimicrobial Agents and Chemotherapy—1969

Mode of Action of Azotomycin

R. W. BROCKMAN, R. F. PITTILLO, SUE SHADDIX, and D. L. HILL

Biochemistry and Microbiology Departments, Kettering-Meyer Laboratories, Southern Research Institute, Birmingham, Alabama 35205

Azotomycin (duazomycin B), an antibiotic with antitumor activity, inhibited purine biosynthesis in neoplastic cells but not the utilization of preformed purines. In L1210 leukemia cells in mice, treatment with azotomycin and ^{14}C-formate resulted in accumulation of radioactive formylglycinamide ribonucleotide (FGAR); higher doses of azotomycin partially inhibited such accumulation of FGAR. However, azotomycin itself, unlike 6-diazo-5-oxo-L-norleucine (DON), did not inhibit the enzymatic synthesis of phosphoribosylamine, a precursor of FGAR. This suggested that azotomycin might be hydrolyzed to DON in vivo. Enzyme preparations from micoorganisms and from tumor cells were shown to degrade azotomycin to DON and glutamic acid; mouse blood plasma appeared to be less active. The biochemical effects of azotomycin in vivo may be accounted for by its hydrolysis to DON. Azotomycin may serve as a transport form of DON in vivo.

Azotomycin (Fig. 1), formerly designated diazomycin B or duazomycin B, is a crystalline antibiotic isolated from culture broths of *Streptomyces ambofaciens* and identified by Rao et al. (11, 12) as a peptide consisting of 1 mole of glutamic acid and 2 moles of 6-diazo-5-oxo-L-norleucine (DON).

Antitumor activity of azotomycin has been observed against sarcoma 180, adenocarcinoma 755, and L1210 leukemia in mice and against Walker 256 tumor in rats (2, 5, 15). Clinical studies of azotomycin in patients with solid tumors indicated some effect, and further evaluation was considered to be warranted (5).

It has been suggested that the mode of action of azotomycin is similar to that of DON and azaserine (15). A major site of action of these inhibitors is known to be inhibition of the biosynthesis of purines de novo (8, 9). Preliminary microbiological experiments in this laboratory indicated similarities of azotomycin, DON, and azaserine. For example, strains of *Escherichia coli* resistant to azaserine and to DON were cross-resistant to azotomycin. Also, azotomycin inhibition of *E. coli,* like that of azaserine and DON, was prevented by purines.

In the present study, we have attempted to establish whether the biochemical effects of azotomycin in tumor cells are similar to those of DON and azaserine, and whether the compound might be enzymatically hydrolyzed to yield DON.

MATERIALS AND METHODS

^{14}C-sodium formate (15 mc/mmole; 55 mc/mmole), adenine-8-^{14}C (3.97 mc/mmole), and hypoxanthine-8-^{14}C (3.79 mc/mmole) were purchased from New England Nuclear Corp., Cambridge, Mass. Azotomycin (NSC 56654) was obtained from the Cancer Chemotherapy National Science Service Center, National Cancer Institute, Bethesda, Md. The antiobiotic was produced by Chas. Pfizer & Co., Inc., Brooklyn, N.Y. Azaserine (NSC 742) and DON (NSC 7365) were obtained several years ago from Parke, Davis & Co., Detroit, Mich., through the courtesy of John Dice. These compounds have been stored at −15 C over a dessicant. The concentrations of the three antibiotics used in the experiments were calculated on the basis of their characteristic absorbance. 5-Phosphoribosyl-1-pyrophosphate was purchased from P-L Biochemicals, Inc., Milwaukee, Wis. Reagent-grade chemicals used in the preparation of buffers and solvents for chromatography and in the enzyme work were obtained from standard sources. Pronase (*Streptomyces griseus* protease), B grade, was purchased from Calbiochem, Los Angeles, Calif.

Microbiological studies. Inhibition of the growth of micoorganisms by azotomycin was studied by the agar-diffusion method of Ehrlich et al. (6). Inhibition was determined by measurement of the diameter of zones around paper discs containing known concentrations of inhibitor. Metabolite reversal of azotomycin inhibition

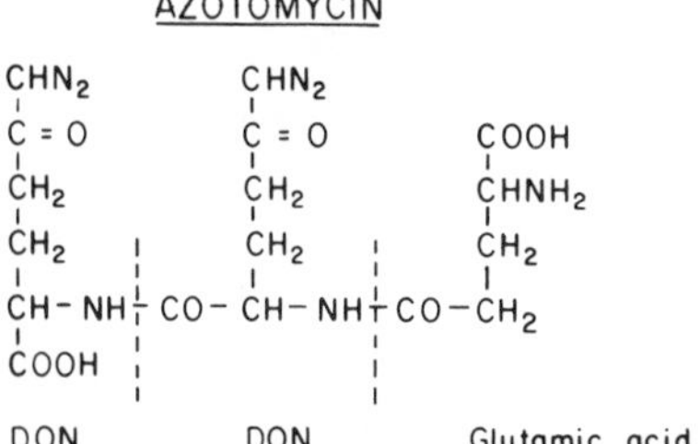

Fig. 1. *Structure of azotomycin (11).*

of *E. coli* was examined by published procedures (10).

Conventional bioautographic procedures were used to detect the presence of azotomycin and DON on paper chromatograms. A strain of *E. coli* which is resistant to amethopterin (methotrexate; *E. coli*/MTX) was found to be more susceptible to DON than to azotomycin. Also, a strain of *E. coli* resistant to *p*-fluorophenylalanine (*E. coli*/FPA) was susceptible to DON but not to azotomycin under the assay conditions. The following descending solvent systems were used in developing the paper chromatograms (Whatman no. 1): (i) 95% ethyl alcohol-1 M ammonium acetate, *p*H 7.5 (75:30, v/v); (ii) 100% ethyl alcohol-*t*-butyl alcohol-88% formic acid-water (60:20:5:15, v/v); (iii) 93.8% aqueous *n*-butyl alcohol-44% aqueous propionic acid (1:1, v/v). A representative chromatogram prepared with the ethyl alcohol-ammonium acetate solvent system is depicted in Fig. 5.

Enzymatic degradation of azotomycin. Soluble extracts were prepared from microorganisms and from tumor cells by sonic disruption of cell suspensions (Branson Sonifier) at ice temperature. The broken-cell suspension was centrifuged at 100,000 × *g* for 1 hr. The supernatant solution was dialyzed overnight against 0.05 M tris(hydroxymethyl)aminomethane (Tris) buffer, *p*H 7.5. Azotomycin and DON were incubated with such extracts in 0.05 M Tris buffer, *p*H 7.5, and 0.3-ml samples were removed at 5-min intervals. Enzyme action was stopped by heating the samples for 1 to 2 min at 100 C. Such treatment did not alter azotomycin or DON in the absence of cell extracts. Samples containing 100 μg of azotomycin or DON were chromatographed for use in ultraviolet light or ninhydrin detection of the compounds. Bioautograms were prepared from chromatograms spotted with 10- or 1-μg amounts of antibiotics.

Purine metabolism studies. Human epidermoid carcinoma cells (HEp-2) and adenocarcinoma 755 cells were maintained in suspension culture; procedures for these as well as for tracer studies in HEp-2 cells have been described (4). In studies on purine metabolism and nucleic acid synthesis, radioactive precursors were added to cell suspensions (3×10^7 cells/100 ml) as follows: ^{14}C-sodium formate, 25 μc; adenine-*8*-^{14}C, 5 μc; hypoxanthine-*8*-^{14}C, 5 μc. For isolation of nucleic acids, at least 200 ml of cell suspension was used. In studying soluble intermediary metabolites arising from ^{14}C-formate, 100 ml of cell suspension was sufficient. Inhibitors were added 1 hr prior to the addition of tracers; cells were harvested 2 hr after the addition of tracers. Procedures for analyses of the soluble intermediary metabolites and of nucleic acids were described in detail previously (4). After incubation with radioactive tracers, the cells were collected by centrifugation, washed with cold physiological saline, resuspended in water, and extracted with hot 80% ethyl alcohol. The soluble extract was concentrated for two-dimensional chromatography-radioautography. The debris was washed with water, with cold 5% trichloroacetic acid, and again with water, and then was extracted with hot 10% sodium chloride adjusted to *p*H 7. The sodium nucleates extracted in this manner were precipitated with ethyl alcohol. Specific activity (nanocuries per milligram) of the sodium nucleates was determined directly, or the nucleic acids were hydrolyzed and the specific activities of adenine and guanine of ribonucleic acid and deoxyribonucleic acid were determined (3).

L1210 ascites tumor cells in BDF_1 mice were used for studies in vivo. Approximately 10^5 leukemia cells were inoculated aseptically into the peritoneal cavity of the mice, and 6 days later the animals were divided into groups of three. Inhibitor was administered intraperitoneally, and after 1 hr ^{14}C-sodium formate was similarly injected (25 μc/mouse). One hour later, the ascites fluid was removed by a syringe, and the L1210 cells were collected by centrifugation. Treatment of the cells was as described above for HEp-2 cells (for more detail, see 10, 11).

The effect of azotomycin and DON on the enzymatic synthesis of phosphoribosylamine was studied with the partially purified 5-phosphoribosyl-pyrophosphate amidotransferase from adenocarcinoma 755 cells. The experimental procedures have been described in detail (7).

RESULTS AND DISCUSSION

An examination of the effect of azotomycin on strains of *E. coli* selected for resistance to azaserine and DON revealed that the resistance of these organisms to azotomycin was increased more than 10-fold (Table 1), which suggested a similar mode of action for these compounds. However, a *p*-fluorophenylalanine-resistant strain (*E. coli*/FPA) retained sensitivity to azotomycin but was resistant to azaserine and DON, and an amethopterin-resistant strain (*E. coli*/MTX) retained sensitivity to azaserine and to DON but was not inhibited by 10 times the concentration of azotomycin that inhibited the parent line. Thus, in these resistant mutants azotomycin could be distinguished from DON. The basis for differences in response of these mutants to azotomycin has not been defined. It

Table 1. *Comparison of inhibition of Escherichia coli by azaserine, DON, and azotomycin*

Bacterial strain[a]	Zone of inhibition (diam in cm)					
	Azaserine		DON		Azotomycin	
	0.1[b]	1.0	0.1	1.0	0.1	1.0
E. coli ATCC 9637	0	2.6	2.8	3.6	2.1	3.2
E. coli/AZA	0	0	0	0	0	0
E. coli/DON	0	0	0	0	0	0
E. coli/FPA	0	0	0	0	1.5	2.8
E. coli/MTX	0	2.0	3.0	3.9	0	0

[a] Resistant strains derived from the parent line: /AZA = azaserine; /FPA = *p*-fluorophenylalanine; /MTX = amethopterin; /DON = 6-diazo-5-oxo-L-norleucine.
[b] Micrograms of inhibitor per disc.

appears that the growth of *E. coli*/FPA is inhibited by azotomycin itself because it did not respond to DON. *E. coli*/MTX was susceptible to DON but did not respond to azotomycin, even though cell-free extracts of the mutant had the capacity to hydrolyze azotomycin to DON. Lack of transport of azotomycin into *E. coli*/MTX could account for this result.

Azotomycin inhibition of *E. coli* ATCC 9637 was prevented by purines, by purine ribonucleosides, and by 4-amino-5-imidazolecarboxamide. This result, similar to that obtained with azaserine and DON (9), indicated that azotomycin inhibited purine biosynthesis.

Azotomycin inhibited the incorporation of ^{14}C-formate into nucleic acids of HEp-2 cells growing in culture (Table 2). DON was a more potent inhibitor; 4 μg of azotomycin per ml was required for 50% inhibition of ^{14}C-formate incorporation, whereas a DON concentration of <0.1 μg/ml caused comparable inhibition. This might be ascribed to differences in uptake of the two agents or to incomplete hydrolysis of azotomycin to DON in HEp-2 cells.

Table 2. *Inhibition of ^{14}C-formate incorporation into nucleic acids of HEp-2 cells in culture*

Inhibitor	Concn[a] (μg/ml)	Specific activity of nucleic acids[b] (% of control)
Azotomycin	0.75	76
	1.5	65
	3.0	62
	6.0	34
	10.0	39
DON	0.1	36
	0.5	15
	1.3	15
	3.25	7
	6.5	5
	13	6

[a] Calculated from spectrophotometric data.
[b] Average of control value = 80 nc/mg (80 × 10^{-9} c/mg); the percentage of the control was calculated for each experiment. Concentration for 50% inhibition: azotomycin, 4.0 μg/ml; DON, <0.1 μg/ml.

Azotomycin did not affect the incorporation of adenine-*8*-^{14}C and hypoxanthine-*8*-^{14}C into the nucleic acids of growing HEp-2 cells (Table 3) at a concentration (6 μg/ml) which produced 66% inhibition of ^{14}C-formate incorporation. Thus, in HEp-2 cells the antibiotic appeared to inhibit the biosynthesis of purines rather than the utilization of preformed purines.

Results of experiments with L1210 leukemia cells in vivo showed azotomycin to be a potent inhibitor of ^{14}C-formate incorporation into nucleic acids in this system (Table 4). In contrast to the results obtained with HEp-2 cells, azotomycin appeared to be more effective than DON in inhibiting ^{14}C-formate incorporation into nucleic acids in L1210 cells in vivo.

By means of chromatographic-autoradiographic techniques, the effects of azotomycin, DON, and azaserine on the purine biosynthetic

Table 3. *Lack of effect of azotomycin on the incorporation of purines into nucleic acids of HEp-2 cells in culture*

Azotomycin concn (μg/ml)	Radioactive precursor	Specific activity of nucleic acid purines[a]			
		Ribonucleic acid		Deoxyribonucleic acid	
		Adenine	Guanine	Adenine	Guanine
Control	Adenine-*8*-^{14}C	283	64.1	112	33.4
6		281	63.4	96.1	31.4
Control	Hypoxanthanine-*8*-^{14}C	176	217	70.0	108
6		171	220	60.9	105

[a] Specific activities expressed as nanocuries per micromole of purine base.

Table 4. *Azaserine, DON, and azotomycin inhibition of ^{14}C-formate incorporation into nucleic acids of L1210 leukemia cells in vivo*

Inhibitor	Dosage[a] (mg/kg)	Specific activity of nucleic acids[b] (% of control)
Azaserine	0.05	20
	0.10	14
	0.50	10
	1.0	9
	6.8	9
DON	0.01	60
	0.05	26
	0.10	18
	0.50	14
	6.0	14
Azotomycin	0.05	17
	0.10	8
	0.50	6
	1.2	4
	6.0	5

[a] Administered by intraperitoneal injection.
[b] Average of control values = 84 nc/mg.

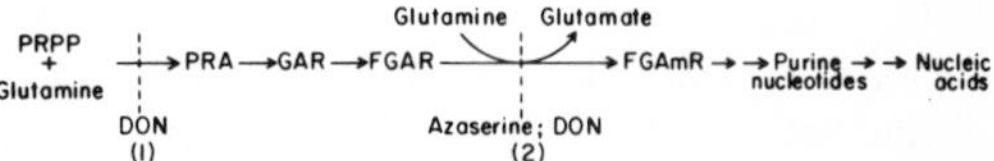

Fig. 2. *Purine biosynthetic pathway showing sites of inhibition by azaserine and DON. Abbreviations are as follows: DON, 6-diazo-5-oxo-L-norleucine; azaserine, O-diazoacetyl-L-serine; PRPP, 5-phosphoribosyl-1-pyrophosphate; PRA, 5-phosphoribosylamine; GAR, glycinamide ribonucleotide; FGAR, formylglycinamide ribonucleotide; FGAmR, formylglycinamidine ribonucleotide.*

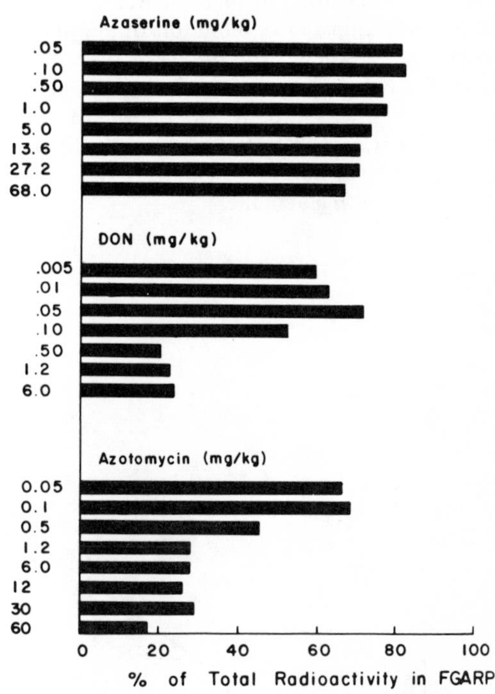

Fig. 3. *Accumulation of formylglycinamide ribonucleoside monophosphate (FGARP) in L1210 leukemia cells in mice as a consequence of treatment with azaserine, DON, or azotomycin at the indicated dosages.*

pathway were examined. Azaserine and DON are known (8) to inhibit the glutamine-mediated amidination of formylglycinamide ribonucleotide (FGAR). In tumor cells, as in microorganisms (14), such inhibition in the presence of ^{14}C-formate or ^{14}C-glycine results in an accumulation of radioactive FGAR (1, 13). Higher concentrations of DON produce a diminution in the amount of FGAR formed as a consequence of inhibition of an earlier step on the purine biosynthetic pathway, namely, the synthesis of phosphoribosylamine (8). Figure 2 serves to summarize these known facts.

A comparative analysis of the effects of a range of dosages of each of these inhibitors on FGAR synthesis in L1210 cells is summarized in Fig. 3 in terms of the amount of labeled FGAR formed as a percentage of the total radioactivity found in the soluble intermediary metabolites. In the case of the untreated control animals the radioactive metabolites in L1210 cells included purines, purine nucleosides, purine nucleotides (adenosine mono-, di-, and triphosphates, inosine monophosphate, guanosine mono- and triphosphates, and nicotinamide adenine dinucleotide), serine, lesser amounts of other amino acids, and small amounts of organic acids. In the animals treated with azaserine, DON, or azotomycin, the major radioactive compound derived from ^{14}C-formate in L1210 cells was FGAR. Significant amounts of compounds that appear to be di- and triphosphate derivatives of FGAR (4) were also found. Small amounts of formylglycinamide ribonucleoside, serine, other amino acids, and organic acids were detected. It is evident from Fig. 3 that, whereas increased doses of azaserine do not significantly decrease the FGAR formation in the L1210 cells, DON and azotomycin are more effective in this respect. The salient point is that higher concentrations of DON and of azotomycin produced a decrease in the amounts of formylglycinamide ribonucleotide formed in L1210 cells. This result is interpreted to mean that DON and azotomycin at higher dosages inhibit an early step on the purine biosynthetic pathway, presumably the synthesis of phosphoribosylamine. Other implications of these results are that azotomycin itself inhibits phosphoribosylamine synthesis or that it is hydrolyzed to DON, which is known to inhibit phosphoribosylamine synthesis.

To examine this further, azotomycin and DON were compared as inhibitors of phosphoribosylamine synthesis. The results of this experiment showed that azotomycin did not inhibit the enzymatic synthesis of phosphoribosylamine, whereas DON was inhibitory (Fig. 4). The Lineweaver-Burk plot shows DON to be competitive with glutamine.

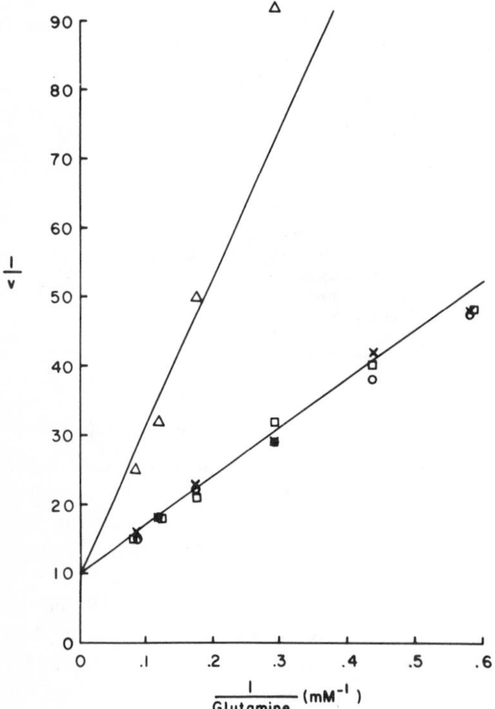

Fig. 4. *Lineweaver-Burk plot showing the effect of DON and of azotomycin on the synthesis of 5-phosphoribosylamine by reaction of 5-phosphoribosyl-1-pyrophosphate with glutamine in the presence of partially purified 5-phosphoribosylpyrophosphate amidotransferase from adenocarcinoma 755 cells (7). Symbols:* ○, *control;* ×, *0.7 mM azotomycin;* □, *0.12 mM azotomycin;* △, *0.14 mM DON.*

The lack of inhibition of the enzymatic synthesis of phosphoribosylamine by azotomycin coupled with the observed inhibition of FGAR synthesis in vivo led us to examine the hydrolysis of azotomycin to DON by micoorganisms, by tumor cells, and by mouse plasma. Azotomycin was incubated for various time intervals with the dialyzed extracts; azotomycin, DON, and glutamic acid were separated chromatographically by use of several different solvent systems. The compounds were located (i) by examination of the chromatograms under ultraviolet light; (ii) by ninhydrin spray reagent; and (iii) by bioautograms with *E. coli*/FPA and *E. coli*/MTX as the assay organisms. As can be seen from the data of Table 1, *E. coli*/FPA was more susceptible to azotomycin and *E. coli*/MTX was more susceptible to DON. The results, which are summarized schematically in Fig. 5, show that incubation of azotomycin with the L1210 extract for 20 min at 37 C resulted in complete loss of azotomycin with formation of a ninhydrin-positive, ultraviolet-absorbing compound that was inhibitory to *E. coli*/MTX and which migrated like DON. Another product of the incubation was a ninhydrin-positive compound which migrated like glutamic acid. Incubation of azotomycin in buffer in the absence of the L1210 cell extract did not alter the compound. DON was recovered unchanged after incubation with the L1210 cell extract, Identical results were obtained with dialyzed extracts prepared from HEp-2 and adenocarcinoma 755 cells. Mouse plasma appeared to be somewhat less active than the extract from L1210 cells. Quantitative comparisons of the activities of L1210 extracts and mouse plasma were not made, but much longer incubations were required to obtain complete hydrolysis of azotomycin by mouse plasma (45 min) compared with L1210 extracts (10 to 15 min).

It is interesting that azotomycin appeared to be somewhat more effective than DON in inhibiting nucleic acid synthesis in L1210 cells in vivo (Table 4). A comparison of these agents in chemotherapeutic trials against L1210 showed them to be about equally effective. At a dosage of 5 mg/kg for azotomycin and 10 mg/kg for DON, administered either intraperitoneally or orally every other day, the life span of treated animals relative to untreated controls (T/C) was 200% (5). Lower dosages of these agents (azotomycin, 0.6 mg/kg; DON, 0.4 mg/kg) gave T/C values of 174 to 214%, respectively.

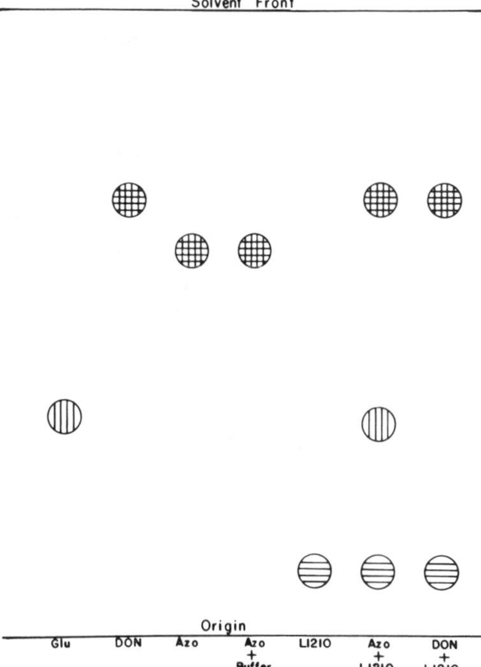

Fig. 5. *Diagram of the paper chromatographic separation of azotomycin (Azo), DON, and glutamic acid (Glu) after incubation of azotomycin with an enzyme extract prepared from L1210 cells. The solvent for development of the chromatogram was 95% ethyl alcohol-1* M *ammonium acetate, pH 7.5 (75:30, v/v). Circles with vertical lines (Glu) indicate ninhydrin-positive spots; circles with horizontal lines, as in those near the origin, represent ultraviolet-absorbing spots; cross-hatched circles indicate spots that were both ninhydrin-positive and ultraviolet light-absorbing. Bioautograms prepared from such chromatograms showed inhibition of Escherichia coli by the cross-hatched spots. Enzyme preparations from HEp-2 cells, adenocarcinoma 755 cells, Streptomyces griseus, and E. coli also hydrolyzed azotomycin.*

A proteolytic enzyme preparation (Pronase) from *S. griseus* rapidly hydrolyzed azotomycin, as did dialyzed extracts from *E. coli* ATCC 9637, *E. coli*/FPA, and *E. coli*/MTX. The results with the *E. coli* strains show that their differences in response to azotomycin (Table 1) cannot be accounted for on the basis of differences in capacity to hydrolyze azotomycin.

The results of this study indicate clearly that azotomycin, like azaserine and DON, inhibited purine biosynthesis in neoplastic cells but did not inhibit the utilization of preformed purines. Azotomycin inhibition of *E. coli,* like that of azaserine and DON, could be prevented by purines and derivatives. However, azotomycin itself did not inhibit the *enzymatic* synthesis of phosphoribosylamine, whereas DON did inhibit this reaction. The simplest explanation for the biochemical effects of azotomycin is that it is hydrolyzed to DON. This view is supported (i) by the observation that DON-resistant *E. coli* also are resistant to azotomycin, (ii) by the lack of inhibition of phosphoribosylamine synthesis in vitro by azotomycin, and (iii) by the observation that formylglycinamide ribonucleotide synthesis was inhibited in vivo.

Azotomycin may prove to be of interest as a transport form of DON. That is, azotomycin may exist as such in the blood for a sufficient length of time to be transported in vivo. Within a given tissue or tumor, its inhibitory effect may be a consequence of its cleavage to DON. If this is the case, then azotomycin could have some selective effect on the basis of its differential uptake, presumably by an active transport mechanism, and subsequent enzymatic hydrolysis. The compound appears to merit further study of its physiological disposition and action in experimental systems. Also, a study of dosage scheduling and combination chemotherapy may provide a basis for enhancement of the antitumor activity of this agent.

ACKNOWLEDGMENTS

This work was supported by contracts PH43-66-29 and PH43-65-594 with the National Cancer Institute.

We gratefully acknowledge the able assistance of Valerie Stringer in the biochemical studies, of Tommie Lou Barker in the animal experiments, of Doris Adamson and Sue Vail in the cell culture work, and of Brenda Cummings in the microbiological work. Tom Herren ably carried out the quantitative determinations of radioactivity.

LITERATURE CITED

1. Anderson, E. P., and R. W. Brockman. 1963. Biochemical effects of duazomycin A in the mouse plasma cell neoplasm 70429. Biochem. Pharmacol. **12**:1335–1354.
2. Ansfield, F. J. 1965. Phase I study of azotomycin (NSC-56654). Cancer Chemother. Rep. **46**:37–40.
3. Bennett, L. L., Jr., H. E. Skipper, L. Simpson, G. P. Wheeler, and W. S. Wilcox. 1960. Searches for exploitable differences between normal and cancer cells. V. Cellular conservation of purines. Cancer Res. **20**:62–81.
4. Brockman, R. W., and S. Chumley. 1965. Inhibition of formylglycinamide ribonucleotide synthesis in neoplastic cells by purines and analogs. Biochim. Biophys. Acta **95**:365–379.
5. Carter, S. K. 1968. Azotomycin (NSC-56654) clinical brochure. Cancer Chemother. Rep. Part 3 **1**:207–217.
6. Ehrlich, J., W. P. Iverson, and D. Kohberger, 1951. Agar diffusion methods for the assay of viomycin. Antibiot. Chemother. **1**:211–216.

7. Hill, D. L., and L. L. Bennett, Jr. 1969. Purification and properties of 5-phosphoribosylpyrophosphate amidotransferase from adenocarcinoma cells. Biochemistry **8**:122–130.
8. Levenberg, B., I. Melnick, and J. M. Buchanan. 1957. Biosynthesis of the purines. XV. The effect of aza-L-serine and 6-diazo-5-oxo-L-norleucine on inosinic acid biosynthesis *de novo* J. Biol. Chem. **225**:163–176.
9. Pittilo, R. F., and D. E. Hunt. 1967. Azaserine and 6-diazo-5-oxo-L-norleucine (DON), p. 481–493. *In* D. Gottlieb and P. D. Shaw (ed), Antibiotics. Springer-Verlag, Berlin.
10. Pittillo, R. F., C. Moncrief, R. W. Brockman, and P. Chambers. 1965. Antimicrobial activity of 2-fluoroadenosine and 2-fluoroadenine. Antimicrob. Agents Chemother.–1964, p. 474–484.
11. Rao, K. V. 1962. Chemistry of the duazomycins. I. Duazomycins A. Antimicrob. Agents Chemother.–1961, p. 178–183.
12. Rao, K. V., S. C. Brooks, M. Kugelman, and A. A. Romano. 1960. Diazomycins A, B, and C, three antitumor substances. I. Isolation and characterization. Antibiot. Ann. 1959–60, p. 943–949.
13. Sartorelli, A. C., and G. A. LePage. 1958. Metabolic effects of 6-thioguanine. II. Biosynthesis of nucleic acid purines. Cancer Res. **18**:1329–1335.
14. Tomisek, A. J., H. J. Kelly, and H. E. Skipper. 1956. Chromatographic studies of purine metabolism. I. The effect of azaserine on purine biosynthesis in *E. coli* using various ^{14}C-labeled precursors. Arch. Biochem. Biophys. **64**:437–455.
15. Weiss, A. J., G. Ramirez, T. Grage, J. Strawitz, L. Goldman, and V. Downing. 1968. Phase II study of azotomycin (NSC 56654). Cancer Chemother. Rep. **52**:611–614.

Antimicrobial Agents and Chemotherapy—1969

Spectrophotometric Studies of the Interaction of an Antimalarial Quinoline Methanol with Deoxyribonucleic Acid

FRED E. HAHN and CHARLES L. FEAN

Department of Molecular Biology, Walter Reed Army Institute of Research, Washington, D.C. 20012

It was predicted and proved that an antimalarial quinoline methanol formed complexes with double-helical deoxyribonucleic acid (DNA). By the stronger of two binding processes, one drug molecule was bound per >three base pairs with an apparent association constant of $>3.6 \times 10^6$ per mole, whereas one drug molecule per one base pair was bound by a weaker process with an apparent association constant of 10^5 per mole. The affinities of the synthetic quinoline methanol for DNA resembled those of quinine, but, on the average, 10 times more of the synthetic drug was bound to DNA. The quinoline methanol shifted the thermal strand separation profile of DNA to higher temperatures and rendered the denaturation process more cooperative. We propose that the binding of synthetic quinoline methanols to DNA resembles that of the natural quinoline methanol, quinine, and that the greater antimalarial potency of our test compound is the direct result of more synthetic drug molecules becoming bound to DNA.

Quinine, one of the oldest chemotherapeutic drugs, possesses selective toxicity for malarial parasites (10). Quinine (Fig. 1) is a 6-methoxy quinoline-4-methanol, substituted with a bridged aliphatic ring system known as quinuclidine. Ainley and King (1) found in 1938 that replacement of the quinuclidine moiety by piperidine yielded an antimalarial quinoline methanol.

Many quinoline methanols, related to quinine, have been synthesized and tested. The survey of Wiselogle (12) for the years 1941 through 1945 tabulated approximately 200 such compounds. These tables show that substitutions with chlorine in positions 6 and 8, and aromatic ring substitution in position 2 of the quinoline moiety, produced substances which were many times more active than quinine in animal screens. One of these highly active compounds, α-piperidyl-6,8-dichloro-2-phenyl-4-quinoline methanol (Fig. 1) was used in the present study.

Quinine itself has been reported from our laboratory to form a molecular complex with double-helical deoxyribonucleic acid (DNA) and to inhibit the DNA polymerase reaction in vitro (4,8). This inhibition is a function of the stabilization by quinine of DNA to forces which cause separation of the component strands of the double helix (4). In plasmodia, quinine is a potent inhibitor of DNA biosynthesis (9, 11). Evidently, the drug poisons the DNA template.

The present work has been based upon the hypothesis that synthetic quinoline methanols,

α-Piperidyl 6,8-dichloro-2-phenyl-4-quinoline methanol hydrochloride

QUININE

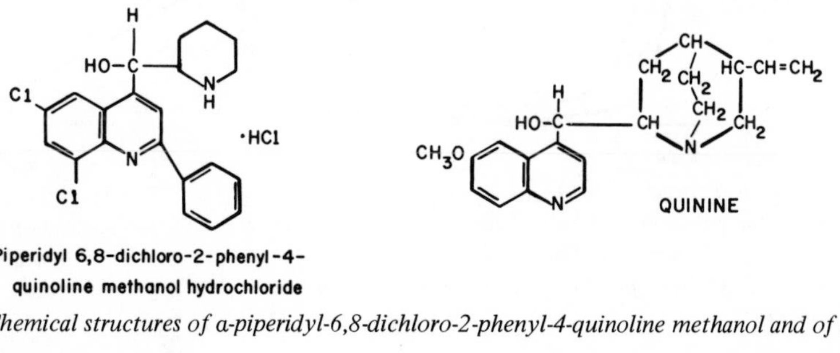

Fig. 1. *Chemical structures of α-piperidyl-6,8-dichloro-2-phenyl-4-quinoline methanol and of quinine.*

related to quinine, will also engage in complex formation with DNA and stabilize the double helix. This has been verified by spectrophotometric titration and "melting" experiments with calf thymus DNA.

MATERIALS AND METHODS

The quinoline methanol compound (Fig. 1) was furnished by the Division of Medicinal Chemistry of our Institute. Calf thymus DNA was purchased from Calbiochem, Los Angeles, Calif. The spectrophotometric titration and construction of the adsorption isotherm (Fig. 3) were carried out as described previously (4) by use of a Cary 14 recording spectrophotometer equipped with optical cells of 10-cm light paths. Melting experiments were performed as previously described (4); no volume corrections were applied to the results depicted in Fig. 4.

RESULTS

The solid line in Fig. 2 represents the absorption spectrum of the quinoline methanol at wavelengths above 300 nm, i.e., over a range at which DNA does not absorb light. The broken line (Fig. 2) shows the spectrum of the test compound in the presence of DNA. First, DNA decreased the intensity of the absorption bands of the drug, indicating that the quinoline methanol interacted with DNA. Second, the absorption maxima of the drug were shifted by DNA to longer wavelengths. It is understood from the pioneer work of Michaelis (7) that such hypsochromic shifts in the absorption spectra of compounds complexing with DNA means that individual drug molecules rather than dimers or aggregates are bound to the polymer.

A spectrophotometric titration of the quinoline methanol with graded concentrations of DNA yielded results which were used to derive the absorption isotherm shown in Fig. 3. On the abscissa is represented r, that is the number of drug molecules bound per atom of DNA phosphorus, and on the ordinate is represented this quantity r divided by the concentration, c, of unbound drug. The curvature of the plot (Fig. 3) indicates that more than one class of binding sites and more than one binding process are involved in the formation of the DNA-drug complex. A tangent to the adsorption isotherm fitted arithmetically to the region of low values of r intercepts with the abscissa at a value of approximately 0.15, corresponding to one drug molecule bound per seven phosphates or per three and one-half base pairs of DNA. The apparent binding constant of this process was calculated from the intercept of the tangent with the ordinate to have a value of the order of 10^6 per mole. This resembles the apparent constant of the binding of quinine to DNA ($>3.6 \times 10^6$ per mole) by the stronger of two processes (4), but the number of quinoline methanols so bound was 12 times larger than the number of bound quinine molecules. This may explain why the quinoline methanol is more potent than quinine as a chemotherapeutic drug.

The tangent to the adsorption isotherm (Fig.

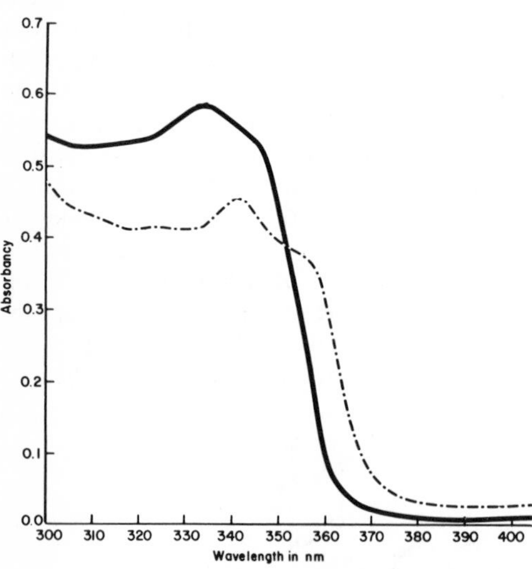

Fig. 2. *Influence of calf thymus DNA upon the absorption spectrum of the quinoline methanol shown in Fig. 1. Drug* (6.2×10^{-6} M *phosphate buffer at pH 7.0:* ———, *alone;* -.-.-., *in the presence of DNA* (6.9×10^{-5} M *phosphorus*).

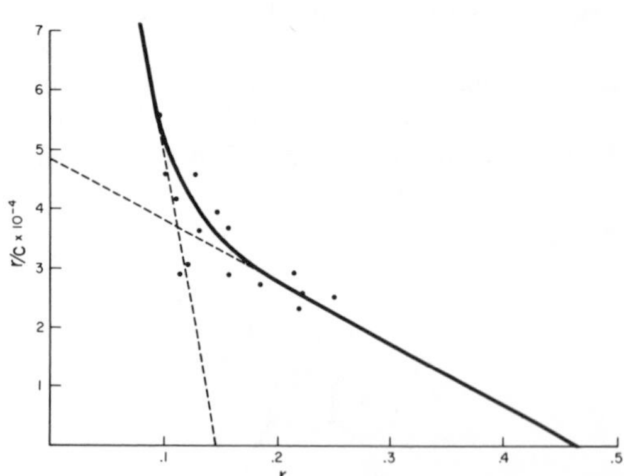

Fig. 3. *Isotherm for the binding of the test quinoline methanol shown in Fig. 1 to calf thymus DNA (r, bound drug per atom of DNA phosphorus; c, concentration of free drug).*

3) fitted to the region of high values of r intercepts with the abscissa at a value of approximately 0.5, corresponding to one drug molecule bound per two phosphates or per one base pair of DNA. The apparent binding constant for this process is of the order of 10^5 per mole, which is almost exactly the apparent constant of the binding of quinine to DNA (1.5×10^5 per mole) by the weaker of two processes (4). The number of quinoline molecules so bound is eight to nine times greater than the number of quinine molecules so bound. Again, this may explain the greater potency of the quinoline methanol.

Like quinine (4) and other antimalarial drugs (5), the quinoline methanol shifted the thermal strand separation profile of DNA to higher temperatures, as shown in Fig. 4. The difference in the shape of the melting curves for DNA alone and for the DNA-drug complex renders the calculation of ΔT_m uncertain. The greater steepness of the denaturation profile of the DNA-drug complex suggests a more highly cooperative type of thermal strand separation, as has been previously shown in this laboratory for

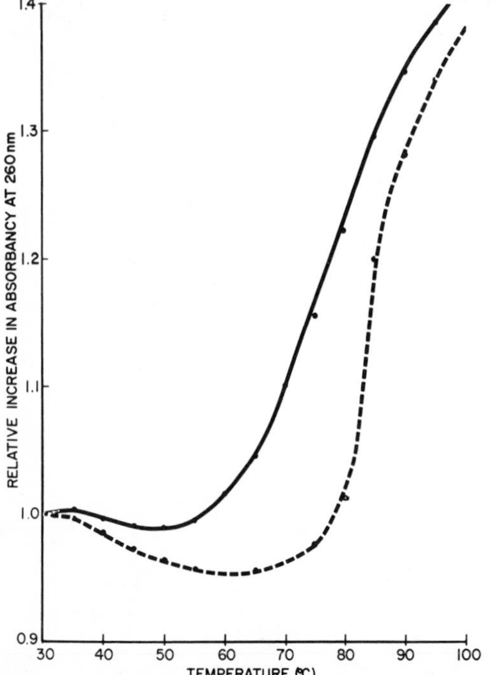

Fig. 4. *Thermal dissociation of DNA (5.2×10^{-5} M phosphorus) in the absence (———) or presence of the test quinoline methanol (1.16×10^{-5} M) (-----) shown in Fig. 1. Phosphate buffer, 10^{-3} M at pH 7.0.*

complexes of DNA with chloroquine (2) and berberine (6).

DISCUSSION

The present work has shown that one representative antimalarial quinoline methanol forms a complex with double-helical DNA and stabilizes DNA to thermal strand separation. Parameters for two binding processes as determined by spectrophotometric titration suggest that the quinoline methanol has affinities for DNA similar to those of quinine, but that, on the average, 10 times more of the synthetic drug is bound per unit of DNA. Another similarity to the DNA-quinine relationship is suggested by the observation that the quinoline methanol percipitated DNA at low concentrations.

It was recognized throughout the course of this study that additional biophysical experiments were desired for a more detailed description of the DNA-quinoline methanol complex. As in the case of quinine (4), such experiments are not feasible because of the precipitation phenomenon.

The most important question to be asked is, of course, that of the structures of the DNA complexes which are formed with the quinoline methanol by either of two binding processes. Our present results afford only a general discussion of this problem. It has been suggested in this laboratory (4) that the strong binding of quinine to DNA involves intercalation of the quinoline ring between base pairs of double-helical DNA. Cairns (3) has proposed that maximal intercalation occurs to the extent of one ligand molecule per two base pairs. The red shift of the absorption maxima of the test quinoline methanol upon complexing with DNA suggests that individual drug molecules are bound, and the stoichiometry of the stronger process, one drug molecule per >three base pairs is within the possible limits of intercalation binding.

The more frequent binding of the drug by the weaker of the two processes occurred to the extent of one molecule per base pair. This exceeds the stiochiometric limitations for intercalation. The only inference which our results permit concerning the possible structure of this complex with DNA is that the drug molecules evidently are not "stacked" alongside the double helix in a manner which could favor drug-drug interactions; such an occurrence would produce a blue shift in the absorption spectrum of the bound drug, i.e., precisely the opposite of the result that was observed. Finally, the limited working range of spectrophotometry and the precipitation of DNA by the drug at low concentrations render it nonfeasible to observe either very strong binding of a few drug molecules or weak binding of numerous molecules which could conceivably attain values of one basic drug molecule per one phosphate group of DNA.

LITERATURE CITED

1. Ainley, A. D., and H. King. 1938. Antiplasmodial action and chemical constitution. II. Some simple synthetic analogs of quinine and cinchonine. Proc. Roy. Soc. (London) Ser. B **125**:60–92.
2. Allison, J. L., R. L. O'Brien, and F. E. Hahn. 1965. DNA: reaction with chloroquine. Science (Washington) **149**:1111–1113.
3. Cairns, J. 1962. The application of autoradiography to the study of DNA viruses. Cold Spring Harbor Symp. Quant. Biol. **27**:311–318.
4. Estensen, R. D., A. K. Krey, and F. E. Hahn. 1969. Studies on a deoxyribonucleic acid-quinine complex. Mol. Pharmacol. **5**:532–541.
5. Hahn, F. E., R. L. O'Brien, J. Ciak, J. L. Allison, and J. G. Olenick. 1966. Studies on modes of action of chloroquine, quinacrine and quinine and on chloroquine resistance. Mil. Med. **131**(Suppl.):1071–1089.
6. Krey, A. K., and F. E. Hahn, 1969. Berberine: complex with DNA. Science (Washington) **166**:755–757.
7. Michaelis, L. 1947. The nature of the interaction of nucleic acids and nuclei with basic dyestuffs. Cold Spring Harbor Symp. Quant. Biol. **12**:131–142.
8. O'Brien, R. L., J. G. Olenick, and F. E. Hahn. 1966. Reactions of quinine, chloroquine, and quinacrine with DNA and their effects on the DNA and RNA polymerase reactions. Proc. Nat. Acad. Sci. U.S.A. **55**:1511–1517.
9. Polet, H., and C. F. Barr. 1968. Chloroquine and dihydroquinine. *In vitro* studies of their antimalarial effect upon *Plasmodium knolesi.* J. Pharmacol. Exp. Ther. **164**:380–386.
10. Romanovsky, D. L. 1891. Specific action of quinine in malaria. Vrach (St. Petersb.) **12**:438–440.
11. Schellenberg, K. A., and G. R. Coatney. 1961. The influence of antimalarial drugs on nucleic acid synthesis in *Plasmodium gallinaceum* and *Plasmodium berghei.* Biochem. Pharmacol. **6**:143–152.
12. Wiselogle, F. Y. 1946. A survey of antimalarial drugs 1941-1945. J. W. Edwards, Ann Arbor, Mich.

Antimicrobial Agents and Chemotherapy—1969

Synthesis of Protocatechuate Oxygenase by *Pseudomonas fluorescens* in the Presence of Actinomycin D

NORMAN N. DURHAM and K. C. KEUDELL

Department of Microbiology, Oklahoma State University, Stillwater, Oklahoma 74074

Pseudomonas fluorescens produces an inducible enzyme, protocatechuate oxygenase (EC 1.99.2.3) in response to protocatechuic acid. Actinomycin D inhibits growth of the organism in a succinate-salts medium but not in a protocatechuate-salts medium. The antibiotic prevented incorporation of leucine-*2-^{14}C* and uracil-*2-^{14}C* by the cells when succinate was the substrate. Neither leucine-*2-^{14}C* nor uracil-*2-^{14}C* incorporation was influenced in the protocatechuate-salts medium. Addition of protocatechuic acid either prevented or reversed, depending on the time of addition, the actinomycin D inhibition of growth and macromolecular synthesis. Uptake studies with ^{14}C-actinomycin D established that the antibiotic readily penetrated the permeability barrier and that protocatechuic acid did not compete with or otherwise influence the uptake mechanism. Since protocatechuic acid can reverse the inhibition, the complexing of the antibiotic with cellular deoxyribonucleic acid apparently is reversible. It is proposed that protocatechuic acid and actinomycin D interact to negate the ability of the antibiotic to affect the cell adversely. The elucidation of this phenomenon may contribute toward a better understanding of the detoxifying potential of the cell by exogenous compounds, as well as the mechanisms for genetic regulation and macromolecular synthesis.

Actinomycin D prevents protein synthesis by inhibiting deoxyribonucleic acid (DNA)-directed ribonucleic acid (RNA) synthesis (4, 7, 9), and there is an accompanying decrease in the uptake of labeled uracil into messenger RNA and of labeled amino acids into protein (12).

Different enzyme systems vary in their sensitivity to the antibiotic. The formation of alkaline phosphatase and α-amylase was inhibited by actinomycin D in *Bacillus subtilis*, but ribonuclease was not (8). Pollock (13) observed a differential effect in enzyme systems of *B. subtilis* and *B. cereus*. Production of gramicidin S in *B. brevis* was not affected by actinomycin D, even though normal RNA and protein syntheses were inhibited (3). Actinomycin D readily inhibited macromolecular syntheses in sarcoma 37 ascites cells (6).

It has been proposed that the binding of actinomycin was specific for double-stranded helical DNA which contained guanine (1). Recently, Wells (15) suggested that the presence of guanine in DNA was not a sufficient requisite for binding but that structural conformation played an important role.

Studies in this laboratory have established that the induced synthesis of protocatechuate oxygenase (EC 1.99.2.3) by *Pseudomonas fluorescens* (2, 10) in response to protocatechuic acid (3,4-dihydroxybenzoic acid) is not affected by actinomycin D. In addition, protocatechuic acid alleviates the actinomycin D inhibition of growth in a synthetic salts medium. As the antibiotic reportedly binds to the DNA of the cell, this investigation was conducted to delineate the apparent resistance of the synthesis of protocatechuate oxygenase and the unique ability of cells to grow in the presence of a DNA-binding compound.

MATERIALS AND METHODS

Test organism. The organism used in this study has been tentatively identified as *P. fluorescens* (10). Stock cultures were maintained on Nutrient Agar and succinate-salts-agar slants stored at 4 C.

Media. The synthetic salts medium had the following composition: 0.42% K_2HPO_4, 0.32% KH_2PO_4, 0.2% NH_4Cl, 0.2% NaCl, and 0.2% of the desired carbon source. The *p*H was adjusted to 7.0. Agar (Difco) was added to give a final concentration of 2.0% when a solid medium was desired. A sterile mineral salts solution (0.1 ml) was added to each 100 ml of synthetic medium (2).

Preparation of substrates and inhibitor. Succinic and protocatechuic acids were prepared fresh for each experiment. The compounds were dissolved in 0.01 M 2-amino-2-(hydroxymethyl)-1,3-propanediol buffer (Tris), and the *p*H was adjusted to 7.0. Actinomycin D was dissolved in distilled water just prior to use.

Cell suspensions. Cells from Nutrient Agar or succinate-agar slants (16 to 18 hr) were suspended in sterile 0.01 M Tris buffer and used to inoculate the surface of the appropriate agar plates. The plates were incubated at 37 C for 16 to 18 hr. The cells were then harvested, washed twice, and suspended in sterile 0.01 M Tris buffer (*p*H 7.0) so that a 1:10 dilution gave the desired absorbance reading at 540 nm with a Bausch & Lomb Spectronic-20 colorimeter (18-mm light path).

Growth studies. Growth experiments were conducted with the use of 18 × 150 mm tubes containing a total of 6 ml of liquid. The tubes were incubated at 37 C on a reciprocal shaker. For experiments in which samples were required at various time intervals, 250-ml Erlenmeyer flasks with side arms containing 40 ml of medium were used. These flasks were incubated at 37 C with constant shaking. Growth was followed by reading the absorbance at 540 nm.

Manometric studies. Enzymatic activity was measured by following oxygen uptake in a Warburg apparatus at 37 C with air as the gas phase (14).

Radioisotope studies. The incorporation of uracil-2-^{14}C (specific activity, 6.15 mc/mmole) was measured simultaneously with the manometric investigations. Uracil-2-^{14}C (0.043 μc/ml, final concentration), 5 μmoles of uracil per ml as a carrier, and the desired substrate were placed in the side arm of Warburg vessels. All ingredients were added to the cells simultaneously. Duplicate flasks (2.4-ml total liquid volume) were prepared, and at various time intervals a flask was removed from the Warburg apparatus, a 1.0-ml sample was pipetted into a thick-walled centrifuge tube, and the sample was frozen in a cellosolve-dry ice bath.

To study incorporation of amino acids, 1.0 ml of leucine-2-^{14}C (161,310 counts per min per ml) was added to a 250-ml Erlenmeyer side-arm flask containing 0.2% succinate, 20 μmoles of leucine per ml as a carrier, and 0.8 μmoles of protocatechuic acid per ml or 30 μg/ml of actinomycin D, or both of the last two components. The flasks were inoculated with succinate-grown cells. At the desired time, absorbance readings were taken, and a 3-ml sample was removed and frozen in a cellosolve-dry ice bath.

A 4-ml amount of cold 5% trichloroacetic acid was added to the tubes containing the frozen samples. The samples were thawed at 4 C and centrifuged at 12,000 × *g* for 15 min at 4 C. The supernatant solution was poured into counting vials. The pellets were suspended in 5 ml of cold 5.0% trichloroacetic acid, incubated at 4 C for 15 min, and centrifuged at 12,000 × *g* for 15 min. The supernatant solution was poured into different counting vials. The cell pellets were washed once with 5 ml of distilled water, suspended in 5 ml of 95% ethyl alcohol, incubated at room temperature for 15 min, and centrifuged. The ethyl alcohol was discarded, and the cells were washed again with distilled water. The pellets were suspended in 5 ml of 5.0% trichloroacetic acid and heated at 90 C for 30 min. The samples were cooled and then centrifuged at 12,000 × *g* for 15 min. The supernatant solution was placed in counting vials, and the contents of the vials were dried at 55 C under vacuum in a desiccator containing anhydrous $CaCl_2$ until about 0.1 ml of fluid remained in the vials. A 10-ml amount of liquid scintillation counting fluid (42 ml of Liquifluor to 1 liter of sulfur-free toluene) was added to each vial. The cell pellets from the leucine experiment were digested overnight in 0.5 ml of NCS Reagent (Nuclear-Chicago Corp., Des Plaines, Ill.) at room temperature. All samples were counted in a Nuclear-Chicago liquid scintillation spectrometer. The system had a counting efficiency of approximately 40% for ^{14}C under these conditions.

Uptake of ^{14}C-actinomycin D. Succinate-grown cells were suspended so that a 1:10 dilution gave an absorbance reading of 1.0 at 540 nm. Uptake was measured in the following substrates: 0.2% succinate, protocatechuic acid (0.8 μmoles/ml), 0.2% succinate plus protocatechuic acid (0.8 μmole/ml), and protocatechuic acid (6.8 μmoles/ml). Unless indicated otherwise, each tube contained 0.2 ml of the substrate, 0.1 ml of actinomycin D (2.5 × 10^7 counts per min per μmole), 0.065 ml of actinomycin D (30 μg/ml) as a carrier, and 0.01 M Tris buffer to bring the total liquid volume to 0.5 ml.

The cell suspension (0.15 ml) was added to the substrates in thick-walled centrifuge tubes (15 × 100 mm), incubated at 37 C for 75 sec, and frozen in a cellosolve-dry ice bath. A 5-ml amount of cold Tris buffer was added to each tube; the pellet was thawed at 4 C, centrifuged at 12,000 × *g* for 15 min, and washed twice by centrifugation. All solutions were saved for counting. A 0.5-ml amount of NCS Reagent (Nuclear-Chicago) was added to each tube, and digestion of the cell pellets was carried out overnight at room temperature. The digested material was poured into a counting vial, and the tube was rinsed with 9.5 ml of counting fluid (42 ml of Liquifluor to 400 ml of absolute ethyl alcohol and 600 ml of toluene).

RESULTS

Effect of actinomycin D on growth. When succinate-grown cells were used as the inoculum, actinomycin D inhibited growth in a succinate-salts medium, and the inhibition was concentration-dependent (Fig. 1). A concentration of 30 μg/ml gave virtually complete inhibition; concentrations of 5 and 10 μg/ml decreased growth, and the total cell density did not attain the same value as the control.

The inoculation of protocatechuate-salts medium with succinate-grown cells showed different results. Actinomycin D, in the concentrations used in this experiment, did not inhibit growth of the cells growing in the protocatechuate-salts medium (Fig. 2). These results establish that actinomycin D did not inhibit cells when protocatechuic acid was used as the sole source of carbon and energy. Thus, in this medium, the antibiotic did not influence synthesis of the induced enzyme (protocatechuate oxygenase) or any other essential metabolic reactions required for growth.

Similar experiments were conducted with protocatechuate-induced cells as the inoculum instead of the noninduced succinate-grown cells. Protocatechuate-induced cells growing in a succinate-salts medium were inhibited in the presence of actinomycin D, but the same cells growing in a protocatechuate-salts medium showed no lag or inhibition of growth in the presence of the antibiotic.

Thus, both protocatechuate-induced and noninduced cells (succinate-grown) were inhibited by actinomycin D when succinate was used as the sole source of carbon and energy. Growth occurred in the protocatechuate-salts medium in the presence of actinomycin D regardless of the medium on which the inoculum was grown. The results establish that protocatechuic acid prevents actinomycin D from inhibiting growth and, at the same time, eliminates the possibility that growth in protocatechuic acid confers a permanent state of resistance.

Reversal of actinomycin D inhibition of growth by protocatechuic acid. Cells growing in a medium containing protocatechuic acid as the sole source of carbon and energy were not inhibited by actinomycin D. Experiments were conducted to determine whether protocatechuic acid could reverse the inhibition of growth by

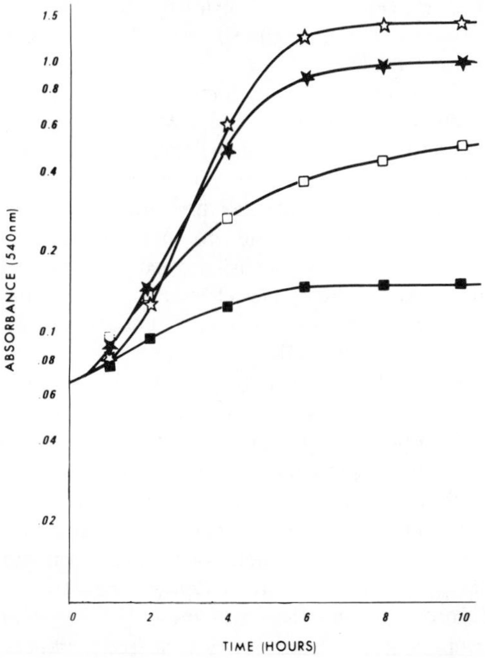

Fig. 1. *Influence of actinomycin D on succinate-grown P. fluorescens cells growing in a succinate-salts medium. Symbols:* ☆, *control;* ★, *actinomycin D (5 μg/ml);* □, *actinomycin D (10 μg/ml);* ■, *actinomycin D (30 μg/ml).*

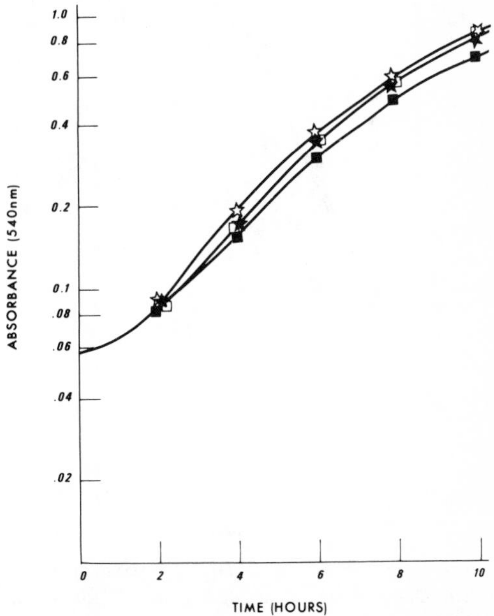

Fig. 2. *Influence of actinomycin D on succinate-grown P. fluorescens cells growing in a protocatechuate-salts medium. Symbols:* ☆, *control;* ★, *actinomycin D (5 μg/ml);* □, *actinomycin D (10 μg/ml);* ■, *actinomycin D (30 μg/ml).*

actinomycin D when succinate was used as the primary carbon and energy source. The results (Fig. 3) indicated that addition of protocatechuate to the inhibited system at the indicated time (3.5 hr) reversed the actinomycin D inhibition of growth. Both protocatechuate concentrations, 0.4 and 0.8 μmole/ml, readily relieved the inhibition produced by 30 μg of actinomycin D per ml. The rate of growth, following reversal of the inhibition by protocatechuate, was similar to the rate of growth in the controls. Appropriate controls run concurrently showed protocatechuate did not affect growth of the cells.

Effect of actinomycin D and protocatechuic acid on cell viability. Viable-cell counts were made of cells growing under the different conditions to substantiate the results obtained with growth (absorbance) studies.

Viable counts of cells growing in a succinate medium (Table 1) showed a steady decrease after 2 to 3 hr in the presence of actinomycin D,

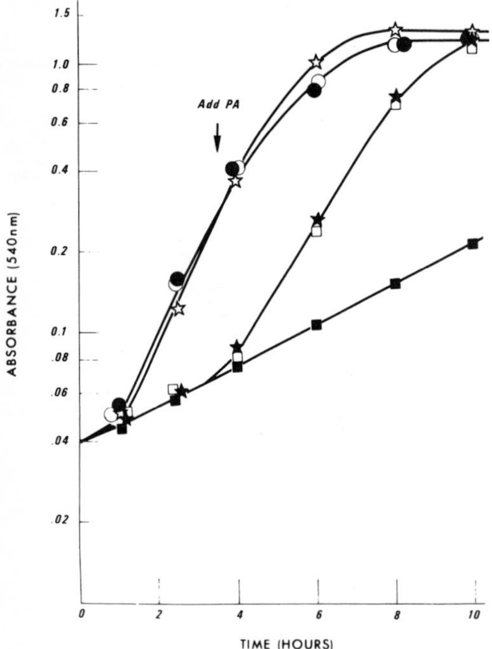

Fig. 3. *Protocatechuic acid (PA) reversal of actinomycin D inhibition of succinate-grown P. fluorescens cells growing in a succinate-salts medium. Protocatechuic acid was added to the cells at 3.5 hr. Symbols:* ☆, *control;* ■, *actinomycin D (30 μg/ml);* □, *actinomycin D (30 μg/ml) + PA (0.8 μmole/ml);* ★, *actinomycin D (30 μg/ml) + PA (0.4 μmole/ml);* ○, *PA (0.8 μmole/ml);* ●, *PA (0.4 μmole/ml).*

Table 1. *Viable counts of cells growing in a succinate-salts medium in the presence and absence of actinomycin D and protocatechuic acid*

Time (hr)	Millions of viable cells[a]				
	Succinate	Succinate, Act. D[b]	Succinate, Act. D, PA[c]	Succinate, Act. D, PA[d]	Succinate, PA[c]
0	266	291	245	288	290
2	348	284	269	278	297
3	790	152	790	157	810
4	1,980	17	1,730	209	1,720
6	2,680	4	2,410	316	2,720
7	2,560	2	2,060	421	1,980

[a] The medium was inoculated to give approximately 250×10^{-6} cells/ml.
[b] Actinomycin D (Act. D) concentration was 30 μg/ml.
[c] Protocatechuic acid (PA), 0.8 μmole/ml (added at 0 hr).
[d] Protocatechuic acid (PA), 0.8 μmole/ml (added at 3 hr).

confirming that actinomycin D was interfering with the viability of cells growing in the succinate-salts medium. Microscopic examination revealed an increase in cell size in the presence of actinomycin D. This would explain the continued slight increase in the absorbance reading (Fig. 1 and 3) in the presence of actinomycin D even though the viable-cell count showed a decline.

Cell counts in the tubes in which actinomycin D and protocatechuic acid were added simultaneously at 0 hr revealed little, if any, inhibition, and the cells grew out to approximately the same total cell mass as the control. Addition of protocatechuic acid to actinomycin D-inhibited cells at 3 hr showed reversal, as indicated by the viable-cell counts. The results obtained from the viable-cell counts readily augment the growth studies in showing that protocatechuic acid may prevent or overcome the inhibition by actinomycin D.

Incorporation of uracil-2-^{14}C and leucine-2-^{14}C in the presence of actinomycin D. Growth studies demonstrated that actinomycin D did not inhibit growth of cells utilizing protocatechuic acid as the sole source of carbon and energy or when an extremely low concentration of protocatechuic acid was present in a system containing a different growth substrate. Experiments were conducted to observe protocatechuate oxygenase synthesis manometrically and simultaneously to measure the incorporation of uracil-*2-^{14}C* into the hot trichloroacetic acid-soluble fraction (RNA).

Actinomycin D did not influence the induced synthesis of protocatechuate oxygenase by cells in the presence of protocatechuic acid as measured by oxygen uptake, and samples taken at several time intervals indicated that uracil-*2-^{14}C* was incorporated into cellular RNA at approximately the same rate in the presence and absence of actinomycin D. Controls indicated that uracil-*2-^{14}C* was not incorporated into the hot trichloroacetic acid-soluble fraction by the cells in the absence of the inducer (protocatechuic acid). Incubation of the cells with actinomycin D for 60 min prior to addition of protocatechuic acid did not influence induced enzyme synthesis.

Amino acid incorporation into protein is decreased in the presence of actinomycin D (5, 12). This inhibition of amino acid incorporation was confirmed for cells growing in a succinate-salts medium (Table 2). Since protocatechuic acid reversed the inhibition of growth, the incorporation of amino acids into proteins was measured in the presence and absence of actinomycin D and protocatechuic acid.

Leucine-*2-^{14}C* incorporation into protein was inhibited by actinomycin D (Table 2). When protocatechuate was added simultaneously with actinomycin D (0 hr), the rate of amino acid incorporation appeared to be slightly reduced, but it was obvious that protein synthesis was in progress. Addition of protocatechuate to inhibited cells at 2.5 hr reversed the inhibition, as incorporation of labeled leucine was evident at the later time intervals. ^{14}C-amino acid incorporation by the cells was evident when protocatechuic acid was added simultaneously with the inhibitor or to actinomycin D-inhibited cells. These results augment the findings from the growth study that protocatechuate may either prevent or overcome the actinomycin D inhibition.

Table 2. *Incorporation of leucine-2-^{14}C into protein of P. fluorescens cells growing in the presence and absence of actinomycin D and protocatechuic acid*

Time (hr)	Counts per min[a]				
	Succinate	Succinate, Act. D	Succinate, Act. D, PA[b]	Succinate, Act. D, PA[c]	Succinate, PA[b]
0	0	0	0	0	0
0.5	5	8	7	10	14
1	24	23	13	18	11
1.5	42	31	40	27	47
2.5	132	40	105	36	82
3.5	191	36	132	95	111
4	199	44	167	124	205

[a] Actinomycin D (Act. D) concentration was 30 μg/ml. All counts were corrected for background.

[b] Protocatechuic acid (PA), 0.8 μmole/ml (added at 0 hr).

[c] Protocatechuic acid (PA), 0.8 μmole/ml (added at 2.5 hr).

Uptake of ^{14}C-actinomycin D by cells. Leive (11) noted that treatment of *Escherichia coli* with ethylenediaminetetraacetate (10^{-3} M) permitted the uptake of actinomycin D with the subsequent inhibition of β-galactosidase synthesis. *P. fluorescens* cells were treated with ethylenediaminetetraacetate (10^{-3} M), and enzyme synthesis was measured in the presence and absence of actinomycin D. Results indicated no difference in the rate of protocatechuate oxygenase synthesis.

The uptake of ^{14}C-actinomycin D by the cells was measured to confirm that the antibiotic was penetrating the permeability barrier of this gram-negative organism. Actinomycin D uptake did occur in the presence of succinate and protocatechuate. The rate of uptake was comparable with both substrates. These studies also suggest that none of the substrates is competing with or otherwise influencing the uptake of actinomycin D by the cells. Therefore, growth of the cells in the presence of actinomycin D with protocatechuate as the substrate cannot be readily explained on the assumption that the substrate and inhibitor compete for entry into the cell.

DISCUSSION

The growth of *P. fluorescens* in a succinate-salts medium was inhibited by actinomycin D, and the effect was concentration-dependent. Actinomycin D did not inhibit growth of the cells when protocatechuic acid was used as the sole source of carbon and energy. Since protocatechuate oxygenase is inducible, this offers an example of microbial protein synthesis that was not sensitive to this antibiotic. Protocatechuic acid did not interfere with the uptake of ^{14}C-actinomycin D by the cell. Absorbance measurements and viable-cell counts established that low concentrations of protocatechuic acid could prevent or alleviate the actinomycin D inhibition of growth in the succinate medium.

Actinomycin D inhibited incorporation of radioactive leucine into protein and uracil into

RNA in the absence of protocatechuate. Incorporation of both the amino acid and pyrimidine was resumed when protocatechuic acid was added to the inhibited cells.

Alleviation of the inhibition suggests that the complexing of actinomycin D with DNA is reversible. This finding augments an earlier observation from this laboratory which noted that transformation of *B. subtilis* was inhibited by actinomycin D but could be reversed by dialysis (16).

It has been suggested that guanine must be present for actinomycin D to bind to DNA (5), but more recently structural conformation has been implicated as an important determinant (15). One possibility is that, if guanine was not present in the genome coding the messenger RNA for protocatechuate oxygenase, then actinomycin D would not be able to bind to the specific loci and enzyme synthesis would occur. Certainly this would offer a plausible explanation for growth in the protocatechuate-salts medium and synthesis of the enzyme when actinomycin D is present. However, the ability of protocatechuic acid to prevent or overcome the inhibition suggests that the effect is general in nature and, as a result, cannot be explained solely on the basis of the presence or absence of guanine or the configuration of the molecule.

Other plausible explanations are that actinomycin D and protocatechuic acid form a complex, and that protocatechuic acid displaces the antibiotic from the DNA or may otherwise function to inactivate the antibiotic. When protocatechuic acid and actinomycin D are added simultaneously, the antibiotic is inactivated before the inhibition is established. In the reversal studies, the antibiotic forms a reversible complex with DNA and, when the inhibitor detaches from the DNA, it may then complex with or otherwise be inactivated by protocatechuic acid. The molecular conformation indicates that protocatechuic acid may complex with the chromophore of the actinomycin molecule, thereby preventing the antibiotic from further interaction with cellular DNA. The structures of the two molecules would permit such a reaction.

ACKNOWLEDGMENTS

This investigation was supported by Public Health Service Grant NIAMD-09396 from the National Institute of Arthritis and Metabolic Diseases and by grant IN-91A from the American Cancer Society.

LITERATURE CITED

1. Cerami, A., E. Reich, D. C. Ward, and I. H. Goldberg. 1967. The interaction of actinomycin with DNA: requirement for 2-amino group of purines. Proc. Nat. Acad. Sci. U.S.A. **57**:1036–1042.
2. Durham, N. N. 1958. Studies on the metabolism of p-nitrobenzoic acid. Can. J. Microbiol. **4**:141–148.
3. Eikhom, T. S., and S. G. Laland. 1965. The effect of actinomycin D on the production of gramicidin S in whole cells of *Bacillus brevis*. Biochim. Biophys. Acta **100**:451–458.
4. Goldberg, I. H., and M. Rabinovitz. 1962. Actinomycin D inhibition of deoxyribonucleic acid-dependent synthesis of ribonucleic acid. Science (Washington) **136**:315–316.
5. Goldberg, I. H., M. Rabinovitz, and E. Reich. 1962. Basis of actinomycin action. I. DNA binding and inhibition of RNA-polymerase synthetic reactions by actinomycin. Proc. Nat. Acad. Sci. U.S.A. **48**:2094–2101.
6. Honig, G. R., and M. Rabinovitz. 1966. Inhibition by actinomycin D of oxidation-dependent biosynthesis in Sarcoma 37 ascites cells. J. Biol. Chem. **241**:1681–1687.
7. Hurwitz, J., J. J. Furth, M. Malamy, and M. Alexander. 1962. The role of deoxyribonucleic acid in ribonucleic acid synthesis. III. The inhibition of the enzymatic synthesis of ribonucleic acid and deoxyribonucleic acid by actinomycin D and proflavin. Proc. Nat. Acad. Sci. U.S.A. **48**:1222–1230.
8. Kadowaki, K., J. Hososda, and B. Maruo. 1965. Effects of actinomycin D and 5-fluorouracil on the formation of enzymes in *Bacillus subtilis*. Biochim. Biophys. Acta **103**:311–318.
9. Kirk, J. M. 1960. The mode of action of actinomycin D. Biochim. Biophys. Acta **42**:167–169.
10. Kirkland, J. J., and N. N. Durham. 1965. Synthesis of protocatechuate oxygenase by *Pseudomonas fluorescens* in the presence of exogenous carbon sources. J. Bacteriol. **90**:15–22.
11. Leive, L. 1965. Actinomycin sensitivity in *Escherichia coli* produced by EDTA. Biochem. Biophys. Res. Commun. **18**:13–17.
12. Levinthal, C., A. Keynan, and A. Higa. 1962. Messenger RNA turnover and protein synthesis in *Bacillus subtilis* inhibited by actinomycin D. Proc. Nat. Acad. Sci. U.S.A. **48**:1631–1638.
13. Pollock, M. R. 1963. The differential effect of actinomycin D on the biosynthesis of enzymes in *Bacillus subtilis* and *Bacillus cereus*. Biochim. Biophys. Acta **76**:80–93.
14. Umbreit, W. W., R. H. Burris, and J. F. Stauffer. 1964. Manometric techniques, 4th ed. Burgess Publishing Co., Minneapolis.
15. Wells, R. D. 1969. Actinomycin binding to DNA: inability of a DNA containing guanine to bind actinomycin D. Science (Washington) **165**:75–76.
16. Wingfield, D. D., T. J. Kerr, and N. N. Durham. 1965. Evaluation of transformation in cell populations containing aberrant cell forms and the inhibition of transformation by selected inhibitors. Can. J. Microbiol. **11**:797–805.

Antimicrobial Agents and Chemotherapy—1969

Cell Walls of Methicillin-Resistant *Staphylococcus aureus*

L. D. SABATH, C. D. LEAF, D. A. GERSTEIN, and M. FINLAND

Thorndike Memorial Laboratory (Channing Laboratory), Harvard Medical Unit, Boston City Hospital, and Department of Medicine, Harvard Medical School, Boston, Massachusetts 02118

Methicillin resistance of *Staphylococcus aureus* is independent of penicillinase (β-lactamase) synthesis and function. The possibility that alterations in cell wall structure parallel changes in susceptibility to methicillin was investigated in naturally occurring isolates by (i) determining the susceptibility of cells to wall-lytic enzymes and (ii) measuring the amino acid composition of cell walls. Egg white lysozyme failed to lyse either methicillin-susceptible (MS) or methicillin-resistant (MR) cells, whereas lysostaphin lysed both, but the latter at significantly slower rates. No difference in amino acid composition was detected in walls of MS and MR cells. In contrast, staphylococci made resistant to methicillin in the laboratory by serial transfers in the presence of drug showed little or no decrease in rates of lysis by lysostaphin. Similarly, MS cells selected for resistance to lysostaphin showed no change in susceptibility to methicillin.

Methicillin-resistant strains of *Staphylococcus aureus* are usually defined as those for which 25 μg or more of methicillin per ml is required to inhibit their growth; in contrast, susceptible strains are usually inhibited by 1.5 to 3.0 μg/ml. Although almost all naturally occurring methicillin-resistant strains produce large amounts of penicillinase, this is probably not the cause of their resistance for the following three reasons: (i) no more penicillinase is produced by methicillin-resistant *S. aureus* than by most other strains (12, 13); (ii) the penicillinase produced by methicillin-resistant strains is not different either qualitatively or in kinetic behavior from that produced by methicillin-susceptible strains (12, 13); (iii) methicillin-resistance is independent of penicillinase synthesis (6, 16) and function (2, 15).

Because penicillins act by inhibiting a cross-linking transpeptidase in the cytoplasmic membrane (20, 21), it seemed possible that methicillin-resistant staphylococci might have cell walls that differed from those of susceptible cells. This communication describes some experiments performed to evaluate this possibility.

With regard to the possibility that cell walls of methicillin-resistant staphylococci are altered, the following two facts were considered. (i) Only about 1 in 1 million colony-forming units from cultures of methicillin-resistant staphylococci is highly resistant to methicillin, i.e., is capable of forming colonies on agar containing 50 μg of methicillin per ml of medium (1–5, 7–11, 14, 15, 17). Therefore, any analysis of cell walls from such a mixed population would be unlikely to detect the characteristics associated with methicillin resistance in that 1 cell in 1 million. (ii) Alterations in cell wall structure might involve changes in any one or more wall component, i.e., in the peptide, sugar, amino sugar, lipid, or some other component.

The problem of having only a small minority of resistant cells in a population was met by selecting for methicillin-resistant cells, so that most or all of the cells being tested would have the resistance trait. The possibility that a difference in wall structure might involve any wall component will eventually have to be met by measuring each wall component. For current studies, amino acid composition (15*a*) and also the susceptibility to wall-lytic enzymes have been determined. Although the sites of action of the enzymes used are known, it is possible that a change in composition of any wall component might influence accessibility of wall-lytic enzymes to their sites of action and thus influence the rate of the reaction.

MATERIALS AND METHODS

Bacteria. The naturally occurring methicillin-resistant strains were isolated from patients at the Boston City Hospital, except for one British isolate kindly supplied by K. G. H. Dyke (6); some of these strains have been previously described (2, 15). The methicillin-susceptible staphylococci were also clinical isolates obtained from the Diagnostic Bacteriology Laboratory at Boston City Hospital, except for one strain (Oxford 167) which was obtained from N. Smith, Sir William Dunn School of Pathology, Oxford, England. Predominantly methicillin-resistant populations of six isolates were obtained by cloning on Difco Heart Infusion (HI) agar containing 50 μg of cloxacillin/ml, and then growing cells from single colonies in Difco Brain Heart Infusion (BHI) containing 50 μg of cloxacillin/ml. Such populations contained 50 to 100% highly resistant organisms (per cent highly resistant equals the colony count on HI agar containing 50 μg of cloxacillin per ml divided by the colony count on HI agar without antibiotic multiplied times 100) whereas the populations of naturally occurring isolates usually contained only 1 in 10^5 to 10^6 highly resistant "cells" or colony-forming units. Similar results had been obtained when methicillin was used for cloning, but cloxacillin was used throughout these experiments because it is more stable.

Laboratory production of resistant strains. Two methicillin-susceptible strains of *S. aureus*, one a penicillinase producer (strain 60/1) isolated in the Boston City Hospital and the other a penicillinase-negative strain (Oxford 167), were made resistant to methicillin by serial passages in the presence of increasing concentrations of drug until the organisms grew in ⩾100 μg/ml. Lysostaphin-resistant strains were also selected under appropriate laboratory conditions.

Antibiotics and enzymes. The methicillin (Bristol Laboratories, Syracuse, N.Y.), cloxacillin (Ayerst Laboratories, New York, N.Y.), cephalothin and cephaloridine (Lilly Laboratories for Clinical Research, Indianapolis, Ind.), and lysostaphin (Mead Johnson Research Laboratories, Evansville, Ind.) were generously donated by the manufacturers or distributors. The egg white lysozyme was purchased from Pentex, Inc. (Kankakee, Ill).

Antibiotic susceptibility testing. Undiluted 18-hr BHI broth cultures were applied with an inocula replicator (18) to the surface of HI agar containing twofold serial dilutions of the appropriate antibiotic. Results were read after 48 hr of incubation at 37 C.

Lysis of bacterial cell suspensions. Overnight cultures of cells were washed twice with 1 M NaCl and then adjusted to optical densities of 1.0 (Coleman Junior spectrophotometer) at 620 nm in a tris(hydroxymethyl) aminomethane (Tris)-NaCl buffer at *p*H 7.5 (23). To each cuvette (12 × 75 mm), 0.5 ml of such cell suspensions and 2 ml of Tris-NaCl buffer were added. The cuvettes were incubated for 10 to 20 min in a water bath at 37 C before the reaction was initiated by adding 0.5 ml of prewarmed Tris-NaCl buffer containing either lysostaphin (usually 2.5 μg) or lysozyme (50 μg). Enzyme was omitted from appropriate control tubes. At intervals of 2 to 10 min, the per cent light transmission at 620 nm was recorded. This is a slight modification of the procedure described by Zygmunt et al. (23).

RESULTS

Susceptibility to lysis by lysozyme. No detectable lysis of methicillin-susceptible or methicillin-resistant cells was noted during 16 hr of incubation.

Susceptibility to lysis by lysostaphin. Lysostaphin lysed both methicillin-susceptible and methicillin-resistant cells, but at quite different rates.

Figure 1 shows the comparative rates of lysis, or change in light transmission at 620 nm, for a predominantly methicillin-resistant cell population (MR) and for the strain from which it was cloned (MS). The susceptible strain showed much greater changes in light transmission than the methicillin-resistant population. When lysostaphin was omitted from control cell suspensions, there was negligible lysis.

This particular strain was isolated from a patient at Boston City Hospital. Epidemiologically distinct isolates of methicillin-resistant *S. aureus* from five other patients showed similar results, in that cell populations in which most of the cells were methicillin-resistant lysed much

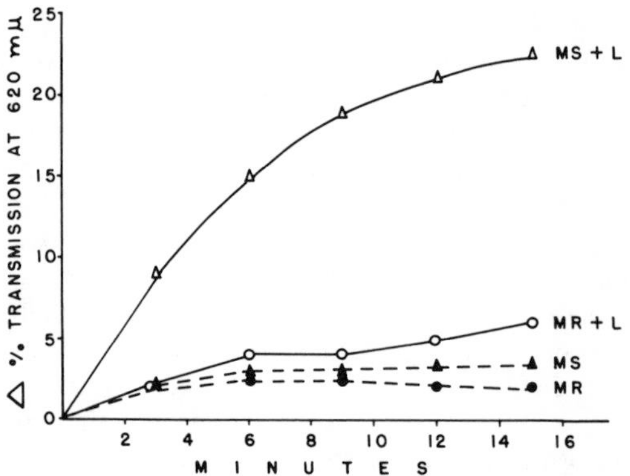

Fig. 1. *Lysostaphin (L) lysis of methicillin-resistant (MR) and methicillin-susceptible (MS) Staphylococcus aureus cells.*

more slowly than did cell populations in which only 1 cell in 10^5 or 10^6 was resistant.

A summary of results with these other isolates is shown in Fig. 2. The rates of lysis of several common methicillin-susceptible strains of *S. aureus* did not differ significantly from the rates of lysis of naturally occurring methicillin-resistant isolates. Cell populations containing mostly methicillin-resistant cells obtained by cloning were significantly more resistant to lysis by lysostaphin.

Two methicillin-susceptible strains that had been made methicillin-resistant in the laboratory were tested for susceptibility to lysostaphin, and compared with their parent strains. One strain (Fig. 3) showed a slight increase in susceptibility to lysostaphin, compared with its parent strain. The other strain (Fig. 4), which had also been "trained" to methicillin resistance in the laboratory, showed a somewhat slower rate of lysis when exposed to lysostaphin than did its parent strain, but this was a smaller decrease in susceptibility to lysostaphin than was shown with cloned naturally occurring methicillin-resistant isolates.

The Oxford strain was also used as a source of a lysostaphin-resistant clone which was highly resistant to lysostaphin (Fig. 5). When these lysostaphin-resistant organisms were tested for susceptibility to methicillin and other semisynthetic penicillins and cephalosporins, they did not differ from the parent, lysostaphin-susceptible strain.

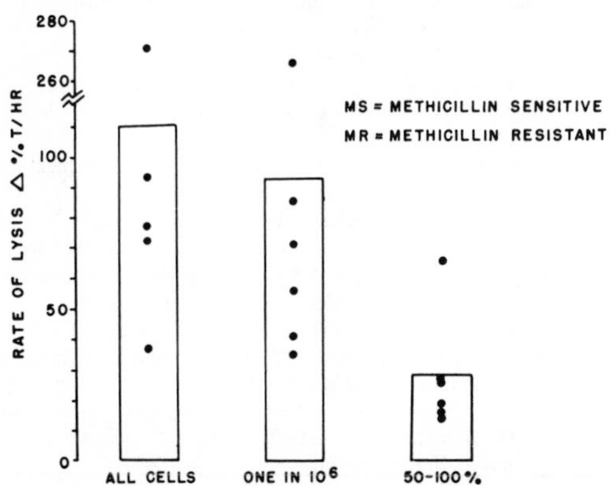

Fig. 2. *Effect of methicillin resistance on rate of lysis of Staphylococcus aureus by lysostaphin. Height of each bar represents mean rate of lysis for individual strains (shown as dots).*

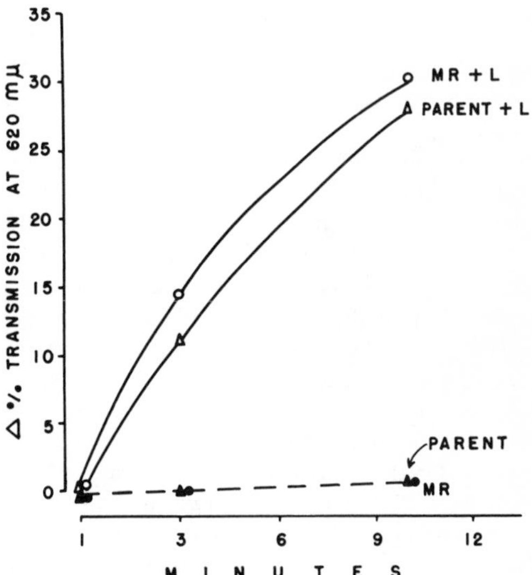

Fig. 3. *Effect of lysostaphin (L) on laboratory-induced methicillin-resistant (MR) Staphylococcus aureus 60/1.*

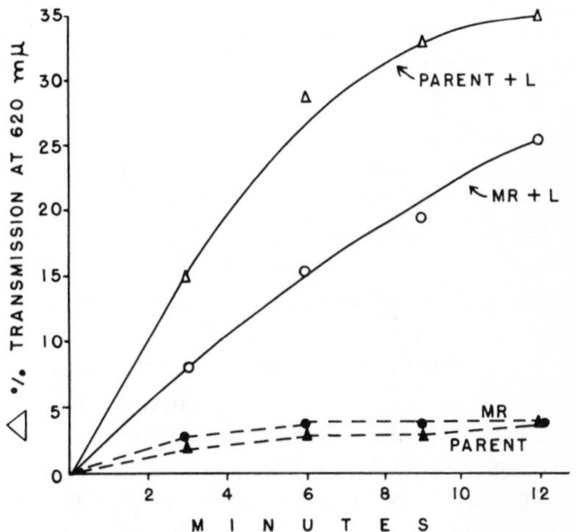

Fig. 4. *Effect of lysostaphin (L) on laboratory-induced methicillin-resistant (MR) Staphylococcus aureus Oxford.*

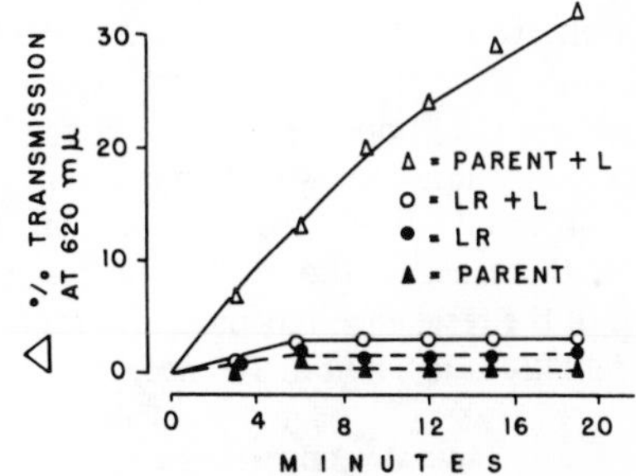

Fig. 5. *Lysostaphin (L) lysis of lysostaphin-resistant (LR) Staphylococcus aureus.*

DISCUSSION

The results of the experiments with enzymes that lyse bacterial cell walls cen be interpreted as follows.

When identically prepared cell suspensions lyse at different rates, their cell walls or surfaces must be considered different because the wall is the substrate of the enzyme. In contrast, when different cell suspensions are lysed at identical rates, they might be identical in wall structure, or they might be quite different in structure, but not in a way that influences the rate of lysis.

Thus, a difference in rate of lysis can have but one interpretation: the walls have to be different. On the other hand, identical rates of lysis can have at least the above two interpretations.

Accordingly, these data indicate that the cell walls or surfaces of cell populations that are predominantly methicillin-resistant are different from those of methicillin-susceptible cells. Because amino acid analysis of walls of these cells showed no difference between those that were methicillin-susceptible and those that were methicillin-resistant (15*a*), it must be assumed that the difference in cell wall or surface structure involves something other than a change in the peptide portion detectable by the methods used. Some other possible explanations of the decreased rate of lysis are consistent with these observations. Among these are an increased number of peptide chains (of the same composition) in the wall (19), incorporation of other (nonpeptide) material in the wall (19) that served to protect the enzyme-susceptible bond, and changes in conformation or configuration of the peptide components. These explanations apply only to naturally occurring methicillin-resistant *S. aureus* cells, for the laboratory-induced methicillin-resistant cells showed much less change in lysostaphin susceptibility. Lysostaphin resistance itself, which has been shown to be associated with a change in cell wall amino acid composition (22), does not necessarily imply methicillin resistance, as was shown here.

The observed difference in wall structure could be the cause of the methicillin resistance, a result of the resistance mechanism, or merely a coincidentally associated difference.

ACKNOWLEDGMENTS

We are indebted to Ruth Jones, Sarah B. Larabee, and Clare Wilcox for valuable technical assistance, and to A. Kathleen Daly and Alice McDonald for providing most of the clinical isolates used in this study.

This investigation was supported by Public Health Service grants 5 RO1-AI-23 and 2 TO1-AI-68 from the National Institute of Allergy and Infectious Diseases.

Dr. Sabath is a Recipient of a Career Development Award from the National Institute of Allergy and Infectious Diseases.

LITERATURE CITED

1. Barber, M. 1962. Coagulase-positive staphylococci resistant to benzylpenicillin, methicillin and other penicillins, p. 89–102. *In* Ciba Foundation, Resistance of bacteria to the penicillins. J. A. Churchill, London.
2. Barrett, F. F., R. F. McGehee, Jr., and M. Finland. 1968. Methicillin-resistant *Staphylococcus aureus* at Boston City Hospital. N. Engl. J. Med. **269**:441–448.
3. Bastin, R., R. Worms, and J. F. Acar. 1967. Clinical aspects of heterogeneous resistance of staphylococci to penicillins and cephalosporins Pathol. Biol. **15**:1205–1211.
4. Churcher, G. M. 1968. A screening test for the detection of methicillin-resistant staphylococci. J. Clin. Pathol. **21**:213–217.
5. Courtieu, A. L., F. N. Guillermet, C. Longeray, G. Maka, and Y. A. Chabbert. 1964. Frequence des staphylocoques presentant une résistance heterogene a la methicilline et l'oxacilline en milieu hospitalier. Ann. Inst. Pasteur (Paris) **107**:691–697.
6. Dyke, K. G. H., M. P. Jevons, and M. T. Parker. 1966. Penicillinase production and intrinsic resistance to penicillins in *Staphylococcus aureus.* Lancet **1**:835–838.
7. Eriksen, K. R., and I. Erichsen, 1963. Clinical occurrence of methicillin resistant strains of *Staphylococcus aureus.* Ugeskr. Laeger **125**:1234.
8. Gill, F. A., and E. W. Hook. 1965. Changing patterns of bacterial resistance to antimicrobial drugs. Amer. J. Med. **39**:780–794.
9. Gravenkemper, C. F., J. L. Brodie, and W. M. M. Kirby. 1965. Resistance of coagulase-positive staphylococci to methicillin and oxacillin. J. Bacteriol. **89**:1005–1010.
10. Harding. J. W. 1963. Infections due to methicillin-resistant strains of *Staphylococcus pyogenes.* J. Clin. Pathol. **16**:268–270.
11. Knox, R., and J. T. Smith. 1961. The nature of penicillin-resistance in staphylococci. Lancet **2**:520–525.
12. Pollock, M. R. 1967. Origin and function of penicillinase: a problem in biochemical evaluation. Brit. Med. J. **2**:71–77.
13. Richmond, M. J. 1966. The properties of penicillinase synthesized by methicillin resistant staphylococci. *In* Antibiotics. Advances in research production and clinical use. M. Herald and Z. Gabriel, p. 43–46.
14. Rolinson, G. N. 1963. Resistance to the newer penicillins. Brit. Med. J. **1**:542–543.
15. Sabath, L. D., F. F. Barrett, C. Wilcox, D. A. Gerstein, and M. Finland. 1969. Methicillin resistance of *Staphylococcus aureus* and *Staphylococcus epidermidis.* Antimicrobial Agents and Chemotherapy–1968, p. 302–306.

15*a*. Sabath, L. D., C. D. Leaf, D. A. Gerstein, and M. Finland. 1970. Altered cell walls of *Staphylococcus aureus* resistant to methicillin. Nature (London) **225**:1074.

16. Seligman, S. J. 1966. Penicillinase-negative variants of methicillin-resistant *Staphylococcus aureus.* Nature (London) **209**:994–996.
17. Seligman, S. J. 1966. Methicillin-resistant staphylococci: genetics of the minority population. J. Gen. Microbiol. **42**:315–322.
18. Steers, E., E. L. Foltz, and B. S. Graves. 1959. Inocula replicating apparatus for routine testing of bacterial susceptibility of antibiotics. Antibiot. Chemother. **9**:307–311.

19. Strominger, J. L., and J. M. Ghuysen. 1967. Mechanisms of enzymatic bacteriolysis. Science (Washington) **156:** 213–221.

20. Tipper, D. J., and J. L. Strominger. 1965. Mechanism of action of penicillins: a proposal based on their structural similarity to acyl-D-alanyl-D-alanine. Proc. Nat. Acad. Sci. U.S.A. **54:**1133–1141.

21. Wise, E. M., and J. T. Park. 1965. Penicillin. Its basic site of action as an inhibitor of a peptide cross-linking reaction in cell wall mucopeptide synthesis. Proc. Nat. Acad. Sci. U.S.A. **54:**75–81.

22. Zygmunt, W. A., H. P. Browder, and P. A. Tavormina. 1967. Lytic action of lysostaphin on susceptible and resistant strains of *Staphylococcus aureus.* Can. J. Microbiol. **13:**845–853.

23. Zygmunt, W. A., E. F. Harrison, H. P. Browder, and P. A. Tavormina. 1968. Comparative inhibition of methicillin-resistant strains of *Staphylococcus aureus* by lysostaphin and other antibiotics. Appl. Microbiol. **16:**1174–1178.

Antimicrobial Agents and Chemotherapy—1969

β-Lactamase Activity and Resistance to Ampicillin, Carbenicillin, and Cephaloridine of *Klebsiella*, *Enterobacter*, and *Citrobacter*

B. SLOCOMBE and R. SUTHERLAND

Beecham Research Laboratories, Betchworth, Surrey, England

Seventy-six strains of gram-negative bacilli were identified as *Klebsiella*, *Enterobacter*, or *Citrobacter*, and their susceptibility to the β-lactam antibiotics ampicillin, carbenicillin and cephaloridine was determined. In general, the majority of strains of *Klebsiella* were resistant to the penicillins but were susceptible to cephaloridine, whereas the *Enterobacter* and *Citrobacter* bacteria were resistant to both ampicillin and cephaloridine but were susceptible to carbenicillin. Most strains of *Klebsiella* inactivated ampicillin as a result of β-lactamase activity, but carbenicillin and cephaloridine were relatively stable to enzymatic destruction by *Klebsiella*. In contrast, *Enterobacter* and *Citrobacter* rapidly inactivated cephaloridine, but generally caused little destruction of ampicillin or carbenicillin. All bacterial strains tested displayed β-lactamase activity, but destruction of the β-lactam antibiotics was not the sole mechanism of resistance.

Early studies with ampicillin showed that the majority of strains belonging to the *Klebsiella-Enterobacter* (*Aerobacter*) group of bacteria were resistant to the action of this broad-spectrum penicillin (12, 17), and that the resistance to ampicillin appeared to be associated with the β-lactamase activities of these organisms (1, 16). In contrast, *Klebsiella* species have been found to be generally susceptible to cephalosporin antibiotics (2, 3), although the closely related *Enterobacter* group has been shown to have virtually uniform resistance to cephalosporins (3, 9, 18). Fleming and co-workers (5, 6) demonstrated that *Enterobacter* species inactivated cephalosporins by β-lactamase activity, and suggested that the resistance of *Enterobacter* to cephalosporins was associated with enzymatic destruction. These workers also observed that *Klebsiella* strains consistently failed to inactivate cephalosporins (5), but Medeiros and O'Brien (10) reported that a significant number of *Klebsiella* isolates produced a cephalosporinase, and that these strains were usually resistant to cephalothin. Carbenicillin, the most recent of the semisynthetic penicillins to be introduced into clinical practice, was found to be inactive against *Klebsiella* species (8, 13) but, unlike ampicillin, the resistance of this group of bacteria to carbenicillin was not associated with β-lactamase activity.

This study was designed to compare the degrees of susceptibility of *Klebsiella*, *Enterobacter*, and *Citrobacter* bacteria to ampicillin, carbenicillin, and cephaloridine, and to attempt to determine the role of β-lactamase production in the resistance of these organisms to the β-lactam antibiotics.

MATERIALS AND METHODS

Cultures. The bacteria used were isolated from clinical specimens (urine, sputum, wounds, and exudates) obtained from a number of hospitals in the United Kingdom. A small number of strains of type species were obtained from the National Collection of Type Cultures, London, England, and were used as taxonomic control strains.

Classification of bacteria. The cultures were identified by standard fermentation and biochemical reactions, and by motility tests, and were classified according to the scheme proposed by Cowan and Steel (4; Fig. 1).

Minimal inhibitory concentrations. The susceptibility of the organisms to ampicillin, carbenicillin, and cephaloridine was determined by twofold serial dilution of the

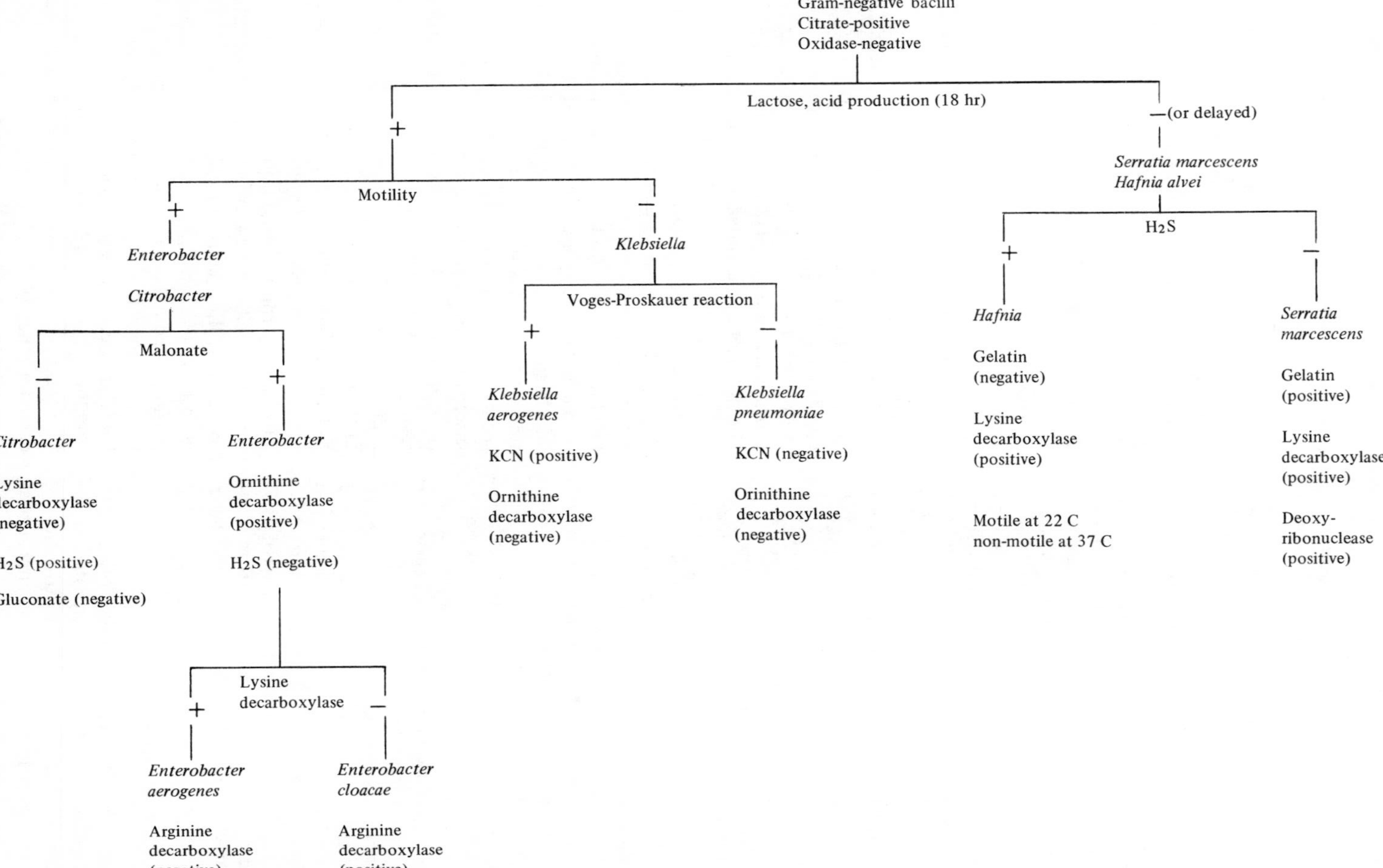

Fig. 1. *Schema for differentiation of citrate-utilizing, gram-negative bacilli [after Cowan and Steel (4)].*

antibiotics in 5-ml volumes of nutrient broth or 18-ml volumes of nutrient agar. For tests in liquid medium, the inoculum was 1 drop (0.03 ml) of an undiluted overnight broth culture, and for tests with solid medium, 1 drop (0.003 ml) of an overnight broth culture delivered with a multiple inoculating device. Minimal inhibitory concentrations were determined after 18 hr of incubation at 37 C.

Viable-count experiments. The test bacteria were incubated at 37 C in nutrient broth containing known concentrations of the antibiotics. Samples were taken at intervals, and 0.02-ml volumes of suitable dilutions of the cultures were pipetted onto nutrient agar plates. Colonies were counted after 18 hr incubation at 37 C, and the number of surviving bacteria was estimated.

Antibiotic assay. Ampicillin, carbenicillin, or cephaloridine concentrations in cultures from serial dilution tests or viable-count experiments were measured by microbiological assay. Samples were suitably diluted and plated in large rectangular plates seeded with *Bacillus subtilis* ATCC 6633 for assay of ampicillin and cephaloridine (16) or with *Pseudomonas aeruginosa* NCTC 10490 for assay of carbenicillin (8).

Transfer of antibiotic resistance. Antibiotic-resistant strains were grown for 6 hr at 37 C in Penassay broth (Oxoid CM287), and 0.2-ml volumes of these donor strains were added to 0.4-ml volumes of a 6-hr culture of the recipient strain of *Escherichia coli* K-12 711 Nx, a lactose-negative, antibiotic-susceptible, nalidixic acid-resistant strain. The mating mixture of donor and recipient bacteria was inoculated into 9-ml volumes of Penassay broth and, after overnight incubation at 37 C, 0.003 ml was plated on MacConkey agar (Oxoid CM3) containing the appropriate antibiotic (20 or 40 μg/ml) and nalidixic acid (20 μg/ml). Control plates containing antibiotic alone (20 or 40 μg/ml), or nalidixic acid alone (20 μg/ml), were also set up, and a control culture of the antibiotic-susceptible, nalidixic acid-resistant recipient strain was always included in the test. The selective media plates were incubated overnight at 37 C, and any lactose-negative colonies growing on the antibiotic-containing plates were subcultured into Penassay broth and incubated overnight at 37 C. These cultures were checked for purity and retested for antibiotic resistance on MacConkey agar containing the appropriate antibiotic and nalidixic acid. A number of tests were also carried out with other suitable recipient strains, namely, *Salmonella typhi* and *S. typhimurium.*

RESULTS

Cultures. A total of 76 strains of bacteria were classified as *Klebsiella, Enterobacter,* or *Citrobacter* (Table 1), and the distribution of positive reactions in the basic biochemical tests is shown in Table 2. The motility tests and ornithine decarboxylase reactions showed good correlation for differentiation between *Klebsiella* and *Enterobacter* groups, and the Voges-Proskauer test and malonate utilization served in most cases to distinguish the *Enterobacter* and *Citrobacter* groups. Twelve strains of indole-positive bacteria, identical in most other respects to *K. aerogenes,* were classified as *K. oxytoca.*

Table 1. *Distribution of Klebsiella-Enterobacter-Citrobacter bacteria tested*

Species	No. of strains	
K. aerogenes	29	48
K. oxytoca	12	
K. pneumoniae	2	
K. ozaenae	2	
K. rhinoscleromatis	1	
K. edwardsii	2	
E. cloacae	8	15
E. aerogenes	4	
E. liquefaciens	1	
E. species	2	
Citrobacter freundii	13	
Total	76	

Antibiotic susceptibility. The results of serial dilution tests to determine the minimal inhibitory concentrations of ampicillin, carbenicillin, and cephaloridine against the 76 strains of bacteria tested are summarized in Fig. 2, which shows the cumulative percentage inhibition of the strains by each antibiotic. It can be seen that *Klebsiella* species were distinctly more susceptible to cephaloridine than to ampicillin or carbenicillin. Thus, 67% of the 48 strains tested were inhibited by 12.5 μg or less of cephaloridine per ml, whereas only 12.5 and 6% of these strains were inhibited by similar concentrations of ampicillin and carbenicillin, respectively. In contrast, *Enterobacter* species were almost uniformly resistant to cephaloridine, as well as ampicillin, and were generally susceptible to carbenicillin. Thus, 11 of 15 strains (74%) were inhibited by 12.5 μg or less of carbenicillin per ml, in contrast to 7% inhibition by ampicillin and cephaloridine. Similarly, *Citrobacter* bacteria were typically susceptible to carbenicillin (11 of 13 strains inhibited by 12.5 μg/ml) and resistant to ampicillin and cephaloridine.

Antibiotic susceptibility and β-lactamase activity. The relationship between the susceptibility of this group of bacteria and their ability to destroy the β-lactam antibiotics as a result of β-lactamase activity was investigated by measurement of residual antibiotic activity of cultures incubated overnight in serial dilution tests. Typical results are shown in Table 3. In general, *Klebsiella* species were resistant to ampicillin, and there was complete destruction of ampicillin in the tubes showing visible growth after overnight incubation. These organisms were also resistant to carbenicillin, but there was usually only slight or partial destruction of the penicillin, and it was obvious that *Klebsiella* bacteria were capable of growing in the presence of relatively high concentrations of carbenicillin. Cephaloridine was active against *Klebsiella,* and there was evidence of destruction only at relatively low concentrations of the antibiotic. In minimal inhibitory concentration tests with cephaloridine against *Enterobacter* and *Citrobacter* species, growth was invariably accompanied by total destruction of the antibiotic, whereas there was relatively little destruction of either ampicillin or carbenicillin, even when the organism was resistant to the penicillin under test.

Examination by thin-layer chromatography of broth cultures of *Klebsiella, Enterobacter,* or *Citrobacter* bacteria for which minimal inhibi-

Table 2. *Biochemical reactions of 76 strains of gram-negative, oxidase-negative bacilli*

Test	Positive reactions					
	Klebsiella (48 strains)		*Enterobacter* (15 strains)		*Citrobacter* (13 strains)	
	No.	Per cent	No.	Per cent	No.	Per cent
Lactose fermentation (18 hr at 37 C)	44	91.7	15	100	13	100
Motility	0	0	15	100	12	92.3
Indole production	11	22.9	0	0	2	15.4
Methyl red	7	14.6	0	0	13	100
Voges-Proskauer reaction	44	91.7	15	100	0	0
Citrate utilization	47	97.7	15	100	13	100
Lysine decarboxylase	45	93.7	6	40.0	0	0
Ornithine decarboxylase	0	0	15	100	8	61.5
H_2S production	0	0	0	0	9	69.2
Gluconate oxidation	44	91.7	15	100	0	0
Malonate utilization	46	95.8	14	93.3	0	0

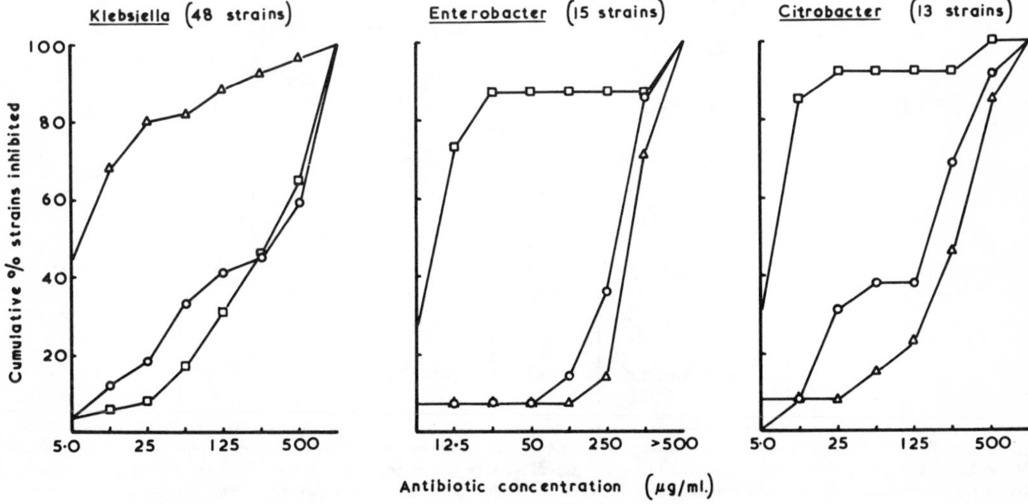

Fig. 2. *Antibiotic susceptibility of 76 strains of Klebsiella-Enterobacter-Citrobacter bacteria. Symbols:* ○, *ampicillin;* □, *carbenicillin;* △, *cephaloridine.*

tory concentration tests indicated a marked loss of ampicillin or carbenicillin activity, as judged by microbiological assay, showed the presence of the penicilloic acids of ampicillin or carbenicillin, confirming that inactivation was due to the β-lactamase activities of the bacteria.

Although the results of these experiments indicated the relative stabilities of the three β-lactam antibiotics to the β-lactamases produced by the *Klebsiella, Enterobacter,* and *Citrobacter* organisms, this type of test gave no indication as to whether growth occured as a result of destruction of the antibiotic, or whether destruction occured as a result of growth of the organism. Accordingly, viable-count experiments were carried out to measure growth of the test organism in the presence of β-lactam antibiotic, and the antibiotic contents of the cultures were assayed over the same period to attempt to elucidate the relationship between growth and destruction. The results of typical viable-count experiments with a strain of *K. aerogenes* and one of *E. aerogenes* are illustrated in Fig. 3 and 4. In Fig. 3, it can be seen that cephaloridine at a concentration of 5 μg/ml reduced the viable count to zero within 3 hr. Both ampicillin and carbenicillin showed significant bactericidal activity at concentrations of 50 and 100 μg/ml during the first 6 hr of the experiment, but failed to prevent growth from increasing to visible levels after 24 hr. With ampicillin, growth appeared to take place after there was marked destruction of the antibiotic, but with carbenicillin growth occurred when there was still a substantial amount of antibiotic remaining.

With the test strain of *E. aerogenes* (Fig. 4), cephaloridine produced a fall in the viable count in the initial 3-hr period while there was still antibiotic present, but growth followed destruction of the antibiotic. Both ampicillin and carbenicillin also showed bactericidal activity during the first 6 hr of the experiment. However, growth occurred after this period, even though 70% of the original ampicillin activity remained after 24 hr in the culture which had originally contained 500 μg of ampicillin per ml. There was no detectable loss of carbenicillin activity.

Table 3. *Relationship between resistance of Klebsiella-Enterobacter-Citrobacter bacteria to ampicillin, carbenicillin, and cephaloridine and the β-lactamase activities of these organisms*

Genus	Antibiotic	Growth[a] and antibiotic concn (μg/ml)						
		500[b]	250	125	50	25	12.5	5.0
K. aerogenes NCTC 8172	Ampicillin	±	+	+	+	+	+	+
		0[c]	0	0	0	0	0	0
	Carbenicillin	±	±	+	+	+	+	+
		>125	125	32	12.6	5.4	1.5	0
	Cephaloridine	–	–	–	–	±	±	+
		500	250	90	40	8.5	2.5	0
E. cloacae NCTC 10005	Ampicillin	±	±	+	+	+	+	+
		500	250	125	23	2.6	0	0
	Carbenicillin	–	+	+	+	+	+	+
		500	200	94	40	18	8	4
	Cephaloridine	+	+	+	+	+	+	+
		0	0	0	0	0	0	0
C. freundii NCTC 9750	Ampicillin	NT	NT	+	+	+	+	+
				43	21	12	0.8	0.3
	Carbenicillin	NT	NT	–	–	–	±	+
							6.6	2.7
	Cephaloridine	NT	NT	+	+	+	+	+
				0	0	0	0	0

[a] The antibiotics were serially diluted in nutrient broth, and the tubes were inoculated with one drop of an overnight broth culture of the test organism. Growth was determined by visual inspection after 24 hr of incubation at 37 C, and the residual antibiotic activities were measured by microbiological assay. Symbols: + = visible growth, ± = trace growth, – = no visible growth; NT = not tested.

[b] Initial antibiotic concentration.

[c] Residual antibiotic concentration at the conclusion of the minimal inhibitory concentration test.

Transfer of antibiotic resistance. A total of 62 strains of *Klebsiella, Enterobacter,* and *Citrobacter* were tested for their ability to transfer ampicillin resistance to *E. coli* K-12 711 Nx. Only one culture, a strain of *K. aerogenes* was found to transfer ampicillin resistance to this organism (Table 4). These strains also failed to transfer ampicillin resistance to recipient strains of *S. typhi* and *S. typhimurium.* Difficulty was experienced in selecting transcipients (ampicillin-resistant *E. coli*) when an undiluted culture was plated on the antibiotic-containing selective medium. Lactose-negative colonies were recovered at a high frequency, but when these were cultured and retested for ampicillin resistance they were found to be susceptible to the antibiotic. These "transcipients" were in fact colonies of the ampicillin-susceptible recipient strain of *E. coli* which had been able to grow as a result of destruction of ampicillin in the selective medium by the β-lactamase activity of the donor strain. This problem was overcome by use of an inoculum diluted 1:5 with sterile saline, or by increasing the ampicillin concentration from 20 to 40 μg/ml.

Thirty-one of these strains, resistant to ampicillin and one or more antibiotics, namely, cephaloridine, chloramphenicol, kanamycin, streptomycin, and tetracycline, were tested for frequency of R factor transfer. Eighteen strains transferred antibiotic resistance at a relatively high rate (Table 4), but none of the strains transferred resistance to cephaloridine, and only one strain (described above) transferred an ampicillin R factor.

In a separate series of experiments, the majority of test strains were examined for ability to transfer carbenicillin R factors, but transfer of carbenicillin resistance was not demonstrated.

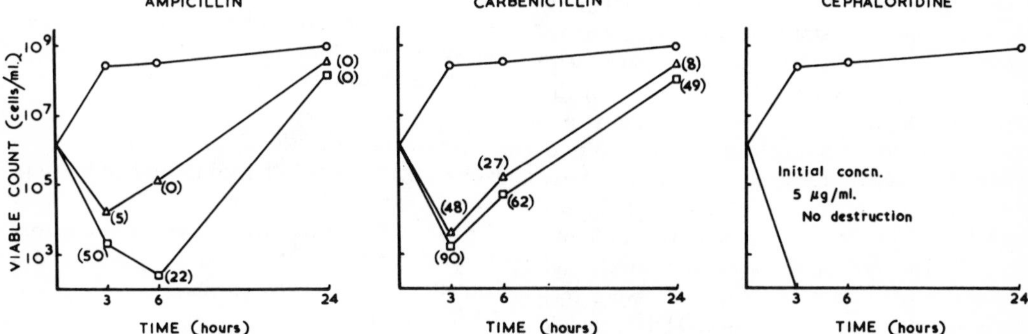

Fig. 3. *Bactericidal activities of ampicillin, carbenicillin, and cephaloridine against Klebsiella aerogenes. Symbols:* ○, *antibiotic-free control;* △, *50 μg/ml;* □, *100 μg/ml. Figures in brackets show residual antibiotic concentration (μg/ml).*

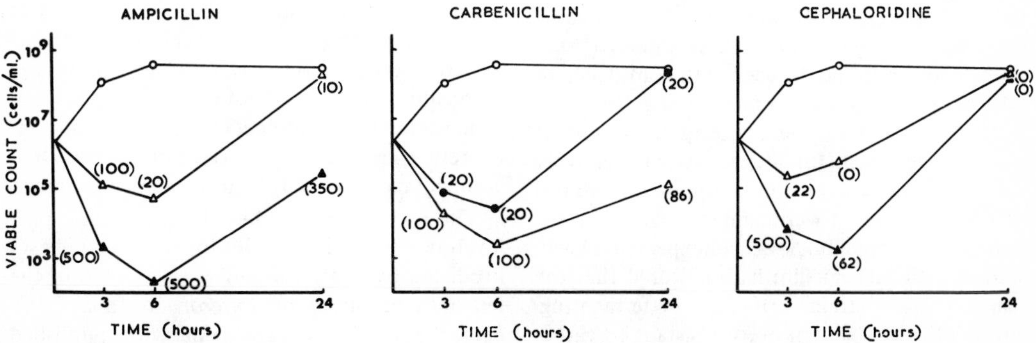

Fig. 4. *Bactericidal activities of ampicillin, carbenicillin, and cephaloridine against Enterobacter aerogenes. Symbols:* ○, *antibiotic-free control;* ●, *20 μg/ml;* △, *100 μg/ml;* ▲, *500 μg/ml. Figures in brackets show residual antibiotic concentrations (μg/ml).*

Table 4. *Incidence of transferable drug resistance in Klebsiella, Enterobacter, and Citrobacter bacteria*

Resistance of donor strain[a]	No. of strains tested			No. of strains transferring resistance			Resistance pattern transferred[a]
	Klebsiella	*Enterobacter*	*Citrobacter*	*Klebsiella*	*Enterobacter*	*Citrobacter*	
A	29	0	0	1	0	0	A
A Cp	0	5	4	0	0	0	–
Cp	0	0	2	0	0	0	–
A S Cp	0	1	0	0	1	0	S
A T	1	0	0	0	0	0	–
A T Cp	1	0	0	1	0	0	T
A T S	1	1	0	1	1	0	T S
A T C	4	0	0	3	0	0	T C (2) C (1)
A C Cp	0	1	0	0	1	0	C
A T C S	7	0	0	6	0	0	T C S
A T C S K	5	0	0	4	0	0	T C S K
Total	48	8	6	16	3	0	

[a] A = ampicillin; C = chloramphenicol; Cp = cephaloridine; K = kanamycin; S = streptomycin; T = tetracycline.

DISCUSSION

The results of this study with a relatively limited number of strains of *Klebsiella, Enterobacter,* and *Citrobacter* are in agreement with published reports showing the resistance of this group to ampicillin (12, 17). Our results also confirm the strikingly different susceptibility of *Klebsiella* species to cephaloridine compared with the high degree of resistance of *Enterobacter* and *Citrobacter* bacteria to this antibiotic (3, 5, 9). However, in this study a relatively high proportion of strains of *Klebsiella* were relatively resistant to cephaloridine. Thus, it would not seem realistic to attempt to use susceptibility to cephaloridine as a means of distinguishing *Klebsiella* species from *Enterobacter,* or conversely to assume that nonmotile strains of this taxonomic group will of necessity be susceptible to cephalosporins. However, P. C. Fleming (*personal communication*) has observed that cephalosporin C may be used with confidence to differentiate *Klebsiella* from *Enterobacter.*

The finding that the majority of strains of *Enterobacter* and *Citrobacter* were relatively susceptible to carbenicillin, as opposed to strains of *Klebsiella* which were almost invariably resistant to carbenicillin, was unexpected. Early studies with carbenicillin had indicated that the majority of strains of lactose-fermenting, citrate-utilizing bacteria were resistant to carbenicillin as well as to ampicillin (8, 13), but it now seems probable that most of the strains tested belonged to the genus *Klebsiella,* although this was not determined at the time. The susceptibility of the *Enterobacter* and *Citrobacter* bacteria to carbenicillin has obvious clinical implications, particularly in view of the resistance of this group to the cephalosporin and other antibiotics.

The similarity of the *Enterobacter* and *Citrobacter* organisms with regard to susceptibility to the β-lactam antibiotics, as well as on the basis of biochemical characteristics, would point to a close relationship between these genera and a distinct difference between these organisms and the *Klebsiella* genus.

The relationship between the resistance of the *Klebsiella, Enterobacter,* and *Citrobacter* groups of bacteria to β-lactam antibiotics and the β-lactamase activities of these organisms is not clear, as, for example, is the case with penicillin-resistant strains of staphylococci. All strains of bacteria tested in this study demonstrated β-lactamase activity, *Klebsiella* strains destroyed ampicillin and, on occasion, carbenicillin and cephaloridine; *Enterobacter* and *Citrobacter* bacteria inactivated cephaloridine invariably, ampicillin occasionally, and carbenicillin rarely.

The results reported here indicate that cephaloridine is usually stable to the β-lactamases produced by *Klebsiella* but is susceptible to the enzymes produced by *Enterobacter* and *Citrobacter* bacteria, in agreement with published reports (2, 5, 10). This suggests that the resistance of the latter group to cephaloridine may be attributable to enzymatic destruction. In contrast, ampicillin is inactivated by *Klebsiella* species, but is relatively stable to destruction by *Enterobacter* and *Citrobacter* organisms. The resistance of the latter organisms to ampicillin is, therefore, not generally associated with β-lactamase activity, whereas the data presented here appear to support suggestions that *Klebsiella* strains are resistant largely as a result of production of β-lactamase (1, 16). However, Seligman (14) has produced evidence suggesting a mechanism of intrinsic resistance for *Klebsiella* in addition to β-lactamase activity.

With carbenicillin, the resistance of *Klebsiella* species was in most cases not associated with inactivation of the antibiotic, unlike ampicillin, and was obviously due to some other mechanism. The susceptibility of *Enterobacter* and *Citrobacter* organisms to carbenicillin and their relative insusceptibility to ampicillin was apparently not due to differences in stability to the β-lactamase activities of this group, as neither antibiotic appeared to be inactivated to any great extent. It must be assumed that the greater activity of carbenicillin against these bacteria is due to some other mechanism, as is the case with *P. aeruginosa,* which is relatively susceptible to carbenicillin but resistant to ampicillin.

The very low transfer frequency of ampicillin resistance (2%) and failure to transfer carbenicillin or cephaloridine resistance indicate that the insusceptibility of the *Klebsiella, Enterobacter,* and *Citrobacter* bacteria to the β-lactam antibiotics is not extrachromosomally mediated, in keeping with the findings of Medeiros and O'Brien (10, 11). However, the results of this study are at variance with those reported by Hinshaw and co-workers (7), who found that ampicillin resistance was transferred frequently as a unit in combination with resistance to other antibiotics, for example, streptomycin, chloramphenicol, and tetracycline. A possible explanation for the discrepancy between these two reports is that conditions in this study were not favorable for transfer of ampicillin, carbenicillin, or cephaloridine resistance. This does not seem likely, as under these conditions resistance to other antibiotics was transferred readily from these bacteria. Also, in other studies in which the same conditions were used, ampicillin and cephaloridine resistance has been transferred readily between other bacterial species (15). The role of transferable resistance and the resistance of the *Klebsiella, Enterobacter,* and *Citrobacter* bacteria to β-lactam antibiotics requires further investigation.

ACKNOWLEDGMENT

It is a pleasure to thank Christine Goater for skilled technical assistance.

LITERATURE CITED

1. Ayliffe, G. A. J. 1963. Ampicillin inactivation and sensitivity of coliform bacilli. J. Gen. Microbiol. **30:**339–348.
2. Barber, M., and P. M. Waterworth. 1964. Penicillin-resistant penicillins and cephalosporins. Brit. Med. J. **2:**344–349.
3. Benner, E. J., J. S. Micklewait, J. L. Brodie, and W. M. M. Kirby. 1965. Natural and acquired resistance of *Klebsiella-Aerobacter* to cephalothin and cephaloridine. Proc. Soc. Exp. Biol. Med. **119:**536–541.
4. Cowan, S. T., and K. J. Steel. 1961. Diagnostic tables for the common medical bacteria. J. Hyg. **59:**357–372.
5. Fleming, P. C., M. Goldner, and D. G. Glass. 1963. Observations on the nature, distribution, and significance of cephalosporinase. Lancet **1:**1399–1401.
6. Goldner, M., D. G. Glass, and P. C. Fleming. 1968. Characteristics of *Aerobacter* beta-lactamase. Can. J. Microbiol. **14:**139–145.
7. Hinshaw, V., J. Punch, M. J. Allison, and H. P. Dalton. 1969. Frequency of R factor-mediated multiple drug resistance in *Klebsiella* and *Aerobracter.* Appl. Microbiol. **17:**214–218.
8. Knudsen, E. T., G. N. Rolinson, and R. Sutherland. 1967. Carbenicillin: a new semisynthetic penicillin active against *Pseudomonas pyocyanea.* Brit. Med. J. **3:**75–78.
9. Lerner, P. I., and L. Weinstein. 1967. The differentiation of Klebsiella from Aerobacter species by sensitivity to cephalothins and penicillins. Amer. J. Med. Sci. **254:**63–68.
10. Medeiros, A. A., and T. F. O'Brien. 1967. Association of cephalosporinase activity, cephalothin resistance, and episome-mediated drug resistance in *Klebsiella* strains. Antimicrob. Agents Chemother.–1966, p. 321–327.
11. Medeiros, A. A., and T. F. O'Brien. 1968. R factor-mediated increments in levels of resistance to and enzymatic degradation of penicillins and cephalosporins. Antimicrob. Agents Chemother.–1967, p. 271–278.
12. Rolinson, G. N., and S. Stevens. 1961. Microbiological studies on a new broad-spectrum penicillin, "Penbritin." Brit. Med. J. **2:**191–196.
13. Rolinson, G. N., and R. Sutherland. 1968. Carbenicillin, a new semisynthetic penicillin active against *Pseudomonas aeruginosa.* Antimicrob. Agents Chemother.–1967, p. 609–613.
14. Seligman, S. J. 1968. Resistance of Klebsiella and Enterobacter to the penicillins. Proc. Soc. Exp. Biol. Med. **127:**915–919.
15. Slocombe, B., and R. Sutherland. 1969. Sensitivity of Gram-negative bacilli to ampicillin after six years clinical usage. J. Clin. Pathol. **22:**644–648.
16. Sutherland, R. 1964. The nature of the insensitivity of Gram-negative bacteria towards penicillins. J. Gen. Microbiol. **34:**85–98.
17. Sutherland, R., and G. N. Rolinson. 1964. Activity of ampicillin *in vitro* compared with other antibiotics. J. Clin. Pathol. **17:**461–465.
18. Zabransky, R. J., J. W. Hall, F. E. Day, and G. M. Needham. 1969. *Klebsiella, Enterobacter,* and *Serratia*: biochemical differentiation and susceptibility to ampicillin and three cephalosporin derivatives. Appl. Microbiol. **18:**198–203.

Antimicrobial Agents and Chemotherapy—1969

Antibiotic Resistance of *Salmonella* in the Eastern United States

E. B. WINSHELL, C. CHERUBIN, J. WINTER, and H. C. NEU

Department of Medicine and School of Public Health, Columbia University, New York, New York 10032, and the Beth Israel Salmonella Center, New York, New York 10003

The antimicrobial resistance of 292 clinical isolates of *Salmonella* was determined. *S. typhimurium* accounted for 44% of the isolates, a frequency which has not changed in the past 5 years. Among the isolates, 21% were resistant to one or more antibiotics. A disproportionate number of the resistant isolates were strains of *S. typhimurium*, representing an increase in the incidence of *S. typhimurium* resistance. Multiple drug resistance occurred with equal frequency in both *S. typhimurium* and other serotypes, as did the ability to transfer drug resistance to an *Escherichia coli* recipient. Levels of antibiotic resistance transferred to *E. coli* or other *Enterobacteriaceae* were identical to that of the donor *Salmonella* isolate. Ampicillin was the antibiotic to which the greatest number of strains were resistant; 63% of the resistant strains were not inhibited by ampicillin, representing an increase from 17% in 1965. No chloramphenicol-resistant strains were encountered. Most isolates with transferable drug resistance came from municipal hospitals and were isolated from children under 10 years of age. There were no apparent differences in symptoms in patients infected with resistant strains as compared with those infected with susceptible strains. The resistant strains were not isolated from hospital-acquired infections.

The transfer of antibiotic resistance from one strain of *Enterobacteriacae* to another has been extensively studied since its discovery in Japan in 1959. Transferable drug resistance is mediated by an episomal element, the R factor. Several surveys of transferable antibiotic resistance in salmonellae in the United States have appeared (5, 9, 10). These studies showed that resistance to streptomycin, tetracycline, and sulfonamides was most common, and that there was a higher incidence of drug resistance in strains of *Salmonella typhimurium* than in other *Salmonella* serotypes. Smith's (10) study at Children's Hospital in Boston, Mass., did not specify the background or age of the children infected with resistant strains of *Salmonella*. Anderson (1) has suggested that the use of antibiotics in rearing livestock plays a role in the development of drug resistance.

The present study was initiated to determine whether there had been any change in the incidence of transferable drug resistance in *S. typhimurium* and other *Salmonella* serotypes in the eastern United States. The influence of age, economic status, urban or rural home background, and hospital contacts of the patients was considered in studying the occurrence of strains with antibiotic resistance. Resistance to ampicillin was extensively evaluated because this drug has assumed a major role in therapy of acute salmonellosis.

MATERIALS AND METHODS

Sequential human isolates of *Salmonella* sent to the New York Salmonella Center at the Beth Israel Hospital from voluntary and municipal hospitals in New York City, upstate New York, and surrounding states were used. Information on the origin of the specimen (age of patient, sex, source, symptoms, and type of hospital) was obtained when available. All duplicate cultures from the same individual were tested but were not included in the statistical analysis.

Antibiotic susceptibility profiles were done by the method of Bauer et al. (2). The following antibiotic susceptibility discs were used: ampicillin, 10 μg; streptomycin, 10 μg; tetracycline, 30 μg; kanamycin, 30 μg; cephalothin, 30 μg; cephalexin, 30 μg; chloramphenicol, 30 μg; carbenicillin, 100 μg; and polymyxin B sulfate, 300 units.

The presence of transferable drug resistance was determined according to the method of Watanabe (12). The recipient strain was *Escherichia coli* W 1485, an F⁻ Lac⁺ organism; therefore, selection of lactose-positive drug resistance colonies could be accomplished by streaking a loopful of the mating mixture on eosin-methylene blue-agar containing the selective drug at two concentrations. Transfer of only the ampicillin and tetracycline determinants was scored. Penicillinase assays were performed by a modification of the Novick (8) micro-iodometric assay.

RESULTS

Table 1 shows the distribution of 292 *Salmonella* serotypes tested from December 1968 to March 1969. The isolates tested are comparable to the 1965 sample of Gill and Hook (5) from the same sources. *S. typhimurium* at a frequency of 44% was the most prevalent human isolate in the eastern United States. In a survey from 45 states by Schroeder et al. (9), *S. typhimurium* accounted for 25.5%, but this is probably related to the fact that less common serotypes (41.5%) are referred to the National Communicable Disease Center for identification. Within the greater metropolitan area of New York, the most frequently isolated types of salmonellae have remained in the same frequency over the past 5 years (3).

The overall resistance of salmonellae to antibiotics has increased from 13.8 to 21.6% in the past 5 years. This is due to the increase in resistance in *S. typhimurium* from 18.5 to 36.7% during this period. In contrast, resistance in serotypes other than *S. typhimurium* has not changed appreciably (Table 2).

The incidence of strains resistant to ampicillin has increased from 3.9% of the isolates in 1965 to 13.5% in 1969 (Table 3). This increase is especially significant because 23% of the strains of *S. typhimurium,* which is the most ubiquitous species, are resistant to ampicillin. The spectrum of carbenicillin is identical to that of ampicillin and presumably is determined by the same resistance gene. Cephalosporin resistance was uncommon and was unrelated to ampicillin resistance. Tetracycline and streptomycin resistance, which had heretofore been the most common, has remained unchanged, but again is seen more frequently in *S. typhimurium* than in other serotypes. It is also notable that no chloramphenicol-resistant isolates were found in this sample.

Multiple drug resistance was found most often in *S. typhimurium*—in 70.2% as compared with 56.3% of other serotypes. Interestingly, single drug resistance occurred in 43.7% of other types of salmonellae and in 29.8% of *S. typhimurim*

Table 1. *Percentage distribution of Salmonella serotypes*

Serotype	1969	1967[a]	1965[b]
S. typhimurium .	44	25.5	42.5
S. enteritidis	14	7.0	9.5
S. heidelberg	6.5	6.5	8.4
S. saintpaul	6.5	4.0	3.2
S. infantis	4.5	4.5	7.1
S. thompson	3.8	5.2	0.79
S. muenchen	3.1	–	0.79
Other	17.6	57.3	27.7
Total	100 (296[c])	100 (400)	100 (254)

[a] Data of Schroeder et al. (9).
[b] Data of Gill and Hook (5).
[c] Total number.

Table 2. *Resistance of Salmonella isolates*

Serotype	Per cent resistant in 1969	Fraction with RTF[a]	Per cent RTF	Per cent resistant 1965
S. typhimurium . .	36.7 (47[b])	19/30	63.5	18.5 (20)
S. enteritidis	4.9 (2)	0/2	0	4.2 (1)
S. heidelberg	10.5 (2)	2/2	100	28.6 (6)
S. saintpaul	21 (4)	1/4	25	12.5 (1)
S. infantis	0	–	–	5.6 (1)
S. thompson	0	–	–	0
S. muenchen	22.2 (2)	0/2	0	50 (1)
S. blockley	0	–	–	0
S. newport	20 (1)	0/1	0	16.7 (3)
S. derby	0	–	–	0
Others	14.7 (5)	3/3	100	3.9 (2)

[a] RTF = resistance transfer factor.
[b] Figures in parentheses represent the actual number of resistant isolates.

Table 3. *Resistance of Salmonella isolates to specific antibiotics*

Drug	Per cent resistant		
	All strains	*S. typhimurium*	Other strains
Ampicillin	13.5	23.4	5.5
Carbenicillin	13.5	23.4	5.5
Streptomycin	15.0	27.3	5.5
Tetracycline	8.2	12.5	3.7
Cephalosporin	3.2	5.5	1.2
Kanamycin	3.3	5.5	1.2
Chloramphenicol . . .	0	0	0
Polymyxin B	0	0	0

isolates. Similar results were found by Schroeder et al (9). In addition, tetracycline resistance almost never occurred alone but was linked to other resistance markers. This was the case less often with ampicillin resistance, which occurred singly at a frequency of 22% in *S. typhimurium* and 50% in other serotypes (Table 4).

We found that 63.3% of *S. typhimurium* strains resistant to ampicillin or tetracycline had demonstrable resistance factors, whereas only 43% (6 of 14) of the other strains contained transfer factors (Table 2). These represent minimal numbers because transfer of antibiotic resistance requires the presence of the transfer factor as well as the resistance determinants. Strains which do not contain the transfer factor would not be revealed by the mating test.

To determine whether the use of different recipients would alter the percentage of transferable resistance, we tested selected resistant strains with *E. coli* strains FW, CR 34 (Nal^R), and AB 282 and *S. typhimurium* strain LT_2 (Nal^R) as recipients. No differences were noted.

All strains of *Salmonella* which could grow on 250 μg of ampicillin per ml, regardless of their ability to transfer resistance, produced a surface penicillinase which could be released by osmotic shock (7). These enzymes reacted with antiserum to purified *Salmonella* penicillinase isolated from an episomal strain. However, strains which were resistant to 10 μg of ampicillin per ml did not release the penicillinase nor did they ever transfer resistance.

Resistant strains of *Salmonella* were isolated from a younger age group than were the susceptible strains (Table 5). There was no correlation of antibiotic resistance with sex of patient. In the patients from whom clinical information was available, no discernible difference in source of isolation (stool, blood, urine) or clinical symptoms could be detected between those infected with susceptible bacteria and those infected with resistant bacteria.

Antibiotic resistance of *S. typhimurium* was more frequent in municipal hospitals and in those voluntary hospitals serving poor socioeconomic areas (Table 6). Out-of-city hospitals which had a high rate of resistant *S. typhimurium* strains were D.C. General and Boston City, both municipal hospitals. These differences were statistically significant with the sample size for *S. typhimurium,* but not for the other serotypes.

Table 4. *Linkage of drug-resistance markers*

Salmonella serotype	Resistance	Per cent
S. typhimurium	Ampicillin	
	Single	22
	Multiple	78
	Tetracycline	
	Single	7
	Multiple	93
Other serotype	Ampicillin	
	Single	50
	Multiple	50
	Tetracycline	
	Single	14
	Multiple	86

DISCUSSION

Previous investigations have demonstrated the importance of R factors as the mechanism of antibiotic resistance in *Salmonella.* For many years, *S. typhimurium* has been the most frequently isolated human serotype from both fecal and nonfecal sites. Smith (10) had noted multiply resistant *Salmonella* strains at Boston

Table 5. *Relationship of patient age and antibiotic susceptibility*

Patient age	*S. typhimurium*[a]		Other serotypes[a]	
	Resistant (27)[b]	Susceptible (50)	Resistant (8)	Susceptible (79)
years	%	%	%	%
<1	48	24	75	34
1-10	30	46	12	29
>10	22	30	12	37

[a] *P* values for both categories <0.05.
[b] Number of isolates.

Table 6. *Geographic distribution of resistant salmonellae*

Hospital source	No. of resistant isolates/ total isolates	
	S. typhimurium	Other serotypes
New York City		
Municipal hospitals	18/36 (50.0%)	2/27 (7.4%)
Voluntary hospitals (low-income area)	8/11 (72.5%)	4/18 (22.2%)
Voluntary hospitals (high-income area)	7/21 (33.3%)	3/36 (14.3%)
Out of city		
Municipal hospitals	4/8 (50.0%)	2/16 (12.5%)
Voluntary hospitals	10/52 (19.2%)	4/67 (5.9%)

Children's Hospital but did not comment on the age of the patients or their economic background. Gill and Hook (5) demonstrated R factor resistance in 71% of the resistant *Salmonella* strains supplied by the New York Salmonella Center, but they did not separate *S. typhimurium* from other serotypes. Both our data and that of Schroeder et al. (9) show that resistance is significantly more common in *S. typhimurium* than in other *Salmonella* serotypes. The increase in resistance has been due mainly to increased numbers of strains resistant to ampicillin. Tetracycline and streptomycin resistance has remained fairly constant over the past few years. Interestingly, single drug resistance is more common in *Salmonella* serotypes other than *S. typhimurium*. Schroeder et al. (9) reported a similar finding.

Ampicillin resistance in *Salmonella* was first reported in Great Britain in 1961, shortly after the introduction of the drug. Studies by Mare (6) in Africa on the fecal bacterial flora of a Kalahari bushman population showed a lower frequency (10%) of resistant enteric bacteria, none of which contained R factors, than in stool flora of a "civilized population" in Praetoria. Anderson (1) and Smith (11) have stressed the selective pressure of intensive use of antibiotics in the spread of drug-resistant bacteria. Ampicillin use in outpatient departments has increased steadily since 1964 and, particularly with the availability of pleasantly flavored syrups, its use in acute febrile illness in children has surpassed the sulfonamides and tetracyclines. The greatest ampicillin resistance was seen in isolates from children who were 1 year or less of age and who were from poor socioeconomic areas. It is possible that the established gut flora of the small child can be more easily converted to a resistant flora. Such would seem the case in young calves (1). In view of the younger age of patients of urban background with resistant strains, it seems unlikely that in the eastern United States animals provide a reservoir, and we would suggest that the reservoir is in the young children.

The higher incidence of antibiotic resistance and R factors in *S. typhimurium* is unexplained. However, we suspect that it is due to a greater fertility with respect to intergenic mating ability of *S. typhimurium* (Winshell and Neu, *in preparation*). The penicillinases of a number of the other serotypes resistant to ampicillin have been shown to be surface enzymes (7). We have purified several penicillinases from these non-R-factor strains, and have found them to be identical to purified *S. typhimurium* penicillinase (Neu, *unpublished data*).

Although antibiotic therapy in *Salmonella* gastroenteritis probably lengthens the duration of excretion of salmonellae (4), ampicillin treatment is common, particularly in the very young. The high incidence of ampicillin resistance makes it exceedingly important to determine the susceptibility of salmonellae if therapy becomes necessary. No strains showed resistance to chloramphenicol, probably because of severe outpatient restriction of its use due to the risk of adverse hematological reactions. In any serious *Salmonella* infection, chloramphenicol would probably remain the agent of choice.

ACKNOWLEDGMENTS

This work was supported by Public Health Service grant AI 06840 from the National Institute of Allergy and Infectious Diseases, by grant 1199 from the Health Research Council of New York City to the New York Salmonella Center, and by a grant from the Saul Singer Foundation to the Salmonella Center. H. C. Neu is a Career Scientist of the New York Health Research Council.

LITERATURE CITED

1. Anderson, E. S. 1968. Drug resistance in *Salmonella typhimurium* and its implications. Brit. Med. J. **3**:333–339.
2. Bauer, A. W., W. M. M. Kirby, J. C. Sherris, and M. Turck. 1966. Antibiotic susceptibility testing by a standardized single disk method. Amer. J. Clin. Pathol. **45**:493–496.
3. Cherubin, C. E., T. Fodor, L. Denmark, C. Master, H. T. Fuerst, and J. Winter. 1969. The epidemiology of salmonellosis in New York City. Amer. J. Epidemiol. **90**:112–125.
4. Dixon, J. M. S. 1965. Effect of antibiotic treatment on duration of excretion of *Salmonella typhimurium* by children. Brit. Med. J. **2**:1343–1345.
5. Gill, F. A., and E. W. Hook. 1966. Salmonellosis strains with transferable antimicrobial resistance. J. Amer. Med. Ass. **198**:1267–1269.
6. Mare, I. J. 1968. Incidence of R factors among gram negative bacteria in drug-free human and animal communities. Nature (London) **220**:1046–1047.
7. Neu, H. C. 1968. The surface localization of penicillinase in *Escherichia coli* and *Salmonella typhimurium*. Biochem. Biophys. Res. Commun. **32**:258–263.
8. Novick, R. P. 1962. Micro-iodometric assay for penicillinase. Biochem. J. **83**:236–240.
9. Schroeder, S. A., J. V. Bennett, and P. M. Terry. 1968. Antibiotic resistance and transfer factor in Salmonella, United States 1967. J. Amer. Med. Ass. **205**:903–906.
10. Smith, D. H. 1966. Salmonella with transferable drug resistance. N. Engl. J. Med. **275**:626–630.
11. Smith, H. W. 1969. Transfer of antibiotic resistance from animal and human strains of *Escherichia coli* to resident *E. coli* in the alimentary tract of man. Lancet **1**:1174–1176.
12. Watanabe, T. 1964. Selected methods of genetic study of episome-mediated drug resistance in bacteria. Methods Med. Res. **10**:202–220.

Antimicrobial Agents and Chemotherapy—1969

Phenotypic Variability in Penicillin Resistance in a Methicillin-Resistant Strain of *Staphylococcus aureus*

STEPHEN J. SELIGMAN

Department of Medicine, State University of New York Downstate Medical Center, Brooklyn, New York 11203

A methicillin-resistant strain of *Staphylococcus aureus* possesses low-level resistance to benzylpenicillin which appears to be independent of the presence of penicillinase. This strain is also capable of giving rise to rare mutants conferring high-level resistance. Factors affecting phenotypic expression of low-level resistance were studied by streaking dilute inocula onto antibiotic-containing agar and determining the viable count. In a penicillinase-negative variant of the methicillin-resistant strain 13137, low-level resistance to benzylpenicillin was increased either by decreasing the incubation temperature below 37 C or by increasing the NaCl concentration to 5%. Stationary-phase cultures had a gradual decline in viable count with increasing antibiotic concentrations; in contrast, the degree of resistance of log-phase cultures remained more uniform. Resistance expressed in a parent methicillin-resistant strain is subject to marked phenotypic variation and should be clearly separated from resistance of its more highly resistant mutants.

Most methicillin-resistant strains of *Staphylococcus aureus* isolated from clinical sources have a relatively low level of resistance to methicillin, but these strains characteristically produce highly resistant mutants (3, 7, 8, 10). Penicillinase-negative variants derived from methicillin-resistant strains continue to have both low-level methicillin resistance and the capacity to mutate to high-level resistance (11).

Variations in experimental conditions are known to influence the apparent resistance of methicillin-resistant *S. aureus* cells. Barber was the first to report increased resistance on hypertonic media (2). Annear found that incubation temperature markedly influenced resistance (1). At 43 C, his strains were as susceptible as methicillin-susceptible staphylococci, but they were considerably more resistant at 31 C. However, with the exception of previous reports attributing increased resistance on hypertonic media to an increase in the low-level resistance of the parent methicillin-resistant strain (3, 10), little attempt has been made to determine whether the variations in experimental conditions affected low-level resistance of the parent strain or high-level resistance of the mutants.

The present study describes the effects of incubation temperature, of growth phase, and of NaCl concentration upon low-level resistance. The use of a penicillinase-negative variant eliminated penicillinase activity and thereby made possible estimation of penicillinase-independent resistance to benzylpenicillin and other penicillinase-susceptible penicillins. The likelihood of appearance of the more highly resistant mutants was minimized by the use of dilute inocula plated onto solid media and by scoring viable count. This technique also permitted evaluation of a graded response rather than the all-or-none response of a broth-dilution susceptibility test.

MATERIALS AND METHODS

Media. Trypticase Soy Agar (TSA) and Trypticase Soy Broth (TSB) were used. For 5% NaCl-agar, sufficient NaCl was incorporated in the TSA to raise the NaCl concentration from 0.5 to 5.0%. Antibiotics were added to liquefied agar at 45 C before it was poured into petri plates. The resulting agar media were incubated at 37 C overnight to dry the surface of the media prior to inoculation.

Bacterial strains. *S. aureus* 13137 is one of the original methicillin-resistant strains reported by Jevons (6). The penicillinase-negative variant of 13137 used in the present study had lost concurrently both penicillinase activity and mercury resistance, presumably as a result of spontaneous loss of an extrachromosomal element or plasmid (11).

S. aureus 209P (ATCC 6538P), the other strain used, is a typical methicillin-susceptible strain which does not produce penicillinase.

Inoculation of strains onto antibiotic-agars. Stationary-phase cultures were prepared by inoculating a single colony into 10 ml of TSB and incubating the culture overnight. Log-phase cultures were prepared by inoculating 1 ml of overnight culture into 9 ml of TSB and incubating at 37 C without shaking for 4 hr. Cultures were diluted in TSB to yield 50 to 100 colony-forming units per 0.05 ml and then were streaked at room temperature in 0.05-ml amounts onto antibiotic-agar (four streaks per plate). After the streaks were dry, the plates were incubated at the indicated temperatures. Viable counts were made after 1 and 2 days. The results after 1 day of incubation are reported but did not differ significantly from 2-day results.

Growth curves at various temperatures. A 6-ml amount of an overnight culture was inoculated into 120 ml of TSB and incubated at the indicated temperature in a reciprocating water-bath shaker (New Brunswick Scientific Co., New Brunswick, N.J.) at 80 rev/min. Samples were removed at intervals for reading of optical density at 650 nm in a Coleman Junior spectrophotometer. Subcultures were made to ascertain the purity of the culture at the end of incubation.

RESULTS

Resistance of the methicillin-resistant strain 13137 to benzylpenicillin was influenced by temperature of incubation, growth phase of inoculum, and salt content of medium. Resistance of the methicillin-susceptible strain 209P was not appreciably influenced by changes in these variables.

Temperature effect. Decreasing the temperature of incubation from 37 to 33 C increased the resistance of the methicillin-resistant strain (Fig. 1). At 37 C, growth did not occur on benzylpenicillin concentrations greater than 0.12 μg/ml. At 33 C, a 32-fold increase in benzylpenicillin concentration was required to achieve a comparable inhibitory effect. Experiments at 31 C gave results similar to those at 33 C and did not reveal an additional increase in resistance.

The 32-fold increase in resistance associated with a 4 C reduction in incubation temperature suggested the possibility that the methicillin-resistant strain was temperature-sensitive. Consequently, growth in the absence of an antibiotic was measured at different temperatures (Fig. 2).

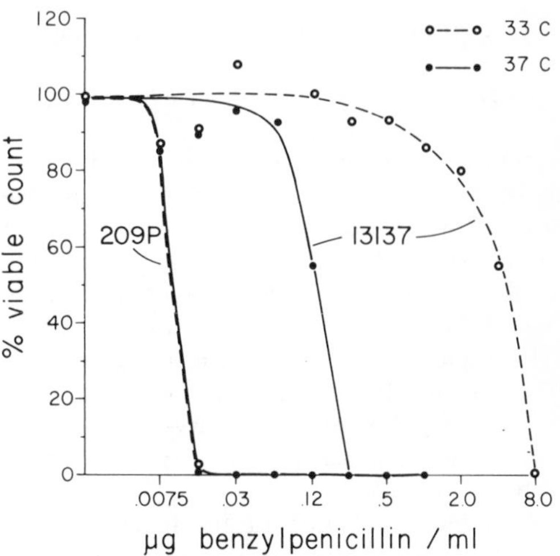

Fig. 1. *Effect of incubation temperature on the percentage of colony-forming particles of Staphylococcus aureus able to grow on penicillin-agar. A penicillinase-negative variant of the methicillin-resistant strain 13137 is compared with the methicillin-susceptible strain 209P. Inocula were from log-phase cultures.*

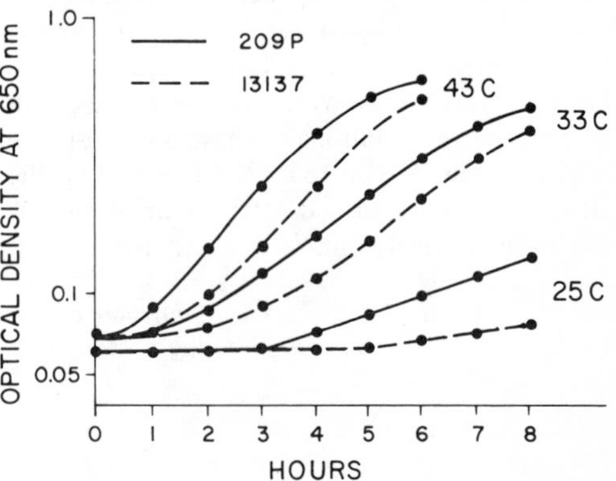

Fig. 2. *Effect of temperature on growth of shake cultures of a methicillin-resistant strain (13137) and methicillin-susceptible strain (209P) of Staphylococcus aureus. Experiments at 29, 31, and 37 C yielded the intermediate results expected on the basis of the temperature curves charted.*

Growth rates of both strain 13137 and strain 209P gradually increased as the incubation temperature was increased from 25 to 43 C. Hence, the markedly increased penicillin susceptibility of strain 13137 at 37 C compared with that at 33 C did not appear to be associated with a gross temperature sensitivity of the growth rate. After 4 to 8 hr of incubation at any given temperature, however, the methicillin-susceptible strain achieved a greater optical density than the methicillin-resistant staphylococcus.

Growth phase of culture. In experiments at 33 C, the number of colonies formed by a stationary-phase culture of the methicillin-resistant strain gradually decreased as the benzylpenicillin concentration was increased from 0.03 to 4.0 μg/ml (Fig. 3). In contrast, the number of colonies of a logarithmically growing culture did not decrease appreciably until benzylpenicillin had been increased to 1 μg/ml, and then the number of colonies decreased more precipitously. For both stationary- and log-phase cultures, 8 μg/ml was necessary to achieve complete inhibition.

Overnight incubation of the inoculum with 0.5 μg of methicillin per ml failed to change either the temperature or growth-phase effects.

NaCl concentration. In agar containing 5% NaCl, penicillin resistance was increased so that 16 μg of benzylpenicillin per ml was necessary for complete inhibition as judged at 24 to 48 hr (Fig. 4). The results on media containing 5% NaCl were similar both at 37 and 33 C; hence, the additional salt greatly diminished the temperature effect. However, the above-noted differences between stationary-phase and log-phase cultures persisted on 5% NaCl-agar. On the salt-agar, colonies formed after 24 hr of incubation were relatively small, but had the appearance of vegetative (normal bacterial) colonies. With 2 to 4 days of additional incubation, a few L-form colonies and mixed colonies containing both L elements and vegetative elements were formed on benzylpenicillin concentrations greater than 8 μg/ml.

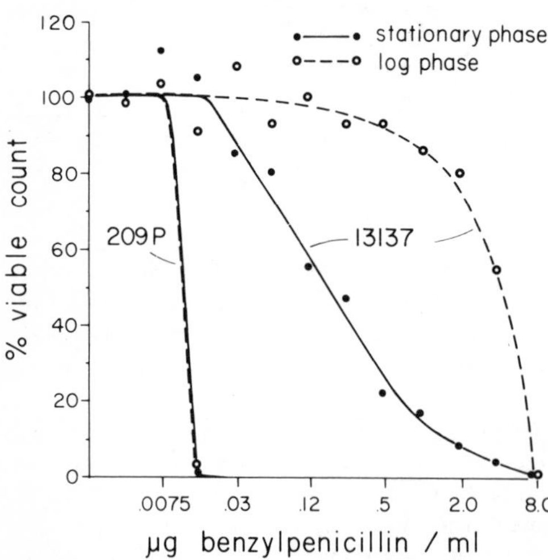

Fig. 3. *Effect of growth phase of inoculum on the percentage of colony-forming particles of Staphylococcus aureus able to grow on penicillin-agar. A penicillinase-negative variant of the methicillin-resistant strain 13137 is compared with the methicillin-susceptible strain 209P. Incubation was at 33 C.*

Other β-lactam antibiotics. Table 1 indicates the relative resistance of strain 13137 to benzylpenicillin and to four other β-lactam antibiotics. Resistance to benzylpenicillin was the one most markedly affected by change in temperature from 37 to 33 C. For all antibiotics, resistance was greater on agar containing 5% NaCl than on TSA. The growth-phase differences (not indicated in Table 1) were comparatively slight with

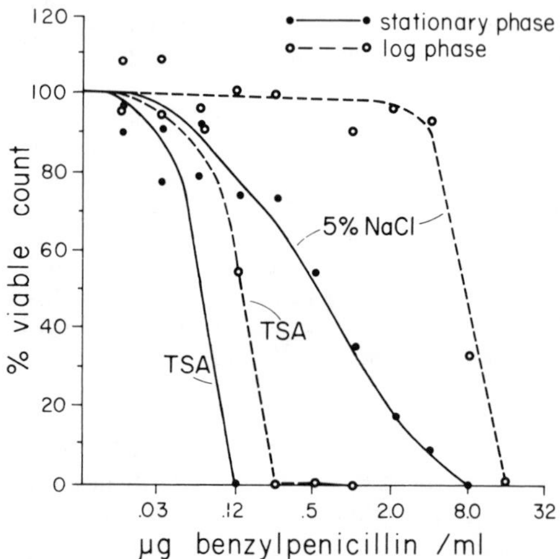

Fig. 4. *Effect of change in NaCl concentration from 0.5% (TSA) to 5.0% on the percentage of colony-forming particles of a penicillinase-negative variant of methicillin-resistant Staphylococcus auresu 13137 able to grow on penicillin-agar at 37 C.*

Table 1. *Highest antibiotic concentration permitting growth of 10% or more of the total number of colony-forming particles of a log-phase culture of strain 13137*

Antibiotic	Antibiotic concn (μg/ml)			
	37 C		33 C	
	TSA	5% NaCl	TSA	5% NaCl
Benzylpenicillin . . .	0.12	8	4	16
Dicloxacillin	0.25	8	0.5	16
Ampicillin	1	16	4	16
Cephalothin	1	⩾32	2	⩾32
Methicillin	2	64	4	64

TSA for antibiotics other than benzylpenicillin, but were consistently observed with 5% NaCl-agar.

DISCUSSION

The results of the present study indicate that the low-level benzylpenicillin resistance of a penicillinase-negative variant of a methicillin-resistant strain of *S. aureus* was increased 32-fold by reducing the incubation temperature from 37 to 33 C. This finding may be related to the increased methicillin resistance with lowered incubation temperature reported by Annear (1); however, in the current study, only a twofold increase in methicillin resistance was found. The temperature sensitivity of benzylpenicillin resistance suggests the possibility that such resistance may be the result of a temperature-sensitive enzyme. The hypothesis of such a temperature-sensitive enzyme is not sufficient to explain either the lack of correspondence between the increase in resistance to benzylpenicillin and methicillin or the ability of 5% NaCl-agar to diminish the temperature effect (Table 1). The highest levels of resistance observed were on hypertonic media. The effect of hypertonic media is probably to protect against lysis and thereby allow survival with a less adequate cell wall.

The findings that stationary-phase cultures showed a gradual decrease in colony count with increasing antibiotic concentration and that log-phase cultures were more uniformly resistant are in contrast to the more usual results of increased penicillin susceptibility of actively growing cultures. Subsequent experiments have indicated that the stationary-phase cultures were more susceptible to autolysis than log-phase cultures, and that autolysis-defective mutants were more uniformly resistant to penicillin (S. J. Seligman, *unpublished data*).

Low-level penicillin resistance in a methicillin-resistant strain of *S. aureus* should be distinguished from resistance attributable to more highly resistant mutants of *S. aureus*. The distinction on a clinical level is important, because growth rate and presumably virulence of the highly resistant mutants are less than those of the parent. In addition, the distinction is helpful to the clinical laboratory in designing screening tests to detect the methicillin-resistant staphylococcus. The disc susceptibility test depends upon low-level resistance. The disc plates should be inoculated at 30 to 33 C and read after 24 hr of incubation (9). If media containing 5% NaCl are used (4), the discs may be incubated at 37 C and should be read at 24 hr. Additional incubation may permit L-form growth, which should not be interpreted as an indication of resistance. Broth-dilution susceptibility tests done with inocula of 10^4 to 10^6 bacteria and with overnight incubation at 37 C give a relatively poor distinction between methicillin-resistant and methicillin-susceptible strains (5). In contrast, broth-dilution susceptibility tests with 10^7 to 10^8 bacteria incubated for 48 hr permit demonstration of the high degree of resistance attributable to the growth of slow-growing mutants (12). Lastly, this distinction is essential for understanding the mechanism of increased resistance in molecular terms. The biochemical bases of low- and high-level resistance may indeed be very different.

ACKNOWLEDGMENTS

These studies were supported by Public Health Service grant AI-01074 from the National Institute of Allergy and Infectious Diseases.

I wish to thank Evelyn Witkin for review of the manuscript.

LITERATURE CITED

1. Annear, D. I. 1968. Effect of temperature on resistance of *Staphylococcus aureus* to methicillin and some other antibiotics. Med. J. Aust. **1**:444–446.
2. Barber, M. 1964. Naturally occurring methicillin-resistant staphylococci. J. Gen. Microbiol. **35**:183–190.
3. Chabbert, Y. A. 1967. Behavior of "methicillin heteroresistant" staphylococci to cephaloridine. Postgrad. Med. J. **43**(Suppl.):40–42.
4. Churcher, G. M. 1968. A screening test for the detection of methicillin-resistant staphylococci. J. Clin. Pathol. **21**:213–217.
5. Dyke, K. G. H., M. P. Jevons, and M. T. Parker. 1966. Penicillinase production and intrinsic resistance to penicillins in *Staphylococcus aureus*. Lancet **1**:835–838.
6. Jevons, M. P. 1961. Celbenin-resistant staphylococci. Brit. Med. J. **1**:126.
7. Knox, R. 1961. Celbenin-resistant staphylococci. Brit. Med. J. **1**:126.
8. Knox, R., and J. T. Smith. 1961. The nature of penicillin resistance in staphylococci. Lancet **2**:520–522.
9. Rountree, P. M., and M. A. Beard. 1968. Hospital strains of *Staphylococcus aureus* with particular reference to methicillin-resistant strains. Med. J. Aust. **2**:1163–1168.
10. Seligman, S. J. 1966. Methicillin-resistant staphylococci: genetics of the minority population. J. Gen. Microbiol. **42**:315–322.
11. Seligman, S. J. 1966. Penicillinase-negative variants of methicillin-resistant *Staphylococcus aureus*. Nature (London) **209**:994–996.
12. Seligman, S. J., and W. L. Hewitt. 1966. Resistance to penicillins and cephalosporins. Antimicrob. Agents Chemother.–1965, p. 387–391.

Antimicrobial Agents and Chemotherapy—1969

Frequency of Transferable Drug Resistance in Clinical Isolates of *Klebsiella*, *Aerobacter*, and *Escherichia*

M. J. ALLISON, J. D. PUNCH, and H. P. DALTON

Departments of Pathology and Microbiology, Medical College of Virginia, Health Sciences Division of Virginia Commonwealth University, Richmond, Virginia 23219

The presence of R factors in multiply drug-resistant clinical isolates of *Klebsiella, Aerobacter,* and *Escherichia* was monitored. Nineteen of 101 *Aerobacter* strains were able to transfer drug resistance to an *E. coli* recipient. Resistance to ampicillin, streptomycin, and tetracycline was observed in 42% of the transfers. *Klebsiella* transferred resistance in 79 of the 98 strains tested. Sixteen patterns of drug resistance were noted; about 33% involved the simultaneous transfer of resistance to streptomycin, chloramphenicol, kanamycin, and neomycin. Fifty-nine of 64 strains of *Escherichia* transferred resistance; a variety of R factor resistance determinants were obtained. The high incidence of R factor-mediated resistance may account for the recent increase in resistance of gram-negative bacteria to antimicrobial agents and the corresponding increase in the incidence of gram-negative sepsis in our institution.

An increased incidence of gram-negative bacteria in serious infections has been noted in recent years (5, 9). Concomitant with the increased incidence of sepsis has been an increase in multiple resistance to antimicrobial agents. R factors have been cited as the cause of the increase in multiple drug resistance by various investigators (4, 7). This communication concerns the incidence of transferable antibiotic resistance in clinical isolates of *Aerobacter, Klebsiella,* and *Escherichia.*

MATERIALS AND METHODS

Sources of bacteria. Strains of multiply drug-resistant *Klebsiella, Aerobacter,* and *Escherichia* were isolated from clinical sources, i.e., urine, sputum, wounds, exudates, and blood. No effort was made to distinguish between hospital- and community-acquired infections, or between bacterial contamination of the sites and true infections. The strains of *Klebsiella* and *Aerobacter* were separated on the basis of motility and ornithine decarboxylase activity (6). Antibiotic susceptibility was determined by a qualitative disc-diffusion technique in which high and low concentrations (BBL) of the following antibiotics were used: ampicillin, tetracycline, chloramphenicol, kanamycin, neomycin, and nalidixic acid. Plates were incubated for 24 hr at 37 C. If the zone size was 2.5 mm or larger with the high concentration, the organism was recorded as susceptible to the antibiotic.

The multiply drug-resistant isolates used for this study included 90 strains of *Aerobacter,* 81 strains of *Klebsiella,* and 64 strains of *Escherichia.* All strains were susceptible to nalidixic acid.

Media. Antibiotic Medium No. 3 (Penassay Broth, Difco) was used as the propagating medium for R factor transfer. MacConkey Agar (Difco), containing the appropriate antibiotics, was used for selection of transcipients (recipients which had acquired an R factor).

Transfer of drug resistance from isolates to E. coli. The technique previously described was employed (7). Essentially, isolates resistant to two or more antibiotics (high- or low-concentration discs) and susceptible to nalidixic acid served as donors. A strain of *E. coli* CSH-2 (F^-, Met^-, Pro^-) was used as the recipient. Mating was accomplished by mixing 0.5-ml amounts from turbid 6-hr cultures of donor and recipient strains with 9 ml of fresh Penassay Broth. After incubation for 18 hr at 37 C, 0.1-ml amounts of the mixed culture were plated on MacConkey Agar plates containing nalidixic acid (1,000 μg/ml) and ampicillin (20 μg/ml), tetracycline (20 μg/ml), streptomycin (20 μg/ml), chloramphenicol (20 μ/ml), or neomycin (20 μg/ml). Alone, neither donor nor recipient would grow on these media, the donor because it was susceptible to nalidixic acid and the recipient, CSH-2 (F^-, Met^-, Pro^-, Nal-r), because it was susceptible to ampicillin, streptomycin, chloramphenicol, tetracycline, and neomycin. A negative control of the recipient was run to assure antibiotic activity of the plates. A positive control containing CSH-2 (F^-, Met^-, Pro^-, Nal-r) and a known competent donor, *E. coli* W677-222 (Lac^-, Met^-, Pro^-), containing the episome (222) which confers resistance to streptomycin, tetracycline, chloramphenicol, and sulfonamides was run to monitor mating efficiency (7).

All plates were incubated for 24 hr at 37 C. Transcipient colonies selected from these plates were restreaked on MacConkey Agar containing the same antibiotics as the original isolation plates to check for purity. Antibiotic susceptibilities of these transcipients were determined as previously described.

RESULTS

The results of a survey to determine the incidence of multiple resistance in *Aerobacter*, *Klebsiella*, and *Escherichia* isolates are presented in Table 1. These data represent the consecutive isolates obtained over a 6-month period. Of the 678 *Aerobacter* isolates, 63% were resistant to

Table 1. *Incidence of Aerobacter, Klebsiella, and Escherichia isolates resistant to two or more antibiotics*[a]

Organism	Percentage isolated from				Total no. of isolates	No. resistant
	Urine	Respiratory tract	Wounds	Blood		
Aerobacter	70	28	62	88	678	428 (63%)
Klebsiella	54	61	48	72	668	380 (57%)
Escherichia	23	12	36	31	1,502	348 (23%)

[a] Collected from July to December 1968.

Table 2. *Incidence of transferable drug resistance from resistant Aerobacter isolates*[a]

Resistance of donor	No. tested	No. transferring resistance	Resistance transferred[b]
Am Sm	5	2	Am Sm (1) Sm (1)
Am Km	1	0	–
Am Tc	3	0	–
Am Sm Tc	4	1	Am Sm Tc (1)
Am Sm Cm	1	0	–
Am Sm Cm Tc	36	9	Am Sm Tc (5) Sm Tc Cm (1) Am Sm Tc (1) Sm (1) Am Sm (1)
Am Sm Km Nm	2	0	–
Am Sm Tc Km	1	0	–
Am Sm Tc Cm Km	10	1	Am Sm Tc (1)
Am Sm Cm Km Nm	2	0	–
Am Sm Cm Tc Nm	4	0	–
Am Cm Tc Km Nm	1	0	–
Am Sm Cm Tc Km Nm	31	6	Am Sm Tc (1) Am Sm Km Nm (1) Sm Cm Tc (1) Sm Km Nm (1) Am Sm Cm Nm (1) Am (1)
Total	101	19	

[a] Abbreviations: Am, ampicillin; Sm, streptomycin; Km, kanamycin; Tc, tetracycline; Cm, chloramphenicol; Nm, neomycin.
[b] Numbers in parentheses indicate number of strains.

two or more antibiotics. A similar figure, 57%, was obtained with 668 *Klebsiella* isolates, whereas 23% of 1,502 *Escherichia* isolates were multiply resistant.

Variability in the incidence of drug resistance was related to the source of specimens. For example, from urine specimens, 70% of all *Aerobacter* isolates, 54% of all *Klebsiella* isolates, and 23% of all *Escherichia* isolates possessed resistance to two or more antibiotics. In contrast, only 28, 61, and 12% respectively, of the *Aerobacter, Klebsiella,* and *Escherichia* isolates from the respiratory tract were multiply resistant. Differences in resistance were also noted between isolates from wounds and blood specimens.

Table 2 lists the antibiotic susceptibility of the 101 *Aerobacter* strains tested for the presence of R factors and shows the pattern of resistance transferred. The transfer of drug resistance occurred with 19 strains (18%). A variety of resistance patterns were found in the transcipients; they possessed from one to four drug-resistance markers. In Table 5, the patterns of drug resistance transferred from the *Aerobacter* strains are grouped according to resistance to antibiotics. Resistance to streptomycin and ampicillin was transferred as a single marker in some cases, but kanamycin and neomycin resistance was transferred only in combination with streptomycin resistance. The most common grouping of R determinants was ampicillin, streptomycin, and tetracycline (42%).

The results obtained with the *Klebsiella* isolates are given in Table 3. In general, the *Klebsiella* strains were multiply resistant to three or more antibiotics. Of the 98 strains, 58 were resistant to six antibiotics (ampicillin, streptomycin, chloramphenicol, tetracycline, kanamycin, and neomycin), and only 12 isolates

Table 3. *Incidence of transferable drug resistance from resistant Klebsiella isolates*[a]

Resistance of donor	No. tested	No. transferring resistance	Resistance transferred[b]
Am Sm	7	3	Sm (1) Am (1) Am Sm (1)
Am Km	1	0	–
Am Cm	1	0	–
Am Tc	1	0	–
Sm Cm	2	0	–
Am Sm Tc	7	7	Am Sm Tc (7)
Am Sm Cm	1	1	Am Sm (1)
Am Sm Cm Tc	12	10	Am (1) Sm Cm (8) Am Sm Tc (1)
Am Sm Cm Tc Km	2	1	Am Sm Cm Tc Km (1)
Am Sm Tc Km Nm	4	2	Am Tc (1) Am Sm Tc Km Nm (1)
Am Sm Cm Km Nm	2	2	Sm Cm Km Nm (2)
Am Sm Cm Tc Km Nm	58	53	Sm Cm Km Nm (23) Am Sm Cm Tc Km Nm (13) Sm Nm (1) Sm Cm Tc Km (2) Am Sm Cm Km Nm (4) Sm Cm Tc Km Nm (5) Sm Cm Km (1) Am Sm Tc (1) Cm Km Nm (2) Am Sm Cm Tc Km (1)
Total	98	79	

[a] Abbreviations as in Table 2.

[b] Numbers in parentheses indicate number of strains.

were resistant to fewer than three antibiotics. R factors were transferred from 79 strains (80%). The highest incidence of transfer occurred with donors possessing resistance to four or more antibiotics. However, a variety of antibiotic-resistance patterns were obtained in the transcipients. This is further illustrated in Table 5, which shows the frequency of isolation of individual R factors. It can be seen that the two resistance patterns transferred from *Klebsiella* strains most frequently accounted for 48% of all R factors. A total of 16 different patterns were transferred from *Klebsiella* isolates, including several transfers of resistance to a single antibiotic.

Table 4 shows the original resistance of the 64 *Escherichia* isolates tested and the pattern of resistance transferred by 59 strains. It can be noted that most *Escherichia* isolates were multiply resistant to only two or three antibiotics, in contrast to the multiple resistance to four to six drugs for the other two groups of isolates. Less than 10% of the *Escherichia* isolates were resistant to five or more antibiotics. Sixteen different patterns of resistance were observed in the transcipients, as shown in Table 5. Approximately 23% of the transfers were to a single antibiotic, either ampicillin or streptomycin. The simultaneous acquisition of resistance to two antibiotics accounted for 43% of all transfers, whereas transfer of resistance to four antibiotics was low (7%).

DISCUSSION

The discovery of infectious drug resistance in Japan about 10 years ago has led to studies attempting to delineate the role of R factors in the increasing incidence of multiple drug resistance in gram-negative organisms. It is apparent from the data obtained during the present study,

Table 4. *Incidence of transferable drug resistance from resistant Escherichia strains*[a]

Resistance of donor	No. tested	No. transferring resistance	Resistance transferred[b]
Am Tc	2	1	Am (1)
Am Sm	5	5	Am (1) Am Sm (4)
Sm Tc	20	16	Sm Tc (10) Sm (5) Tc (1)
Am Sm Tc	23	23	Am Sm Tc (9) Am (2) Sm (2) Sm Tc (1) Am Sm (7) Am Tc (2)
Sm Tc Cm	3	3	Sm Tc Cm (3)
Am Sm Tc Cm	4	4	Am Sm Tc Cm (1) Am Sm Cm (1) Am (1) Sm Cm (1)
Am Sm Tc Cm Nm (Km)[c]	4	4	Am Sm Tc Nm (1) Am Sm Tc Cm (1) Nm (1) Sm Tc Nm (1)
Sm Tc Cm Nm (Km)	2	2	Sm Cm Nm (1) Sm Tc Cm Nm (1)
Sm Tc Nm (Km)	1	1	Sm Tc Nm (1)
Total	64	59	

[a] Abbreviations as in Table 2.
[b] Numbers in parentheses indicate number of strains.
[c] Km in parentheses indicates that it was not tested for transfer.

Table 5. *Drug-resistance patterns of transferred R factor*

Resistance patterns[a]	R factors transferred from		
	Aerobacter	*Klebsiella*	*Escherichia*
Am	5[b]	3	8
Sm	11	1	12
Nm	–	–	2
Tc	–	–	2
Sm Cm	–	10	2
Sm Nm	–	1	–
Am Sm	11	3	19
Am Tc	–	1	3
Sm Tc	–	–	18
Am Sm Tc	42	11	15
Sm Km Nm	5	–	–
Sm Cm Tc	11	–	5
Sm Cm Km	–	1	–
Cm Km Nm	–	3	–
Am Sm Cm	–	–	2
Sm Tc Nm	–	–	3
Sm Cm Nm	–	–	2
Am Sm Km Nm	5	–	–
Am Sm Tc Cm	5	–	3
Am Sm Cm Nm	5	–	–
Sm Cm Km Nm	–	32	–
Sm Cm Tc Km	–	3	–
Am Sm Cm Km	–	5	–
Am Sm Tc Nm	–	–	2
Sm Tc Cm Nm	–	–	2
Am Sm Tc Km Nm	–	1	–
Am Sm Cm Tc Km	–	3	–
Sm Cm Tc Km Nm	–	6	–
Am Sm Cm Tc Km Nm	–	16	–
Total	100	100	100

[a] Abbreviations as in Table 2.
[b] Percentage of total R factors isolated.

as well as from other reports (8), that multiple drug resistance in many cases is due to demonstrable R factors. It is also evident that the organisms are closely associated with nosocomial infections (15, 16).

The high frequency of R factor transfer from clinical *Escherichia* isolates to the *E. coli* recipients might be interpreted as reflecting a high mating compatability between the donor and the recipient. *Klebsiella* strains also transferred resistance at a high rate to the *E. coli* recipient. With *Aerobacter* strains, however, R factor transfer was observed in less than 20% of the matings. The basis for this apparent variability in transferable drug resistance among these groups is not clear. Whether this represents a low mating compatability between *Aerobacter* and *E. coli* or a high incidence of chromosomal resistance in the *Aerobacter* strains raises some interesting questions. Another possible explanation resides in the model of Anderson (1–3). In this model, transferable resistance may not form a single linkage group. Each determinant maintains an independent relationship with the R transfer factor, Δ. Furthermore, a loss of the Δ factor will result in loss of transferability of the resistance determinants, although the resistance determinants are complete replicans and are still present in the cell as episomes (1–3). The low level of resistance transferability from the *Aerobacter* isolates may represent a natural restriction between the *Aerobacter* genome and the Δ factor. Studies in which the triparental cross is used for identifying wild strains of *Enterobacteriaceae* carrying drug-resistance determinants without transfer factors should clarify this possibility (11, 13).

The data presented in this study indicates that nosocomial *Escherichia* isolates are not the source of R factors for the clinical isolates of *Klebsiella* and *Aerobacter.* Two facts support this position: the relatively low incidence of multiple resistance in the 1,502 *Escherichia* strains and the lack of R factors conferring wide multiple resistance (four to six antibiotics) in the *Escherichia* group. However, the data do not eliminate the possibility that *Escherichia* can serve as the source of transfer factors with or without some resistant determinants and that the R factors are formed by recombination between drug-resistance determinants and transfer factors within the *Klebsiella* and *Aerobacter* isolates. Both Anderson and Mitsuhashi et al. have proposed such a mechanism for R factor formation (3, 13).

During these studies, no attempt was made to cure the resistant clinical isolates of the drug-resistance determinants. Thus, information regarding the contribution of the R factor to the total drug-resistance pattern of the isolates was not defined. Medeiros and O'Brien (10) recently reported that, in *Serratia,* R factors often serve only to augment the total level of resistance.

The serious problem of gram-negative bacterial sepsis now faced by hospital patients is of national concern. Smith and Armour reported R factors in 69% of the multiply resistant strains of *E. coli, Proteus, Klebsiella,* and *Pseudomonas* isolated from the urinary tract (18). A high incidence of R factors in clinical isolates of *Shigella, Salmonella, Escherichia, Klebsiella,* and *Aerobacter* has also been reported by various investigators (12, 14, 17). This study supports the noted high incidence of R factors in nosocomial environments and provides a comparison under standard conditions of the incidence in three common groups. The variety of drug-resistance patterns observed, some of which were partially or completely transferable, emphasizes the dynamic picture of drug resistance in clinical isolates and demands a constant monitoring for drug-resistance patterns. Such information is essential to both the clinician and the epidemiologist.

LITERATURE CITED

1. Anderson, E. S. 1965. A rapid screening test for transfer factors in drug sensitive *Enterobacteriaceae.* Nature (London) **208**:1016–1017.
2. Anderson, E. S. 1965. Origin of transferable drug-resistance factor in *Enterobacteriaceae.* Brit. Med. J. **2**:1289–1291.
3. Anderson, E. S., and M. J. Lewis. 1965. Characterization of a transfer factor associated with drug resistance in *Salmonella typhimurium.* Nature (London) **208**:843–849.
4. Bulger, R. J., C. E. Roberts, and J. C. Sherris. 1967. Changing incidence of antibiotic resistance among *Staphylococcus auresus, Escherichia coli, Aerobacter-Klebsiella,* and *Pseudomonas* encountered in a teaching hospital over a 7-year period. Antimicrob. Agents Chemother–1966, p. 42–46.
5. Dalton, H. P., and M. J. Allison. 1967. Etiology of bacteremia. Appl. Microbiol. **15**:808–814.
6. Edwards, P. R., and W. H. Ewing. 1962. Identification of *Enterobacteriaceae,* p. 7. Burgress Publishing Co., Minneapolis.
7. Hinshaw, V., J. Punch, M. J. Allison, and H. P. Dalton. 1969. Frequency of R factor-mediated multiple drug resistance in *Klebsiella* and *Aerobacter.* Appl. Microbiol. **17**:214–218.
8. Kabins, S. A., and S. Cohen. 1966. Resistance transfer factor in enteric bacteria. N. Engl. J. Med. **275**:248–252.
9. Marin, C. M. 1969. Editorial: a national bacteremia registry. J. Infec. Dis. **120**:495–496.
10. Medeiros, A. A., and T. F. O'Brien. 1969. Contribution of R factors to the antibiotic resistance of hospital isolates of *Serratia.* Antimicrob. Agents Chemother.–1968, p. 30–35.
11. Meynell, E., G. G. Meynell, and N. Datta. 1968. Phylogenetic relationships of drug-resistance factors and other transmissible bacterial plasmids. Bacteriol. Rev. **32**:55–83.
12. Mitsuhashi S., H. Hashimoto, R. Egawa, T. Tanaka, and Y. Nagai. 1967. Drug resistance of enteric bacteria. IX. Distribution of R factors in gram-negative bacteria from clinical sources. J. Bacteriol. **93**:1242–1245.
13. Mitsuhashi, S., M. Kameda, K. Harada, and M. Suzuki. 1969. Formation of recombinants between nontransmissible drug-resistance determinants and transfer factors. J. Bacteriol. **97**:1520–1521.
14. Naide, G., T. Kawamura, K. Makino, H. Tamura, and T. Watanabe. 1967. Prevalence of transferable drug-resistance in drug resistant bacteria isolated from urinary tract infections in Japan. Jap. J. Microbiol. **2**:87–94.
15. Salzman, T. C., J. J. Clark, and L. Klemm. 1968. Hand contamination of personnel as a mechanism of cross-infection in nosocomial infections with antibiotic-resistant *Escherichia coli* and *Klebsiella-Aerobacter.* Antimicrob. Agents Chemother.–1967, p. 97–100.
16. Salzman, T. C., and L. Klemm. 1967. Transferable drug resistance (R factors) in *Enterobacteriaceae*: relationship to nosocomial infections. Antimicrob. Agents Chemother.–1966, p. 212–220.
17. Smith, D. H. 1967. Drug resistance of enteric bacteria mediated by R factors. Antimicrob. Agents Chemother.–1966, p. 274–280.
18. Smith, D. H., and I. Armour. 1966. Transferable R factors in enteric bacteria causing infection of the genitourinary tract. Lancet **2**:15–18.

Antimicrobial Agents and Chemotherapy—1969

Unusual Resistance of *Staphylococcus aureus* to Lincomycin and 7-Chlorolincomycin

E. JACK BENNER and ALLEN P. ADAMS, JR.

Section of Infectious and Immunologic Diseases, Department of Internal Medicine, School of Medicine, University of California, Davis, California 95816, and the Sacramento Medical Center, Sacramento, California 95823

We found 8 of 38 methicillin-resistant strains of *Staphylococcus aureus* resistant to lincomycin and 7-chlorolincomycin. Additionally, 2% of 259 recent clinical isolates which appeared susceptible when tested with a 10-μg content disc of either drug were resistant by tube and plate minimal inhibitory concentration (MIC) tests. These discordant strains contained naturally resistant mutants not present in the susceptible strains. The discordant strains, like erythromycin-resistant strains, rapidly developed resistance to lincomycin and 7-chlorolincomycin during serial transfer in these drugs, whereas resistance was acquired in a slow stepwise fashion by all other strains tested. The finding that lincomycin was not inactivated by the susceptible strains, the discordant strains, classically resistant strains, or strains with acquired resistance due to serial passage in drug indicated that resistance was a result of tolerance. Since the discordant strains were not detected by the 10-μg content disc of either drug, therapy of infections caused by such strains could lead to the selection of naturally resistant mutants. Tube or plate MIC tests and tests with 2-μg content discs detected all the resistant strains.

Lincosamide antibiotics, lincomycin and 7-chlorolincomycin, are usually effective in vitro against most strains of *Staphylococcus aureus* (5, 6). However, a few strains of *S. aureus* not susceptible to erythromycin were resistant, or rapidly became resistant, to lincyomycin during in vitro drug exposure tests (3, 4). In tests with 297 different clinical isolates of *S. aureus* from several sources, some strains appeared susceptible when tested with a disc containing 10 μg of either lincomycin or 7-chlorolincomycin but were actually resistant in tube or plate minimal inhibitory concentration (MIC) tests. A comparison of susceptible strains, naturally occurring resistant strains, and strains made resistant by in vitro antibiotic exposure is presented.

MATERIALS AND METHODS

Susceptibility tests. All of the staphylococci were recovered from clinical infections. Cultures were prepared by overnight incubation in Trypticase Soy Broth (TSB). Disc susceptibilities were determined by a standard single-disc method (1). The same TSB culture of each isolate was diluted 10^{-3} with TSB, and 0.5 ml was added to 0.5 ml of broth containing the appropriate amount of antibiotic to yield final drug concentrations of 0.5, 1, 2, 4, 8, 16, 31.3, 62.5, 125, 250, 500, or 1,000 μg/ml. After 18 hr of incubation at 37 C, the tubes were examined, and the lowest drug concentration which had prevented visible growth was accepted as the MIC. Trypticase-soy-yeast extract-agar plates containing 1, 2, 3, 4, 8, 10, 16, 20, 31.3, 40, 62.5, 80, 125, 160, 250, 500, and 1,000 μg of lincomycin or 7-chlorolincomycin powders per ml were prepared fresh for each replicate-plate MIC test. A hand replicator which added 10^6 bacteria was used to deliver organisms which had been grown in broth for 18 hr at 37 C. After incubation, the lowest concentration of drug which prevented visible growth of bacteria on the plate was considered to be the MIC.

Population analysis. Trypticase Soy Agar plates containing antibiotic were prepared as in the plate MIC tests. Each organism tested was grown overnight in broth, and then diluted in broth so that the addition of 0.1 ml to the antibiotic-containing plate would provide an inoculum of 10^8, 10^6, or 10^2 bacteria. Each inoculum was added and spread by pipette tip on the surface of a plate at each drug concentration. All plates were incubated at 37 C for 48 hr. Counts of colony-forming units were made after 24 hr of incubation and again after the 48-hr growth period. Control plates without antibiotic were made in duplicate for each inoculum size.

Development of drug resistance in vitro. Strains of *S. aureus* were serially transferred once daily in broth containing from 0.5 to 1,000 μg of lincomycin or 7-chlorolincomycin per ml. After 24 hr of incubation at 37 C, 0.1 ml was removed from the tube with the highest concentration of antibiotic and diluted 10^{-2} in broth. For the next transfer, 0.5 ml of this dilution was used to inoculate 0.5 ml of broth with antibiotic. This was continued for 26 transfers or until growth occurred in the presence of an antibiotic concentration of 500 μg/ml.

Tests to detect inactivation of lincomycin. Actively growing cultures of each strain tested were added directly to broth solutions of lincomycin so that 10 ml of culture contained 10 μg of antibiotic per ml. The tubes were incubated at 37 C with constant shaking for 24 hr. Samples from each culture and from an incubated broth control tube with 10 μg of lincomycin per ml were Seitz-filtered and frozen simultaneously with freshly prepared standard solutions of lincomycin. These were then assayed by the agar-well method of Bennett et al. (2)

RESULTS

Comparison of broth-dilution MIC and disc test results. When a 2-μg content disc of lincomycin or 7-chlorolincomycin was used, 23 of 297 isolates had zones of inhibition 15 mm or less in diameter, and all were resistant by the MIC test. The other 274 isolates yielded zones more than 25 mm in diameter and were inhibited by 2 μg or less of either drug per ml. Of the 23 resistant isolates, 10 possessed intrinsic resistance to methicillin.

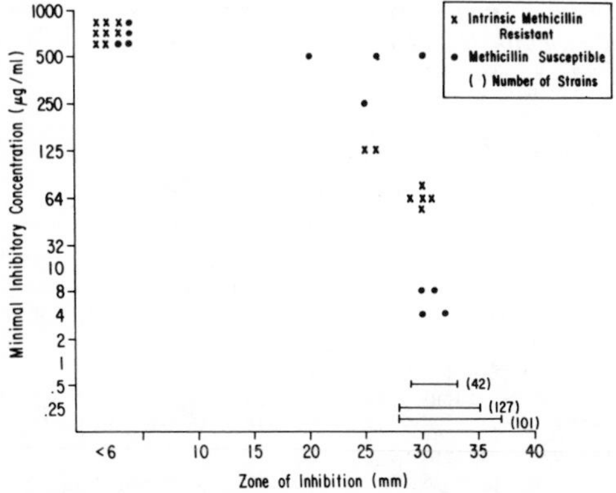

Fig. 1. *Minimal inhibitory concentrations (broth) versus diameters of zones of inhibition with 10-μg content discs of 7-chlorolincomycin; 297 isolates of S. aureus.*

In contrast, 15 isolates repeatedly produced inhibition zones of 20 mm or more in diameter when a 10-μg content 7-chlorolincomycin disc was used, yet required from 4 to 1,000 μg of this antibiotic per ml for inhibition in plate or tube MIC tests (Fig. 1). When a 10-μg content lincomycin disc was used, 11 isolates repeatedly gave similar discordant results when compared with tube or replicate plate MIC results (Fig. 2).

Population characteristics of susceptible, discordant, and resistant strains. It was found that strains which appeared resistant by the 10-μg content disc test and by plate or tube MIC tests were composed of a uniform population of cells with a high level of resistance to both lincomycin and 7-chlorolincomycin (Fig. 3). Three susceptible strains were composed of cells

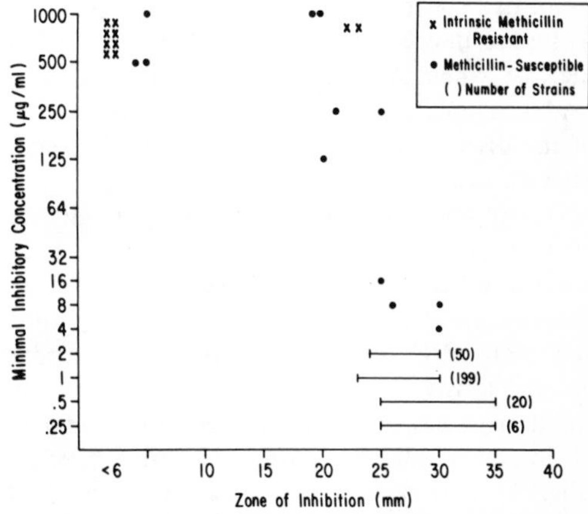

Fig. 2. *Minimal inhibitory concentrations (broth) versus diameters of zones of inhibition with 10-μg content discs of lincomycin; 297 isolates of S. aureus.*

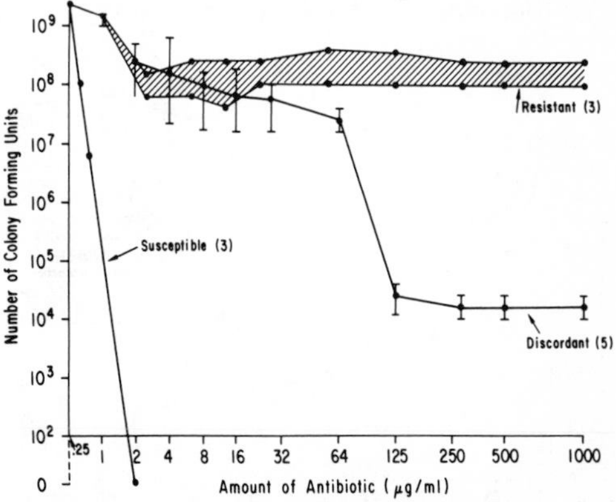

Fig. 3. *Population analysis with lincomycin-resistant (three), lincomycin-susceptible (three), and discordant strains (five).*

which were all killed by a 2 μg/ml concentration of either antibiotic. However, the discordant strains (methicillin-susceptible) possessed "heterogeneity," and a significant proportion of cells were resistant to 4 to 64 μg of either drug per ml. A small number of cells of each strain (0.01 to 0.001%) were resistant to as much as 1,000 μg of each drug per ml.

During study of the discordant strains, small and large colonies were observed on agar plates after a 24-hr growth period. The small colonies were seen only rarely on antibiotic-free plates. The progeny of a small and a large colony were found to be quite different. Most of the progeny of a large colony were very resistant to both antibiotics (Fig. 4, line d), whereas the progeny of the small colony were similar to the parent strain in respect to "heterogeneity" of resistance (compare line b in Fig. 4 with "discordant" in Fig. 3). When colonies were picked from drug-containing plates used in the population studies of the discordant strain, 10 of 27 such colonies gave discordant disc and MIC results.

Development of lincosamide drug resistance by in vitro transfer in antibiotic. Tests with 21 isolates which were susceptible to lincomycin, 7-chlorolincomycin, and erythromycin by tube and plate MIC tests showed that these strains became resistant in a slow stepwise manner, and could grow in only 10 μg of 7-chlorolincomycin or lincomycin per ml after 25 serial passages (Fig. 5). However, strains that gave discordant test results against lincosamide antibiotics developed resistance much more rapidly. Ten such strains, five of which were resistant to erythromycin and five of which were susceptible to erythromycin, all developed resistance which allowed growth in at least 500 μg of the lincosamide drugs per ml after only five serial passages in either drug. In addition, all strains were resistant to erythromycin after serial transfer five times in either lincomycin or 7-chlorolincomycin. Strains that required 25 serial passages in lincomycin before tolerating this drug in a concentration of 10 μg/ml had no cross-resistance with erythromycin.

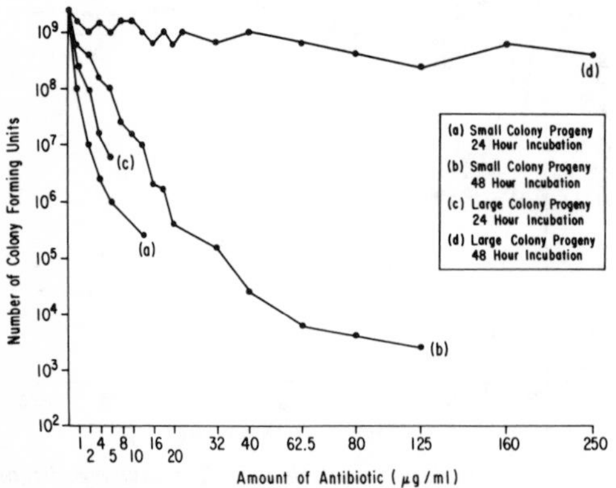

Fig. 4. *Population characteristics of a "discordant" strain of S. aureus.*

Effect of actively growing staphylococci on lincomycin. There was no loss in the biological activity of lincomycin as a consequence of the growth of staphylococci (Table 1). None of the strains inactivated lincomycin despite prolific growth during 24 hr of incubation, regardless of the source or nature of the resistance.

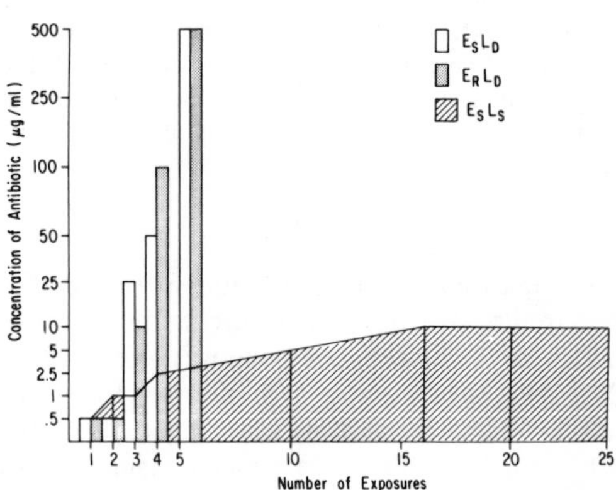

Fig. 5. *Rapid acquisition of resistance by in vitro transfer with strains which were erythromycin-susceptible and lincomycin-discordant (E_sL_d), strains which were erythromycin-resistant and lincomycin-discordant (E_rL_d), strains which were susceptible to both erythromycin and lincomycin (E_sL_s). The highest concentration of antibiotic in which visible growth occurred after 24 hr of incubation is shown.*

Table 1. *Residual lincomycin after 12 and 24 hr of incubation with actively growing staphylococci*

Strain of *S. aureus* tested for drug inactivation	Inoculum (bacteria/ml)	Drug concn (μg/ml)		
		0 hr	12 hr	24 hr
Lincomycin-susceptible . . .	2.4×10^8	10.0	10.0	10.1
Lincomycin-resistant (natural)	2.5×10^8	9.9	10.1	10.0
Lincomycin-resistant after 25 in vitro passages	7.5×10^8	9.9	10.0	10.0
Parent strain of the preceding strain	4.0×10^8	10.2	9.9	10.1
Discordant parent strain . .	3.9×10^8	10.1	10.0	10.1
Resistant after five transfers	2.8×10^8	10.0	10.2	9.9

DISCUSSION

These results show that both lincomycin and 7-chlorolincomycin susceptibility tests done with a 10-μg content disc will fail to detect resistance to these drugs in 2% of methicillin-susceptible strains of *S. aureus*. When methicillin-resistant strains were included, approximately 5% of tested strains appeared susceptible (zone of inhibition, 20 mm or greater) although they were, in fact, resistant to lincomycin and 7-chlorolincomycin (MIC, 4 to 1,000 μg/ml). These discordant results did not occur in tests with a 2-μg content disc when the inoculum was regulated as described by Bauer et al. (1).

Although most clinical isolates of *S. aureus* develop resistance to the lincosamide antibiotics in a slow, stepwise manner, strains resistant to erythromycin, as well as the strains yielding discordant susceptibility test results, achieved a high level of resistance with only one to five exposures to lincosamide antibiotics. It seems necessary to detect these strains to allow their eradication from hospitals and to prevent the emergency of the resistant progeny that appear after brief drug exposure.

It was apparent that discordant test results occurred because of "heterogeneity" within some strains of *S. aureus* with regard to resistance to both lincomycin and 7-chlorolincomycin. The discordant strains contained a small number of cells with a high level of drug resistance and a larger number of cells which tolerated from 4 to 64 μg of antibiotic per ml. However, the presence of the drug retarded the development of colonies. After a standard 18 hr incubation period, the majority of the colony-forming units had not appeared on the plate near the antibiotic-containing discs, or on agar plates containing antibiotic. However, incubation of the 10-μg content disc tests for 48 hr allowed the resistant population in the discordant strains to form colonies around the disc. In MIC tests in which heavy inocula were used, growth was apparent after overnight incubation, even though no inactivation of the drug occurred. The population characteristics of the discordant strains and the absence of drug inactivation are consistent with the natural occurrence of inherently resistant staphylococci. The nature of this resistance awaits elucidation.

ACKNOWLEDGMENT

This study was supported by a grant-in-aid from The Upjohn Co.

LITERATURE CITED

1. Bauer, A. W., D. M. Perry, and W. M. M. Kirby. 1959. Single disc antibiotic sensitivity testing of staphylococci. Arch. Intern. Med. **104**:208–216.
2. Bennett, J. V., J. L. Brodie, E. J. Benner, and W. M. M. Kirby. 1966. Simplified, accurate method for antibiotic assay of clinical specimens. Appl. Microbiol. **14**:170–177.
3. Duncan, I. B. R. 1968. Development of lincomycin resistance by staphylococci. Antimicrob. Agents Chemother.–1967, p. 723–729.
4. Garrison, D. W., R. M. DeHaan, and J. B. Lawson. 1968. Comparison of in vitro antibacterial activities of 7-chloro-7-deoxylincomycin, lincomycin, and erythromycin. Antimicrob. Agents Chemother–1967, p. 397–400.
5. Kaplan, K., and L. Weinstein. 1968. Lincomycin. Pediat. Clin. N. Amer. **15**:131–139.
6. Meyers, B. R., K. Kaplan, and L. Weinstein. 1969. Microbiological and pharmacological behavior of 7-chlorolincomycin. Appl. Microbiol. **17**:653–657.

Antimicrobial Agents and Chemotherapy—1969

Susceptibility of "Methicillin"-Resistant *Staphylococcus aureus* to 12 Antimicrobial Agents

PAUL D. HOEPRICH, E. JACK BENNER, and FRITZ H. KAYSER[1]

Section of Infectious and Immunologic Diseases, Department of Internal Medicine, School of Medicine, University of California, Davis, California 95616

Seventy clinical isolates of "methicillin"-resistant *Staphylococcus aureus* were tested for susceptibility to 12 antimicrobial agents under the following conditions: 10^5 cocci per ml for inocula; molar definition of antimicrobial agents; a synthetic, protein-free broth culture medium; and 48 hr of incubation with subculture of 5% of the test volume to distinguish bacteriostatic from bactericidal action. At concentrations relevant to therapeutics, vancomycin and fusidic acid were bactericidal to all 70 strains; rifampin, coumermycin, gentamicin, and cycloserine were also quite active. Molecule for molecule, rifampin was the most potent of the agents tested; however, the record of rifampin was marred by five instances of skipped tubes among the 70 tests (350 tubes). Skipping was productive of highly resistant progeny, but was difficult to reproduce; the significance of the phenomenon to therapeutics is as yet unclear.

There is clearly a burgeoning clinical importance to strains of *Staphylococcus aureus* that are resistant to the β-lactamase-resistant penicillins and cephalosporins (1, 2, 7). Accordingly, the potential of both established and investigational antimicrobial drugs for use against these ominously peculiar staphylococci must be determined.

Identical inocula of 70 isolates of "methicillin"-resistant *S. aureus*, collected from Europe and the United States, were exposed to equimolar quantities of the antimicrobial agents under study in a totally defined, protein-free, broth medium. Ranked in descending order of effectiveness, as judged at concentrations attainable in the blood of patients given doses it is possible to administer, the agents studied were: vancomycin, fusidic acid, rifampin, coumermycin, gentamicin, cycloserine, cephalothin, dicloxacillin, benzylpenicillin, nafcillin, cephalexin, and bacitracin.

MATERIALS AND METHODS

Culture medium. A formula was developed that provides a synthetic, protein-free, alanine-free, *p*-aminobenzoic acid-free, isosmolal broth medium that is low in concentration of glucose (0.0014 M—the only fermentable carbohydrate) and ligands capable of binding metallic cations (phosphate, 0.002 M). The medium, dubbed synthetic amino acid medium (SAAM), is well buffered with 2-(*N*-morpholino) propane sulfonic acid (0.018 M) and 2-amino-2-(hydroxymethyl)-1,3-propanediol (0.042 M). Commercially available sterile solutions, as used in compounding tissue culture media, conveniently provide accessory growth substances (Eagle's basal medium vitamins solution, 100X) and most of the amino acids (Eagle's minimal essential medium amino acids solution with D-glutamine, 50X). Fumaric acid, pyruvate, uracil, L-asparagine, L-proline, L-cysteine, glycine, and metallic cations (Mg^{++}, Fe^{++}, Mn^{++}) complete the list of ingredients. Overnight cultures of *S. aureus* in SAAM broth regularly attained densities of 5×10^8 to 1×10^9 per ml.

Bacteria. For testing, the isolates of "methicillin"-resistant *S. aureus* were grown overnight in 10 ml of SAAM broth. On the basis of direct counts in a Petroff-Hausser chamber, dilutions were prepared in SAAM to yield a suspension containing 100,000 cocci per 0.9 ml of medium.

Antimicrobial agents. Antimicrobial agents were supplied by: Bristol Laboratories, Syracuse, N.Y. (dicloxacillin, sodium, lot 68F2966); Chas. Pfizer & Co., Inc., Brooklyn, N.Y. (benzylpenicillin, potassium, lot 7Y601; bacitracin A, lot OX190); Ciba Pharmaceutical Co., Summit, N.J. (rifampin, Lapetit lot T/389); Eli Lilly &

[1] Visiting Microbiologist for the year 1969 from the Institute of Medical Microbiology, University of Zurich, Zurich, Switzerland.

Co., Indianapolis, Ind. (cephalothin, sodium, lot XS 1620 AMX; cephalexin, lot XT 1611 AMX; cycloserine, lot P86379; vancomycin sulfate, lot 302-392 AD 15 TB); Hoffman-La Roche, Inc., Nutley, N.J. (coumermycin A_1, lot C77798); Leo Laboratories, Ltd., Hayes, Middlesex, England (fusidic acid, sodium, batch 193); Schering Corp., Bloomfield, N.J. (gentamicin sulfate, batch 3765-139); and Wyeth Laboratories, Inc., Philadelphia, Pa. (nafcillin, sodium, control no. W673827).

Working solutions of each antimicrobial agent were prepared in SAAM to contain 1.0, 0.1, and 0.01 μmole/ml. Additional working solutions of some agents were made to provide concentrations of special interest (Fig. 4) or of therapeutic relevance, i.e., concentrations attainable in the blood of patients with doses practical in therapy (*see* Fig. 5). After transfer of 0.1-ml portions of these working solutions to snap-top, polycarbonate tubes (11 X 75 mm), the tubes were stored at −20 C until used.

Special problems arose with some antimicrobial agents. (i) The molecular weight of vancomycin is not precisely known but falls in the range of 3,200 to 3,500; for preparation of solutions of vancomycin, a molecular weight of 3,350 was assumed. (ii) The commercially available gentamicin (3) consists of gentamicin C_1 (molecular weight, 477.6), gentamicin C_2 (molecular weight, 463.6), and gentamicin C_{1a} (molecular weight, 449.6); a molecular weight of 463.6 was taken as a reasonable average for work with gentamicin. (iii) The addition of four parts (by weight) of *N*-methylglucamine per part of coumermycin A_1 largely offsets the tendency of coumermycin to form stable colloids in aqueous systems (according to Stanley Gould, Hoffman-La Roche, Inc.); nevertheless, to obtain a working solution containing 1.0 μmole (1,132 μg) of coumermycin A_1 per ml, it was necessary to use SAAM with 25% dimethylsulfoxide (v/v). (iv) The problems of solution and maintenance of rifampin in the reduced form were met as previously described (9).

Tests. Mechanical (vortex) mixing was carried out as soon as inoculation was completed and was repeated after 12 hr of incubation at 37 C and again after 48 hr when the tests were concluded. Growth, evident as turbidity or a fall in *p*H, or as both, was assumed to indicate resistance.

From each of the tubes without visible growth,

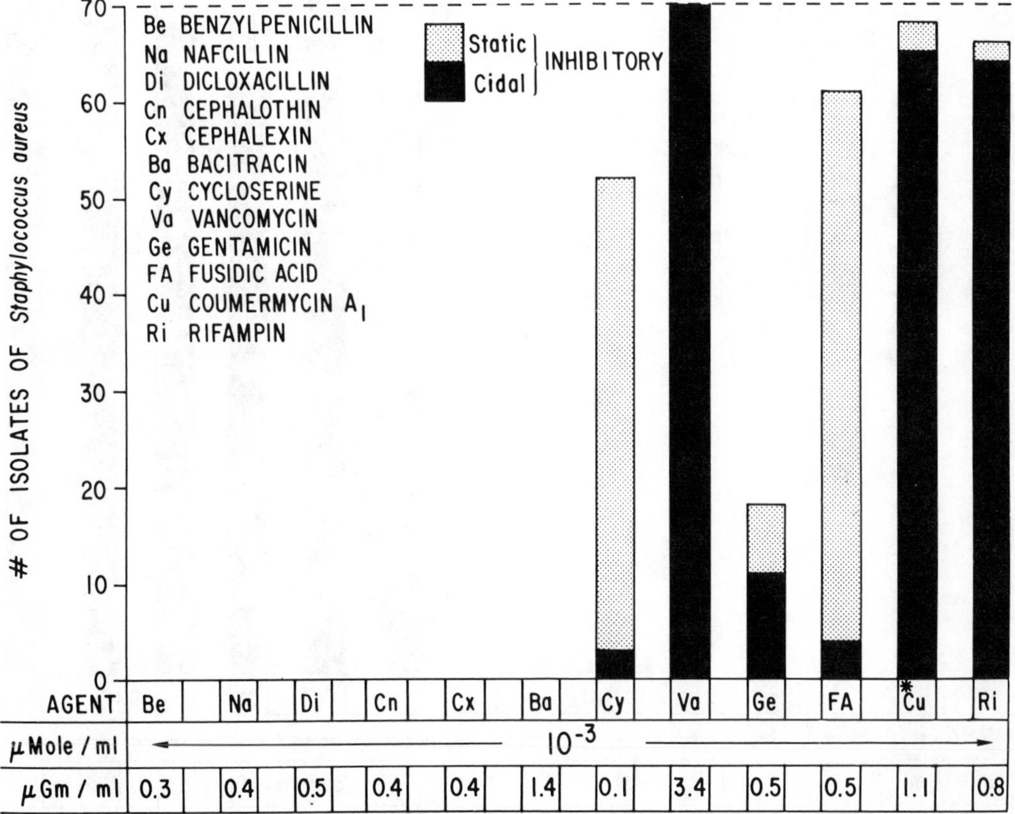

Fig. 1. *Effect of a concentration of* 10^{-3} *μmole/ml of 12 antimicrobial agents on 70 clinical isolates of "methicillin"-resistant Staphylococcus aureus. Vancomycin, fusidic acid, coumermycin* A_1, *and rifampin were the most active agents.*

0.05 ml (5% of the volume) was removed and deposited on a one-fifth sector of a 100 X 15 mm agar plate [commercial tryptic digest of casein-papaic digest of soybean broth base, without glucose, plus 0.9% Ionagar No. 3 (Colab Laboratories, Inc., Chicago Heights, Ill.)]. After 48 hr at 37 C in a moist-air candle jar, growth was considered to indicate a bacteriostatic effect, and lack of growth a bactericidal effect, in the original broth test.

RESULTS

Molecule for molecule, the penicillins, cephalosporins, and bacitracin were markedly less active against "methicillin"-resistant *S. aureus* than were any of the other agents tested (Fig. 1-3). Indeed, none of the penicillins in concentrations ranging from 10^{-3} to 10^{-1} μmole/ml kept any of the strains from growing. The cephalosporins were also inactive at 10^{-3} μmole/ml (Fig. 1). However, cephalothin at 10^{-2} μmole/ml prevented growth of 7 (10%) strains (Fig. 2), and growth of 12 (17%) strains was prevented at 10^{-1} μmole/ml (Fig. 3). Cephalexin was less active. Although bacitracin was inactive at 10^{-3} and 10^{-2} μmole/ml (Fig. 1 and 2, respectively), 63 (90%) strains were susceptible to 10^{-1} μmole (141.3 μg) per ml (Fig. 3).

Of the remaining agents, vancomycin was the most active; it had a bactericidal effect on all 70 strains in the range from 10^{-3} to 10^{-1} μmole/ml (Fig. 1-3). The other antimicrobial agents, in order of descending activity, were: coumermycin A_1, rifampin, fusidic acid, gentamicin, and cycloserine. Cycloserine was primarily bacteriostatic at all concentrations, as was fusidic acid at 10^{-3} μmole (0.5 μg) per ml (Fig. 1). When active, gentamicin, coumermycin A_1, and rifampin were primarily bactericidal, as was fusidic acid at concentrations $\geqslant 10^{-2}$ μmole (5.2 μg) per ml (Fig. 2).

Lower concentrations of vancomycin, coumermycin A_1, and rifampin were tested, enabling extension of molecular comparison by

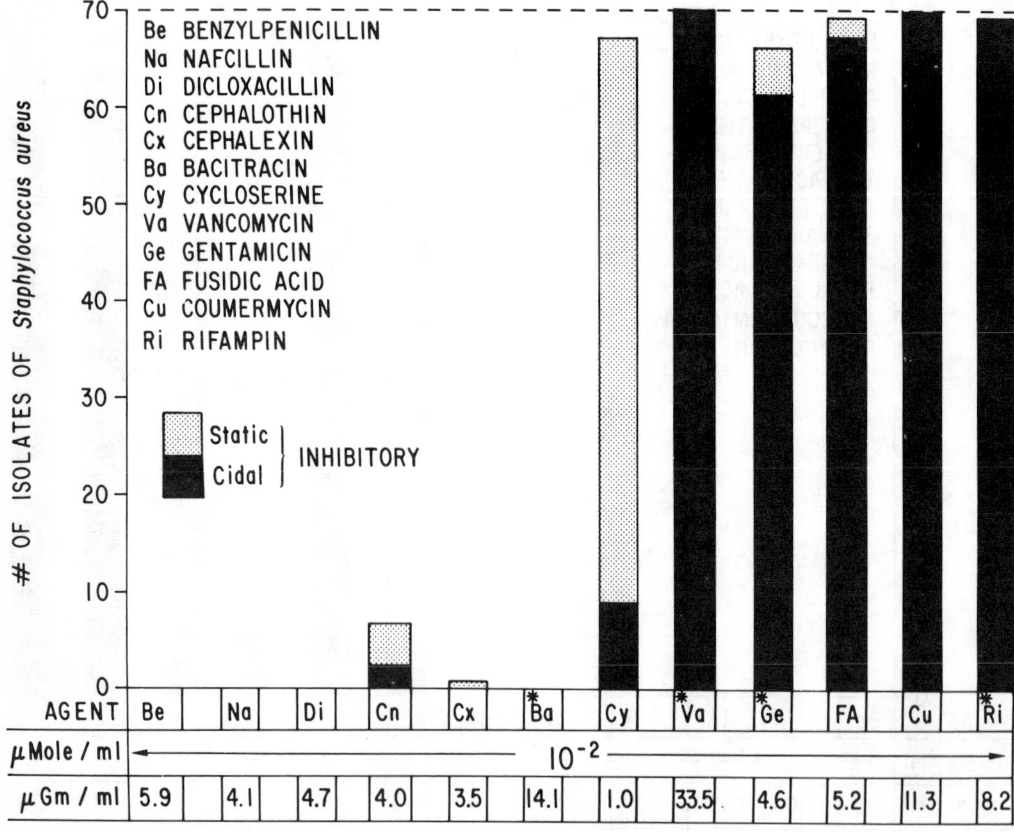

Fig. 2 *Effect of a concentration of 10^{-2} μmole/ml of 12 antimicrobial agents on 70 isolates of "methicillin"-resistant Staphylococcus aureus. In addition to vancomycin, fusidic acid, coumermycin A_1, and rifampin, gentamicin and cycloserine were significantly active.*

decimally decremental steps from 10^{-1} through 10^{-5} µmole/ml (Fig. 4). At 10^{-5} µmole/ml, vancomycin was without effect, coumermycin A_1 was bacteriostatic to four isolates, and rifampin inhibited seven isolates and was lethal to one additional strain. With a 10-fold increase in concentration to 10^{-4} µmole/ml, both vancomycin and rifampin were primarily bacteriostatic against 68 and 67 strains, respectively; 41 isolates were susceptible to coumermycin A_1.

The results at practical concentrations, i.e., concentrations attainable in the blood of patients, are plotted in Fig. 5. None of the penicillins tested, and only cephalothin of the two cephalosporins, displayed significant activity, even at 0.5 µmole (198.2 µg of cephalothin) per ml. Sixty-six (94%) of the isolates were affected by cephalothin, and the effect was bactericidal against 47 (67%) of these isolates. Cycloserine [0.25 µmole (25.5 µg) per ml] was active against 69 (98%) isolates; however, the effect was bacteriostatic for 43 (61%) strains. Vancomycin [10^{-2} µmole (33.5 µg) per ml] and fusidic acid [10^{-1} µmole (51.7 µg) per ml] were uniformly bactericidal. One isolate was resistant to rifampin (10^{-2} µmole (8.2 µg) per ml], whereas the other 69 (99%) were killed by this agent. Coumermycin A_1 [10^{-3} µmole (1.1 µg) per ml] was bactericidal to 65 (93%) isolates and bacteriostatic to three additional isolates. Gentamicin [10^{-2} µmole (4.6 µg) per ml] was active against 66 (94%) isolates and its effect was bactericidal against 61 (87%) of these strains.

Among the 70 tests (350 tubes) carried out with rifampin, there were five instances of skipped tubes.

DISCUSSION

Of the antimicrobial agents that act by interfering with synthesis of bacterial cell walls, only cephalothin and cycloserine displayed

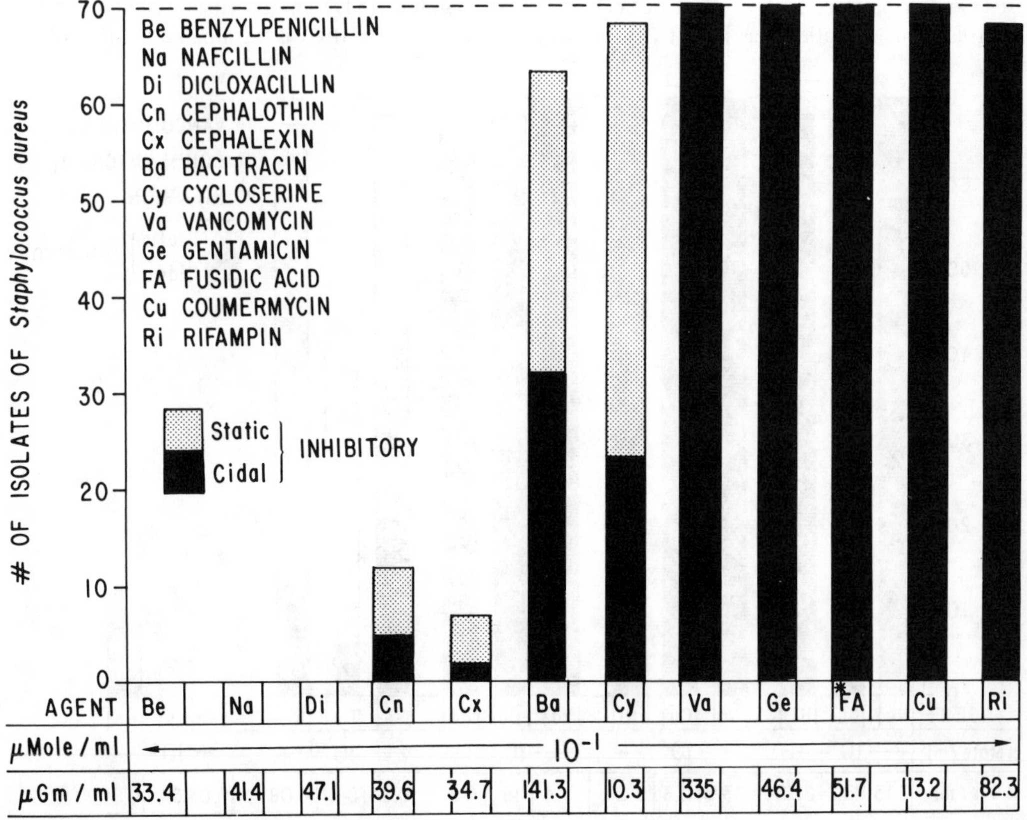

Fig. 3 *Effect of a concentration of* 10^{-1} *µmole/ml of 12 antimicrobial agents. At this concentration, bacitracin joined cycloserine, vancomycin, gentamicin, fusidic acid, coumermycin* A_1*, and rifampin in being active against most of the 70 strains of "methicillin"-resistant Staphylococcus aureus that were tested.*

significant activity in vitro against the 70 strains of "methicillin"-resistant *S. aureus* that were tested. Cephalothin has been given to humans in the treatment of infections caused by "methicillin"-resistant staphylococci (1), but the results were not encouraging. It may be that heterogeneity of resistance, as is demonstrable in the laboratory, is of clinical consequence. That is, in the patient, as in the test tube, only a portion of the staphylococcal cells will be inhibited by a given concentration of cephalothin; some cocci will be quite tolerant, not merely surviving but actually proliferating in the presence of the agent. Moreover, the doses employed in treating patients infected with "methicillin"-resistant staphylococci have not always been massive–to the degree of attaining 0.5 μmole (198.2 μg) per ml of blood. There is no reported clinical experience on the use of cycloserine in the therapy of infections caused by "methicillin"-resistant staphylococci.

Vancomycin, on the other hand, has been used, and it appears to be fully as effective in the treatment of patients as its activity in vitro would suggest. However, vancomycin is inconvenient to use, there are side effects and allergic reactions, and staphylococci that are resistant to vancomycin do cause illness (8).

In earlier work in which an agar-dilution method of testing was used (10), all of 20 strains of "methicillin"-resistant *S. aureus* were inhibited by gentamicin. The larger experience reported herein, based on broth-dilution testing, showed that 66 of 70 (94%) strains were susceptible to concentrations of gentamicin that are of clinical relevance, a result in keeping with previous work with unselected clinical isolates of *S. aureus* (9).

Resistance to fusidic acid, in the form of growth from an inoculum of undefined size in the presence of ⩾ 16 μg in a complex protein-rich culture medium, appears to occur in nature, and may or may not, arise during therapy (4). By our testing, as defined above, all 70 isolates of "methicillin"-resistant *S. aureus* that were examined suffered a bactericidal effect from 0.10 μmole (51.7 μg) of fusidic acid per ml, a concentration that is attainable in the blood

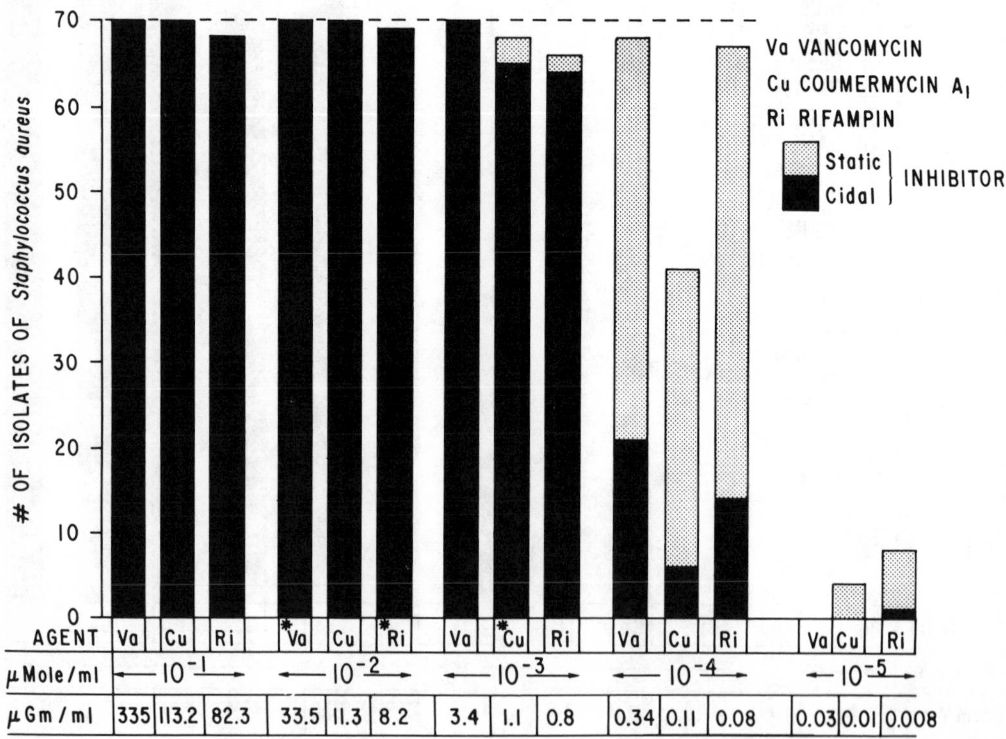

Fig. 4 *Effect of decimally decremental concentrations of vancomycin, coumermycin A_1, and rifampin against 70 clinical isolates of "methicillin"-resistant Staphylococcus aureus. The remarkable potency of rifampin and coumermycin A_1 is apparent.*

during treatment (13). Although our inoculum of 10^5 cells must be considered large, heterogeneity in regard to susceptibility and resistance might still be present; we did not carry out population analyses.

Clinical application of coumermycin A_1 to the treatment of infections caused by *S. aureus* has yet to be reported. With the development of a formulation that appears to assure adequate absorption after peroral administration (from data supplied by William B. Abrams, Department of Clinical Pharmacology, Hoffman-La Roche, Inc.), clinical trial is feasible.

In our previous work, as in the present study, rifampin was the most potent of 20 antimicrobial agents tested simultaneously and identically for effectiveness against 62 clinical isolates of *S. aureus* (9). Neither in our earlier report (9) nor in the earlier work of others (5, 6, 14, 15) was the so-called skipped-tube phenomenon noted. McCabe et al. (12) and Kunin et al. (11) reported observing growth in the presence of concentrations of rifampin that were greater than those which inhibited *S. aureus* in the same test series.

However, in the work reported herein, there were five instances of skipped tubes among 70 tests (350 tubes) with rifampin. Several differences in our methods of testing are pertinent. In 1967, the inoculum used was 10^4 cocci per ml, the culture medium was complex and contained protein, and incubation was overnight with subculture of about 0.8% of the volume of the test broth to agar (incubated overnight). In the present work, the inoculum was 10^5 cocci per ml, the culture medium was totally defined and free from protein, and incubation was for 48 hr with subculture of 5% of the volume of the test broth to agar (incubated 48 hr).

To assess the reproducibility of skipped

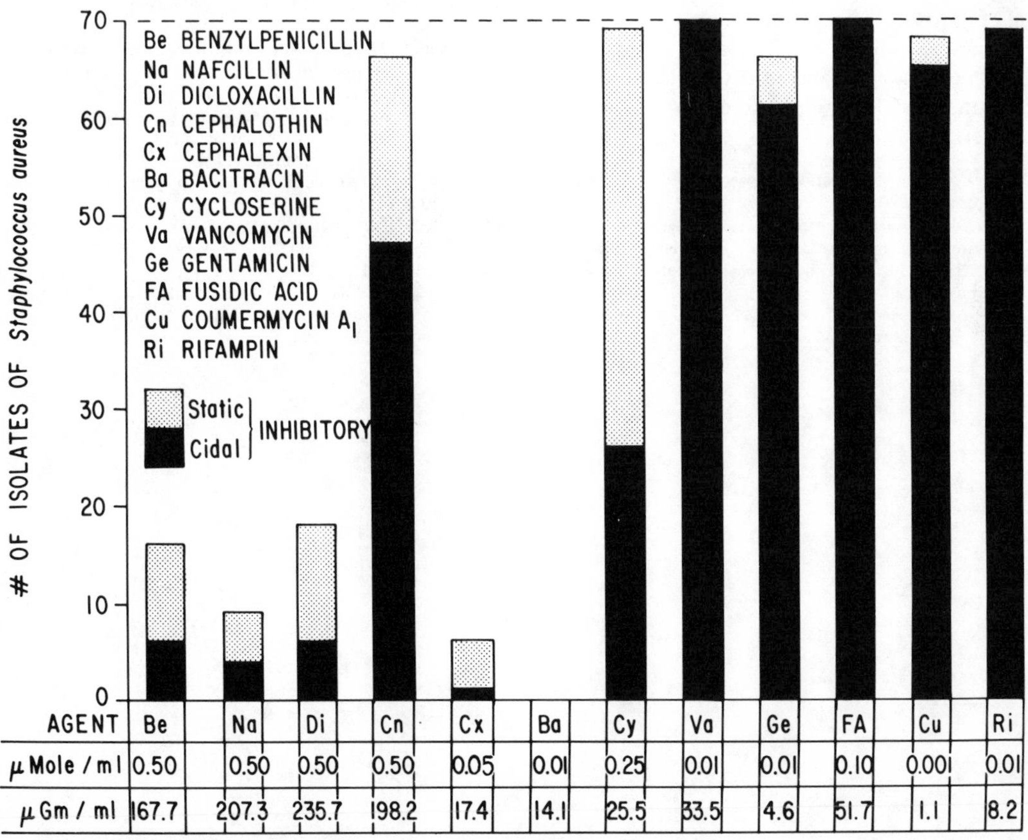

AGENT	Be	Na	Di	Cn	Cx	Ba	Cy	Va	Ge	FA	Cu	Ri
µMole / ml	0.50	0.50	0.50	0.50	0.05	0.01	0.25	0.01	0.01	0.10	0.001	0.01
µGm / ml	167.7	207.3	235.7	198.2	17.4	14.1	25.5	33.5	4.6	51.7	1.1	8.2

Fig. 5 *Activity of 12 antimicrobial agents in concentrations that are attainable in the blood of patients against 70 isolates of "methicillin"-resistant Staphylococcus aureus. Significant susceptibility to cephalothin, cycloserine, vancomycin, gentamicin, fusidic acid, coumermycin A_1, and rifampin is evident. Of these agents, cephalothin has been used with doubtful success, whereas vancomycin appears to be clinically effective.*

tubes, the five strains associated with skipping in the tests reported herein were set up in quintuplicate, exactly as the tests of this report. In addition, a second series was set up, also in quintuplicate, but with an inoculum of 10^6 cocci per ml. There were no skipped tubes among the 125 tubes inoculated with 10^5 cocci per ml; skipping did occur with three of the five strains when the inoculum was 10^6 cocci per ml.

Staphylococci that skipped to grow out at concentrations higher than those inhibitory in the same series of tubes were tested for susceptibility to rifampin. All grew in all concentrations of rifampin that were tested [maximum: 0.10 μmole (82.3 μg) per ml]. Apparently, among *S. aureus* cells in nature there are a very few that are natively resistant to rifampin, perhaps on the order of 1 in 10^8, as suggested by Kunin et al. (11). Certainly, the frequency of occurrence of this phenomenon is not nearly so great as that claimed by McCabe and co-workers (12). Further, we cannot concur in the dour outlook expressed by the latter authors with respect to the probable utility of rifampin in the treatment of infections caused by non-acid-fast bacteria.

ACKNOWLEDGMENTS

This work was supported by grants-in-aid from Abbott Laboratories and Schering Corp., and by Public Health Service Grant AI 08955-01 from the National Institute of Allergy and Infectious Diseases.

The essential technical assistance of Fred L. Atchison and Molly Yim is sincerely appreciated.

LITERATURE CITED

1. Benner, E. J., and F. H. Kayser. 1968. Growing clinical significance of methicillin-resistant *Staphylococcus aureus*. Lancet **2**:741–744.
2. Benner, E. J., and V. Morthland. 1967. Methicillin-resistant *Staphylococcus aureus*: antimicrobial susceptibility. N. Engl. J. Med. **277**:678–680.
3. Cooper, D. J., H. M. Mariagliano, M. D. Yudis, and T. Traubel. 1969. Recent developments in the chemistry of gentamicin. J. Infec. Dis. **119**:342–344.
4. Evans, R. J., and P. M. Waterworth. 1966. Naturally-occurring fusidic acid resistance in staphylococci and its linkage to other resistances. J. Clin. Pathol. **19**:555–560.
5. Furesz, S., V. Arioli, and R. Pallanza. 1966. Antimicrobial properties of new derivatives of rifamycin SV. Antimicrob. Agents Chemother.–1965, p. 770–777.
6. Furesz, S., and R. Scotti. 1960. Rifomycin. IV. Some laboratory and clinical experiences with rifomycin B. Antibiot. Ann. 1959-1960, p. 285–292.
7. Garrod, L. P. 1968. Methicillin-resistant staphylococci. Lancet **2**:871.
8. Hoeprich, P. D. 1961. Intracommunity admixture of human associated staphylococci. J. Lab. Clin. Med. **57**:781–806.
9. Hoeprich, P. D. 1968. Susceptibility of staphylococci to new antimicrobial agents. Antimicrob. Agents Chemother.–1967, p. 697–704.
10. Hoeprich, P. D. 1969. Gentamicin versus *Staphylococcus aureus*. J. Infec. Dis. **119**:391–392.
11. Kunin, C. M., D. Brandt, and H. Wood. 1969. Bacteriologic studies of rifampin, a new semisynthetic antibiotic. J. Infec. Dis. **119**:132–137.
12. McCabe, W. R., and V. Lorian. 1968. Comparison of the antibacterial activity of rifampicin and other antibiotics. Amer. J. Med. Sci. **256**:255–265.
13. Stewart, G. T. 1964. Steroid antibiotics. Pharmakotherapia **2**:137–148.
14. Timbal, M. T. 1960. Rifomycin. II. Antibacterial activity of rifomycin B. Antibiot. Ann. 1959-1960, p. 271–276.
15. Timbal, M. T., R. Pallanza, and S. Furesz. 1963. Further experimental data on the bactericidal activity of rifamycin SV. International symposium on rifamycins. Chemotherapia **7**:213–219.

Antimicrobial Agents and Chemotherapy—1969

Interaction of Various Tetracyclines with Metallic Cations in Aqueous Solutions as Measured by Circular Dichroism

L. A. MITSCHER, A. C. BONACCI, B. SLATER-ENG, A. K. HACKER, and T. D. SOKOLOSKI

Divisions of Natural Products, Chemistry, and Pharmaceutics, College of Pharmacy, The Ohio State University, Columbus, Ohio 43210

Circular dichroism measurements provide a sensitive optical probe for simultaneous measurement of the molecular conformation of the tetracycline A and BCD rings in dilute aqueous solutions under a variety of conditions. Binding with various metal ions alters the conformation of both chromophoric regions; thus, circular dichroism is a powerful tool for studying this important property. A variety of tetracyclines were studied at various *p*H levels in the presence of various molecular proportions of Ca^{++}, Mg^{++}, Cu^{++}, and Al^{+++} ions. No binding could be detected spectroscopically below *p*H 3. Al^{+++} ions bind to the BCD ring juncture at *p*H 4.9, and all four ions bind to this region at *p*H 7.5. The conformational change measured shows a stoichiometric ratio of 1 metal ion per tetracycline molecule at *p*H 4.9. At *p*H 9.3, a level at which the dimethylamino group is partially deprotonated, a stoichiometry of 2 metal ions per tetracycline molecule is observed, and the A ring chromophore changes in addition to the BCD chromophore changes. When glycine buffers are used at *p*H 7.5 in the presence of Al^{+++} ions, the resulting complex is quite insoluble. Tetracyclines oxygenated at C_5 (oxytetracycline, *α*-6-deoxyoxytetracycline, 6-methylene-oxytetracycline) are more complicated in their response to changing *p*H and the addition of various ions, and considerable data have been accumulated indicating that *α*-6-deoxyoxytetracycline is different in its binding response at high *p*H levels as compared with 6-demethyl-6-deoxytetracycline. The chemical and possible clinical implications of these findings are briefly discussed.

Basically, circular diochroism is differential absorption of right and left circularly polarized light, and as such is sensitive to the direction and intensity of twisting of the chromophores in a molecule such as the tetracyclines. There are two chromophores present in the clinically useful tetracyclines, one in the A ring which consists of the tricarbonyl system ranging from C_1 to C_3, and the other consisting of the lower peripheries of rings B and C and the aromatic D ring. The A ring chromophore gives rise to an intense band at 262 nm whose degree of twisting is determined, in our view, by the degree of interaction between the diaxial C_4 dimethylamino function and the 12a-hydroxyl group. The BCD chromophore is dominated to a major extent by the configuration of the 5a-hydrogen atom. The circular dichroism spectra can be best interpreted upon the basis of the fundamental rule of circular dichroism measurements that the two dominating influences are the absolute configuration of the molecule and the solution conformation (13).

Preliminary evidence presented in 1968 (13) suggested that chelation occurred at the BCD chromophore first, upon raising the *p*H, and then the A ring chromophore became involved if the *p*H was raised high enough to liberate the dimethylamino function from its acid addition salt. The differential nature of circular dichroism measurements, as opposed to ultraviolet measurements, provides a powerful tool for measuring these effects of metal ions at various *p*H levels when changes in chirality (twisting) of the chromophores are involved. The following new evidence confirms and extends our previously expressed views.

MATERIALS AND METHODS

The tetracycline derivatives used in this study are the purest samples available and were obtained through the generosity of J. M. Boothe, Jr., of Lederle Laboratories and W. Celmer of Charles Pfizer & Co. Sample preparation and the technique of measurement have been described in detail previously (13).

RESULTS AND DISCUSSION

In the tetracycline series, chelation mimics the ultraviolet effects of adding base (bathochromic effect). That this occurs at lower *p*H values when ions are present reveals the greater efficiency of chelation (4). This property is a convenient phenomenon for examining this effect.

Al^{+++} ion is especially convenient for illustrating the range and nature of our extensive findings with a wide variety of ions and tetracyclines. At *p*H 4.9, Al^{+++} ion clearly chelated with 6-deoxy-6-demethyltetracycline, whereas Ca^{++} and Mg^{++} ions give only little evidence for binding at this *p*H. In solutions with this degree of acidity, the dimethylamino group is strongly protonated and would not be expected to play a role in the chelation, and the circular dichroism spectrum clearly shows this (Fig. 1). Only the peaks associated with the BCD chromophore are affected, for the band at 262 nm is essentially unchanged. Adding increasing increments of metal ion to a fixed concentration of tetracycline enables one to estimate the relative equivalency. When this is done, the spectral changes are mainly accomplished when a molar ratio of 1 Al^{+++} ion per tetracycline molecule is reached (Fig. 2). One site requires one ion to accommodate it. This does not reflect on the question of how many tetracyclines can interact with a given molecular equivalent of ion, but rather just how many ions are involved with a single tetracycline.

Al^{+++} ion forms octahedral complexes (7), and Ni^{++} ion was shown by reflectance measurements to do so with tetracyclines at *p*H 7. Only oxygen atoms were involved in the complex (1). A 2:1 ratio of tetracyclines to metal was involved. This is illustrated schematically in Fig. 3. Our data can be rationalized satisfactorily with this model. It will be noted that the A ring is not

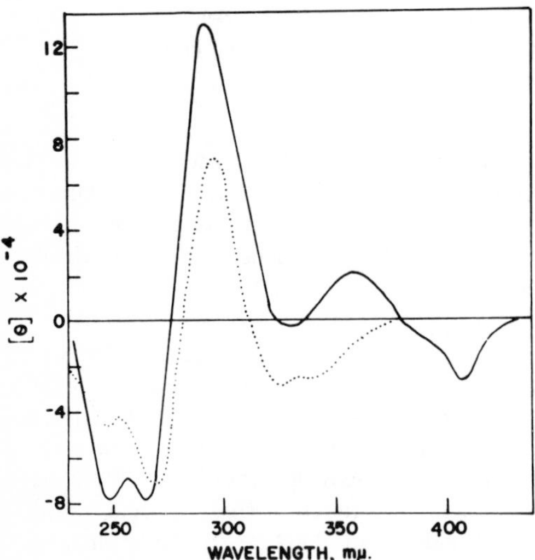

Fig. 1. *Circular dichroism spectrum of 6-demethyl-6-deoxytetracycline at pH 4.9 with (solid line) and without (dotted line) four molar equivalents of Al^{+++} ion.*

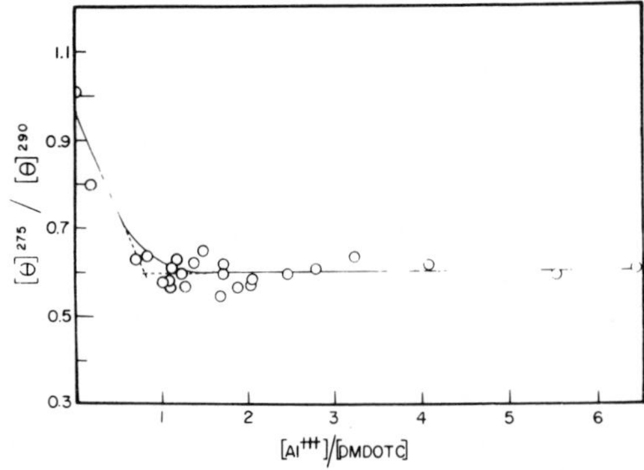

Fig. 2. *Ratios analysis of the interaction of Al^{+++} ions with 6-demethyl-6-deoxytetracycline at pH 4.90.*

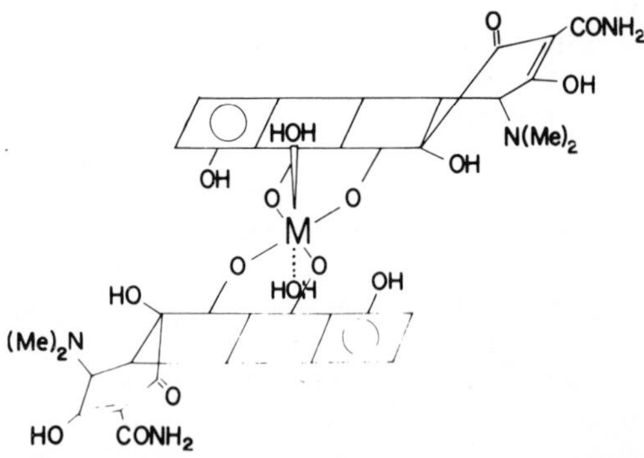

Fig. 3. *Schematic representation of octahedral tetracycline-metal chelate.*

hindered in this view. Up to this point, our findings agree with numerous previous studies, and the effects noted provide a satisfactory rationale for the spectroscopic findings. Some studies, but by no means all, have suggested a possible second ion binding site, although the evidence was never wholly convincing (1, 2, 4-6, 8, 9, 17).

At *p*H 9.23, a level at which the dimethylamino group is substantially deprotonated and can participate in binding, the spectra (Fig. 4) show that both chromophoric regions are involved. Equivalency analysis (Fig. 5) demonstrated that the complex formation was largely completed when 2 moles of metal ion had been added. Two sites require two metal ions. The spectrum also demonstrated the interesting finding that both sites compete for the first mole of metal ion added. This is not revealed by the corresponding ultraviolet spectra. These findings provide a very satisfactory rationale for the previous reports on this vexatious problem, for until now, this *p*H dependence seems not to have been generally recognized. The special utility of circular dichroism measurements in allowing one to see both ends of the molecule simultaneously makes this an especially useful tool. Similar data for other tetracyclines and Mg^{++} or Ca^{++} ions will be reported in a more detailed communication. Acidification of solutions containing the metal chelates in each case restores the typical nonchelated tetracycline spectrum. This indicates that the reactions observed are rapidly reversible and that no permanent or deep-seated structural change has occurred.

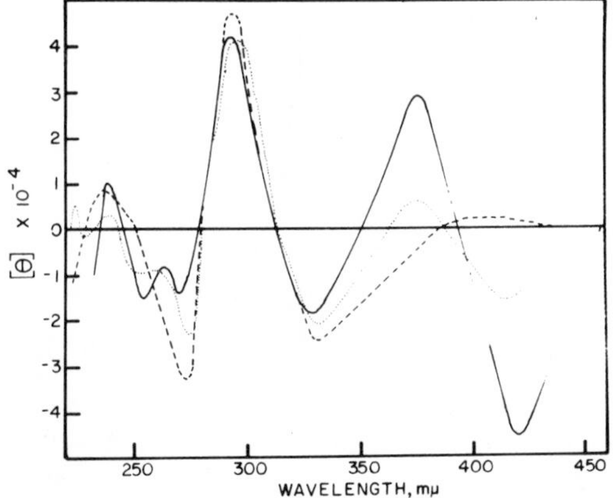

Fig. 4. *Circular dichroism spectra of 6-demethyl-6-deoxytetracycline at pH 9.23. No* Al^{+++} *(---). One molar equivalent* Al^{+++} *(····). Two molar equivalents (——).*

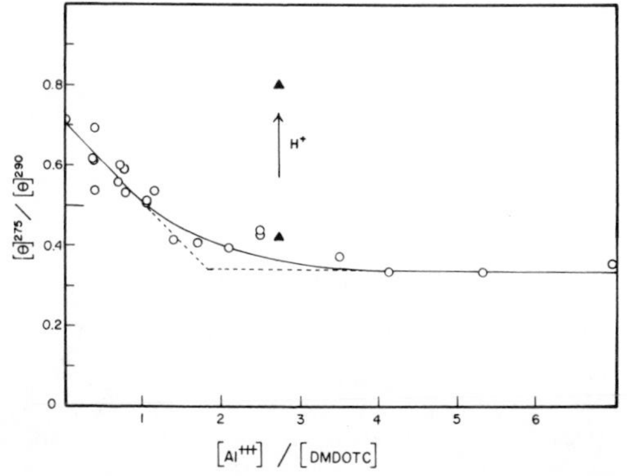

Fig. 5. *Ratios analysis of the interaction between* Al^{+++} *ions and 6-demethyl-6-deoxytetracycline at pH 9.23.*

At *p*H 7.5, which represents a more realistic solution *p*H from a biological standpoint, the BCD chelate is formed and the A ring complex is less evident (Fig. 6). This is consistent with expectation, for the dimethylamino group is more protonated than at *p*H 9.23. There is a definite buffer effect which was noted while making these measurements and which is potentially quite significant. When glycine buffers are used, the spectra have the characteristic diffuse nature which Urry and Ji recently noted for suspensions (19). In this case, the solutions became quite turbid. When phosphate, citrate, or acetate buffer was used, this effect was not

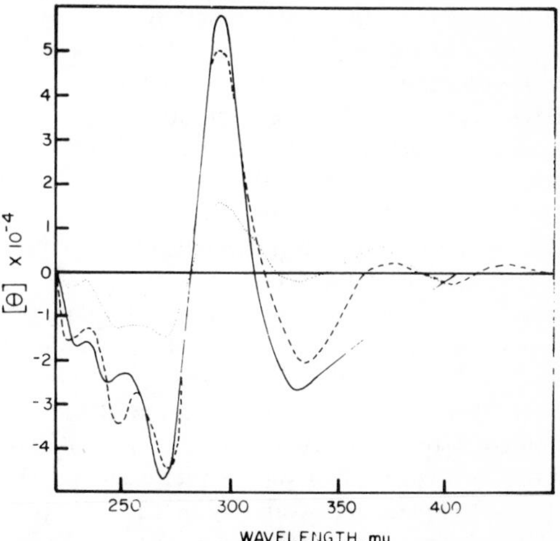

Fig. 6. *Circular dichroism spectra of 6-demethyl-6-deoxytetracycline at pH 7.53. No* Al^{+++}*, glycine buffer (——). Three molar equivalents of* Al^{+++}*, glycine buffer (····) or phosphate buffer (---).*

seen. Al^{+++} ion formulations increase tetracycline solubility at intermediate *p*H levels (14, 15), although they prevent one's obtaining useful drug concentrations in the blood when the preparations are given orally (16). It is possible to rationalize this anomaly by suggesting that the glycinate ion replaces the waters (or one of them) of hydration in the complex. This would neutralize the complex and lead to the formation of an insoluble ternary complex. Presumably this would occur at the *p*H of the intestine, and subsequent precipitation of the drug on the intestinal wall could account for the clinical observations. Recently, Japanese workers have reached the same conclusion, based on data from a different experimental system (10, 11). Interestingly, their intestinal wall penetration studies showed an ion equivalency of 1:1 at *p*H 6 and 2:1 at *p*H 8. These studies are in mutual agreement, and furthermore our theoretical analysis provides a satisfactory rationale for the Japanese findings. At *p*H 8, in the presence of two molar equivalents of Ca^{++} ions, the tetracycline disappeared from the intestinal lumen but did not appear in the blood on the opposite side of the mucosa. Histological examination showed that the tetracycline was adhering to the intestinal wall.

Recent reports (12, 17) that 6-deoxyoxytetracycline gives adequate concentrations in the blood even when taken orally with cation-rich foods such as milk, although not with Al^{+++} ions, led us to study oxytetracycline derivatives as well. It is clear that both 6-methyleneoxytetracycline and 6-deoxyoxytetracycline possess solution conformations identical with that of oxytetracycline and the other clinically useful tetracyclines in acidic solutions, and that they are also incapable of detectable metal ion binding under these conditions (Fig. 7 and 8). When the *p*H is raised to approximately 9, all three 5-hydroxylated tetracyclines possess very similar circular dichroism curves, suggesting similar conformations, and they all form similar complexes with Ca^{++} and Mg^{++} ions. 6-Deoxyoxytetracycline, then, does complex with these metals. Its improved oral activity in the presence of ions must be explained in some other fashion. The simplest explanation would be that the complex is simply more soluble under the conditions extant in the intestine. This possibility is currently under investigation in our laboratory. It is also possible that binding to proteins in tissue depots may be more readily reversible with this substance than with the other clinically useful tetracyclines.

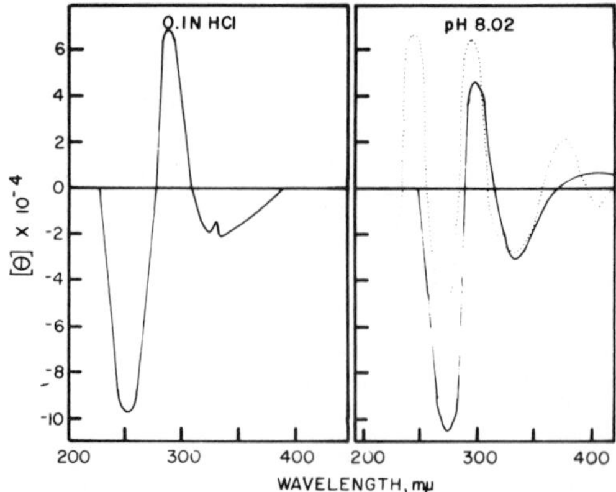

Fig. 7. *Circular dichroism spectra of 6-methyleneoxytetracycline at pH 1 and 8.02 in the presence (dotted lines) and absence (solid lines) of Mg^{++} ions. At pH 1, both curves overlap completely.*

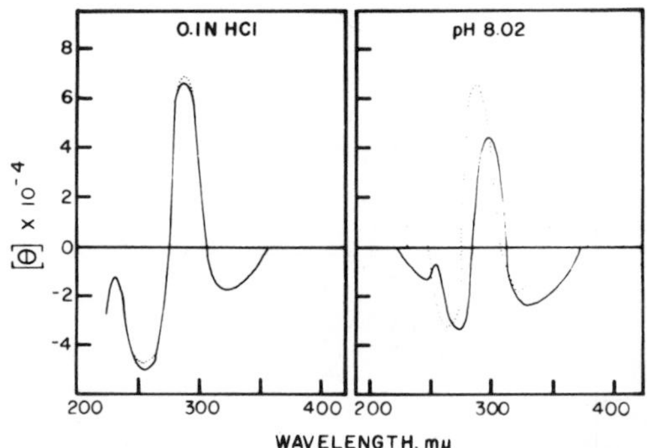

Fig. 8. *Circular dichroism spectra of α-6-deoxyoxytetracycline at pH 1 and 8.02 in the presence (dotted lines) and absence (solid lines) of Mg^{++} ions.*

ACKNOWLEDGMENTS

We are grateful for support of this work provided by Public Health Service grant AI-09247 from the National Institute of Allergy and Infectious Diseases. Figures 1-6 are reproduced by permission of the editors of *Infection and Immunity*, whose cooperation is appreciated.

LITERATURE CITED

1. Baker, W. A., Jr., and P. M. Brown. 1966. Metal binding in tetracyclines. Cobalt (II) and nickel (II) complexes. J. Amer. Chem. Soc. **88**:1314–1317.
2. Benet, L. Z., and J. E. Goyan. 1965. Determination of the stability constants of tetracycline complexes. J. Pharm. Sci. **54**:983–987.
3. Colaizzi, J. L., A. M. Knevel, and A. N. Martin. 1965. Biophysical study of the mode of action of tetracycline antibiotics. J. Pharm. Sci. **54**:1425–1436.

4. Conover, L. H. 1956. Progress in the chemistry of oxytetracycline and related compounds. Chem. Soc. (London), Spec. Publ. No. 5, p. 48–81.
5. Doluisio, J. T., and A. N. Martin. 1963. Metal complexation of the tetracycline hydrochlorides. J. Med. Chem. **6**:16–20.
6. Doluisio, J. T., and A. N. Martin. 1963. The binding of tetracycline analogs to conalbumin in the absence and presence of cupric ions. J. Med. Chem. **6**:20–23.
7. Graddon, D. P. 1968. An introduction to co-ordination chemistry, 2nd ed. Pergamon Press, New York.
8. Ibsen, K. H., M. R. Urist, and S. Uyeno. 1962. Calcium and magnesium complexes with oxytetracycline. Proc. Soc. Exp. Biol. Med. **109**:797–801.
9. Ishidate, M., and T. Sakaguchi. 1955. Metal chelate compounds of tetracycline derivatives. I. Aureomycin. Chem. Pharm. Bull. (Tokyo) **3**:147–155.
10. Kakemi, K., H. Sezaki, H. Ogata, and T. Nadai. 1968. Absorption and excretion of drugs. XXXVI. Effect of Ca^{++} on the absorption of tetracycline from the small intestine (1). Chem. Pharm. Bull. (Tokyo) **16**:2200–2205.
11. Kakemi, K., H. Sezaki, M. Hayashi, and T. Nadai. 1968. Absorption and excretion of drugs. XXXVII. Effect of Ca^{++} on the absorption of tetracycline from the small intestine (2). Chem. Pharm. Bull. (Tokyo) **16**:2206–2212.
12. Migliardi, J. R., and M. Schach von Wittenau. 1967. Pharmacodynamic properties of doxycycline in man. Proc. 5th Int. Congr. Chemother. **4**:165–171.
13. Mitscher, L. A., A. C. Bonacci, and T. D. Sokoloski. 1969. Circular dichroism and solution conformation of the tetracycline antibiotics. Antimicrob. Agents Chemother.–1968, p. 78–86.
14. Remmers, E. G., W. C. Barringer, G. M. Sieger, and A. P. Doerschuk. 1964. Metal-acid complexes with members of the tetracycline family. J. Pharm. Sci. **53**:1452–1456.
15. Remmers, E. G., W. C. Barringer, G. M. Sieger, and A. P. Doerschuk. 1964. Metal-acid complexes with members of the tetracycline family. II. Development of stable preconstituted parenteral formulations. J. Pharm. Sci. **53**:1534–1536.
16. Remmers, E. G., W. C. Barringer, G. M. Sieger, N. Anagnostakos, J. J. Corbett, and A. P. Doerschuk. 1965. Metal-acid complexes with members of the tetracycline family. III. Summary of blood level studies. J. Pharm. Sci. **54**:49–52.
17. Rosenblatt, J. E., J. E. Barrett, J. L. Brodie, and W. M. M. Kirby. 1967. Comparison of in vitro activity and clinical pharmacology of doxycycline with other tetracyclines. Antimicrob. Agents and Chemother.–1966, p. 134–141.
18. Sakaguchi, T., M. Toma, T. Yoshida, H. Omura, and H. Takasu. 1958. Metal chelate compounds with tetracycline derivatives. VII. The structure of tetracycline chelates. Chem. Pharm. Bull. (Tokyo) **6**:1–9.
19. Urry, D. W., and T. H. Ji. 1968. Distortions in circular dichroism patterns of particulate (or membranous) systems. Arch. Biochem. Biophys. **128**:802–807.

Antimicrobial Agents and Chemotherapy—1969

Conformation of Macrolide Antibiotics

IV. Nuclear Magnetic Resonance, Circular Dichroism, and Chemical Studies of Erythromycin Derivatives

T. J. PERUN, R. S. EGAN, P. H. JONES, J. R. MARTIN, L. A. MITSCHER, and B. J. SLATER

Scientific Divisions, Abbott Laboratories, North Chicago, Illinois 60064, and College of Pharmacy, Ohio State University, Columbus, Ohio 43210

A conformation of the aglycone ring of erythromycin is proposed which is based on nuclear magnetic resonance (NMR), circular dichroism, and chemical data. This solution conformation is essentially identical with that present in the crystal as determined by a previous X-ray crystallographic study. High-resolution NMR studies of many erythromycin aglycone derivatives have shown that all such compounds have basically the same solution conformation, which is stable over a large temperature range. The mutual relationships of protons on the aglycone ring were determined by consideration of their coupling constants. Circular dichroism studies of the same compounds in hydroxylic solvents have confirmed their conformational homogeneity, and have provided evidence for the orientations of the ketone and lactone functions. Application of various theoretical rules for interpretation of circular dichroism curves indicate that the orientations in solution are the same as in the crystal. Chemical reactions in the erythronolide B series that are readily explained by the proposed conformation include the internal hemiketal and enol ether formation of the hydroxyl on C-6 with the ketone on C-9, and the highly specific eliminations involving hydroxy groups on C-6 and C-11.

Macrolide antibiotics have been the subject of many studies involving their chemical structure, biochemistry, and mechanism of action (18), and new members of this series are continually being discovered. Biochemical studies have elucidated portions of the biosynthetic pathway, especially in the erythromycin series (6, 15, 16), and studies of the mode of action of macrolides have reached the molecular level (14, 25). These studies have reached the point of sophistication where information about the three-dimensional shape of macrolide molecules in solution is necessary in order to dilineate more of the details of the mode of action, and to allow rational design of chemical reactions for purposes of structural modification and possibly synthesis.

The three-dimensional shape of the 14-membered macrolide erythromycin A in the crystal form was reported in 1965 from results of an X-ray crystallographic study (11). Although the shape of a molecule in the crystal state is often a good approximation to its conformation in solution, this correlation is somewhat uncertain with potentially flexible structures such as the large ring present in erythromycin. At about the same time that the crystal structure of erythromycin was determined (and also its complete stereochemistry), Celmer reported the configurations of aglycone carbon atoms of oleandomycin which were identical with the related carbon atoms in the erythromycin molecule (2, 3). In some pioneering work on macrolide conformations, he used the stereochemistry in proposing an aglycone conformation in solution based on the best steric fit of these highly substituted rings to the strain-free conformation of the 14-membered ring hydrocarbon cyclotetradecane (4).

This strain-free ring conformation (as proposed by Dale) is taken from the diamond-lattice arrangement of carbon atoms (7), as shown in Fig. 1. Celmer found, by fitting the oleandomycin ring to this conformation, that there was only one arrangement of atoms that minimized internal steric interactions and ring strain. Furthermore, he found that this arrange-

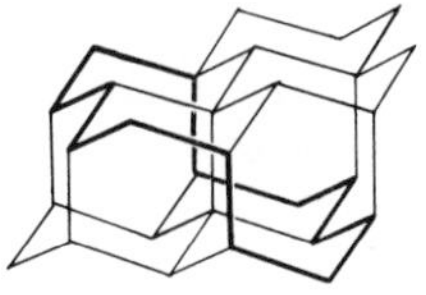

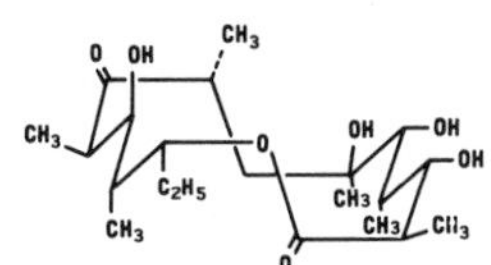

Fig. 1. *Celmer-Dale diamond-lattice conformation.*

ment closely approximated the crystal structure of erythromycin A.

Examination of models shows that this proposed conformation of the oleandomycin and erythromycin aglycones is very similar to that found in the crystal except for the orientations of the lactone grouping, and the tertiary hydroxyl at C-6. We have evidence to show that the orientations of these groups, in solution, are identical with those in the crystal. Furthermore, it appears that a better conformational model for the 14-membered macrolide ring is not the diamond-lattice arrangement of Dale, but rather an alternate diamond-lattice arrangement as shown in Fig. 2. Although this alternate diamond-lattice structure is not the lowest energy conformation of the cyclic hydrocarbon, it serves as a useful model for the 14-membered lactone of macrolides.

The use of this alternate conformational model correctly orients the lactone grouping as it is in the crystal, and requires less reorganization of the C-6 to C-8 region to place the C-6 hydroxyl in a proximate relationship with the ketone. A model of the macrolide ring in this diamond-lattice arrangement shows the presence of serious 1,3-diaxial interactions between the methyls on C-4, C-6, and C-8 (see Ia in Fig. 3). These steric interactions are all relieved when the tertiary hydroxyl is reoriented toward the ketone (as shown by Ib in Fig. 3), and probably provide the driving force for this internal rearrangement. In the conformation used by Celmer the 1,3-diaxial interaction between methyls on C-4 and C-6 remains unrelieved.

The conformation we have proposed for the aglycone of erythromycin is shown in Fig. 4. This conformation fits all experimental data we have obtained from nuclear magnetic resonance (NMR), circular dichroism, and chemical studies.

MATERIALS AND METHODS

All compounds discussed have been the subject of earlier publications regarding their isolation or synthesis. NMR spectra were recorded by use of Varian Associates HA-100 and HR-220 spectrometers, in deuterated solvents. Circular dichroism spectra were obtained with a Durrum-Jasco model ORD/UV-5 instrument equipped with a CD attachment and operating at ambient temperature in spectra-grade methanol solvent.

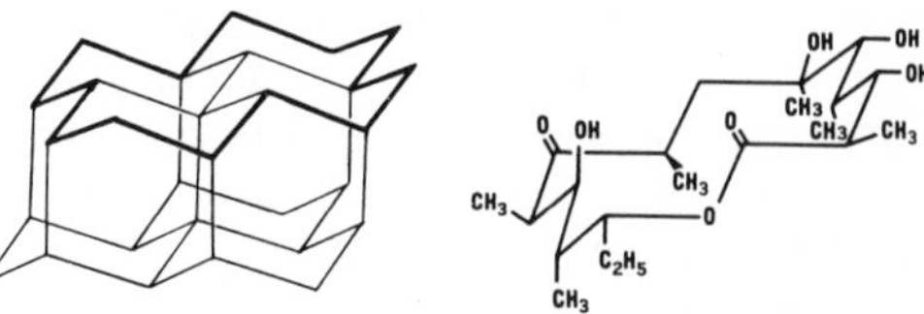

Fig. 2. *Alternate diamond-lattice conformational model.*

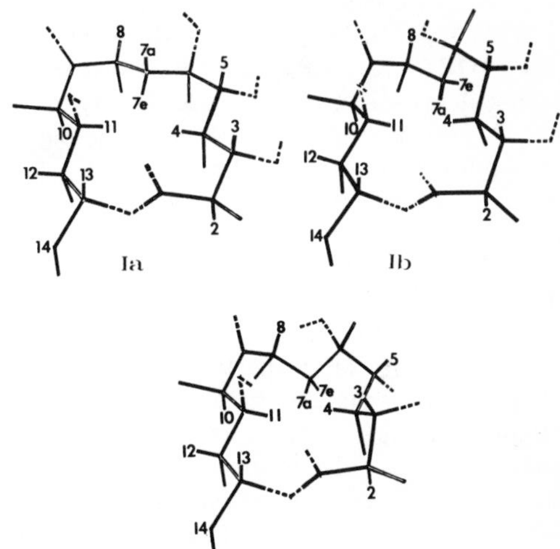

Fig. 3. *Framework molecular models of macrolide aglycone conformation.*

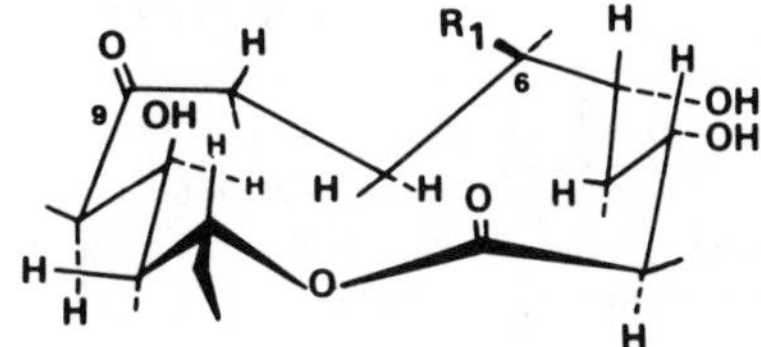

Fig. 4. *Aglycone conformation showing proton relationships.*

RESULTS

NMR studies. Earlier attempts to analyze the 60-MHz NMR spectra of macrolide antibiotics were not very successful because of the large number of protons in the molecule and the complex nature of the spectra with many overlapping resonances. NMR spectra were used to some extent in making configurational assignments of the anomeric protons of the attached glycoside moieties (3, 5, 10, 11, 15, 20).

In our studies of the chemistry and biochemistry of the erythromycins, we were fortunate to obtain a number of aglycone derivatives which were well suited for detailed analysis with an HA-100 NMR spectrometer. Some of the structures included in this NMR study (Fig. 5) were erythronolide B (R_1 = OH; R_2, R_3, R_4 =H), 6-deoxyerythronolide B (R_1, R_2, R_3, R_4 = H), their various acetate esters (R_2, R_3, R_4 = H or acetyl), 3-*0*-α-L-mycarosylerythronolide B (R_1 = OH; R_2, R_4 = H; R_3 = mycarose), 5-*0*-β-D-desosaminylerythronolide B (R_1 = OH; R_3, R_4 = H; R_2 = desosamine), and the parent antibiotics erythromycin A, B, and C. Also included were various 9-dihydroerythronolide structures (23). Initial work centered on the most deshielded protons in the NMR spectra, and some of these results have been reported in an earlier communication (22). More recent studies with 220-MHz spectra have confirmed these initial results and have made possible a complete analysis of all of the ring protons in these aglycones. The results of these analyses show that there is an invariance of nearly all of the coupling constants of related protons throughout the series, indicating that all aglycones are conformationally homogeneous. This was further supported by the observation that the coupling constants did not change when the spectra were obtained in solvents of differing polarity or over a wide temperature range. If the coupling constants represented a time-averaged spectrum of different conformers in a rapid equilibrium, the populations of these conformers would have been changed by these differences in solvent polarity or solution temperature.

Having been convinced that we were observing a single stable conformation of the aglycone ring, the values of the coupling constants were used to determine vicinal proton relationships by use of the well-known Karplus equation which correlates the magnitude of a coupling constant with the dihedral angle of the vicinal protons (13). The vicinal proton relationships determined from the observed coupling constants correspond closely with those for vicinal protons on a cyclohexane ring. Examination of the diamond-lattice arrangement of a 14-membered ring shows that these same vicinal proton relationships are found in the larger ring (axial-axial, axial-equatorial, etc.) with the additional proviso that in these larger rings a new equatorial-equatorial relationship is possible in which the protons are 180° opposed. Applying the general rule that coupling constants with a large absolute value (9 to 14 Hz) correspond to axial-axial or equatorial-equatorial (opposed) relationships and that coupling constants with small values (1 to 5 Hz) correspond to equatorial-axial proton relationships made it apparent that the observed coupling constants in the erythronolide ring corresponded closely to the proton relationships in the modified diamond-lattice conformation shown in Fig. 4.

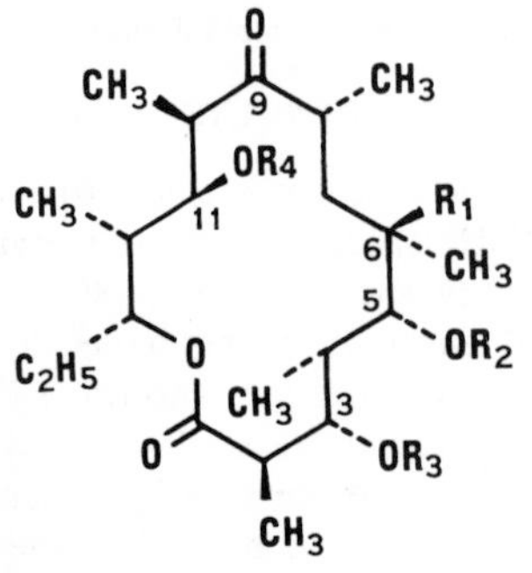

It should be pointed out that the Karplus equation gives two possible solutions for the angle between vicinal protons, and this factor has to be considered when one examines the experimental coupling constants in a large potentially flexible ring such as that present in macrolide structures. When other factors such as steric interactions, solvent effects on chemical shifts (8, 23), and chemical reactivity are considered, however, only one solution produces a conformation consistent with all of the data.

The coupling constants and corresponding proton relationships for 6-deoxyerythronolide B are given in Table 1. This compound has been chosen as a model structure for the erythronolide series of compounds because it contains the greatest number of vicinal protons on the 14-membered ring, thus providing the most complete experimental data.

When the NMR study was expanded to include the parent erythromycins, a remarkably consistent pattern of coupling constants was observed for nearly all protons equivalent to those in the aglycone series. The only coupling constant which was changed significantly was $J_{4,5}$, which had increased from ∿ 2.5 Hz in the unsubstituted aglycones to ∿ 7 Hz in the erythromycins. This we explained as a result of a slight

Fig. 5. *Erythromycin derivatives.*

Table 1. *Nuclear magnetic resonance data for 6-deoxyerythronolide B (in deuteriochloroform)*

Proton coupling	Coupling constant	Proton relationship
$J_{2,3}$	10.5	a,a
$J_{3,4}$	<1	a,e
$J_{4,5}$	2.5[a]	e,a
$J_{5,6}$	4.7[a]	a,e
$J_{6,7a}$	4.7	e,a
$J_{6,7e}$	10.2	e,e (opposed)
$J_{7a,7e}$	15.0	
$J_{7a,8}$	13.0	a,a
$J_{7e,8}$	4.0	e,a
$J_{10,11}$	2.0	a,e
$J_{11,12}$	10.2	e,e (opposed)
$J_{12,13}$	1.5	e,a
$J_{13,14a}$	8.9	
$J_{13,14e}$	4.6	
$J_{14e,14a}$	14.0	

[a] The earlier values reported for these coupling constants (22) have been reversed.

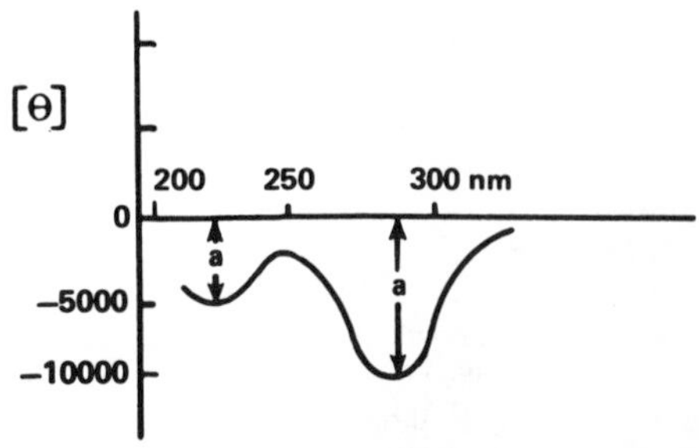

Fig. 6. *Circular-dichroism curve of erythromycin B.*

rotation of the C-4, C-5 bond to relieve interactions between the bulky sugar groups on C-3 and C-5 (22). The value of $J_{4,5}$ in other aglycones also substituted on C-3 and C-5 showed the same increase. Thus, the triacetate esters of erythronolide B and 6-deoxyerythronolide B had $J_{4,5}$ values of 5.5 and 6 Hz, respectively. The NMR spectra of monoglycoside derivatives 3-mycarosylerythronolide B and 5-desosaminylerythronolide B were analyzed and values for $J_{4,5}$ were found to be 3.6 and 2.5 Hz, respectively. These values are in accord with the interpretation of results on the basis of interactions between substituents on both C-3 and C-5. Part Ic of Fig. 3 shows the effect of increasing the angle between H_4 and H_5. The conformation of the rest of the ring remains unchanged.

When the C-3 and C-5 hydroxyls were tied up as part of a cyclic ester, such as a 3,5-phenylboronate, the $J_{4,5}$ value remained the same as the unsubstituted aglycone. This is a result of the fact that the hydroxyl groups are locked in a parallel orientation with each other, which also is the most favorable orientation in the unsubstituted aglycones.

Circular-dichroism studies. Further data supporting the aglycone conformation shown in Fig. 4 came from circular-dichroism studies of erythromycins and erythronolides (17). Figure 6 shows the circular-dichroism curve of erythromycin B, which is representative of the curves of most compounds in this series. Over 50 members of the erythromycin-erythronolide series of compounds have been studied, and the signs and relative intensities of the curves agree with one another quite closely for members of similar structure and chromophoric type. This observation provides further support for the conformational homogeneity of the macrolide ring.

Table 2 lists the circular-dichroism data for a number of compounds studied. The separation of ketone and lactone functions in the erythronolide ring allowed the conformational analysis of both groupings from their circular dichroism data. This information was complementary to the NMR data because the NMR spectra alone could not be used to determine the orientations of the ketone or lactone groupings.

Figure 7 shows a representation of the proposed macrolide conformation as viewed down the axis of the carbonyl group. Application of the well-known octant rule for ketones as modified for moderately twisted systems (9) predicts a negative circular dichroism curve for this conformation, and this is what is observed. The most dominant influence on the sign determination is the methyl on the C-8 α carbon which lies in a negative octant. Its counterpart on C-10 lies very nearly in a nodal plane and, therefore, does not contribute significantly to the sign determination.

The tertiary hydroxyl on C-6 stands in a positive octant and would be expected to diminish somewhat the negativity of the ketone peak. It is significant that removal of this function in 6-deoxyerythronolide B does indeed result in increased negative molecular amplitude. The C-11 hydroxyl is in a negative octant, and increasing its bulk by acetylation would be expected to increase the negative amplitude, as indeed it does in 11-acetylerythronolide B.

The circular-dichroism curve for the lactone chromophore was analyzed by use of both the

Table 2. *Circular-dichroism data of erythromycin and erythronolide derivatives*

Compound	Ketone amplitude	Lactone amplitude
Erythromycin A	290 nm ([θ]-6,600, a-80.5)	220 nm ([θ]-2,400, a-29.3)
Erythromycin B	288 nm ([θ]-10,800, a-131.8)	210 nm ([θ]-3,600, a-43.9)
Erythronolide B	290 nm ([θ]-12,200, a-148.8)	210 nm ([θ]-4,300, a-52.5)
11-*O*-acetylerythronolide B	292 nm ([θ]-17,900, a-218.1)	218 nm ([θ]-3,200, a-39.1)
6-Deoxyerythronolide B	290 nm ([θ]-17,500, a-213.5)	215 nm ([θ]-5,400, a-65.9)
3-*O*-α-L-mycarosylerythronolide B	292 nm ([θ]-13,500, a-164.7)	205 nm ([θ]-4,200, a-51.2)
5-*O*-β-D-desosaminylerythronolide B	290 nm ([θ]-13,700, a-167.1)	220 nm ([θ]-5,700, a-69.5)

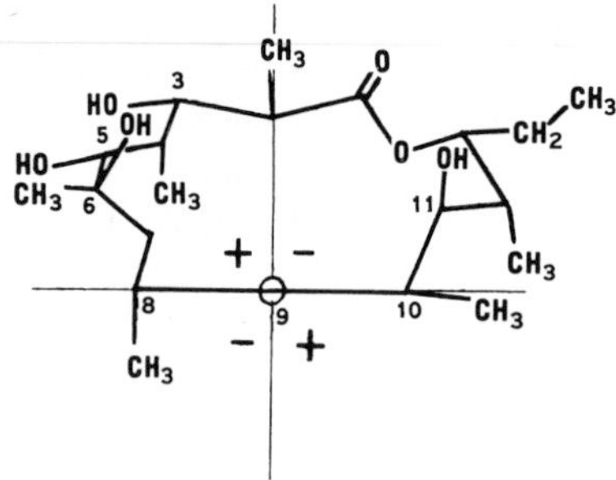

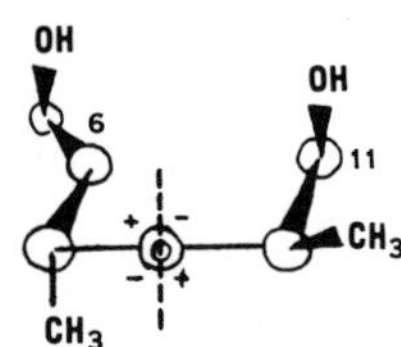

Fig. 7. *Carbonyl octant projection of the erythronolide conformation.*

chirality rules of Beecham et al. (1, 19, 26) and the modified lactone sector rule (12, 24). Both of these analyses lead to a predicted negative sign for the lactone curve when the lactone is oriented as in Fig. 4, whereas the alternate lactone orientation would lead to a predicted positive sign.

The chirality rule is the most straightforward of the two to apply to the macrolide ring, and it is represented in Fig. 8. In this analysis, the lactone ring is considered as a twisted chromophore, and the helicity of the twist is determined by whether the carbon β to the carbonyl lies above or below the plane of the lactone function. In the macrolide case, carbon-3 lies below the lactone plane and thus imparts a negative sign to the circular-dichroism curve.

Fig. 8. *Application of the chirality rule for lactones to the erythronolide conformation.*

It should be noted, however, that previous circular dichroism and optical rotatory dispersion studies have involved only lactones with *syn* geometries, whereas in the larger macrolide rings the energetically favored geometry is s-*anti.* One would expect the same electronic effects to be operating in these larger rings, but since these are the first known examples of large ring lactones studied, one must be cautious in applying rules developed from smaller rings.

Chemical studies. Earlier studies of the acid-catalyzed degradation of the erythronolide ring showed that a facile reaction occurs between the C-6 hydroxyl and the C-9 ketone, leading to the formation of an enol ether III (Fig. 9), presumably via the intermediacy of a hemiketal II (21). Although this reaction was first observed in aqueous and nonaqueous acid solutions, it has recently been found that the reaction will occur even in weakly basic solvents when catalyzed by the presence of a strong acid salt of the weak base. Although this reaction by itself does not provide conclusive evidence for a proximate relationship between the C-6 hydroxyl and the C-9 ketone, it is explained very nicely by the conformation determined from spectroscopic data, which shows the close spatial arrangement of the two reacting groups. This reaction can occur with little change in the conformation of the rest of the ring.

Circular dichroism studies of this internal rearrangement were carried out by adding a drop of acid to the methanol solution of various erythromycins and erythronolides. Table 3

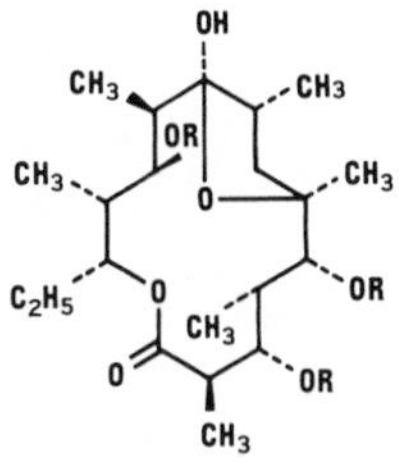

II III IV

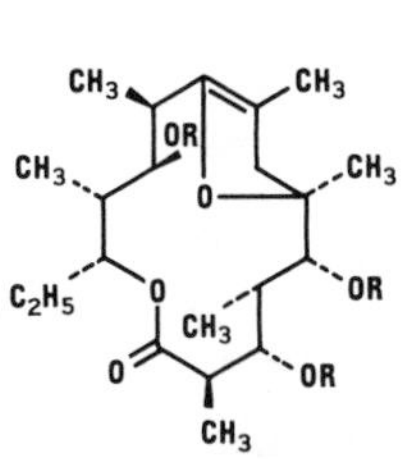

Fig. 9. *Erythronolide hemiketal and enol ether structures.*

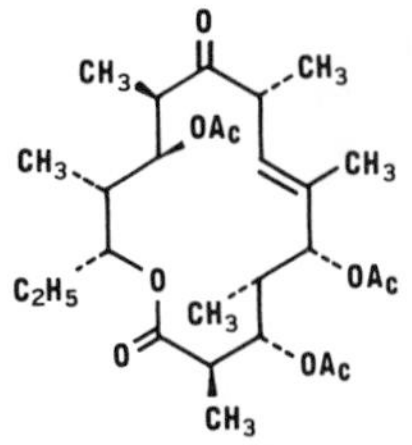

Table 3. *Effect of catalytic hydrochloric acid on the 290 nm absorption curve*

Compound	[θ] Reduction	Time
	%	*min*
Erythromycin B	92	1
Erythronolide B	90	1
3,5,11-Tri-*O*-acetylerythronolide B	89	2
6,7-Anhydro-3,5,11-tri-*O*-acetylerythronolide B	0	120
6-Deoxyerythronolide B	31	1
3,5,11-Tri-*O*-acetyl-6-deoxyerythronolide B	0	120

shows the effect of added acid on the ketone absorption curve. Compounds containing a C-6 hydroxyl exhibit a very rapid loss of the ketone absorption, whereas compounds without the C-6 hydroxyl show either no change in the spectrum or, in the case of 6-deoxyerythronolide B, a partial loss of ketone absorption (presumably by some other type of reaction). The lactone absorption is relatively unaffected by this acid treatment.

Elimination of the C-6 hydroxyl with thionyl chloride (21) occurs specifically endocyclic and in high yield to give the 6,7-anhydro derivative in most erythronolide compounds (see IV or V in Fig. 10). This *trans* double bond is accommodated very nicely by the erythronolide conformation, as no new steric interactions are introduced and the vinyl proton remains as the internally positioned substituent. In a C-8 epimeric erythronolide derivative (VII) under the same reaction conditions, only exocyclic elimination occurs, giving VIII (Fig. 11). The apparent reason for this complete change in reaction specificity is the presence of severe steric interactions between methyls on C-6 and C-8 in the transition state leading to an endocyclic double bond in the 8-epi compound.

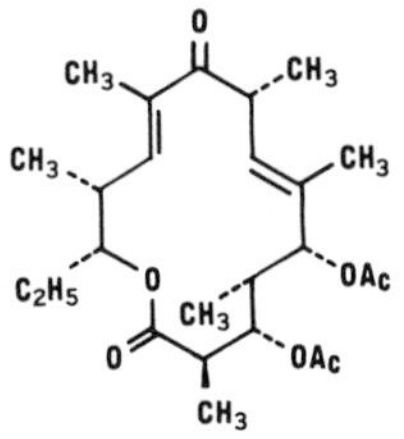

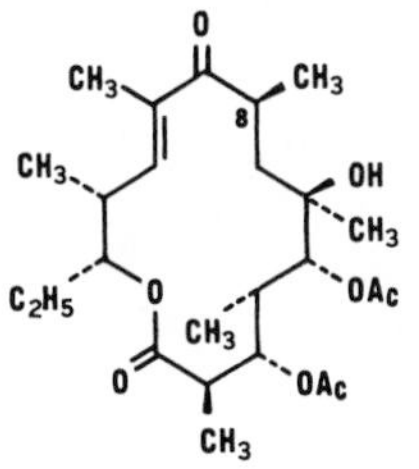

V VI

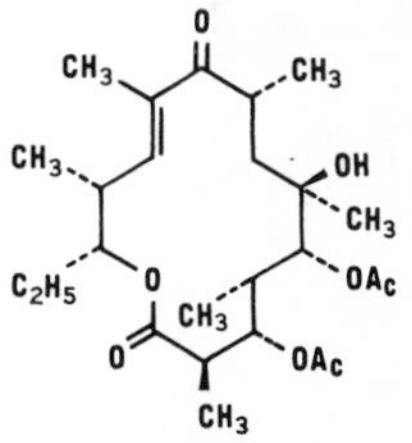

Fig. 10. *Anhydroerythronolides.*

VII 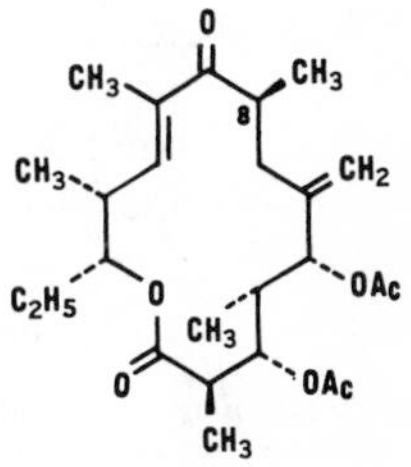 VIII

Fig. 11. *8-Epi-anhydroerythronolides.*

The elimination of the 11-acetoxyl to give the 10,11-anhydro compound V (21) is facilitated by the *trans* geometry of the leaving groups in the erythronolide conformation. The conformation again allows the formation of the 10,11-double bond because no new steric interactions are introduced and the internally positioned group is a hydrogen. Both the 6,7- and 10,11-double bonds are accommodated without any conformational change in the rest of the ring. NMR studies on anhydro derivatives have confirmed their conformational similarity to the saturated compounds. Table 4 shows the coupling constants for two anhydroerythronolide B derivatives IV and V.

It is quite probable that the conformation shown in Fig. 4 is not unique to the erythro-

Table 4. *Nuclear magnetic resonance data for 6,7-anhydro-3,5,11-tri-O-acetylerythronolide B (IV) and 6,7-10,11-dianhydro-3,5-di-O-acetylerythronolide B (V), in deuteriobenzene*

Proton coupling	Coupling constants (Hz)	
	IV	V
$J_{2,3}$	10.5	11.0
$J_{3,4}$	<1	<1
$J_{4,5}$	1.8	2.8
$J_{5,7}$ (allylic)	1.0	1.3
$J_{7,8}$	11.2	10.1
$J_{10,11}$	1.5	–
$J_{11,12}$	10.0	9.0
$J_{12,13}$	1.0	2.0

mycin series, but is also the most stable conformation of other 14-membered macrolides. Slight changes in the conformation may occur because of substitution changes, but the overall conformation should remain the same. Preliminary NMR studies of some aglycone derivatives of the 14-membered macrolide lankamycin have given evidence for an identical conformation. Studies of the conformation of oleandomycin are currently underway by Egan and Bauer.

ACKNOWLEDGMENTS

That portion of this work carried out at Ohio State University was supported by Public Health Service grant AI-09247 from the National Institute of Allergy and Infectious Diseases.

We sincerely thank Lewis W. Cary of Varian Associates for obtaining 220-MHz NMR spectra. Special thanks are due Robert Oheim of Abbott Laboratories for his efforts in photographing the molecular models of the conformations.

LITERATURE CITED

1. Beecham, A. F. 1968. Optical activity and lactone ring configurations. Tetrahedron Lett., p. 3591–3594.
2. Celmer, W. D. 1965. Macrolide stereochemistry. I. The total absolute configuration of oleandomycin. J. Amer. Chem. Soc. **87**:1797–1799.
3. Celmer, W. D. 1965. Macrolide stereochemistry. II. Configurational assignments at certain centers in various macrolide antibiotics. J. Amer. Chem. Soc. **87**:1799–1801.
4. Celmer, W. D. 1966. Biogenetic, constitutional, and stereochemical unitary principles in macrolide antibiotics. Antimicrob. Agents Chemother.–1965, p. 144–156.
5. Celmer, W. D., and D. C. Hobbs. 1965. The α-L and β-D-pyranose linkages in oleandomycin. Carbohyd. Res. **1**:137–144.
6. Corcoran, J. W. 1964. The biosynthesis of erythromycin. Lloydia (Cincinnati) **27**:1–14.
7. Dale, J. 1963. Macrocyclic compounds. III. Conformation of cycloalkanes and other flexible macrocyles. J. Chem. Soc. (London), p. 93–111.
8. Demarco, P. V. 1969. Pyridine solvent shifts in the NMR analysis of erythromycin algcones. Tetrahedron Lett., p. 383–386.
9. Djerassi, C., and W. Klyne. 1962. Optical rotatory dispersion: Application of the octant rule to some structural and stereochemical problems. J. Chem. Soc. (London), p. 4929–4950.
10. Grisebach, H., and W. Hofheinz. 1963. Die Konfiguration der Glykosidbindungen in Erythromycin und Magnamycin. Chem. Ber. **96**:2867–2869.
11. Harris, D. R., S. G. McGeachin, and H. H. Mills. 1965. The structure and stereochemistry of erythromycin A. Tetrahedron Lett., p. 679–685.
12. Jennings, J. P., W. Klyne, and P. M. Scopes. 1965. Optical rotatory dispersion. XXIV. Lactones. J. Chem. Soc. (London), p. 7211–7229.
13. Karplus, M. 1963. Vicinal proton coupling in nuclear magnetic resonance. J. Amer. Chem. Soc. **85**:2870–2871.
14. Mao, J. C-H., and M. Putterman. 1969. The intermolecular complex of erythromycin and ribosome. J. Mol. Biol. **44**:347–361.
15. Martin, J. R., T. J. Perun, and R. L. Girolami. 1966. Studies on the biosynthesis of the erythromycins. I. Isolation and structure of an intermediate glycoside, 3-α-L-mycarosylerythronolide B. Biochemistry **5**:2852–2856.
16. Martin, J. R., and W. Rosenbrook. 1967. Studies on the biosynthesis of the erythromycins. II. Isolation and structure of a biosynthetic intermediate, 6-deoxyerythronolide B. Biochemistry **6**:435–440.
17. Mitscher, L. A., B. J. Slater, T. J. Perun, P. H. Jones, and J. R. Martin. 1969. The conformation of macrolide antibiotics. III. Circular dichroism and the conformation of erythromycins. Tetrahedron Lett., p. 4505–4508.
18. Morin, R., and M. Gorman. 1967. Macrolide antibiotics. Kirk-Othmer encyclopedia of chemical technology, 2nd ed. **12**:632–661.
19. Okuda, T., S. Harigaya, and A. Kiyomoto. 1964. Studies on optical rotatory dispersion of five-membered sugar lactones: configuration and the sign of an optical rotatory dispersion curve. Chem. Pharm Bull. (Tokyo) **12**:504–506.
20. Omura, S., M. Katagiri, H. Ogura, and T. Hata. 1968. The chemistry of leucomycins. II. Glycosidic linkages of mycaminose and mycarose on leucomycin A_3. Chem. Pharm. Bull. (Tokyo) **16**:1167–1173.
21. Perun, T. J. 1967. Chemistry of erythronolide B. Acid-catalyzed transformations of the aglycone of erythromycin B. J. Org. Chem. **32**:2324–2330.
22. Perun, T. J., and R. S. Egan. 1969. The conformation of erythromycin aglycones. Tetrahedron Lett., p. 387–390.
23. Perun, T. J., R. S. Egan, and J. R. Martin. 1969. The conformation of macrolide antibiotics. II. Configurational and conformational studies of dihydroerythronolides. Tetrahedron Lett., p. 4501–4504.
24. Snatzke, G., H. Ripperger, C. Horstmann, and K. Schreiber. 1966. Circulardichroismus. XIX. Nitrosamine und Nitrosaminoketale. Sektorregel für Nitrosamine, Nitroverbindungen und Lactone. Tetrahedron **22**:3103–3116.
25. Wilhelm, J. M., N. L. Oleinick, and J. W. Corcoran. 1968. Interaction of antibiotics with ribosomes: structure-function relationships and a possible common mechanism for the antibacterial action of the macrolides and lincomycin. Antimicrob. Agents Chemother.–1967, p. 236–250.
26. Wolf, H. 1966. Cotton-Effekt und Konformation des δ-Lactonringes. Tetrahedron Lett., p. 5151–5156.

Antimicrobial Agents and Chemotherapy—1969

Chemical Modifications of Erythromycin Antibiotics

II. Synthesis of 4′-Hydroxyerythromycin A

PETER H. JONES, KISHORI S. IYER, and WALTON E. GRUNDY

Research Division, Abbott Laboratories, North Chicago, Illinois 60064

The basic macrolide antibiotics contain either desosamine or mycaminose as the amino sugar. Generally, the 12- and 14-membered ring macrolides contain desosamine whereas those with 16-membered rings contain mycaminose. Since these two sugars have the same configuration and differ only by a 4′-hydroxyl group, addition or removal of this group would effect a conversion of one sugar to the other. We have added a 4′-hydroxyl substituent to the desosamine moiety of erythromycin, thereby converting its amine sugar to mycaminose. This modification was accomplished by first converting erythromycin into its N-oxide. Pyrolysis of the amine oxide led to the Δ3′,4′-allylic alcohol, which was converted into the *cis*-epoxide with *m*-chloroperbenzoic acid. Epoxide ring opening with sodium azide gave both the 3′- and 4′-azides. Reductive alkylation with formaldehyde and hydrogen gave the corresponding dimethylamino derivatives. The *gluco* configuration of the 3′ isomer and the *gulo* configuration of the 4′ isomer were determined by nuclear magnetic resonance on the acetylated form of the acid-cleaved amino sugars. 4′-Hydroxyerythromycin A has the same antimicrobial spectrum as erythromycin A but is approximately 60% as active in vitro. The 3′-hydroxy isomer was completely devoid of antimicrobial activity.

A macrolide antibiotic was defined by Woodward in 1957 as an antibiotic possessing a many-membered lactone ring (19). Since then, it has become apparent that macrolide antibiotics have other common structural features (11). The carbohydrate moieties which are glycosidically attached to the lactone are always 6-deoxyhexoses. One of the sugars is from the D series related to 6-deoxyglucose and is attached to the aglycone ring by a β-glycoside bond. In the 12-membered ring macrolides methymycin and neomethymycin, and in the 14-membered ring macrolides erythromycin, oleandomycin, narbomycin, and pikromycin, the D-sugar is the amino sugar desosamine (Fig. 1). The 16-membered ring antibiotics spiramycin, magnamycin, leucomycin, and niddamycin all contain the D-amino sugar mycaminose, whereas the neutral macrolides neutramycin, chalcomycin, and lankamycin all contain the related D-sugar chalcose (11).

Since most of the microbiologically active macrolides contain one of these three sugars, we felt it would be interesting to interconvert one sugar for another on the aglycone. By this method, one could better study the role of the various D-sugars in their biological action. With our present synthetic tools, it would be quite difficult to remove one sugar and replace it with another. However, if one inspects the three sugars, mycaminose and chalcose differ from desosamine by only one substituent. Thus, if one replaces the dimethylamine of desosamine with a methoxyl group, he has converted desosamine into chalcose. Likewise, if a hydroxyl group is added to the 4 position of desosamine, the resulting sugar is mycaminose. This paper describes our studies of the conversion of the desosamine sugar of erythromycin A (1) into mycaminose.

MATERIALS AND METHODS

An infrared and nuclear magnetic resonance (NMR) spectrum was obtained on each compound, and in each case was consistent with the assigned structure. The

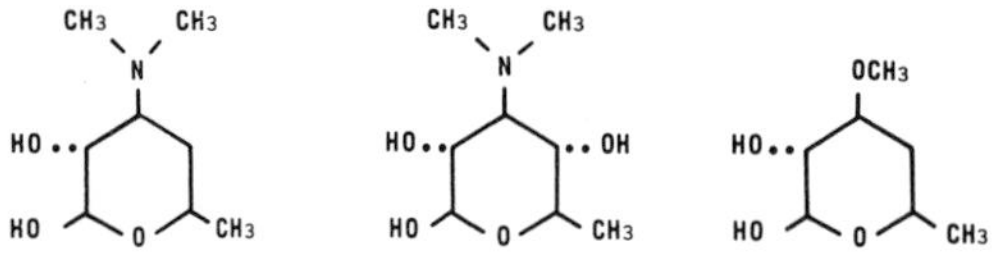

Fig. 1. *Macrolide antibiotic* D*-sugars.* D*-Desosamine (left),* D*-mcaminose (center),* D*-chalcose (right).*

infrared spectra were run on a Perkin-Elmer model 21 grating spectrophotometer. The NMR spectra were recorded on a Varian HA-100 instrument with the use of 10% deuteriochloroform solutions. Values are measured in Hertz downfield from tetramethylsilane as an internal standard. Thin-layer chromatography (TLC) was carried out on silica gel G plates activated at 100 C for 2 hr. The plates were developed by use of the following solvent systems: (A) chloroform-methanol, 95:5; (B) benzene-methanol, 80:20; (C) benzene-methanol, 70:30; (D) benzene-methanol-ammonium hydroxide, 78:19:3; (E) carbon tetrachloride-dimethylformamide-ammonium hydroxide, 14:1:trace. The spots were detected by spraying with arsenomolybdate reagent (12) and heating for several minutes at 100 C. Since the R_F values varied widely from plate to plate, they were not recorded. Optical rotations were determined with a Hilger and Watts polarimeter on 1% solutions in methanol.

(3′S,4′S)-3′-de-(dimethylamino)-3′,4′-epoxyerythromycin A (4). *m*-Chloroperbenzoic acid (85% assay; 20 g, 0.1 mole) was slowly added (1 hr) with stirring to a solution of 14 g (0.02 mole) of 3′-de-(dimethylamino)-3′,4′-dehydroerythromycin A (3) dissolved in 500 ml of chloroform (25 C). After the addition was complete, the solution was stirred at 0 C for 24 hr. The reaction mixture was poured into cold 6% Na_2SO_3. The chloroform layer was washed three times with cold 2% Na_2SO_3, once with cold 5% $NaHCO_3$, and once with water; it was then dried (Na_2SO_4) and concentrated. Upon addition of 30 ml of hot acetone, the residue dissolved and quickly crystallized, yielding 11 g (78%) of **4**: melting point (mp), 221 to 223 C; TLC (systems A, D, E), single spot; $[\alpha]^{26}{}_D$,–107°; infrared ($CHCl_3$), 1,723 cm^{-1} (lactone C=O) and 1,684 (ketone C=O); NMR ($CDCl_3$), no vinyl protons at 550 Hz. *Analysis.* Calculated for $C_{35}H_{60}O_{14}$: C, 59.64; H, 8.58; O, 31.78. Found: C, 59.62; H, 8.32; O, 31.62.

(3′S,4′S)-3′-de-(dimethylamino)-3′-azido-4′-hydroxyerythromycin A (5) and (3′R,4′R)-3′-de-(dimethylamino)-4′-azido-3′-hydroxyerythromycin A (6). To a solution of **4** (8.4 g, 0.012 mole) dissolved in dimethylformamide (300 ml) and water (8 ml) were slowly added (0.5 hr) sodium azide (7.8 g, 0.12 mole) and magnesium perchlorate (2.5 g, 0.01 mole). After being stirred at 80 C for 24 hr, the solution was cooled to 25 C and added to 300 ml of water. After standing for 24 hr, the solution was filtered, and the filtrate was set aside for the isolation of **5**. The solid was refluxed with a solution of chloroform (25 ml) and methanol (20 ml). The solution was filtered, and 250 ml of ether was added to the filtrate. After cooling to 0 C, the solid was collected by filtration, yielding 3.5 g (39%) of **6**: mp, 223 to 224 C; TLC (system A), single spot; infrared (Nujol), 1,725 cm^{-1} (lactone C=O), 1,678 cm^{-1} (ketone C=O), and 2,103 cm^{-1} (azide); $[\alpha]^{26}{}_D$,–104° ($c = 1$, dimethylformamide). *Analysis.* Calculated for $C_{35}H_{61}N_3O_{14}$: C, 56.21; H, 8.22; N, 5.62; O, 29.95. Found: C, 56.27; H, 8.12; N, 5.67; O, 30.15.

The filtrate from above was extracted four times with chloroform. The combined chloroform extracts were washed twice with water, dried (Na_2SO_4), and evaporated to dryness. The residual oil was dissolved in ether and washed twice with water. The volume of the wet ether solution was reduced to 10 ml and cooled to 0 C. The 3′-azide (**5**) was collected by filtration and recrystallized from wet ether to yield 2.5 g (28%) of **5**: mp, 202 to 204 C; $[\alpha]^{26}{}_D$,–74°; TLC (system A), single spot moving behind **6**; infrared ($CHCl_3$), 1,733 cm^{-1} (lactone C=O), 1,687 cm^{-1} (ketone C=O), and 2,102 cm^{-1} (azide). *Analysis.* Calculated for $C_{35}H_{61}N_3O_{14}$: C, 56.21; H, 8.22; N, 5.62; O, 29.95. Found: C, 56.11; H, 8.07; N, 5.55; O, 29.65.

(4′S)-4′-hydroxyerythromycin A (7). The 3′-azide (**5**), 1.0 g, was dissolved in 100 ml of absolute ethyl alcohol. To this solution was added 1.2 ml of 37% aqueous formaldehyde and 0.85 g of 5% palladium on carbon catalyst. The resulting mixture was hydrogenated on a Parr shaker under several atmospheres of pressure for 24 hr. The solution was filtered and the solvent was removed. The residue was dissolved in 50 ml of methylene chloride and 300 ml of cold 0.1 M KH_2PO_4 (pH∼4.5). The methylene chloride layer was discarded and the aqueous layer was washed twice with 50 ml of methylene chloride. The pH of the aqueous layer was adjusted to 10 with Na_2CO_3, and the basic solution was washed four times with chloroform. The combined choloform extracts were dried (Na_2SO_4) and evaporated to dryness to yield 0.7 g of a colorless glass. The glass was crystallized from methylene chloride-hexane to yield 0.6 g (60%) of **7** as prisms: mp, 148 to 150 C; $[\alpha]^{26}{}_D$,–76°; infrared ($CHCl_3$), 1,725 cm^{-1} (lactone C=O) and 1,684 cm^{-1} (ketone C=O); TLC (system C), single spot; NMR ($CDCl_3$), 250 Hz (CH_3-N). *Analysis.* Calculated for $C_{37}H_{67}NO_{14}$: C, 59.26; H, 9.01; N, 1.87; O, 29.87. Found: C, 58.99; H, 9.06; N, 1.88; O, 29.86.

(3′R,4′R)-3′-de-(dimethylamino)-4′-dimethylamino-3′-hydroxyerythromycin A (9). The 4′-dimethylamine **9** was prepared from the 4′-azide **6** by a procedure analogous with the synthesis of the 3′-dimethylamine **7**. Reductive alkylation of 1.0 g of **6** yielded 0.75 g (72%) of **9** from methylene chloride-hexane: mp, 221 to 224 C; $[\alpha]^{26}{}_D$,–96°; TLC (system C), single spot faster moving than **7**; infrared ($CHCl_3$), 1,725 cm^{-1} (lactone C=O) and 1,689 cm^{-1} (ketone C=O); NMR ($CDCl_3$), 245 Hz (CH_3-N). *Analysis:* Calculated for $C_{37}H_{67}NO_{14}$: C, 59.26; H, 9.01; N, 1.87; O, 29.87. Found: C, 59.45; H, 9.07; N, 1.70; O, 29.95.

(4′S)-4′-acetoxy-2′-O-acetylerythromycin A (8). To a solution of (4′S)-4′-hydroxyerythromycin A (7; 300 mg, 0.4 mmole) in 5 ml of acetone containing 300 mg of sodium bicarbonate was added 0.4 ml (4.0 mmoles) of acetic anhydride. After stirring at 25 C for 2 hr, the reaction mixture was poured into ice water. After 2 hr, the solid was filtered and crystallized from acetone-water to yield 270 mg (81%) of the diacetate **8**: mp, 174 to 176 C; TLC (system B), single spot faster moving than **7**; infrared ($CHCl_3$), 1,743 cm^{-1} (lactone and ester C=O) and 1,683 cm^{-1} (ketone C=O); NMR ($CDCl_3$), 232 Hz (CH_3-N), 201, 202 Hz (acetate). *Analysis.* Calculated for $C_{41}H_{71}NO_{16}$: C, 59.04; H, 8.58; N, 1.68; O, 30.70. Found: C, 59.10; H, 8.43; N, 1.71; O, 30.90.

The diacetate (**8**), 2 mg, was dissolved in 2 ml of methanol and several microliters were applied to a TLC plate which was developed with system B. After 4 hr, the sample was 50% converted back to **7**, after 8 hr 75%, and after 24 hr >95%. On each plate, the presence of a new spot (the monoacetate) was less than 5%.

(4′S)-4′-benzoyloxy-2′-O-benzoylerythromycin A. The dibenzoate ester was prepared from **7** by a procedure analogous to the preparation of the acetate. A sample (300 mg, 0.4 mmole) of **7** was treated with 900 mg (4.0 mmoles) of benzoic anhydride. The product on crystallization from methylene chloride-hexane yielded 298 mg (75%) of the dibenzoate ester: mp, 222 to 226 C; TLC (system E), single spot faster than **7**; infrared ($CHCl_3$), 1,723 cm^{-1} (lactone and ester C=O) and 1,683 cm^{-1} (ketone C=O); NMR ($CDCl_3$), 232 Hz (N-methyl). *Analysis.* Calculated for $C_{51}H_{75}NO_{16}$: C, 63.93; H, 7.89; N, 1.46; O, 26.72. Found: C, 63.92; H, 7.90; N, 1.52; O, 26.80.

The dibenzoate (2 mg) was dissolved in 2 ml of methanol, and the rate of hydrolysis in methanol was studied by TLC (system B). After 2 days, the sample was 50% hydrolyzed to **7**, and after 8 days the sample was more than 90% **7**. At any time during the hydrolysis, the amount of a new spot (the monobenzoate) never exceeded 10%.

Structure proof of 7 and 9. 9-Dihydroerythronolide A (**11**) and methyl cladinoside (**12**) were both isolated from **7** and **9** by previously described methods and were shown to be identical in all respects to authentic samples (5, 10, 18). Mycaminose·HCl (**13**) was isolated by the method of Hamill et al. (6) and had the identical physical constants. The triacetate ester **14** was prepared by the method of Hochstein and Murai (8), and the NMR peaks are reported in Table 2.

4,6-Dideoxy-4-dimethylamino-D-*gulo*-hexose hydrochloride (15) from 9. Compound **9**, 3 g, was refluxed for 2 hr with 30 ml of 3 N HCl. The amine sugar **15** was isolated as the hydrochloride salt by the same procedure (16). Two crystallizations from 95% ethyl alcohol and C_6H_6 yielded 400 mg (44%) of **12**: mp, 185 to 187 C; $[\alpha]^{25}{}_D -18°$ (c = 1, water, 24 hr). *Analysis.* Calculated for $C_8H_{18}ClNO_4$: C, 42.20; H, 7.97; N, 6.15; Cl, 15.57. Found: C, 42.08; H, 7.93; N, 6.00; Cl, 15.34.

The mother liquors from the above crystallizations were concentrated in vacuo and the residue was dissolved in 10 ml of water. The salt was converted into the free base by passing the solution over a column (1 × 12 cm) of IRA 400 (OH^-). The effluent was evaporated to dryness in vacuo, and the residue (320 mg) was dissolved in 10 ml of pyridine and 1 ml of Ac_2O. After 24 hr at 25 C, the solution was poured into cold 5% $NaHCO_3$, and after 15 min it was extracted twice with $CHCl_3$. The $CHCl_3$ extract was washed (water) and dried (Na_2SO_4). Removal of the solvent yielded 500 mg (94%) of triacetate **16** as a colorless oil. An NMR spectrum ($CDCl_3$) showed the presence of three acetate groups; a gas-liquid phase chromatographic analysis showed the presence of a major peak (91%) and a minor peak (9%). A small sample of the major component was collected by repeated gas-liquid phase chromatography runs and examined by NMR ($CDCl_3$). The chemical shifts are tabulated in Table 2 and demonstrate that the major component is the β anomer **14**: $[\alpha]^{25}{}_D, -37°$. *Analysis.* Calculated for $C_{14}H_{23}NO_7$: C, 52.99; H, 7.30. Found: C, 52.83; H, 7.14.

Antimicrobial activity in vitro. The antimicrobial spectrum was determined by the twofold broth-dilution procedure with the use of Brain Heart Infusion and 24-hr incubation at 37 C. The two *Mycoplasma* species were tested in PPLO broth (Difco) fortified with 20% calf serum and 10% fresh yeast extract.

Antimicrobial activity in vivo. Mouse protection tests were carried out comparing 4′-hydroxyerythromycin A with erythromycin A. The mice were infected intraperitoneally with 10 to 100 LD_{50} of *Staphylococcus aureus* Smith and were medicated either orally or intramuscularly.

RESULTS AND DISCUSSION

Recently, the synthesis of 3′-de-(dimethylamino)-3′,4′-dehydroerythromycin A (3) from the amine oxide by elimination of erythromycin A N-oxide (2) was reported (10). The allylic alcohol 3 was used as the starting point in this study because the double bond at the 3′ and 4′ positions allows exclusive substitution at these centers. By forming the epoxide of the allylic alcohol and subsequent epoxide ring opening with a nitrogen nucleophile, the nitrogen group would be replaced at C-3′ and a hydroxyl group would be introduced at C-4′. If the epoxide is *cis* to the 2′-hydroxyl group (*allo* configuration), ring opening of the epoxide at C-3′ leads to a derivative with the same configuration as mycaminose.

It has been well established by Henbest and Wilson that the formation of epoxides from cyclic allylic alcohols occurs by attack of the peracid on the side *cis* to the hydroxyl group

(7). Treatment of the allylic alcohol **3** with *m*-chloroperbenzoic acid produced the *cis*-epoxide **4** in high yield. A TLC of the crude reaction product showed a second spot (<10%) which was attributed to the *trans* isomer. Positive structural assignments of the products from the epoxide **4** which are discussed in a later section of this paper confirm its assigned *allo* configuration (Fig. 2).

Treatment of the epoxide **4** with dimethylamine in either refluxing methanol or ethylene glycol produced a mixture of new compounds. An NMR spectrum of the crude reaction product showed only a trace of an N-methyl absorption, demonstrating the absence of epoxide opening. However, when sodium azide was substituted as the nucelophile (9), the epoxide was completely converted into the two azides **5** and **6** which were assumed to have the *gluco* and *gulo* configuration, respectively. As illustrated in Table 1, the ratio of the two azides was not affected by changing the reaction solvent from dimethylsulfoxide to dimethylformamide. In each case, when only a trace of water was used as a proton source, the ratio of **5** to **6** was 1:9. However, when the percentage of water in the reaction mixture was raised, the amount of **5** increased proportionately, until at 5% water the ratio became constant at 2:3. When the 2′-hydroxyl group was protected by an acetate ester, the water concentration no longer was a factor, and the ratio again was 5:95.

The direction of epoxide ring opening is determined by the Fürst-Plattner rule whereby the nucleophile attacks the epoxide from the axial side, breaking the equitorial bond of the oxide, and the oxygen remains attached to the axial position (4; A. Fürst and P. A. Plattner, Abstr. 12th Int. Congr. Pure Appl. Chem., p. 409–411, 1951). However, the Fürst-Plattner rule is not always valid in the carbohydrate series owing to the flexibility of the ring (2, 3, 13, 15-17). When a carbohydrate is held in a rigid conformation by a 1:6-anhydro ring or a 4:6-O-benzylidene group, the rule almost always predicts the correct product (14). When such a group is not present, as in the present case, the sugar freely interconverts from one conformation to the other, i.e., **4a** to **4b** (Fig. 3).

Table 1. *Effect of solvent on isomer ratio*

2′-Substituent	Solvent[a]	3′-*Gluco* isomer	4′-*Gulo* isomer
		%	%
OH	DMSO-trace water	10	90
OH	DMF-trace water	10	90
OH	DMSO-5% water	40	60
OH	DMF-5% water	40	60
O-C(=C)-CH_3	DMSO-5% water	5	95

[a] DMSO = dimethylsulfoxide; DMF = dimethylformamide.

As can be seen in Fig. 3, epoxide ring opening of the **4b** conformation occurs at the 3′-position, producing the 3′-*gluco* isomer (**5**), whereas attack of **4a** produces the 4′-*gulo* isomer **6**. By examination of the two conformations, one can see that **4b** is more unstable than **4a** because **4b** has three axial groups whereas **4a** has none. Therefore, conformation **4a** might be expected to predominate in solution, and the major product of the epoxide ring opening might be expected to be **6**. (The structure of **6** was first assigned on the basis of this assumption.) As evidenced from Table 1, addition of water to the reaction solvent changes the product ratio. This result indicates that conformation **4b** is no longer so unstable with respect to **4a**. One explanation is that an excellent hydrogen bonding solvent, such as dimethylsulfoxide, bonds to the hydroxyl group, thereby preventing it from hydrogen-bonding to the other groups. When water is added, the hydrogen-bonding ability of the solvent is reduced. In conformation **4b**, the hydroxyl group can bond to both the epoxide oxygen and to the ring oxygen, thus stabilizing this conformation. When the hydroxyl group is esterfied, it can no longer stabilize conformation **4b**, and the addition of water would no longer change the product ratio. This effect was indeed noted (Fig. 4).

Reductive alkylation of the azide **5** with formaldehyde and hydrogen by use of palladium on carbon catalyst led smoothly to the dimethylamine **7**. Mild acetylation led smoothly to the 2′,4′-diacetate ester **8** from which the parent **5** was regenerated by mild hydrolysis with methanol. The facile esterification and hydrolysis is typical of hydroxyl and ester groups which are adjacent to a dimethylamine and is a good indication of the structure of **5**. Likewise, the azide **6** was alkylated to the dimethylamine **9**. In this case, mild acetylation led to only a monoacetate **10** from which the parent **9** was regenerated by hydrolysis with methanol. The formation of the monoacetate was good evidence for the structure of **9**.

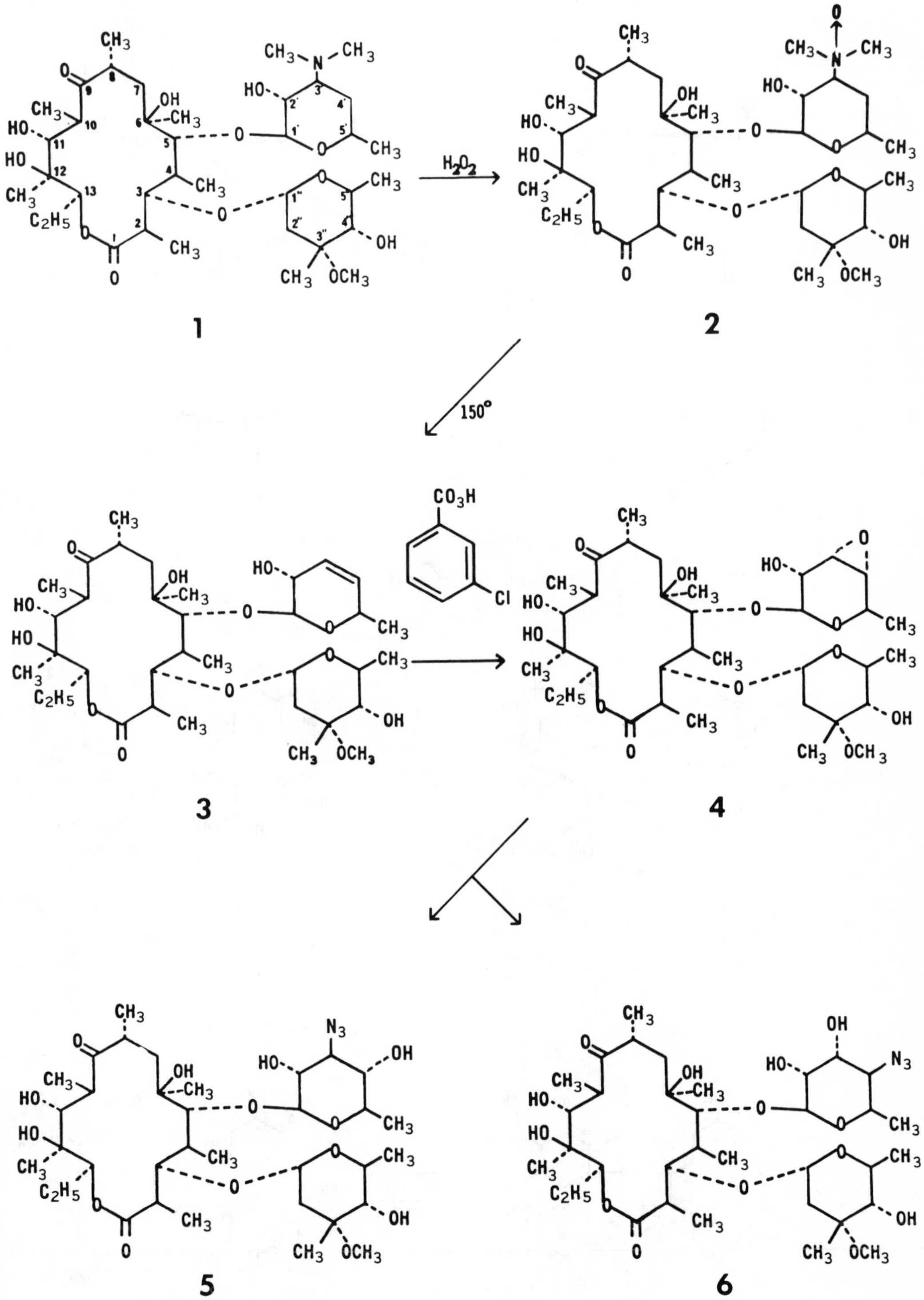

Fig. 2. *Synthesis of 3′- and 4′-azides.*

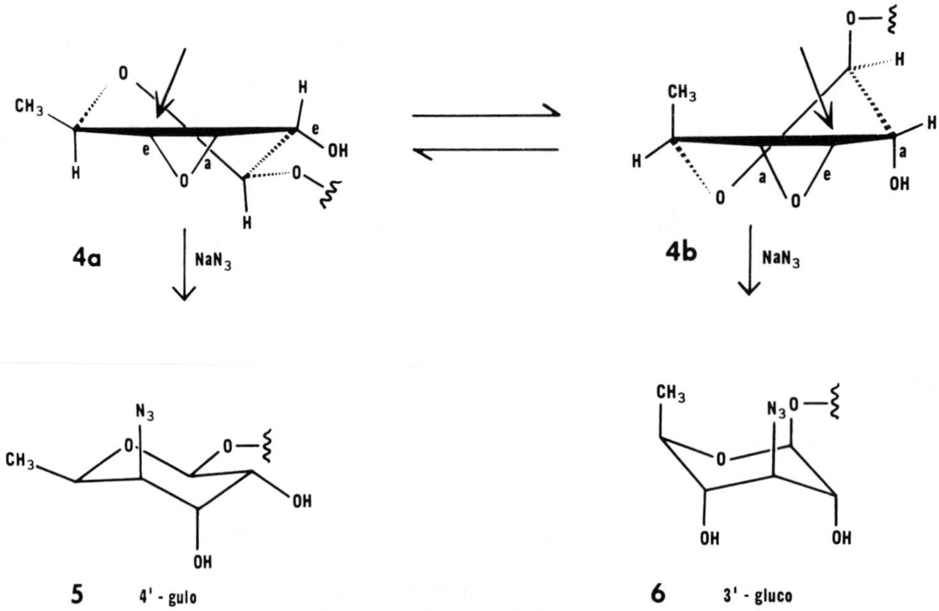

4a
NaN$_3$
4b
NaN$_3$

5 4'-gulo
6 3'-gluco

Fig. 3. *Fürst-Plattner rule of epoxide ring opening.*

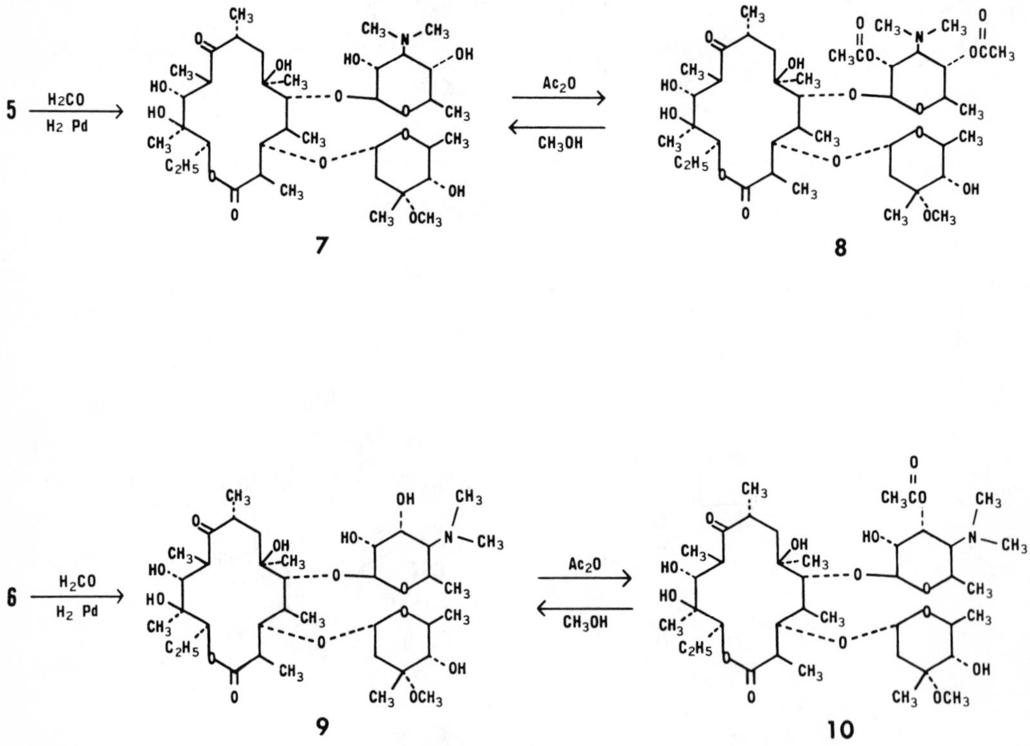

5 $\xrightarrow[H_2\ Pd]{H_2CO}$ 7 $\underset{CH_3OH}{\overset{Ac_2O}{\rightleftarrows}}$ 8

6 $\xrightarrow[H_2\ Pd]{H_2CO}$ 9 $\underset{CH_3OH}{\overset{Ac_2O}{\rightleftarrows}}$ 10

Fig. 4. *Reductive alkylation of azides.*

Further evidence for the structure of **7** and **9** was provided by chemical degradation to 9-dihydroerythronolide A (**11**), methyl cladinoside (**12**), and the corresponding amino sugars **13** and **15** (Fig. 5). The ketone in the aglycone portion of **7** and **9** was reduced with sodium borohydride to the 9-dihydro derivative; the free aglycone **11** was isolated after removal of the sugar by aqueous acid hydrolysis and was shown to be identical with that derived from erythromycin A by the method of Sigal et al. (18). Methyl cladinoside (**12**) was removed from **7** and **9** with methanolic hydrogen chloride and shown to be unchanged (5, 10). Mycaminose **13** was isolated from **7** by the method of Hamill et al. (6) and was shown to have the identical physical properties. Acetylation of **13** produced the triacetate **14** whose structure was confirmed by NMR, the results of which are listed in Table 2. The new amino sugar **15** was isolated from **9** by a similar procedure and was converted into its triacetate **16**. The structure and configuration of **16** were assigned by NMR (Table 2). The characteristic peaks of the three acetates, the dimethylamino, and the secondary methyl groups indicate that **16** is a triacetyldimethylamino-6-deoxy sugar. The peaks at 578, 566, and 512 Hz are typical of protons adjacent to acetate groups. Likewise, the peaks at 243 and 426 Hz are assigned to the protons adjacent to the dimethylamine and the methyl groups, respectively.

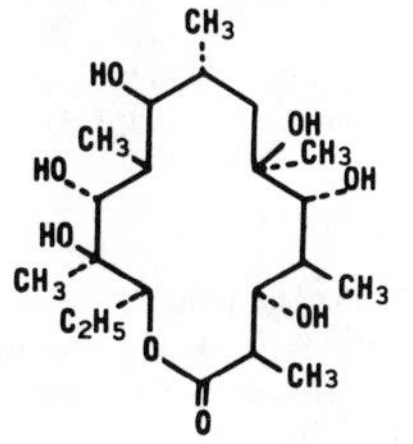

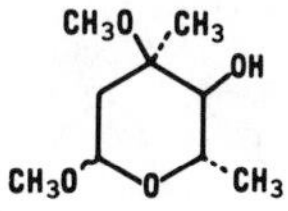

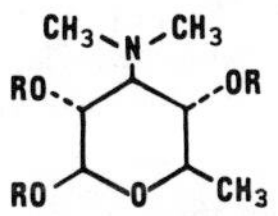

Fig. 5. *Degradation products of compounds 7 and 9.*

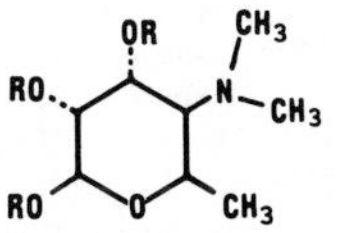

The doublet at 578 Hz (J=8 Hz) can only be assigned to H-1. The only 8 Hz coupling is at 512 Hz, and must be assigned to H-2, indicating that these protons are axial (1). The remaining ring protons all have small coupling constants indicating axial-equitorial or equitorial-equitorial configurations. We then turned to decoupling experiments to assign the remaining protons. By this method, the peak at 566 Hz was assigned to H-3, the 243 Hz peak to H-4, and 426 Hz peak to H-5, which confirms the 1,2,3-triacetyl-4-dimethylamino structure. Since $J_{2,3}$ is small (3.5 Hz) and H-2 is axial, H-3 must be equitorial. $J_{3,4}$ is also small, so that the configuration of H-4 is uncertain. Finally, $J_{4,5}$ (3.5 Hz) indicates only that H-4 and H-5 cannot both be axial. The choice of possible structures is narrowed to the three shown in Fig. 6. Structures **17** and **18** must be eliminated because they both are L-sugars which would have required the unlikely epimerization at C-5 during one of the steps. It, therefore, is reasonable to assign the structure of **16** as β-1,2,3-tri-*O*-acetyl-4-dimethylamino-4,6-dideoxy *gulo* hexopyranoside.

Microbiology. The antimicrobial spectrum of 4′-hydroxyerythromycin A (**7**) is identical with that of erythromycin A and appears to be about one half as active, as is shown by the data in Table 3. Turbidimetric assays with the Heatley strain of *Staphylococcus aureus* indicated that 4′-hydroxyerythromycin A was 60% as active.

Table 2. *NMR spectra of the amino sugar acetates (all values in Hertz)*

Proton	Compound 14		Compound 16	
	Chemical shift	Coupling constant	Chemical shift	Coupling constant
H-1	562 (d)	J = 8.0	578 (d)	J = 8
H-2	507 (q)	J = 8.0, 10.5	512 (q)	J = 8, 3.5
H-3	284 (t)	J = 10, 10	566 (t)	J = 3.5, 3.0
H-4	478 (q)	J = 10, 9	243 (t)	J = 3.0, 3.5
H-5	359 (m)	J = 9, (7)	426 (m)	J = (3.5) (6.5)
CH_3-	119 (d)	J = 7	134 (d)	J = 6.5
$(CH_3)_2N$	233 (s)	–	251 (s)	–
CH_3CO	201 (s)	–	210 (s)	–
	204 (s)	–	210 (s)	–
	206 (s)	–	203 (s)	–

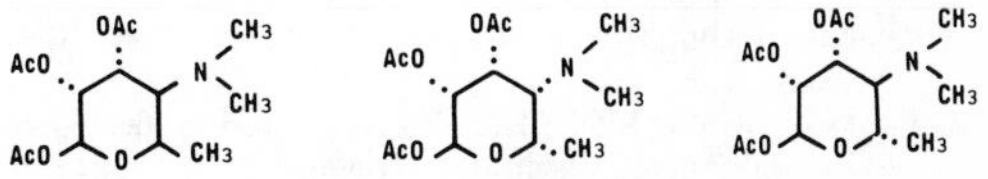

Fig. 6. *4-Amino sugars;* **16** *(left),* **17** *(center), and* **18** *(right).*

Table 3. *Antimicrobial spectrum of 4′-hydroxyerythromycin A*

Organism	Minimal inhibitory concn (μg/ml)[a]	
	4′-Hydroxy-erythromycin (7)	Erythro-mycin A
Diplococcus pneumoniae ATCC 6301	0.05	0.05
Enterobacter aerogenes ATCC 13048	>100	100
Escherichia coli Juhl	100	50
Haemophilus influenzae ATCC 9334	6.2	3.1
Klebsiella pneumoniae ATCC 10031	12.5	25.
Mycoplasma gallisepticum 86	0.2	0.1
M. pneumoniae FH	0.2	0.1
Proteus mirabilis Finland #9	>100	100
P. vulgaris JJ	>100	>100
Pseudomonas aeruginosa ATCC 9027	>100	>100
Salmonella typhimurium ED #9	50	25
S. typhi ATCC 9902	100	25
Shigella sonnei ATCC 9290	25	25
Staphylococcus aureus Smith	0.39	0.2
S. aureus Smith ER[b]	>100	>100
S. aureus Quinones[c]	>100	>100
S. aureus Wise[c]	>100	>100
S. epidermidis Abbott 3519	0.39	0.2
S. epidermidis Abbott 3519 ER[b]	>100	>100
Streptococcus faecalis ATCC 10541	0.2	0.05
S. pyogenes C203	0.05	0.025

[a] The 3′-hydroxy isomer **9** was ineffective against all organisms tested (minimal inhibitory concentration >100 μg/ml).

[b] Resistance to erythromycin induced in the laboratory.

[c] Naturally resistant strains.

Table 4. *In vivo activity of 4′-hydroxyerythromycin A against Staphylococcus aureus*

Antibiotic	Route of Medication	CD_{50}
		mg/kg
4′-Hydroxyerythromycin A	Intramusclar	10-20
	Oral	150
Erythromycin A	Intramuscular	2.5-5.0
	Oral	50

Bactericidal tests carried out with *S. aureus* and *Streptococcus pyogenes* showed no differences in the behavior of the two compounds. The 3′-hydroxy-4′-dimethylamine isomer **9** exhibited no antimicrobial activity.

The mouse protection data with *Staphylococcus aureus* presented in Table 4 indicate that the 4′-hydroxy derivative **7** is between one-half and one-quarter as active as erythromycin A.

ACKNOWLEDGMENTS

We thank R. S. Egan and Ruth Stanaszek for the NMR spectra, A. J. Kammer for the infrared spectra, E. Baker, S. Harris, and D. Nelson for the chromatographic analyses, V. Rauschel for the elemental analyses, M. Freifelder and D. Dunnigan for the reductive alkylations, and D. Kenney, C. Vojtko, S. Bell, and R. Bower for the microbiological studies.

LITERATURE CITED

1. Bible, R. H. 1965. Interpretation of NMR spectra, an empirical approach, p. 16 and 36. Plenum Press, New York.
2. Cookson, R. C. 1954. The direction of ring-opening of 2:3-anyhdrosugars. Chem. Ind. (London), p. 223–224.
3. Dick, A. J., and J. K. N. Jones. 1967. Epoxide ring opening of methyl 2,3-anhydro-4-azido-4-deoxypentopyranosides. Can. J. Chem. **45**:2879–2885.
4. Eliel, E. L. 1956. Substitution at saturated carbon atoms, p. 130–134. *In* M. S. Newman (ed.), Steric effects in organic chemistry. John Wiley & Sons, Inc., New York.
5. Flynn, E. H., M. V. Sigal, Jr., P. F. Wiley, and K. Gerzon. 1954. Erythromycin. I. Properties and degradation studies. J. Amer. Chem. Soc. **76**:3121–3131.
6. Hamill, R. L., M. E., Haney, Jr., M. Stamper, and P. F. Wiley. 1961. Tylosin, a new antibiotic. II. Isolation, properties, and preparation of desmycosin, a microbiologically active degradation product. Antibiot. Chemother. **11**:328–334.
7. Henbest, H. B., and R. A. L. Wison. 1957. Aspects of stereochemistry. I. Stereospecificity in formation of epoxides from cyclic allylic alcohols. J. Chem. Soc. (London), p. 1958–1965.
8. Hochstein, F. A., and K. Murai. 1954. Magnamycin B, a second antibiotic from *Streptomyces halstedii.* J. Amer. Chem. Soc. **76**:5080–5083.
9. Ingham, J. D., W. L. Petty, and P. L. Nichols, Jr. 1956. The addition of azide ion to epoxides. J. Org. Chem. **21**:373–375.
10. Jones, P. H., and E. K. Rowley. 1968. Chemical modifications of erythromycin antibiotics. I. 3′-De(dimethylamino) erythromycin A and B. J. Org. Chem. **33**:665–670.
11. Morin, R., and M. Gorman. 1967. Macrolide antibiotics, p. 632–661. *In* Encylopedia of chemical technology, 2nd ed. John Wiley & Sons, Inc., New York.
12. Nelson, N. 1944. A photometric adaptation of the Somogyi method for the determination of glucose. J. Biol. Chem. **153**:375–380.
13. Newth, F. H. 1959. Sugar epoxides. Quart. Rev. (London) **13**:30–47.
14. Newth, F. H., and R. F. Homer. 1953. The action of acidic reagents on ethylene oxide anhydro-sugars. II. The action of hydrochloric acid on methyl 2:3-anhydro-4:6-O-benzylidene-α-D-mannoside. J. Chem. Soc. (London), p. 989–992.
15. Overend, W. G., and G. Vaughan. 1955. Sugar transformations. The direction of ring-opening of anhydro-sugars of the ethylene-oxide type. Chem. Ind. (London), p. 995–1000.
16. Peat, S., and L. F. Wiggins. 1938. The preparation of 2:3-anhydro-, 3:4-anhydro-, and 3:6-anhydro-methylhexosides from 3-p-toluenesulphonyl methylglucoside. J. Chem. Soc. (London), p. 1088–1097.
17. Peat, S., and L. F. Wiggins. 1938. The behaviour of anhydro-methylhexosides towards akaline reagents. Preparation of derivatives of 3-amino-glucose and 2-aminoaltrose. J. Chem. Soc. (London), p. 1810–1815.
18. Sigal, M. V., Jr., P. F. Wiley, K. Gerzon, E. H. Flynn, U. C. Quarck, and O. Weaver. 1956. Erythromycin. VI. Degradation studies. J. Amer. Chem. Soc. **78**:388–395.
19. Woodward, R. B. 1957. Struktur und Biogenese der Makrolide. Agnew. Che. **69**:50–58.

Antimicrobial Agents and Chemotherapy—1969

Spectrophotometric Assay for Cephalosporin C in Fermentation Broths

C. A. CLARIDGE, RICHARD W. VAUGHAN, PETER KRESEL, and A. GOUREVITCH[1]

Research Division, Bristol Laboratories, Division of Bristol-Myers Co., Syracuse, New York 13201

Cephalosporin C has an absorption peak in the ultraviolet region at 260 nm. This property was used as the basis for a new spectrophotometric assay for this antibiotic in fermentation broths. There was good correlation between this spectrophotometric assay for cephalosporin C and a bioassay in which *Alcaligenes faecalis* is used as the test organism. The assay did not distinguish between cephalosporin C and its deacetyl derivative. Neither cephalosporin N nor cephalosporin P interfered.

Methods for the estimation of cephalosporin C in fermentation broths have depended upon biological assay procedures (2, 5, 7, 10) or upon a chemical process (4) requiring preliminary treatment of the sample with penicillinase to remove cephalosporin N (penicillin N). We were interested in developing a specific and rapid method for the estimation of cephalosporin C concentrations in experimental fermentations which would exclude interference by cephalosporins N and P, two other antibiotics that are generally present.

Cephalosporin C has a peak absorbance in the ultraviolet (UV) region at 260 nm (1). This property has been used for locating cephalosporin C and its derivatives on paper chromatograms, and even for quantitative estimation after their elution (8). Cephalosporin C is also decomposed by UV light (6), and Sabath et al. (11) used this characteristic as part of an assay designed to measure individually penicillin, cephalothin, and chloramphenicol when they are all present in mixtures.

The direct estimation of cephalosporin C in fermentation broths by measurement of the absorbance at 260 nm is complicated by the preparation of a suitable blank for the spectrophotometer. Various ingredients used in the experimental media are known to interfere.

The procedure described here is a rapid, simple one which overcomes these difficulties and permits concentrations of cephalosporin C above 500 μg/ml to be estimated in fermentation broths.

The standard error of the method ranged from 1 to 3% of the mean, whereas the amount of cephalosporin C measured was 1 to 13% more than the actual amount present.

MATERIALS AND METHODS

Apparatus. A Beckman model DU spectrophotometer with 1-cm quartz cells was used to measure the absorbance at 260 nm. A Bausch & Lomb model 505 recording spectrophotometer was used to obtain complete UV spectra.

Reagents. The following buffer solutions were required: (i) 0.2 M potassium chloride-sodium hydroxide (*p*H 12.5), (ii) 0.1 M potassium phosphate (*p*H 7.0), and (iii) 0.2 M potassium phosphate (*p*H 6.0).

Biological assay. The method of Claridge and Johnson (5) with *Alcaligenes faecalis* as the test organism was used for the estimation of cephalosporin C.

Preparation of samples for assay. The broth samples were first centrifuged to remove cell growth, and the resulting supernatant fluid was used for estimation of potency by the UV assay. Because the broth supernatant fluid showed nonspecific absorption at 260 nm, it was necessary to dilute the supernatant fluid at least 50-fold to overcome this effect. The lowest concentration of cephalosporin C which could be effectively measured was 5 μg/ml; thus, with the dilutions required during the assay, the minimum detectable level in broth samples was 500 μg/ml.

Fermentation samples. The cephalosporin C fermentations were produced by growing *Cephalosporium* sp. CMI 49137 in a variety of experimental media prepared in the laboratory.

[1] Deceased.

RESULTS AND DISCUSSION

The observation that the absorbance of cephalosporin C at 260 nm could be destroyed by treating the preparation with alkali suggested that this could be used as the basis for an assay of this antibiotic, both in its pure form and in fermentation broths. The difference in absorbance at 260 nm between an alkali-treated sample used as a reference blank and a nontreated sample should give a measure of the cephalosporin C content.

Early in the work on the development of this assay, we found that destroying the cephalosporin C chromophore with 0.2 N NaOH resulted in an unsatisfactory reference blank which yielded variable absorbances with standard concentrations of the antibiotic. The alkali treatment destroyed the chromophore, but, as the sample aged, the absorbance at this wavelength slowly increased leading to an erroneous value for the sample not treated with alkali. The difference in absorbance between the blank and the sample was thus dependent upon the length of time the portion to be used as a reference blank was heated with base.

We noticed that the NaOH solution did not control the *p*H of the diluted broth samples adequately at this step. However, the cephalosporin C chromophore could be destroyed by the use of a suitable alkaline buffer of a *p*H greater than 12 (Table 1).

The absorbances shown in Table 1 were obtained with a 60 μg/ml solution of cephalosporin C prepared in 0.2 N NaOH or various alkaline buffers. Because this preparation was to be used as the reference blank, the condition yielding the lowest absorbance was the most desirable because it would give the most sensitive assay. It can be seen that a *p*H greater than 12 was required and that either 5 min at 37 C or 10 to 20 min at 30 C satisfied this requirement. Use of the longer time required at 30 C proved to be more convenient for carrying out the assay procedure. Broth samples diluted in the same *p*H 12.5 buffer were found to reach their lowest absorbance after 25 min at 30 C. The results obtained with 0.2 N NaOH are shown for comparison.

The low absorbance of the samples to be used as the blank could be stabilized readily by neutralization, most conveniently by making a twofold dilution with 0.2 M potassium phosphate buffer (*p*H 6.0). The resulting *p*H was near 7.2.

The UV absorption spectra of cephalosporin C, cephalosporin N, and corresponding alkali-treated samples are shown in Fig. 1. These data show that absorbance of cephalosporin C at 260 nm was reduced by the alkaline treatment and, in addition, that cephalosporin N did not interfere.

Similarly, the absorption spectra of a clarified cephalosporin C fermentation broth and an alkali-treated portion are shown in Fig. 2. Typical fermentation broths required an initial 50-fold dilution of the blank because of nonspecific interfering material from the complex ingredients of the media.

The procedure selected for the preparation of a standard line was as follows. A series of solutions containing cephalosporin C at concentrations of 5, 10, 20, 30, 40, and 50 μg/ml were prepared in *p*H 7.0 phosphate buffer. Another series of solutions to be used as reference blanks containing cephalosporin C at concentrations of 10, 20, 40, 60, 80, and 100 μg/ml were prepared

Table 1. *Absorbance at 260 nm of alkali-treated cephalosporin C blank*[a]

Time	23 C (NaOH)	30 C			37 C		
		*p*H 11.0	*p*H 12.0	*p*H 12.5	*p*H 11.0	*p*H 12.0	*p*H 12.5
min							
5		0.90	0.56	0.26	0.90	0.48	0.25
10	0.37	0.92	0.48	0.25	0.87	0.41	0.28
20		0.89	0.44	0.26	0.81	0.36	0.31
30	0.29	0.88	0.41	0.28	0.77	0.35	0.35
50	0.32	0.82	0.35	0.33	0.71	0.34	0.43
90	0.41	0.80	0.34	0.39	0.66	0.40	0.51

[a] Cephalosporin C was prepared at 60 μg/ml in 0.2 N NaOH, in Na_2HPO_4–NaOH (*p*H 11.0 and 12.0), or in KCl-NaOH (*p*H 12.5). The optical density was measured at 260 nm after the indicated times at each temperature, with each buffer or NaOH solution as a blank.

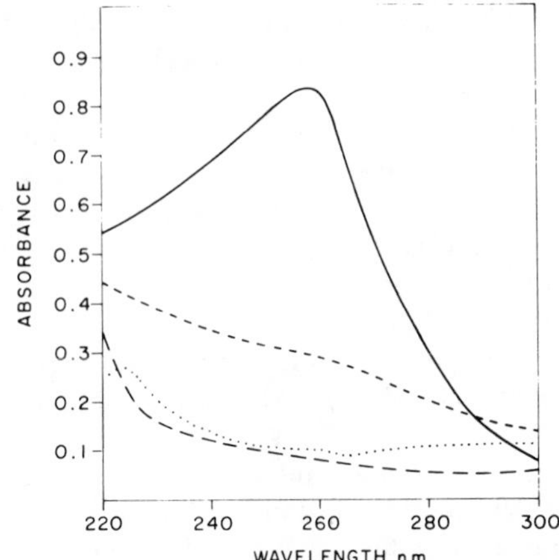

Fig. 1. *Absorption spectra of alkali-treated and non-treated cephalosporin C and cephalosporin N. The spectra of the nontreated samples were obtained from 50 µg/ml solutions in 0.1 M potassium phosphate buffer (pH 7.0). Spectra of the alkali-treated samples were obtained from solutions (50 µg/ml, final concentration) prepared as described in the text. Symbols:——, cephalosporin C; - - - - -, alkali-treated cephalosporin C; . . . ., cephalosporin N; — — — alkali-treated cephalosporin N.*

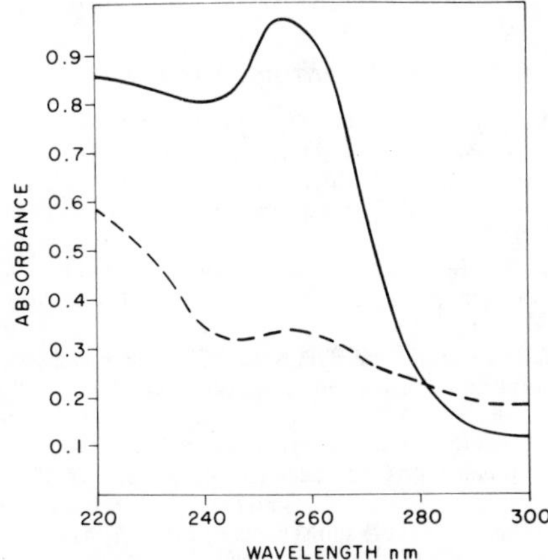

Fig. 2. *Absorption spectra of a cephalosporin C fermentation broth and an alkali-treated sample. The clarified cephalosporin C broth was diluted 100-fold with pH 7.0 buffer. The alkali-treated sample was prepared as described in the text. Symbols:——, cephalosporin C broth; - - - - -, alkali-treated cephalosporin C broth.*

in the *p*H 12.5 buffer and transferred immediately to a water bath at 30 C. After 15 min, the samples were removed from the water bath and diluted with an equal volume of 0.2 M potassium phosphate buffer (*p*H 6.0) to bring the final *p*H near neutrality. Absorbances at 260 nm of the solutions of cephalosporin C prepared in *p*H 7.0 phosphate buffer were then determined, with the proper alkali-treated samples being used as reference blanks for the spectrophotometer. A plot of the cephalosporin C concentration versus absorbance at 260 nm was linear from 10 to 50 µg/ml (Fig. 3).

The standard line obtained by this procedure remained stable for at least 20 hr (Table 2).

For the estimation of the concentration of cephalosporin C in fermentation broths, a slight

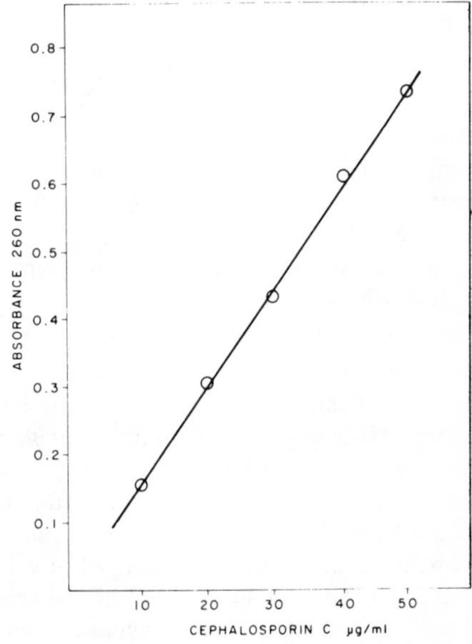

Fig. 3. *Dose-response curve of cephalosporin C at 260 nm. The equation for the line is* $y=0.0146x \dot{-} 0.0026$. *The regression coefficient* $r=0.998$.

Table 2. *Stability of assay standard line*[a]

Cephalosporin C	Absorbance (260 nm)		
	25 min	2 hr	20 hr
µg/ml			
10	0.14	0.14	0.13
20	0.29	0.29	0.29
30	0.42	0.44	0.44
40	0.60	0.60	0.59
50	0.72	0.72	0.72

[a] The absorbance recorded is the difference between the alkali-treated sample used as a blank and the nontreated sample. Times indicated represent the period following neutralization of the samples used as blanks.

change in the treatment of the sample to be used as the blank was required. The fermentation broth was clarified by centrifugation; then the supernatant fluid was diluted in *p*H 7.0 phosphate buffer so that the estimated concentration of cephalosporin C fell within the range of 5 to 50 μg/ml. Another portion of the supernatant fluid was diluted in the *p*H 12.5 buffer to one-half the dilution used for the assay sample and was placed in a water bath at 30 C for 25 min. At the end of this time, it was further diluted with an equal volume of *p*H 6.0 phosphate buffer. When the absorbance of the sample at 260 nm was obtained with the alkali-treated sample as a blank, its potency could then be calculated from the standard line.

Variations within the bioassay and spectrophotometric procedures were investigated by assaying a single broth sample 10 times by each method. The coefficient of variation for the bioassay was 2.1, the range varying from 88 to 110% of the mean; for the spectrophotometric procedure, the coefficient of variation was 1.5, the range being 96 to 111% of the mean.

To investigate the sensitivity of the assay, seven concentrations of the cephalosporin C reference standard were added to a previously assayed fermentation broth. The broths were reassayed with five replications, and the data were analyzed by computing the mean and standard error of the mean of each set of values. The results (Table 3) show that the sensitivity was well within the limits expected from an assay of fermentation broths and that the added cephalosporin C was measured accurately.

Table 3. *Addition of known amounts of cephalosporin C to a fermentation broth*

Cephalosporin C added	Mean amt of cephalosporin C ± SE[a]	Mean increase over basal	Increase over amount added
μg/ml	*μg/ml*	*μg/ml*	%
0	2,289 ± 44.3	0	0
200	2,510 ± 52.8	221	10.0
400	2,751 ± 72.6	462	13.2
600	2,894 ± 95.0	605	0.7
800	3,166 ± 42.8	877	9.5
1,000	3,373 ± 42.8	1,084	8.4
1,300	3,741 ± 62.9	1,452	11.6
2,000	4,424 ± 63.0	2,135	6.8

[a] All mean values are based on five assays.

This assay has proven to be a rapid and simple method for the determination of cephalosporin C in fermentation broths. Although deacetylcephalosporin C (9) is measured by this procedure, we have not found it to be as significant a contaminant in our fermentations as in those reported by Huber et al. (8).

Cephalosporin P (3) is found in some fermentation samples when they are examined by paper chromatography, but it is known that this antibiotic does not interfere when the bioassay of cephalosporin C is done with *A. faecalis* (5). Two equally potent cephalosporin C samples (as measured by bioassay), one containing cephalosporin P and the other none, have also given equivalent values by the spectrophotometric method.

If the standard colorimeter which accompanies most equipment used for the automation of chemical assays is replaced by a more sensitive spectrophotometer able to measure absorbance at 260 nm, it should be possible to automate this assay for use in monitoring cephalosporin C concentrations in fermentation broths.

LITERATURE CITED

1. Abraham, E. P., and G. G. F. Newton. 1961. The structure of cephalosporin C. Biochem. J. **79**: 377–393.
2. Bond, J. M., R. W. Brimblecomb, and R. C. Codner. 1962. Biological assay of cephalosporin C. J. Gen. Microbiol. **27**:11–19.
3. Burton, H. S., E. P. Abraham, and M. E. Cardwell. 1956. Cephalosporin P and helvolic acid. Biochem. J. **62**:171–176.
4. Caltrider, P. G., and H. F. Niss. 1966. Role of methionine in cephalosporin synthesis. Appl. Microbiol. **14**:746–753.
5. Claridge, C. A., and D. L. Johnson. 1963. A specific bio-assay for cephalosporin C in fermentation broths. Antimicrob. Agents Chemother.–1962, p. 682–686.
6. Demain, A. L. 1966. Destruction of cephalosporin C by ultraviolet light. Nature (London) **210**:426–427.
7. Demain, A. L., and J. F. Newkirk. 1962. Biosynthesis of cephalosporin C. Appl. Microbiol. **10**:321–325.
8. Huber, F. M., R. H. Baltz, and P. G. Caltrider. 1968. Formation of desacetylcephalosporin C in cephalosporin C fermentation. Appl. Microbiol. **16**:1011–1014.
9. Jeffery, J. D. 'A., E. P. Abraham, and G. G. F. Newton. 1961. Deacetylcephalosporin C. Biochem. J. **81**:591–596.
10. Kavanagh, F. 1963. Cephalosporin C, p. 265–270. *In* F. Kavanagh (ed.), Analytical microbiology. Academic Press Inc., New York.
11. Sabath, L. D., P. B. Loder, D. A. Gerstein, and M. Finland. 1968. Measurement of three antibiotics (penicillin, cephalothin, and chloramphenicol) when present together in mixtures. Appl. Microbiol. **16**:877–880.

Antimicrobial Agents and Chemotherapy—1969

Constituents of Amphomycin

M. BODANSZKY, N. C. CHATURVEDI, J. A. SCOZZIE, R. K. GRIFFITH, and A. BODANSZKY

Case Western Reserve University, Cleveland, Ohio

In addition to a fatty acid moiety (mostly 3-isododecenoic acid and 3-anteisotridecenoic acid), L-aspartic acid (3 moles), L-β-methylaspartic acid, glycine (2 moles), L-proline, L-valine, D-pipecolic acid, and α,β-diaminobutyric acid (about 2 moles) were found to be constituents of amphomycin In the hydrolysate, the L-threo and D-erythro forms of α,β-diaminobutyric acid were found, the threo form being more abundant. Also some additional yet unidentified basic amino acids were detected.

Isolation of the antibiotic amphomycin was described by Heinemann et al. in 1953 (8). In the 16 years since then, several new peptide antibiotics have been reported to be closely related to amphomycin: zaomycin in 1954 (9), crystallomycin in 1958 (5), aspartocin in 1959 (16), glumamycin in 1961 (17), tsushimycin in 1968 (18), and laspartomycin in 1968 (15).

The detailed amino acid composition is known for aspartocin (14, 16), and a tentative sequence of the components has been proposed for glumamycin (3). In addition to amino acids, fatty acids also occur among the constituents of amphomycin and the related antibiotics (Table 1).

The identification of the fatty acid in glumamycin (11) as 3-isotridecenoic acid has to be corrected. According to Inoue (11), oxidation of the fatty acid gave 1.2 moles of acetic acid and on ozonolysis of the unsaturated compound an optically active acid was obtained; thus, it follows that the fatty acid from glumamycin belongs not to the iso but rather to the anteiso series. In the case of aspartocin, a thorough study of the fatty acids was carried out, and the two main components, 3-isopentadecenoic acid and 3-anteisopentadecenoic acid, were fully characterized.

Table 1. *Reported fatty acid constituents of the amphomycin group of antibiotics*

Antibiotic	Fatty acids	Reference
Amphomycin	3-Isododecenoic and 3-anteiso-tridecenoic acid	1
Zaomycin	Isoundecenoic acid (tentative)	18
Crystallomycin	Saturated C_{17} fatty acid	13
Aspartocin	3-Isopentenoic and 3-anteiso-pentenoic acid (1:1)	7
Glumamycin	"Isotridecenoic acid" (probably anteisotridecenoic acid)	11
Tsushimycin	Isotetradecenoic and anteiso-pentadecenoic acid	18, 19
Laspartomycin	None reported	15

Apart from its crystallinity, surface activity, amphoteric properties, specific rotation, and peptide character, little was known about amphomycin. Therefore, a detailed investigation into the structure of this antibiotic was undertaken. After acid hydrolysis of amphomycin, an oil could be extracted with ether or hexane. The composition of this mixture, containing fatty acids and lactones, has already been described (1); here we only summarize, in Fig. 1, the major components isolated and identified. The C_{13} unsaturated acid is also the source of the C_{13} lactone; similarly, the C_{12} lactone originates from 3-isododecenoic acid. The formation of the lactones seems to be characteristic of the unsaturated fatty acids from amphomycin.

MATERIALS AND METHODS

Amphomycin calcium salt was generously provided by L. Szabo of H. Lundbeck and Co., Copenhagen-Valby, Denmark, and the sodium salt of aspartocin used for some comparison studies, by E. E. Patterson of Lederle Laboratories, Pearl River, N.Y. Synthetic erythro-α,β-diaminobutyric acid was obtained from J. Meienhofer of the Children's Cancer Research Foundation, Inc., Boston, Mass.

Countercurrent distribution of amphomycin was carried out with a 60-tube Craig apparatus (10-ml lower layer volume) in an *n*-butyl alcohol-pyridine-acetic acid-water (4:2:1:7) solvent system.

$$\begin{array}{l} CH_3 \\ \quad\quad \searrow CH{-}(CH_2)_5{-}CH{-}CH_2{-}CH_2{-}CO \\ CH_3{-}CH_2 \nearrow \quad\quad\quad\quad\quad\; \llcorner\!\!-\!O\!-\!\!\lrcorner \end{array}$$

(+)4-hydroxy-anteisotridecanoic acid lactone
[(+)4-hydroxy-10-methyldodecanoic acid lactone]

$$\begin{array}{l} CH_3 \\ \quad\quad \searrow CH{-}(CH_2)_5{-}CH{=}CH{-}CH_2{-}COOH \\ CH_3{-}CH_2 \nearrow \end{array}$$

(+)3-anteisotridecenoic acid
[(+)10-methyl-3-dodecenoic acid]

$$\begin{array}{l} CH_3 \\ \quad\quad \searrow CH{-}(CH_2)_5{-}CH{-}CH_2{-}CH_2{-}CO \\ CH_3 \nearrow \quad\quad\quad\quad\quad\quad\; \llcorner\!\!-\!O\!-\!\!\lrcorner \end{array}$$

4-hydroxy-isododecanoic acid lactone
[4-hydroxy-10-methylundecanoic acid lactone]

Fig. 1. *Fatty acids in amphomycin.*

The antibiotic, amphomycin, was hydrolyzed at 100 C in 6 N HCl for 16 hr in a nitrogen atmosphere or in vacuo. For qualitative identification of the amino acid residues, descending and circular paper chromatography on Whatman no. 1 paper and thin-layer chromatography on precoated silica gel F-254 plates (distributed by Brinkmann Instruments Inc., Westbury, N.Y.) were employed with an *n*-butyl alcohol-acetic acid-water (4:1:1) solvent system. A Beckman model 120C amino acid analyzer was used for quantitative amino acid analysis. The amino acids were isolated from the hydrolysate by column chromatography on Dowex 50W-X12 cation-exchange resin (4 cm × 30 cm). Gradient elution with hydrochloric acid was used (water to 6 N HCl for the preliminary separation and a 0.12 to 0.60 N HCl for separation of the acidic and neutral amino acids).

Optical rotation of the isolated amino acids was measured with a Perkin-Elmer model 141 Polarimeter in a 1-decimeter cell with 5 N HCl as solvent. The nuclear magnetic resonance (nmr) spectra were obtained on a 60-Hz Varian instrument in D_2O with sodium 2,2-dimethyl-2-silapentane-5-sulfonate (DSS) as the internal reference standard.

RESULTS AND DISCUSSION

The occurrence of several fatty acids in the hydrolysate prompted us to attempt the separation of the individual members of the amphomycin family. A solvent system consisting of *n*-butyl alcohol-pyridine-acetic acid-water (4:2:1:7) was found to give a partition coefficient less dependent on concentration than that obtained with other systems tried. The calcium salt of the antibiotic (1.0 g) was converted into the amphoteric form by acidification of its suspension in water with hydrochloric acid to *p*H 2.6 and extraction of the resulting clear solution with *n*-butyl alcohol. The organic layer was washed with water and dried; the solvent was then removed in vacuo, leaving a solid residue (0.72 g). This material (0.60 g) was dissolved in 20 ml of the upper layer of the solvent system described above, placed into the first two tubes of a Craig apparatus, and distributed through 60 transfers. The bulk of the antibiotic was found in a band with a maximum at tube no. 45. The distribution curve (Fig. 2) was in good agreement with a curve calculated for $K = 3.0$. Samples from several sections of the peak showed no difference in their fatty acid and amino acid composition, and the conclusion had to be drawn that no separation of the members of the antibiotic family took place. Although the material is obviously not homogenous, its heterogeneity could not be demonstrated on paper chromatograms or thin-layer chromatograms. The amino acid constituents were studied, therefore, on such heterogenous material (referred to as amphomycin).

Samples of amphomycin were hydrolyzed, and quantitative amino acid analysis was carried out by the Spackman-Stein-Moore method (20). The results are summarized in Table 2, which also shows the reported amino acid components of the related antibiotics.

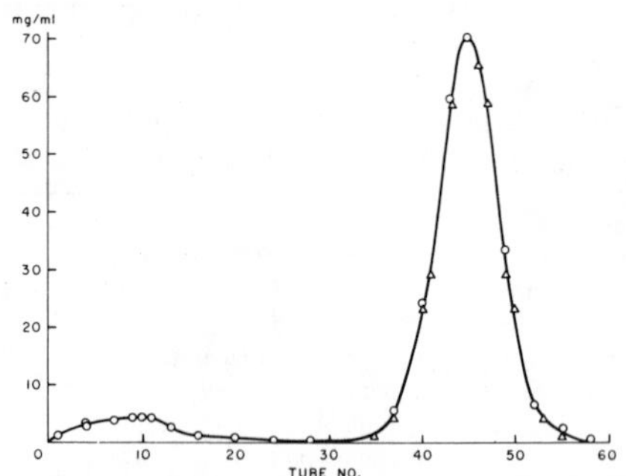

Fig. 2. *Countercurrent distribution of amphomycin in n-butyl alcohol-pyridine-acetic acid-water (4:2:1:7); $n = 60$, $r_{max} = 45$. Symbols: O, experimental curve; Δ, calculated curve ($K = 3.0$).*

Table 2. *Amino acid constituents of the amphomycin group of antibiotics*[a]

Amino acid	Amphomycin	Crystallo-mycin(5)	Aspartocin (6, 14, 16)	Glumamycin (10, 12)	Tsushi-mycin (18)	Lasparto-mycin[b](15)
α,β-Diaminobutyric acid . .	2[c]	6[d]	+	2	U[e]	1
Aspartic acid	3	8	4	3	4[f]	4
β-Methylaspartic acid	1		+	1	—	—
Glycine	2	6	2	2	2	4
L-Valine	1	3	1	1	1	—
D-Pipecolic acid	1	3	+	1	+	+
L-Proline	1	+	1	1	1	1

[a] For zaomycin (9), no amino acid composition was reported. The constituents of amphomycin were determined in the study reported here; data for the other antibiotics are from the references given after the name of each antibiotic. The amounts of each amino acid are expressed in moles.
[b] Contains also threonine (1 mole), isoleucine (1 mole), and two unknown amino acids (one of these basic).
[c] Several additional as yet unidentified basic, ninhydrin-positive constituents were also detected.
[d] No α,β-diaminobutyric acid, but a $C_7H_{14}N_2O_2$ compound was isolated.
[e] Unidentified basic amino acid.
[f] Includes aspartic and β-methylaspartic acids.

A large sample of amphomycin (10 g) was hydrolyzed, the fatty acids were removed by extraction with ether, and the excess hydrochloric acid was removed by evaporation in vacuo. The residue was applied on a Dowex 50W-X12 column. The elution of fractions was followed (Fig. 3) by weight measurement of the residues after evaporation of the eluant under nitrogen. The material from the first peak was rechromatographed on the same column but with a less steep gradient of hydrochloric acid. The elution pattern (Fig. 4) shows good separation between a peak containing both aspartic acid and β-methylaspartic acid, a second peak representing glycine, and the third peak which was identified as L-valine. Finally, a less well-separated section is composed of overlapping areas of L-proline and D-pipecolic acid.

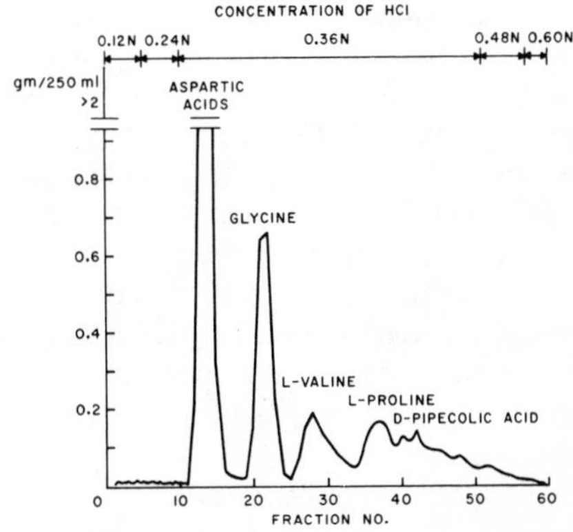

Fig. 4. *Separation of the acidic and neutral amino acids from amphomycin.*

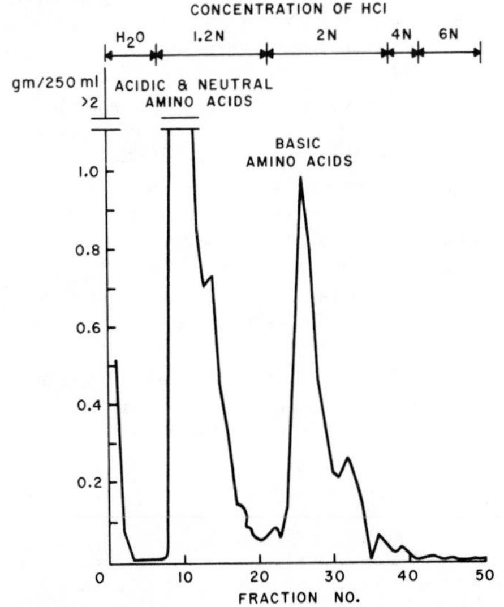

Fig. 3. *Preliminary separation of the components from a total hydrolysate of amphomycin.*

For identification of the amino acids, nmr spectra and comparison with authentic samples on paper chromatograms were used, and the configuration of each component was determined by measurement of the optical rotation. The data thus obtained show that 3 moles of L-aspartic acid, 1 mole of β-methylaspartic acid, 2 moles of glycine, and 1 mole each of L-valine, L-proline, and D-pipecolic acid occur in the antibiotic. The basic amino acids (cf. Fig. 3) consist mainly of α,β-diaminobutyric acid, a part of which (1.0 g) was obtained in crystalline form as a monohydrochloride monohydrate. The nmr spectrum of this material, on comparison with the spectra published by Hausmann, Borders, and Lancaster (6), revealed that in the crystals an equimolar mixture of the threo and erythro forms was at hand. Dakin degradation (2) gave D-alanine, as in the case of the α,β-diaminobutyric acid from glumamycin (4). Thus, the mixture consists of L-threo and D erythro α,β-diaminobutyric acids. However, in the mother liquor of the crystalline α,β-diaminobutyric acid, the threo form was found to be more abundant than the erythro isomer.

In amino acid composition, thus far no major differences have been found among the members of the amphomycin group (with the exception of laspartomycin). In the fatty acid component, the differences are more pronounced, but even in this respect there seems to be at least a close similarity between amphomycin and glumamycin. The study of the sequence of amphomycin currently in progress might reveal that the sequence of the constituents is not the same in these antibiotics. Some of the earlier comparisons of the different members of this group of antibiotics need to be revised. For example, contrary to earlier reports by Shoji et al. (18), amphomycin does indeed contain α,β-diaminobutyric acid. Similar reassessments may be required for other members of this antibiotic group.

ACKNOWLEDGMENTS

This work was supported by Public Health Service grant AI 07515.04 from the National Institute of Allergy and Infectious Diseases. One of the authors (J.A.S.) is a National Institutes of Health predoctoral fellow.

LITERATURE CITED

1. Bodanszky, M., N. C. Chaturvedi, and J. A. Scozzie. 1969. The structure of fatty acids from the antibiotic amphomycin. J. Antibiot. (Tokyo) **22**:399–408.
2. Dakin, H. D. 1905. The oxidation of amino acids with the production of substances of biological importance. J. Biol. Chem. **1**:171–176.
3. Fujino, M. 1965. On glumamycin, a new antibiotic. VI. An approach to the amino acid structure. Bull. Chem. Soc. Jap. **38**:517–522.
4. Fujino, M., M. Inoue, J. Ueyanagi, and A. Miyake. 1965. On glumamycin, a new antibiotic. V. The steric configuration of α,β-diaminobutyric acid. Bull. Chem. Soc. Jap. **38**:515–516.
5. Gause, G. F., T. P. Preobrazhenskaya, V. K. Kovalinkova, N. P. Ilicheva, M. G. Brazhnikova, N. N. Lomakina, I. N. Kovsharova, V. A. Shorin, I. A. Kunrat, and S. P. Shapovalova. 1957. Crystallomycin, a new antibacterial antibiotic. Antibiotiki **6**:9–14.
6. Hausmann, W. K., D. B. Borders, and J. E. Lancaster. 1969. α,β-diaminobutyric acid obtained from aspartocin. J. Antibiot. (Tokyo) **22**:207–210.
7. Hausmann, W. K., A. H. Struck, J. H. Martin, R. H. Barritt, and N. Bohonos. 1964. Structure determination of fatty acids from the antibiotic aspartocin. Antimicrob. Agents Chemother.–1963, p. 352–359.
8. Heinemann, B., M. A. Kaplan, R. D. Muir and I. R. Hooper. 1953. Amphomycin, a new antibiotic. Antibiot. Chemother. **3**:1239–1242.
9. Hinuma, Y. 1954. Zaomycin, a new antibiotic from streptomyces sp. Studies on the antibiotic substances from actinomyces. XXXIII. J. Antibiot. (Tokyo) Ser A **7**:134–136.
10. Inoue, M. 1962. On glumamycin, a new antibiotic. II. Isolation and identification of amino acids constituting glumamycin. Bull. Chem. Soc. Jap. **35**:1249–1254.
11. Inoue, M. 1962. On glumamycin, a new antibiotic. III. Fatty acid, a constituent of the antibiotic. Bull. Chem. Soc. Jap. **35**:1255–1257.
12. Inoue, M. 1962. On glumamycin, a new antibiotic. IV. The amino acid moiety. Bull. Chem. Soc. Jap. **35**:1566.
13. Lomakina, N. N., and M. G. Brazhnikova. 1959. The chemical composition of crystallomycin. Biokhimiya **24**:399–405.
14. Martin, J. H., and W. K. Hausmann. 1960. Isolation and identification of D-α-pipecolic acid, α[L],β-methylaspartic acid and α,β-diaminobutyric acid from the polypeptide antibiotic aspartocin. J. Amer. Chem. Soc. **82**:2079.
15. Naganawa, H., M. Hamada, K. Maeda, Y. Okami, T. Takeuchi, and H. Umezawa. 1968. Laspartomycin, a new antistaphylococcal peptide. J. Antibiot. (Tokyo) **21**:55–62.
16. Shay, A. J., J. Adam, J. H. Martin, W. K. Hausmann, P. Shu, and N. Bohonos. 1960. Aspartocin. I. Production, isolation and characteristics. Antibiot. Ann. 1959/1960, p. 194–198.
17. Shibata, M., T. Kanzaki, N. Nakazawa, M. Inoue, H. Hitomi, K. Mizuno, M. Fujino, and A. Miyake. 1962. Glumamycin, a new antibiotic. J. Antibiot. (Tokyo) Ser. A **15**:1–6.
18. Shoji, J., S. Kozuki, S. Okamoto, R. Sakazaki, and H. Otsuka. 1968. Studies on tsushimycin. I. Isolation and characterization of an acidic acylpeptide containing a new fatty acid. J. Antibiot. (Tokyo) **11**:439–443.
19. Shoji, J., and H. Otsuka. 1969. Studies on tsushimycin. II. The structures of constituent fatty acids. J. Antibiot. (Tokyo) **22**:473–479.
20. Spackman, D. H., W. H. Stein, and S. Moore. 1958. Automatic recording apparatus for use in the chromatography of amino acids. Anal. Chem. **30**:1190–1206.

Antimicrobial Agents and Chemotherapy—1969

Biosynthesis of Coumermycin A_1: Incorporation of L-Proline into the Pyrrole Groups

J. SCANNELL and Y. L. KONG

Hoffman-La Roche Inc., Chemical Research Department, Nutley, New Jersey 07110

The incorporation by a *Streptomyces* strain of radioactive atoms in glucose, proline, δ-aminolevulinic acid (ALA), and methionine into coumermycin A_1 and into the methyl pyrrole groups was examined. Glucose was incorporated into the nonpyrroyl portions of the molecule and methionine into both the pyrrole and the nonpyrroyl moieties. Proline was incorporated into the pyrrole groups to a 10-fold greater extent than was ALA. Moreover, in a cold precursor competition experiment, ALA had no effect on proline incorporation but proline lowered ALA incorporation. We conclude that the pyrrole ring is synthesized from proline, rather than from ALA as is the case in the porphyrin biosynthetic pathway.

The chemical similarity of portions of coumermycin A_1 (Fig. 1A) to novobiocin (Fig. 1B) permits certain analogies on biosynthetic pathways to be made. Thus, for coumermycin it is likely that glucose is the precursor of the noviose moieties (3), that tyrosine is the origin of the coumarin moieties (4), and that methionine is a source of the coumarin C-methyl and noviose O-methyl groups, as well as of one methyl of the gem dimethyl group (2). We have, therefore, focused our attention on the pyrrole moieties unique to coumermycin. [The proposed structures and nomenclature of the known components of the coumermycin complex were summarized previously (7). Whereas A_1 has two terminal methyl pyrroyl groups, D-2 has only one. D-1b and D-1c have one terminal methyl pyrroyl group and one terminal pyrroyl group; A_2 has two terminal pyrroyl groups.

Our experiments were facilitated by the ease with which all three pyrrole groups can be removed pyrolytically and purified and assayed by the vapor-phase chromatography (VPC) procedure (7). Thus, it was possible to study methionine as a precursor of the C-methyl groups specifically on the pyrroles. On the basis of some possible metabolic pathways of pyrrole synthesis, summarized in Fig. 2, it was of interest to determine whether δ-aminolevulinic acid (ALA) is the preferred precursor of the pyrrole group, as is the case in prophyrin biosynthesis (6), or whether proline is incorporated, as appears to be the case in the biosynthesis of prodigiosin (8). Since it has not yet been possible to obtain sufficient coumermycin production by *Streptomyces* cells grown on a simple defined medium, cells grown on a complex medium and washed cells previously grown on a complex medium were used in our experiments.

MATERIALS AND METHODS

A strain of *S. hazeliensis* (1) was used in all experiments. An inoculum (3 ml), prepared from a slant culture by incubation at 28 C for 3 days, was added to a 1-liter flask containing 100 ml of medium. Incubation, unless otherwise stated, was in shaken flasks for 10 days at 28 C. Both inoculum and fermentation media consisted of (per liter): cottonseed flour (Pharmamedia), 20 g; cornstarch, 20 g; lard oil, 20 g; debittered yeast, 4 g; $K_2HPO_4 \cdot 3HO_2$, 2.5 g; $CaCl_2 \cdot 2H_2O$, 0.5 g; and $CoCl_2 \cdot 6H_2O$, 202 μg.

In washed-cell experiments, the cells plus insoluble fermentation medium components were separated from the growth medium by centrifugation, resuspended in 0.1 M potassium phosphate (pH 6.3), and again collected by centrifugation. After repetition of the phosphate wash, the cells and solids were suspended in 100 ml of the same buffer. Preliminary experiments had shown that the insoluble medium components were necessary for antibiotic production. To the suspended cells was added 5 to 10 μc of ^{14}C-labeled compounds or 50 μc of

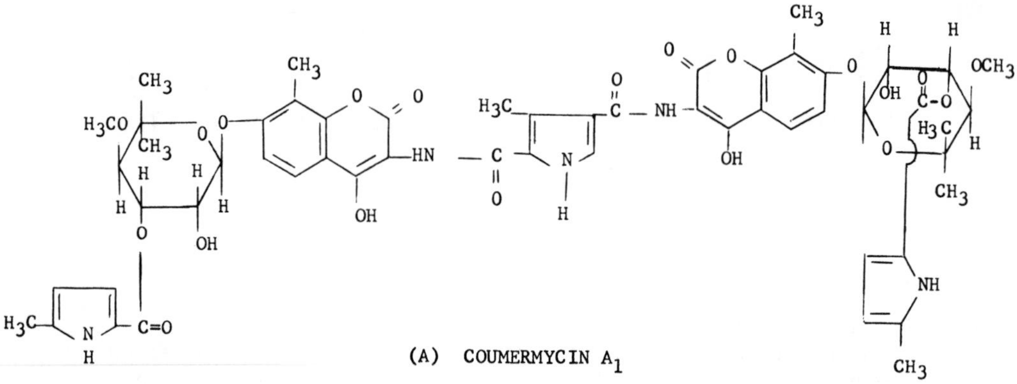

(A) COUMERMYCIN A_1

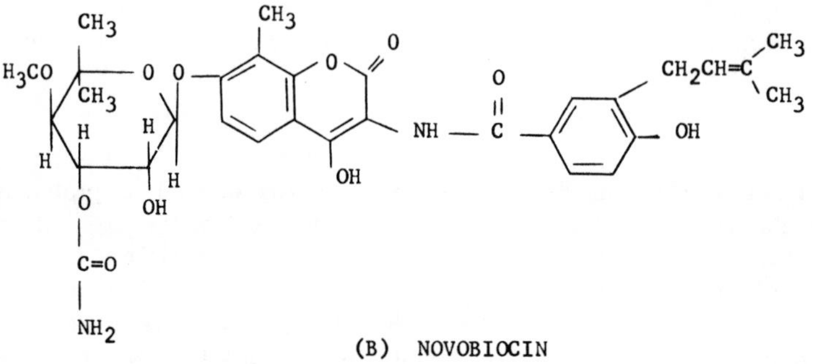

(B) NOVOBIOCIN

Fig. 1. *Structure of coumermycin* A_1 *and Novobiocin.*

^{3}H-labeled compounds. The specific activities of the substances were such that the absolute amount of presumed precursor added to the 100 ml was about 0.1 μmole. No attempts were made to estimate or take into consideration pool sizes. After 10 hr of incubation, 20 mg of nonradioactive pure coumermycin A_1 was added as carrier, and the total coumermycin complex was isolated by adjustment of the *p*H of the whole broth to 7.5 and addition of one-half volume of acetone. After filtration with Celite filter aid, the filter cake was suspended twice in 25 ml of 50% aqueous acetone and filtered. The combined filtrate and washes were evaporated at 35 C under reduced pressure until the low-boiling solvent was removed. The concentrate and 0.5 g of Celite filter aid were stirred while the *p*H was slowly adjusted to 4.1 with 2 N HCl. The crude antibiotic complex precipitated on the filter aid was filtered on a sintered-glass funnel and washed with about 10 ml of water until the wash was colorless. Additional colored impurities were removed by two successive suspensions of the precipitate in 2 ml of methanol at 0 C followed by filtration. The filter cake was then extracted twice with 5 ml of tetrahydrofuran. The filtrates from this step were combined and concentrated under reduced pressure to about 1 ml; 2.5 ml of methanol was added, and the antibiotic suspension was concentrated again to 1 ml. This step was repeated, another 2.5 ml of methanol was then added, and the cooled suspension was filtered without addition of filter aid on a fine-porosity, sintered-glass funnel. The antibiotic complex was washed once with 1 ml of cold methanol and three times with 0.5 ml of ethyl ether. The isolated material, yield 90%, was 95 to 100% antibiotic complex. The same isolation procedure was used with growing cultures. In the nonradioactive experiments (Table 1), the procedure was scaled up 10-fold and no carrier coumermycin A_1 was added. The analysis for coumermycin D-2 was by the ultraviolet spectral ratios of the isolated complex (7).

For determination of total incorporation into coumermycin A_1, the complex was separated into various components by thin-layer chromatography on Merck silica gel F-254 developed with ethyl acetate-water-tetrahydrofuran: 4:5:1, upper layer. The coumermycin A_1 area was scraped off, and radioactivity was determined as described below. Quantitation was based on the isolated weight as checked by bioassay (1) and ultra-

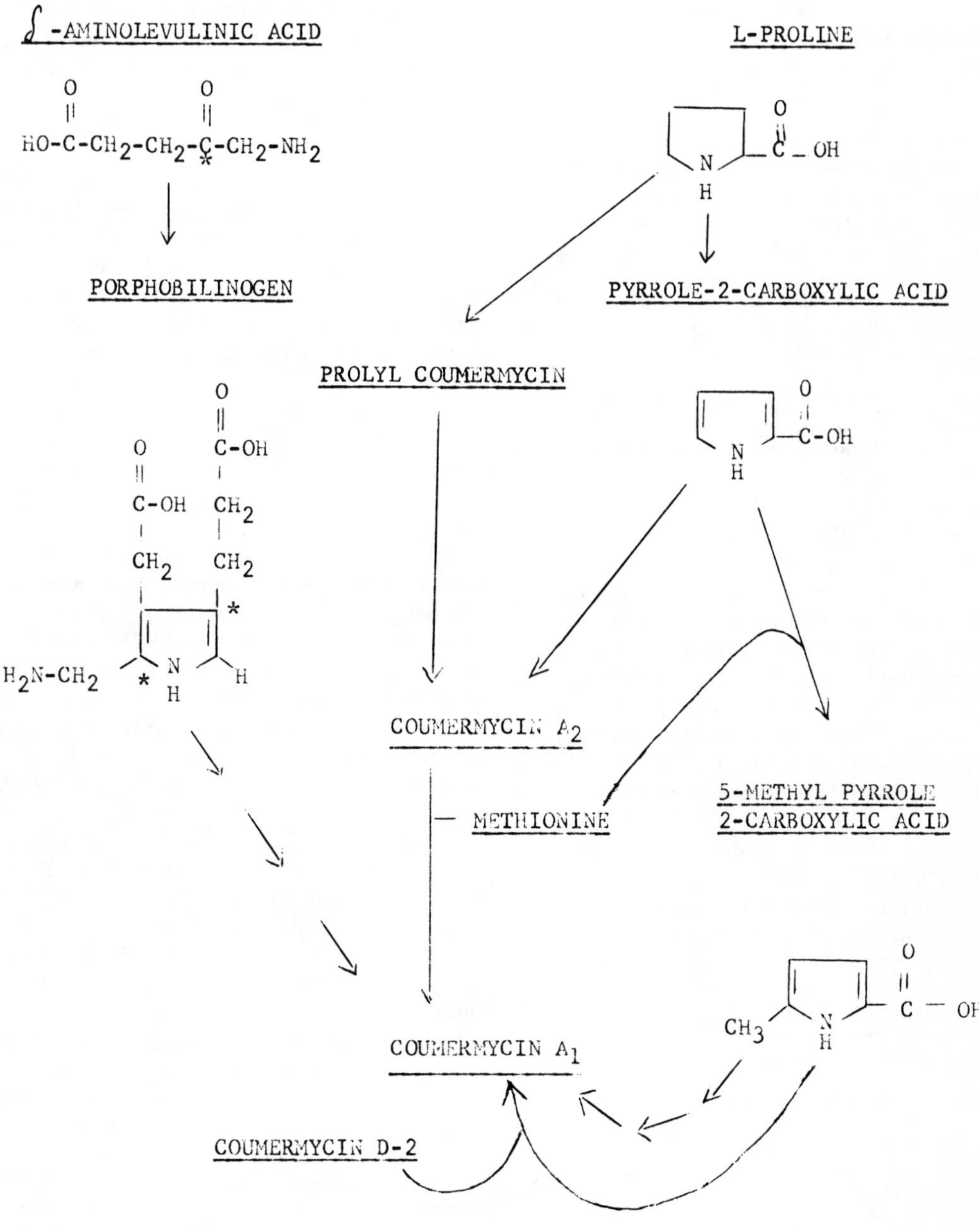

Fig. 2. *Some possible pathways of coumermycin A_1 biosynthesis.*

violet spectroscopy (7). Thus, an error was introduced by the presence of other analogues; however, in all cases this error was small since coumermycin A_1 was added as a carrier, and a check on the amounts of other analogues present was afforded by the thin-layer chromatography separation and by spectral ratios (7) of the isolated material.

Incorporation of label into pyrrole groups was determined after isolating these moieties by means of the pyrolysis-VPC method (7). An F & M model 80 pyrolyzer operated at 8.5 amp and an F & M 5750 chromatograph equipped with a 10/1 splitter and preparative take off were used. The methyl pyrrole was trapped in ethyl alcohol at 0 C, and the amounts were determined by ultraviolet absorption at 230 nm, measured with a Beckman DB-G spectrophotometer. The amounts of radioactivity in coumermycin A_1 and in methyl pyrrole were determined with a Packard model 3375 scintillation counter by use of a scintillation solution consisting of 16 g of 2,5-bis-[2-(5-*t*-butylbenzoxazolyl)]-thiophene, 2,400 ml of toluene, 320 g of naphthalene, and 160 ml of methylcellosolve.

^{14}C-L-proline (U) and δ-aminolevulinic-*4-C*^{14} acid were purchased from New England Nuclear Corp., Boston, Mass. L-Methionine (methyl-C^{14}), ^{14}C-D-glucose (U), L-methionine (methyl-T), L-proline-T(G), and 4-hydroxyproline-T(G) were purchased from Nuclear-Chicago Corp., Des Plaines, Ill.

RESULTS AND DISCUSSION

In small-scale experiments, great variation in fermentation yield and in consequent per cent incorporation of radioactive precursors was encountered. However, each experiment was repeated several times and the relative incorporation of the various precursors did not change. The results presented below are representative of those experiments in which good fermentation yields of coumermycin A_1 were obtained.

Production of coumermycin A_1 and D-2. As is apparent from Table 1, antibiotic began to appear at about the third day after inoculation. The concentration gradually increased until about the 12th day, after which the activity remained essentially constant. The D-2 analogue was apparently formed early in the fermentation, for after the fifth day there was no significant change in concentration. This would indicate that A_1 is not formed by direct pyrroylation of D-2, although the insolubility of the antibiotic complex may also prevent the pyrrolylation of D-2. Addition of Co^{++} to the medium (5) kept the nor forms, A_2 and D-1-b/c, at barely detectable levels, <5 mg/liter, at all times.

Table 1. *Time course of the coumermycin fermentation*

Day	Coumermycin complex isolated[a]	Coumermycin D-2[b]
	mg/liter	*mg/liter*
3	17	2
4	47	3
5	126	7
7	156	6
9	225	7
11	276	8
13	333	6
15	295	6
17	324	7
19	348	7
23	355	7

[a] No added carrier was employed here.
[b] Determined by the ultraviolet spectral ratios of the isolated complex (7).

Incorporation of methionine ($C^{14}H_3$) into coumermycin A_1. The results presented in Table 2 show significant incorporation at all dosing times, with a maximum at 5 days. In view of the many alternate metabolic reactions of methionine, the complex and ill-defined nature of the fermentation medium, and the long time course of the fermentation, these may be considered very good incorporations. On the assumption that methylation is a terminal step in the biosynthesis, we chose to dose with other radioactive precursors at 4 days rather than at 5 days.

Relative incorporation of radioactive precursors into the whole molecule and into the pyrrole groups of coumermycin A_1. The results of experiments summarized in Table 3 show that proline is incorporated to about the same extent as methionine and about 10 times more than ALA, even though there are two potential sites of incorporation for ALA in each pyrrole. Moreover, in a competition experiment in which washed cells were used, the incorporation of radioactive L-proline was not appreciably changed by the addition of either 20 or 100 mg of nonradioactive ALA to a 100-ml washed-cell suspension; however, the incorporation of radioactive ALA was depressed to one-fourth of the control level by the addition of 20 mg of nonradioactive L-proline. It is unlikely that 4-hydroxy-L-proline is an oxidative intermediate during the utilization of L-proline as tritium

Table 2. *Incorporation of methionine ($^{14}CH_3$) into coumermycin A_1 in a growing culture of Streptomyces hazeliensis*

Day of dosing	Incorporation
	%
3	2.2
4	4.1
5	10.6
6	8.4
7	6.1
8	3.8
9	2.2
10	1.7

Table 3. *Incorporation of labeled precursors into coumermycin A_1*

Precursor	Per cent incorporation			
	Washed cells		Growing cells	
	Whole molecule	Pyrroles	Whole molecule	Pyrroles
L-Methionine	14.9	12.2	10.0	7.9
L-Proline	7.0	6.9[a]	7.6	8.0[a]
δ-Aminolevulinic acid	0.5	1.0	0.9	0.4
D-Glucose	0.01	0	1.0	0

[a] Corrected for pyrolytic loss of carboxyl label, assuming uniform labeling of the molecule.

from the former was incorporated to only one-tenth the extent of tritium from the latter.

Although the incorporation of radioactive carbon from glucose was low compared with that of other precursors, this may only reflect the rapid utilization of glucose for other metabolic purposes, particularly in the nutrient-starved, washed-cell experiments. A further complication was the finding that the addition of glucose to washed cells results in complete inhibition of coumermycin production.

It seems apparent that when dosed at the fourth day methylation by methionine occurs predominantly on the pyrroles. However, since no direct measurements were made specifically on other parts of the molecule, this inference is based on the difference between two experimentally distinct measurements of total incorporation and pyrrole incorporation. Nevertheless, the good agreement in the proline incorporation into pyrroles and the whole molecule lends confidence to the methods and the conclusion. The differences (Table 3) between the incorporation of ALA into the whole molecule and into the pyrroles in washed cells as compared with growing cells are probably not experimentally significant, because the actual number of counts per minute was quite small.

Our major conclusion is that proline serves as a direct precursor of the pyrrole groups of coumermycin A_1. The mechanism of incorporation may be more complex than a simple pyrroylation of coumermycin D-2. Moreover, questions remain as to when and how proline is oxidized and at what stage methylation takes place.

ACKNOWLEDGMENTS

We thank J. Berger and D. Perlman for their critical interest in this work. We are also indebted to H. Laurencot for radioactivity measurements.

LITERATURE CITED

1. Berger, J., A. J. Schocher, A. D. Batcho, B. Pecherer, O. Keller, J. Maricq, A. E. Karr, B. P. Vaterlaus, A. Furlenmeier, and H. Spiegelberg. 1966. Production, isolation, and synthesis of the coumermycins (sugordomycins), a new streptomycete antibiotic complex. Antimicrob. Agents Chemother.–1965, p. 778-785.
2. Birch, A. J., D. W. Cameron, P. W. Holloway, and R. W. Rickards. 1960. Further examples of biological C-methylation: novobiocin and actinomycin. Tetrahedron Lett. **25**:26–31.
3. Birch, A. J., P. W. Holloway, and R. W. Rickards. 1962. The biosynthesis of noviose, a branched chain monosaccharide. Biochim. Biophys. Acta **57**:143–145.
4. Bunton, C. A., G. W. Kenner, M. J. T. Robinson, and B. R. Webster. 1963. Experiments related to the biosynthesis of novobiocin and other coumarins. Tetrahedron **19**:1001–1010.
5. Claridge, C. A., V. Z. Rossomano, N. S. Buono, A. Gourevitch, and J. Lein. 1966. Influence of cobalt on fermentative methylation. Appl. Microbiol. **14**:280–283.
6. Lascelles, J. 1964. Tetrapyrrole biosynthesis and its regulation. W. A. Benjamin, New York.
7. Scannell, J. 1968. Characterization and analysis of the antibiotic coumermycin by means of pyrolysis-vapor-phase chromatography and ultraviolet spectra. Antimicrob. Agents Chemother.–1967, p. 470–474.
8. Williams, R. P., and W. R. Hearn. 1967. Prodigiosin, p. 410–432. *In* D. Gottlieb and P. D. Shaw (ed.), Antibiotics, vol. 2. Biosynthesis. Springer-Verlag, New York.

Antimicrobial Agents and Chemotherapy—1969

Printed in USA

Moenomycin A: Further Characterization and Chemistry

D. LENOIR, R. TSCHESCHE, W. WUCHERPFENNIG, G. HUBER, and H. L. WEIDENMÜLLER

Institut für Organische und Biochemie, Bonn, and Farbwerke Hoechst AG, Frankfurt/M-Hoechst, Germany

Moenomycin A, which is primarily effective against gram-positive bacteria, is the principal component of the antibiotic moenomycin. It is a phosphorus-containing glycolipid and a tetrabasic acid with a strongly acid function (phosphoric acid diester group) and three medium strength acid groups. In aqueous solution, moenomycin behaves like a strong surfactant. This is consistent with its molecular structure, which consists of a polar part (chromophore, oligosaccharide, phosphoric acid diester group) and a non polar lipid residue (moenocinol). On hydrolysis, a number of cleavage products were found, and the following either were identified or their structure was elucidated: D-glucosamine, D-glucose, ultraviolet chromophore (2-amino-cyclopentanedione-1,3), the lipid alcohol named moenocinol, and a phosphoric acid diester group. The structure of the hydrolysis product Z_1 described in an earlier paper has been elucidated.

Moenomycin A is the principal component of the antibiotic moenomycin isolated from *Streptomyces bambergiensis,* and is highly effective against gram-positive bacteria (4, 9). Moenomycin consists of several components which are chemically similar, and it belongs to a new group of antibiotics which are phosphorus-containing glycolipids. The recently described antibiotics 11 837 R.P. (D. Mancy et al., Abstr. Int. Congr. Microbiol., Moscow, p. 165, 1966) and prasinomycin contain a number of structural components (sugars, a lipid moiety called moenocinol) which are also found in moenomycin (6, 10).

Moenomycin A has the approximate empirical formula $C_{70}H_{121}N_5O_{40}P$ and reacts like a tetrabasic acid. On potentiometric titration of the acid form (produced over Dowex-50) with 0.1 N sodium hydroxide solution, two equivalence points in a ratio of 1:3 were obtained. An equivalent weight of 450 was calculated from the base comsumption. One acid function is relatively strong ($pK_a < 2$) and may be ascribed to the phosphoric acid diester group; the other three acid functions are of medium strength ($pK_a = 4.5$) and probably correspond to carboxyl groups. In aqueous solution, moenomycin behaves as a strong surfactant. The dependence of the surface tension on the molar concentration is approximately the same as is found in aqueous solutions of soaps and alkyl sulfates (Fig. 1). In contrast, the concentration dependence of the equivalent conductance is different from the usual surfactant compounds so that it was not possible to derive a defined concentration of micell formation.

On splitting the lipid moiety from the intact molecule, both antibiotic and surfactant prop-

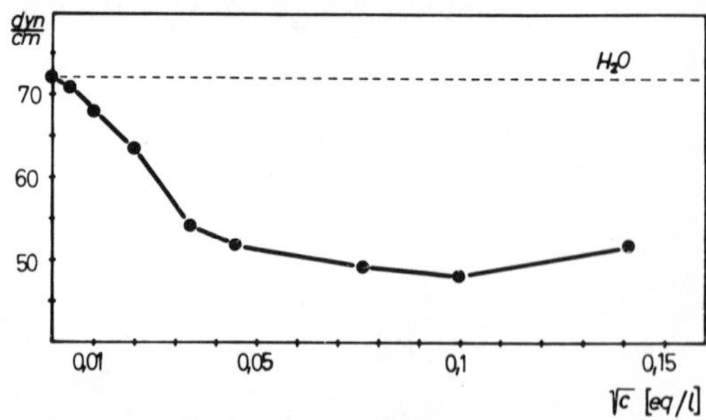

Fig. 1. *Dependence of the surface tension of moenomycin (potassium salt) in aqueous solution on the equivalent concentration.*

erties disappeared completely. From this result, it follows that the known high molecular weight aggregates of moenomycin probably have a micellar structure (from the magnitude of the sedimentation and diffusion constant in the pH range from 3 to 7, particle weights between 20,000 and 70,000 are calculated). The molecular structure of moenomycin, consisting of hydrophobic hydrocarbon residue (lipid) adjacent to a highly polar moiety (oligosaccharide and phosphoric acid ester), satisfies the requirements for a micellar structure in aqueous solution. In such micelles, the aggregates of high molecular weight are oriented as a result of the hydrophobic interaction of the hydrocarbon residues to form complexes of 20 to 40 monomeric units, with a decrease in free energy content.

For elucidation of the molecular structure of moenomycin A, a number of cleavage products, which are formed on hydrolysis with dilute boiling mineral acid, were isolated and their structures were determined. The molecule is relatively stable to dilute alkali, but treatment with acid very quickly leads to decomposition of the compound.

Lipid part. On short-term hydrolysis (2 N HCl, 12 min at 100 C), a water-insoluble fraction separates as an oily residue (lipid part) which can be extracted with benzene or chloroform. This fraction was separated into three components. The structures of these compounds (moenocinol, isomoenocinol, and moenocene) were clarified by us recently (7; Fig. 2).

We have shown that moenocinol posesses the same structure as the lipid portion of moenomycin and is probably linked as an ether to the remainder of the molecule. During the hydrogenation of moenomycin (aqueous methanol, Pt catalyst), hydrogenolysis of some of the lipid part takes place with formation of a perhydrogenated compound which is identical with the product obtained from the hydrogenation of moenocene. It is thus demonstrated that the lipid components isolated during acid hydrolysis do not represent a rearrangement product of the carbon skeleton. [It is possible that the biogenesis of this compound does not take place by means of the stepwise building up of isoprene units but by direct alkylation of a sesquiterpene unit (of the caryophylene type, for example) with geranyl pyrophosphate.]

The following findings indicate an ether linkage of the lipid part with the molecular residue. (i) It is not possible to cause cleavage with alkali treatment (10% sodium hydroxide solution, 2 hr at 100 C); what is more, no additional titratable acid function is formed by acid cleavage. An ester bond is consequently *improbable.* (ii) No reaction takes place with hydroxylamine hydrochloride; an acetal or ketal linkage is therefore improbable. (iii) The cleavage of the lipid moiety generally takes place readily under solvolysis conditions; in highly polar solvents such as formic acid or HBr-glacial acetic acid, it proceeds almost instantaneously at room temperature; in dilute mineral acid at 100 C, it is complete after approximately 10 min; and in a dimethylsulfoxide-sulfuric acid system in a ratio of 9:1 it takes 1 to 2 hr. The moenocinol and isomoenocinol split off are in a state of reversible equilibrium. On the basis of this result the cleavage suggests solvolysis of a protonated allyl ether (Fig. 3). From the amount of the lipid part (ca. 15 to 20%) obtained on hydrolysis, it may be deduced that moenocinol (molecular weight, 358) is present only once in the molecule.

Sugars. If allowed to react with acid for an extended period, a number of sugars are split

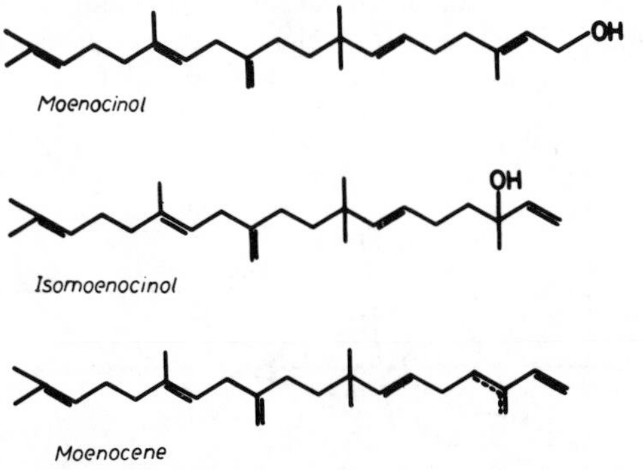

Fig. 2. *Structure of the lipid components from moenomycin.*

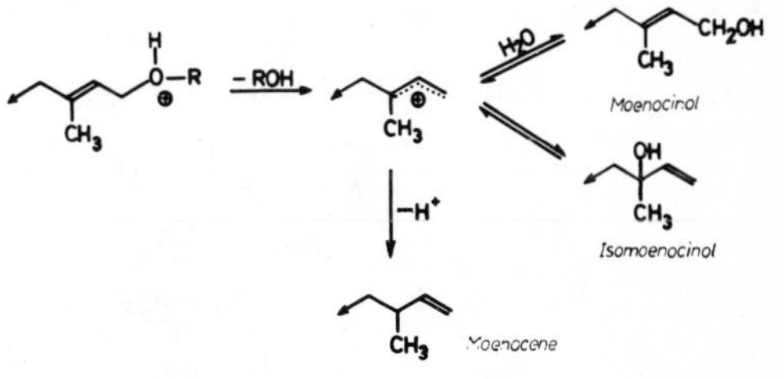

Fig. 3. *Proposed mechanism of lipid splitting of moenomycin.*

off, the isolation and characterization of which have already been reported (4). After hydrolysis for 30 min, glucose is detectable, and after 2 hr the amino sugars glucosamine and quinovosamine are found (Table 1). These sugars are determined quantitatively in the hydrolysate. The amino sugars were determined in a Beckman amino acid analyzer (ninhydrin) after hydrolysis for 14.5 hr with semiconcentrated HCl (6 N) at 100 C. The losses on hydrolysis were corrected. Glucose was determined by gas chromatography after silylation and enzymatically by means of glucose oxidase.

The values in Table 1 show that both amino sugars occur once in the molecule. Since moenomycin does not possess basic properties and neither reacts with ninhydrin nor consumes nitrite, the amino sugars must be present in acylated form. The relatively large acetyl content of moenomycin (12 to 13%) is an indication of *N*-acetyl groups.

Since the reaction of moenomycin itself with Morgan-Elson reagent is negative, it is likely that both amino sugars are in the pyranose form (5).

Moenomycin reacts with both aqueous sodium periodate and lead tetraacetate in acetic acid. The quantitative comsumption of both oxidizing agents shows that 2 oxidation equivalents are taken up so that two vicinal diol groups may be present. Further hydrolysis of the oxydized product produces the amino sugars, but no glucose; thus, at least one of the diol groups must be located on a glucose residue.

Chromophore part. 2-Amino-cyclopentanedione-1,3 (Fig. 4) was recognized as the chromophore in moenomycin (8); it is liberated by acid hydrolysis (2 hr at 100 C) and can be isolated by ion exchange. This very unstable amino reductone was converted into a stable *N*-acetyl derivative which we were able to characterize.

Table 1. *Quantitative determination of glucosamine, quinovosamine, and glucose in moenomycin A*

Sugar	Per cent	Per molecule of moenomycin
Glucosamine	11.38	1.05
Quinovosamine	9.45	0.95
Glucose		
(by gas chromatography)	7.0	0.66
Glucose (oxidase)	7.11	0.67

Fig. 4. *"Chromophor" and N-acetyl "chromophor" from moenomycin A.*

The compound was obtained synthetically for the first time by Corbella et al. (2). We prepared it in a different way and characterized its spectroscopic properties. The chromophore as such is inherently symmetrical and only becomes a chiral system through its linkage with the molecular residue which then exhibits a characteristic circular dichroism. The sign and band intensity are dependent on the solvent and *p*H (Fig. 5).

Apart from the free "chromophore," we succeeded in isolating from the hydrolysate a chromophore containing cleavage product which, on further acid treatment, could be split into "chromophore" and quinovosamine. This compound exhibits the same circular dichroism as moenomycin. Thus, it is demonstrated that this unit represents the chiral center of the molecule.

Sugarlike hydrolysis product Z_1. On prolonged acid hydrolysis (5 hr at 100 C), a sugarlike, strongly reducing cleavage product Z_1 is split off from moenomycin; its isolation has already been reported (4). It was possible to purify this compound by means of careful chromatography on silica gel and Sephadex, followed by crystallization. The structure was derived on the basis of its spectroscopic properties (mass spectrum, ultraviolet, nuclear magnetic resonance, and infrared spectra) as 3-methyl-4,5-dihydroxycylopentene-2-one-1 (W. Wucherpfennig, Diplomarbeit, Universität Bonn, Bonn, Germany, 1969; Fig. 6). The sugarlike compound could also be converted into its diacetate. Similar dihydroxy-cyclopentenones have been found in nature as metabolites of moulds, e.g., terrein, which possesses a propenyl group instead of the methyl group of Z_1 (1).

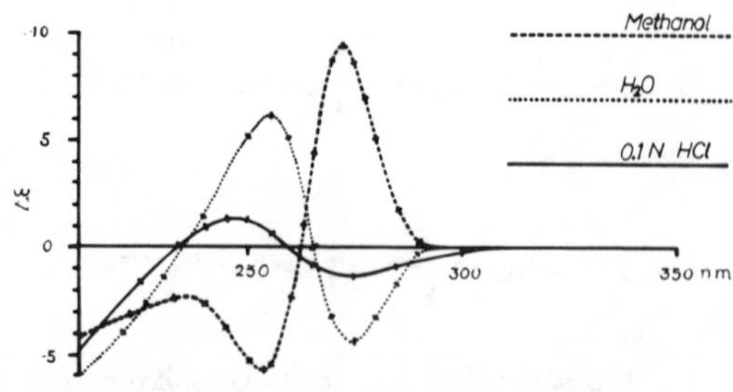

Fig. 5. *Circular dichroism of moenomycin A.*

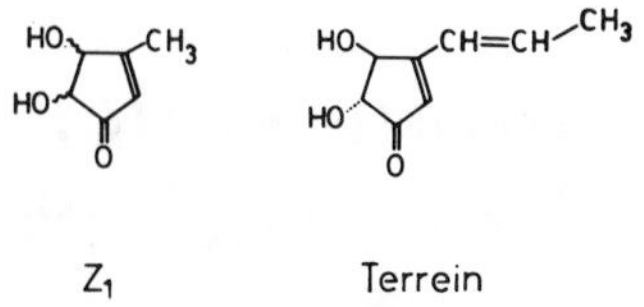

HO, CH3 / HO / O — Z_1 HO, CH=CH–CH3 / HO / O — Terrein

Fig. 6. *Structure of Z_1 and terrein.*

Since a corresponding enone chromophor is not observed in moenomycin, nor is a carbonyl group detectable, Z_1 ought to represent a secondary product. However, it could also be present in the parent molecule as a ketal. The optical activity of Z_1 indicates that the configuration during hydrolysis must have been retained in at least one center of asymmetry. Finally, it could be shown that none of the known cleavage products leads to Z_1 after further hydrolysis.

LITERATURE CITED

1. Barton, D. H. R., and E. Müller. 1955. The constitution and stereochemistry of terrein. J. Chem. Soc. (London), p. 1028.
2. Corbella, A., G. Jommi, G. Ricci, and G. Russo. 1965. Sui 2-amino-1,3-dichetoni cicilici. Gazz. Chim. Ital. **95**:948–965.
3. Huber, G., U. Schacht, H. L. Weidenmüller, J. Schmidt-Thomé, J. Duphorn, and R. Tschesche. 1966. Moenomycin, a new antibiotic. II. Characterization and chemistry. Antimicrob. Agents Chemother.–1965, p. 737–742.
4. Huber, G. 1967. Moenomycin. IV. Säurehydrolyse und Charakterisierung der Spaltprodukte. Liebigs Ann. Chem. **707**:170–176.
5. Kuhn, R., and G. Krüger. 1956. 3-Acetaminofuran aus N-Acetyl-D-Glucosamin; ein Beitrag zur Theorie der Morgan-Elson-Reaktion. Chem. Ber. **89**: 1473–1486.
6. Slusarchyk, W. A., and F. L. Weisenborn. 1969. The structure of the lipid portion of the antibiotic prasinomycin. Tetrahedron Lett., p. 659–662.
7. Tschesche, R., F.-X. Brock, and J. Duphorn. 1968. Moenomycin. V. Strukturaufklärung des Lipoidteils von Moenomycin. Liebigs Ann. Chem. **720**:58–70.
8. Tschesche, R., D. Lenoir, and H. L. Weidenmüller. 1969. Über die Struktur des "Chromophors" in Antibiotkum Moenomycin. Tetrahedron Lett., p. 141–144.
9. Wallhausser, K. H., G. Nesemann, P. Prave, and A. Steigler. 1966. Moenomycin, a new antibiotic. I. Fermentation and isolation. Antimicrob. Agents Chemother.–1965, p. 734–736.
10. Weisenborn, F. L., J. L. Bouchard, D. Smith, F. Pansy, G. Maestrone, G. Miraglia, and E. Meyers. 1967. The prasinomycins: Antibiotics containing phosphorus. Nature (London) **213**:1092–1094.

Antimicrobial Agents and Chemotherapy—1969

Printed in USA

Pharmacology of Polyriboinosinic: Polyribocytidylic Acid, a New Antiviral and Antitumor Agent

RICHARD H. ADAMSON, SERGIO FABRO, ELTON R. HOMAN, ROGER W. O'GARA, and ROBERT P. ZENDZIAN

National Cancer Institute, Bethesda, Maryland 20014, The George Washington University, Washington, D.C. 20005, and Hazleton Laboratories, Falls Church, Virginia 22042

Polyriboinosinic: polyribocytidylic acid (poly rI:poly rC), an effective inducer of interferon, was tested for antitumor activity in mice, rats, and primates. Poly rI:poly rC was especially active against a mouse reticulum cell sarcoma (A-RCS) and against the Walker 256 rat carcinosarcoma. Poly rI:poly rC was examined for potential embryotoxic, carcinogenic, and pharmacological properties in several animal species. In the rabbit, poly rI:poly rC caused 100% resorptions when administered subcutaneously on days 8 and 9 of pregnancy. In dogs and rhesus monkeys, daily intravenous doses of poly rI:poly rC greater than 1 mg/kg were lethal; doses of 1 mg/kg and less were tolerated. The most consistent changes in blood chemistry in dogs and monkeys were dose related increases in serum transaminases and prothrombin time.

Polyriboinosinic: polyribocytidylic acid (poly rI:poly rC), a synthetic double-stranded ribonucleic acid, was shown by Field et al. and Hilleman to be an effective inducer or releaser of interferon and also to have activity against viral infection in vivo and in vitro (4, 5). Park and Baron reported that poly rI:poly rC was useful in the treatment of herpetic keratoconjunctivitis in rabbits (11), and other investigators have used it in the treatment of other virus-induced diseases in various animal species. Levy and co-workers reported that poly rI:poly rC was active against several transplantable mouse tumors and was especially active in the reticulum cell sarcoma J 96132 (9). The antitumor effect of this compound has also been tested with various other tumors (2, 6, 12). The present report summarizes some of our data on the antitumor effects, pharmacological properties, and toxicity of poly rI:poly rC.

MATERIALS AND METHODS

Source of compound. The poly rI:poly rC used in these studies was kindly supplied by Hilton Levy and the Cancer Chemotherapy National Service Center (CCNSC) of the National Cancer Institute. The individual polyribonucleotides, poly rI and poly rC, were also supplied by the CCNSC. The polyriboguanylic: polyribocytidylic acid (poly rG:poly rC) was purchased from Biopolymers Inc., Chagrin Falls, Ohio.

Antitumor effect. The effect of poly rI:poly rC on several transplantable mouse tumors was studied. The compound was also evaluated for activity against the Walker 256 carcinosarcoma transplanted intraperitoneally (ip) in Sprague Dawley rats. Poly rI:poly rC was administered ip 24 hr after the mice or rats were inoculated with the tumor. Poly rI:poly rC was given at doses of 5, 10, and 20 mg/kg on a variety of dose schedules—daily, every other day, every third day, and every fourth day. The optimal dose and schedule for increasing survival time are reported for each type of tumor. A related compound, poly rG:poly rC, was also evaluated for antitumor activity in three rodent tumors—leukemia L1210, Adamson reticulum cell sarcoma (A-RCS), and Walker 256 carcinosarcoma. Poly rI:poly rC was tested for cytotoxic activity against L1210 in tissue culture. L1210 cells were maintained in static culture in R.P.M.I. #1630 medium (20% fetal calf serum) as described previously (3). Stock cultures were counted and diluted so that there were 10^5 cells/ml and a total of 5 ml in each experiment. A total of 0.1 ml of poly rI:poly rC at various concentrations or 0.1 ml of saline was added to 5 ml of these cells. Cell counts were taken every 24 hr for 3 days by use of a Coulter counter (3). Poly rI:poly rC was examined for potential antitumor effect against liver tumors induced in rhesus monkeys by ip administration of *N*-nitrosodiethylamine (DENA). The monkeys were examined by palpation and were biopsied; the tumors were measured and photographed (8). Poly rI:poly rC was administered intravenously (iv) three times a week for 4 months, at which time a second biopsy and measurement of the tumor were taken. In addition, serum α-feto-protein levels were followed weekly in monkeys treated with poly rI:poly rC (7).

Embryotoxic studies. Virgin New Zealand white rabbits and Sprague Dawley rats were used in these studies. The animals were mated with proven males of the same strain and were maintained with Purina chow and water *ad libitum*. In the rabbits, poly rI:poly rC was injected subcutaneously (sc) at 1 or 2 mg/kg on days 8 and 9 or days 11 and 12 of pregnancy. In addition, the effects of poly rG:poly rC on the rabbit fetus was studied by administration of a dose of 2 mg/kg on days 8 and 9 of pregnancy. Eight pregnant rats were injected sc with a dose of 8 mg of poly rI:poly rC per kg on days 7 and 8; 11 pregnant rats injected with saline served as controls.

On the 28th day of pregnancy, each rabbit was killed by an iv injection of an overdose of sodium pentobarbital; each rat was likewise killed on the 20th day of pregnancy. The uterus of the animal was then exposed and carefully opened; the number of implantations, resorptions, and fetuses was recorded. The viable fetuses were examined for external and internal gross abnormalities.

Carcinogenic studies. Potential carcinogenic activity of poly rI:poly rC was determined by sc injection into General Purpose newborn mice (noninbred albinos) at doses ranging from nontoxic to lethal. The compound was given both as a single injection and in multiple doses. The animals were held for 6 months, and then they were killed and examined for possible tumors.

Toxicity studies and pharmacology. Poly rI:poly rC was evaluated for acute toxicity (14-day observation period) in CD_2F_1 male mice after ip administration. The LD_{50} was obtained by determining the effect of four dose levels (10 mice/dose). Computations for determining the LD_{50} were done according to the method of Litchfield and Wilcoxon (10).

The toxicity of poly rI:poly rC was evaluated in beagle dogs and rhesus monkeys. The design of the experiments allowed daily dosing for as long as 28 days, followed by an observation period of approximately 100 days. Gross pharmacotoxic signs were evaluated, and various biochemical and hematological tests were performed on all animals (1). Gross and microscopic pathology was done on the animals that died or were sacrificed (1).

The effects of poly rI:poly rC on contractions of the isolated guinea pig ileum (1) were studied. Dose-response curves were obtained for control measurements with acetylcholine and histamine. Poly rI:poly rC was added to the 50-ml bath at doses up to 20 μg/ml as a challenge against the spasmogenic agents. The effect of poly rI:poly rC on the isolated guinea pig uterus and the isolated rat uterus was also studied. After a standard response to acetylcholine had been obtained, poly rI:poly rC was added to the 50-ml bath and the response to acetylcholine was repeated. The effects of the compound on the blood pressure of anesthetized dogs and monkeys were also studied (1).

RESULTS AND DISCUSSION

Antitumor activity. Results presented in Table 1 summarize the activity of poly rI:poly rC against several transplantable rodent tumors. All of these experimental tumors were mouse tumors with the exception of the Walker 256 carcinosarcoma which was carried in Sprague Dawley rats. Poly rI:poly rC had minimal but definite activity against leukemia L1210; it also had minimal activity against a plasma cell tumor, YPC-1. The compound was more effective against the Walker 256 carcinosarcoma, producing a 100% increase in median life span over that of untreated controls. Poly rI:poly rC was also active in the reticulum cell sarcoma A-RCS, but it was not active when tested against the ovarian reticulum cell sarcoma. The compound was also ineffective against leukemia P388 or the Kelly leukemia, K1964. Generally, the optimal antitumor dose was 10 mg/kg every day or 20 mg/kg every other day.

Table 1. *Effect of poly rI:poly rC on various experimental tumors*

Tumor	Route of tumor transplantation	Optimal dose	Optimal schedule	Increase in median survival over control
		mg/kg		%
Leukemia L1210	ip	10	Daily	35
Plasma cell YPC-1	ip	10	Every other day	39
Carcinosarcoma Walker 256	ip	10	Daily	100
Reticulum cell sarcoma, A-RCS	sc	20	Every other day	89
Reticulum cell sarcoma, ovarian	sc	20	Every other day	20
Leukemia P388	ip	10	Daily	16
Leukemia K1964	sc	10	Every other day	12

Poly rI:poly rC was not cytotoxic when tested against leukemia L1210 in vitro at doses up to 40 μg/ml. However, this lack of effect is mitigated by the recent observation of several investigators at the National Cancer Institute that fetal calf serum as well as human serum may break down the compound when in contact with it for several hours. This modification of the activity of poly rI:poly rC is currently being investigated.

Because poly rI:poly rC produced marked antitumor activity in the Walker 256 carcinosarcoma, other synthetic polyribonucleotides were evaluated for antitumor effect in this experimental system. As can be seen from Table 2, poly rG:poly rC was also highly effective in prolonging survival time. However, the individual homopolymers poly rI and poly rC were without effect in this tumor. Poly rG:poly rC was tested against leukemia L1210 and the Adamson reticulum cell sarcoma (A-RCS), both of which are responsive to treatment with poly rI:poly rC, but was found to be inactive.

Poly rI:poly rC was not active against DENA-induced liver tumors in rhesus monkeys. Four monkeys (592G, 593G, 595G, and 603G) treated with 1 mg of the compound per kg three times per week for 4 months showed no response, as evidenced by growth of the original tumor nodule(s) and the emergence of new liver tumors upon a second biopsy. The pathology, when the monkeys were killed after 4 months of treatment, revealed multiple hepatic cell carcinomas of the liver in all four animals, with metastasis to the lung in three of the monkeys. Generally, megakaryocytic hyperplasia of the bone marrow and hyperplasia of lymphoid tissue was also seen. In addition, the α-feto-protein levels never decreased in any of these four monkeys, and frequently the titer increased as the treatment and tumor progressed.

Table 2. *Effect of polyribonucleotides on Walker 256 carcinosarcoma*

Polyribonucleotide	Optimal daily dose	Increase in median survival over control
	mg/kg	%
Poly I	10	0
Poly C	10	0
Poly rI:poly rC	10	100
Poly rG:poly rC . . .	5 or 10	100

Embryotoxic studies. As can be seen from Table 3, poly rI:poly rC produced 100% resorptions when given sc on days 8 and 9 to pregnant rabbits. Similar effects were obtained with 1 mg/kg, since 80% of the implantations underwent resorption. The compound was also embryotoxic when given on days 11 and 12. Poly rI:poly rC does not seem to possess significant teratogenic activity under these experimental conditions; only three fetuses were grossly malformed as compared with two controls. The administration of poly rG:poly rC at doses of 2 mg/kg sc did not increase the number of resorptions over that of saline-treated controls. It is of interest that poly rI:poly rC treatment of pregnant rats at 8 mg/kg on days 7 and 8 of pregnancy did not produce any resorptions or malformations. This dose is an effective antitumor dose in the rat and is four times greater than that which produced 100% resorptions in the rabbit.

Carcinogenic studies. Because of its interferon-inducing ability and its embryotoxic effects, poly rI:poly rC was tested in newborn mice for possible carcinogenic properties. Results presented in Table 4 demonstrate that the

Table 3. *Embryotoxic activity of poly rI:poly rC and poly rG:poly rC in New Zealand white rabbits*

Treatment	Days of pregnancy treated	No. of does	Total no. of implantations	Total no. of resorptions	No. of normal fetuses	No. of malformed fetuses
Saline, sc	8 and 9	12	84	6 (7%)	76	2
Poly rI:poly rC						
1 mg/kg, sc . . .	8 and 9	7	55	44 (80%)	9	2
1 mg/kg, sc . . .	11 and 12	5	39	24 (61%)	14	1
2 mg/kg, sc . . .	8 and 9	6	47	47 (100%)	0	0
Poly rG:poly rC						
2 mg/kg, sc . . .	8 and 9	5	39	3 (8%)	35	1

Table 4. *Carcinogenic test of poly rI:poly rC in newborn mice*

Doses[a]	Schedule	Total dose administered	Mortality/ total[b]	No. of mice with pulmonary tumors/total[c]
mg/kg		*mg/mouse*		
9.2	Single	0.046	4/12	0/12
4.6	Single	0.023	0/8	0/8
9.2	1/wk × 8[d]	1.196	0/9	2/9
4.6	1/wk × 8	0.607	1/9	0/9
0.9	1/wk × 8	0.114	6/10	0/10
0.09	1/wk × 8	0.015	0/7	0/7

[a] Administered subcutaneously.
[b] Within the 24-week observation period.
[c] All mice were examined 24 weeks after treatment. No other tumors were observed.
[d] Once per week for 8 weeks.

Table 5. *Lethality of iv poly rI:poly rC in rhesus monkeys*

Daily dose	No. of monkeys	No. of doses	Lethality
mg/kg			
30	1	1.5	Died day 2
15	1	8	Died day 8
5	2	4	One died on day 4
1	2	28	Not lethal
0.3	2	28	Not lethal
0.1	2	28	Not lethal

compound did not possess significant carcinogenic activity when evaluated on a variety of doses and schedules. Only two pulmonary tumors were observed in the 55 mice treated, an incidence of pulmonary tumors comparable to that in untreated mice in our colony. No other tumors could be detected in other organs or tissues.

Toxicity studies and pharmacology. The acute LD_{50} of poly rI:poly rC administered ip to mice was 34.7 mg/kg (95% confidence interval of 30.1 to 39.9; slope of 1.34). Beagle dogs tolerated 28 daily iv injections of poly rI:poly rC at doses of 0.03 to 1 mg/kg. Injections of 3, 5, or 10 mg/kg iv resulted in lethality after one to four doses. Autopsy of dogs at death revealed congestion of several organs and engorgement of the cerebral vasculature. Signs of toxicity preceding death from single iv doses were reminiscent of anaphylactic or endotoxin shock except for the relative slowness of the response. Typically, the dog vomited repeatedly and passed loose watery stools. The extremities became cold to the touch, although the rectal temperature rose 2 to 3 degrees F (1.1 to 1.7 C). The dog then became ataxic, the blood pressure fell to 35 to 50 mm of Hg, and the animal lost its ability to stand; finally, it lost consciousness, and 3 hr after dosing the animal died of respiratory failure. At 2 hr after dosing, the blood did not coagulate and prothrombin activity was undetectable. Serum transaminase and alkaline phosphatase activities had increased 4- to 10-fold at that time. The most consistent biochemical response observed in dogs at all dose levels was abnormally high serum glutamic oxalacetic transaminase (SGOT), serum glutamic pyruvic transaminase, and alkaline phosphatase. Prolonged increases in prothrombin time and decreased hemoglobin and hematocrit were also seen. Return of hematocrit and hemoglobin values to normal levels required 1 to 3 weeks after the last dose. As is shown in Table 5, rhesus monkeys also tolerated doses greater than 1 mg/kg for only a few days but were able to survive 28 daily doses of 0.1, 0.3, or 1 mg/kg. Animals dying at high doses exhibited salivation, emesis, and depression; upon autopsy, myocardial infarction and engorgement of a variety of organs, including heart, liver, lung, and kidney, were observed. Frequent hematological and biochemical changes seen at all dose levels included anemia, and elevated SGOT and lactic dehydrogenase activities.

Poly rI:poly rC administered to four pentobarbital-anesthetized rhesus monkeys produced mild cardiovascular effects. Doses of 1 mg/kg caused a decrease of 30 mm of Hg in blood pressure in three animals. The hypotensive response was reversible and showed tachyphylaxis. Pressor and depressor responses to classical pharmacological agents remained unchanged. However, iv administration of poly rI:poly rC to four beagle dogs at doses up to 5 mg/kg produced no change in blood pressure. Depressor responses to histamine were prolonged in these animals and the pressor response to bilateral carotid occlusion was blocked for about 1 hr, after which it slowly returned.

Poly rI:poly rC at doses up to 20 μg/ml produced no effect either on the isolated guinea pig ileum or on the isolated uterus from guinea pigs or rats. In addition, the response of the ileum to histamine or acetylcholine was not modified. The response of the uterus to acetylcholine also remained unchanged after addition of poly rI:poly rC to the tissue bath.

ACKNOWLEDGMENTS

This work was supported by Public Health Service grant GM-13749 from the National Institute of General Medical Sciences and by contracts PH 43-66-84 and NIH 69-2067 from the National Cancer Institute.

LITERATURE CITED

1. Adamson, R. H., R. L. Dixon, M. Ben, L. Crews, S. B. Shohet, and D. P. Rall. 1965. Some pharmacologic properties of vincristine. Arch. Int. Pharmacodyn. Ther. **157**:299–311.
2. Adamson, R. H., and S. Fabro. 1969. Embryotoxic effect of poly I:poly C. Nature (London) **223**:718.
3. Adamson, R. H., L. G. Hart, V. T. DeVita, and V. T. Oliverio. 1968. Antitumor activity and some pharmacologic properties of anthramycin methyl ether. Cancer Res. **28**:343–347.
4. Field, A. K., A. A. Tytell, G. P. Lampson, and M. R. Hilleman. 1967. Inducers of interferon and host resistance. II. Multistranded synthetic polynucleotide complexes. Proc. Nat. Acad. Sci. U.S.A. **58**:1004–1010.
5. Hilleman, M. R. 1968. Interferon induction and utilization. J. Cell Physiol. **71**:43–59.
6. Homan, E. R., R. P. Zendzian, and R. H. Adamson. 1969. Some aspects of the pharmacology and toxicity of polyinosinic: polycytidylic acid. Proc. Amer. Ass. Cancer Res. **10**:40.
7. Hull, E. W., P. P. Carbone, D. Gitlin, R. W. O'Gara, and M. G. Kelly. 1969. α-Feto-protein in monkeys with hepatoma. J. Nat. Cancer Inst. **42**:1035–1044.
8. Kelly, M. G., R. W. O'Gara, R. H. Adamson, K. Gadekar, C. C. Botkin. W. H. Reese, Jr., and W. T. Kerber. 1966. Induction of hepatic cell carcinomas in monkeys with N-nitrosodiethylamine. J. Nat. Cancer Inst. **36**:323–351.
9. Levy, H., L. W. Law, and A. Rabson, 1969. Inhibition of tumor growth by polyinosinic-polycytidylic acid. Proc. Nat. Acad. Sci. U.S.A. **62**:357–361.
10. Litchfield, J. T., and F. Wilcoxon. 1949. A simplified method of evaluating dose-effect experiments. J. Pharmacol. Exp. Ther. **96**:99–113.
11. Park, J. H., and S. Baron. 1968. Herpetic keratoconjunctivitis: Therapy with synthetic double-stranded RNA. Science (Washington) **162**:811–813.
12. Zeleznick, L. D., and B. K. Bhuyan. 1969. Treatment of leukemic L1210 mice with double stranded polyribonucleotides. Proc. Soc. Exp. Biol. Med. **130**:125–128.

Antimicrobial Agents and Chemotherapy—1969

Antiviral Activity and Molecular Features of Benzimidazoles

D. G. O'SULLIVAN, C. LUDLOW, D. PANTIC, and A. K. WALLIS

Courtauld Institute of Biochemistry, Middlesex Hospital Medical School, London, W1P 5PR, England

Compounds related to 2-(α-hydroxybenzyl)benzimidazole (HBB) selectively inhibit the replication of many picornaviruses, but viruses from most other groups are affected less or not at all. The pattern of the structure-activity relationships of these compounds for polioviruses is summarized and compared briefly with the pattern for other picornaviruses. Broad similarities, but also clear differences, exist. The protective activity of 5-phenyl and 5-amino derivatives of HBB toward poliovirus and coxsackievirus A21 is given as an example. The general pattern of activity for polioviruses is compared with the well-known structure-activity patterns of isatin thiosemicarbazone derivatives. Although the assays were performed under entirely different conditions (in mice with isatin thiosemicarbazone derivatives and in tissue culture with HBB derivatives), interesting similarities were observed. For example, substitution with simple alkyl groups at the heterocyclic N-atom enhanced the respective antiviral activity but larger substituents anywhere tended to reduce it. The fused benzene ring was necessary for high activity in both series, and substituents in this ring usually reduced activity. However, 5-fluoro-HBB is an example of such a substituted compound possessing greater protective activity than HBB. The introduction of solubilizing groups, such as $-NH_2$ or $-CO_2H$, often appeared detrimental to activity.

Since Hollinshead and Smith (7) discovered that 2-(α-hydroxybenzyl)benzimidazole (HBB, I; R = H) could exert a protective action against

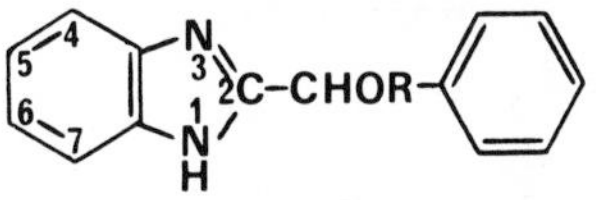

(I)

type 2 poliovirus in tissue culture and in vivo, the antiviral effect of the 2-substituted benzimidazole structure has received detailed study. HBB itself was the most selectively active of a number of related compounds examined by Tamm et al. (23), although they found 5-chloro-HBB to be both more active and more toxic, giving it a slightly lower selective activity. Recently Tamm et al. (24) reported a survey relating to the toxicity and activity of 42 benzimidazoles and similar compounds toward echovirus 6 in monkey kidney cells. We have prepared and tested many substituted benzimidazoles and related compounds for their cytotoxic effects and their activities towards the three polioviruses (type 1, *L Sc* 2 *ab*; type 2, *P* 712 *Ch* 2 *ab*; and type 3, *Leon* 12 *ab*) in ERK cells (9-17, 19, 20) and have determined their influence on the onset of cytopathic effects due to other picornaviruses and viruses from other groups (10). Akihama et al. (1) have examined some substituted bis-benzimidazolylmethyl compounds, and numerous other HBB derivatives have been prepared for study [e.g., by Sinnur et al. (22)]. The molar activity of a compound (sometimes expressed as the reciprocal of the molar concentration required to produce a given degree of inhibition of viral multiplication) has less practical significance than its selective activity (molar activity divided by toxicity). In general, however, the latter will be known with less accuracy than the former because of the difficulties often encountered in measuring toxicities accurately. Unfortunately, different experimental approaches for assessing activities and toxicities, the use of different cell systems, and other conditions make only qualitative comparisons possible in data from different sources. Also, many hundreds of benzimidazoles and related compounds would have to be tested to solve with certainity the complete structure-activity problem. Consequently, generalizations on structure-activity relations must involve some overall impressions and include a measure of speculative inference from the body of existing results.

The isatin 3-thiosemicarbazone series of antiviral compounds has also received extensive structure-activity study, particularly in relation to activity against vaccinia virus (3, 21). Some superficial structural similarity exists between these isatin thiosemicarbazones and the substituted benzimidazoles, but the broad differences in the methods used for bioassay of these two types of compound make a comparison of their relative effects difficult. Nevertheless, observation of some definite similarities between the two series has been possible.

MATERIALS AND METHODS

ERK and HeLa cells were grown in continuous culture. The initial growth medium consisted of Eagle's basal medium containing 10% calf serum, 0.044% $NaHCO_3$, and antibiotics [benzyl-penicillin (200 units/ml), streptomycin (200 μg/ml), and amphotericin B (5 μg/ml)]. To maintain the cells in culture, the medium was replaced on the third or fourth day by medium containing 5% calf serum and 0.18% $NaHCO_3$.

Experiments were carried out on monolayers grown in test tubes. The initial growth medium was discarded and replaced by medium (2 ml per tube) containing 10 or 5% calf serum, for ERK and HeLa cells, respectively, 0.18% $NaHCO_3$, and also virus, compound, or both at the desired concentrations. The tubes were closed with silicone-rubber bungs and were then allowed to rotate slowly at 37 C. The cultures were examined repeatedly for cytopathic effect, and the times, to the nearest quarter day, were noted when half the cells in each tube were affected.

The concentrations of virus, expressed as tissue culture infective dose (TCD_{50}) units per milliliter, were determined by preparing serial dilutions of virus suspension and finding the dilution factor (= TCD_{50}) necessary to reduce the concentration to 1 infective dose unit per ml. The latter was taken as the concentration of virus producing a mean 50% cytopathic effect in six tubes, 7 days after addition to ERK cell monolayers.

Viruses. To replenish virus stocks, the viruses were grown in ERK cells and, after the cytopathic end point was reached, the virus-containing supernatant fluid was centrifuged to remove cell debris. A second and third passage of virus through cells could then be carried out, if necessary, and the concentrated virus suspension was stored at −20 C.

When used in testing compounds, serial 10-fold dilutions of stock virus were prepared in either plain medium or medium containing compound in solution at the appropriate concentration.

RESULTS

The results presented exemplify or emphasize certain points regarding the structure-activity relationships. The maximal concentrations of the test compounds that just failed to produce any microscopically visible toxic effects on ERK cells after 4.5 days are listed in Table 1. Compounds were normally tested for their effects on virus-infected cells at half of these tabulated concentrations. Table 1 also contains the melting points of the compounds.

The effects of various modifications of HBB upon activity are shown in Fig. 1 with poliovirus (type 2) growing in ERK cells and in Fig. 2 with poliovirus (types 1 and 3) growing in HeLa cells. Each compound was tested against three concentrations of each virus. Uninfected ERK cell cultures had their 50% degeneration end point at 9.5 days, and uninfected HeLa cell cultures had their 50% degeneration point at 4.5 days after the time of infection of the noncontrol cultures in these experiments.

Table 1. *Maximal concentrations tolerated by ERK cells for a period of 4.5 days*

Compound	Melting point	Maximal tolerated concn
	C	μM
2-(α-Hydroxybenzyl)benzimidazole (HBB)	206–207	210
1-(*p*-Methoxybenzyl)-HBB	110–111	50
1-(*p*-Chlorobenzyl)-HBB hydrochloride	187–188.5	<5
1-(β-Dimethylaminoethyl)-HBB	115.5–116.5	450
1-Ethyl-*O*-acetyl-HBB	124–125	100
4-Methyl-HBB	193.5–194.5	220
5-Amino-HBB	180–181	420
5-Fluoro-HBB	207.5–208.5	160
5-Bromo-HBB	200–201	50
5-Bromo-1-propyl-HBB	159–160.5	100
5-Phenyl-HBB	183.5–184.5	70
5-Nitro-HBB	170–171	40
2-(α-Aminobenzyl)-benzimidazole	204–205	180
2-(α-Hydroxybenzyl)-benzothiazole	122–123	110
3-(α-Hydroxybenzyl)-indazole	166	120

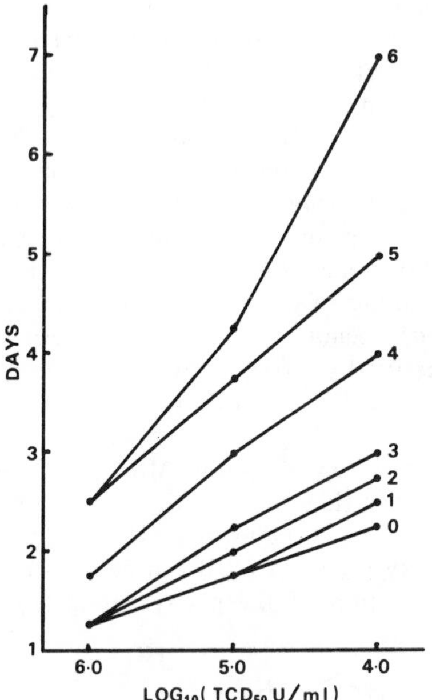

Fig. 1. *Effects of compounds at half their maximal tolerated concentrations on the time interval between addition of media containing poliovirus (type 2) to ERK cells and the subsequent 50% cytopathic end point of the cultures. The lines are labeled as follows: 0 = control (no compound) or one of the inactive compounds, 5-amino-HBB, 4-methyl-HBB, or 1-(p-methoxybenzyl)-HBB; 1 = 5-nitro-HBB or 1-(p-chlorobenzyl)-HBB hydrochloride (1.0 μM); 2 = 5-bromo-HBB or 1-(β-dimethylaminoethyl)-HBB; 3 = 5-bromo-1-propyl-HBB; 4 = 1-ethyl-O-acetyl-HBB; 5 = HBB; and 6 = 5-fluoro-HBB.*

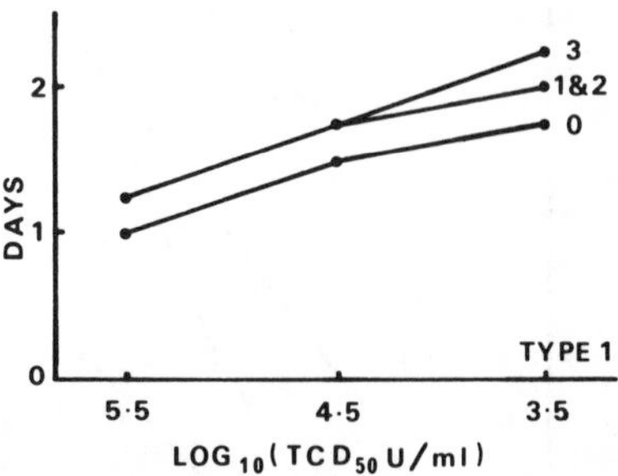

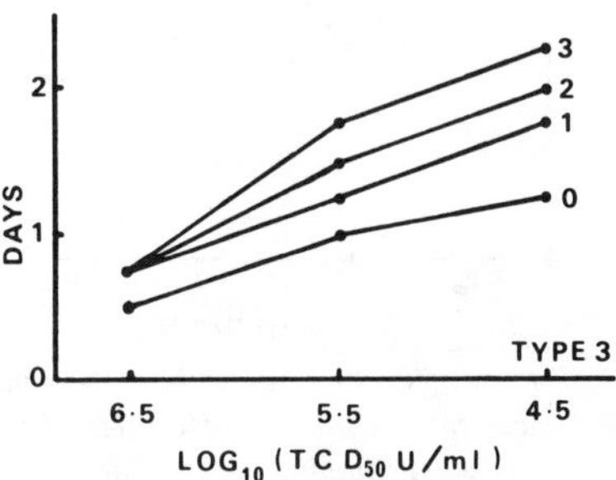

Fig. 2. *Effects of compounds at half their maximal tolerated concentrations (to ERK cells) on the time interval between the addition of media containing poliovirus (type 1 and type 3) to HeLa cells and the subsequent 50% cytopathic end point of the cultures. In both parts of Fig. 2, the lines are labeled as follows: 0 = control (no compound) or one of the inactive compounds, 5-amino-HBB, 5-bromo-HBB, 5-nitro-HBB, 1-(p-chlorobenzyl)-HBB hydrochloride (1.0 μM), or 1-(p-methoxybenzyl)-HBB; 1 = HBB; 2 = 5-bromo-1-propyl-HBB or 1-ethyl-O-acetyl-HBB; 3 = 5-fluoro-HBB.*

Figures 1 and 2 show that 5-fluoro-HBB gave cells more protection than HBB, whereas other HBB derivatives with substituents in the fused benzene ring tended to be less active than HBB.

In Fig. 3, each line joins four points obtained in an experiment with ERK cells infected with coxsackievirus A21 and simultaneously treated with one of several HBB derivatives. Uninfected control cultures reached their 50% degeneration point at 9 days. Naturally, compounds that failed to show activity in these experiments might give some protection if lower initial virus concentrations were used.

Coxsackievirus A21 is less sensitive than many other picornaviruses to the inhibiting effect of HBB derivatives, but the 5-phenyl and 5-amino compounds showed notable protective effects. The 5-amino derivative had no effect on cells infected with high concentrations of coxsackievirus A21, but its effect increased rapidly at low virus concentrations. The marked activity of the 5-phenyl derivative towards coxsackievirus A21 was much less than that previously obtained with the 1-phenyl derivative (10). Neither HBB nor 5-fluoro-HBB showed any effects in the experiment described here.

Comparison of the activity of HBB with that of its 5-phenyl derivative, each compound being tested at one-half its maximal tolerated concentration for the cells, disclosed that HBB was the better agent for protection of ERK cells from infection with poliovirus type 2, whereas 5-phenyl-HBB was the more active against infection with poliovirus type 1 or 3.

DISCUSSION

Activities and selectivities toward polioviruses. HBB (I; R = H) was taken as the parent

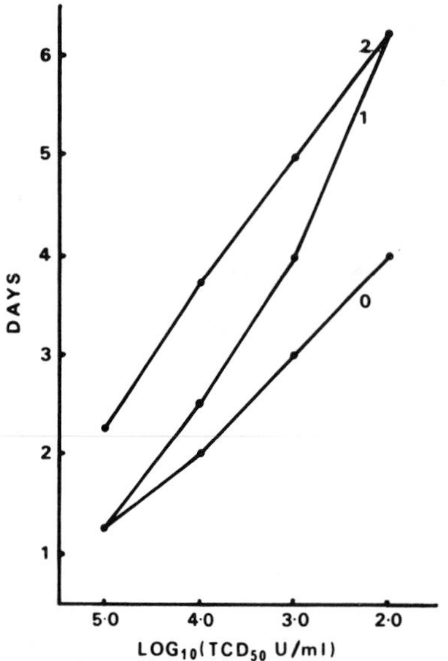

Fig. 3. *Effects of compounds at half their maximal tolerated concentrations on the time interval between the addition of media containing coxsackievirus A21 to ERK cells and the subsequent 50% cytopathic end point of the cultures. The lines are labeled as follows: 0 = control (no compound) or one of the compounds showing no activity, HBB, 5-fluoro-HBB, 5-bromo-HBB, 5-nitro-HBB, 5-bromo-1-propyl-HBB, 1-ethyl-O-acetyl-HBB, or 1-(p-methoxybenzyl)-HBB; 1 = 5-amino-HBB; 2 = 5-phenyl-HBB.*

compound of this series. A 35 μM concentration effected 75% inhibition of the growth of type 2 poliovirus in ERK cells after 16 hr (9), and 36 μM had the same effect in MK cells after 48 hr (23). The toxicities (needed to assess the selective activities) of HBB and its derivatives differ in different cell lines. The following sequence is nearly always preserved: activity (or selectivity) of compound in inhibiting the growth of type 2 poliovirus >its activity (or selectivity) towards type 1 poliovirus ⩾its activity (or selectivity) towards type 3 poliovirus.

2-Substituent of HBB. Benzimidazole itself (II; R = H) has very low activity and selectivity, and its more active 2-benzyl and 2-benzoyl derivatives are both much less active and selective than HBB (23), demonstrating the importance of the composition of the substituent at position 2 of the imidazole. The inactivity of the 2-hydroxymethyl and 2-hydroxyethyl derivatives (II; R = $-CH_2OH$ and R = $-CH_2CH_2OH$, respectively) demonstrates the importance of the phenyl group (23). Substituents in this phenyl group appear to reduce the activity of HBB (19), and some substituents and some modifications of this ring greatly reduce activity towards echovirus 6 (24). However, 2-(2-thienyl-hydroxymethyl)benzimidazole is nearly as active as HBB towards echovirus 6 (24).

(II)

The methoxy derivative MBB (I; R = Me) is similar to HBB in activity and selectivity towards type 2 poliovirus (13, 16), and the α-hydroxy group of HBB can be transferred to the *o* position of the phenyl group (III) with

(III)

little loss in activity (17). Also, we found 2-(α-aminobenzyl)benzimidazole to be active. In spite of the use of DMSO to dissolve this compound as the free base at 90 μM, it was not as effective as HBB in protecting ERK cells against the cytopathic effects of types 1, 2, and 3 polioviruses.

O'Sullivan and Wallis (19) found the glycol (IV; R = R^2 = H, R^1 = OH) to have protective

(IV)

activity against type 1 poliovirus, and Akihama et al. (1) showed that this activity was increased by substituents, particularly the methoxy group, in the 5 position (IV, R = H, R^1 = OH, R^2 = OMe).

Replacement of the H atom attached to the α-carbon atom by an Me group (V; R = OH, R^1 = Me) led to some reduction in protective activity against type 2 poliovirus (19), but it led to increases in activity and selectivity toward echovirus 6 (24).

(V)

To summarize, a 2-substituent is necessary for high activity, and, if not the α-hydroxybenzyl group itself, it must be a substituted methyl group with such substituents that it forms a specifically suitable alternative to the α-hydroxybenzyl group.

Effect of substituents in the 1 position. Simple alkyl, alkenyl, and aryl substituents (VI;

(VI)

$R^1 = R^2 = R^3 = H$, R = alkyl, etc.) increase the activity of HBB (19). This is shown for alkyl substituents in Fig. 4. The activities and selectivities are at a maximum with the propyl (or butyl) substituent, and we have found that they

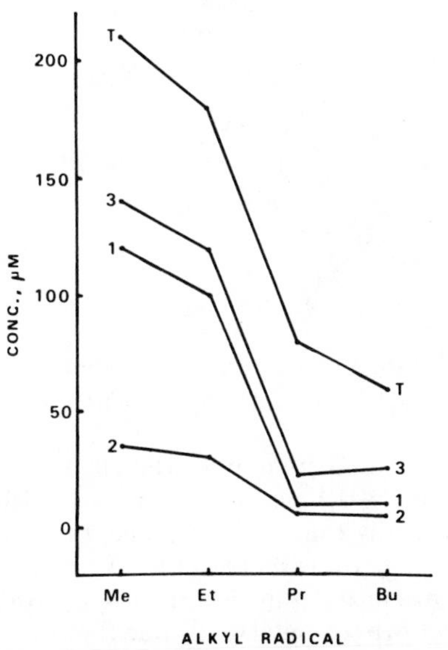

Fig. 4. *Effect of carbon chain length of 1-alkyl-HBB derivatives on maximal concentrations tolerated in ERK cells for 4.5 days (line T) and on concentrations required to reduce type 1 (line 1), type 2 (line 2), and type 3 (line 3) poliovirus yields in ERK cells by 75%.*

decline on passing to the pentyl substituent. 1-Phenyl (14), 1-benzyl (12), 1-allyl and 1-crotyl (*to be published*), and 1-β-methoxyethyl (13) derivatives of HBB are all highly active and selective compounds. However, Fig. 1, 2, and 3 show that some 1-substituted HBB derivatives (e.g., 1-*p*-methoxybenzyl, 1-*p*-chlorobenzyl, and 1-β-dimethylaminoethyl derivatives) have little or no protective activity.

Effect of substituents in the fused benzene ring. Figures 1 and 2 show that 5-fluoro-HBB has greater protective activity than HBB. The 5-chloro derivative is similar in activity to HBB (15, 23), but most substituents appear to reduce or remove activity (Fig. 1 and 2).

Quaternization. Benzimidazoles form quaternary ions (VII). Several of the quaternary

(VII)

iodides have been shown to be active against polioviruses, but activities are lower than that of HBB (20). The activities of 1-akyl bases and 1,3-dialkyl quaternary salts make it unlikely that the activity of HBB is connected with the formation of HBB-containing nucleosides.

Optical enantiomorphs. Formula VIII shows that HBB and its derivatives have an asymmetric

$$R{-}CHOH{-}R^1$$

(VIII)

carbon atom and exist in D and L forms. The activity of HBB is largely associated with its D isomer (8, 9, 11), and the activity of the 5-chloro derivative is probably entirely associated with its D isomer (15). However, the DL and D forms of the 1-alkyl derivatives have similar activity (11).

Modification to the benzimidazole ring system. Modifications to the fused benzene ring destroy activity. Chatterjee et al. (5) reported that 2-(α-hydroxybenzyl)-imidazo(4,5-*b*)- and (4,5-*c*)-pyridines [analogues of HBB with an N-atom replacing the CH group at positions 4(7) and 5(6), respectively] have no antipoliovirus activity, and Haggerty et al. (6) reported inactivity of 8-(α-hydroxybenzyl)purine [the HBB analogue with N-atoms at positions 4(7) and 6(5) of HBB] toward types 1 and 2 polioviruses. 2-(α-hydroxybenzyl)imidazole itself failed to demonstrate antiviral activity (24).

Modifications to the five-membered ring of HBB appear damaging to the selective activity. We found that 2-(α-hydroxybenzyl)benzothiazole shows much less protective activity than HBB toward type 2 poliovirus and no activity toward the type 1 and type 3 viruses. 3-(α-hydroxybenzyl)indazole, when tested by us at half its maximal tolerated concentration (Table 1), failed to protect ERK cells from the cytopathic effects of types 1, 2, and 3 polioviruses. The benzothiazole derivative offers some protection to echovirus 6-infected MK cells (24).

Effect of inserting salt-forming groups. Increases in the solubility of HBB derivatives in water could have practical advantages for in vivo testing, but attempts to modify the molecule to increase water solubility appeared detrimental to antipoliovirus activity. Thus, quaternizing reduced antipolio activity, and the insertion of an amino group at the 5 position gave a compound with little or no protective action against polioviruses. Two carboxylic acids [2-(*o*-carboxybenzyl)benzimidazole and β-2-(1-methylbenzimidazolyl)glyceric acid] showed little or no activity (13). Tamm et al. (24) reported that the α-carboxymethyl derivative of HBB (as the ammonium salt) and the 1-carboxymethyl derivative of α-methyl-HBB have no activity in relation to echovirus 6.

Activities towards other picornaviruses. HBB derivatives can inhibit the replication of many, but not all, picornaviruses. Results from tests on a selection of the more active derivatives against some entero- and rhinoviruses suggests that, for susceptible viruses, those compounds that are the most active in relation to one virus will be among the most active in relation to other viruses (10). However, this is probably an oversimplification, and the results given in this paper for the influence of 5-fluoro-, 5-amino-, and 5-phenyl-HBB on poliovirus and coxsackievirus A21 infection of cells demonstrates that variations in pattern are possible.

Comparison with antivaccinial activity of isatin thiosemicarbazones. Isatin 3-thiosemicarbazone and many of its derivatives (IX) inhibit the multiplication of poxviruses, and detailed structure-activity studies in relation to

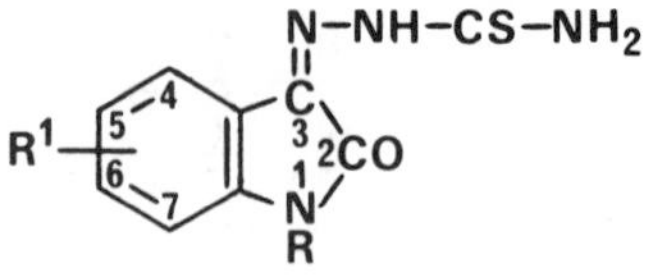

(IX)

their action against vaccinia (3, 21) and ectromelia (2, 4, 18) infections have been carried out. As both HBB and isatin 3-thiosemicarbazone consist of fused benzene and five-membered nitrogen-containing rings, with a single side chain attached to the heterocyclic ring, there is some similarity in structure. However, the heterocyclic systems differ in properties, and the characters of the side chains are quite different. Also, as different groups of viruses are involved and the methods used for antiviral testing were different, one might not expect similarities to emerge. In spite of this, there are some distinct similarities between the patterns of antivaccinia and antipolio activities.

The thiosemicarbazone side chain of isatin 3-thiosemicarbazone must be preserved for antivaccinia activity (3), and any change in the substituents in this side chain, as indicated in formula X, removes this activity. The activity of

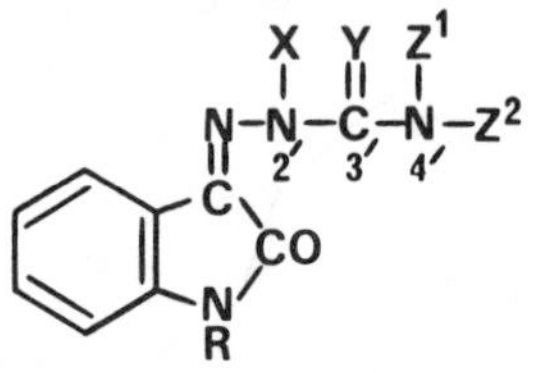

(X)

isatin 3-thiosemicarbazone is even more sensitive to changes in the side chain than the activity of HBB.

The introduction of small alkyl groups at position 1 (IX) increases the antivaccinial activity of isatin 3-thiosemicarbazone, the maximum being reached with the ethyl substitutent (3). The maximal antipoliovirus activity occurs at the propyl (or butyl) substituent in the 1-alkyl HBB series (9, 19).

The insertion of substituents in the benzene ring of isatin 3-thiosemicarbazone reduces the activity, the magnitude of the reduction depending on the size of the substituent (3). There is a similar tendency with HBB derivatives and, although the 5-fluoro derivative gives more protection than HBB, the sequence of activities, F > Cl > Br, is similar in the two series of compounds. However, 5-phenyl-HBB is still comparatively active in relation to polioviruses.

Interfering with the fused ring systems is damaging to activity in both series of compounds, and the insertion of solubilizing salt-forming groups reduces or abolishes the antivaccinial activity of isatin 3-thiosemicarbazone derivatives (3). The similar tendency with the activities of HBB derivatives has been discussed.

ACKNOWLEDGMENTS

We thank Franco Piozzi of the University of Palermo for providing a sample of 3-(α-hydroxybenzyl)indazole and the National Fund for Research into Crippling Diseases for supporting this research.

LITERATURE CITED

1. Akihama, S., M. Okude, K. Sato, and S. Iwabuchi. 1968. Inhibitory effect of 1,2-bis-(2-benzimidazolyl)-1,2-ethanediol derivatives on poliovirus. Nature (London) **217**:562–3.
2. Bauer, D. J. 1963. The chemotherapy of ectromelia infection with isatin β-dialkylthiosemicarbazones. Brit. J. Exp. Pathol. **44**:233–242.
3. Bauer, D. J., and P. W. Sadler. 1960. The structure-activity relationships of the antiviral chemotherapeutic activity of isatin β-thiosemicarbazone. Brit. J. Pharmacol. **15**:101–110.
4. Bauer, D. J., and P. W. Sadler. 1961. Derivatives of isatin beta-thiosemicarbazone with anti-viral chemotherapeutic activity against ectromelia infection. Nature (London) **190**:1167–1169.
5. Chatterjee, S. K., P. C. Jain, and N. Anand. 1965. Potential purine antagonists. VI. Synthesis of 2-benzyl- and 2-(α-hydroxybenzyl)imidazopyridines. Indian. J. Chem. **3**:138–139.
6. Haggerty, W. J., R. H. Springer, and C. C. Cheng. 1965. Studies on 2-(α-hydroxybenzyl)benzimidazole (HBB) analogues. I. Synthesis of 8-(α-hydroxybenzyl)purines, the diaza analogues of HBB. J. Med. Chem. **8**:797–802.
7. Hollinshead, A. C., and P. K. Smith. 1958. Effects of certain purines and related compounds on virus propagation. J. Pharmacol. Exp. Ther. **123**:54–62.
8. Kadin, S. B., H. J. Eggers, and I. Tamm. 1964. Synthesis and virus-inhibitory activity of D- and L- isomers of 2-(α-hydroxybenzyl)benzimidazole. Nature (London) **201**:639–640.
9. O'Sullivan, D. G. 1965. Viruses and the chemotherapy of viral diseases. Royal Institute of Chemistry, Lecture Series, No. 2, p. 1–44.
10. O'Sullivan, D. G., D. Pantic, D. S. Dane, and M. Briggs. 1969. Protective action of benzimidazole derivatives against virus infections in tissue culture and *in vivo*. Lancet **1**:446–448.
11. O'Sullivan, D. G., D. Pantic, and A. K. Wallis. 1964. Action of D-1-alkyl-2-(α-hydroxybenzyl)benzimidazoles on tissue-culture cells infected with poliovirus. Nature (London) **201**:378–379.
12. O'Sullivan, D. G., D. Pantic, and A. K. Wallis. 1964. Protection of poliovirus-infected tissue-culture cells using the 1-benzyl, 1-pentyl and 1-isopropyl derivatives of 2-(α-hydroxybenzyl)benzimidazole. Nature (London) **203**:433–434.
13. O'Sullivan, D. G., D. Pantic, and A. K. Wallis. 1965. Protection offered to poliovirus-infected tissue-culture cells by methoxy- and hydroxy-methyl compounds related to 2-benzylbenzimidazole. Nature (London) **205**:262–264.
14. O'Sullivan, D. G., D. Pantic, and A. K. Wallis. 1967. New 1,2-disubstituted benzimidazoles with high inhibiting effects on poliovirus replication. Experientia (Basel) **23**:704–706.
15. O'Sullivan, D. G., D. Pantic, and A. K. Wallis. 1968. D-5-Chloro-2-(α-hydroxybenzyl)benzimidazole and 1-alkyl-5-chloro-2-(α-hydroxybenzyl)benzimidazoles as inhibitors of poliovirus multiplication. Experientia (Basel) **24**:661–663.
16. O'Sullivan, D. G., D. Pantic, and A. K. Wallis. 1968. The inhibiting actions on poliovirus multiplication of 1-alkyl-2-(α-methoxybenzyl)benzimidazoles. Experientia (Basel) **24**:1185–1187.
17. O'Sullivan D. G., and P. W. Sadler. 1961. New agents with high activity against type 2 poliovirus. Nature (London) **192**:341–343.
18. O'Sullivan, D. G., P. W. Sadler, and C. Webley. 1963. A study of the chemotherapeutic activity of isatin β-4′,4′-dialkylthiosemicarbazones against ectromelia infection. Chemotherapia **7**:17–26.
19. O'Sullivan, D. G., and A. K. Wallis. 1963. New benzimidazole derivatives with powerful protective action on tissue-culture cells infected with types 1, 2 and 3 poliovirus. Nature (London) **198**:1270–1273.
20. O'Sullivan, D. G., and A. K. Wallis. 1963. 2-(α-Hydroxybenzyl)benzimidazolium salts and their influence on cultured cells infected with poliovirus. Nature (London) **200**:1101–1103.
21. Sadler, P. W., D. G. O'Sullivan, and D. J. Bauer. 1963. A study of substances of potential value in the treatment of pox virus and entero virus infections. Antibiot. Chemother. **2**:403–412.
22. Sinnur, K. H., G. R. Revankar, and S. Siddappa. 1966. Benzimidazoles. III. Synthesis of (α-hydroxybenzyl)-benzimidazoles. Monatsh. Chem. **97**:417–422.
23. Tamm, I., R. Bablanian, M. M. Nemes, C. H. Shunk, F. M. Robinson, and K. Folkers. 1961. Relationship between structure of benzimidazole derivatives and selective virus inhibitory activity. Inhibition of poliovirus multiplication and cytopathic effects by 2-(α-hydroxybenzyl)benzimidazole, and its 5-chloro derivative. J. Exp. Med. **113**:625–655 + plates.
24. Tamm, I., H. J. Eggers, R. Bablinian, A. F. Wagner, and K. Folkers. 1969. Structural requirements of selective inhibition of enteroviruses by 2-(α-hydroxybenzyl)benzimidazole and related compounds. Nature (London) **223**:785–788.

Antimicrobial Agents and Chemotherapy—1969

Antiviral Activity of Calcium Elenolate on Parainfluenza Infection of Hamsters

M. G. SORET

Department of Virology Research, The Upjohn Co., Kalamazoo, Michigan 49001

The in vivo antiviral activity of calcium elenolate was demonstrated in hamsters infected with parainfluenza 3 virus. The drug was virucidal when given within minutes of the viral inoculation. Calcium elenolate also showed a "therapeutic" effect when given 8 hr after infection. This antiviral activity, after establishment of the infection, reduced the severity of the infectious process. The minimal effective dose of calcium elenolate produced only minimal histological changes in the sensitive olfactory epithelium of the hamster while exerting significant therapeutic antiviral activity. The effects obtained suggest that calcium elenolate may affect viral components of cellular origin in both free and cell-associated virus.

In the search for antiviral drugs, calcium elenolate was found to have in vitro activity against a variety of viruses (6), including several agents of human "common colds."

As a potential in vivo antiviral drug, calcium elenolate was tested in parainfluenza 3 infection of hamsters. These tests, which mimic the infection, treatment, and sampling procedures employed in "common cold" studies in human volunteers (1, 2, 9), are the subject of this report.

MATERIALS AND METHODS

A detailed description of the materials and methods employed in this study has been published (8). A simplified description is given here.

Animals. Sendai-free, 100-g golden syrian hamsters, obtained from Lakeview Hamster Colony, Newfield, N.J., were used. In most experiments, groups of 10 hamsters were used. The animals were housed in units of five hamsters per cage.

Virus. The infecting virus, myxovirus parainfluenza type 3 (HA-1 virus, strain C-243) obtained from the American Type Culture Collection, was maintained in frozen pools of infected HEp-2 cell cultures. Only pools with titers higher than 10^7 plaque-forming units (PFU) per ml were used to infect hamsters.

Virus inoculation. Nonanesthetized hamsters were inoculated with 10^4 to 4×10^4 PFU of HA-1 virus in a 0.01-ml volume of Hanks' balanced salt solution (BSS). This small volume was given into the right nasal chamber by use of a 0.25-ml syringe with a 27-gauge needle attached. The syringe was operated by a microdispenser, and the needle was tipped with a small piece of plastic tubing.

Drug administration. Drug or placebo treatment was given in 0.05-ml volumes per nostril each time to nonanesthetized hamsters.

Nasal passage washings. Sampling of the infected nasal cavity was accomplished by means of nasal douches taken 3 hr after the last treatment or at 24 or 32 hr postinfection. In either case, about 3 to 4 ml of BSS was forced into one nostril and the wash was collected from the other nostril. The nasal wash was quick-frozen until used.

Viral titrations. Viral titrations of the nasal washes were made on plate cultures of HEp-2 cells under agar overlay. Plaque counts were made 48 to 72 hr later.

Analysis of the data. The mean value obtained from each treated group was compared with the mean of the control (placebo-treated) group. The significance of the observed difference was determined by the one-tailed t test, since it was known that the drug was at least as effective as the control treatment. Dunnett's (3) test was used when more than one treatment group was compared with the control group.

RESULTS AND DISCUSSION

Preliminary work. A number of preliminary tests were carried out to obtain basic information about the in vivo characteristics of the drug. Comparison with saline-treated controls showed that multiple treatments with calcium elenolate, as close as 3 hr before virus inoculation, did not affect the course of the infection. Treatment at 2 hr, or at 18 hr postinfection, also had no antiviral effect. Such observations indicated that, for the drug to exert its "contact" activity, treatments should be given closer to the time of inoculation of virus. Virus shedding in nasal washes taken 24 hr postinfection was reduced somewhat by treatment either 15 min before or after inoculation and to an even greater degree by treatment both before and after inoculation. Reduction of the interval from 15 min to 10 to 5 min before and after the time of infection increased the effectiveness of calcium elenolate. These findings coincide with the in vitro activity of the drug (6).

Explanation for the narrow interval between inoculation of virus and effective application of treatment may reside in the very rapid disappearance of the drug from the nasal passages of hamsters. Within 15 min after treatment with a 2% solution of calcium elenolate, less than 5% of the drug was recovered from the nasal washes of hamsters and guinea pigs. Evidence was found that calcium elenolate rapidly binds to proteins, which could account for its rapid disappearance from the nasal cavity as free drug.

In vivo virucidal effect at the time of infection. The in vivo virucidal effect of calcium elenolate is shown in Table 1. In this test, 25 hamsters were treated with a 2% solution of the drug in saline, and 24 others received saline as placebo. In both cases, 0.05 ml per nostril was given 10 min before and 10 min after the inoculation of 10^4 PFU of HA-1 virus in 0.01 ml of BSS. Nasal douches were taken 24 hr postinfection, and the viral content was determined by the plaque assay method in HEp-2 cell plates. The drastic viral reduction in the nasal washes of drug-treated animals indicated the efficiency of calcium elenolate in reducing virus shedding. Statistical analysis showed the difference between placebo and drug-treated groups to be significant ($P < 0.01$). To ascertain further the antiviral effectiveness of the drug, the rate of viral spread to the lungs was determined. From each group of animals, 10 were selected at random at 72 hr postinfection. As shown in Table 2, virus was recovered from all 10 lungs of placebo-treated animals, but no virus was recovered from the drug-treated animals. The highly significant difference indicated a very efficient viral inactivation in the nasal cavity, preventing spread of the virus to the lungs. This in vivo effect was interpreted as due to an in situ virucidal action of the drug, which effectively reduced the number of infectious particles before their penetration into susceptible cells. If this were so, then the drug would similarly affect newly formed virus emerging from primarily infected cells and thus prevent or reduce the number of secondary foci of infection.

Table 1. *In vivo virucidal effect of calcium elenolate at the time of infection*

Treatment[a]	No. of animals	Mean PFU/ml[b]	Statistical analysis		
			Mean $\log_{10}$ PFU/ml[c]	SEM[d]	Observed t[e]
Saline	24	603	2.78	0.09	
Drug, 2% ..	25	9	0.97	0.16	–9.68**

[a] Intranasal treatment, 10 min before and 10 min after virus inoculation.
[b] Viral count in nasal washes taken 24 hr postinfection.
[c] Obtained as $1/N\ \Sigma\log_{10}(X + 1)$.
[d] Standard error of the mean.
[e] Significance (one-sided) of the observed t judged by Dunnett's procedure: $^{**}P<0.01$.

Virucidal effect after the eclipse phase. To determine whether the drug would affect newly formed virus, 100 hamsters in groups of 10 were inoculated as aforementioned and treated intranasally with either saline or 1% calcium elenolate in saline. The hamsters were treated from one to five times with 0.05 ml per nostril, at 2-hr intervals with treatment starting 8 hr postinfection. Since the nasal douches were done 3 hr after final treatment, the time of these samplings varied from 11 hr postinfection in the groups receiving one treatment to 19 hr postinfection in the groups treated five times. Results shown in Table 3 indicate that when treatment was initiated 8 hr postinfection, either in a single dose or in repeated doses at 2-hr intervals, up to 16 hr postinfection, recovery of virus 3 hr after the last treatment was significantly reduced in all cases. Viral titrations of a second nasal wash taken from the same animals

Table 2. *Virus spread to the lungs of 20 randomly selected hamsters, 10 per group, 72 hr postinfection (from Table 1)*

Treatment[a]	Mean PFU/g of lung	No. of infected lungs[b]
Saline	229×10^3	10/10
Drug, 2%	0	0/10

[a] Intranasal treatment, 10 min before and 10 min after virus inoculation.
[b] Infected/total. Analysis of data on the basis of presence or absence of virus in the lungs resulted in a corrected chi-square value of 16.20 ($P<0.001$).

Table 3. *Virucidal effect of 1% calcium elenolate given intranasally after the eclipse phase*

Treatment		Recovery of virus in nasal washes							
		3 hr after last treatment				32 hr postinoculation			
			Statistical analysis				Statistical analysis		
Solution	Doses[a]	Mean PFU/ml[b]	Mean $\log_{10}$PFU/ml[c]	SEM[d]	Observed t[e]	Mean PFU/ml	Mean $\log_{10}$PFU/ml	SEM	Observed t
Saline	1	32	1.50	0.07		29,600	4.47	0.22	
Drug	1	5	0.68	0.15	–4.90**	5,500	3.74	0.08	–8.72**
Saline	2	74	1.87	0.13		27.000	4.43	0.04	
Drug	2	2	0.38	0.15	–7.75**	8,150	3.91	0.11	–4.22**
Saline	3	355	2.55	0.08		36,400	4.56	0.03	
Drug	3	7	0.84	0.14	–10.56**	5,750	3.76	0.17	–4.79**
Saline	4	148	2.17	0.09		21,400	4.33	0.09	
Drug	4	5	0.73	0.15	–8.07**	3,720	3.57	0.13	–5.00**
Saline	5	708	2.85	0.13		28,200	4.45	0.09	
Drug	5	20	1.29	0.15	–7.77**	5,900	3.77	0.15	–3.82**

[a] Doses given at 2-hr intervals, beginning 8 hr postinfection.
[b] Viral count per milliliter of nasal wash.
[c] Obtained as $1/N\Sigma\log_{10}(X + 1)$.
[d] Standard error of the mean.
[e] Significance (one-sided) of the observed t judged by Dunnett's procedure: $^{**}P<0.01$.

Table 4. *Antiviral effect of graded concentrations of calcium elenolate, given intranasally*

	Recovery of virus in nasal washes							
	3 hr after last treatment				32 hr postinoculation			
		Statistical analysis				Statistical analysis		
Treatment[a]	Mean PFU/ml[b]	Mean $\log_{10}$PFU/ml[c]	SEM[d]	Observed t[e]	Mean PFU/ml	Mean $\log_{10}$PFU/ml	SEM	Observed t
Saline	245	2.39	0.06	–	50,120	4.70	0.09	–
Drug, 1.0%	9	0.96	0.16	–7.82**	1,413	3.15	0.21	–6.31**
Drug, 0.5%	5	0.71	0.14	–9.17**	2,570	3.41	0.16	–5.26**
Drug, 0.25%	43	1.63	0.16	–4.12**	8.318	3.92	0.23	–3.20**
Drug, 0.10%	115	2.06	0.11	–1.81	15,490	4.19	0.17	–2.11†

[a] Two doses given at 8 and 12 hr postinfection.
[b] Viral count per ml of nasal wash.
[c] Obtained as $1/N\Sigma\log_{10}(X + 1)$.
[d] Standard error of the mean.
[e] Significance (one-sided) of the observed t judged by Dunnett's procedure: $^{**}P<0.01$; †$P = 0.06$.

at 32 hr postinfection revealed a persistent antiviral effect. The number of animals involved, the persistent effect, and the consistency of the results clearly indicated the drug's "therapeutic" value in diminishing the number of infectious virus particles, and thus the degree of the infection.

Minimal effective dose. To establish a minimal effective dose, groups of 10 hamsters were treated with graded concentrations of calcium elenolate, ranging from 1 to 0.1% and given at 8 and 12 hr postinfection. Results in Table 4 show significant antiviral activity with 0.25% concentration 15 hr postinfection. When second nasal washings were collected at 32 hr postinfection, dose response was even more readily observed. Further, animals that had been treated with a 0.25% solution of drug continued to show a significantly lower yield of virus than controls ($P<0.01$). Even in those animals treated with a

0.1% solution, reduction of virus then approached significance ($P = 0.06$). The minimal effective dose was estimated to be lower than that tested, especially if multiple treatments are used.

Minimal effective dose in multiple treatments. Efforts were continued to establish a minimal effective dose in an adequate regimen of treatment. In the next test, beginning 8 hr postinfection, six treatments with graded drug concentrations (from 0.5 down to 0.01%) were given at 4-hr intervals. The last treatment was administered at 28 hr postinfection, and the nasal washes were taken 4 hr later. Table 5 shows that the 0.075% concentration of calcium elenolate was significantly effective ($P<0.05$). This appeared to be the minimal effective dose.

Effect of medication on the nasal tissue of hamsters. The extraordinary sensitivity of hamster olfactory epithelium to a considerable number of drugs tested has been reported (8). Presumably, the size and the complexity of the hamster olfactory area and its position in the nasal cavity make this tissue an easy target for irritants placed in the nasal chamber. Figure 1 shows some anatomical features of the nasal cavity of the hamster. Occupying the anterior portion of the chamber are the simple naso and maxillo turbinates, covered with respiratory ciliated epithelium. This tissue is the one primarily involved in myxovirus infection (4, 5). Posteriorly are the complicated ethmo turbinates, covered with olfactory epithelium. Figure 2 shows histological details of the same areas. The preponderance of olfactory epithelium is

Table 5. *Minimal effective dose of calcium elenolate in multiple treatments*

Treatment[a]	Mean PFU/ml[b]	Statistical analysis: Mean $\log_{10}$ PFU/ml[c]	SEM[d]	Observed t[e]
Saline	38,020	4.58	0.13	
Drug, 0.5%	2,512	3.40	0.13	−6.34**
Drug, 0.1%	10,470	4.02	0.10	−3.03**
Drug, 0.075% . .	12,020	4.08	0.14	−2.70*
Drug, 0.050% . .	26,920	4.43	0.13	−0.81
Drug, 0.025% . .	23,990	4.38	0.16	−1.08
Drug, 0.010% . .	25,120	4.40	0.12	−1.00

[a] Six doses at 4-hr intervals, beginning 8 hr postinfection.
[b] Viral count per milliliter of nasal wash.
[c] Obtained as $1/N \Sigma \log_{10} (X + 1)$.
[d] Standard error of the mean.
[e] Significance (one-sided) of the observed t judged by Dunnett's procedure: $*P<0.05$; $**P<0.01$.

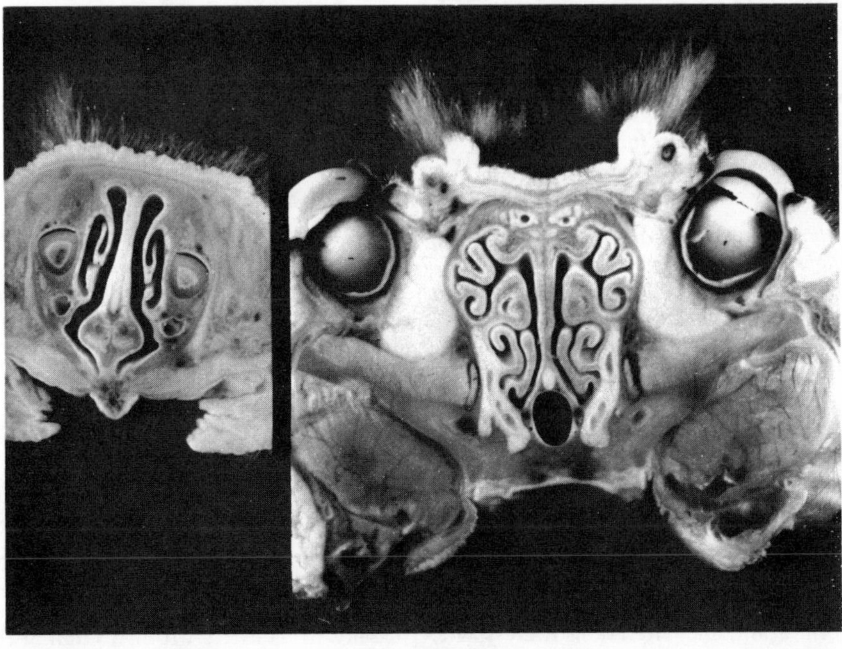

Fig. 1. *Gross anatomical features of the nasal cavity of the hamster. Frontal sections made at 6 and 12 mm from the nasal tip. Respiratory area (left) and olfactory area (right), respectively (× 5).*

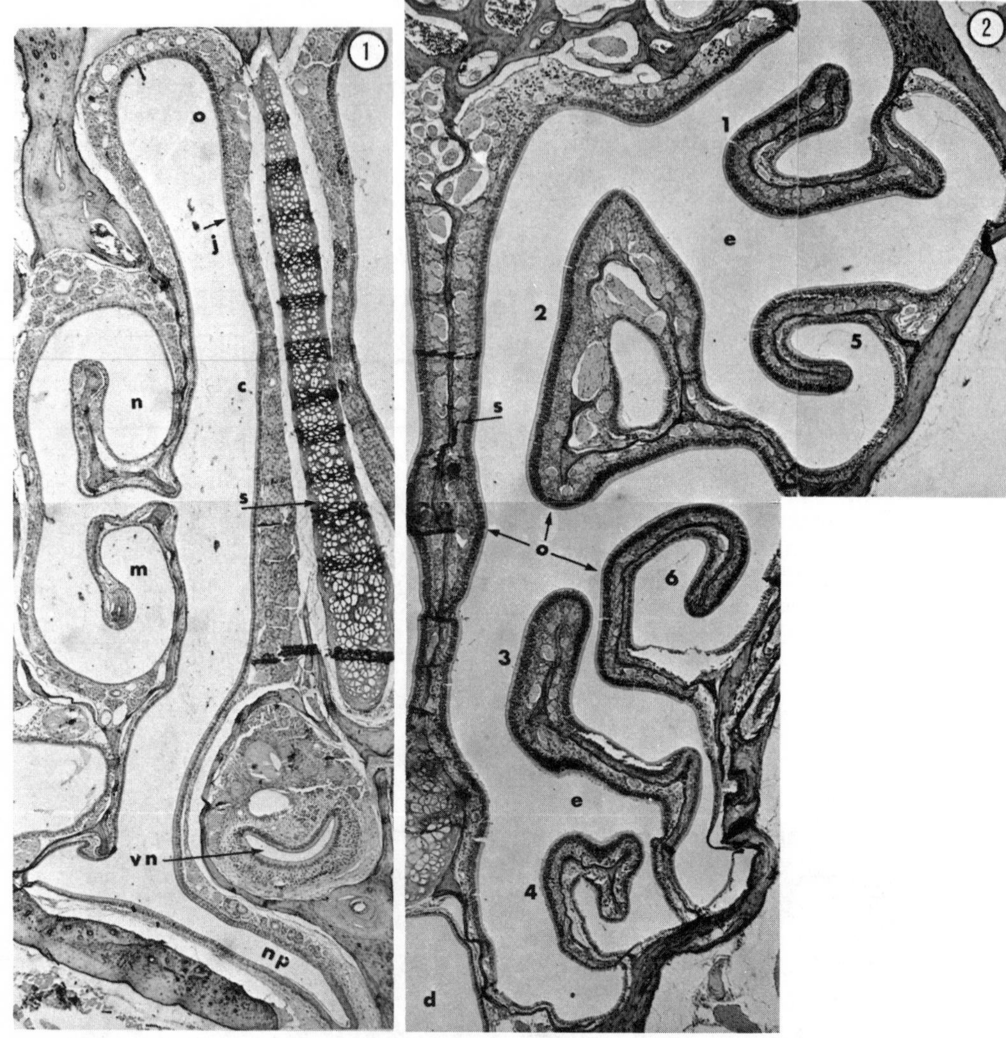

Fig. 2. *Histological details of the nasal tissue of the hamster: n = nasoturbinate; m = maxilloturbinate; e = ethmoturbinates (1, 2, 3, and 4 are endoturbinates and 5 and 6 are ectoturbinates); s = nasal septum; c = ciliated epithelium; o = olfactory epithelium; j = junction of ciliated and olfactory epithelia; d = subseptal duct; vn = vomero-nasal organ of Jacobson; np = naso-palatine canal.* ① *Respiratory area: frontal section, about 6 mm from the nose tip, at the level of the vomero-nasal organ of Jacobson and of the naso and maxilloturbinates (× 35).* ② *Olfactory area: frontal section, about 12 mm from the nose tip, at the level of the ethmoturbinals (× 35).*

apparent. Instillation of solutions containing more than 0.5% calcium elenolate into the nose of hamsters altered mainly the olfactory epithelium (Fig. 3), the ciliated one being affected mostly at the junction of the two epithelia (Fig. 4). However, with reduced drug concentrations, fewer alterations resulted. At the minimal effective concentration, the alterations were slight. Although, in the the experimental animal (and even in humans), a minor degree of tissue damage or irritation could be tolerated in favor of a definite reduction of the disease, it was of practical importance to obtain antiviral effect with almost no histological changes in the nasal tissues.

In the tests described here, calcium elenolate has shown virucidal effect when given intranasally to hamsters within 15 min of HA-1 virus inoculation. Calcium elenolate also showed a "therapeutic" effect when treatment was ini-

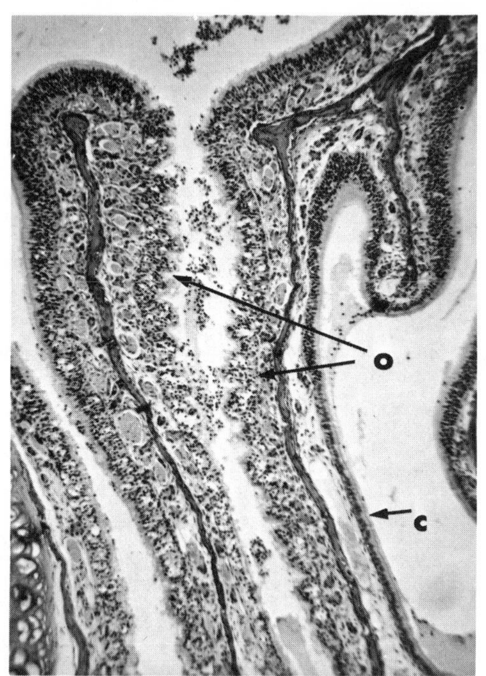

Fig. 3. *Alterations of the olfactory epithelium (o) induced by four doses of 0.5% calcium elenolate, 24 hr after the last treatment. Ciliated epithelium (c) not affected (X 80).*

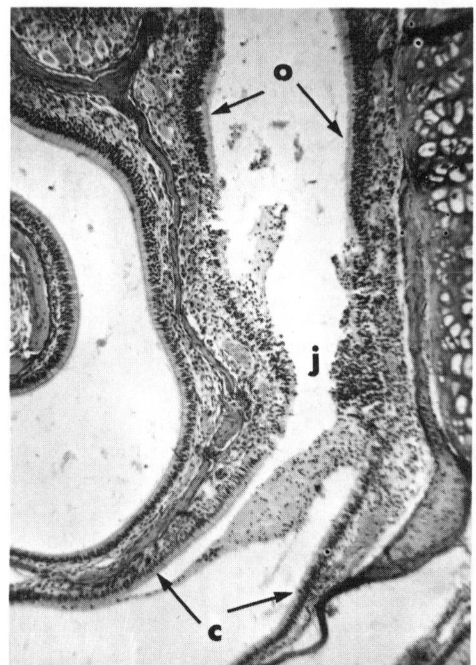

Fig. 4. *As in Fig. 3–the ciliated epithelium (c) is only affected at the junction (j) with the olfactory epithelium (o) (X 80).*

tiated at 8 hr postinfection, either in a single dose or in repeated doses at various intervals up to 28 hr postinfection. This effect was indicated by the significant reduction of the amount of virus in nasal washes taken as early as 11 hr or as late as 32 hr after inoculation. This antiviral effect, once the infection has taken place, results in a drastic reduction of the infectious process and minimizes the spread of the infection to the environment. The sustained effect obtained suggests that calcium elenolate may affect viral components of cellular origin in both free and cell-associated virus.

The olfactory epithelium of the hamster [and other laboratory animals (7)], although not primarily involved in myxovirus infection, is generally very sensitive to medication. However, the minimal effective concentration of calcium elenolate, 0.075%, allows the administration of six treatments within a 28-hr period postinfection, producing only minimal histological changes while exerting statistically significant therapeutic antiviral activity.

Lack of effect of the tissue-bound drug on virus attachment and penetration is indicated by its relative inactivity when administered intranasally earlier than 15 min before inoculation. Lack of effect on intracellular viral multiplication is shown by its inactivity when administered from 15 min to 2 hr after inoculation, at the beginning of the eclipse phase. However, drug given after the eclipse phase, when new virus emerges from the infected cell, results in decreased virus in the nasal cavity. At this time, any unbound drug may affect free new virus, rendering it noninfective. However, if the drug has already been bound to the infected cell surface, the emerging virus may take drug-modified cellular material into its envelope, making this new virus similarly noninfective.

The drug's rapid disappearance from washes of the nasal cavity of hamsters substantiates that the viral reduction observed did not result from in vitro activity of residual free drug in the collected washings.

The drug seems to exert its antiviral activity by affecting viral components of cellular origin.

ACKNOWLEDGMENTS

I acknowledge the skillful technical assistance of Frank Skreko, Jr., and the statistical analysis of the data provided by John Schultz.

LITERATURE CITED

1. Cate, T. R., R. B. Couch, and K. M. Johnson. 1964. Studies with rhinoviruses in volunteers: production of illness, effect of naturally acquired antibody and demonstration of a protective effect not associated with serum antibody. J. Clin. Invest. **43**:56–67.
2. Couch, R. B., T. R. Cate, R. G. Douglas, Jr., P. J. Gerone, and V. Knight. 1966. Effect of route of inoculation on experimental respiratory viral disease in volunteers and evidence for airborne transmission. Bacteriol. Rev. **30**:517–529.
3. Dunnett, C. W. 1964. New tables for multiple comparisons with a control. Biometrics **20**:482–491.
4. Hers, J. F. P. 1955. The histopathology of the respiratory tract in human influenza, p. 67. H. E. Stenfert Kroese N. V.- Leiden.
5. Mulder, J. 1960. Broad aspects of the problem of human virulence in influenza viruses. Virus virulence and pathogenicity. Ciba Found. Study Group No. 4, p. 43. Little Brown & Co., Boston.
6. Renis, H. E. 1970. In vitro antiviral activity of calcium elenolate. Antimicrob. Agents Chemother.–1969, p. 167–172.
7. Smith, C. G. 1938. Changes in the olfactory mucosa and the olfactory nerves following intranasal treatment with one per cent zinc sulphate. Can. Med. Ass. J. **39**:138.
8. Soret, M. G. 1969. System for antiviral drug evaluation in hamsters infected with HA-1 virus. Antimicrob. Agents Chemother.–1968, p. 220–224.
9. Tyrrell, D. A., M. L. Bynoe, K. Petersen, and R. N. P. Sutton. 1959. Inoculation of human volunteers with para-influenza types 1 and 3 (HA2 and HA1). Brit. Med. J. **2**:909–911.

Antimicrobial Agents and Chemotherapy—1969

In Vitro Antiviral Activity of Calcium Elenolate

HAROLD E. RENIS

Department of Virology Research, The Upjohn Co., Kalamazoo, Michigan 49001

Calcium elenolate $[(C_{11}H_{13}O_6)_2Ca]$ is a multifunctional monoterpene which can be isolated from acid-hydrolyzed aqueous extracts of various parts of olive plants. This compound has been shown to be virucidal for all viruses against which it has been tested. No change in infectivity was noted when infectious ribonucleic acid (prepared from coxsackievirus A21) was incubated with calcium elenolate. Incubation of calcium elenolate with influenza A (PR8) virus resulted in loss of infectivity at concentrations which caused no observable change in hemagglutination titer or neuraminidase activity. The virucidal activity of this compound was shown to be greatest under alkaline conditions (*p*H 7.5). The quantity of virus inactivated was dependent on the calcium elenolate concentration and the time of incubation. Incubation of calcium elenolate with several nucleic acid constituents prior to the addition of virus caused no alteration in virucidal activity. However, when the incubation was carried out with amino acids prior to incubation with virus, losses in virucidal activity were detected with glycine, lysine, cysteine, and histidine, and to a lesser extend with phenylalanine, tryptophan, serine, and threonine. Pretreating cells with calcium elenolate did not alter coxsackievirus A21 attachment.

Elenolic acid can be obtained, after mild acid hydrolysis, from the aqueous extracts of various parts of the olive plant (*Olea europa*) (3, 7). The structure of the calcium salt, which may be obtained in cyrstalline form from the hydrolysates, is shown in Fig. 1.

We have found calcium elenolate to be virucidal for a broad spectrum of viruses in vitro, to reduce virus yields from hamsters infected with parainfluenza 3 virus (11), and to have a low order of toxicity after intranasal instillation (6). The results of our in vitro studies with calcium elenolate form the basis of this report.

MATERIALS AND METHODS

Virucidal activity. Calcium elenolate was prepared in 0.9% NaCl at the indicated concentrations. Equal volumes of calcium elenolate and virus were incubated at 37 C for 30 min. The residual infectivity of the mixture was determined by the plaque method on monolayers of susceptible cells.

Infectious ribonucleic acid (I-RNA) from coxsackievirus A21 infected cells. The preparation and assay of I-RNA from coxsackievirus A21 was as previously described (10). Equal volumes of calcium elenolate (1 mg/ml) and I-RNA were incubated at 37 C for 30 min, and then the residual infectivity was determined.

Viruses. Coxsackievirus A21, parainfluenza 3 virus, herpesvirus (MRS), and pseudorabies virus were obtained from D. A. Buthala. Vesicular stomatitis virus (Indiana), encephalomyocarditis virus, Newcastle disease virus (GB), and poliovirus 1, 2, and 3 were obtained from G. E. Underwood. The influenza A virus (PR8) was adapted to chick kidney monolayers, and the Sindbis virus was obtained from the American Type Culture Collection. Reovirus 3 (Deering) was obtained from P. J. Gomatos (Sloan-Kettering Institute, New York, N.Y.).

Cells. Monolayers prepared from trypsinized 10- or 11-day-old chick embryos were used for the cultivation and plaque assay of Sindbis and vesicular stomatitis viruses. Chick kidney cell monolayers, prepared from

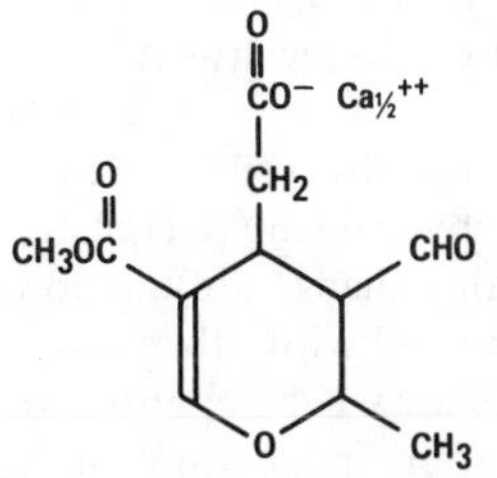

Fig. 1. *Structure of calcium elenolate. This structure has been revised from that reported. This information will be subsequently reported by R. C. Kelly and F. A. MacKellar of these laboratories.*

19-day-old embryos, were used for the cultivation and plaque assay of Newcastle disease and influenza A (PR8) viruses. Reovirus 3 and encephalomyocarditis virus were cultivated in and plaque-assayed on L929 cells. ML cells, obtained from D. A. Buthala, were used for the culitvation and plaque assay of coxsackievirus A21 and polioviruses 1, 2, and 3. Parinfluenza 3 virus was grown on ML monolayers, and HEp-2 monolayers were used for the plaque assay. Herpesvirus (MRS) was grown and assayed on primary rabbit kidney monolayers.

Eagle's medium with 3% inactivated fetal bovine serum was used for the propagation of all viruses except parainfluenza 3 virus, for which medium 1066 with 3% fetal bovine serum was used. Medium 199 supplemented with 5% fetal calf serum and Eagle's amino acid and vitamin mixtures, and containing 1% Noble agar, was used for plaque assays.

Determination of hemagglutinin titer. Serial twofold dilutions of influenza A (PR8) virus treated with calcium elenolate for 30 min at 37 C were made in 0.9% sodium chloride and were incubated with an equal volume of 0.5% red cells from chickens at 4 C for 60 min. The reciprocal of the highest dilution of virus giving definite hemagglutination was taken as the end point.

Neuraminidase activity. Influenza A (PR8) virus, which had been treated for 30 min at 37 C with calcium elenolate, was diluted with 2 volumes of 1 M acetate buffer (pH 6.0). The resulting mixture (0.1 ml) was incubated with 0.1 ml of neuraminyl-lactose (1 mg/ml) for 60 min at 37 C, and the free neuraminic acid was determined colorimetrically (14).

Table 1. *Spectrum of virucidal activity of calcium elenolate*[a]

Virus	Cell	Plaque-forming units/0.5 ml	
		Control	Treated
Herpes	Rabbit kidney	3.3×10^5	$<10^1$
		8.4×10^5	1.7×10^2
Vaccinia	Chick embryo	3.7×10^6	$<10^1$
Pseudorabies	Rabbit kidney	6.5×10^4	$<10^1$
		1.8×10^6	9.6×10^3
Influenza A (PR8)	Chick kidney	9.1×10^5	$<10^1$
		6.0×10^5	$<10^1$
Newcastle disease	Chick kidney	4.2×10^5	1.4×10^2
		2.1×10^6	8.5×10^1
Parainfluenza 3	HEp-2	1.4×10^4	$<10^1$
		2.3×10^3	$<10^1$
Coxsackie A21	ML	5.0×10^5	$<10^2$
		1.1×10^7	2.4×10^2
Encephalomyocarditis	L929	1.4×10^6	1.1×10^5
		1.0×10^6	6.1×10^4
Polio 1	ML	3.0×10^7	8.6×10^4
		2.8×10^7	1.2×10^5
Polio 2	ML	4.1×10^5	2.1×10^3
		3.1×10^5	3.6×10^3
Polio 3	ML	3.7×10^4	5.7×10^3
		4.0×10^4	3.6×10^3
Vesicular stomatitis	Chick embryo	2.1×10^6	4.0×10^1
		2.0×10^6	2.2×10^2
Sindbis	Chick embryo	5.7×10^5	$<10^1$
		9.0×10^4	$<10^1$
Reovirus 3 (Deering)	L929	8.1×10^6	4.2×10^5

[a] Calcium elenolate (1 mg/ml) or 0.9% NaCl was incubated with an equal volume of virus suspension at 37 C for 30 min.

RESULTS

The virucidal activity of calcium elenolate was studied with several different viruses. As shown in Table 1, titers of all viruses were reduced after incubation with calcium elenolate at 0.5 mg/ml for 30 min at 37 C. Reovirus 3 (Deering) and poliovirus 3 appeared to be the least susceptible to inactivation (about 1 log reductions in virus titers were observed), whereas the remainder of the viruses tested were highly susceptible to inactivation by this agent. During the course of studies with coxsackievirus A21, it was observed that prolonged storage of virus stocks at −70 C decreased the susceptibility of the virus to inactivation by calcium elenolate. The reasons underlying this change are unknown, and it has not been observed with other viruses.

Figure 2 shows a comparison of the residual infectivity after incubation of coxsackievirus A21 contained in tissue culture fluid and virus which had been purified by density gradient centrifugation (generously supplied by L. Slechta of these laboratories) with different

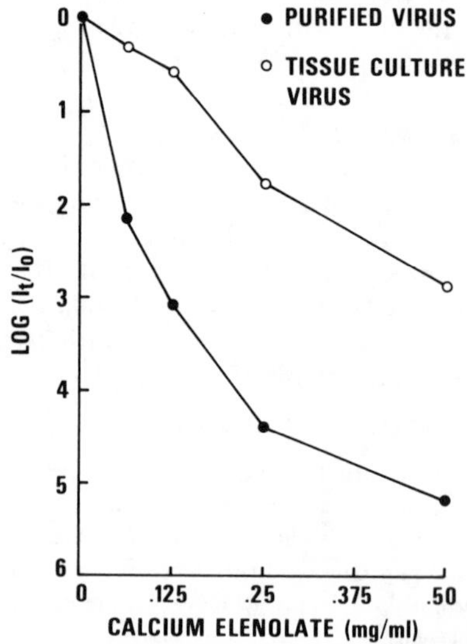

Fig. 2. *Inactivation of purified coxsackievirus A21 and of coxsackievirus A21 in tissue culture fluid. Virus (0.5 ml), calcium elenolate (0.5 ml in saline), and buffer (phosphate, 0.1 ml, pH 8.0, 0.5 M) were incubated at 37 C for 40 min.* I_t *= infectivity of the treated sample;* I_0 *= infectivity of saline control.*

concentrations of calcium elenolate. It is clear from these data that calcium elenolate is much more effective in inactivating the purified virus than the unpurified virus. These results indicate that the crude tissue culture fluid protects the virus from inactivation and suggest that the agent reacts with components in the tissue culture fluid.

The effect of *p*H on the inactivation of coxsackievirus A21 by calcium elenolate is shown in Fig. 3. At *p*H values lower than 6.5, little inactivation was observed. The virucidal activity of calcium elenolate increased as the medium was made more alkaline, with maximal activity occurring at *p*H 7.5 to 8.0. At *p*H 8.0, the titer of the control sample was greatly decreased.

Table 2 shows data obtained by incubating different preparations of I-RNA prepared from coxsackievirus A21 with calcium elenolate. Clearly, even though the whole virus was readily inactivated by calcium elenolate, no inactivation of the infectivity of the isolated RNA occurred. These data suggest that calcium elenolate exerts its virucidal activity by interacting with the protein of the virus particle.

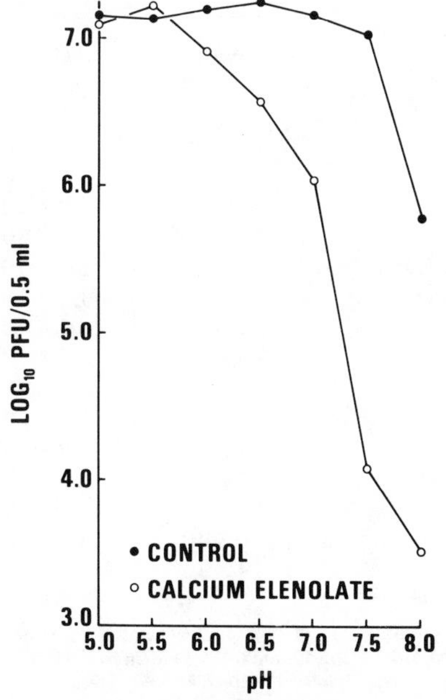

Fig. 3. *Inactivation of coxsackievirus A21 by calcium elenolate at different pH values. Virus (0.5 ml), calcium elenolate (0.5 ml in 0.55 mg/ml), and buffer (phosphate, 0.1 ml, 0.5* M*) were incubated at 37 C for 3 min. Residual infectivity was determined by the plaque method.*

Studies of the effect of the concentration of calcium elenolate on the infectivity, hemagglutinin, and neuraminidase activity of influenza A virus (PR8) showed that all of these parameters were decreased at high concentrations (1 mg/ml) of calcium elenolate (Table 3). However, at lower drug concentrations (e.g., 0.25 mg/ml), the infectivity of the virus was decreased by nearly 2.5 logs, but no change was observed in the hemagglutination titer nor in the neuraminidase activity. These data suggest that the infectivity of the virus particle is more susceptible to inactivation by calcium elenolate than are the other two virus properties.

The inactivation of parainfluenza 3 virus at *p*H 7.5 by calcium elenolate appears to follow first-order kinetics (Fig. 4). With the concentrations of drug used, the inactivation in all cases was rapid at first and was concentration-dependent. With concentrations of 0.10 and 0.05 mg/ml, the virus titers decreased steadily for about the first 60 min; then the rate of inactivation leveled off, and very little virus was inactivated during the next 2 hr.

Table 2. *Effect of calcium elenolate on coxsackievirus A21 infectious RNA (I-RNA)*[a]

I-RNA prepn	Plaque-forming units/0.2 ml	
	Control	Treated
A	4.5×10^4	5.5×10^4
B	1.9×10^4	3.0×10^4
C	2.9×10^4	2.8×10^4

[a] Equal volumes of calcium elenolate (1 mg/ml) and I-RNA were incubated at 37 C for 30 min. The resulting infectivity was determined by plating on ML monolayers.

Table 3. *Effect of calcium elenolate on the infectivity, hemagglutination titer, and neuraminidase activity of influenza A (PR8) virus*

Calcium elenolate[a] (mg/ml)	Infectivity[b]	Hemagglutination titer	Neuraminidase activity[c]
1.0	$<10^{-1}$	32	25.2
0.5	$<10^{-1}$	128	31.2
0.25	5×10^1	128	36.9
0.125	7×10^2	128	33.0
0.06	4.3×10^3	128	32.4
0	1.3×10^4	128	37.0

[a] The concentrations given are those of the stock solutions.
[b] Expressed as plaque-forming units per 0.5 ml.
[c] Expressed as nanomoles of neuraminic acid cleaved.

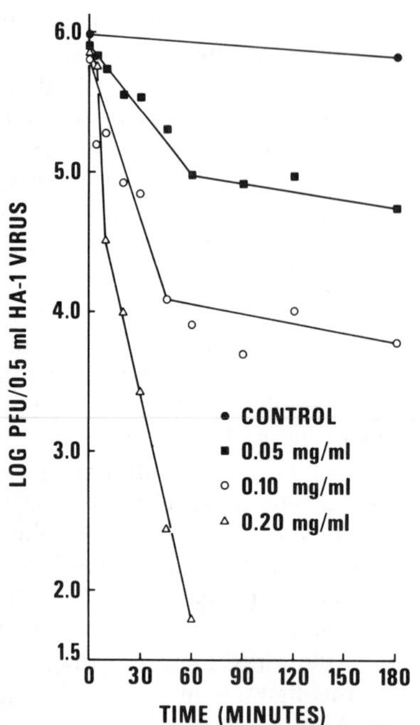

Fig. 4. *Kinetics of inactivation of parainfluenza 3 virus by calcium elenolate. Virus (1 ml), calcium elenolate (1 ml), and buffer (phosphate, pH 7.5, 0.5 M, 0.2 ml) were incubated for different times at 37 C.*

The effect of treating ML monolayers with calcium elenolate (0.25 mg/ml in Hanks' solution) for 1 hr prior to adding coxsackievirus A21 is shown in Fig. 5. In these studies, the calcium elenolate was removed from the monolayers, and the monolayers were washed before the diluted virus was added. At the indicated times, the excess virus was removed and the monolayers were washed with Hanks' solution. At the concentrations used calcium elenolate had no effect on the subsequent attachment and plaque formation of coxsackievirus A21. Similar results have been obtained with herpesvirus and parainfluenza 3 virus.

Incubation of calcium elenolate with several nucleic acid constituents, including bases, nucleosides, nucleotides of purines and pyrimidines, RNA, or deoxyribonucleic acid, did not alter the virucidal activity toward coxsackievirus A21. However, several amino acids decreased the virucidal activity of calcium elenolate after prior incubations with 2 molar equivalents of amino acids (Table 4). Cysteine, histidine, lysine, and glycine were most active in this regard, and phenylalanine, tryptophan, serine, and threonine were intermediate in activity. No change in activity was observed with isoleucine, leucine, valine, and tryosine. The data shown in Table 5 indicate that the amino group of cysteine is necessary for the inactivation of the effect of calcium elenolate. Cysteine, *S*-methyl cysteine,

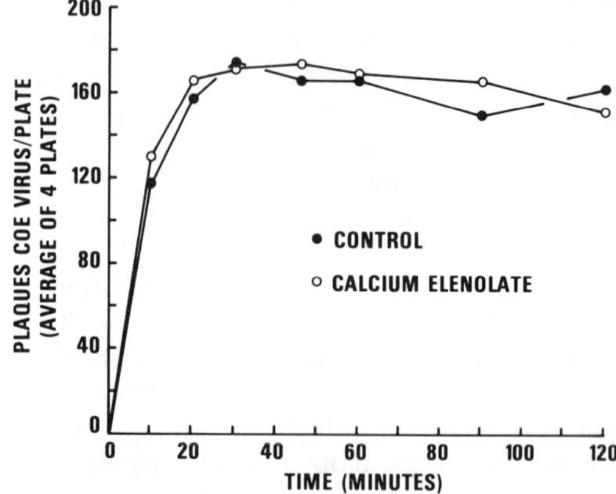

Fig. 5. *Attachment of coxsackievirus A21 to ML monolayers pretreated with calcium elenolate (○) or saline (●). ML monolayers were treated with calcium elenolate (0.25 mg/ml in Hanks' solution) for 1 hr at 37 C. The attachment of coxsackievirus A21 was determined at different times by washing the monolayers and allowing plaques to form under agar medium.*

Table 4. *Effect of incubating calcium elenolate with 2 molar equivalents of amino acids prior to adding coxsackievirus A21*[a]

Amino acid	Plaque-forming units/0.5 ml	
	Treated	Control
Serine	1.6×10^4	3.5×10^6
Threonine	1.8×10^4	7.6×10^6
Lysine	3.3×10^6	3.0×10^6
Glycine	2.2×10^6	2.9×10^6
Alanine	4.9×10^2	2.1×10^6
Phenylalanine	2.5×10^5	3.9×10^6
Tryptophan	5.4×10^5	1.3×10^7
Tryosine	5.2×10^3	8.5×10^5
Valine	9.9×10^3	1.7×10^6
Leucine	5.8×10^3	3.2×10^6
Isoleucine	4.0×10^3	5.1×10^6
Saline	3.7×10^3	1.9×10^6
Cysteine	1.9×10^7	2.0×10^7
Cystine	1.2×10^4	1.2×10^7
Histidine	2.0×10^7	2.1×10^7
Saline	1.4×10^4	1.1×10^7

[a] Equal volumes of calcium elenolate or saline were incubated at 37 C for 30 min (*p*H 7.5); then coxsackievirus A21 was added. After 30 min, the infectivity was determined.

Table 5. *Effect of incubating calcium elenolate with cysteine derivatives on its virucidal activity for coxsackievirus A21*[a]

Derivative	Calcium elenolate	Saline	Calcium elenolate/ saline X100
Cysteine	2.5×10^5	37×10^5	6.8
S-methyl cysteine	0.98×10^5	17×10^5	5.7
N-acetyl cysteine	0.41×10^5	290×10^5	0.14
Cysteine ethyl ester ..	10.0×10^5	220×10^5	4.5
Saline	1.0×10^2	10^6	<0.01

[a] The conditions used are described in Table 4.

and the ethyl ester of cysteine were quite effective, whereas that derivative of cysteine which blocked the amino group (i.e., *N*-acetyl cysteine) was only slightly effective. Other derivatives of histidine (i.e., histamine, histidinol, and histidine methyl ester) were effective in preventing virucidal activity in similar studies, whereas imidazole, imidazole acetic acid, and urocanic acid were ineffective.

DISCUSSION

The results described in this paper indicate that calcium elenolate is virucidal for a broad spectrum of viruses. Except for reovirus 3 (Deering) and poliovirus 3, all of the viruses against which calcium elenolate was tested were highly susceptible to inactivation. The infectivity of influenza A virus (PR8) was destroyed at concentrations of drug that had little or no effect upon hemagglutination titer or upon neuraminidase activity of the virus preparation. These data suggest that viruses inactivated by calcium elenolate are still capable of attaching to cells. Incubation of infectious RNA prepared from coxsackievirus A21 with calcium elenolate did not result in decreased infectivity. From these data, it is tentatively concluded that the virucidal activity of calcium elenolate is mediated through an interaction with the protein coat of the viral particle rather than its nucleic acid. Such a conclusion is further supported by the observation that, whereas some constituents of nucleic acids were ineffective as blocking agents, several amino acids interfered with the virucidal activity of calcium elenolate.

In many regards, the action of calcium elenolate is similar to that which has been reported for several sulfhydryl reagents (1, 2, 4, 5, 8, 9, 15). The sulfhydryl reagents, like calcium elenolate, inactivate a broad spectrum of viruses. Viruses inactivated by certain sulfhydryl reagents (i.e., mercurials or oxidizing agents) may be reactivated with cysteine or reduced glutathione, whereas those reagents which form thio-ethers are not reactivated (1, 5, 8, 9). All attempts to reactivate calcium elenolate-inactivated coxsackievirus A21 have been unsuccessful.

The virucidal activity of calcium elenolate differs significantly from that of other virucidal agents, such as the α-ketoaldehydes, which are also inactivated by cysteine (12). For example, kethoxal does not inactivate several picornaviruses (10, 13), whereas calcium elenolate does, and kethoxal destroys the infectivity of I-RNA prepared from coxsackievirus A21 (10), but calcium elenolate is ineffective.

ACKNOWLEDGMENT

I thank Barbara Court for technical assistance.

LITERATURE CITED

1. Allison, A. C. 1962. Observations on the inactivation of viruses by sulfhydryl reagents. Virology **17**:176–183.
2. Allison, A. C., F. E. Buckland, and C. H. Andrewes. 1962. Effects of sulfhydryl reagents on infectivity of some viruses. Virology **17**:171–175.
3. Beyerman, H. C., L. A. vanDijck, J. Levisalles, A. Melera, and W. L. C. Veer. 1961. The structure of elenolide. Bull. Sci. Chem. France No. 10, p. 1812–1820.
4. Buckland, F. E. 1960. Inactivation of virus hemagglutins by *para*-chloromercuribenzoic acid. Nature (London) **188**:768.
5. Choppin, P. W., and L. Philipson. 1961. The inactivation of enterovirus infectivity by the sulfhydryl reagent *p*-chloromercuribenzoate. J. Exp. Med. **113**:713–734.
6. Elliott, G. A., D. A. Buthala, and E. N. DeYoung. 1970. Preliminary safety studies with calcium elenolate, an antiviral agent. Antimicrob. Agents Chemother.–1969, p. 173–176.
7. Panizzi, L., M. L. Scarpati, and G. Oriente. 1960. The constitution of Oleuropein, a bitter glycoside having hypotensive action, from olives. Gazz. Chim. Ital. **90**:1449–1485.
8. Philipson, L., and P. W. Choppin. 1960. On the role of virus sulfhydryl groups in the attachment of enteroviruses to erythrycytes. J. Exp. Med. **112**:455–478.
9. Philipson, L., and P. W. Choppin. 1962. Inactivation of enteroviruses by 2,3-dimercaptopropanol (BAL). Virology **16**:405–413.
10. Renis, H. E. 1970. Antiviral studies with kethoxal. Ann. N.Y. Acad. Sci., *in press.*
11. Soret, M. G. 1970. Antiviral activity of calcium elenolate on parainfluenza infection of hamsters. Antimicrob. Agents and Chemother.–1969, p. 160–166.
12. Underwood, G. E., R. A. Siem, S. A. Gerpheide, and J. H.

Hunter. 1959. Binding of an antiviral agent (kethoxal) by various metabolites. Proc. Soc. Exp. Biol. Med. **100**:312–315.

13. Underwood, G. E., and S. D. Weed. 1961. The effect of carbonyl compounds on poliovirus. Virology **13**:138–139.
14. Warren, L. 1959. The thiobarbituric acid assay of sialic acids. J. Biol. Chem. **234**:1971–1975.
15. Yuki, H., F. Sano, S. Takama, and S. Suzuki. 1966. Studies of antiviral agents. I. Relationship between chemical reactivity of sulfhydryl reagents and their inactivating activity of adenovirus type 5. Chem. Pharm. Bull. (Tokyo) **14**:139–146.

Antimicrobial Agents and Chemotherapy—1969

Preliminary Safety Studies with Calcium Elenolate, an Antiviral Agent

G. A. ELLIOTT, D. A. BUTHALA, and E. N. DeYOUNG

The Upjohn Co., Kalamazoo, Michigan 49001

The LD_{50} of calcium elenolate for rats was approximately 1,700 mg/kg when the drug was administered orally as a single dose. When the drug was given intraperitoneally the LD_{50} was 160 mg/kg in rats and 120 mg/kg in mice. Daily oral doses of 30, 100, and 300 mg/kg for 30 days were well tolerated in rats. Calcium elenolate was also well tolerated in dogs at 3, 10, and 30 mg/kg per day for 1 month, except for mild gastric irritation at the highest dose tested. The intranasal instillation of 1 and 2% aqueous solutions as drops three times daily in chickens was accompanied by nasal exudation and alterations in the epithelium and lamina propria of the nasal turbinates after 2 days of treatment. Changes in the olfactory epithelium were more pronounced than those in the respiratory epithelium. Similar though much milder changes were seen in rabbits subjected to aqueous intranasal sprays in concentrations as high as 0.6% four times daily for periods up to 14 days. Histologically, the reactions of rabbits treated with concentrations of 0.1 and 0.3% were not different from those of control animals after 7 days of treatment; however, the 0.3% concentration when given for 14 days was moderately irritating. Differences in the distribution of epithelium and total area of the epithial surface of the human nasal cavity suggest that the rabbit nasal cavity may be more sensitive than that of the human.

The routine test procedures used in the preclinical in vivo safety evaluation of chemotherapeutic agents include systemic administration of both single and multiple doses of the drugs to several animal species. Single doses are given in an effort to establish the LD_{50} of a drug, and multiple doses are given to evaluate systemic effects. The route of administration and the duration of treatment are determined in part by the intended clinical protocol. Additional studies are conducted when agents are to be used in a specialized fashion. The purpose of this paper is to report the results of such an evaluation of the antiviral agent calcium elenolate.

MATERIALS AND METHODS

Single-dose studies. Aqueous solutions of calcium elenolate were given intraperitoneally at 0.1-log intervals to groups of five male and five female Carworth CF-1 mice weighing approximately 20 g each. Groups of five male Upjohn Sprague-Dawley specific pathogen-free (SPF) rats weighing approximately 150 g each were injected with calcium elenolate in a similar fashion. Additional groups, each consisting of five male rats from the same source, were treated orally with aqueous solutions of calcium elenolate at 0.2-log intervals. Both mice and rats were observed for 7 days after administration of the drug, and animals surviving at the end of that time were necropsied. The LD_{50} was determined by the Spearman-Karber method (2).

Subacute oral studies. Aqueous solutions were given orally to groups of 10 male and 10 female rats (Upjohn Sprague-Dawley SPF) at levels, of 0, 30, 100, and 300 mg per kg per day for 1 month. Calcium elenolate also was given orally as a dry powder in encapsulated form to groups of two male and two female purebred beagle dogs approximately 7 months of age. Single doses of 0, 3, 10 and 30 mg per kg per day were administered to these animals for 1 month. Terminal hematological examinations were performed on all rats. Pretreatment and terminal hematological examinations, urinalyses, and clinical chemistry determinations were performed on all dogs. Tissues from both rats and dogs were examined grossly at necropsy and microscopically after sectioning.

Intranasal studies. Intranasal studies were of two types. In the initial pilot work, 1 and 2% aqueous solutions of calcium elenolate were instilled as drops three times daily in 1-day-old Leghorn chicks (SPAFAS, Inc., Norwich, Conn.) Administration was continued for various intervals up to 14 days, and daily clinical observations were made. At necropsy, nasal turbinates and paranasal sinuses, along with major organs, were examined histologically. Pilot studies also were conducted in rabbits. In these studies, New Zealand rabbits were sprayed intranasally with 0.1, and 0.25, and 1% solutions three times daily for a 2-day period.

More extensive tolerance studies were conducted in New Zealand rabbits. Several concentrations, up to and including 0.6% were administered for 1- and 2-week periods. In these studies, calcium elenolate was administered as an aqueous spray at the rate of 0.2 ml per nostril four times daily. Animals were necropsied at the end of each study. Nasal turbinates, paranasal sinuses, and major organs were examined histologically. The spray technique and the procedure used for obtaining representative samples of structures within the rabbit nasal cavity have been described (1).

RESULTS

Single-dose studies. The LD_{50} of calcium elenolate in mice was 120 mg/kg when the drug was administered by the intraperitoneal route. In rats, the LD_{50} was 160 mg/kg when the drug was administered intraperitoneally and 1,700 mg/kg when it was given orally.

Subacute oral studies. In the 1-month study with rats, all doses of calcium elenolate were well tolerated. The only drug-associated change seen was a gross yellowing of the nonglandular forestomach in 8 of the 20 rats receiving 300 mg/kg (the highest dose tested). No histological alterations were seen. In dogs given calcium elenolate for 1 month, changes occurred only in the animals receiving 30 mg/kg (the highest dose tested). A mild gastric irritation manifested by sporadic vomiting and the development of a few small gastric erosions occurred in three of the four animals in this group.

Intranasal studies. In pilot studies, the intranasal administration of calcium elenolate to chicks produced gross nasal exudates and alterations in the epithelium and underlying lamina propria of the nasal turbinates after 2 days of treatment. These alterations were dose-related and were more prominent in the olfactory epithelium than in the respiratory epithelium. They were characterized by flattening of the epithelium and in some instances by focal necrosis. Inflammatory cell infiltrates also were found in the lamina propria. In preliminary studies, changes similar both in degree and in distribution were found in the nasal cavity of rabbits sprayed with 1% calcium elenolate. However, rabbits receiving 0.1 and 0.25% solutions of the drug were free from drug-related change.

In the more definitive studies, the nasal cavities of rabbits were sprayed four times daily with 0.1, 0.3, and 0.6% solutions for both 7- and 14-day periods. Five rabbits were tested under each set of conditions, and in each study additional groups of five rabbits were maintained as untreated and vehicle controls. Nasal tissues of rabbits that received the 0.1% solution for 7 days were difficult to distinguish from the nasal tissues of rabbits that received the 0.3% solution for 7 days. These two groups did not differ substantially from the vehicle control group except in terms of an increased nasal exudate and a more marked inflammatory response in the lamina propria of the maxilloturbinals (Fig. 1–3). The 0.6% concentration was

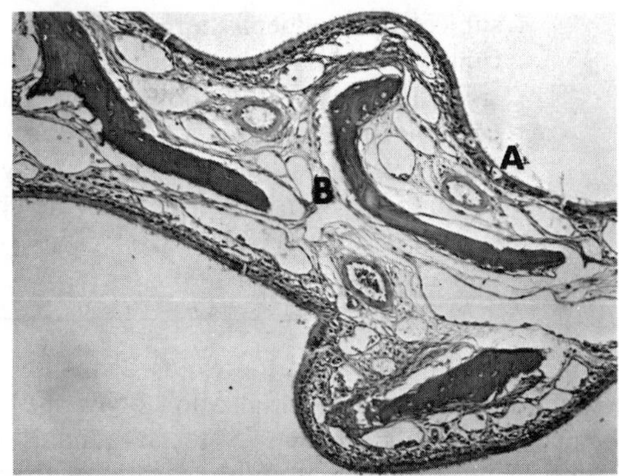

Fig. 1. *Maxillo-turbinal from untreated control rabbit, showing epithelium (A) and lamina propria (B).* × *140.*

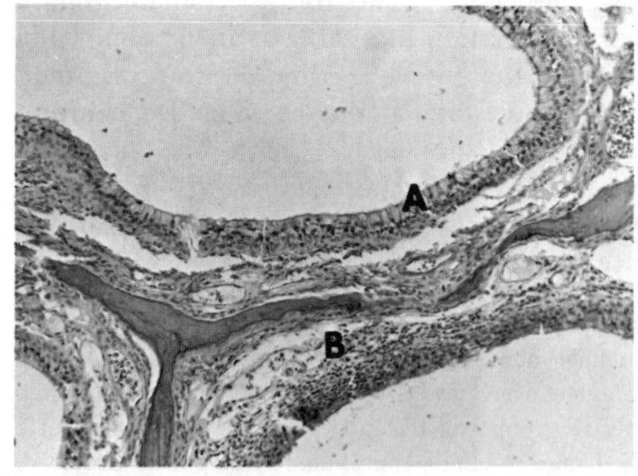

Fig. 2. *Maxillo-turbinal from vehicle control rabbit, showing higher epithelium than usual (A) and inflammatory cell infiltrate in lamina propria (B).* × *140.*

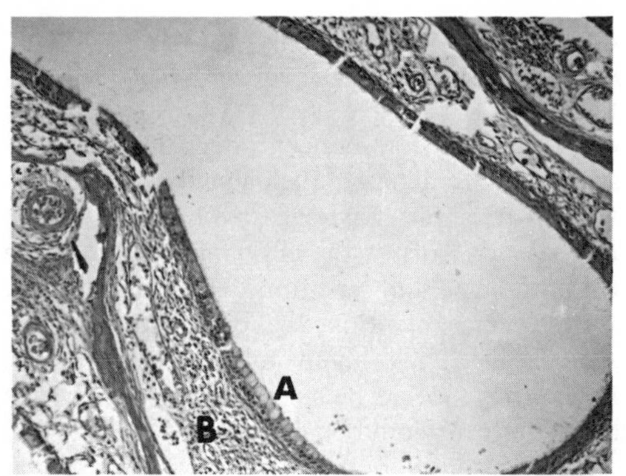

Fig. 3. *Maxillo-turbinal from rabbit treated with 0.1% calcium elenolate for 7 days, showing changes essentially like those seen in Fig. 2.* × *140.*

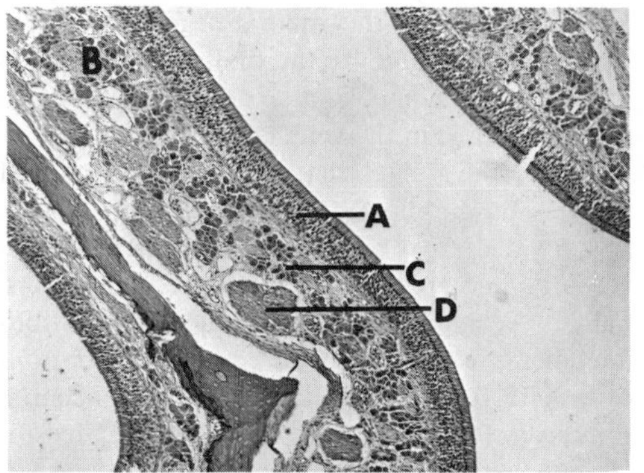

Fig. 4. *Ethmo-turbinal from vehicle control rabbit, showing epithelium (A) and lamina propria (B) glands (C) and nerves in cross section (D); no change from normal.* × *88.*

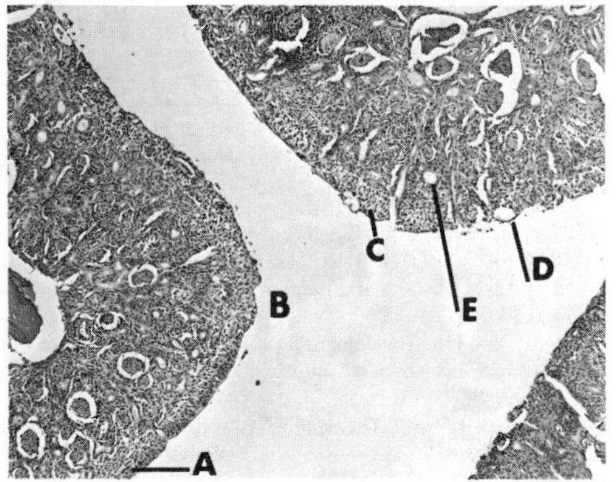

Fig. 5. *Ethmo-turbinal from rabbit treated with 0.6% calcium elenolate, showing flattening of epithelium (A), thinning and irregularity of epithelium (B), decrease in number of nuclei (C), vacuolation (D), and dilatation of glands (E).* × *88.*

mildly irritating, as shown by the increased prominence of the columnar epithelium and the increased numbers of goblet cells in the maxillo-turbinals. Some of these same changes were seen in the maxillo-turbinals of rabbits receiving the 0.1 and 0.3% solutions, but they were much less severe. The olfactory epithelium of the ethmo-turbinals also was moderately distorted in two of the five rabbits receiving the 0.6% solutions.

In the 14-day study, the 0.1% solution of calcium elenolate was well tolerated. Changes differed little from those seen in the vehicle control group or from those seen after 7 days of treatment. However, in 0.3 and 0.6% solutions the compound was a mild to moderate irritant. This was shown by the prominent columnar epithelium covering the maxillo-turbinals where it is usually flatter and by more pronounced and consistent changes in the olfactory epithelium than were present at 7 days. These changes were characterized by flattening, thinning, and vacuolation of olfactory cells (Fig. 4 and 5). Similar focal but much less marked alterations were seen in the olfactory epithelium of two of the five rabbits receiving the 0.1% solution.

In both the 7-day and the 14-day studies, drug-related effects were confined to the nasal cavity. The incidence of sinusitis was not different from that in the controls.

DISCUSSION

To relate the effects observed in animals to those that might be anticipated in humans, it may be helpful to compare some aspects of the rabbit nasal cavity with that of the human.

The rabbit nasal cavity has three sets of turbinates (4; Fig. 6). The most anterior of

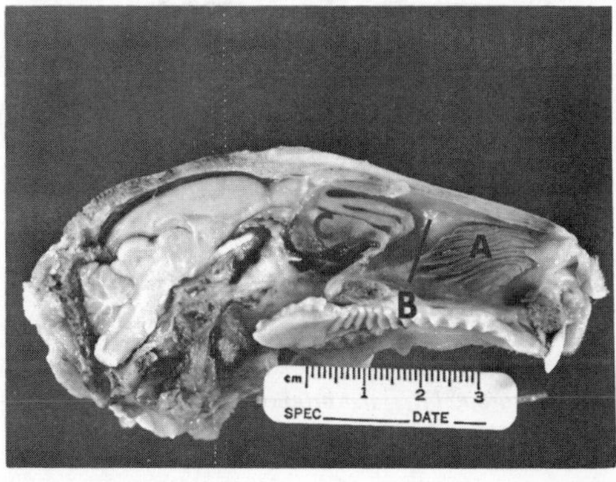

Fig. 6. *Interior of rabbit nasal cavity, showing maxillo-turbinal (A), nasoturbinal (B), and ethmo-turbinal (C).*

these, the branched maxillo-turbinal, is covered with a low stratified epithelium about two cell layers thick. The ethmo-turbinal, located posteriorly, and the naso-turbinal, dorso-laterally, are covered almost entirely by olfactory epithelium. Ciliated columnar epithelium is limited primarily to the nasal septum and the paranasal sinuses. This distribution differs from that in humans in whom the bulk of the nasal epithelium is ciliated columnar or respiratory (4, 5). The distribution of olfactory epithelium also differs in that in man it is found in a small area over the superior and supreme turbinals, a small part of the middle turbinal, on the septum, and on the roof (Fig. 7). It is interesting to note, however, that the total area covered by olfactory epithelium in rabbits is reported (4) to be close to that of humans (7.5 versus to 10 to 12.5 cm^2). Figures comparing the total area of the nasal cavity of man with that of rabbits are difficult to obtain. Negus (4), however, stated that the total area of nasal epithelium in humans is approximately three times that of rabbits.

With these points in mind, it seems that the intranasal testing of calcium elenolate in man should be feasible, even though mild to moderate changes were seen when rabbits were treated for an extended period. The greater regional concentration of the olfactory epithelium in rabbits may render them especially susceptible to damage from materials placed in the nose. The human nasal cavity, in which the epithelium is less concentrated, may be less susceptible to damage. Such an enhanced susceptibility of rabbits was suggested by Gundrum on the basis of work with sulfonamides (3). On the basis of Negus's observation (4) on comparative surface areas mentioned above, one also may speculate that the same volume sprayed into the human nose would be spread over a greater area and its effects would be diluted.

In addition, it is reasonable to postulate that the increased numbers of goblet cells and the appearance of columnar epithelium covering the maxillo-turbinals in calcium elenolate-treated rabbits reflects primarily a defensive or physiological response rather than a degenerative one. This is substantiated by the finding of changes in the epithelium and lamina propria, along with nasal exudates, in the vehicle control groups.

Further evidence that the nasal mucosa of rabbits may be more sensitive than that of man is provided by pilot and tolerance studies recently completed in human volunteers. Calcium elenolate sprays applied in cautious increments were well tolerated in concentrations of 0.0085 to 2%. Subsequently, a 1% concentration given four times daily was well tolerated for 14 days.

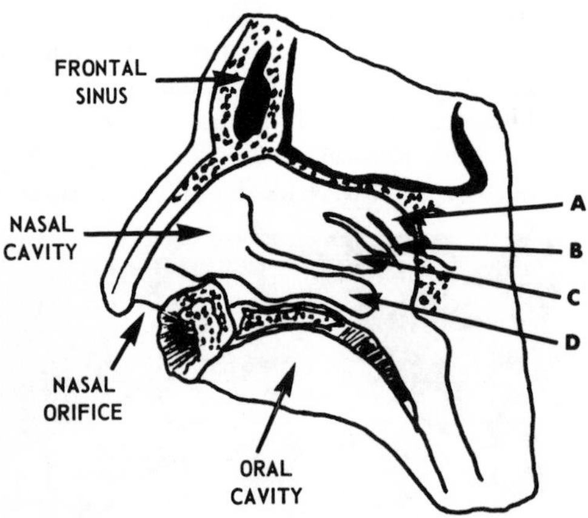

Fig. 7. *Diagram of interior of human nasal cavity, showing supreme turbinal (A), superior turbinal (B), middle turbinal (C), and inferior turbinal (D).*

ACKNOWLEDGMENTS

We are grateful to R. Shattuck, Department of Pathology and Toxicology Research, for assistance in the preparation of photographs, and to G. E. Underwood, Department of Virology Research, The Upjohn Co., for his comments and suggestions concerning the manuscript.

LITERATURE CITED

1. Elliott, G. A., and E. N. DeYoung. 1969. Intranasal toxicity testing of antiviral agents. 2nd Conf. on Antiviral Substances, N.Y. Acad. Sci.
2. Finney, D. J. 1964. Statistical methods in biological assay, 2nd ed. Hafner Publishing Co., New York.
3. Gundrum, L. K. 1943. Effect of the newer sulfanilamide derivatives on the nasal mucosa of rabbits. Arch. Otolaryngol. 37:209.
4. Negus, V. 1958. The comparative anatomy and physiology of the nose and paranasal sinuses. E. and S. Livingstone Ltd., Edinburgh.
5. Shaeffer, J. P. 1942. The respiratory system, p. 136–1420. *In* J. P. Schaeffer (ed.), Morris' human anatomy, 10th ed. The Blakiston Co., Philadelphia.

Antimicrobial Agents and Chemotherapy—1969

Inhibitory Effect of Statolon on Virus-Induced Sarcoma of Mice

JOHNG S. RHIM and ROBERT J. HUEBNER

Microbiological Associates, Inc., and National Cancer Institute, Bethesda, Maryland 20014

Statolon, an extract of the mold *Penicillium stoloniferum*, provided a significant degree of protection against the development of sarcomas in newborn NIH Swiss mice injected subcutaneously with Friend pseudotype sarcoma virus. The best results were obtained when 100 μg/mouse was administered prior to virus inoculation and then was repeated every second or third day; inhibition was also observed when the repeated treatements were started as late as 7 days after sarcoma virus inoculation. No effects were noted when a single pretreatment was given 24 hr before virus inoculation. Treated mice developed tumors later than untreated mice and survived longer.

Statolon, an extract of the mold *Penicillium stoloniferum*, has been shown to exert its antiviral action by stimulating the in vitro and in vivo production of interferon (6, 8). Statolon, whose activity is due to a mycophage (x,y) containing double-stranded ribonucleic acid (1, 7), was reported to inhibit Friend leukemia virus infection in mice (10, 15) and in tissue culture (12). In addition, statolon inhibited the in vitro cellular transformation induced by murine sarcoma viruses (13). We now describe the inhibitory effect of statolon on murine sarcoma virus in mice.

MATERIALS AND METHODS

Antiviral agents. The statolon used was supplied through the kindness of W. J. Kleinschmidt, Lilly Research Laboratory, Indianapolis, Ind. Stock solution was prepared as 1 mg of statolon per ml of 2% fetal bovine serum in Eagle's minimal essential medium with antibiotics.

The synthetic double-stranded ribonucleic acid polyinosinic acid: polycytidylic acid (poly I:poly C) was purchased from P-L Biochemical, Inc., Milwaukee, Wis. Stock solution was prepared as 1 mg of poly I:poly C per ml of phosphate-buffered saline (*p*H 7.2).

Hanks balanced salt solution (HBSS) was used for inoculation of infected control mice.

Murine sarcoma virus. Virus stocks of Moloney sarcoma virus were prepared as partially purified virus concentrates (9). Pseudotype of this virus with the coat of Friend leukemia virus (5) was used. The virus stock was stored at –70 C. The infectivity titers were determined by tumor induction assay in NIH Swiss mice and by focus assay in NIH Swiss mouse embryo cell cultures (4).

Mice. Newborn NIH Swiss mice used in these experiments were obtained from the animal production section of National Institutes of Health. In all experiments, 10^3 focus-forming units of the murine sarcoma virus was inoculated subcutaneously into the back region of the mice on the day of birth or the day following. Treatment with statolon and control HBSS was given by subcutaneous injection in the same area as virus inoculation.

RESULTS

Tumor inhibition by statolon. The initial experiment was designed to determine the inhibitory effect of statolon on the induction of tumors by the Friend pseudotype of mouse sarcoma virus. Treatment was commenced 1 day before virus inoculation and was continued at 2- or 3-day intervals during a 17- to 22-day observation period as follows. Newborn mice were each injected subcutaneously with 0.1 ml of statolon (100 μg per mouse). Control mice were similarly injected with HBSS. The next day, all mice were injected with 10^3 focus-forming units of the Friend pseudotype of mouse sarcoma virus. On the following day and on alternate days thereafter, the mice were treated with statolon and HBSS as described above. This experiment was repeated twice to confirm the observations.

The results (Table 1) indicated that the induction of tumors in NIH Swiss mice by this

Table 1. *Inhibitory effect of statolon on Friend pseudotype murine sarcoma virus-induced tumors in newborn NIH Swiss mice*[a]

Expt no.	Treatment	No. of mice with tumors/total mice surviving						
		Day 7	Day 10	Day 14	Day 17	Day 19	Day 22	Day 24
1	Statolon	0/10	0/10	1/10	1/10	3/10	3/10	4/10
	HBSS[b]	0/10	1/10	6/10	8/9	8/9	8/9	8/8
2	Statolon	0/8	0/8	2/8	3/8	3/8	–	–
	HBSS	2/17	7/17	16/17	10/11	10/11	–	–
3	Statolon	0/10	0/10	2/10	3/10	3/10	3/10	–
	HBSS	0/11	1/11	5/11	7/11	9/11	11/11	–

[a] Statolon (100 μg/mouse) was given subcutaneously 24 hr before virus inoculation and at 2- or 3-day intervals for 14 to 17 days.
[b] Hanks balanced salt solution.

inoculation of the Friend pseudotype sarcoma virus was significantly suppressed by statolon. In the control mice, tumors started to appear at the site of inoculation in 6 or 7 days and were observed in almost all of the mice after 17 days. However, in 60 to 70% of the mice treated with statolon, tumors failed to develop during the period of observation.

Optimal treatment regimen. In an experiment designed to determine the optimal treatment of mice with statolon, the effect of statolon exposure period relative to time of virus infection was examined. The dose of virus, the volume of inoculum, and the route of statolon administration were the same as the preceding experiment. Three tests were conducted: in one, statolon (100 μg/mouse) was given to mice as a single treatment 24 hr before virus infection; in a second test, treatment was begun prior to virus inoculation and was repeated every second or third day (as in the initial experiment described above); in the third test, treatment was started 7 days after virus inoculation and repeated at 2- or 3-day intervals. The effect of these regimens on tumor formation is shown in Fig. 1. Best inhibitory effects were obtained when treatment was begun prior to virus inoculation and repeated every 2 or 3 days, but inhibition (about one-third) was also observed when the drug treatment started as late as 7 days after virus inoculation and was followed by repeated treatment. No significant effect was noted when a single pretreatment was given 24 hr before virus inoculation, but a delay in the appearance of tumors was evident even with a single pretreatment.

Table 2 shows the effect of statolon treatment on the survival of mice infected with Friend pseudotype murine sarcoma virus. In the mice treated with statolon before virus inoculation and then every second or third day, the rate of survival was increased and the time of death of those mice that died was delayed. In addition, most of the surviving mice were resistant to rechallenge with sarcoma virus.

Effect of route of treatment. The effect of various routes of statolon administration on the inhibition of virus-induced sarcoma of mice was next determined. Statolon (100 μg/mouse) was administered (i) intraperitioneally, (ii) intraperitoneally and subcutaneously, or (iii) subcutaneously, according to the regimen previously determined to be optimal. Statolon injected intraperitoneally or intraperitoneally and subcutaneously was toxic and resulted in the death of most of the mice; in the few surviving mice, tumors usually appeared earlier and were larger than those in the control mice and in the mice treated subcutaneously. Thus, the best protection was afforded by subcutaneous administration of statolon. Two different lots of statolon produced similar degrees of inhibition (Fig. 2).

Comparison of statolon and poly I:poly C. Experiments were next designed to compare the efficacy of statolon with that of the synthetic double-stranded ribonucleic acid poly I:poly C in the inhibition of mouse sarcoma virus. Sarma et al. (14) previously reported inhibition of sarcoma virus-induced tumor of mice by poly I:poly C. Statolon (100 μg/mouse) and poly I:poly C (100 μg/mouse) were given subcutane-

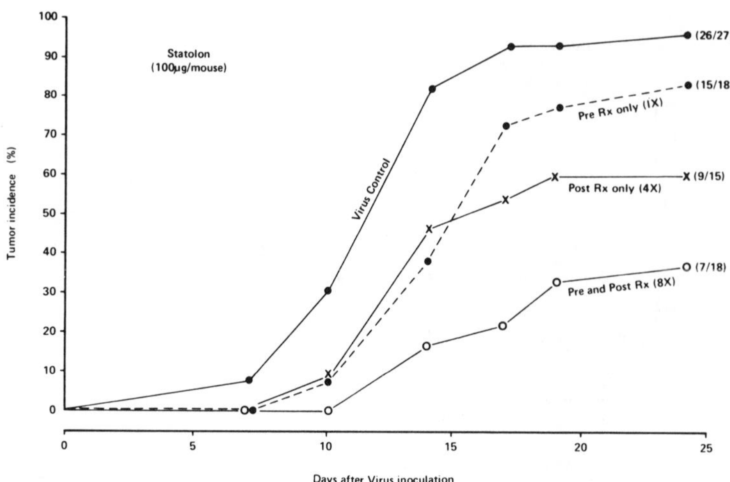

Fig. 1. *Effect of time and duration of exposure to statolon on its inhibition of Friend pseudotype sarcoma virus in mice. Treatment regimens are defined in Table 2. Numbers in parentheses show the number of mice developing tumors/total mice inoculated. Data are from two separate experiments.*

Table 2. *Effect of statolon treatment on survival of mice treated with Friend pseudotype murine sarcoma virus*

Expt no.	Treatment[a]	Days of observation	No. of deaths/ no. inoculated	Days of observation	No. of deaths/ no. inoculated
1	Statolon				
	Pre only (1X)	27	3/8 (38%)	51	4/8 (50%)
	Post only (4X)	27	2/8 (25%)	51	2/8 (25%)
	Pre + post (8X)	27	1/9 (11%)	51	1/9 (11%)
	HBSS	27	4/8 (50%)	51	4/8 (50%)
2	Statolon				
	Pre only (1X)	24	0/10	31	0/10
	Post only (5X)	24	0/8	31	0/8
	Pre + post (9X)	24	0/10	31	0/10
	HBSS	24	2/10 (20%)	31	4/10 (40%)
3	Statolon				
	Pre only (1X)	24	1/8 (13%)		
	Post only (4X)	24	1/7 (14%)		
	Pre + post (8X)	24	0/8		
	HBSS	24	6/17 (35%)		

[a] Pre only (1X) = a single 24-hr treatment before virus infection. Post only (4X) = treatment beginning 7 days after virus inoculation and repeated at 2- or 3-day intervals for four times. Pre + post (8X) = treatment was begun prior to virus inoculation and repeated at 2- or 3-day intervals for eight times. The dose of statolon administered was 100 μg per mouse. HBSS = Hanks balanced salt solution.

ously 24 hr before virus inoculation and at 2- or 3-day intervals for 14 to 16 days. Two such experiments were conducted. As shown in Table 3, the degree of protection provided by 100 μg of poly I:poly C was similar to that obtained with statolon.

DISCUSSION

The inhibitory effects of statolon against mouse sarcoma virus in mice observed in this study were in agreement with our previous results in vitro (12, 13). Optimal results were

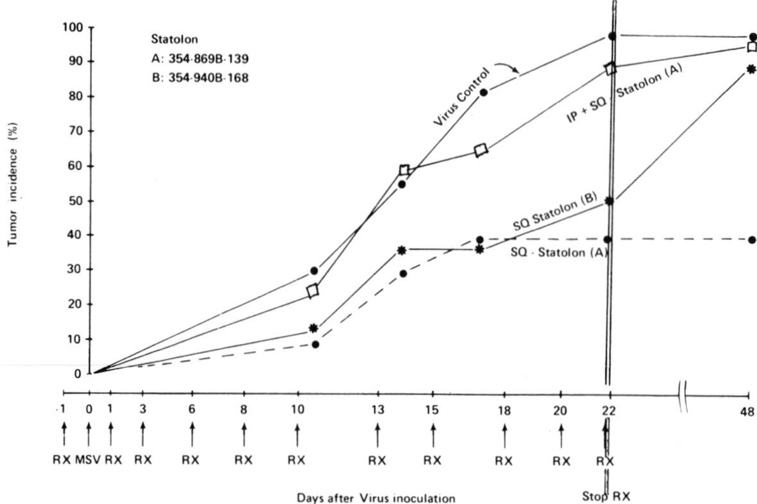

Fig. 2. *Effect of route of administration of statolon on inhibition of Friend pseudotype sarcoma of mice. Two lots of statolon were tested: (A) = lot 354-869B-139; (B) = lot 354-940B-168. SQ = subcutaneously; IP + SQ = intraperitoneally and subcutaneously.*

Table 3. *Comparison of the inhibitory effects of statolon and poly I:poly C on Friend pseudotype murine sarcoma virus-induced sarcoma of mice*

Expt. no.	Treatment[a]	No. of mice with tumors / total mice inoculated		
		Days 7–10	Days 14–17	Days 20–22
1	Statolon	1/10	3/10	4/9
	Poly I:poly C	0/8	3/8	4/8
	HBSS	1/9	4/9	8/9
2	Statolon	2/9	5/9	5/9
	Poly I:poly C	1/9	4/9	5/9
	HBSS	2/9	9/10	10/10

[a] Statolon (100 μg/mouse) and poly I:poly C (100 μg/mouse) were given subcutaneously 24 hr before virus inoculation and at 2- or 3-day intervals for 22 days. HBSS = Hanks balanced salt solution.

obtained when treatment was begun prior to virus inoculation and repeated doses of statolon were given thereafter. Our previous results (11) and those of Sarma et al. (14) had shown that the best protection against murine sarcoma virus infection in mice and in tissue culture was obtained by repeated treatment with poly I:poly C. Gresser reported that the repeated administration of an interferon preparation delayed the evolution of Friend leukemia in mice (3) and also resulted in a marked increase in the survival of tumor-inoculated mice (2).

Our present results also indicated that better protection was achieved by subcutaneous than by intraperitoneal injections of statolon. Kleinschmidt (2nd Conf. on Antiviral Substances, New York, N. Y. 1967) previously reported that statolon injected intraperitoneally did not provide protection against influenza PR8 in mice; however, protection was seen when statolon was administered intranasally.

The mechanism by which statolon exerts a protective effect against virus-induced sarcoma of mice remains to be investigated, since Kleinschmidt reported that the antigenicity of statolon is low. The evidence might be construed to favor the interpretation that the observed tumor inhibition was mediated through the induction of endogenous interferon, but this remains to be established.

ACKNOWLEDGMENTS

This work was supported by contract PH 43-68-705 with the National Cancer Institute.

We thank Robert Donahoe and Han Y. Cho for excellent technical assistance.

LITERATURE CITED

1. Banks, G. T., K. W. Buck, E. B. Chain, F. Himmelweib, J. E. Marks, J. M. Tyler, M. Hollings, F. T. Last, and O. M. Stone, 1968. Viruses in fungi and interferon stimulation. Nature (London) **218**:542–545.
2. Gresser, I. Bourali, C., J. P. Levy, D. Fontaine-Brouty-Boye, and M. T. Thomas. 1969. Increased survival in mice inoculated with tumor cells and treated with interferon preparations. Proc. Nat. Acad. Sci. U.S.A. **63**:51–57.

3. Gresser, I., J. Coppey, E. Falcoff, and D. Fontaine. 1967. Interferon and murine leukemia. I. Inhibitory effect of interferon preparations on development of Friend leukemia in mice. Proc. Soc. Exp. Biol. Med. **124**:84–91.

4. Hartley, J. W., and W. P. Rowe, 1966. Production of altered cell foci in tissue culture by defective Moloney sarcoma virus particles. Proc. Nat. Acad. Sci. U.S.A. **58**:780–786.

5. Huebner, R. J., J. W. Hartley, W. P. Rowe, W. T. Lane, and W. I. Capps. 1966. Rescue of the defective genome of Moloney sarcoma virus from a noninfectious hamster tumor and the production of pseudotype sarcoma viruses with various leukemia viruses. Proc. Nat. Acad. Sci. U.S.A. **56**:1164–1169.

6. Kleinschmidt, W. J., J. C. Cline, and E. B. Murphy. 1964. Interferon production induced by statolon. Proc. Nat. Acad. Sci. U.S.A. **52**:741–744.

7. Kleinschmidt, W. J., L. F. Ellis, R. M. Van Frank, and E. B. Murphy. 1968. Interferon stimulation by a double-stranded RNA of a mycophage in statolon preparations. Nature (London) **220**:167–168.

8. Kleinschmidt, W. J., and E. B. Murphy, 1965. Investigations on interferon induced by statolon. Virology **27**:484–489.

9. Moloney, J. B. 1956. Biological studies on the Rous sarcoma virus. V. Preparation of improved standard lots of the virus for use in quantitative investigations. J. Nat. Cancer. Inst. **16**:877–888.

10. Regelson, W., and O. Foltyn. 1966. Prevention and treatment of Friend leukemia virus (FLV) infection by polyanions and phytohemagglutinin. Proc. Amer. Ass. Cancer Res. **1**:58.

11. Rhim, J. S., C. Greenawalt, and R. J. Heubner, 1969. Synthetic double-stranded RNA: inhibitory effect on murine leukemia and sarcoma viruses in cell cultures. Nature (London) **222**:1164–1165.

12. Rhim, J. S., R. J. Huebner, and S. Gisin. 1969. Inhibitory effect of Statolon on murine leukemia and sarcoma viruses in cell culture. Antimicrob. Agents Chemotherapy–1968, p. 190–193.

13. Rhim, J. S., R. J. Huebner, and S. Gisin. 1969. Effect of statolon on acute and persistent murine leukemia and sarcoma virus infections. Proc. Soc. Exp. Biol. Med. **130**:181–187.

14. Sarma, P. S., G. Shiu, R. H. Neubauer, S. Baron, and R. J. Heubner, 1969. Virus-induced sarcoma of mice: inhibition by a synthetic polyribonucleotide complex. Proc. Nat. Acad. Sci. U.S.A. **62**:1046–1051.

15. Wheelock, E. F. 1967. Effect of statolon on Friend virus leukemia in mice. Proc. Soc. Exp. Biol. Med. **124**:855–858.

Antimicrobial Agents and Chemotherapy—1969

Antiviral Comparisons of Statolon and Polyinosinic-Polycytidylic Acid

GERALD D. MAYER and RUSSELL F. KRUEGER

Department of Microbiology, The Wm. S. Merrell Co., Division of Richardson-Merrell Inc., Cincinnati, Ohio 45215

In an investigation of the utility of interferon inducers as broad-spectrum antiviral agents, statolon and polyinosinic-polycytidylic acid (poly I:C) were tested in mice, rats, and rabbits against viruses with similar and dissimilar pathogeneses. Both interferon inducers were more effective against the neurotropic viruses than against respiratory infections caused by influenza viruses. Tail lesions caused by vesicular stomatitis virus were significantly reduced by prophylactic treatment with statolon and poly I:C, yet neither reduced tail lesions caused by vaccinia viruses. Although both compounds increased survival time of mice given lethal challenges of vesicular stomatitis virus or vaccinia virus, neither decreased mortality. Rats were protected from the paralytic effects of Semliki Forest virus by statolon and poly I:C, and both compounds significantly reduced vaccinia-induced lesions in rabbits. In vitro susceptibility to different interferons appears to bear little correlation to what can be expected from interferon inducers in vivo. From these studies, we conclude that such compounds will have similar antiviral capabilities, and these will be determined, at least in part, by viral pathogenesis and the pharmacodynamics of the inducer and the interferon induced.

Statolon and the double-stranded polyribonucleotide complex of inosinic and cytidylic acids (poly I:C) are both interferon inducers (1–3). The term inducer is used here in the general sense of stimulation, and is not meant to distinguish between substances that cause de novo synthesis and those that stimulate release of preformed interferons.

A recent report (5) disclosed that, in vitro, the relative susceptibility of certain viruses to interferons varies with the source of interferon induced in different animal species. The purpose of this study was to learn against which in vivo virus systems interferon inducers might be effective and to determine whether consistent activity in vivo can be obtained with such compounds.

MATERIALS AND METHODS

Animals. White CF-1 male mice weighing 15 to 20 g each and white CFE male rats weighing 100 to 120 g each were obtained from Carworth Farms. New Zealand white rabbits (male and female) weighing 2.5 kg each, from Sweetwater Farm rabbitry, were used.

Compounds. Statolon, kindly supplied by W. J. Kleinschmidt of Eli Lilly & Co. (Indianapolis, Ind.), was diluted in 0.15% hydroxyethylcellulose for testing. Poly I:C, purchased from Biopolymers (Dover, N.J.), was diluted in 0.85% saline.

Viruses. Mouse brain passages of encephalomyocarditis (EMC) virus, Semliki Forest virus (SFV), mengovirus, and vaccinia virus were used for subcutaneous, intracranial, or intradermal challenges. Influenza viruses Jap/305 and PR8, used to infect mice intranasally, were prepared from mouse lung passages. The vesicular stomatitis virus (VSV) used in the interferon assays was propagated in infected mouse L (929) cells.

Animal techniques. Subcutaneous viral inoculations were given to mice (0.1 ml) and rats (0.2 ml) in the groin area, except in the nonlethal VSV and vaccinia tail lesion tests for which 0.1 ml of virus was administered subcutaneously in the mid-portion of the tail (Yoshimura et al., Proc. 6th Int. Congr. Chemother., *in press*). For intracranial challenge, mice were inoculated in the temporal region with 0.03 ml of virus. Intranasal inoculation of mice was achieved by nasal instillation of 0.05 ml of virus. Intradermal inoculation of rabbits with vaccinia virus was done with 0.2 ml of virus injected into the shaved side of the rabbit.

In treatment of mice and rats, doses of preparations of drugs given were as follows: subcutaneously, 0.25 ml; intraperitoneally, 0.25 ml; and intravenously, 0.1 ml.

Interferon assays. Sera collected from mice, rats, and rabbits were diluted in Eagle's basal medium (Earle's salts with 2% fetal calf serum and 10% sodium bicarbonate for maintenance) and assayed for interferon on homologous cell cultures. Homologous sera were left on monolayers of mouse L (929), rat embryo, and rabbit kidney (RK_{13}) cells for 24 hr. The cells were then washed twice with Hank's balanced salt solution and challenged with 100 to 1,000 $TCID_{50}$ of VSV diluted in Eagle's basal medium.

RESULTS

Comparison of mouse serum interferon levels. The data in Table 1 show that, after the same interval postinjection, intraperitoneal administration of statolon to mice yielded higher interferon levels than did subcutaneous treatment. Although the best interferon titers were seen at 6 or 24 hr after intraperitoneal treatment with statolon, activity (titer of 1:40) was still detectable 96 hr post-treatment. Poly I:C, in single doses, induced higher serum interferon levels when given intravenously than when given intraperitoneally.

Effect of time of prophylactic treatment with statolon and poly I:C upon activity against EMC virus and SFV. The effect of time of prophylactic injection into mice of single doses of statolon or poly I:C upon antiviral activity is shown for EMC virus in Fig. 1 and for SFV in Fig. 2. In both cases, statolon afforded protection over much longer intervals before infection than did poly I:C. Consistently, with both inducers, early preinfection treatments were observed to provide greater protection against SFV than against EMC virus.

The antiviral spectra of statolon and poly I:C in mice are compared in Table 2. A very high level of protection from lethal challenges of neurotropic viruses was observed. Activity against EMC virus with statolon was high when either intraperitoneal or subcutaneous routes of

Table 1. *Interferon levels in mouse serum after administration of statolon and poly I:C*

Compound	Route[a]	Dose (mg/kg)	Serum sample: Time after treatment (hr)	Serum sample: Interferon titer[b]
Statolon	ip	250	96	1:40
	ip	250	24	1:1,200
	ip	100	24	1:1,400
	ip	100	6	1:2,400
	sc	250	24	1:150
Poly I:C	iv	2.500	7	1:700
	iv	2.500	2	1:2,800
	iv	1.250	6	1:2,000
	iv	0.625	3	1:2,400
	iv	0.625	6	1:480
	iv	0.625	2	1:480
	ip	2.500	7	1:250
	ip	2.500	2	1:600
	ip	1.250	4	1:160

[a] Routes of drug administration: ip, intraperitoneal; sc, subcutaneous; iv, intravenous.

[b] Concentration at which 50% of the cell sheet remained when the control sheets were completely destroyed by the virus.

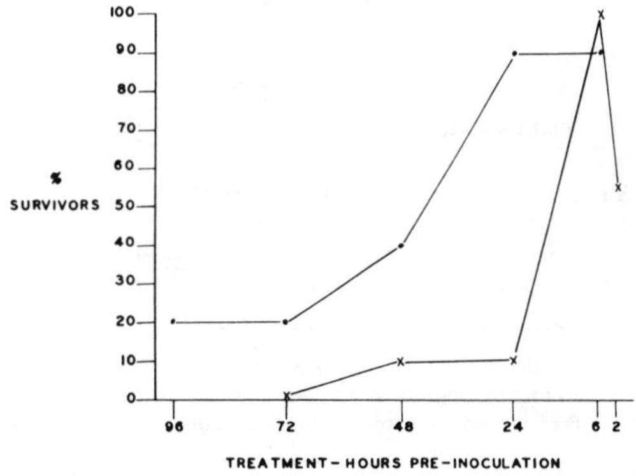

Fig. 1. *Effect of time of prophylactic treatment with statolon and poly I:C upon activity against encephalomyocarditis virus (10 LD_{50}). Statolon, 100 mg/kg intraperitoneally (●); poly I:C, 0.625 mg/kg intravenously (X).*

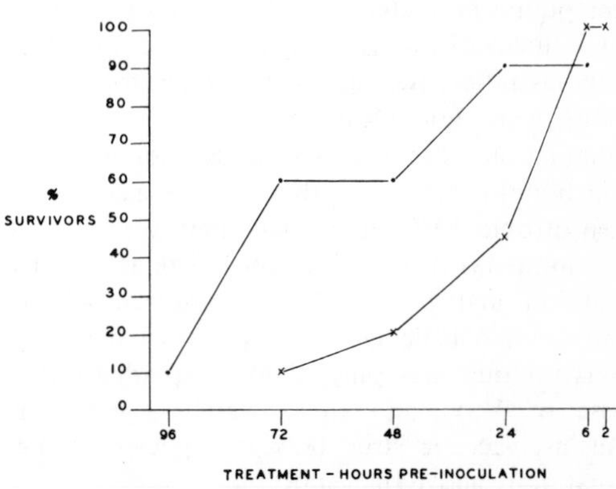

Fig. 2. *Effect of time of prophylactic treatment with statolon and poly I:C upon activity against Semliki Forest virus (30 LD_{50}). Statolon, 100 mg/kg intraperitoneally (●); poly I:C, 0.625 mg/kg intravenously (X).*

Table 2. *Activity of statolon and poly I:C against fatal virus infections of mice*

Infection		Compound	Prophylactic treatment			% S[c]	Mean day of death		Activity analysis
Virus	Route[a]		Route[b]	Dose (mg/kg)	Time (hr)		Treated	Controls	
Encephalomyocarditis	sc	Statolon	ip	100	24	90	10.3	4.3	High
			sc	250	24	65	8.2	4.4	High
		Poly I:C	iv	0.625	6	100	11.0	4.3	High
			ip	1.6	6	100	11.0	4.6	High
Semliki Forest	sc	Statolon	ip	100	24	90	10.8	7.3	High
		Poly I:C	iv	0.625	6	100	11.0	7.3	High
Mengo	sc	Statolon	ip	250	24	100	11.0	5.3	High
		Poly I:C	iv	0.625	3	55	10.0	5.1	High
Influenza									
Jap/305	in	Statolon	sc	250	24,2	40	8.4	6.4	Moderate
		Poly I:C	ip	1.6	6	0	6.2	6.7	None
PR8	in	Statolon	sc	250	24,2	0	5.7	5.7	None
		Poly I:C	ip	1.6	6	0	6.2	6.6	None
Vesicular stomatitis	ic	Statolon	ip	250	24,2	0	4.6	4.0	Weak
		Poly I:C	iv	0.625	3	0	5.9	5.4	Weak
Vaccinia	ic	Statolon	ip	250	48	10	7.8	6.8	Weak
					24	0	6.8	6.8	None
		Poly I:C	iv	0.625	6	20	8.0	6.8	Weak
					2	30	8.3	6.0	Weak

[a] Routes of infection: sc, subcutaneous; in, intranasal; ic, intracranial.
[b] Routes of drug administration: ip, intraperitoneal; sc, subcutaneous; iv, intravenous.
[c] Per cent survivors over 10-day period; there were no survivors in any untreated control group.

treatment were used. Poly I:C was equally effective against EMC virus when the compound was given intravenously or intraperitoneally. Statolon administered subcutaneously was moderately active against influenza Jap/305, but poly I:C given intraperitoneally was not. Neither compound protected mice from fatal challenges of influenza PR8. Although the routes of drug administration used against the respiratory infections were not ideal for optimal interferon stimulation (Table 1), both compounds were much more active by these routes against the neurotropic EMC virus than they were against the influenza viruses. Only very weak activity by statolon and poly I:C was observed against intracranial challenges of VSV or vaccinia virus. Survival time was only slightly extended in the case of VSV, and there were no survivors. Against vaccinia virus, poly I:C appeared somewhat more active than statolon.

In contrast to the weak activity against lethal challenges of VSV, both statolon and poly I:C were highly active in the VSV tail lesion test (Table 3). Neither compound was active against vaccinia-induced mouse tail lesions. Quantitation in this test was made by visual observation of the number and severity of lesions on the seventh or eighth day after subcutaneous inoculation of virus into the tail (Yoshimura et al., *in press*). Tail lesion scores of 10 mice per group were averaged.

In an experiment designed to determine the ability of statolon and poly I:C to protect rats from paralytic challenges of SFV, protection was complete with both drugs. Statolon (100 mg/kg subcutaneously) was administered 24 hr before and poly I:C (5 mg/kg intravenously) 5 hr before subcutaneous inoculation of the virus. Paralysis was recorded over a 15-day period. There was no paralysis in either treatment group, whereas paralysis in the control groups ranged from 50 to 70%. No interferon was detected in sera from the rats treated with statolon or poly I:C.

Intradermal inoculation of vaccinia virus into rabbits induces good lesions in 72 hr (4). A 1,000-fold dilution of our virus preparation produced discernible lesions (Fig. 3A). When statolon (100 mg/kg) was administered 24 hr before inoculation, a 100-fold greater concentra-

Table 3. *Activity of statolon and poly I:C against vesicular stomatitis and vaccinia viruses in mouse tail lesion tests*

Virus	Compound	Prophylactic treatment			Tail lesion scores[b]		Activity analysis
		Route[a]	Dose (mg/kg)	Time (hr)	Treated	Controls	
Vesicular stomatitis	Statolon	ip	250	24	0.3	1.3	High
	Poly I:C	iv	1	3	0.4	1.5	High
Vaccinia	Statolon	ip	250	24,2	1.6	1.9	None
	Poly I:C	iv	1.6	6	2.0	1.8	None

[a] Routes of drug administration: ip, intraperitoneal; iv, intravenous.
[b] Lesions of 10 mice were averaged; scoring system ranges from no lesions (0) to a maximal condition (3).

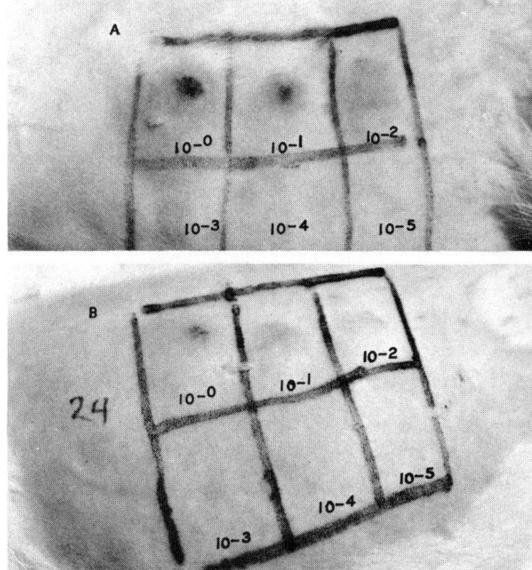

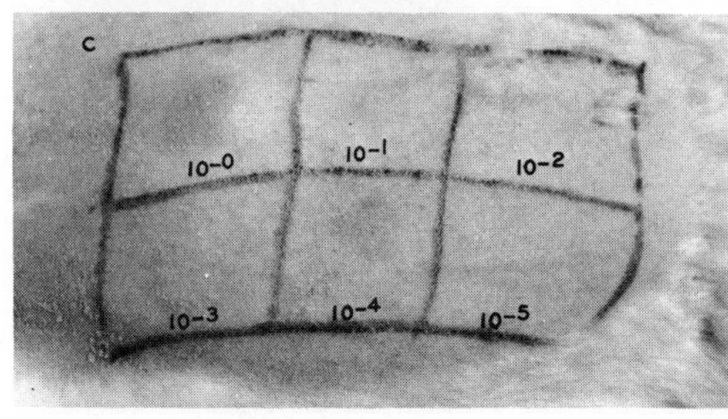

Fig. 3. *Effect of statolon (100 mg/kg intraperitoneally) and poly I:C (0.5 mg/kg intravenously) on preventing vaccinia-induced lesions in rabbits. (A) Infected controls:* 10^{-0} *= ++++;* 10^{-1} *= +++;* 10^{-2} *= ++;* 10^{-3} *= +;* 10^{-4} *and* 10^{-5} *= 0. (B) Statolon-treated (24 hr preinoculation):* 10^{-0} *= ++;* 10^{-1} *= +;* 10^{-2} *to* 10^{-5} *= 0. (C) Poly I:C-treated (2 hr preinoculation):* 10^{-0} *= +;* 10^{-1} *to* 10^{-5} *= 0. Test read 72 hr postinoculation.*

tion of virus was needed to produce a similar effect (Fig. 3B). Results in animals treated with poly I:C (0.5 mg/kg intravenously 2 hr preinoculation) were still more dramatic; undiluted virus suspension provoked only a very slight reaction (Fig. 3C). Rabbit serum interferon levels were greater than 1:2,500 with poly I:C at protective doses 2 hr after treatment; no interferon levels were detectable in serum from statolon-treated animals 6, 24, or 48 hr after treatment.

DISCUSSION

Interferon inducers such as statolon and poly I:C were more effective in vivo against the neurotropic viruses than against respiratory infections caused by influenza viruses. In mice, both compounds were only slightly active against lethal challenges of VSV but were effective in reducing tail lesions induced by this virus. Weak activity against intracranial challenges of vaccinia virus was also observed, but neither inducer reduced tail lesions caused by this virus in mice. Stewart et al. (5) reported the order of sensitivity to mouse interferon in vitro to be: vaccinia>VSV>SFV. Results of in vivo protection tests reported here indicate a different order of sensitivity to interferon inducers, namely: SFV>VSV>vaccinia.

Stewart et al. (5) also reported that vaccinia virus was far less susceptible in vitro to rabbit interferon than were VSV, SFV, and Sindbis virus. Our data with rabbits show excellent activity with the interferon inducer poly I:C against vaccinia virus; statolon was less active. Furthermore, high interferon titers were seen in serum from poly I:C-treated rabbits, whereas no interferon was detected in serum from statolon-treated rabbits. Compounds for which antiviral activity is mediated through induction of interferon will probably have similar qualitative antiviral potential. Relative in vitro susceptibility of viruses to interferons from different animal sources appears to bear little correlation to protection afforded by interferon inducers in animals; activity in vivo is dependent on such variables as viral pathogenesis, probable stimulation of other physiological factors, and the general pharmacodynamics of the inducer and the interferon induced.

ACKNOWLEDGMENTS

We gratefully acknowledge the technical assistance provided by Sei Yoshimura, Frank Bray, and Betsy Dresser in the in vivo work. Sincere appreciation is extended to Barbara Fink, Caroll Hull, and Dennis Richter for assistance with the interferon assays.

LITERATURE CITED

1. Field, A. K., G. P. Lampson, A. A. Tytell, and M. R. Hilleman. 1967. Inducers of interferon and host resistance. II. Multistranded synthetic polynucleotide complexes. Proc. Nat. Acad. Sci. U.S.A. **58**:1004–1010.
2. Kleinschmidt, W. J., J. C. Cline, and E. B. Murphy. 1964. Interferon production induced by statolon. Proc. Nat. Acad. Sci. U.S.A. **52**:741–744.
3. Kleinschmidt, W. J., and E. B. Murphy. 1965. Investigations on interferon induced by statolon. Virology **27**:484–489.
4. Šmejkal, F., and F. Sorm. 1962. The effects of 6-azauracil-riboside against vaccinia virus in rabbits. Acta Virol. **6**:282.
5. Stewart, W. E., II, W. D. Scott, and S. E. Sulkin. 1969. Relative sensitivities of viruses to different species of interferon. J. Virol. **4**:147–153.

Antimicrobial Agents and Chemotherapy—1969

Interferon Induction by and Ribonuclease Sensitivity of Thiophosphate-Substituted Polyribonucleotides

E. DE CLERCQ,[1] F. ECKSTEIN, H. STERNBACH, and T. C. MERIGAN

Division of Infectious Diseases, Department of Medicine, Stanford University School of Medicine, Stanford, California 94305, and Max-Planck-Institut für Experimentelle Medizin, Göttingen, West Germany

Substitution of thiophosphate for phosphate in the alternating copolymer of riboadenylic acid and ribouridylic acid [poly r(A-U)] caused a significant increase of induction of interferon and cellular resistance to virus infection. The resulting poly r(AS-US) reduced vesicular stomatitis virus plaque formation in human skin fibroblasts at a 100- or 10,000-fold lower concentration and produced 20-fold (human skin fibroblasts) or 100-fold (rabbits) higher amounts of interferon. The partially substituted poly r(A-US) was intermediate in activity between the unmodified poly r(A-U) and the completely substituted poly r(AS-US). The sensitivity of poly r(A-U), poly r(A-US), and poly r(AS-US) to pancreatic ribonuclease, as measured by antiviral activity, closely paralleled their capacity to induce cellular resistance to virus infection. Both antiviral activity and resistance to pancreatic ribonuclease increased in the order: poly r(A-U), poly r(A-US), poly r(AS-US) (of lower molecular weight), and poly r(AS-US) (of higher molecular weight). Poly r(AS-US) did not differ significantly from the polyriboinosinic acid/polyribocytidylic acid homopolymer pair [(poly rI)·(poly rC)] either in antiviral activity or in sensitivity to pancreatic ribonuclease. Although susceptibility to pancreatic ribonuclease does not necessarily reflect the pattern of degradation within or outside the cell, the striking parallelism between antiviral activity and sensitivity to enzymatic degradation suggests that enzymatic degradation may play a critical role in the antiviral activity of polynucleotides. Further similar work may be useful in rationally evolving interferon inducers with higher activities than heretofore observed, as well as in increasing understanding of the mechanism by which interferon production is stimulated.

Substitution of thiophosphate for phosphate in the alternating copolymer of riboadenylic acid and ribouridylic acid [poly r(A-U)] resulted in a significant increase of interferon production in vitro and in vivo (2). The thiophosphate-substituted poly r(A-U), designated as poly r(AS-US), was also more resistant to degradation by several enzymes, such as spleen phosphodiesterase, snake venom phosphodiesterase, micrococcal nuclease, and pancreatic ribonuclease (4), and the increased resistance to pancreatic ribonuclease paralleled the increased cellular resistance to virus infection in vitro (2).

These studies have now been extended to preparations of poly r(A-U) and poly r(AS-US) with different molecular weight and to the partially substituted copolymer poly r(A-US), an alternating copolymer of rAMP (adenosine-5′-monophosphate) and rUMPS (uridine-5′-monophosphorothioate).

The general structure of thiophosphate-substituted polynucleotides is shown in Fig. 1. The introduction of sulfur in the phosphate

[1] Lilly International Fellow and "Aspirant" of the Belgian N.F.W.O. (Nationaal Fonds voor Wetenschappelijk Onderzoek).

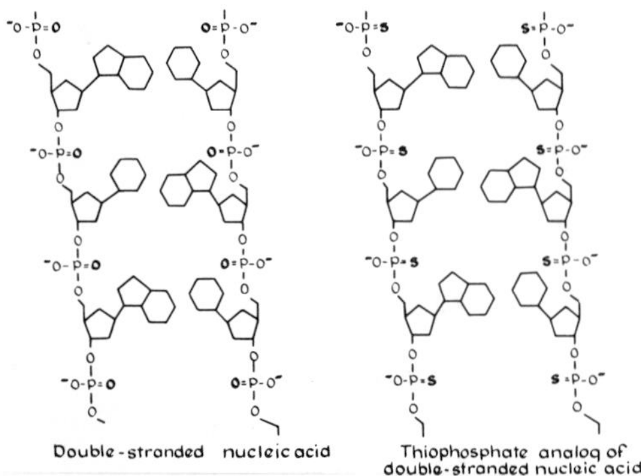

Fig. 1. *General structure of the thiophosphate-substituted polynucleotides. Left: unmodified nucleic acid with alternating base sequence [e.g., poly r(A-U)]. Right: completely thiophosphate-substituted nucleic acid with –P=S linkages instead of –P=O [e.g., poly r(AS-US)].*

linkages did not interfere with the formation of double-stranded complexes, as identical melting profiles were obtained for poly r(A-U), poly r(A-US), and poly r(AS-US) (4, 5).

MATERIALS AND METHODS

Polyribonucleotides and thiophosphate analogues. The alternating copolymer poly r(A-U) and its analogues poly r(A-US) and poly r(AS-US) were prepared essentially by methods described elsewhere (2, 5). A first preparation of poly r(A-U) (I) had a sedimentation value ($S_{20,w}$) of 7.7; a second one (II) had a sedimentation value of 7.6 (molecular weight, 128,200). The sedimentation value of poly r(A-US) was 7.4 (molecular weight, 105,000). Sedimentation values for poly r(AS-US) were 3.2 for preparation I and 5.0 (molecular weight, 30,000) for preparation II. The homopolymer pair (poly rI)·(poly rC) was prepared by mixing the individual homopolymers polyinosinic acid and polycytidylic acid (purchased from Miles Laboratories, Elkhart, Ind.) in equimolar concentrations in saline and allowing them to stand at room temperature for about 4 hr. Hypochromicity and finding of the characteristic melting profile indicated that the double-stranded base-paired complex had formed. Concentrations of the polymers were determined spectrophotometrically (1). They were dissolved in normal saline and stored at –20 C.

Cellular resistance to virus infection in vitro. Induction of cellular resistance to bovine vesicular stomatitis virus (VSV), Indiana strain, was measured by virus plaque reduction in human skin fibroblasts. Confluent cell cultures were treated for 20 to 24 hr with various concentrations of polymer in minimal Eagle's essential medium (MEM). Polymers were removed before challenging the cells with VSV and virus plaques were counted 2 days later.

Interferon production in vitro. Production of interferon was followed in confluent human skin fibroblasts in petri dishes exposed to 8 μg of the polymer in 1 ml of MEM for 3 hr. Polymers were removed and cells were exhaustively washed with MEM until the last washing was found free from residual polynucleotide (or polynucleotide analogue). A 4-ml amount of MEM was added to each petri dish, and the cell cultures were incubated for 5 hr. Culture fluid was harvested at the end of this 3- to 8-hr incubation period and the interferon level was measured. The cell cultures were incubated with fresh medium (4 ml per petri dish) for another 16 hr. The supernatant fluid collected at the end of this 8- to 24-hr incubation period was also examined for interferon content. Interferon assays were carried out in human skin fibroblasts challenged with VSV. The titer of interferon corresponded to the reciprocal of the highest dilution of sample which reduced VSV plaque formation by 50%. Interferon was characterized by its sensitivity to trypsin (0.25 mg/ml, 1 hr, 37 C), resistance to pancreatic ribonuclease [40 μg/ml, 1 hr, 37 C, 10^{-3} M ethylenediaminetetraacetate (EDTA)], and lack of activity in heterologous (mouse L929) cells.

Interferon production in vivo. Rabbits (weight, 1.5 to 2.0 kg) were injected intravenously with 20 μg of the polymer. Blood samples were taken 2 and 4 hr later, and the serum was assayed for interferon with the plaque reduction technique in RK 13 or primary rabbit kidney cell cultures, again with VSV as the challenge virus. Interferon was characterized by its sensitivity to trypsin (0.35 mg/ml, 1 hr, 37 C), resistance to pancreatic ribonuclease (40 μg/ml, 1 hr, 37 C, 10^{-3} M EDTA), and lack of activity in heterologous cells (human skin fibroblasts).

Sensitivity to pancreatic ribonuclease. Polymers were exposed to various concentrations of pancreatic ribonuclease (bovine pancreatic ribonuclease A, five times crystallized, purchased from Sigma Chemical Co., St. Louis, Mo.) for 1 hr at 37 C in MEM, *p*H 7.5 (+ 10^{-3} M EDTA). Their residual antiviral activity was measured by VSV plaque reduction in human skin fibroblasts as described above.

RESULTS

Cellular resistance to virus infection in vitro. When compared with preparations I and II of poly r(A-U), poly r(AS-US) reduced VSV plaque formation in human skin fibroblasts at a 100-fold (preparation I) or 10,000-fold (preparation II) lower concentration (Table 1). The partially substituted copolymer r(A-US) showed an intermediate antiviral activity, reducing virus plaque formation at a 10-fold lower concentration than poly r(A-U) I. In the same conditions, (poly rI)·(poly rC) proved 4 to 40 times less active in inducing cellular resistance than poly r(AS-US) I and II.

Table 1. *Cellular resistance to vesicular stomatitis virus in human skin fibroblasts*

Polymer	Minimal inhibitory concn[a] (μg/ml)
Poly r(A-U) I	0.1
Poly r(A-U) II	1.0
Poly r(A-US)	0.01
Poly r(AS-US) I	0.001
Poly r(AS-US) II	0.0001
(Poly rI)·(poly rC)	0.004

[a] Reducing virus plaque formation by 50%.

Table 2. *Interferon production in human skin fibroblasts*

Polymer[a]	Interferon titer (units/4 ml[b])	
	3–8 hr	8–24 hr
Poly r(A-U) II	⩽1	⩽1
Poly r(A-US)	12	⩽1
Poly r(AS-US) II	20	6
(Poly rI)·(poly rC)	20	⩽1

[a] Concentration: 8 μg/ml.
[b] Tissue culture fluid.

Table 3. *Interferon production in the rabbit*

Polymer[a]	Interferon titer (units/4/ml[b])	
	At 2 hr	At 4 hr
Poly r(A-U) II	<10	15
Poly r(AS-US) II	⩾1,000	600
(Poly rI)·(poly rC)	>1,000	>1,000

[a] Twenty micrograms per rabbit, intravenously.
[b] Serum.

Interferon production in vitro. The thiophosphate analogues were capable of interferon induction in human skin fibroblasts under conditions with which the unmodified compound was not (Table 2). Poly r(AS-US) II and (poly rI)·(poly rC) did not differ in interferon production during the 3- to 8-hr incubation period, but poly r(AS-US) II continued to produce interferon beyond that period whereas (poly rI)·(poly rC) did not. As observed for the cellular resistance, poly r(A-US) showed an interferon-inducing capacity intermediate between those of poly r(A-U) and the completely substituted poly r(AS-US).

Interferon production in vivo. In the rabbit, poly r(AS-US) II stimulated the production of significantly larger amounts of circulating interferon than poly r(A-U) II (Table 3). In the same animal model, (poly rI)·(poly rC) surpassed poly r(AS-US) in antiviral activity.

Sensitivity to pancreatic ribonuclease. As increased resistance to enzymatic breakdown might offer a reasonable explanation for the increased antiviral activity following sulfur substitution, the nucleic acids and their thiophosphate analogues were tested for sensitivity to treatment with pancreatic ribonuclease. Much higher enzyme concentrations were required for poly r(AS-US) than for poly r(A-U) to destroy the residual antiviral activity against VSV in human skin fibroblasts (Table 4). The sensitivity of the tested polymers to pancreatic ribonuclease closely paralleled their degree of antiviral activity. Both resistance to ribonuclease (Table 4) and antiviral activity (Tables 1-3) increased in the order poly r(A-U), poly r(A-US), poly r(AS-US) I (lower molecular weight), and poly r(AS-US) II (higher molecular weight). The relationship between the induction of cellular resistance to virus infection and the sensitivity to ribonuclease treatment was nearly quantitative. Poly r(A-U) was about 100 times (preparation I) to 10,000 times (preparation II) more sensitive to ribonuclease than poly r(AS-US) and 10 to 100 times more sensitive than poly r(A-US). In parallel, poly r(AS-US) reduced VSV plaque formation at a 100-fold (preparation I) or 10,000-fold (preparation II) lower concentration and poly r(A-US) at a 10- to 100-fold lower concentration than poly r(A-U). Finally, the respective sensitivities of (poly rI)·(poly rC) and poly r(AS-US) to ribonuclease treatment did not differ significantly, nor did their respective antiviral activities.

DISCUSSION

Marked changes in interferon production and antiviral activity can be brought about by minimal changes in the chemical structure of polyribonucleotides. Substitution of → P=S link-

Table 4. *Sensitivity to pancreatic ribonuclease as measured by the ability to confer cellular resistance to vesicular stomatitis virus in human skin fibroblasts*

Polymer	Concn of polymer (μg/ml)	Per cent virus plaque reduction by given concentrations of the polymer after prior exposure to the indicated concentrations of ribonuclease					
		100X higher	10X higher	Equal	10X lower	100X lower	Control (no ribonuclease)
Poly r(A-U) I	4	–	0	0	50	–	100
	0.4	0	0	0	50	–	50
Poly r(A-U) II	4	–	0	0	0	0	50
Poly r(A-US)	0.4	0	0	0	100	100	100
Poly r(AS-US) I	0.4	0	0	100	100	100	100
	0.04	0	75	100	100	100	100
Poly r(A-US) II	0.04	0	100	100	100	100	100
	0.004	40	100	100	100	100	100
(Poly rI)·(poly rC)	4	–	0	100	100	100	100
	0.4	0	50	100	100	100	100
	0.04	0	100	100	100	100	100

ages for →P=O linkages in the alternating copolymer r(A-U) caused a significant increase of its antiviral activity and decreased in parallel its susceptibility to several enzymes. Introduction of sulfur did not interfere with the formation of a stable, double-stranded complex or with the polyanionic character of the molecule, both of which are essential structural features of synthetic polymers in acting as interferon inducers (1, 3). The increased antiviral activity upon substitution of thiophosphate for phosphate in poly r(A-U) has been demonstrated in several test systems, both in vitro and in vivo, and has recently been confirmed for the thiophosphate analogues of poly r(I-C), the alternating copolymer of riboinosinic acid and ribocytidylic acid (E. De Clercq et al., *to be published*). The striking parallelism between the increase of antiviral activity and decrease of sensitivity to ribonuclease degradation after introduction of sulfur suggests that the two phenomena might be interrelated. For poly r(A-US), the greater antiviral activity over poly r(A-U) does not seem to be due solely to an increased resistance to pancreatic ribonuclease, as poly r(A-U) and poly r(A-US) would be expected to have identical susceptibilities to pancreatic ribonuclease. Pancreatic ribonuclease cleaves poly r(A-U) between the phosphate attached to the 3′-hydroxyl group of uridine and the 5′-hydroxyl group of adenosine. This linkage is free from sulfur in poly r(A-US): the phosphate which is replaced by thiophosphate in poly r(A-US) is the one attached to the 3′-hydroxyl group of adenosine, which pancreatic ribonuclease does not cleave. Accordingly, Matzura and Eckstein (5) did not find marked differences in degradation of poly r(A-U) and poly r(A-US) by pancreatic ribonuclease as followed by radioactivity. However, poly r(A-US) proved more active than poly r(A-U) in inducing interferon and cellular resistance to virus infection and was also more resistant to pancreatic ribonuclease as measured by residual antiviral activity in vitro. The differing results on resistance of poly r(A-US) to pancreatic ribonuclease can presumably be explained by the much greater sensitivity of the biological assay as compared to the one used by Matzura and Eckstein (5).

It is likely that enzymatic degradation is a limiting factor for the antiviral potency of polynucleotides. Nucleolytic activity of the serum may account for the short-lived antiviral activity of polynucleotides in the whole animal. Substitution of sulfur for oxygen not only increased interferon production and resistance to enzymatic breakdown, but also rendered the polymers more resistant to inactivation by fetal calf serum (E. De Clercq et al., *to be published*). Both antiviral activity and resistance to enzymatic degradation and to sero-inactivation increased in the order: (i) poly r(A-U), (ii) poly r(A-US), and (iii) (poly rI)•(poly rC) and poly r(AS-US). These findings further suggest that the inactivation of polynucleotides by serum is nuclease-mediated and that chemical modification of the existing polynucleotides to structures with a reduced sensitivity to enzymatic degradation might increase interferon production and antiviral protection in vivo, because of the longer persistence of the polymer in the animal.

ACKNOWLEDGMENTS

This investigation was supported by Public Health Service grant AI 05629 from the National Institute of Allergy and Infectious Diseases and by the Deutsche Forschungsgemeinschaft.

LITERATURE CITED

1. De Clercq, E., and T. C. Merigan. 1969. Requirement of a stable secondary structure for the antiviral activity of polynucleotides. Nature (London) **222:**1148–1152.
2. De Clercq, E., F. Eckstein, and T. C. Merigan. 1969. Interferon induction increased through chemical modification of a synthetic polyribonucleotide. Science (Washington) **165:**1137–1139.
3. De Clercq, E., F. Eckstein, and T. C. Merigan. 1969. Structural requirements for synthetic polyanions to act as interferon inducers. 2nd Conf. on Antiviral Substances, Ann. N.Y. Acad. Sci., *in press.*
4. Eckstein, F., and H. Gindl. 1969. Polyribonucleotides containing a thiophosphate backbone. Fed. Eur. Biochem. Soc. Lett. **2:**262–264.
5. Matzura, H., and F. Eckstein. 1968. A polyribonucleotide containing alternating →P=O and →P=S linkages. Eur. J. Biochem. **3:**448–452.

Antimicrobial Agents and Chemotherapy—1969

Printed in USA

Antiviral Activity of 9-β-D-Arabinofuranosyladenine

VI. Effect of Delayed Treatment on Herpes Simplex Virus in Mice

F. A. MILLER, B. J. SLOAN, and C. A. SILVERMAN

Biological Research and Development Department, Medical and Scientific Affairs Division, Parke, Davis & Co., Detroit, Michigan 48232

The purine nucleoside 9-β-D-arabinofuranosyladenine (ara-A) was administered subcutaneously to mice at 24, 48, 72, and 96 hr after intracerebral inoculation of herpes simplex virus (HSV) type 1. Increases in the rate of survival varied inversely with the extent of the delay in treatment. Upon administration of three doses of ara-a (each 1,000 mg/kg) during 6-hr periods starting at the times indicated above, survival rates of 57, 41, 22, and 11, respectively, were obtained. Survivors rechallenged with 1,000 LD_{50} of homologous virus showed high resistance. HSV was present in brain suspensions of treated animals at the final period tested in all groups. A 10% suspension of brain tissue from mice surviving at 21 days showed no evidence of HSV when titrated in vivo. Virus in brain suspensions obtained from previously exposed drug-treated survivors of the delayed-therapy experiment was inoculated into normal mice, and these animals were treated with ara-A. No indication that the virus had developed resistance to ara-A was observed.

The purine nucleoside 9-β-D-arabinofuranosyladenine (ara-A) has been reported to have therapeutic and prophylactic activity against a broad spectrum of deoxyribonucleic acid viruses, both in cell culture and in animals (2, 4, 5, 7-9). Most of our in vivo testing has been done in mice or rats, and we have obtained high survival rates in animals which were treated after inoculation with lethal intracerebral doses of herpes simplex virus (HSV) or vaccinia virus. The drug was effective when administered by peroral, intraperitoneal, subcutaneous, and percutaneous treatment routes over a wide range of regimens and drug levels.

We soon observed in our animal chemotherapy trials that survival rates were high even when treatment was delayed 24 hr after intracerebral inoculation of HSV. This truly therapeutic effect is significant when one considers that we are dealing with a central nervous system infection and that the drug must cross the blood-brain barriers. We have, therefore, continued studying delayed treatment of this virus infection.

In this report, we describe experiments involving delayed treatment, rechallenge of survivors, and treatment of animals inoculated with virus from animals previously treated with ara-A.

MATERIALS AND METHODS

The crystalline ara-A used in these experiments was obtained from the research laboratories of Parke, Davis & Co. This material was "micronized" to 5 μm or less and suspended in phosphate-buffered saline containing 0.4% carboxymethyl cellulose. The mice were Swiss albino males weighing 18 to 20 g (obtained from Carworth Farms, Portage, Mich.). The HSV was the Parke-Davis REM strain, which is a type 1 virus and has been carried in mouse brain for 10 years and approximately 25 passages. The stock seed was maintained frozen in glass vials at –60 C. The mouse intracerebral LD_{50} titer is 10^{-5}/0.03 ml.

Infected brain tissue was obtained by sacrifice of the animals at the indicated time intervals and removal of the entire brain; the tissue was stored at –60 C. The 10% tissue suspensions were prepared in a Ten-Broeck tissue grinder with Eagle's basal medium supplemented with

2% chicken serum. After centrifugation at approximately 310 × *g*, the supernatant fluid was rapidly frozen in an alcohol-dry ice mixture and stored at −60 C for later assay. Infectivity titers were determined on the basis of the rates of death after intracerebral inoculation of 0.03 ml of appropriate dilutions of tissue supernatant fluids into groups of six mice each; the LD_{50} was calculated by the method of Reed and Muench (6).

Experimental methods. Approximately 500 mice were inoculated intracerebrally with 32 LD_{50} of HSV. Starting 24 hr after inoculation, one group of 100 mice was treated subcutaneously with 1,000 mg of ara-A/kg three times on a single day, approximately every 2 hr over a 6-hr period. Starting at 48, 72, and 96 hr after inoculation, three other groups of 100 mice each were similarly treated. Thus, there were four groups of 100 mice, each receiving at 24-hr intervals the same series of drug treatments. A group of 100 inoculated but untreated mice were held as virus controls. Groups of five uninoculated mice receiving only drug were observed for deaths due to drug alone. The suspending vehicle was determined to have no therapeutic activity against HSV in mice. Table 1 shows the schedule of inoculation, treatment, and autopsy.

Beginning at 6 hr after inoculation and continuing at 12, 24, 48, 72, 96, 120, 144, and 168 hr after inoculation, groups of five untreated animals were killed and brain tissue was removed. Virus-inoculated animals, which had been treated as shown in Table 1, were killed in groups of five at 24, 48, and 72 hr after the start of treatment and brain tissue was removed. The brain tissue from each group was pooled for processing as described above.

The remaining treated and control animals were observed for 21 days, at which time numbers of survivors were recorded and the average survival times for those mice that had died were calculated. On the 21st day, approximately half of the survivors in all groups were killed, and brain tissue was processed for titration in mice to determine the presence of residual virus 21 days after inoculation and subsequent treatment. The remaining half of the survivors of the original experiment were rechallenged with 1,000 LD_{50} of HSV and were observed for an additional 21 days to determine resistance to infection. Normal animals of the same age were inoculated as controls. A trial was conducted to determine whether passage of virus in ara-A-treated animals had any effect upon the virulence of the virus or its susceptibility to ara-A. Brain suspensions from treated and control groups from the delayed-treatment experiment were titrated in normal mice for infectivity, and suspensions from six representative groups were used to inoculate mice intracerebrally for a therapy test. At 24 hr after inoculation, these animals were treated with three 1,000-mg doses of ara-A/kg administered subcutaneously at 2-hr intervals. The mice were observed for 21 days, and then the number of survivors was determined.

RESULTS

Table 2 shows the effects of delayed treatment upon survival of HSV-infected mice and on the response of survivors to rechallenge with the virus. When treatment was delayed up to 72 hr, there were still significant effects on survival ($P = 0.001$) and delay of death ($P = <0.001$) of animals not surviving. Treatment delayed as long as 96 hr after inoculation produced a slight but not significant increase in survivors and no delay in death time. A time response in the percentage of survivors was evident over the period used, varying inversely with the length of time treatment was delayed. There were no deaths in the uninoculated-treated group. The inoculated and treated 21-day survivors had become resistant to a large virus challenge. In contrast, when normal mice of the same age were challenged with the same virus inoculum, all of them succumbed by the fifth day.

Data in Table 3 indicate that virus can be detected in brain tissue from treated, as well as untreated, animals at several early time periods. Virus remained detectable for at least 72 hr after treatment, which was the longest interval tested after treatment in each group. The virus titers of brain suspensions from the animals treated at 24 and 48 hr after inoculation did not increase as

Table 1. *Schedule of inoculation, treatment, and autopsy of groups of 100 mice*[a]

Group	Time after inoculation										
	0 hr	6 hr	12 hr	24 hr	48 hr	72 hr	96 hr	120 hr	144 hr	168 hr	21 days
1	I	–	–	ara-A	S	S	S	–	–	–	S
2	I	–	–	–	ara-A	S	S	S	–	–	S
3	I	–	–	–	–	ara-A	S	S	S	–	S
4	I	–	–	–	–	–	ara-A	S	S	S	S
Control	I	S	S	S	S	S	S	S	S	S	–

[a] I = inoculated; ara-A = treated; S = autopsied.

Table 2. *Effect of delayed ara-A dosing on mice inoculated with 32 LD_{50} of herpes simplex virus*

Original test						21-day survivors[f] rechallenged	
Period dosed[a] after inoculation	Survivors[b] at 21 days			Increase in avg day of death			
(hr)	S/T[c]	Per cent	p[d]	No. of days	p[e]	S/T[c]	Per cent
24–30	49/85	57[g]	<0.001	1.5	<0.001	22/25	88
48–54	35/85	41	<0.001	1.2	<0.005	15/16	93
72–78	19/85	22	0.001	1.4	<0.001	12/12	100
96–102	10/85	11	<0.05	0	–	5/5	100
Untreated	2/60	3	–	–	–	–	–

[a] Three doses of 1,000 mg/kg subcutaneously during a 6-hr period. No deaths in uninoculated but treated control group.
[b] Mice autopsied were subtracted from total.
[c] Number of survivors at 21 days/total in test.
[d] Probability (chi-square analysis) that the observed increase in *survivor number* was due to chance.
[e] Probability (*t* test) that the observed increase in survival *time* of virus-infected, treated groups compared with the virus control group was due to chance.
[f] Survivors of original test were reinoculated on day 21 with 1,000 LD_{50} of HSV and were observed for an additional 21 days.
[g] The average percentage of survivors from seven experiments done with the same regimen was 51%.

Table 3. *Effect of delayed ara-A dosing on titer of HSV in mouse brain*[a]

Period dosed after inoculation (hr)	Time of brain autopsy after inoculation									
	6 hr	12 hr	24 hr	48 hr	72 hr	96 hr	120 hr	144 hr	168 hr	21 days[b]
24–30	–	–	–	2.97	2.7	2.25	–	–	–	<1
48–54	–	–	–	–	2.6	3.7	5.5[c]	–	–	<1
72–78	–	–	–	–	–	4.1	>5.5[c]	5.0	–	<1
96–102	–	–	–	–	–	–	>5.5[c]	4.1	5.0[c]	<1
Untreated	<1	<1	2.23	3.3	4.2	4.3	>5.5[c]	5.0	5.1[c]	–

[a] Results are expressed as LD_{50} titer (negative $\log_{10}$) based on the method of Reed and Muench (6). The 48-, 72-, and 96-hr titration results are an average of two tests.
[b] Titer of brain suspension from 21-day survivors, other than those rechallenged.
[c] This brain suspension virus also was used for inoculating mice in chemotherapy "susceptibility test" as shown in Table 4.

rapidly as that from the untreated controls autopsied at the same time. Approximately the same amount of virus was detected in both the treated groups and the untreated controls, starting with the 120-hr harvest and irrespective of the delay in dosing. However, no virus was detectable by mouse titration of brain tissue from treated animals surviving at 21 days.

Brain tissue harvested at 120 and 168 hr after inoculation, and at various postinoculation treatment periods, was used as seed material for inoculating mice, to determine whether virus susceptibility to ara-A had changed. The therapeutic effect against virus from previously treated groups was comparable with the effect against virus not previously exposed to ara-A (Table 4).

DISCUSSION

The data presented here are consistent with our previous reports showing that ara-A is a truly therapeutic agent. Previous studies with HSV in cell culture showed no evidence of decreased susceptibility to ara-A after three passages (4). The present experiment provides in vivo evidence that HSV does not, in one passage, acquire decreased susceptibility to ara-A. Decreased virus susceptibility to guanidine (in vivo) and 5-iodo-2′-deoxyuridine (in vitro) has been reported after exposure of virus to these drugs (1, 3). Ara-A apparently did not eradicate potentially infectious virus from the brain within 72 hr after the initiation of treatment in mice whose treatment was started from 24 to 96 hr after inoculation. However, brain tissue from

Table 4. *Activity of ara-A against herpes simplex virus previously exposed to ara-A in mice*

Delayed-dosing test		Virus susceptibility test		
Dosing period (hr)[a]	Autopsy period (hr)[a]	Virus inoculum (no. of LD_{50})	No. of survivors at 21 days/total in test	
			Treated[b]	Untreated
48–54	120	100	8/10	0/7
72–78	120	320	4/10	0/10
96–102	120	320	4/10	0/10
96–102	168	100	5/10	0/10
Untreated virus,	120	320	2/10	0/10
controls	169	100	5/10	0/10

[a]After inoculation.

[b]Treated: 1,000 mg of ara-A/kg subcutaneously three times between 24 and 30 hr after inoculation.

animals surviving at 21 days contained no detectable virus, and these mice were resistant to a large challenge of homologous virus.

The large numbers of treated 21-day survivors were from the same groups of animals whose randomly selected members, killed at 2 to 7 days after inoculation, showed high virus titers in their brain tissue when this was passed intracerebrally into normal mice.

These data suggest at least two possibilities regarding the ara-A control mechanisms for this infection. (i) Infected cells in which virus replication has progressed beyond some critical stage prior to the introduction of ara-A continue to yield infectious virus. The yield is sufficiently large to stimulate immunity, but further viral replication in normal cells is prevented by the drug. (ii) Infected cells after treatment with ara-A yield incomplete virus or noninfectious viral antigens, or both. These remain non-infectious in the treated animal and stimulate immunity. On passage without drug, the incomplete virus matures in the new host and can then establish a fatal infection. In either case, treatment was followed by the development of immunity in nearly all surviving animals, and infectious virus could not be detected by the 21st day.

LITERATURE CITED

1. Buthala, D. A. 1964. Cell culture studies on antiviral agents. I. Action of cytosine arabinoside and some comparisons with 5-iodo-2′-deoxyuridine. Proc. Soc. Exp. Biol. Med. **115**:69–77.
2. Dixon, G. J., R. W. Sidwell, F. A. Miller, and B. J. Sloan. 1969. Antiviral activity of 9-β-D-arabinofuranoxyladenine. V. Activity against intracerebral vaccinia virus infections in mice. Antimicrob. Agents Chemother.–1968, p. 172–179.
3. Melnick, J. L., D. Crowther, and J. Berrera-Oro. 1961. Rapid development of drug resistant mutants of poliovirus. Science (Washington) **134**:557.
4. Miller, F. A., G. J. Dixon, J. Ehrlich, B. J. Sloan, and I. W. McLean, Jr. 1969. Antiviral activity of 9-β-D-arabinofuranosyladenine. I. Cell cultures studies. Antimicrob. Agents Chemother.–1968, p. 136–147.
5. Privat de Garilhe, M., and J. de Rudder. 1964. Effet de deux nucleosides de l'arabinose sur la multiplication des virus de l'herpes et de la vaccine en culture cellulaire. Compt. Rend. **259**:2725–2728.
6. Reed, L. J., and H. Muench. 1938. A simple method of estimating fifty percent endpoints. Amer. J. Hyg. **27**:493–498.
7. Sidwell, R. W., G. J. Dixon, F. M. Schabel, Jr., and D. H. Kaump. 1969. Antiviral activity of 9-β-D-arabinofuranosyladenine. II. Activity against herpes simplex keratitis in hamsters. Antimicrob. Agents Chemother.–1968, p. 148–154.
8. Sidwell, R. W., G. J. Dixon, S. M. Sellers, and F. M. Schabel, Jr. 1968. In vivo antiviral properties of biologically active compounds. II. Studies with influenza and vaccinia viruses. Appl. Microbiol. **16**:370–392.
9. Sloan, B. J., F. A. Miller, J. Ehrlich, I. W. McLean Jr., and H. E. Machamer. 1969. Antiviral activity of 9-β-D-arabinofuranosyladenine. IV. Activity against intracerebral herpes simplex virus infections in mice. Antimicrob. Agents Chemother.–1968, p. 161–171.

Antimicrobial Agents and Chemotherapy—1969

Effect of *Mycoplasma pneumoniae* on Rhinovirus Ribonucleic Acid Synthesis in KB Cells

W. H. MILLIGAN, III and R. D. FLETCHER

School of Dental Medicine, University of Pittsburgh, Pittsburgh, Pennsylvania 15213

Studies were performed to determine the effect of *Mycoplasma pneumoniae* (ATCC 15293) on rhinovirus replication in KB cells. Rhinovirus ribonucleic acid (RNA) synthesis in KB cell monolayers was measured by tritiated uridine uptake in the presence of actinomycin D. Groups of KB cells were inoculated at selected times with *M. pneumoniae* (grown on glass) and were subsequently infected with rhinovirus. Tritiated uridine uptake in these systems was then compared with that in virus-infected KB cells not previously inoculated with *M. pneumoniae.* Viral RNA synthesis was stimulated throughout the entire period of observation in cells previously inoculated with *M. pneumoniae.* Uptake of tritiated uridine by the virus was 20 to 138% greater in *Mycoplasma*-treated cells than in control cells. Additional evidence indicates that this enhancement is not produced by an extracellular element, but requires the presence of intact *Mycoplasma.* Furthermore, stimulation seems to occur at an early stage in the viral replication cycle.

Since the initial demonstration by Robinson, Wichelhausen, and Roizman (6) that a number of tissue culture systems were contaminated with *Mycoplasma,* there have been several similar reports. Because of our interest in rhinovirus replication, we chose to determine the effect of *Mycoplasma* on this virus. Since *M. pneumoniae,* like rhinovirus, is pathogenic for the human respiratory tract, it was the *Mycoplasma* of choice for this study. Synthesis of viral ribonucleic acid (RNA), an indication of viral replication, was measured by the rate of incorporation of ^{3}H-uridine. This report describes the stimulatory effect of *M. pneumoniae* on rhinovirus RNA replication.

MATERIALS AND METHODS

Tissue culture. The KB cell monolayers were purchased from Flow Laboratories, Rockville, Md., in 16 × 125 mm screw-cap tubes. These cells were used as a source of starter cells for preparation of monolayers in 32-oz (942-ml) prescription bottles and also for assay of viral RNA synthesis. Medium for growing the cells consisted of Earle's tissue culture medium (BME) with glutamine, supplemented with 10% calf serum, whereas media used for maintenance of the cells was BME with glutamine plus 2% calf serum. Neither the growth nor the maintenance medium contained antibiotics. Periodically, the cells were tested for contamination with pleuropneumonia-like organisms (PPLO) by inoculation of cell suspensions on PPLO agar plates.

Rhinovirus. Rhinovirus type 1A strain 2060 was initially purchased from the American Type Culture Collection. The stocks employed for our studies were prepared by infecting KB cell (human carcinoma of the nasopharynx) monolayers in the presence of BME (with glutamine, 2% calf serum) followed by incubation at 33 C. After a 4+ cytopathic effect was observed, the virus was harvested. The cells were subjected to three cycles of freezing and thawing (−60 to 25 C); the resultant mixture was centrifuged at 2,484 × g for 10 min at 4 C. The supernatant fluids were then titered and stored at −60 C. Rhinovirus stock was titered in KB cell monolayers at 33 C on a roller drum (1 rev/min), and after 7 days the tissue culture-infecting dose, 50% ($TCID_{50}$), per milliliter was calculated by the method of Reed and Muench (5). Virus stocks prepared in this manner had a $TCID_{50}$/ml of 10^6 to 10^7. In subsequent ^{3}H-uridine uptake studies, the KB cell monolayers were infected at a multiplicity of infection (MOI) of 4 or 40. Virus stocks proved negative for mycoplasma when cultured on suitable PPLO medium.

M. pneumoniae. *M. pneumoniae* (Eaton agent) was initially procured from the American Type Culture Collection (ATCC 15293) and was propagated in PPLO growth medium consisting of 70% PPLO broth (Difco), 20% horse serum (Grand Island Biological Co., Grand Island, N.Y.), and 10% fresh yeast extract (Grand Island Biological Co.). In addition, the medium contained 0.5% dextrose and 0.004% phenol red. *M. pneumoniae* stocks were prepared by the inoculation of approximately 5×10^7 acid-forming units (AFU) of *M. pneumoniae* into 32-oz sterile prescription bottles containing 15 ml of the above PPLO growth medium. The inoculated bottles were then placed horizontally in an incubator at 37 C. After a suitable period of incubation (usually 4 to 5 days), the supernatant fluid was decanted, and the confluent *M. pneumoniae* colonies adhering to the glass were rinsed three times with Earle's salt solution containing 10% calf serum, 0.85% $NaHCO_3$, and glutamine. The bottles were drained; the adherent colonies of *M. pneumoniae* were scraped from the surface of the glass with a rubber policeman and were resuspended in the aforementioned rinse solution. The titer of the resultant *M. pneumoniae* grown on glass (MP-G) was then determined in triplicate. Serial 10-fold dilutions of the MP-G in PPLO medium were incubated for 21 days at 37 C. The final dilution of MP-G giving acid production (red to yellow change of the phenol red indicator) was recorded, and the *Mycoplasma* titer was calculated by the method of Reed and Muench (5) and expressed in AFU. Because the PPLO growth medium has been reported by Fletcher, Milligan, and Albertson (Bull. Czech. Soc. Microbiol. and Folia Microbiol., *in press*) to enhance the effect of mycoplasma on rhinovirus RNA replication, MP-G suspended only in rinse solution was employed throughout this study.

Assay procedure for viral nucleic acid synthesis. KB cell monolayers in screw-cap tubes were drained, and 0.9 ml of tissue culture maintenance medium was added to each tube. These tissue monolayer systems were then divided into three groups: the first group received 0.1 ml of MP-G (4 AFU) in BME with glutamine plus 10% calf serum; the second and third groups received 0.1 ml of BME with glutamine plus 10% calf serum. All tissue monolayer systems were then incubated at 37 C for 12 hr. At the end of this incubation period, all tubes were drained, and the cell sheets were rinsed with tissue culture maintenance medium (BME with glutamine and 2% calf serum). Groups 1 and 2 were then inoculated with 1 ml of rhinovirus 2060 stock (MOI, 40), whereas the tubes of group 3 (uninfected tissue controls) received 1 ml of maintenance medium. The time of rhinovirus inoculation was recorded as zero time. All tissue monolayer systems were then incubated on a roller (1 rev/min) at 33 C for 1 hr. At 1 hr postinfection, these systems were drained, and the cell sheets were rinsed with 1 ml of maintenance medium to remove unadsorbed virus. Then 0.5 ml of maintenance medium containing 5 μg of antinomycin D (Calbiochem, Los Angeles, Calif.) was added to each tube, and the preparations were incubated at 33 C on the roller drum for an additional 1.5 hr. At this time (2.5 hr postinfection), ^{3}H-uridine in maintenance medium (specific activity, 8.0 c/mmole) was added to a final concentration of 5 μc/ml. Incubation was continued at 33 C on the roller drum. Triplicate samples were removed from each group at selected times and processed as follows: cell sheets were drained, washed three times with 4-ml portions of chilled (4 C) 5% trichloroacetic acid, and drained; the tissue sheets were then solubilized in 0.5 ml of hydroxide of hyamine and 10 ml of scintillation counting fluid [4 of 2,5-diphenyloxazole; 200 mg of 1,4-bis-2-(4-methyl-5-phenyloxazolyl)-benzene; 95 ml of toluene, and 50 ml of absolute ethyl alcohol]. ^{3}H-uridine uptake per sample in counts per minute was then monitored by use of a Packard Tri-Carb scintillation counter (model 3320).

Experiments designed to determine the effect of the size of the *Mycoplasma* inoculum on viral RNA synthesis were performed as follows: 0.1-ml portions of suitable dilutions of MP-G were inoculated into tubes containing KB cell monolayers and 0.9 ml of tissue culture maintenance medium. The tissue systems were then incubated at 37 C for 12 hr, at which time monolayers were rinsed, infected with rhinovirus (MOI, 4), and assayed for viral RNA synthesis as previously described.

RESULTS

The stimulatory effect of *M. pneumoniae* on rhinovirus 2060 RNA synthesis in KB cells (Table 1) was evident during the viral RNA replication period. The stimulation was 138, 46, 20, 36, and 46% respectively, at 7, 8, 9, 10, and 11 hr after viral infection. At the peak of synthesis, viral RNA was 20% greater in the *M. pneumoniae* preinoculated cells than in the control virus-infected cells. The values have been corrected by subtracting ^{3}H-uridine uptake of

Table 1. *Effect of Mycoplasma pneumoniae (MP-G) on RNA synthesis by rhinovirus 2060 in KB cells*[a]

Time after viral infection	Infectious agent		Per cent stimulation
	Rhinovirus + MP-G	Rhinovirus alone	
hr	*counts/min*	*counts/min*	
5	0	0	–
6	1,684	0	–
7	23,828	10,032	137.5
8	51,341	35,214	45.8
9	56,840	47,369	20.0
10	55,461	40,883	35.7
11	42,727	29,195	46.4

[a] The results given are the averages from three separate experiments. The per cent stimulation was calculated by dividing the counts per minute of virus-infected cells preinoculated with *Mycoplasma* by the counts per minute of virus-infected cells, and multiplying by 100.

tissue controls (KB cells plus actinomycin D plus ^{3}H-uridine). Initially, additional controls in which KB cells were previously inoculated with *M. pneumoniae* were included, but these were found to be unnecessary; the ^{3}H-uridine uptake of such cells was identical to that of KB cells not inoculated with *Mycoplasma.*

The effect of the number of AFU of *M. pneumoniae* on rhinovirus RNA synthesis in KB cells is demonstrated in Table 2. Stimulation was observed at 16.5, 8.25, and 4.1 AFU of *M. pneumoniae* per cell, whereas apparent inhibition was observed at 33 AFU per cell. The per cent stimulation in these experiments was less than that shown in Table 1 because of the lower MOI of the rhinovirus inoculum (see Materials and Methods). With 33 AFU of *M. pneumoniae,* no effect on the number of viable KB cells was observed throughout the 12-hr period of exposure. ^{3}H-uridine uptake of KB cells inoculated with MP-G was identical to that of KB cells not inoculated with MP-G, regardless of the number of AFU per cell. We have been unable to demonstrate stimulation of viral RNA synthesis with 3 AFU or less of *M. pneumoniae* at 12 hr before viral infection. Experiments are now in progress to define the MOI of rhinovirus and the AFU of *M. pneumoniae* necessary to give maximal stimulation of viral nucleic acid replication.

Preliminary experiments on the effect of different times of pre-exposure of KB cells to *M. pneumoniae* inoculum prior to viral infection indicate that viral nucleic acid stimulation occurs when *M. pneumoniae* is inoculated at 48 or 12 hr prior to viral infection, but is not evident when *M. pneumoniae* is inoculated at 24 hr prior to and at the time of virus infection. This is consistent with the observations of Singer, Barile, and Kirschstein (7), who reported increased interferon production in tissue systems previously (−24 hr) treated with *Mycoplasma* and subsequently challenged with virus.

It was initially thought that the *M. pneumoniae* inoculum might be carrying a soluble factor which was responsible for the stimulation. To test this possibility, a portion of the *M. pneumoniae* stock (suspended in BME, 10% calf serum) was filtered through a 0.45-nm filter. The filtrate was cultured for viable *M. pneumoniae* and no *Mycoplasma* was detected. This filtrate was then used to pretreat KB cells 12 hr prior to virus infection. No effect upon viral RNA synthesis was observed, and the pattern of viral RNA synthesis in the "filtrate-treated cells" was identical to that of the virus controls.

Table 2. *Effect of various concentrations of Mycoplasma pneumoniae (MP/G) on RNA synthesis by rhinovirus 2060 in KB cells*

Acid-forming units of *M. pneumoniae*	Peak of rhinovirus RNA synthesis	
	Time	Per cent stimulation[a]
	hr	
33.0	10	–[b]
16.5	11	7
8.25	10	10
4.1	10	9
2.1	11	0
none	10	0

[a] Average results of three separate experiments.
[b] Inhibition, 13%.

DISCUSSION

Our results show that *M. pneumoniae* has a stimulatory effect on rhinovirus 2060 RNA synthesis. *Mycoplasma*-induced viral stimulation has previously been reported by Singer, Kirchstein, and Barile (8) working with vesicular stomatitis virus and *M. arginini,* and by Gafford, Sinclair, and Randall (1) with *M. gallisepticum* and fowlpox virus. In contrast to these reports of stimulation, an inhibitory relationship has been demonstrated between selected arboviruses and *Mycoplasma* (2) and between Rous sarcoma virus and a *Mycoplasma*-like factor (4). Thus, it appears that the nature of the effect of *Mycoplasma* on viral replication depends upon the system being studied.

Mycoplasma alone, or in association with KB cells, is clearly not eliciting a soluble stimulatory substance, indicating that intact *Mycoplasma* is necessary for the stimulation. The mechanism of stimulation is presently under investigation. Initial mode-of-action studies indicate that enhancement occurs early in the viral replication cycle.

The results of in vitro studies may be misleading when extended to in vivo conditions, but recently Kasza et al. (3) reported that inoculation of germ-free pigs with *M. hyponeumoniae* and a swine adenovirus (both of which are pathogenic for swine) resulted in a pneumonia of greater severity than that produced by either agent alone. These results, coupled with our observations, may indicate that the interaction of *M. pneumoniae* with rhinovirus 2060 could result in a more severe upper respiratory tract infection.

ACKNOWLEDGMENTS

This investigation was supported by Public Health Service Training Grant DE-00108-07 and by U.S. Army Grant DAHC 19-69-G-0011.

LITERATURE CITED

1. Gafford, L. G., R. Sinclair, and C. C. Randall, 1969. Growth cycle of fowlpox virus and change in plaque morphology and cytopathology by contaminating mycoplasma. Virology **37**:464–472.
2. Kagan, G. Y., K. S. Kulikova, V. V. Neustroeva, A. J. Rezepova, and Z. D. Sultanova. 1968. The effect of Mycoplasma infection of culture cells on reproduction, cytopathic activity and hemagglutinating capacity of certain viruses. Vop. Virusol. (Transl.) **5**:600–604.
3. Kasza, L., R. T. Hodges, A. O. Betts, and P. C. Trexler. 1969. Pneumonia in gnotobiotic pigs produced by simultaneous inoculation of a swine adenovirus and *Mycoplasma hyopneumoniae*. Vet. Rec. **84**:262–267.
4. Ponten, J., and I. Macpherson. 1966. Interference with Rous sacroma virus focus formation by a mycoplasma-like factor present in human cell cultures. Ann. Med. Exp. Biol. Fenn. **44**:260–264.
5. Reed, L. I., and H. Muench. 1938. A simple method for estimating fifty per cent endpoints. Amer. J. Hyg. **27**:493.
6. Robinson, L. B., R. H. Wichelhausen, and B. Roizman. 1956. Contamination of human cell cultures by PPLO. Science (Washington) **124**:1147–1148.
7. Singer, S. H., M. F. Barile, and R. I. Kirschstein. 1969. Enhanced virus yields and decreased interferon production in mycoplasma-infected hamster cells. Proc. Soc. Exp. Bio. Med. **131**:1129–1134.
8. Singer, S. H., R. L. Kirschstein, and M. F. Barile. 1969. Increased yields of stomatitis virus from hamster cells injected with Mycoplasma. Nature (London) **222**:1087–1089.

Antimicrobial Agents and Chemotherapy—1969

Preparation of Semisynthetic Coumermycin A_1 Derivatives

IV. Aliphatic Acyl and Related Derivatives of 3-Amino-4-Hydroxy-8-Methyl-7-[3-*O*-(5-Methyl-2-Pyrrolylcarbonyl) Noviosyloxy] Coumarin

J. G. KEIL, I. R. HOOPER, R. H. SCHREIBER, C. L. SWANSON, and J. C. GODFREY

Department of Biochemical Research, Bristol Laboratories, Division of Bristol-Myers Co., Syracuse, New York 13201

A number of acylamido semisynthetic coumermycin derivatives prepared either by the transacylation reaction with ditetrahydropyranylcoumermycin A_1 or by direct condensation with 3-amino-4-hydroxy-8-methyl-7-[3-*O*-(5-methyl-2-pyrrolylcarbonyl)noviosyloxy]coumarin (*PNC*-amine) are presented. The preparation of this key intermediate is detailed. Further, the preparation of a number of related coumermycin derivatives prepared by direct condensation with *PNC*-amine is also presented. Some structure-activity relationships have evolved. Most of the derivatives prepared, however, are low in activity or are too highly serum bound to be of any particular value.

The series of reactions by which coumermycin A_1 (Ia, Fig. 1) has been converted to a variety of new, semisynthetic antibiotics, as well as a discussion of the probable mechanisms of the reactions involved, has been presented in the first three papers of this series (2,3,5). Although the transacylation reactions described therein were useful for the preparation of a large number of semisynthetic coumermycin antibiotics, many of which possessed physical and biological properties more desirable than coumermycin A_1 itself, these reactions were found to be generally applicable only to acid chlorides and anhydrides. The present paper discloses the isolation of a number of aliphatic semisynthetic coumermycin derivatives prepared either by the usual transacylation method with the use of ditetrahydropyranylcoumermycin A_1 (2) or by direct acylation of 3-amino-4-hydroxy-8-methyl-7-[3-*O*-(5-methyl-2-pyrrolylcarbonyl) noviosyloxy]coumarin, "*PNC*-amine." A number of sulfonamide, ureide, thioureide, Schiff base, and secondary amine derivatives at the coumarin-3-amine are also discussed. Because the mechanism of the transacylation reaction necessarily precludes the preparation of these types of compounds, we believed that *PNC*-amine would be a versatile intermediate if a satisfactory way could be found for its preparation.

MATERIALS AND METHODS

Coumermycin A_1 (Ia, Fig. 1) was isolated as a pure, crystalline material according to the procedure described by Kawaguchi et al. (1) by use of the actinomycete *Streptomyces rishiriensis*. The acids, acid chlorides, and anhydrides used were generally obtained from commercial sources. Exceptions were the 3-substituted-4-hydroxyphenylacetic and 3-substituted-4-hydroxyphenylpropionic acids, which were made as described by Schmitz and co-workers (5).

The preparation of 2′,2′-*O,O*-ditetrahydropyranylcoumermycin A_1 (Ib, Fig. 1) from coumermycin A_1 was previously described (2,3) as were the reaction conditions for the preparation of semisynthetic coumermycin A_1 derivatives from ditetrahydropyranylcoumermycin A_1 via the transacylation route (2,3).

The quantitative estimation of residual coumermycin A_1 in semisynthetic coumermycins isolated by transacylation procedures was determined by a complexing reaction with nickel sulfate in dimethylsulfoxide (DMSO). This method, developed by Peter Monteleone of the Chemical Control Department, Bristol Laboratories, has been described (2,3). Under the conditions of this test, as little as 0.1% coumermycin A_1 can be determined.

Further indications of purity were obtained by chromatography on 0.5-inch (1.3-cm) strips of S & S 589 Blue Ribbon paper (Schleicher & Schuell Co., Keene, N.H.) in the solvent system acetone-0.1 M triethanolamine, adjusted to *p*H 7.0 with glacial acetic acid (2:3), as well as by bioautography on agar plates seeded with *Staphylococcus aureus* ATCC 6538P. Calibration of the paper chromatography-bioautograph system with coumermycin A_1 permitted ready quantitation of 0.5% or more contamination of the sample by coumermycin A_1 Samples containing ⩽0.5% (weight) coumermycin A_1 were judged to be pure on a bioactivity basis (procedures devised by C. A. Claridge and V. Z. Rossomano, Microbiological Research Department, Bristol Laboratories).

Chemical purity of semisynthetic coumermycins was demonstrated by infrared spectra, integrated nuclear magnetic resonance (NMR) spectra, and combustion analyses.

EXPERIMENTAL

The various stages in the preparation of *PNC*-amine are shown in Fig. 1. The melting points given for the compounds described below are uncorrected.

Bis-benzyloxycarbonyl imide of coumermycin A_1 (II). Monosodium coumermycin A_1 (60 g, 0.053 mole) was dissolved in 1,250 ml of tetrahydrofuran with slight warming on a steam bath. After allowing the deep golden-yellow solution to cool to 25 C, 44.6 ml of triethylamine (6 equivalents) was carefully added with vigorous stirring. The mixture immediately started to gel, although rapid stirring kept the gel mobile. Five equivalents (36 ml) of benzyloxycarbonyl chloride, diluted to 250-ml volume with tetrahydrofuran, was added dropwise to the vigorously stirred gel solution at 25 C over a 30-min period. After 1 hr, the gel disappeared and the presence of triethylamine hydrochloride precipitate was noted. The stirring of the yellow solution was continued at 25 C for an additional 24 hr. The solution was filtered to remove the triethylamine hydrochloride, and then was concentrated in vacuo to approximately one-tenth its original volume. The light yellow-orange solution was poured into 3,000 ml of Skellysolve B with vigorous stirring. An immediate precipitate of a light cream-colored solid appeared. After being stirred for 1 hr at 25 C, it was filtered, washed with four 100-ml portions of *n*-hexane, and dried to yield 77.4 g of semipure *bis*-benzyloxycarbonyl imide of courmermycin A_1 (melting point: softens at 145 to 150 C and decomposes with effervescence at 190 to 200 C). It is probable that this solid, consisting mainly of the desired product, contained small quantities of tri- and tetra-substituted carbobenzoxy side products, since one or both of the 4-hydroxyl functions of the coumarin moieties of coumermycin A_1 are capable of being carbobenzoxylated as well, These small quantities of side products do not interfere with

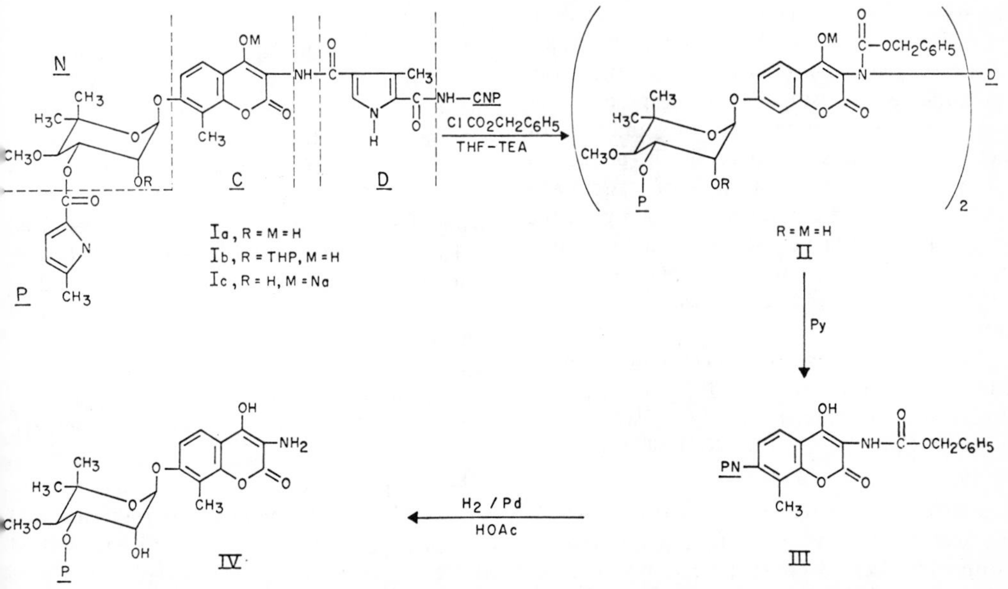

Fig. 1. *Preparation of PNC-amine. THF = tetrahydrofuran; TEA = triethylamine.*

the subsequent steps and are either eliminated or converted to desired product in the course of further processing. The infrared spectrum of the solid product showed a very weak amide II band near 1,530 cm^{-1}, indicating the presence of little, if any, starting material.

3-Benzyloxycarbonylamido-4-hydroxy-8-methyl-7-[3-0-(5-methyl-2-pyrrolylcarbonyl) noviosyloxy] coumarin (III). By dissolving 75 g of the *bis*-benzyloxycarbonyl imide of coumermycin A_1 (II) in 1,200 ml of pyridine at 25 C, a light orange-colored solution was obtained. It was warmed to 50 to 55 C for at least 24 hr, during which time it was stirred. The resulting orange-brown solution was concentrated in vacuo to about one-fifth its original volume and was poured into 3,000 ml of ice water with vigorous stirring. The *p*H was adjusted to ca. 1 to 2 with 6 N hydrochloric acid, and the solution was then stirred for an additional 1 hr. The suspension was filtered to yield 57.9 g of light cream-tan solids which were dried in vacuo to constant weight. The benzyloxycarbonyl amide is quite chloroform-soluble whereas the undesired side products are not. The whole product (50.0 g) was placed in a Soxhlet extraction apparatus and continuously extracted with chloroform until further materials extracted from the whole became negligible. Evaporation of the chloroform extracts produced approximately 15 g of chloroform-soluble materials. This residue was redissolved in a small portion of chloroform and extracted with 5% aqueous sodium bicarbonate to remove any acidic impurities. The chloroform solution was dried over anhydrous sodium sulfate, and the product was fractionally precipitated by the addition of increasing amounts of Skellysolve B (petroleum solvent, boiling point 60 to 68 C, essentially *n*-hexane) to yield a pure fraction, 4.5 g, of the title compound as a white, crystalline solid (melting point: softens at 110 C, gelling at 125 C, and melts with effervescence at 155 to 160 C).

The infrared and NMR spectra were consistent with the structure of the title compound.

Analysis. Calculated for $C_{32}H_{34}O_{11}N_2$ $1/2H_2O$: C, 60.84; H, 5.59; N, 4.44. Found: C, 61.14; H, 5.65; N, 4.83.

3-Amino-4-hydroxy-8-methyl-7-[3-O-*5-methyl-2-pyrrolyl-carbonyl-noviosyloxy] coumarin (IV). 3-Benzyloxycarbonylamido-4-hydroxy-8-methyl-7-[3-*O*-(5-methyl-2-pyrrolylcarbonyl) noviosyloxy] coumarin (III, 1.8 g, 2,90 mmoles) was dissolved in 150 ml of glacial acetic acid to produce a pale yellow solution. To this solution was added 450 mg of 30% palladium on diatomaceous earth catalyst, and the resulting solution was treated with hydrogen in a Parr hydrogenation apparatus at an initial pressure of 52.5 psi. The reduction was run for 24 hr at room temperature, during which time the total uptake of hydrogen was 15.7 psi. The catalyst was removed by filtration over a filter-aid pad under a nitrogen atmostphere, and the filter pad was washed with five 20-ml portions of glacial acetic acid. The solution was immediately evaporated to dryness in vacuo and stored under vacuum; yield, 1.26 g. It was recrystallized from acetone and *n*-hexane and was dried in vacuo over sodium hydroxide pellets to give 0.90 g (64%) of a light yellow-gold solid (melting point: 196 to 200 C). Infrared and NMR analyses of this solid were consistent with the structure of the title compound. It is sensitive to oxidation, particularly when in solution.

Analysis. Calculated for $C_{24}H_{28}O_9N_2$: C, 59.01; H, 5.79; N, 5.75. Found: C, 58.76; H, 6.02; N, 5.70.

3-Undecanamido-4-hydroxy-8-methyl-7-[3-O-(5-methyl-2-pyrrolylcarbonyl)noviosyloxy] coumarin (compound 7, method A). A solution of 500 mg (1.02 mmoles) of *PNC*-amine in 15 ml of pyridine was treated with a solution of 314.5 mg (1.536 mmoles) of undecanoyl chloride (Eastman Kodak Co., Rochester, N.Y.) in 2.0 ml of tetrahydrofuran at 25 C. The solution was stirred at 25 C for 20 hr. It was then poured into 600 ml of ice water with vigorous stirring and was adjusted to *p*H 1.5 with 6 N hydrochloric acid. After 15 min, the precipitate was filtered, washed with fresh water, and dried, giving 589 mg of crude product. It was dissolved in 10 ml of ethyl acetate and fractionally precipitated by addition of *n*-hexane, yielding 347 mg (51.7%) of the title compound. Infrared and NMR spectra were consistent with the expected structure.

Analysis. Calculated for $C_{35}H_{48}O_{10}N_2$: C, 64.00; H, 7.37; N, 4.26. Found: C, 63.62; H, 6.99; N, 4.63.

3-(N-Cyclohexyl-β-alanyl)-4-hydroxy-8-methyl-7-[3-O-(5-methyl-2-pyrrolylcarbonyl) noviosyloxy]coumarin (compound 43, method B). A solution of 300 mg (0.614 mmole) of *PNC*-amine in 10 ml of acetone was treated with

0.150 ml (106 mg, 1.04 mmoles) of triethylamine and was cooled to 3 C. In another flask, 210.3 mg (1.228 mmoles) of *N*-cyclohexyl-β-alanine (Abbott Laboratories North Chicago, Ill.) was dissolved in a mixture of 10 ml of acetone and 1.0 ml of water at 25 C. Triethylamine, 0.310 ml (224 mg, 2.21 mmoles), was added, and the solution was cooled to 2 C. Then 0.180 ml (200 mg, 1.84 mmoles) of ethyl chloroformate (Eastman Kodak Co.) was added all at once, and the solution was stirred at 0 to 5 C for 30 min to allow the mixed anhydride to form. The mixed anhydride solution was added rapidly to the *PNC*-amine solution; the mixture was stirred at 0 to 5 C for 2 hr, and then at 25 C for 16 hr. It was poured into 300 ml of ice water and acidified to *p*H 1.5 with 6 N hydrochloric acid. The crude product, 408 mg, was filtered, washed, and dried. It was dissolved in 15 ml of ethyl acetate and fractionally precipitated with *n*-hexane to afford 279 mg (70.6%) of the title compound. Its anticipated structure was substantiated by infrared and NMR spectra.

Analysis. Calculated for $C_{33}H_{43}O_{10}N_3$: C, 61.77; H, 6.75; N, 6.55. Found: C, 61.70; H, 6.84; N, 6.17.

3-[N-carbobenzoxy-α-D-(2-thienyl)glycyl]-4-hydroxy-8-methyl-7-[3-O-(5-methyl-2-pyrrolylcarbonyl)noviosyloxy]coumarin (compound 41, method C). To a solution of 250 mg (0.512 mmole) of *PNC*-amine in 15 ml of methyl ethyl ketone were added 190 mg (0.922 mmole) of *N,N'*-dicyclohexylcarbodiimide (Aldrich Chemical Co., Inc., Milwaukee, Wis.) and 224 mg (0.768 mmile) of *N*-carbobenzoxy-α-D-(2-thienyl)glycine. A precipitate of *N,N'*-dicyclohexylurea was noted after 30 min, and the solution was stirred at 25 C for 16 hr. A few drops of glacial acetic acid were added, and *N,N'*-dicyclohexylurea was removed by filtration. The filtrate was concentrated in vacuo to a brown-orange residue which was dissolved in 50 ml of ethyl acetate and extracted with three 25-ml portions of 6 N hydrochloric acid and three 25-ml portions of 5% sodium bicarbonate solution. The ethyl acetate solution was dried over sodium sulfate, and the product, 107 mg (27.4%) of golden-yellow solid, was recovered by fractional precipitation with *n*-hexane. Its infrared and NMR spectra fully supported the structure.

Analysis. Calculated for $C_{38}H_{39}O_{12}N_3S \cdot 1/2H_2O$: C, 59.21; H, 5.23; N, 5.45; S, 4.16. Found: C, 58.96; H, 5.52; N, 5.40; S, 3.89.

3-N'-ethylureido-4-hydroxy-8-methyl-7-[3-O-(5-methyl-2-pyrrolylcarbonyl)noviosyloxy]coumarin (compound 44, method D). A solution of 500 mg (1.02 mmoles) of *PNC*-amine in 25 ml of pyridine was treated with 0.120 ml (103 mg, 1.44 mmoles) of ethyl isocyanate (Aldrich Chemical Co.), and the solution was heated at reflux for 24 hr. It was poured into 300 ml of ice water and adjusted to *p*H 1.5 with 6 N hydrochloric acid. The resulting suspension was stirred for 30 min, and the product was recovered by filtration, washed, and dried to give 458 mg of crude material. It was recrystallized from ethyl acetate, giving 261 mg (45.8%) of purified product, of which the infrared and NMR spectra were entirely consistent with the proposed structure.

Analysis. Calculated for $C_{27}H_{33}O_{10}N_3$: C, 57.95; H, 5.94; N, 7.51. Found: C, 57.89; H, 6.08; N, 7.28.

3-(N'-phenylthioureido)-4-hydroxy-8-methyl-7-[3-O-(5-methyl-2-pyrrolylcarbonyl)noviosyloxy]coumarin (compound 49, method E). A solution of 392 mg (0.803 mmole) of *PNC*-amine in 25 ml of pyridine was treated with 0.140 ml (151mg, 1.12 mmoles) of phenylisothiocyanate (Eastman Kodak Co.) and refluxed for 2.0 hr. It was poured into 300 ml of ice water and acidified to *p*H 1.5 with 6 N hydrochloric acid. The crude product (411 mg) which precipitated was filtered, washed, and dried. It was purified by fractional precipitation from ethyl ether and *n*-hexane to yield 190 mg (38.0%) with a melting point of 180 C (decomposition). This compound had very weak antibacterial activity.

Analysis. Calculated for $C_{31}H_{33}O_9N_3S$: C, 59.70; H, 5.33; N, 6.73; S, 5.14. Found: C, 60.00; H, 5.28; N, 6.17; S, 4.83.

3-*n*-Propylamino-4-hydroxy-8-methyl-7-[3-O-(5-methyl-2-pyrrolylcarbonyl)noviosyloxy]coumarin (compound 50, method F). A solution of 500 mg (1.02 mmoles) of *PNC*-amine in 25 ml of pyridine was treated with 118 mg (1.51 mmoles) of 1-chloropropane and refluxed for 6.0 hr. It was poured into 300 ml of ice water and acidified to *p*H 1.5 with 6 N hydrochloric acid; the precipitate which formed was filtered and dried; [melting point: 205 C (decomposition)]. Infrared and NMR spectra supported the proposed structure of the title compound, and the product had very weak antibacterial activity.

Analysis. Calculated for $C_{27}H_{34}O_9N_2$: C, 61.12; H, 6.46; N, 5.28. Found: C, 61.05; H, 6.41; N, 5.29.

3-(4-Methylbenzenesulfonamido)-4-hydroxy-8-methyl-7-[3-O-(5-methyl-2-pyrrolylcarbonyl) noviosyloxy] coumarin (compound 48, method G). A solution of 543 mg (1.11 mmoles) of *PNC*-amine in 25 ml of pyridine was treated with 296 mg (1.55 mmoles) of *p*-toluenesulfonyl chloride (Eastman Kodak Co.) and stirred at 25 C for 65 hr. The solution was then poured into 300 ml of ice water and acidified to *p*H 1.5 with 6 N hydrochloric acid. After 1 hr, the precipitate was removed by filtration, washed, and dried to give 590 mg of crude product. Crystallization from ethyl ether and *n*-hexane yielded 200 mg (28.1%) of the title compound, as shown by its infrared and NMR spectra.

Analysis. Calculated for $C_{31}H_{34}O_{11}N_2S$: C, 57.93; H, 5.33; N, 4.35; S, 4.98. Found: C, 58.15; H, 5.70; N, 4.45; S, 5.34.

3-(N′-4-aminophenylureido)-4-hydroxy-8-methyl-7-[3-O-(5-methyl-2-pyrrolylcarbonyl) noviosyloxy] coumarin (compound 47, method H). 3-(*N*′-4-nitrophenylureido)-4-hydroxy-8-methyl-7-[3-*O*-(5-methyl-2-pyrrolylcarbonyl) noviosyloxy] coumarin (compound 46), 200 mg (0.306 mmole), was dissolved in a mixture of 50 ml of glacial acetic acid and 5 ml of dimethylformamide. Catalyst, 30 mg of 5% palladium on charcoal (Engelhard Industries, Inc., Newark, N.J.), was added, and the mixture was reduced at 25 C and an initial hydrogen pressure of 39.6 psi for 24 hr in a Parr apparatus. The catalyst was filtered, and the deep yellow filtrate was concentrated in vacuo. Ethyl acetate was added and distilled several times to displace all of the dimethylformamide. The brown residue weighed 176 mg. It was crystallized from acetone and *n*-hexane to give 63 mg (33%) of the title compound.

Analysis. Calculated for $C_{31}H_{34}O_{10}N_4$: C, 59.80; H, 5.50; N, 8.99. Found: C, 59.61; H, 5.94; N, 8.45.

RESULTS AND DISCUSSION

A number of hopefully selective hydrolytic procedures were tried on coumermycin A_1. None of them yielded any evidence of liberation of the 3-amino function from the 3-methylpyrrole-2,5-dicarboxamide which is the central link in the otherwise symmetrical coumermycin A_1 molecule, Ia. Treatment of coumermycin A_1 with aqueous or alcoholic sodium or barium hydroxide under various conditions of time, concentration, and temperature gave only general degradation via opening of the ester and lactone linkages prior to any significant attack on the amides. Mild acid hydrolysis fared no better, giving either no reaction or cleavage of the glycosidic bonds.

It seemed that transacylation of ditetrahydropyranylcoumermycin A_1 (Ib) with benzyloxycarbonyl chloride (carbonbenzoxy chloride) should yield the desired intermediate *PN*(O-THP)*C*-$NHCO_2C_7H_7$, which could then be cleaved in two steps to *PNC*-amine. Diligent investigation of reaction conditions led finally to the discovery that treatment of the sodium salt of coumermycin A_1 (Ic, Fig. 1), dissolved in tetrahydrofuran containing six molar equivalents of triethylamine, with a large excess (five molar equivalents) of benzyloxycarbonyl chloride led directly and in high yield to the *bis*-benzyloxycarbonyl imide (II, Fig. 1). Evidently, the 2′-hydroxyl of the noviose moieties is not sufficiently nucleophilic under these conditions to attack benzyloxycarbonyl chloride to produce the carbonate ester. It is not known whether transacylation in this case occurs via the mechanism suggested previously (2), although it would seem to be most likely in view of the

Table 1. *Comparison of minimal inhibitory concentrations of PNC-NHCOCH(CH$_3$)$_2$ and related antibiotics*[a]

Organism	Minimal inhibitory Concn (μg/ml)		
	Coumermycin A_1	PNC-$NHCOC_6H_5$	PNC-$NHCOCH(CH_3)_2$
Staphylococcus aureus Smith	0.004	0.25	0.16
S. aureus Smith (+ serum)	1.6	8.8	6.2
Streptococcus pyogenes Digonnet #7	0.062	1.6	1.3
Diplococcus pneumoniae A9585	0.16	1.5	1.3

[a] All tests were performed by the dilution method in heart infusion broth.

ailure of ditetrahydropyranylcoumermycin A_1 Ib) to react with isocyanates, isothiocyanates, nd alkyl and aryl sulfonyl chlorides.

Cleavage of the *bis*-imide II in warm pyridine, solation of the crude product, and separation of he desired compound III from it by continuous xtraction into chloroform afforded a moderate yield of pure III, 3-benzyloxycarbonamido-4-hydroxy-8-methyl-7-[3-*O*-(5-methyl-2-pyrrolylcarbonyl)noviosyloxy]coumarin.

Hydrogenolysis of carbobenzoxy intermediate III was attempted in a variety of solvents and with several catalysts. Most conditions gave evidence of the formation of *PNC*-amine, but in

Table 2. *Comparison of the CD_{50} of PNC-NHCOCH(CH_3)$_2$ with those of related antibiotics against three microbial species*[a]

Organism	Oral CD_{50} (mg/kg)		
	Coumermycin A_1	PNC-$NHCOC_6H_5$	PNC-$NHCOCH(CH_3)_2$
taphylococcus aureus Smith	8.00	5.5	3.0
treptococcus pyogenes Digonnet #7	>200	100	90
iplococcus pneumoniae A9585	>200	90	38

[a] Two treatments at 0 and 4 hr postchallenge. Mice were infected by intraperitoneal administration of a sufficient number of acterial cells (>100 LD_{50}) to kill all nontreated mice within 48 hr. In the case of *S. aureus* Smith, the challenge dose was dministered in 5% gastric mucin. The curative doses for 50% of the animals (CD_{50}) were calculated at 96 hr postchallenge.

Table 3. *Minimal inhibitory concentration ratios for aliphatic acyl derivatives of PNC-amine, PNC-NH-CO-R*[a]

Compound no.	R	Synthetic method[b]	*D. pneumoniae*	*S. pyogenes*	*S. aureus* Smith
1	CH_3	A_T, A, B	2.5	1.2	48
2	CH_2CH_3	A_T	1.0	2.0	>4.0
3	$(CH_2)_5CH_3$	A_T	8.0	2.0	4.0
4	$(CH_2)_6CH_3$	A_T	31	2.0	4.0
5	$(CH_2)_7CH_3$	A_T	16	1.0	>4.0
6	$(CH_2)_8CH_3$	A_T	16	≤0.25	4.0
7	$(CH_2)_9CH_3$	A	16	0.31	4.0
8	$(CH_2)_{10}CH_3$	A	4.0	≤0.50	>4.0
9	$(CH_2)_{11}CH_3$	A	2.0	≤0.50	>4.0
10	$(CH_2)_{12}CH_3$	A_T	8.0	≤0.50	20
11	$(CH_2)_{17}CH_3$	A_T	32	–	>4.0
12	$(CH_2)_{20}CH_3$	A_T	32	16	>4.0
13	$CH{=}CHCH_3$	A_T	1.0	2.5	2.0
14	$CH{=}C(CH_3)_2$	A_T	4.0	>2.5	2.0
15	$C(CH_3){=}CHCH_3$	A_T	4.0	8.0	2.0
16	$CH(CH_3)_2$	A_T, A	2.0	1.0	5.0
17	$C(CH_3)_3$	A_T	4.0	2.5	2.0
18	$CH_2CH(CH_3)_2$	A_T	2.0	4.0	2.0
19	$CH_2C(CH_3)_3$	A_T	4.0	8.0	2.0
20	$CH(C_2H_5)_2$	A_T	2.0	2.0	1.0
21	$CH_2CH_2CH(CH_3)_2$	A_T	2.0	2.0	2.0
22	$CH(CH_2CH_2CH_3)_2$	A_T	8.0	2.0	4.0

[a] Results are given as the ratio of the minimal inhibitory concentrations of each compound to those of *PNC*-NH-COC_6H_5 enzamido). The minimal inhibitory concentrations were determined by the twofold dilution method in antibiotic assay broth BBL). All observations were made after 18 hr of incubation at 37 C. Minimal inhibitory concentrations for *D. pneumoniae* were etermined with 5% human serum in the medium; those for *S. aureus* Smith were determined at *p*H 6.

[b] Procedures indicated are for reactions with *PNC*-NH_2 with the exception of the designation A_T, which indicates reaction of an cid chloride or anhydride with ditetrahydropyranyl coumermycin A_1 under the usual transacylation conditions (2, 3). A, acid hloride; B, mixed anhydride; C, carbodiimide; D, condensation with isocyanate; E, isothiocyanate; F, alkyl halide; G, sulfonyl hloride.

neutral solvents (tetrahydrofuran, dioxane, ethyl alcohol, methanol) the *PNC*-amine appeared to be very susceptible to oxygen-induced transformations during the isolation procedure. These changes were apparent from the rapid development of red color in filtrates containing the product. The difficulties were largely overcome by carrying out the reduction over 30% palladium on diatomaceous earth catalyst in glacial acetic acid at about 3 atm of hydrogen pressure. The product was blanketed with nitrogen at all stages during the workup, and was isolated as a pure, crystalline solid which was then found to be stable for a period of several weeks.

In Table 1, the in vitro activity of coumermycin A_1 and of the benzamido derivative against three species of microorganisms is shown to establish a standard basis of comparison for the new compounds reported in this paper. Compound 16 (the isobutyramido derivative) is also included here because it is of particula interest, as will be indicated below, and it activity relative to coumermycin A_1 is of impor tance. In addition, the oral CD_{50} of each o these three compounds against the same organ isms in mice is detailed in Table 2.

Tables 3 through 5 provide a comparison o the activity of each of the semisynthetic cou mermycins with that of the others. Comparativ minimal inhibitory concentration (MIC) data ar expressed as the ratio of the MIC of each com pound to that of a standard compound *PNC*-$NHCOC_6H_5$ (Benzamido). It should b noted that a number of the derivatives had activ ity equal to or superior to that of the standard (ratio less than 1.0). Generally, most of the com pounds listed were found to be serum inactivated to a high degree.

Extensive investigation of compound 16 (iso butyramido) with respect to MIC, CD_{50}, resis

Table 4. *Minimal inhibitory concentration ratios for aliphatic acyl derivatives of PNC-amine, PNC-NH-CO-R*[a]

Compound no.	R	Synthetic method[b]	*D. pneumoniae*	*S. pyogenes*	*S. aureus* Smith
23	CH_2CH_2–(S)	A_T	8.0	1.0	1.0
24	$CH_2CH_2CH_2$–(S)	A_T	16	1.0	1.0
25	$CH_2C_6H_5$	A_T	31	4.0	>4.0
26	$CH_2C_6H_3$ [4-OH-3-$CO(CH_2)_5CH_3$]	B	4.0	2.0	8.0
27	$(CH_2)_2C_6H_3$ [4-OH-3-$CH(CH_3)CH{=}CH_2$]	B	0.50	⩽0.50	1.0
28	$(CH_2)_2C_6H_3$ [4-OH-3-$CH(CH_3)CH_2CH_3$]	H	1.0	⩽0.50	4.0
29	$(CH_2)_2C_6H_3$(4-OH-3-$CH_2CH{=}CHCH_3$)	A, B	8.0	1.2	4.0
30	$(CH_2)_2C_6H_3$ [4-OH-3-$(CH_2)_3CH_3$]	H	4.0	4.0	1.0
31	$CH(C_6H_5)CH_2CH_3$	A_T	8.0	2.0	1.0
32	$CH_2CH(C_6H_5)CH_3$	A_T	2.0	0.25	1.0
33	$CH(C_6H_5)_2$	A_T	1.6	2.0	2.0
34	$CH(OH)C_6H_5$	A_T	8.0	2.0	0.25
35	$CH(CH_2C_6H_4NH_2\text{-}3)C_2H_5$	A_T, H	8.0	2.0	2.0
36	$(CH_2)_7(CHOH)_2(CH_2)_5CH_2OH$	A_T	2.0	1.0	2.0

[a] Results are given as the ratio of the minimal inhibitory concentrations of each compound to those of *PNC*-NH-COC_6H (Benzamido). The minimal inhibitory concentrations were determined by the twofold dilution method in antibiotic assay brot (BBL). All observations were made after 18 hr of incubation at 37 C. Minimal inhibitory concentrations for *D. pneumoniae* we determined with 5% human serum in the medium; those for *S. aureus* Smith were determined at *p*H 6.

[b] Procedures indicated are for reactions with *PNC*-NH_2 with the exception of the designation A_T, which indicates reaction of a acid chloride or anhydride with ditetrahydropyranyl coumermycin A_1 under the usual transacylation conditions (2, 3). A, aci chloride; B, mixed anhydride; C, carbodiimide; D, condensation with isocyanate; E, isothiocyanate; F, alkyl halide; G, sulfony chloride; H, catalytic reduction of a previously prepared derivative.

Table 5. *Minimal inhibitory concentration ratios for related derivatives of PNC-amine, PNC-NH-R*[a]

Compound no.	R	Synthetic method[b]	*D. pneumoniae*	*S. pyogenes*	*S. aureus* Smith
37	$COOCH_2C_6H_5$	—[c]	2.0	0.25	1.0
38	H	—[c]	8.0	8.0	>4.0
39	$COCH_2$(3-indolyl)	B	2.0	4.0	>4.0
40	$COCH(CH_2C_6H_4OH$-4)-NH*CBZ*[d]	B, C	63	≤0.25	4.0
41	COCH(2-thienyl)-NH*CBZ*[d]	B, C	63	2.0	2.0
42	$COCH_2CH_2NHCOC_6H_5$	B	4.0	2.0	>4.0
43	$COCH_2CH_2NH$—(S)	B	16	>2.5	8.0
44	$CONHCH_2CH_3$	D	4.0	2.0	>4.0
45	$CONHC_6H_5$	D	–	2.0	4.0
46	$CONHC_6H_4NO_2$-4	D	–	1.0	>4.0
47	$CONHC_6H_4NH_2$-4	H	8.0	4.0	>4.0
48	$SO_2C_6H_4CH_3$-4	G	16	1.0	>4.0
49	$CSNHC_6H_5$	E	–	–	–
50	$CH_2CH_2CH_3$	F	–	–	–

[a] Results are given as the ratio of the minimal inhibitory concentrations of each compound to those of *PNC*-NH-COC_6H_5 (benzamido). The minimal inhibitory concentrations were determined by the twofold dilution method in antibiotic assay broth (BBL). All observations were made after 18 hr of incubation at 37 C. Minimal inhibitory concentrations for *D. pneumoniae* were determined with 5% human serum in the medium; those for *S. aureus* Smith were determined at *p*H 6.

[b] Procedures indicated are for reactions with *PNC*-NH_2 with the exception of the designation A_T, which indicates reaction of an acid chloride or anhydride with ditetrahydropyranyl coumermycin A_1 under the usual transacylation conditions (2, 3). A, acid chloride; B, mixed anhydride; C, carbodiimide; D, condensation with isocyanate; E, isothiocyanate; F, alkyl halide; G, sulfonyl chloride; H, catalytic reduction of a previously prepared derivative.

[c] See Experimental.

[d] *CBZ* = benzyloxycarbonyl (carbobenzoxy).

tance development, concentration in blood, serum binding, and other factors indicated it to be far superior to all other compounds listed. Detailed biological data on this isobutyramido derivative, as well as on a number of other semisynthetic coumermycins, are reported separately by Price and co-workers (4).

Of 12 organisms chosen to give a representative MIC spectrum, compound III (no. 37), *PNC*-$NHCO_2C_7H_7$, exhibited significant activity only against *Diplococcus pneumoniae, Streptococcus pyogenes,* and three strains of *Staphylococcus aureus.* It was surprisingly active in vivo (mice) against *S. aureus* Smith, showing a CD_{50} of 1.0 mg/kg via the intramuscular route, but it had no activity orally. Compound IV (no. 38), *PNC*-amine, was found to be active only against *D. pneumoniae* and *S. pyogenes* in vitro, and, of course, afforded no measurable protection against *S. aureus* Smith infection in mice.

PNC-amine condensed readily with isocyanates to form ureides, as well as with isothiocyanates to form thioureides, which were stable and readily purified. *PNC*-amine also condensed with alkyl halides to form secondary amines, with aldehydes to form Schiff bases, and with sulfonyl chlorides to form sulfonamides. However, all products of this type had very weak antibacterial activity.

ACKNOWLEDGMENTS

We are indebted to the following people for valuable technical assistance: R. M. Downing, C. M. Kalinowski, H. Schmitz, A. L. Vulcano, and D. F. Whitehead. We are also indebted to the Microbiological Research Department of Bristol Laboratories, and in particular to M. Misiek for the in vitro minimal inhibitory concentration data and to D. Chisholm for the CD_{50} data.

LITERATURE CITED

1. Kawaguchi, H., H. Tsukiura, M. Okanishi, T. Miyaki, T. Ohmori, K. Fujisawa, and H. Koshiyama. 1965. Studies on coumermycin, a new antibiotic. I. Production, isolation, and characterization of coumermycin A_1. J. Antibiot. (Tokyo) Ser. A **18**:1–10.
2. Keil, J. G., I. R. Hooper, M. J. Cron, O. B. Fardig, D. E. Nettleton, F. A. O'Herron, E. A. Ragan, M.A. Rousche, H. Schmitz, R. H. Schreiber, and J. C. Godfrey, 1968. Semisynthetic coumermycins. I. Preparation of 3-acylamido-4-hydroxy-8-methyl-7-[3-O-(5-methyl-2-pyrrolylcar-

bonyl)-noviosyloxy] coumarins. J. Antibiot. (Tokyo) Ser. A **21**:551–566.

3. Keil, J. G., I. R. Hooper, M. J. Cron, H. Schmitz, D. E. Nettleton, and J. C. Godfrey. 1969. The preparation of semisynthetic coumermycin A_1 derivatives. III. Aromatic and heteroaromatic derivatives of 3-amino-4-hydroxy-8-methyl-7-[3-*O*-(5-methyl-2-pyrrolylcarbonyl)noviosyloxy] coumarin. Antimicrob. Agents Chemother.–1968, p. 120–127.
4. Price, K. E., D. R. Chisholm, F. Leitner, and M. Misiek. 1970. Microbiological and pharmacological evaluation of BL-C 43, a new semisynthetic derivative of coumermycin A_1. Antimicrob. Agents Chemother.–1969, p. 000–000.
5. Schmitz, H., R. L. DeVault, C. D. McDonnell, and J. C. Godfrey. 1968. Semisynthetic coumermycins. II. Preparation and properties of 3-(substituted benzamido)-4-hydroxy-8-methyl-7-[3-O-(5-methyl-2-pyrrolylcarbonyl)] coumarins. J. Antibiot. (Tokyo) Ser. A **21**: 603–610.

Antimicrobial Agents and Chemotherapy—1969

Microbiological and Pharmacological Evaluation of BL-C 43, a New Semisynthetic Derivative of Coumermycin A_1

K. E. PRICE, D. R. CHISHOLM, F. LEITNER, AND M. MISIEK

Research Division, Bristol Laboratories, Division of Bristol-Myers Co., Syracuse, New York 13201

BL-C 43, sodium 3-isobutyramido-4-hydroxy-8-methyl-7-[3-*O*-(5-methyl-2-pyrrolylcarbonyl)noviosyloxy]coumarin, is primarily of interest because of its inhibitory effects against gram-positive bacteria and certain gram-negative species such as *Neisseria gonorrhoeae, Haemophilus influenzae,* and *Pasteurella multocida.* In comparative tests with novobiocin, lincomycin, oleandomycin, and erythromycin, the minimal inhibitory concentrations of BL-C 43 for *Staphylococcus aureus, N. gonorrhoeae,* and *H. influenzae* were equal to or lower than those of all other antibiotics except novobiocin. In vitro tests against *Diplococcus pneumoniae* and *Streptococcus pyogenes* showed that the compound was less inhibitory than erythromycin and slightly less active than the other antibiotics. Despite this finding, BL-C 43 proved to be markedly superior to the other antibiotics in therapeutic tests when compounds were administered orally to mice infected with *S. aureus* (four strains), *D. pneumoniae, S. pyogenes,* or *P. multocida.* The surprising in vivo effectiveness of BL-C 43 can probably be attributed to its unusual pharmacological behavior. Tissue distribution studies in mice suggested that the compound is not eliminated by the kidneys, but is removed through biliary excretion. Furthermore, there is strong evidence that reabsorption of the antibiotic occurs as bile is excreted into the small intestine. The net effect of this excretory mechanism is that extremely high and prolonged concentrations of BL-C 43 in mouse blood are attained after oral or parenteral administration.

Coumermycin A_1, an antibiotic characterized by its marked inhibitory activity against staphylococci, was found to be poorly absorbed by the oral route and to cause local irritation when administered parentrally. Because of this, a large series of semisynthetic coumermycin A_1 derivatives were prepared and their biological properties were investigated (1, 4*a*). BL-C 43, sodium-3-isobutyramido-4-hydroxy-8-methyl-7-[3-*O*-(5-methyl-2-pyrrolylcarbonyl) noviosyloxy]coumarin, was selected from this group because of its relatively broad spectrum of antibacterial activity, its high degree of oral absorbability, and its low toxicity. In addition, the irritation caused by parenteral administration of BL-C 43 was found to be less than that caused by coumermycin A_1 (5). The antibacterial spectrum of BL-C 43 closely resembles those of erythromycin, novobiocin, lincomycin, and oleandomycin. The latter group of antibiotics have been used extensively for clinical purposes, particularly in patients with infections caused by gram-positive bacteria and in patients in whom the administration of penicillins is contraindicated. The present report compares the microbiological and pharmacological properties of BL-C 43 with this group of commercially available antibiotics.

MATERIALS AND METHODS

Antibiotics. BL-C 43 was prepared by members of the Bristol Laboratories Biochemistry Department (2). This new derivative of coumermycin A_1 is a pale yellow, semicrystalline solid that is very soluble in water (>200 mg/ml at 25 C). Its activity in vitro was compared with that of a group of antibiotics supplied through the courtesy of the indicated manufacturers: sodium novobiocin, lincomycin hydrochloride, and erythromycin base from The Upjohn Co., Kalamazoo, Mich., and triacetyloleandomycin from Chas. Pfizer & Co., Inc., Brooklyn, N.Y. The same antibiotics, with one exception, were used in studies of the drug concentrations in blood after oral administration, as well as in all determinations of therapeutic efficacy in experimental infections of mice. Commercially obtained erythromycin estolate (Ilosone, Eli Lilly & Co., Indianapolis, Ind.), a dosage form rerecommended for oral use, was substituted for erythromycin base in these studies. Antibiotics compared with BL-C 43 in studies involving parenteral administration were sodium novobiocin, lincomycin hydrochloride, and commercially acquired oleandomycin phosphate (Oleandomycin Intravenous, J. B. Roerig, New York, N.Y.) and erythromycin ethylsuccinate (Erythrocin, Abbott Laboratories, North Chicago, Ill.).

Antibacterial activity (in vitro). The minimal inhibitory concentrations (MIC) of the various antibiotics were determined by a twofold agar-dilution method that utilized the Steers multiple inoculator apparatus (6). A 10^{-1} dilution of an overnight culture of each of the *Streptococcus pyogenes* and *Diplococcus pneumoniae* strains was added to plates containing Trypticase Soy Agar (BBL) plus 2% defibrinated sheep blood. *Haemophilus influenzae* and *Neisseria gonorrhoeae* strains were also tested at a 10^{-1} dilution, but on Brain Heart Infusion Agar (BBL) containing 2% blood and 1% supplement C (Difco). The MIC for the remaining species was determined by adding a 10^{-2} dilution of an overnight culture to Nutrient Agar (Difco) plates. The end point (MIC), which was considered to be the lowest concentration at which bacterial growth was completely inhibited, was determined after overnight incubation at 37C. The influence of the size of the inoculum of *Staphylococcus aureus* A9537 on the MIC of BL-C 43 and several other antibiotics was determined by means of standard twofold dilution tests in which Nutrient Broth (Difco) was used as the growth medium. Inocula were prepared by making 10^{-2}, 10^{-4}, and 10^{-6} dilutions of an 18-hr Nutrient Broth culture that contained 4.5×10^{8} cells/ml. The MIC was determined after culture tubes had been incubated for 18 hr at 37 C.

The bactericidal potential of BL-C 43 and the other antibiotics for two *S. aureus* strains (A9537 and A9606) was measured as follows. Tubes of Nutrient Broth containing various concentrations of the compounds were inoculated with a standard number of cells of either *S. aureus* A9537 or *S. aureus* A9606. Cultures were incubated at 37 C and sampled at 24 hr for determination of the number of viable cells present. Samples were appropriately diluted, spread over the surface of Nutrient Agar plates, and then incubated overnight at 37 C. The number of viable cells per milliliter was then estimated by counting colonies. The MIC was defined as the lowest concentration which prevented grossly detectable growth, and the minimal bactericidal concentration (MBC) was the lowest concentration tested that gave a count of $<$10 cells/ml.

Resistance development studies. The rate of development of resistance by *S. aureus* A9497 to BL-C 43, novobiocin, erythromycin, and lincomycin was determined by transferring a portion of overnight growth from Brain Heart Infusion Agar plates to a new series of antibiotic-containing plates. In every instance, the plate selected as the source of inoculum contained the highest concentration of antibiotic permitting full growth of the organism. Overall, the *S. aureus* A9497 lines were subjected to 12 consecutive transfers on antibiotic-containing media. After the last transfer, each of the strains that had developed resistance was tested against all of the other agents (including oleandomycin) to investigate cross-resistance patterns.

Acid stability and serum binding. Among the properties of BL-C 43 examined were its stability to acid (*p*H 2.0) and the extent to which it is bound to human serum. Acid stability was determined by incubating the compound at 37 C (at a concentration of 100 μg/ml) in citric acid-HCl buffer at *p*H 2.0. Samples were removed periodically, neutralized, and then assayed on *S. aureus* 209P plates for residual activity. The half-life or length of exposure causing a 50% decrease in antimicrobial activity was then calculated.

The extent to which BL-C 43 is bound to human serum was determined by measuring the relative potency against *S. aureus* 209P of antibiotic solutions in *p*H 7.2, 0.001 M phosphate buffer and 95% human serum. Antibiotic potency was measured by an agar-diffusion technique (5) over a BL-C 43 concentration range of 15 to 250 μg/ml.

Activity in experimental mouse infections. Experimental infections were produced in male Swiss-Webster mice weighing 18 to 22 g each. In each experiment, the number of bacterial cells given by the intraperitoneal route was sufficient to kill all of the nontreated mice, generally within 48 hr. Challenge doses of the staphylococcal strains were given as suspensions in 5% mucin; no mucin was utilized for the other infecting agents. Antibiotics were administered orally by stomach tube at the time of challenge (0 hr) and 4 hr later, or at 0, 2, 4, and 6 hr postchallenge. The dose response was determined by increasing drug concentrations by twofold increments; 10 mice were used at each dose level. The *Pasteurella multocida* experiment was terminated after 7 days; all others, after 4 days. At that time, the number of surviving mice was recorded, and the CD_{50} (the total dose in milligrams per kilogram required to cure 50% of the infected mice) was estimated by means of a log-probit plot.

Antibiotic concentrations in the blood of mice. The concentration of drug in the blood after parenteral and oral administration was determined by bleeding fasted, male, Swiss-Webster mice from orbital sinuses at various times after administration of the antibiotics. The techniques used for dosing and bleeding were identical to those previously described by Price et al. (4). BL-C 43 was assayed against *S. aureus* 209P; the other antibiotics were assayed according to the methods outlined by Kirshbaum and Arret (3).

Distribution of BL-C 43 in mice. Concentrations of

BL-C 43 were determined as a function of time after intravenous administration of a 20 mg/kg dose. Tissues to be examined were removed, and their wet weight was determined; then they were placed in 4 parts *p*H 6.0, 0.01 M phosphate buffer and ground in a VirTis 45 homogenizer (VirTis Co., Inc., Gardiner, N.Y.) until homogeneous suspensions were obtained. These were diluted with an equal volume of acetone and then centrifuged. The resulting supernatants fluids were bioassayed on *S. aureus* 209P plates. Bile and urine samples were similarly assayed after being appropriately diluted in *p*H 6.0 phosphate buffer. The urine specimens were collected over dry ice from a pool of 20 mice maintained in a single rodent metabolism cage.

RESULTS

The in vitro antibacterial spectra of BL-C 43 and several other antibiotics are shown in Table 1.

It is apparent that BL-C 43 is active against both gram-positive and gram-negative bacteria. However, the concentrations required to inhibit organisms in the latter group are probably too high to be of significance from the clinical standpoint. Thus, BL-C 43 can be considered of interest primarily because of its gram-positive spectrum. On the other hand, it should be noted that a few gram-negative species, such as *H. influenzae, N. gonorrhoeae,* and *P. multocida,* which are susceptible to many penicillins, are also quire susceptible to BL-C 43. Lincomycin and oleandomycin are active only against gram-positive bacteria, their level of potency against these organisms being generally comparable to that of BL-C 43. Erythromycin, on the other hand, possesses the same broad spectrum of antibacterial activity found for BL-C 43 and novobiocin. However, it is considerably more inhibitory for gram-positive bacteria than are either of these antibiotics.

The distribution of the minimal inhibitory concentrations of BL-C 43 and the commercial antibiotics for a large number of strains of selected gram-positive and gram-negative bacterial species is presented in Tables 2 and 3. These strains were predominantly of clinical origin.

Data in Table 2 show that novobiocin, which inhibited about 98% of the *S. aureus* strains at a concentration of 0.25 μg or less per ml, is by far the most potent antistaphylococcal agent. BL-C 43 and erythromycin were almost as active; 85 and 91% of the strains, respectively, were inhibited at a concentration of 0.5 μg/ml. Lincomycin and oleandomycin were only slightly less inhibitory than the latter antibiotics.

Results obtained with 17 *Streptococcus pyogenes* strains are also presented in Table 2. All of these strains were inhibited by 0.13 μg of erythromycin per ml. Lincomycin was only slightly less inhibitory, as all of the cultures were

Table 1. *Antimicrobial spectrum of BL-C 43 and several commercial antibiotics*

Organism	No. of strains tested	Minimal inhibitory concn[a]				
		BL-C 43	Novobiocin	Lincomycin	Oleandomycin	Erythromycin
Staphylococcus aureus (non-penicillinase producer)	2	0.5	<0.01	1.6	3.2	0.18
S. aureus (penicillinase producer)	4	0.9	0.18	2	6.3	2
Streptococcus pyogenes	4	2	0.5	0.5	4	0.05
S. faecalis	4	16	1	8	8	0.18
Diplococcus pneumoniae	4	3.2	1	0.5	1.8	0.05
Listeria monocytogenes	2	6.3	6.3	8	8	0.18
Haemophilus influenzae	2	2	0.25	32	>32	1
Neisseria gonorrhoeae	2	2	8	>16	8	1
Pasteurella multocida	2	0.25	0.35	22.6	32	1.4
Escherichia coli	3	180	56	>250	400	28
Klebsiella pneumoniae	1	63	32	>500	>500	63
Enterobacter aerogenes	2	>500	250	>500	>500	125
Proteus mirabilis	2	63	16	>500	>500	250
Proteus sp. (indole-positive)	8	70	32	>500	>500	250
Pseudomonas aeruginosa	4	300	80	>500	>500	300

[a] Geometric mean in micrograms per milliliter.

susceptible to 0.5 μg/ml. The other antibiotics were less effective; concentrations of 2 to 4 μg/ml were required to inhibit all 17 strains.

A similar distribution of drug effectiveness was found in tests against 17 *D. pneumoniae* strains. Erythromycin was again the most active antibiotic. Although BL-C 43 displayed the least activity, it did inhibit all strains at a concentration of 4 μg/ml. Lincomycin, novobiocin, and oleandomycin each inhibited all of the strains at a concentration of 1 or 2 μg/ml.

Table 3 summarizes results obtained with 18 *H. influenzae* strains. Outstandingly active was novobiocin, which inhibited all strains at 1 μg/ml. BL-C 43 and erythromycin were effective at somewhat higher concentrations, but no measurable activity was found for lincomycin or oleandomycin.

Erythromycin was the most active antigonococcal antibiotic. All 14 strains of *N. gonorrhoeae* were inhibited by 1 μg of erythromycin per ml (Table 3). BL-C 43, the next most

Table 2. *Relative inhibitory activity of BL-C 43 and several commercial antibiotics for Staphylococcus aureus, Streptococcus pyogenes, and Diplococcus pneumoniae*

Organism	Compound	Minimal inhibitory concn (μg/ml)									
		0.016	0.032	0.063	0.125	0.25	0.5	1	2	4	>4
S. aureus (88 strains)	BL-C 43	–	–	–	–	7[a]	85	98	–	–	100
	Novobiocin	–	–	9	66	98	–	–	–	–	100
	Lincomycin	–	–	–	–	–	9	91	100	–	–
	Oleandomycin	–	–	–	–	–	6	74	98	–	100
	Erythromycin	–	–	–	21	89	91	–	92	100	–
S. pyogenes (17 strains)	BL-C 43	–	–	–	–	–	–	–	–	100	–
	Novobiocin	–	–	–	–	–	12	71	100	–	–
	Lincomycin	–	–	–	–	18	100	–	–	–	–
	Oleandomycin	–	–	–	–	–	–	–	100	–	–
	Erythromycin	–	18	59	100	–	–	–	–	–	–
D. pneumoniae (17 strains)	BL-C 43	–	–	–	–	–	12	41	65	100	–
	Novobiocin	–	–	6	–	35	77	94	100	–	–
	Lincomycin	–	–	–	12	77	94	100	–	–	–
	Oleandomycin	–	–	–	–	6	35	71	100	–	–
	Erythromycin	71	100	–	–	–	–	–	–	–	–

[a] Total percentage of strains inhibited at the indicated concentration.

Table 3. *Relative inhibitory activity of BL-C 43 and several commercial antibiotics for Haemophilus influenzae and Neisseria gonorrhoeae*

Organism	Antibiotic	Minimal inhibitory concn (μg/ml)									
		0.06	0.13	0.25	0.5	1	2	4	8	16	>16
H. influenzae (18 strains)	BL-C 43	–	–	–	–	50[a]	83	89	100	–	–
	Novobiocin	–	61	83	89	100	–	–	–	–	–
	Lincomycin	–	–	–	–	–	–	–	–	28	100
	Oleandomycin	–	–	–	–	–	–	–	–	–	100
	Erythromycin	–	–	–	11	50	67	100	–	–	–
N. gonorrhoeae (14 strains)	BL-C 43	–	7	–	–	14	93	100	–	–	–
	Novobiocin	–	–	–	7	–	–	29	93	100	–
	Lincomycin	–	–	–	–	–	–	–	–	7	100
	Oleandomycin	–	14	–	–	–	–	43	100	–	–
	Erythromycin	14	–	–	36	100	–	–	–	–	–

[a] Total percentage of strains inhibited at indicated concentration.

ctive compound, was only slightly more effec-ive than oleandomycin and novobiocin. Linco-nycin did not inhibit any of the strains at the ighest concentration tested (16 μg/ml).

Data showing the effect of inoculum size on he MIC of BL-C 43 and of the other antibiotics or *S. aureus* A9537 are presented in Table 4.

Results indicate that even a 4-log difference in noculum size (4.5×10^6 versus 4.5×10^2 ells/ml) did not markedly influence the MIC of he antibiotics for *S. aureus* A9537. The biggest hange occurred with oleandomycin and eryth-omycin. With these drugs, the MIC for the argest inoculum was fourfold greater than that or the smallest inoculum.

It was considered of interest to determine whether BL-C 43 could be classified as an ntibiotic whose effects on bacteria are pri-narily "bacteriostatic" or "bactericidal." Since enicillins, which are considered to be primarily actericidal in their behavior, usually sterilize ultures at concentrations only two- to fourfold igher than the MIC, any antibiotic showing a imilarly small range between the MIC and the IBC might be considered a bactericidal drug. Results obtained with BL-C 43 and the com-nercial antibiotics are summarized in Table 5.

On the basis of the definition stated above, oth BL-C 43 and novobiocin might be con-idered bactericidal antibiotics. Classification of he other antibiotics was not so clear-cut, as heir action on the staphylococcal strains varied onsiderably. Erythromycin concentrations re-uired for sterilization of the *S. aureus* A9606 nd *S. aureus* A9537 cultures were, respectively, and 16 times the MIC. The response to leandomycin and lincomycin was even more ariable. With these drugs, there was no difference between the MIC and the MBC in tests against *S. aureus* A9537, whereas against *S. aureus* A9606 the difference between MIC and MBC was at least 4-fold for oleandomycin and 16-fold for lincomycin. This finding might be expected if a significant portion of the population in the *S. aureus* A9606 culture had high resistance to these antibiotics.

The rate at which *S. aureus* A9497 develops resistance to BL-C 43, novobiocin, erythromycin, and lincomycin was determined by serially transferring the culture in subinhibitory concentrations of the agents. The changes in the MIC of each drug after various numbers of transfers are shown in Table 6.

The resistance of *S. aureus* A9497 to each of the antibiotics increased rapidly within four transfers and continued to rise throughout the entire 12-transfer experiment. The rates at which the culture developed resistance to BL-C 43, novobiocin, and erythromycin were comparable, and were somewhat faster than the rate

Table 4. *Effect of inoculum size on the activity of BL-C 43 and several other antibiotics against Staphylococcus aureus A9537*

Antibiotic	Dilution of an 18-hr culture[a] of *S. aureus* A9537		
	10^{-6}	10^{-4}	10^{-2}
L-C 43	0.2[b]	0.2	0.4
ovobiocin	0.025	0.05	0.05
leandomycin	3.1	6.3	12.5
incomycin	0.8	1.6	1.6
rythromycin	0.2	0.4	0.8

[a] Contained 4.5×10^8 viable cells/ml.
[b] Minimal inhibitory concentration in micrograms per illiliter.

Table 5. *Bactericidal effect of BL-C 43 and several other antibiotics against Staphylococcus aureus A9537 and A9606*

Antibiotic	*S. aureus* strain[a]			
	A9537		A9606	
	MIC[b]	MBC[b]	MIC	MBC
BL-C 43	0.5	⩽2	0.25	0.5
Novobiocin	0.25	⩽1	0.06	0.06
Lincomycin	2	2	2	>32
Oleandomycin	2	2	⩽4	16
Erythromycin	0.5	8	2	8

[a] Initial cell counts were 5.9×10^4 for *S. aureus* A9537 and 2.9×10^4 for *S. aureus* A9606.
[b] Minimal inhibitory concentration (MIC) and minimal bactericidal concentration (MBC), both in micrograms per milliliter.

Table 6. *Rate of resistance development of Staphylococcus aureus A9497 to various antibiotics*

Antibiotic	No. of transfers on antibiotic-containing plates[a]			
	0	4	8	12
BL-C 43	0.63[b]	32	500	1,000
Novobiocin	0.16	8	250	1,000
Erythromycin	0.16	16	63	⩾500
Lincomycin	0.32	2	32	63

[a] Heart Infusion Agar.
[b] Highest concentration (micrograms per milliliter) of antibiotic permitting maximal growth.

at which resistance to lincomycin developed. A similar "emergence of resistance" pattern occurred with three other strains studied in this manner. These were *S. aureus* S9537 and one strain each of *D. pneumoniae* and S. *pyogenes.*

All organisms grown on media containing BL-C 43 were cross-resistant to novobiocin, but not to erythromycin, lincomycin, or oleandomycin. Strains made resistant to novobiocin also proved to be resistant to BL-C 43. A considerable amount of cross-resistance among lincomycin, erythromycin, and oleandomycin was also noted.

BL-C 43 was found to be remarkably stable to low *p*H. Its half-life or the time required for destruction of one-half of the original 100 μg/ml concentration at *p*H 2.0 was estimated to be in excess of 10 hr. This suggests that the compound will not undergo significant degradation as a result of exposure to highly acidic gastric juices following its oral administration.

The extent to which BL-C 43 is bound to human serum protein was estimated by comparing the relative antibacterial potency of the antibiotic in buffer and serum at concentrations ranging from 15 to 250 μg/ml. The percentage of binding found by this technique ranged from 76 to 79%, values that are significantly lower than those found for coumermycin A_1 (87%), the parent compound, and for novobiocin (96 to 98%), an antibiotic that also possesses noviose and coumarin moieties.

The relative effectiveness of BL-C 43 and the other antibiotics in experimental bacterial infections of mice was determined. The CD_{50} (curative dose, 50%) of the various antibiotics i shown in Table 7.

As can be observed, BL-C 43 had excellen activity against all four *S. aureus* strains. Novobiocin, lincomycin, and oleandomycin were als active against all four staphylococcal strains, bu considerably less so than BL-C 43. Erythromycin had a very low level of activity agains these strains. As expected, the ability to produc penicillinase did not influence responses of th test organisms to these agents.

BL-C 43 was found to be considerably mor active than novobiocin, lincomycin, oleandomycin, and erythromycin in tests against *S. pyogenes* and *D. pneumoniae*. Interestingly, i the case of BL-C 43, novobiocin, and erythromycin, there seemed to be little if any advantag in treating four times rather than two. Howeve there was some indication that lincomycin an oleandomycin were more effective when fou doses were administered.

The infection caused by *P. multocida,* the on gram-negative species tested, responded ver well to BL-C 43 therapy, but was quite refractory to treatment with the other antibiotics.

The concentrations of BL-C 43, sodium novobiocin, oleandomycin phosphate, erythromycin ethylsuccinate, and lincomycin hydrochloride in blood were determined at various times afte each was administered as a single 25 mg/kg intramuscular (im) dose to each of eight mice Results of this absorption study are shown i Fig. 1.

It is readily apparent that the peak concentra-

Table 7. *In vivo antibacterial activity of BL-C 43 and several other antibiotics*

Challenge orgamism	No. of treatments	BL-C 43	Novobiocin (Na)	Lincomycin (HCl)	Oleando-mycin-triacetyl	Erythro-mycin estolate
Staphylococcus aureus A9537	2	8[a]	26	76	66	124
(non-penicillinase producer)	4	4	24	108	88	80
S. aureus A9497						
(non-penicillinase producer)	2	10	88	140	92	320
S. aureus A9606						
(penicillinase producer)	2	10	38	54	22	230
S. aureus A9631						
(penicillinase producer)	2	40	120	104	114	260
Streptococcus pyogenes A9604	2	196	>500	1,000	560	280
	4	140	–	140	176	216
Diplococcus pneumoniae A9585	2	180	800	>1,000	>1,000	580
	4	160	600	880	680	376
Pasteurella multocida A20139	4	92	560	>1,000	1,000	800

[a] Total dose (milligrams per kilogram) required to protect 50% of the infected mice.

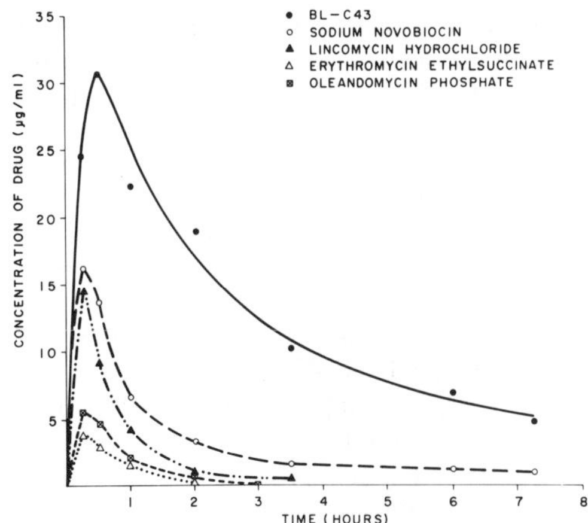

Fig. 1. *Concentrations of BL-C 43 and several other drugs in the blood of mice (eight mice/compound) after intramuscular administration of a 25 mg/kg dose.*

tion of BL-C 43 in blood after im administration was markedly higher than that obtained with any of the other antibiotics. Novobiocin and lincomycin peaked at about 15 µg/ml (one-half the peak value for BL-C 43), whereas the highest concentrations attained with oleandomycin and erythromycin were in the order of 5 µg/ml.

BL-C 43 was demonstrable in the blood for a relatively long time; 5 µg/ml was still present at 7.5 hr postinjection. Detectable amounts of novobiocin also persisted for at least 7.5 hr.

Impressive concentrations of BL-C were also found in the blood after oral administration of a 25 mg/kg dose. Concentrations of this compound, sodium novobiocin, lincomycin hydrochloride, erythromycin estolate, and triacetyloleandomycin in blood are shown in Fig. 2.

BL-C 43 peaked at 1 hr postadministration, with a concentration in excess of 11 µg/ml being attained. The antibiotic tended to persist in the blood, and a 3 µg/ml concentration was still present at 12 hr postadministration. Novobiocin also peaked at a high level (about 9 µg/ml) and persisted for at least 9 hr. Of the remaining antibiotics, the highest peak occurred with triacetyloleandomycin (1.3 µg/ml). This compound could not be detected at 2 hr, and erythromycin and lincomycin were not found in the 6-hr samples.

Figure 3 shows the concentrations obtained in blood when a wide range of dosages of BL-C 43 were administered as single oral doses to mice. As far as peak concentrations are concerned, a generally linear response occurred with doses of 50 mg or less per kg; i.e., for each twofold increase in dose, there was an approximate doubling of the peak concentration. However, at the highest doses studied, 100 and 200 mg/kg, the peak concentrations in blood tended to be disproportionately high. Furthermore, the time of appearance of the peak concentrations was considerably delayed for these doses. The remarkable extent of the decrease in BL-C 43 disappearance rate that occurs after administration of 100 and 200 mg/kg doses can best be appreciated by noting the differences in the concentrations in blood at 1 and 6 hr post-

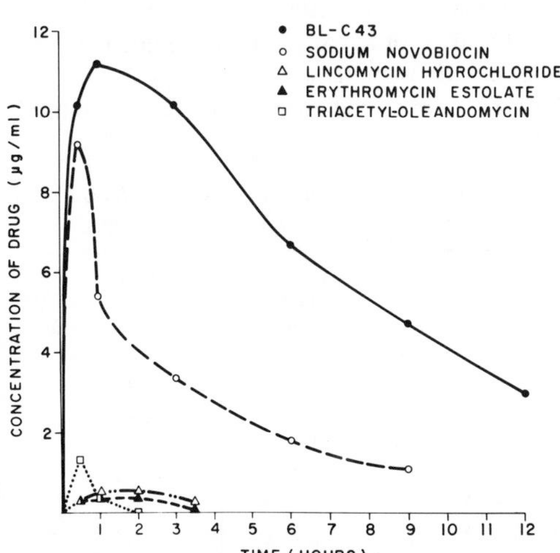

Fig. 2. *Concentrations of BL-C 43 and several other drugs in the blood of mice (eight mice/compound) after oral administration of a 25 mg/kg dose.*

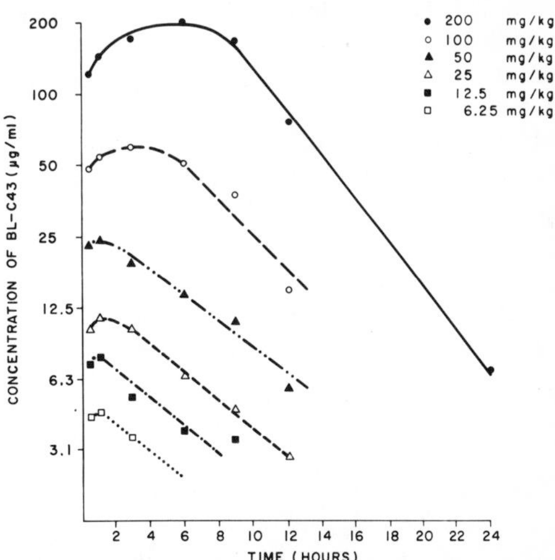

Fig. 3. *Concentrations of BL-C 43 in the blood of mice (eight mice/dose) after oral administration of various doses.*

injection. At doses of 50 mg or less per kg, the concentrations in blood at 6 hr were about 40 to 60% of those measured at 1 hr. With the 100 and 200 mg/kg doses, the concentrations at 6 hr were, respectively, 94 and 128% of the 1-hr concentrations. Results obtained at the higher doses could stem from saturation of the mechanism by which BL-C 43 is eliminated or inactivated, or both. However, it is more likely that the disproportionately high levels occur as a consequence of entero-hepatic recycling. In the latter case, blood concentrations would not decline if the absorption rate approximated the excretion rate. When BL-C 43 was administered im, a prolongation of the presence of the antibiotic in the blood, similar to that achieved with the 100 mg/kg oral dose, became apparent as the dosage level reached 40 to 60 mg/kg.

The BL-C 43 concentrations in the blood after intravenous (iv) administration of a 10 mg/kg dose are shown in Fig. 4. In contrast to most drugs, with which immediate peaks are seen, BL-C 43 did not reach its maximal level until 15 to 20 min postadministration. A significant concentration was still present in blood at 4 hr postinjection. The possibility that the results obtained were merely an artifact induced by the sampling technique (bleeding from orbital sinuses) was eliminated when similar findings were obtained in iv-dosed animals bled from the tail vein or by cardiac puncture. The unusual findings noted in this study can best be explained by the hypothesis that some of the antibiotic is being reabsorbed from the intestine after biliary excretion.

In an effort to throw additional light on the mechanism by which this drug is excreted, a study to determine antibiotic concentrations in tissue as a function of time after iv administration of a 20 mg/kg dose was undertaken. Table 8 shows the concentration and percentage recovery of BL-C 43 in urine samples collected up to 4.5 hr after dosing.

It is clear from these results that significant excretion of BL-C 43 does not occur via the kidney. There is no concentrating effect by this organ since, as can be seen in Fig. 5, at this dose (20 mg/kg) the peak concentration in blood was higher than the maximal concentration found in urine. Although BL-C 43 was detectable in the blood as early as 1 min postinjection, the peak concentration (about 18 μg/ml) did not occur until 15 to 20 min after dosing. Thus, these results are very similar to those previously found (Fig. 4) with a 10 mg/kg iv dose.

Also shown in Fig. 5 are concentrations of BL-C 43 found in various tissues and organs of mice receiving the 20 mg/kg iv dose. The antibiotic was detected very quickly in the heart, lung, and kidney, but was not concentrated by any of them. In contrast, the liver tended to concentrate BL-C 43 rapidly, with a peak level occurring at about 10 min postadministration. Amounts of antibiotic found in the gall bladder during the first 5 min were not significant. However, after this time, extremely high concentrations were present. The small intestine (and its contents) was also antibiotic-free for the first 5 min but then acquired measurable amounts of the drug concurrently with the appearance of antibiotic in the bile. Antibiotic was not present initially in the large intestine but could be found in detectable quantities by 10 to 15 min postadministration. All results obtained in this study are consistent with the hypothesis that BL-C 43 is excreted principally via the biliary route.

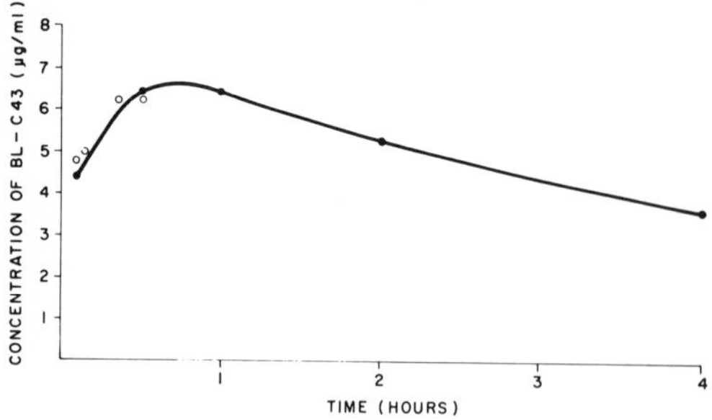

Fig. 4. *Concentrations of BL-C 43 in the blood of mice after intravenous administration of a 10 mg/kg dose. Open and closed sumbols represent average values of separate groups of animals (eight mice/group).*

Table 8. *Urinary excretion of BL-C 43 after intravenous administration of a 20 mg/kg dose to mice*

Sampling interval (hr)	BL-C 43 concn (μg/ml)	Percentage of administered drug recovered
0–1	9.1	.11
1–1.5	7.8	.17
1.5–2	3.4	.08
2–2.5	2.7	.09
2.5–3	2.7	.03
3–3.5	1.7	.05
3.5–4	2.0	.04
4–4.5	<1.5	—
Total		.57

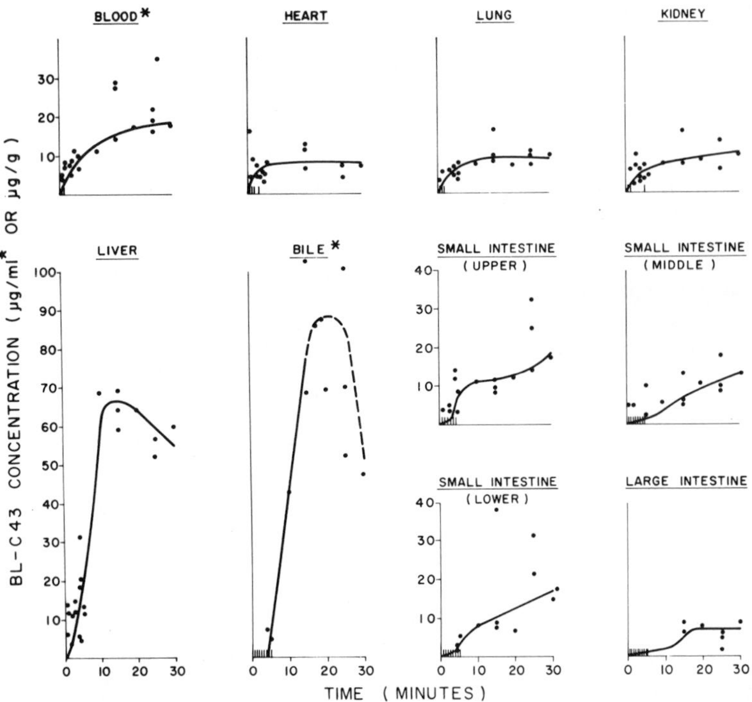

Fig. 5. *Distribution of BL-C 43 in the tissues of the mouse after intravenous administration of a 20 mg/kg dose. Antibiotic concentrations are in micrograms per milliliter for blood and bile specimens, and in micrograms per gram for all others.*

DISCUSSION

BL-C 43 was found to possess a moderately broad spectrum of antibacterial activity. A concentration of 1 µg or less per ml inhibited almost all staphylococcal strains evaluated, and the MIC was 4 µg or less per ml for all strains of *S. pyogenes, D. pneumoniae, H. influenzae,* and *N. gonorrhoeae* tested. Its antibacterial action was not appreciably affected by inoculum size and it was bactericidal at concentrations only slightly higher than the MIC. Despite the fact that the in vitro activity of BL-C 43 was only equivalent to or in some instances inferior to that of novobiocin, erythromycin, lincomycin, and oleandomycin, it was significantly more effective than these antibiotics in orally treated experimental infections of mice produced by strains of *S. aureus, S. pyogenes, D. pneumoniae,* and *P. multocida.* A possible explanation for this phenomenon was brought to light when pharmacological properties of BL-C 43 were examined. Peak concentrations in the blood of mice after im or oral administration of the new antibiotic were considerably higher than those found with erythromycin, oleandomycin, and lincomycin. Peak concentrations were also moderately higher than those obtained with novobiocin. In addition, BL-C 43 was maintained in the blood stream for a much longer time than the other antibiotics, although novobiocin also tended to persist for fairly long periods. Thus, the superior therapeutic effectiveness of BL-C 43 in mouse infections (relative to erythromycin, lincomycin, and oleandomycin) is probably due to its high and persistent concentrations in the blood of this species. Novobiocin, although it also gave fairly high and prolonged concentrations in blood, was considerably less effective in vivo than BL-C 43. This difference in activity can probably be attributed to the fact that the susceptibility of novobiocin to serum protein binding is much greater than that of BL-C 43. This premise holds true, of course, only if the same antibiotic binding relationship exists for mouse serum as is found for human serum, in which novobiocin is 96 to 98% bound and BL-C 43 is 76 to 79% bound.

There is strong circumstantial evidence that the primary route of elimination of BL-C 43 is via biliary excretion. Less than 1% of a dose administered iv was recovered in the urine, and there is no evidence that kidney, heart, or lung tissues concentrate the drug. The antibiotic appears to be accumulated by the liver, concentrated in bile, and then released into the small intestine where it is probably reabsorbed to a considerable extent. If the administered dose is sufficiently high, the absorption rate may approach the excretion rate.

ACKNOWLEDGMENTS

We thank Grace E. Wright, Robert Buck, Kathleen Furness, Richard Goodhines, Thomas Ingram, and Linda Ranieri for capable technical assistance.

LITERATURE CITED

1. Cron, M. J., J. C. Godfrey, I. R. Hooper, J. G. Keil, D. E. Nettleton, K. E. Price, and H. Schmitz. 1970. Studies on semisynthetic antibiotics derived from coumermycin. Abstr. 6th Int. Congr. Chemother., 1969, p. 494.

2. Keil, J. G., I. R. Hooper, R. H. Schreiber, C. L. Swanson, and J. C. Godfrey, 1970. Preparation of semisynthetic coumermycin A_1 derivatives. IV. Aliphatic acyl and related derivatives of 3-amino-4-hydroxy-8-methyl-7-[3-*O*-(5-methyl-2-pyrrolylcarbonyl)noviosyloxy] coumarin. Antimicrob. Agents Chemother.–1969, p. 200–208.

3. Kirshbaum, A., and B. Arret. 1967. Outline of details for official microbiological assays of antibiotics. J. Pharm. Sci. **56:**511–515.

4. Price, K. E., J. A. Bach, D. R. Chisholm, M. Misiek, and A. Gourevitch. 1969. Preliminary microbiological and pharmacological evaluation of 6-(R-α-amino-3-thienylacetamido) penicillanic acid (BL-P 875). J. Antibiot. (Tokyo) **22:**1–11.

4*a*. Price, K. E., D. R. Chisholm, J. C. Godfrey, M. Misiek, and A. Gourevitch. 1970. Semisynthetic coumermycins: structure-activity relationships. Appl. Microbiol. **19:**14–26.

5. Scholtan, W., and J. Schmid. 1962. Die Bindung der Penicilline and die Eiweisskorper des Serums und des Gewebes. Arzneimittel-Forschung **12:**741–750.

6. Steers, E., E. L. Foltz, and B. S. Graves. 1959. An inocula replicating apparatus for routine testing of bacterial susceptibility to antibiotics. Antibiot. Chemother. **9:**307–311.

Antimicrobial Agents and Chemotherapy—1969

Printed in USA

Preparation of Semisynthetic Kasugamycin Derivatives

I. Aliphatic Amidino Derivatives of Kasuganobiosamine

M. J. CRON, R. E. SMITH, I. R. HOOPER, J. G. KEIL, E. A. RAGAN, R. H. SCHREIBER, G. SCHWAB, and J. C. GODFREY

Department of Biochemical Research, Bristol Laboratories, Division of Bristol-Myers Co., Syracuse, New York 13201

Kasugamycin is an antibiotic with interesting gram-negative activity, but one with limited use because of poor oral absorption and potential toxicity. This report discloses the preparation of a number of aliphatic amidino analogues wherein the oxalamidino group is replaced through the following sequence of reactions. The 2-amine group of the kasugamine moiety was protected by formation of the dimedone derivative, and subsequent hydrolysis by aqueous alkali removed the oxalamidine group and left the key kasuganobiosamine derivative in which the 4-amine group is free and the 2-amine group is still blocked. New amidino groups were introduced at the 4-position by reaction of this intermediate with a number of aliphatic imido esters prepared from the corresponding aliphatic nitriles or amides. Removal of the dimedone group was accomplished by treatment with bromine water. Some of the resultant compounds show enhanced biological properties.

The discovery and chemistry of kasugamycin (Fig. 1), first reported in 1965 by Umezawa and co-workers, resulted from a screening program designed to find effective antibiotic control agents for the serious rice blast disease caused by *Piricularia oryzae.* The structure was established both by chemical methods and by X-ray crystallographic analysis as 5-(2-amino-2,3,4,6-tetradeoxy-4-oxalamidino-α-D-arabinohexopyranosyl)-(1R:2S:3S:4R:5R:6R)-inositol (7, 9). Large quantities are now being produced for agricultural purposes.

Kasugamycin was subsequently shown to be an antibiotic with gram-negative activity, effective in the treatment of urinary-tract infections and especially useful against *Pseudomonas* organisms. However, it was shown to produce severe kidney damage in chronic toxicity studies. In addition, it possesses little or no oral activity. Because of its unique oxalamidine group and the ease with which this group could be removed, and because the toxicity of kasugamycin could be related to the potentially available oxalic acid, kasugamycin appeared to be a promising candidate for molecular modifications. A logical approach appeared to be one in which the relatively stable kasugamine-inositol portion of the molecule would be retained with the introduction of a new series of amidine analogues on the 4-amine group of the kasugamine. Such a series would remove the possibility of in vivo formation of oxalic acid and might be expected to change both the antibacterial spectrum and the toxicity level. The kasuganobiosamine dimedone derivative (3) was expected to be a versatile intermediate for the preparation of a series of new compounds based upon its available free amine group. The procedure followed is indicated in Fig. 2.

MATERIALS AND METHODS

Kasugamycin was prepared by the fermentation of *Streptomyces kasugaensis* as described by Umezawa et

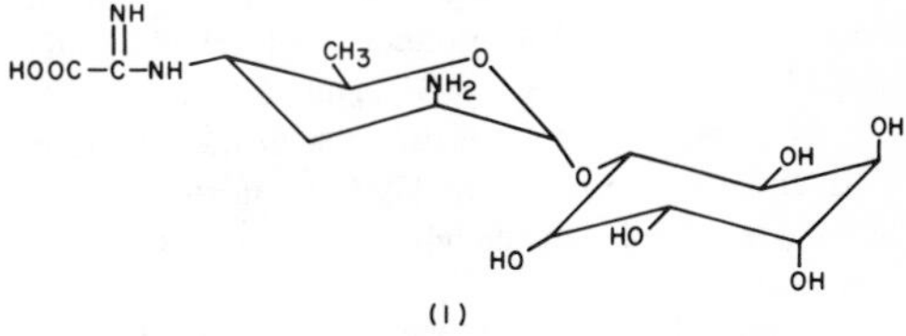

Fig. 1. *Kasugamycin.*

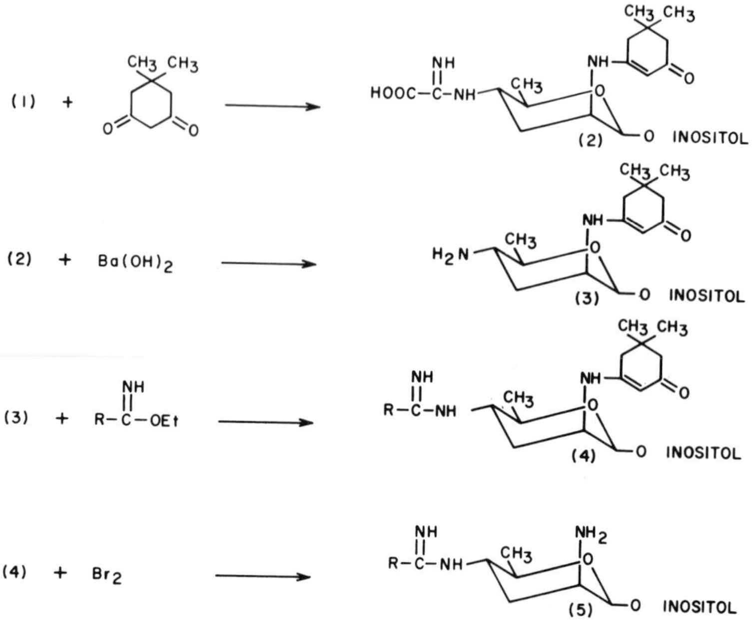

Fig. 2. *Preparation of amidino analogues of kasugamycin. R = members of aliphatic series shown in Table 1.*

al. (9). It was isolated and purified by means of Dowex 50 4X (H^+) columns and crystallization procedures.

The imido esters were prepared according to the method of Pinner (4) by use of the appropriate nitrile with alcohol and dry HCl. Cyanogen was used for the preparation of diethyloxalimidate dihydrochloride with ethyl alcohol and dry HCl, and in this case tetrahydrofuran was used as solvent. An exception to the Pinner method was the preparation of ethyl formimidate hydrochloride, which was prepared from formamide and ethyl chloroformate according to the procedure of Suydam et al. (8).

Dimedone derivative of kasugamycin, 2. A solution of 150 g (0.34 mole) of kasugamycin hydrochloride was dissolved in 2 liters of water, and the *p*H was adjusted to 8.0 by addition of 10% NaOH solution. The solution was diluted with 1 liter of methanol and to it was then added 50 g (0.36 mole) of dimedone (5,5-dimethyl-1,3-cyclohexanedione) dissolved in 400 ml of methanol. The solution was maintained at reflux temperature for 10 hr with stirring and was then cooled. A 147-g yield of crystalline product gradually precipitated. This material was dissolved in warm water at *p*H 1.0 and treated with activated charcoal; the *p*H was adjusted to 2.0, and the material was cooled. The product yielded had a satisfactory elemental analysis, infrared and nuclear magnetic resonance (NMR) spectra consistent with the structure, and a melting point of 226 to 229 C. In most cases, this product was carried immediately into the next step with no purification.

Dimedone derivative of kasuganobiosamine, 3 A 140-g portion of the kasugamycin dimedone derivative was dissolved in 2.8 liters of saturated barium hydroxide solution and heated at reflux for 10 hr. After cooling, the precipitated barium oxalate was recovered by filtration and air-dried. The yield was 58 g, 92% of theory. The *p*H of the filtrate was adjusted to 7.0 with 50% H_2SO_4, and the insoluble $BaSO_4$ was removed by filtration. The *p*H was then adjusted to 11.5 with 10% NaOH, and the solution was concentrated in vacuo to dryness. Addition of several portions of absolute ethyl alcohol, followed in each case by distillation in vacuo, helped remove the last traces of water. The residue was dissolved in approximately 700 ml of methanol, heated to boiling, and then treated with Darco G60. The Darco was removed by filtration and washed with methanol. The total methanol volume was about 800 ml. The solution was placed in a 3-liter Erlenmeyer flask, heated to boiling, and, with stirring, 1,500 ml of boiling absolute ethyl alcohol was added to it. As the solution cooled with continued stirring, 500 ml of acetone and then about 250 ml of ether were slowly added. It was chilled for 10 hr. The crystalline product was recovered by filtering, washing with ethyl alcohol and acetone, air-drying, and then drying in a vacuum oven at 65 C for 4 hr. A 61-g yield was obtained, 45% of theory.

Recrystallization from ethyl alcohol-acetone yielded a product with satisfactory elemental analysis for $C_{20}H_{34}O_8N_2 \cdot CH_3COCH_3$ which melted with decomposition between 220 and 235 C, showed a sharp peak with absorptivity of 63.2 at 289 nm, and showed a specific rotation, $[\alpha]_{589}^{25}$ 24.2° (*c*, 1.0, water). The infrared (in KBr disc) and NMR spectra are shown in Fig. 3.

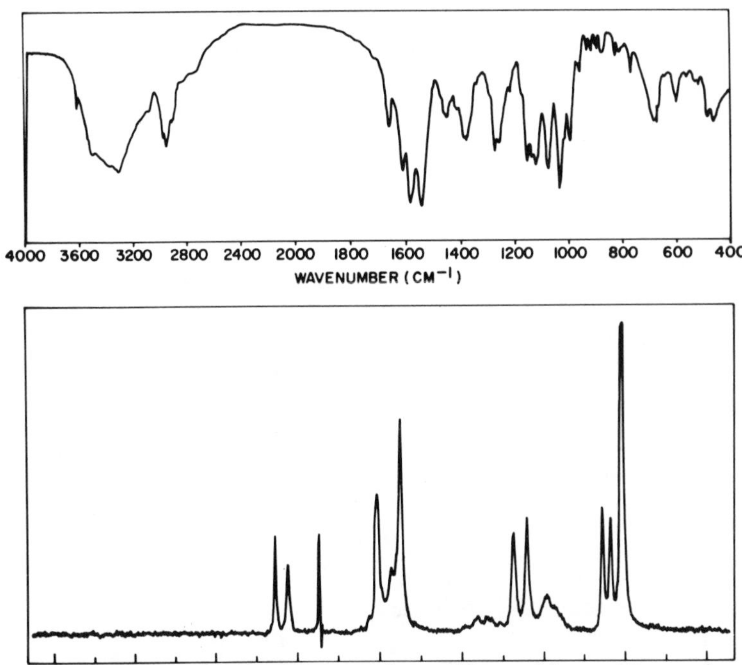

Fig. 3. *Spectra of dimedone derivative of kasuganobiosamine,* 3. *NMR in D_2O solution of sample lyophilized in D_2O.*

Reaction of the kasuganobiosamine derivative with imido esters. A typical preparation for the derivatives listed in Table 1 would be that for the preparation of the acetamidino analogue as follows (Fig. 2, R = CH_3). A 10-g portion of the kasuganobiosamine dimedone derivative (23 mmoles) was added to 175 ml of refluxing methanol, and the *p*H was adjusted to 7.0 to 7.5 with methanolic HCl. The solution was refluxed for a 48-hr period, and during this time a 6 molar excess of the ethyl acetimidate hydrochloride was added in 6 to 10 small portions. After each addition, methanolic sodium methoxide solution was added until a *p*H meter reading of 7.0 to 7.5 was obtained. The reaction mixture was then cooled, methanolic HCl was added until a *p*H reading of 5.5 was obtained, and the solution was concentrated to a volume of 70 ml. The insoluble NaCl was removed by filtration, the filtrate was then concentrated to dryness, and the crude product was recovered (**4**). The dimedone blocking group was next removed without purifying the intermediate by dissolving the residue in 50 ml of water and adding saturated bromine water until a persistent yellow color of bromine was obtained. The insoluble dimedone dibromide formed was removed by filtering, and the filtrate was taken to dryness by distillation in vacuo. Traces of water were removed by adding and distilling off small quantities of *n*-butyl alcohol. The residue was dissolved in 20 ml of methanol, and the product was precipitated by the addition of 300 ml of acetone. A yield of 9.0 g was obtained. The product was purified by adding 8.5 g in 20 ml of water to the top of a Dowex 50 4X (H^+) 100 to 200 mesh column (2.5 by 48 cm), washing the column with water, and then developing with 1 N HCl. The acid eluate was collected in 20- to 25-ml fractions. Fractions numbered 15 to 60 were combined, adjusted to *p*H 4.0 by the addition of NaOH solution, and then concentrated in vacuo to dryness. The residue was then leached with methanol and the solution was again taken to dryness. During this concentration, precipitated sodium chloride was removed by filtering two times. The residue was then dissolved in 20 ml of methanol and precipitated by the addition of 300 ml of acetone and 200 ml of ether. The precipitated product was recovered by filtration, washed with ether, and dried. A yield of 3.6 g was obtained (**5** R = CH_3) which proved to be about 75% pure.

The product was crystallized as the monohydrochloride by dissolving in water, adjusting the *p*H to 8.5 to 9.2 with Dowex 1-4X, and then concentrating the solution to a syrup in vacuo. The residue was dissolved in methanol, and the solution was then diluted with ethyl alcohol. Further concentration produced a white crystalline precipitate. With initial *p*H adjustment to 2.0 with dilute hydrochloric acid, the product was recovered as the dihydrochloride. To obtain samples with satisfactory elemental analyses, it was usually necessary to recrystallize several times.

The acetamidino compound described here is the

only one obtained in the crystalline form. The others have been obtained in the form of white amorphous powders.

For those derivatives larger than $R = CH_3$, it was found that elution from the Dowex 50 chromatographic column was very slow with HCl. In these cases, the column was first washed with water, then with HCl, and then developed with 0.1 N NaOH solution. The active product was eluted from the column in a narrow band just before the alkaline breakthrough.

The course of this reaction series could most easily be followed by thin-layer chromatography. A chromatogram of the intermediates in the preparation of a representative member of the series was made by use of Avicel plates; an *n*-propanol-pyridine-water-acetic acid (15:10:12:3) solvent mixture was used for developing the plates, and ninhydrin spray was used as indicator (Fig. 4A). A slower developing but better resolving system (Fig. 4B) was found when silica gel plates were developed in methyl acetate-2-propanol-NH_4OH (45:105:60). The products obtained in each step of the reaction are different enough in R_F and appearance to indicate the consumption of the starting material and the formation of the desired product.

RESULTS AND DISCUSSION

Although there is considerable literature (4–6) available on the preparation of amidine compounds, the desired amidination reaction in this case was found to be difficult to carry out. For example, Hunter and co-workers (3) reported on the reaction in aqueous solution of proteins and related small molecules with imido esters to form amidine derivatives. It was our experience that none of the desired product could be prepared in an aqueous system. Unsuccessful attempts were made to carry out the amidination reaction in a variety of solvents other than refluxing methanol. No reaction was observed when benzene, tetrahydrofuran, dimethylsulfoxide, or pyridine was used. The use of these solvents with higher temperatures, ranging up to 100 C, resulted in extensive decomposition with blackening of the reaction mixtures. At room temperature or lower, no reaction seemed to take place. Any significant deviation from the procedure described in Materials and Methods resulted in lower yields or complete loss of the final active product.

The *p*H or total acidity of the nonaqueous methanol solution used also appeared to be important. At *p*H meter readings below 6 or above 9, little or no product could be isolated. Hand and Jencks (2) discussed the mechanism of

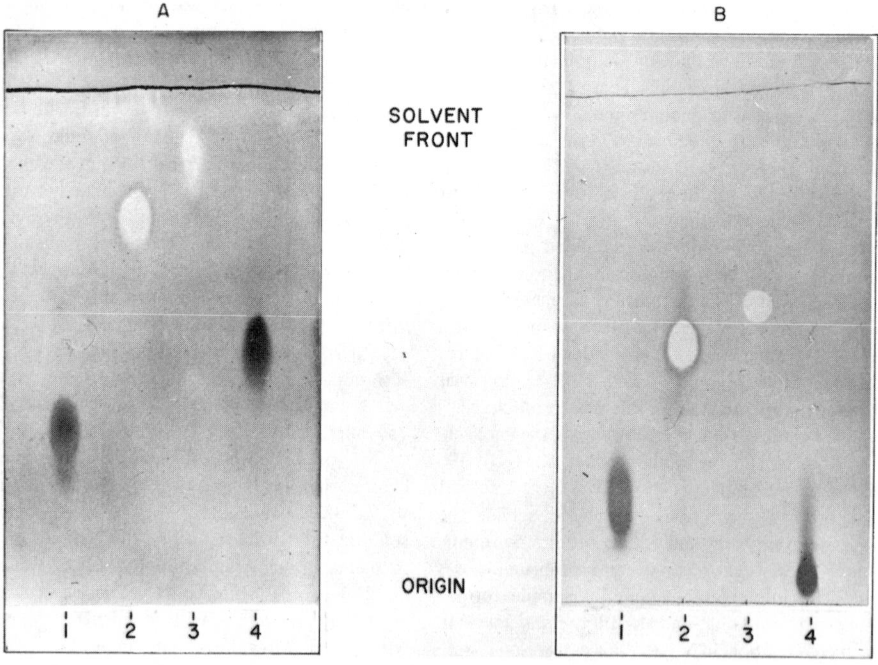

Fig. 4. *Comparative chromatography of the intermediates in the reaction sequence. (1) Kasugamycin,* 1. *(2) Kasuganobiosamine dimedone derivative,* 3. *(3) Dimedone derivative of acetamidino analogue,* 4. *(4) Acetamidino analogue of kasugamycin.* 5.

reaction and the sharp *p*H dependence of the reaction of imido esters with amines. In our preparations, it was apparent that the imido ester reagents were unstable in the reaction medium used. This was evidenced by the fact that upon the addition of a fresh increment of imido ester the reaction would appear to continue for a matter of 3 to 4 hr and then cease. This would indicate the need for a fresh increment of the reagent after which the reaction would continue. Usually the addition of about six equivalents would drive the reaction to completion.

As described by Halpern and James (1), the dimedone blocking group could be removed either by the addition of HNO_2 with the formation of the dimedone oxime or by the addition of bromine with the formation of dibromodimedone. However, in the case of the former, it was found that other components in the complex reaction mixture were also reacting with the HNO_2, and thus it was not possible to add the stoichiometric amount calculated and find the removal of the dimedone complete. On the other hand, use of excess reagent resulted in loss of the desired end product. Excess bromine, however, apparently had no effect on the desired final product, and thus large excesses were allowable and the removal of the blocking group could be pushed to completion with ease.

The feasibility of the above route was first established by allowing the kasuganobiosamine dimedone intermediate to react with diethyl oxalimidate, removing the dimedone block and then hydrolyzing the ethyl amidine moiety to yield fully active crystalline kasugamycin with infrared and NMR spectra identical to those of the natural product. A 16% yield of the expected activity was obtained.

The derivatives prepared are listed in Table 1. With the exception of the acetamidine analogue, they have not been obtained in crystalline form, and thus have been difficult to purify. The infrared and NMR spectra of each are consistent with the proposed structures, and thin-layer chromatograms indicate only one component for each. The observed molecular rotation values should be one measure of the purity. The molecular rotation of kasugamycin monohydrochloride is 53,000. Because of its dipolar ion structure, both basic groups are charged. The acetamidine (R = CH_3-) and the butyramidine [R = $CH_3(CH_2)_2$-) dihydrochlorides, again with

Table 1. *Characterization of amidino analogues of kasugamycin*

R	Melting point (C)[a]	$[M]_{589}^{25}$	Relative activity[b]
–COOH(kasugamycin) . .	236–239	53,000	1.0
–H	165–195	42,000	0.5
$-CH_3$	197–198	53,000	0.25
$-CH_2CH_3$	155–180	44,400	2.0
$-CH_2CH_2CH_3$	196–215	52,000	0.5
$-CH(CH_2)_2$	165–175	39,700	>30
$-(CH_2)_3CH_3$	185–190	44,400	>30
$-CH_2CH(CH_3)_2$	195–200	38,900	>35
$-(CH_2)_4CH_3$	145–150	43,300	>30
$-(CH_2)_2CH(CH_3)_2$	196–200	45,000	15

[a] Decomposition.

[b] Minimal inhibitory concentration of compound/minimal inhibitory concentration of kasugamycin.

both basic groups charged, are pure by all standards, including elemental analysis, and the molecular rotation for each of these compounds is also +52,000 to +53,000. It is reasonable to believe, therefore, that for other members of this series the same value will hold. The lower values reported for the remaining members would thus indicate them to be in the order of 75 to 85% pure.

Although the microbiological evaluation of these compounds is the subject of a separate paper, the in vitro efficacy against *Pseudomonas* organisms as compared with kasugamycin is shown in the last column of Table 1. The values express the ratio of the minimal inhibitory concentration of the compound to that of kasugamycin. Under the conditions used, kasugamycin exhibits a minimal inhibitory concentration of 32 μg/ml. It can be seen that only three members of this series are more active than kasugamyçin and that as the substituted groups become larger this activity disappears.

ACKNOWLEDGMENTS

We are indebted to the following people for valuable technical assistance: R. M. Downing and C. M. Kalinowski, for microanalytical data, and D. F. Whitehead and A. L. Vulcano for spectral data and interpretation. We are also indebted to R. U. Lemieux for many helpful discussions.

LITERATURE CITED

1. Halpern, B., and L. B. James. 1964. Dimedone (5,5-dimethyl-1,3-cyclohexane-1,3-dione) as a protecting agent for amine groups in peptide synthesis. Aust. J. Chem. **17**:1282–1287.
2. Hand, E. S., and W. P. Jencks. 1962. Mechanism of the reaction of imido esters with amines. J. Amer. Chem. Soc. **84**:3505–3514.
3. Hunter, M. J., and M. L. Ludwig. 1962. The reaction of imido

esters with proteins and related small molecules. J. Amer. Chem. Soc. **84**:3491–3504.

4. Rodd, E. H. (ed.) 1965. Rodd's chemistry of carbon compounds. Elsevier Publishing Co., vol. 1, part C, p. 183–200.
5. Roger, R., and D. G. Neilson. 1961. The chemistry of imidates. Chem. Rev. **61**:179–211.
6. Shriner, R. L., and F. W. Neumann. 1944. The chemistry of the amidines. Chem. Res. **35**:351–425.
7. Suhara, Y., K. Maeda, H. Umezawa, and M. Ohno. 1968. Kasugamycin in deoxy sugars. Advan. Chem. Ser. No. 74, p. 15–40.
8. Suydam, F. H., W. E. Greth, and N. R. Langerman. 1969. The synthesis of imidate hydrochlorides by reaction of ethyl chloroformate with amides and thionamides. J. Org. Chem. **34**:292–296.
9. Umezawa, H., M. Hamada, Y. Suhara, T. Hashimoto, T. Ikekawa, N. Tanaka, K. Maeda, Y. Okami, and T. Takeuchi. 1966. Kasugamycin, a new antibiotic. Antimicrob. Agents and Chemother.–1965, p. 753–757.

Antimicrobial Agents and Chemotherapy—1969

Preliminary Microbiological and Pharmacological Evaluation of a Semisynthetic Kasugamycin, BL-A 2

M. MISIEK, D. R. CHISHOLM, F. LEITNER, and K. E. PRICE

Research Division, Bristol Laboratories, Division of Bristol-Myers Co., Syracuse, New York 13201

Structure-activity relationships were examined for a series of semisynthetic kasugamycins which had a straight-chain, branched-chain, or halogen-containing alkyl group substituted for the carboxyl group in the iminoacetic acid moiety of kasugamycin. Several derivatives were found to be two- to fourfold more active than kasugamycin in vitro against certain gram-negative bacteria, including *Pseudomonas.* Additional in vitro and in vivo data are presented on one of these, BL-A 2, 5(2-amino-2,3,4,6-tetradeoxy-4-acetamidino-α-D-arabino-hexopyranosyl)-(1R:2S:3S:4R:5R:6R)inositol. This compound, at 63 μg/ml, inhibited most of the clinical strains of *Escherichia* (77%), *Klebsiella-Enterobacter* (90%), and *Pseudomonas* (96%) tested. High concentrations of BL-A 2 were found in mouse urine: the concentration was about 1,535 μg/ml in the sample collected 0 to 4 hr after intramuscular administration of a 100 mg/kg dose, and about 440 μg/ml in that collected 0 to 6 hr after oral administration of 500 mg/kg. Mice receiving a 100 mg/kg oral dose had average drug concentrations in the urine of about 79 and 34 μg/ml in samples collected from 0 to 6 and 6 to 24 hr, respectively. During the 24-hr collection period, 5.3% of the orally administered dose was recovered. BL-A 2 was found to be relatively nontoxic for mice; the acute intravenous LD_{50} and oral LD_{50} were 1,650 and >10,000 mg/kg, respectively. The data presented show that BL-A 2 is therapeutically effective against both systemic gram-negative infections of mice and urinary-tract infections of rats.

Kasugamycin, a weakly basic, water-soluble, aminoglycosidic antibiotic produced by *Streptomyces kasugaensis,* was discovered by Umezawa and associates (9) during their search for antifungal agents capable of preventing infection of young rice plants by the phytopathogenic fungus *Piricularia oryzae.* The antibiotic is of considerable interest because, in addition to its activity against rice blast, it inhibits growth of a number of gram-negative bacteria, including *Pseudomonas.* Furthermore, it is rapidly absorbed and is excreted in high concentration in the urine (3, 4, 8). Unfortunately, use of the antibiotic has been limited because of its tendency to be nephrotoxic. The present report is primarily concerned with the characterization of a less toxic, semisynthetic kasugamycin derivative, BL-A 2, 5(2-amino-2,3,4,6-tetradeoxy-4-acetamidino-α-D-arabino-hexopyranosyl)-(1R:2S:3S:4R:5R:6R)inositol (Fig. 1). Data presented show its spectrum of in vitro activity against a variety of bacteria, including a number of gram-negative clinical strains, the extent of its absorbability (estimated by determinations of its concentration in blood and urine), as well as its efficacy in experimental infections of rodents.

MATERIALS AND METHODS

Kasugamycin and the semisynthetic kasugamycins used in this study were hydrochlorides, and were synthesized by the Biochemistry Research Department of Bristol Laboratories (2). The minimal inhibitory concentration (MIC) of these kasugamycin derivatives was determined by the standard twofold broth-dilution technique. In most cases, Nutrient Broth (BBL) and an inoculum of 10^5 to 5×10^5 cells/ml were used. A 1:1 mixture of Nutrient Broth and Antibiotic Assay Broth (BBL) containing 5% human serum was used to grow *Diplococcus pneumoniae* and *Streptococcus pyogenes.* In tests designed to determine the susceptibility of clinical strains of gram-negative bacteria to kasugamycin

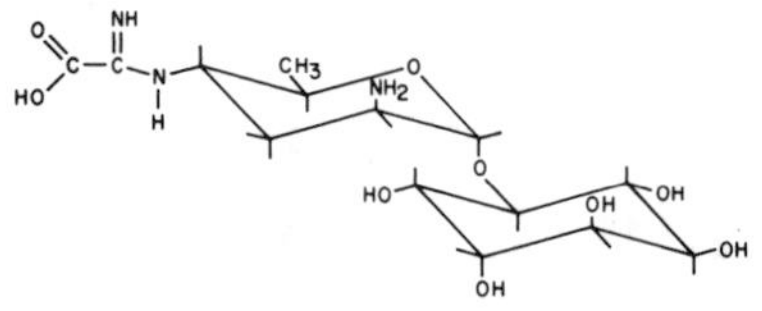

KASUGAMYCIN: 5(2-AMINO-2,3,4,6-TETRADEOXY-4-OXALAMIDINO-α-D-ARABINO-HEXOPYRANOSYL)-(1R: 2S: 3S: 4R: 5R: 6R)-INOSITOL.

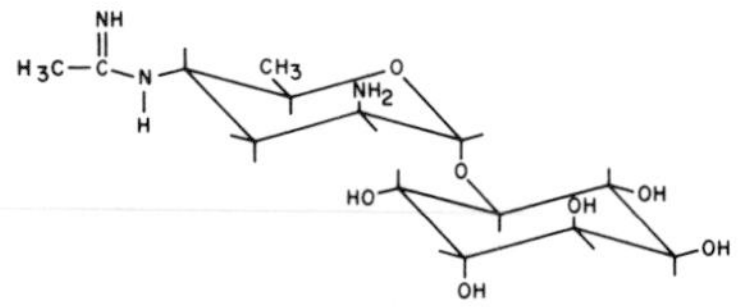

BL-A2: 5(2-AMINO-2,3,4,6-TETRADEOXY-4-ACETAMIDINO-α-D-ARABINO-HEXOPYRANOSYL)-(1R: 2S: 3S: 4R: 5R: 6R)-INOSITOL.

Fig. 1. *Chemical structures of kasugamycin and the semisynthetic kasugamycin BL-A 2. Nomenclature from Cahn et al. (1).*

and BL-A 2, the MIC was determined by a twofold agar-dilution method. In this procedure, antibiotics were incorporated into Nutrient Agar (Difco) by mixing 1 ml of drug solution with 19 ml of liquefied agar medium in a petri dish (100 × 15 mm). After the agar mixture had solidified, the surface was inoculated with 10^{-2} dilutions of overnight broth cultures by means of the Steers multiple inoculator apparatus (7). This instrument permitted the simultaneous inoculation of up to 32 different bacterial strains on a single dish. The end points (MIC) in both procedures were determined after overnight incubation at 37 C. These were accepted as the lowest concentrations at which grossly detectable growth did not occur.

The drug dosage producing 50% mortality (LD_{50}) in normal male Swiss-Webster mice was determined after intraperitoneal, intramuscular (im), and oral administration of kasugamycin and BL-A 2. Survivors on the 10th day after administration of a single dose were noted, and the LD_{50} was calculated (5). Subacute toxicity studies were conducted with Sprague-Dawley male rats by daily intraperitoneal administration of 200 mg/kg for 16 days. Four rats were used for each drug. Blood-urea nitrogen (BUN) determinations were made on the 1st, 5th, 10th, and 15th days. The kidneys of all animals were eventually examined for gross evidence of tissue damage.

Drug concentrations in the blood of male Swiss-Webster mice were determined at various times after administration of the antibiotics. Ten mice were used per dose level. The techniques used for dosing, bleeding, and assaying were identical to those previously described by Price et al. (6). A kasugamycin-susceptible isolate of *Serratia marcescens* ATCC 15365 was used as the assay organism.

The rate or urinary excretion of the hydrochlorides of kasugamycin and BL-A over a 24-hr period was determined after administration of the drug to fasted mice at 100 and 500 mg/kg orally, and 100 mg/kg intramuscularly. Urine samples were collected over dry ice at various intervals post-treatment. Samples from each time period were pooled and the pool was assayed against a standard prepared by spiking normal urine with known quantities of drug. Urine samples were assayed by the agar diffusion-cylinder plate method. In this procedure, Nutrient Agar at *p*H 8.5 seeded with a kasugamycin-susceptible isolate of *S. marcescens* ATCC 15365 was used. Urine volumes for each collection period were recorded, and the values were used to calculate total urinary excretion of the drugs.

Median curative doses of kasugamycin and BL-A 2 were determined for several experimental gram-negative systemic infections of mice. The mice were infected intraperitoneally with a number of bacterial cells sufficient to kill all nontreated control animals within 72 hr. Challenge doses of *Salmonella enteritidis* and *Pseudomonas aeruginosa* were given as suspensions in 5% mucin; *Klebsiella pneumoniae* was administered as an aqueous suspension. The antibiotics were administered at the time of challenge and 4 hr later, by the im route in the case of the *Salmonella* infection, and by both im and oral routes with the *Klebsiella* infection. For treatment of the *Pseudomonas* systemic infection, the antibiotics were administered subcutaneously at the time of challenge and at 2, 4, 6, 24, and 26 hr postinfection. Five mice were used at each dose level for the *Salmonella* infection, and 10 mice per dose level were used for the *Klebsiella* and *Pseudomonas* infections. At the termination of each experiment (5 days post-challenge), the CD_{50} (total dose in milligrams per kilogram required to cure 50% of infected mice) was estimated by means of a log-probit plot of dosage versus percentage survivors.

The relative effectiveness of kasugamycin and BL-A 2 was also determined in an experimental *P. aeruginosa* urinary-tract infection of Long-Evans rats. Animals averaging about 200 g in weight were infected by injecting 0.1 ml of a suspension containing 10^7 cells/ml into the surgically exposed right kidney. The antibiotics were administered subcutaneously for a total of 24 treatments at each of several dose levels (50, 25, and 12.5 mg/kg). Treatments were given at the time of challenge as well at 2, 4, and 6 hr postchallenge on the 1st day and at corresponding time intervals on 4 consecutive days. On the 6th and 7th days, treatments were reduced to two per day given 6 hr apart. Ten rats were used for each dose level. The rats were sacrificed on the 8th day of the experiment, at which time the bladder and kidneys were removed and examined. The bladder was cut open and deposited, along with any residual urine, in a tube containing 10 ml of sterile saline. After the kidneys were macerated by forcing them twice through the end of a 5-ml hypodermic syringe, all tissue for each pair of kidneys was deposited in 10 ml of sterile saline. After thorough mixing, 0.1-ml samples of the kidney suspension and bladder washings were plated on MacConkey Agar. The plates were incubated overnight at 37 C, and the *P. aeruginosa* colonies were counted to determine the number of viable bacterial cells present in the organs.

RESULTS AND DISCUSSION

In vitro studies. The in vitro antibacterial activity of kasugamycin was compared with that of several kasugamycin derivatives in which the carboxyl group in the iminoacetic acid moiety of kasugamycin was replaced by hydrogen, straight-chain, branched-chain, or halogen-containing alkyl groups (Table 1). In general, activity against gram-negative bacteria was enhanced and activity against gram-positive organisms was reduced when kasugamycin's carboxyl group was replaced with a hydrogen or methyl group. Of these two analogues, the methyl-substituted preparation, hereafter referred to as BL-A 2, was more active. BL-A 2 was about four times as active as kasugamycin against *Escherichia coli, K. pneumoniae, S. typhosa,* and *P. aeruginosa* strains. There was a significant decrease in activity against gram-negative bacteria as the length of the straight-chain alkyl group was increased from three to five carbons. Replacement of kasugamycin's carboxyl group with branched-chain radicals, such as isopropyl and isoamyl, resulted in a loss of activity against both gram-positive and gram-negative bacteria. The halogen-containing alkyl substituent, bromopropyl-, was less active than its nonhalogenated counterpart. None of the modifications resulted in greater anti-*Proteus* activity than that of kasugamycin.

Table 2 shows the cumulative percentage of clinical gram-negative bacterial strains susceptible to kasugamycin and BL-A 2. As suggested by the data in Table 1, BL-A 2 was more active in vitro than kasugamycin against many gram-negative bacteria. At a concentration of 63 μg/ml, BL-A 2 inhibited 77.4% of 62 *Escherichia* strains, 90.6% of 32 *Klebsiella-Enterobacter* strains, 96% of 48 *Pseudomonas* strains, and 85% of 40 *Salmonella-Shigella* strains. When the same concentration of kasugamycin was tested against these organisms, it inhibited only 11.3% of the *Escherichia* strains, 9.4% of the *Klebsiella-Enterobacter* strains, 41.7% of the *Pseudomonas* strains, and 50% of the *Salmonella-Shigella* strains. BL-A 2 was less active than kasugamycin against the 64 strains of *Proteus.* At 250 μg/ml, BL-A 2 inhibited only 25% of these strains, whereas all of them were inhibited by the same concentrations of kasu-

Table 1. *Relative in vitro antimicrobial activity of kasugamycin and several kasugamycin derivatives that contain various substituents in the iminoacetic acid moiety* [a]

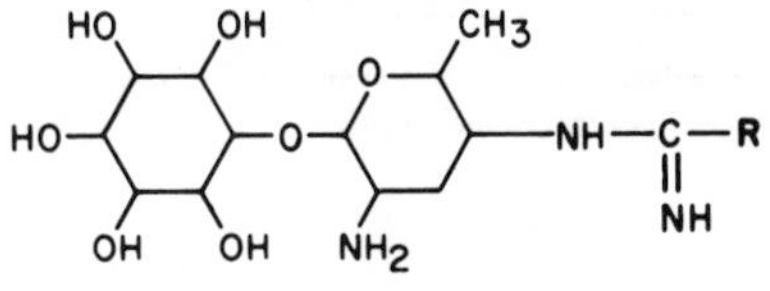

HO OH CH3 O HO— —O— —NH—C—R ‖ NH OH OH NH2

R	Minimal inhibitory concn (μg/ml) for							
	Diplococcus pneumoniae	*Streptococcus pyogenes*	*Staphylococcus aureus*	*Escherichia coli*	*Klebsiella pneumoniae*	*Proteus morganii*	*Salmonella typhosa*	*Pseudomonas aeruginosa*
–COOH (kasugamycin)	32	125	500	32	32	125	63	32
–H	250	1,000	1,000	16	16	125	63	16
$-CH_3$ (BL-A 2)	125	500	1,000	8	8	125	16	8
$-CH_2CH_2CH_3$	250	1,000	>1,000	63	32	500	63	16
$-CH(CH_3)_2$	>1,000	>1,000	>1,000	>1,000	>1,000	>1,000	>1,000	>1,000
$-CH_2CH_2CH_2Br$	500	1,000	1,000	125	125	500	250	63
$-(CH_2)_4CH_3$	500	1,000	>1,000	500	500	>1,000	500	1,000
$-CH_2CH_2CH(CH_3)_2$	>1,000	>1,000	>1,000	>1,000	>1,000	>1,000	>1,000	>1,000

[a] For all organisms, the inoculum was 10^5 to 5×10^5 cells per ml of Nutrient Broth (BBL). *D. pneumoniae* and *S. pyogenes* were tested in 5% human serum in a 1:1 mixture of Antibiotic Assay Broth (BBL) and Nutrient Broth (BBL). All other organisms were tested in Nutrient Broth.

gamycin. All six of the clinical strains of *S. marcescens* available for testing were inhibited by BL-A 2 at 32 μg/ml, whereas none was inhibited by kasugamycin at this concentration. Kasugamycin concentrations of 63 to 250 μg/ml were required to inhibit these strains.

In vivo studies. A study was made of the absorption of BL-A 2 in mice after im administration of single 25, 50, and 100 mg/kg doses and oral administration of single 250, 500, and 1,000 mg/kg doses. Average drug concentrations in the blood at various times after dosing are shown in Fig. 2.

It can be seen that peak concentrations of BL-A 2 in the blood were attained by both routes within 0.5 hr after administration. The antibiotic gave high concentrations when administered parenterally, but was less well absorbed from the gastrointestinal tract. At 15 min after im administration of BL-A 2 in doses of 100, 50, and 25 mg/kg, the concentrations were 46.1, 22.5, and 9.4 μg/ml, respectively. The concentrations in blood dropped rapidly, and the drug was practically undetectable (minimum assayable level = 1.2 μg/ml) by 1.5 hr postadministration.

Oral administration of BL-A 2 at 1,000 and 500 mg/kg gave peak concentrations in the blood at 0.5 hr of 31.8 and 19.9 μg/ml, respectively. Antibiotic concentrations in the blood

Table 2. *Susceptibility of clinical gram-negative bacterial strains to kasugamycin and BL-A 2*

Organism	Compound	Minimal inhibitory concn (μg/ml)[a]							
		4	8	16	32	63	125	250	>250
Escherichia coli (62 strains)	Kasugamycin	—	—	—	1.6[b]	11.3	98.4	100	—
	BL-A 2	1.6	3.2	—	14.5	77.4	100	—	—
Klebsiella-Enterobacter sp. (32 strains)	Kasugamycin	—	—	—	—	9.4	53	96	100
	BL-A 2	—	9.4	—	43.8	90.6	100	—	—
Proteus sp. (64 strains)	Kasugamycin	—	—	—	—	4.7	32.8	100	—
	BL-A 2	1.6	—	—	—	3.2	10.9	25	100
Pseudomonas aeruginosa (48 strains)	Kasugamycin	—	—	—	—	41.7	98	100	—
	BL-A 2	—	—	4.2	60.4	96	—	100	—
Salmonella-Shigella sp. (40 strains)	Kasugamycin	—	—	—	10	50	80	100	—
	BL-A 2	—	—	2.5	22.5	85	100	—	—
Serratia marcescens (6 strains)	Kasugamycin	—	—	—	—	16.7	83.3	100	—
	BL-A 2	—	—	33.3	100	—	—	—	—

[a] Determined by use of a Steers multiple replicator apparatus (7) and 10^{-2} dilutions of overnight broth cultures.
[b] Cumulative percentage of strains susceptible to each concentration.

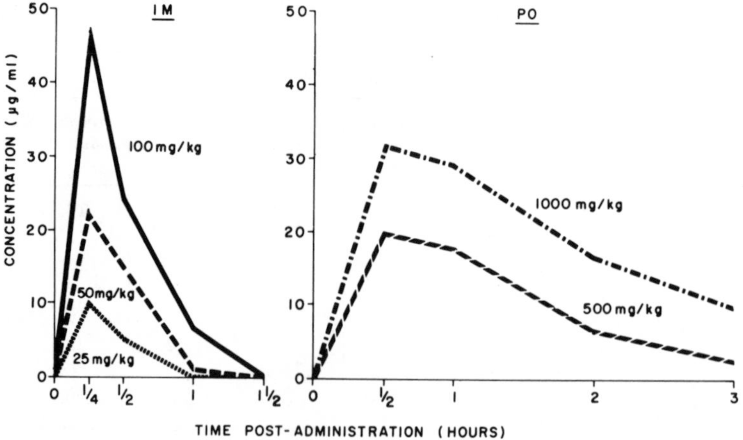

Fig. 2. *Average BL-A 2 concentrations in blood after intramuscular (IM) and oral (PO) administration. Eight mice per dose level were used for IM administration, and 16 mice per dose level were used for PO administration.*

after oral administration were more persistent than after im administration. Detectable amounts were still present at 3 hr after oral administration of 1,000 or 500 mg/kg. No detectable amounts of BL-A 2 were found in blood when a dose of 250 mg/kg was administered orally.

A comparative study was made of the relative extent to which kasugamycin and BL-A 2 are eliminated via the urinary tract of mice after their administration by im and oral routes. As with other aminoglycosidic antibiotics, concentrations found in the urine when the drugs were administered parenterally were higher than those obtained after oral administration.

Figure 3 shows the concentrations of kasugamycin and BL-A 2 in urine after im administration of 100 mg/kg doses to mice. Maximal concentrations of both drugs occurred within 4 hr postadministration. In pooled samples collected between 0 and 4 hr, the concentrations of kasugamycin and BL-A 2 were 1,734 and 1,535 μg/ml, respectively. The concentrations dropped rapidly to an average of 217 and 179 μg/ml, respectively, during the next 4-hr interval. Urine collected between 12 and 24 hr postadministration still contained 40 μg of kasugamycin and 36 μg of BL-A 2 per ml. Approximately 50% of the administered dose of kasugamycin and 64% of that of BL-A 2 were recovered in the urine during the 24-hr period after drug administration.

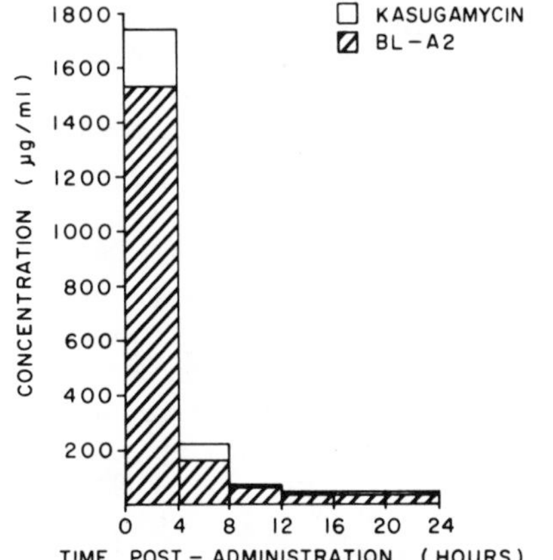

Fig. 3. *Concentrations of kasugamycin and BL-A 2 in the urine of mice after intramuscular administration of a 100 mg/kg dose. Ten mice were used for each antibiotic.*

When kasugamycin and BL-A 2 were administered orally to mice in doses of 100 and 500 mg/kg, maximal concentrations of both antibiotics occurred in the urine within 6 hr (Fig. 4). With the 500 mg/kg dose, the maximal concentrations of kasugamycin and BL-A 2 in the urine were 566 and 440 μg/ml, respectively, and decreased by 4 and 25%, respectively, during the next 6 hr. The concentrations of kasugamycin were higher than those of BL-A 2 at all sampling times. Urine samples collected between 12 and 24 hr postadministration from mice receiving 500 mg/kg contained 292 μg of kasugamycin and 190 μg of BL-A 2 per ml. With the 100 mg/kg dose, the kasugamycin concentration was 61 μg/ml and the BL-A 2 concentration was 32 μg/ml. Over a 24-hr collection period after the oral administration of 500 mg/kg, about 9.4% of the kasugamycin and 5.4% of the BL-A 2 were recovered in the urine. Recovery after a 100 mg/kg oral dose was 6.8 and 5.3%, respectively, for kasugamycin and BL-A 2.

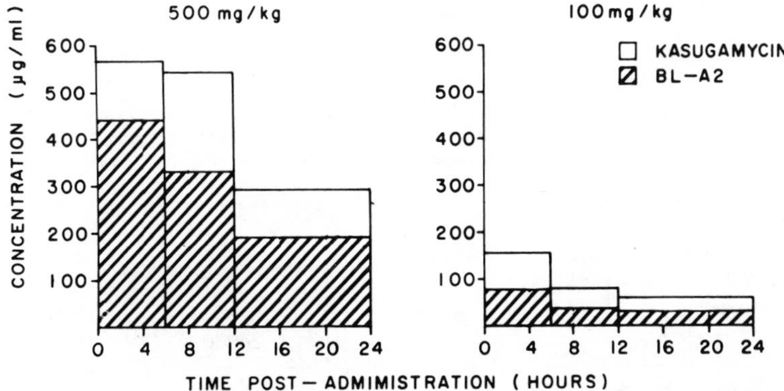

Fig. 4. *Concentrations of kasugamycin and BL-A 2 in the urine of mice after oral administration of 100 and 500 mg/kg doses. Ten mice were used for each dose level.*

The acute toxicity of kasugamycin and BL-A 2 in mice was determined after administration of the antibiotics by oral and parenteral routes. As can be seen in Table 3, both antibiotics possess acute toxicity of a very low order. Overall, kasugamycin appeared to be somewhat better tolerated than BL-A 2.

Kasugamycin and BL-A 2 were also compared in subacute toxicity studies in rats. Animals given kasugamycin by the intraperitoneal route in a daily dosage of 200 mg/kg showed toxic signs, such as decreased food intake, dehydration, and elevated BUN values within 5 days. During this same period, BL-A 2-treated rats appeared normal.

By the 9th day, one death had occurred among the kasugamycin-treated rats, and all remaining animals in this group displayed very high BUN levels and other symptoms of extreme toxicity. These rats maintained their elevated BUN values until they were sacrificed on the 13th, 14th, and 15th days. Over this same period, BL-A 2-treated rats showed no toxic symptoms. Animals in this group were sacrificed on the 16th day. Kasugamycin-treated rats showed gross kidney lesions, whereas BL-A 2-treated rats showed no lesions.

Table 3. *Acute toxicity in mice of orally and parenterally administered BL-A 2 and kasugamycin*

Route	Kasugamycin		BL-A 2	
	LD_0[a]	LD_{50}[b]	LD_0	LD_{50}
Intraperitoneal	2,750	7,600	2,700	5,900
Intravenous	1,800	3,850	900	1,650
Oral	–	>14,000	–	>10,000

[a] Highest dose (in milligrams per kilogram) causing no deaths.
[b] The dose (in milligrams per kilogram) killing 50% of the animals.

The relative effectiveness of kasugamycin and BL-A 2 in experimental systemic infections of mice caused by *S. enteritidis, K. pneumoniae,* and *P. aeruginosa* was determined. The results shown in Table 4 indicate that BL-A 2 was therapeutically more effective than kasugamycin in experimental systemic infections of mice caused by *K. pneumoniae* and *P. aeruginosa.* When the antibiotics were administered im in the treatment of *K. pneumoniae* infections, the CD_{50} of BL-A 2 was 46 mg/kg, and that of kasugamycin was 168 mg/kg. In the treatment of *P. aeruginosa* infections of mice, the CD_{50} of BL-A 2 was 240 mg/kg and that of kasugamycin was 780 mg/kg when the drugs were administered by the subcutaneous route. Although only five mice per dose were used in the treatment of *S. enteritidis* infections by the im route, there was an indication that BL-A 2 (CD_{50} = 220 mg/kg) was again more effective than kasugamycin (CD_{50} = 360 mg/kg). BL-A 2 was much less effective against *K. pneumoniae* when administered orally than when given parenterally. The CD_{50} by the im route was 46 mg/kg, whereas the oral CD_{50} was 700 mg/kg. The efficacy of the two antibiotics in the treatment of an experimental *P. aeruginosa* urinary-tract infection of rats was also studied (Table 5). Against this infection, BL-A 2 was therapeutically effective. When administered subcutaneously in 24 doses of 50 mg/kg each, for a total of 1,200 mg/kg over a period of 7 days, BL-A 2 completely cleared the infecting organism from the bladder and kidneys. When the same regimen was used with doses of 25 mg/kg, BL-A 2 substantially reduced the viable-

Table 4. *Relative effectiveness of kasugamycin and BL-A 2 in experimental systemic infections*[a] *of mice*

Challenge organism	No. of mice per dose level	Treatment		CD_{50} (total mg/kg)	
		Route[b]	Time (hr postinfection)	Kasugamycin	BL-A 2
Klebsiella pneumoniae	10	im	0, 4	168	46
K. pneumoniae	10	po	0, 4	>1,600	700
Salmonella enteritidis[c]	5	im	0, 4	360	220
Pseudomonas aeruginosa[c]	10	sc	0, 2, 4, 6, 24, 26	780	240

[a] Mice were infected intraperitoneally with a number of bacterial cells sufficient to kill all nontreated controls within 72 hr.
[b] Intramuscular (im), oral (po), or subcutaneous (sc).
[c] Challenge organisms were given as suspensions in 5% mucin.

Table 5. *Relative effectiveness of kasugamycin and BL-A 2 in an experimental Pseudomonas aeruginosa urinary-tract infection [a] of rats*

Antibiotic	No. of rats	Dose level (mg/kg)[b]	Treatment effect[c]		
			Avg log viable count		Avg wt per rat (g)
			Bladder	Kidneys	
Controls (infected untreated)	15	–	3.1	6.0	206
Kasugamycin	10	12.5	3.0	4.2	182
Kasugamycin	10	25	<1.0	<1.0	176
Kasugamycin	10	50	<1.0	4.3	172
BL-A 2	10	12.5	3.1	4.5	203
BL-A 2	10	25	1.9	3.3	205
BL-A 2	10	50	<1.0	<1.0	209

[a] Infection initiated via right kidney with an inoculum of 0.1 ml containing 10^6 *P. aeruginosa* cells.

[b] Antibiotics were administered subcutaneously at the individual dose levels indicated for a total of 24 times as follows: four times per day at 2-hr intervals for 5 days, and two times per day at 6-hr intervals on the 6th and 7th days postinfection.

[c] Treatment effect was determined 8 days after initiation of infection (1 day post-treatment).

cell count in these organs. At all dose levels of BL-A 2, the rats continued to gain weight, and their kidneys remained normal in function and appearance.

Results when kasugamycin was administered in the same manner were more erratic. With doses of 25 mg/kg, the bacteria were eliminated from both organs. With doses of 50 mg/kg, however, they were cleared from the bladder but not the kidneys. The lower degree of effectiveness with the higher dose might be attributable to kasugamycin toxicity. Treatment with kasugamycin caused grossly swollen and discolored kidneys as well as severe weight loss. Neither antibiotic had a significant antimicrobial effect at a dose level of 12.5 mg/kg. However, the kasugamycin-treated rats continued to lose weight and their kidneys still appeared to be grossly abnormal.

In summary, the semisynthetic kasugamycin BL-A 2 was two to four times more active in vitro than kasugamycin against strains of *E. coli, P. aeruginosa,* and *Klebsiella-Enterobacter.* Concentrations of BL-A 2 in the urine of mice were comparable to those of kasugamycin. The improved therapeutic effectiveness of BL-A 2 over kasugamycin in experimental gram-negative infections of rodents appeared to be at least of the same order of magnitude as would be expected on the basis of its superiority shown by in vitro MIC tests. These results, along with those obtained in the experimental *P. aeruginosa* urinary-tract infection and in subacute toxicity studies, show clearly that BL-A 2 is relatively nontoxic, despite the fact that it is highly concentrated in the urine. It is therefore suggested that this antibiotic be given consideration as a therapeutic agent for treatment of gram-negative urinary-tract infections, especially those caused by *P. aeruginosa.*

ACKNOWLEDGMENTS

We acknowledge the capable technical assistance of Robert Buck, James Quigley, and Grace E. Wright. We also extend our appreciation to V. Kadar for conducting the acute toxicity study in mice as well as the mouse urinary excretion experiments, and to H. Madissoo for carrying out the subacute toxicity study in rats.

LITERATURE CITED

1. Cahn, R. S., C. K. Ingold, and V. Prelog. 1956. The specification of asymmetric configuration in organic chemistry. Experientia (Basel) **12:**81-124.
2. Cron, M. J., R. E. Smith, I. R. Hooper, J. G. Keil, E. A. Ragan, G. Schwab, and J. C. Godfrey. 1970. Preparation of semisynthetic kasugamycin derivatives. I. Aliphatic amidino derivatives of kasuganobiosamine. Antimicrob. Agents Chemother.–1969, p. 219-224.
3. Hamada, M., T. Hashimoto, T. Takahashi, S. Yokoyama, M. Miyake, T. Takeuchi, Y. Okami, and H. Umezawa. 1965. Antimicrobial activity of kasugamycin. J. Antibiot. (Tokyo) **18:**104-106.
4. Ichikawa, T. 1966. Kasugamycin treatment of *Pseudomonas* infection of the urinary tract. Antimicrob. Agents Chemother.–1965, p. 758-764.
5. Litchfield, J. T., Jr., and F. Wilcoxon. 1949. A simplified method of evaluating dose-effect experiments J. Pharmacol Exp. Ther. **96:** 99-113.
6. Price, K. E. J. A. Bach, D. R. Chisholm, M. Misiek, and A.

Gourevitch. 1969. Preliminary microbiological and pharmacological evaluation of 6-(R-α-amino-3-thienylacetamido) penicillanic acid (BL-P 875). J. Antibiot. (Tokyo) **22**:3-11.

7. Steers, E., E. L. Foltz, and B. S. Graves. 1959. An inocula replicating apparatus for routine testing of bacterial susceptibility to antibiotics. Antibiot. Chemother. 9:307-311.

8. Takeuchi, T., M. Ishizuka, H. Takayama, K. Kurcha, M. Hamada, and H. Umezawa. 1965. Pharmacology of kasugamycin and the effect on Pseudomonas infection. J. Antibiot. (Tokyo) **18**:107-110.

9. Umezawa, H., M. Hamada, Y. Suhara, T. Hashimoto, T. Ikekawa, N. Tanaka, K. Maeda, Y. Okami, and T. Takeuchi. 1966. Kasugamycin, a new antibiotic. Antimicrob. Agents Chemother.–1965, p. 753-757.

Antimicrobial Agents and Chemotherapy—1969

Fermentation, Isolation, and Characterization of LL-Z1220, a New Antibiotic

D. B. BORDERS, F. BARBATSCHI, A. J. SHAY, and P. SHU

Lederle Laboratories Division, American Cyanamid Co., Pearl River, New York 10965

LL-Z1220 is a new antibiotic produced by an undetermined fungal species. The antibiotic was extracted from the culture filtrate with chloroform and purified by crystallization and sublimation. It was obtained as colorless crystals: melting point, 148 C (decomposition); $[\alpha]^{25}{}_{D}$,–123° (*c*, 0.591, $CHCl_3$). It has a molecular weight of 204 and a molecular formula of $C_{11}H_8O_4$. The compound is neutral, gives a positive epoxide test, and has an ultraviolet-absorption maximum at 269 nm (ϵ, 16,800) and a carbonyl absorption near 1,653 cm^{-1}. The antibiotic inhibited a number of gram-negative and gram-positive bacteria in vitro, but it afforded no protection against a series of lethal bacterial infections in mice. The maximal tolerated dose of LL-Z1220 was 20 mg/kg subcutaneously and 80 mg/kg orally.

In our antibiotic screening program, an unidentified fungal species which yielded only chlamydospores and did not have other diagnostic spores types was found to produce a new antibiotic designated LL-Z1220. The antibiotic had in vitro activity against gram-negative and gram-positive bacteria but was inactive in vivo. This paper describes the fermentation and isolation, and some of the chemical and biological properties, of this new compound.

MATERIALS AND METHODS

Fermentation. An inoculum of the culture Z1220, a filamentous fungus, was prepared by growing the organism at 28 C in aerated 20-liter bottles for 48 hr in a medium of the following composition (grams per liter): soybean meal, 10; glucose, 20; corn steep liquor, 5; and calcium carbonate, 3. Twelve liters of inoculum was used to seed 300 liters of medium containing the following ingredients (grams per liter): cane molasses, 20; glucose, 10; soyflour, 10; corn steep liquor, 5; and calcium carbonate, 3. The fermentation was carried out under standard conditions of agitation and aeration for 140 hr at 28 C.

Analytical procedures. The antibiotic activity was followed during fermentation by assaying samples of fermentation filtrate by the agar-diffusion method. The assay organism was *Bacillus subtilis* Stansly R-78 grown on Mycin Assay Agar (nutrient agar, *p*H 7.9, Difco).

Paper electrophoresis studies on Whatman no. 1 paper were run at 300 v with *p*H 8.8 and 3.0 buffers, and the antibiotic zones were detected by bioautography with *B. subtilis*. The *p*H 8.8 buffer was 2% ammonium carbonate in water, and the acidic buffer was 2% acetic acid in water.

The antibiotic had the following R_F values when it was chromatographed on thin layers of E. Merck silica gel F_{254} with the indicated solvents: methanol, 0.52; acetone, 0.47; ethyl acetate, 0.06. The antibiotic zones were readily detected by ultraviolet quenching or with 1% aqueous potassium permanganate spray.

Isolation procedure. The 300 liters of harvested mash was filtered, the filtrate was adjusted to *p*H 7.0 with dilute sodium hydroxide and extracted with 150 liters of chloroform, and the resulting extract was concentrated to dryness under vacuum at a temperature below 40 C. The residual mass was dissolved in about 1 liter of chloroform. The solution was filtered, mixed with 2 liters of acetone, and maintained at 4 C for 20 hr. The crystalline product which separated (58 g) was filtered off, washed with a small volume of acetone, and dried in vacuo at room temperature. The product readily recrystallized with methylene chloride-cyclohexane or sublimed at 125 to 140 C and 0.2 mm of Hg to a white powder.

RESULTS AND DISCUSSION

LL-Z1220 was isolated as colorless needles, melting point 148 C (decomposition), by recrystallizing the residue from a chloroform extract of the fermentation filtrate. Analytical samples were obtained by recrystallization or sublimation. Elemental analyses were variable but showed that nitrogen was not present.

Analysis: Found: C, 60.88, 65.03; H, 3.83, 4.00; O, 30.17, 30.04. Consideration of the

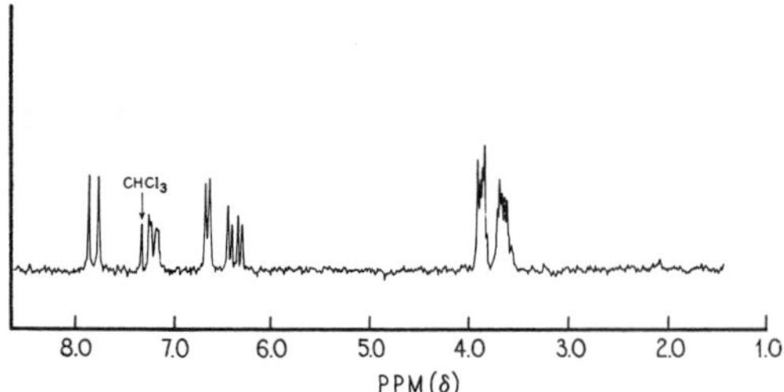

Fig. 1. *Nuclear magnetic resonance spectrum (60 MHz) of LL-Z1220 in* $CDCl_3$.

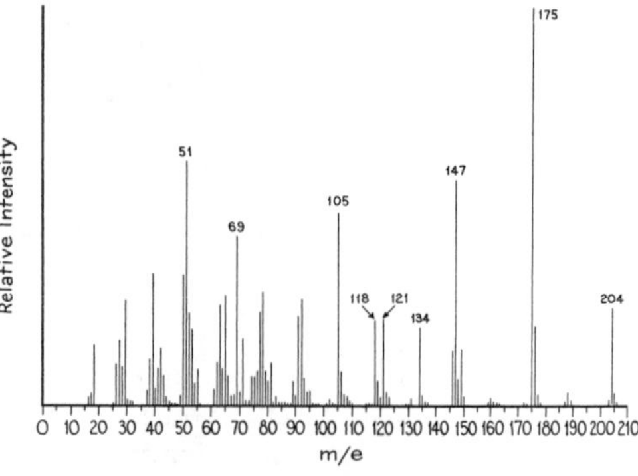

Fig. 2. *Mass spectrum (70 ev) of LL-Z1220.*

Table 1. *In vitro antimicrobial spectrum of LL-Z1220*[a]

Test organism	Minimal inhibitory concn (μg/ml)
Bacillus cereus ATCC10702	250
B. subtilis ATCC 6633	50
Corynebacterium xerosis NRRL-B1397	250
Sarcina lutea ATCC 9341	250
Staphyloccus aureus Smith ATCC 13709	250
S. epidermidis ATCC 12228	250
Streptococcus faecalis ATCC 8043	250
S. pyogenes C203	100
Streptococcus sp., gamma-hemolytic #11	250
Streptococcus sp., beta-hemolytic #80	250
Alcaligenes sp. ATCC 10153	100
Enterobacter cloacae ATCC 222	250
Escherichia coli ATCC 10536	250
Klebsiella pneumoniae AD	100
Proteus mirabilis ATCC 4671	250
P. morganii ATCC 8019	250
P. vulgaris ATCC 6380	100
Pseudomonas aeruginosa ATCC 10145	250
Salmonella typhosa ATCC 6539	50
Shigella flexneri I	250

[a] The agar-dilution method was used and all test organisms were grown on Trypticase Soy Agar (BBL).

nuclear magnetic resonance (NMR) (Fig. 1, eight protons) and the mass spectra (Fig. 2) with a parent ion at *m/e* 204 established the molecular formula as $C_{11}H_8O_4$. The NMR spectrum (Fig. 1) has a one-proton doublet at δ 7.79 coupled (J = 6.0 Hz) to a one-proton doublet of doublets at δ 6.35, which in turn is coupled (J = 2.5 Hz) to a one-proton doublet at δ 6.64. There is another low-field proton at δ 7.14 which is coupled (J = 1.2 and 4.3 Hz) to the remaining high-field protons. The ultraviolet-absorption spectrum of LL-Z1220 had a maximum at 267 nm (ε, 16,800) with no shifts in acid or base. The presence of an epoxide group was indicated by a positive thiosulfate reaction (2). A strong absorption in the infrared-absorption spectrum (Fig. 3) near 1,653 cm^{-1} suggested the presence of a carobonyl group. Paper electrophoresis studies indicated that LL-Z1220 was neutral. A consideration of the chemical and physical properties of LL-Z1220 showed that it was a new antibiotic with no obvious close relationship to any family of known antibiotics.

LL-Z1220 was active in vitro against gram-negative and gram-positive bacteria (Table 1).

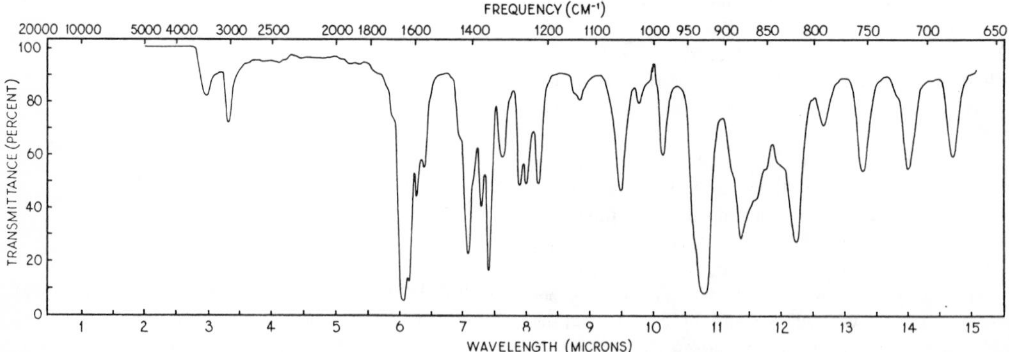

Fig. 3. *Infrared-absorption spectrum of LL-Z1220 in KBr.*

No protection was obtained by subcutaneous administration of the antibiotic to mice infected with lethal doses (1) of the following organisms: *Staphylococcus aureus* Smith, *Escherichia coli* 311, *Diplococcus pneumoniae* SVI, *Klebsiella pneumoniae* AD, *Pasteurella multocida* 310, *Streptococcus pyogenes* C203, *Salmonella typhosa*, *Staphylococcus aureus* Rose, *Aerobacter aerogenes*, *Proteus mirabilis*, *Pseudomonas aeruginosa*, and *Mycobacterium tuberculosis*. The maximal tolerated dose was 20 mg/kg subcutaneously and 80 mg/kg orally.

ACKNOWLEDGMENTS

We thank W. Fulmor and staff for spectral data, J. N. Porter and staff for initial fermentation material, H. Tresner for the isolation and taxonomic studies of the organism, L. Brancone and staff for microanalytical determinations, A. C. Dornbush for in vitro antimicrobial determinations, and G. Redin for the in vivo antibacterial assays.

LITERATURE CITED

1. Redin, G. S. 1967. Antibacterial activity in mice of minocycline, a new tetracycline. Antimicrob. Agents Chemother.–1966, p. 371-376.
2. Ross, W. C. 1950. The reaction of certain expoxides in aqueous solutions. J. Chem. Soc. (London), p. 2257-2272.

Antimicrobial Agents and Chemotherapy—1969

In Vitro and In Vivo Evaluation of Cefazolin, a New Cephalosporin C Derivative

MINORU NISHIDA, TADAO MATSUBARA, TAKEO MURAKAWA, YASUHIRO MINE, YOSHIKO YOKOTA, SHOGO KUWAHARA, and SACHIKO GOTO

Research Laboratories, Fujisawa Pharmaceutical Co., Ltd. Osaka, Japan and Department of Microbiology, Toho University School of Medicine, Tokyo. Japan

Cefazolin, 7-[1-(1H)-tetrazolylacetamido]-3-[2-(5-methyl-1,3,4-thiadiazolyl)-thiomethyl]-Δ^3-cephem-4-carboxylic acid, is a new antibiotic derived from 7-aminocephalosporanic acid. Cefazolin is a broad-spectrum antibiotic, also active against penicillinase-producing strains of *Staphylococcus aureus,* is apparently bactericidal in vitro at or above the minimal inhibitory concentration. In mice, cefazolin provided excellent protection against experimental infections caused by various strains of *S. aureus* (both penicillin-susceptible and penicillin-resistant), *Diplococcus pneumoniae, Escherichia coli,* and *Proteus mirabilis.* In volunteers, satisfactory concentrations of cefazolin in serum and urine were obtained after intramuscular administration of single doses. The maximal concentration in serum was 44.6 μg/ml, which is about twice as high as that of cephaloridine (17.2 μg/ml). This concentration was obtained in volunteers receiving a single dose of 500 mg of cefazolin. The recovery of cefazolin in the 24-hr urine was 95.9% of the administered dose for a dose of 250 mg and 82.4% for a dose of 500 mg (70.2% for 500 mg of cephaloridine). Therapeutically effective concentrations in the serum and urine were maintained as long as 10 hr after administration. Biliary excretion of cefazolin studied in dogs revealed that 3.3% of the intramuscularly administered dose (20 mg/kg) was recovered in the 24-hr bile. This rate seemed to be of an order similar to that of ampicillin, and was markedly higher than the rate of excretion of cephaloridine or cephalothin. When administered intramuscularly to rats as a single dose of 20 mg/kg, cefazolin was widely distributed in the kidneys, liver, heart, spleen, and lungs.

Cefazolin is a new cephalosporin C derivative with the chemical structure shown in Fig. 1. This substance has a tetrazolylacetyl side chain on the amino group and a 5-methyl-thiadiazolyl-thiomethyl group on the 3 position of 7-amino-cephalosporanic acid.

In the present study, the in vitro and in vivo activity of cefazolin was evaluated in comparison with that of related antibiotics.

Cefazolin was established to be a bactericidal antibiotic with a wide range of activity against gram-positive and gram-negative pathogens. Its therapeutic efficacy was tested in mice infected with *Staphylococcus aureus, Diplococcus pneumoniae, Escherichia coli,* and *Proteus mirabilis.* In addition, drug concentration in serum, urinary and biliary excretion, and tissue distribution were studied after administration of cefazolin and related antibiotics to rats, dogs, and healthy volunteers.

MATERIALS AND METHODS

Antibiotics. The antibiotics used were cefazolin (945 μg/mg; Fujisawa Research Laboratories, Osaka, Japan), cephaloridine (988 μg/ml; Glaxo Laboratories,

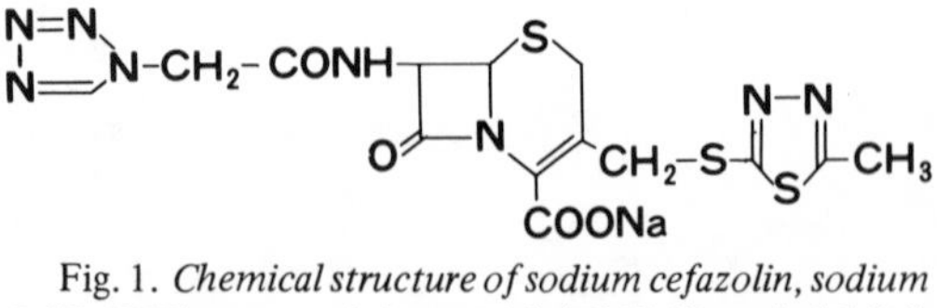

Fig. 1. *Chemical structure of sodium cefazolin, sodium 7-[1-(1H)-tetrazolylacetamido]-3-[2-(5-methyl-1,3,4-thiadiazolyl)-thiomethyl]-Δ^3-cephem-4-carboxylate ($C_{14}H_{13}O_4N_8S_3Na$; molecular weight, 476.3).*

England), cephalothin (971 μg/ml; Eli Lilly & Co., Indianapolis, Ind.), and ampicillin (840 μg/ml; Beecham Research Laboratories, Betchworth, Surrey, England).

Bacterial strains. Standard strains stored in our laboratory were used, in addition to clinical isolates of various species of bacteria supplied by several hospitals in Japan.

Animals. The mice used were dd strain, male albino mice, each weighing 17 to 21 g. Sprague-Dawley white male rats weighing 200 to 270 g and female mongrel dogs weighing 10 to 12 kg were also used. All animals except mice were fasted overnight before use, but were supplied with water *ad libitum.*

Assay of drug. Petri dishes containing 10 ml of nutrient agar, with about 10^5 spores of *Bacillus subtilis* ATCC 6633 per ml, were used for the microbiological assay of antibiotics. Paper discs were placed on the plates, and the diameters of the zones of inhibition were measured after incubation at 37 C for 20 hr.

Susceptibility tests. In vitro antibacterial activity of cefazolin was determined by the agar-dilution method. One loopful of an overnight broth culture was streaked on Heart Infusion Agar containing graded concentrations of cefazolin. The minimal inhibitory concentration (MIC) was determined after incubation at 37 C for 20 hr.

Bactericidal activity. Nutrient broths containing cefazolin at concentrations equal to one-fourth of the MIC, the MIC, and four times the MIC were inoculated with *S. aureus* 209P (10^6/ml). The cultures were incubated at 37 C with shaking, and viable cells were counted at regular intervals.

Protein binding. The degree of binding of cefazolin and related antibiotics to serum proteins was measured by ultrafiltration through Visking tubing (size, 8/32). The antibiotic present in protein-free ultrafiltrates was assayed by the disc method.

Experimental infection. For infection with *S. aureus,* each animal was intravenously challenged with 0.5 ml of the broth culture. For infection with *D. pneumoniae, E. coli,* and *P. mirabilis,* each animal was intraperitoneally challenged with the same amount of the culture. The antibiotics, in single doses of various sizes, were administered subcutaneously 1 hr after the challenge.

Determination of drug concentrations in serum and urinary excretion in healthy volunteers. The drug concentrations in serum and urine of five healthy volunteers were determined by means of a crossover procedure. Each volunteer received a single intramuscular dose of 250 and 500 mg of cefazolin and 500 mg of cephaloridine.

Urine was collected at regular intervals over a period of 24 hr after administration. The concentrations of cefazolin and cephaloridine in the serum and urine were assayed by the disc method.

Identification of active substances excreted in human urine. Cefazolin was administered intramuscularly to two healthy male volunteers as a single dose of 250 mg. The urine was collected over a period of 24 hr after drug administration and was examined by thin-layer chromatography and bioautography.

For thin-layer chromatography, the following solvent systems were used: *n*-butyl alcohol-acetic acid-water (4:1:5, top layer), butyl alcohol-ethyl alcohol-water (4:1:5), and methyl alcohol-*n*-propyl alcohol-water (6:1:2). The adsorbent was Eastman Chromagram Sheet no. 6061.

For bioautography, the dried sheet, developed by the use of aforementioned solvents, was plated on agar previously seeded with 0.2% of a spore suspension (2 × 10^8 spores/ml) of *B. subtilis* ATCC 6633.

Determination of biliary excretion. Dogs were anesthetized with ether and cannulated with a polyethylene tube by a standard laboratory procedure. Cefazolin and related antibiotics were administered intramuscularly as a single dose of 20 mg/kg. The bile was collected for 24 hr.

Determination of tissue distribution. Cefazolin and related antibiotics, each at 20 mg/kg, were given intramuscularly to 12 rats. At 0.5, 1, 2, and 3 hr after dosage, three rats in each group were killed by cervical dislocation. The liver, kidneys, lungs, heart, and spleen were removed and washed with saline. Each organ was then homogenized with three volumes of 99% ethyl alcohol in a Waring Blendor. The homogenates were centrifuged at 6,800 × *g* for 10 min, and the supernatant fluids were used for bioassay.

RESULTS

Antibacterial spectrum. The antibacterial spectra of cefazolin and related antibiotics are summarized in Table 1. Cefazolin was active against a wide range of bacteria, both gram-positive and gram-negative, but not against *Pseudomonas aeruginosa, Proteus vulgaris,* or *Streptococcus faecalis.* Strains of *Staphylococcus aureus* were slightly less susceptible to cefazolin than to cephaloridine or ampicillin, whereas gram-negative bacteria as a whole were more susceptible to cefazolin than to cephaloridine. Accordingly, cefazolin is designated as a broad-spectrum antibiotic.

Distribution of susceptibility of clinical isolates. The distribution of the MIC of cefazolin and related antibiotics against several clinically isolated organisms is shown in Table 2.

Cefazolin was strongly active, though slightly less efficient than cephaloridine, against 64 strains of *S. aureus,* most of which were penicillinase producers. Of the 42 strains of *E. coli* tested, 40 were susceptible to cefazolin. The activity of cefazolin against these strains seemed to be nearly equal to that of cephaloridine and

Table 1. *Antimicrobial spectra of cefazolin and related antibiotics*

Organism	Minimal inhibitory concn (μg/ml)[a]				
	Cefazolin	Cephaloridine	Cephalothin	Cephalexin	Ampicillin
Staphylococcus aureus 209P	0.39	0.1	0.39	3.13	0.2
S. aureus Newman	0.39	0.1	0.78	6.25	0.2
S. aureus Terashima	0.78	0.2	0.78	12.5	0.39
S. aureus Smith	0.39	0.1	0.39	3.13	0.2
Streptococcus hemolyticus S-23[b]	0.2	0.05	0.1	1.56	0.05
S. faecalis 6733[b]	50	12.5	25	>100	1.56
Diplococcus pneumoniae I[b]	0.2	0.05	0.39	3.13	0.05
D. pneumoniae II[b]	0.2	0.05	0.2	6.25	0.05
D. pneumoniae III[b]	0.2	0.1	0.39	3.13	0.1
Corynebacterium diphtheriae P.W.8[b]	0.39	0.1	0.39	1.56	0.2
Clostridium perfringens PB6K[c]	1.56	3.13	3.13	25	3.13
Mycobacterium tuberculosis $H_{37}Rv$[d]	12.5	6.25	25	50	50
Bacillus subtilis ATCC 6633	0.39	0.025	0.05	0.39	0.39
Sarcina lutea PC1–1001	0.78	0.05	0.2	0.39	0.01
Neisseria gonorrhoeae Nakanishi[e]	1.56	1.56	3.13	6.25	0.78
Salmonella typhi T-287	1.56	3.13	1.56	3.13	0.2
S. typhi 0–901	1.56	3.13	1.56	3.13	0.2
S. enteritidis	6.25	12.5	12.5	25	3.13
Klebsiella pneumoniae ST-101	1.56	6.25	12.5	25	1.56
Escherichia coli NIHJ	1.56	3.13	3.13	6.25	1.56
Shigella flexneri 2a	1.56	3.13	6.25	6.25	1.56
S. sonnei I	0.78	3.13	6.25	6.25	3.13
Proteus vulgaris IAM-1025	>100	50	100	100	>100
Pseudomonas aeruginosa IAM-1095	>100	>100	>100	>100	>100

[a] Determined by the agar-dilution method on heart infusion agar (10^8 organisms/ml).
[b] With the addition of 10% serum.
[c] Zeissler's glucose-blood-agar.
[d] Dubos medium.
[e] GC chocolate-agar.

superior to the activity of the other antibiotics. Of the 30 strains of *P. mirabilis,* 26 were suppressed by cefazolin at concentrations ranging from 3.13 to 12.5 μg/ml. The remaining four strains were cefazolin-resistant. Of the 33 strains of *Klebsiella pneumoniae* tested, 19 were suppressed by 1.56 to 3.13 μg of cefazolin per ml, and 8, by 6.25 to 12.5 μg/ml.

These data suggest that, on the whole, cefazolin is more effective than the other antibiotics against the clinical isolates of gram-negative bacteria tested.

Bactericidal activity. The bactericidal activity of cefazolin was compared with that of cephaloridine against *S. aureus* 209P. Figure 2 shows that a marked decrease in the viable-cell count of *S. aureus* occurred when it was exposed to cefazolin at levels equal to the MIC and four times the MIC. At one-fourth the MIC, the count decreased in the initial stage, but increased from 8 hr of incubation onward. A similar tendency was noted in *E. coli*. Cefazolin, accordingly, was considered to be bactericidal, with activity comparable to that of cephaloridine in degree.

Protein-binding effect. Table 3 shows the degree of binding of cefazolin and other antibiotics to serum proteins from different species of animals. In general, the degree of binding depended on the animal species, except with dicloxacillin. Specificity of protein binding was remarkably evident with cefazolin, the extent of the initial amount being only 20% in dogs, 74% in humans, and 90% in rabbits. The protein binding of cefazolin, though somewhat higher than that of cephaloridine or cephalexin, did not seem to be so firm as to reduce the antimicrobial activity in vitro and in vivo.

Protective effect in experimental infections of mice. The protective effect of cefazolin against experimental infections in mice was compared with that of related antibiotics. The MIC and

Table 2. *Distribution of clinical isolates according to susceptibility to cefazolin and related antibiotics*[a]

Organism	Antibiotic	Minimal inhibitory concn (μg/ml)						
		⩾100	50-25	12.5-6.25	6.25-3.13	3.13-1.56	0.78-0.1	⩽ .05
Staphylococcus aureus (64 strains)	Cefazolin	–	–	–	13	–	51	–
	Cephaloridine	–	1	–	18	–	20	25
	Cephalothin	–	–	–	–	–	62	2
	Cephalexin	–	31	–	33	–	–	–
	Ampicillin	14	18	–	21	–	10	1
Escherichia coli (42 strains)	Cefazolin	–	2	23	–	17	–	–
	Cephaloridine	–	3	37	–	2	–	–
	Cephalothin	14	27	1	–	–	–	–
	Cephalexin	39	2	1	–	–	–	–
	Ampicillin	1	18	23	–	–	–	–
Proteus mirabilis (30 strains)	Cefazolin	3	1	11	–	15	–	–
	Cephaloridine	2	9	19	–	–	–	–
	Cephalothin	3	5	22	–	–	–	–
	Cephalexin	10	20	–	–	–	–	–
	Ampicillin	2	–	5	–	21	–	–
Klebsiella pneumoniae (33 strains)	Cefazolin	2	4	8	–	19	–	–
	Cephaloridine	4	17	10	–	2	–	–
	Cephalothin	4	23	6	–	–	–	–
	Cephalexin	24	7	2	–	–	–	–
	Ampicillin	33	–	–	–	–	–	–

[a] Each figure indicates the number of strains which showed the indicated minimal inhibitory concentration.

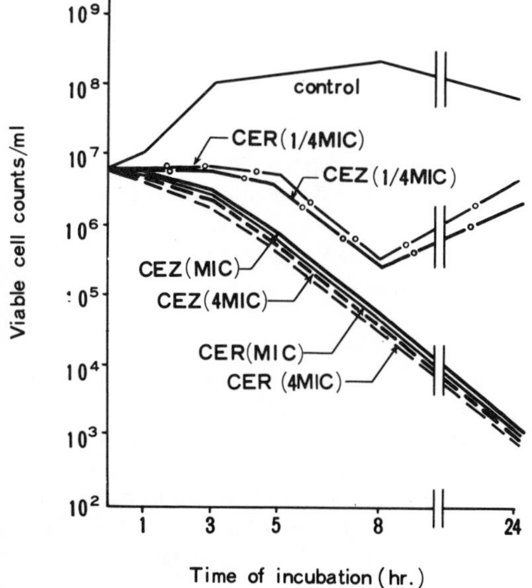

Fig. 2. *Bactericidal activity of cefazolin (CEZ) and cephaloridine (CER) against Staphylococcus aureus 209P.*

Table 3. *Extent of binding of cefazolin and related antibiotics to serum of humans and animals*[a]

Antibiotic	Percentage bound to serum of			
	Humans	Dogs	Rabbits	Rats
Cefazolin	74	20	90	91
Cephaloridine	31	11	29	11
Cephalothin	79	50	85	73
Cephalexin	12	3	15	5
Penicillin G	41	8	43	6
Dicloxacillin	95	92	96	93

[a] Serum, 9 volumes; antibiotic (500 μg/ml), 1 volume; 37 C for 1 hr, then ultrafiltration.

ED_{50} of these antibiotics for various strains of bacteria are summarized in Table 4.

Against infection with *S. aureus* or *E. coli*, the protective effect of cefazolin, like its in vitro activity, was nearly equal to that of cephaloridine. Cefazolin was somewhat less effective than cephaloridine or ampicillin against *D. pneumoniae* and *P. mirabilis*.

Table 4. *Protective effect of cefazolin and related antibiotics against experimental infections in mice*

Organism	MIC (μg/ml)			ED_{50} (mg/mouse)[a]		
	CEZ[b]	CER	AB-PC	CEZ	CER	AB-PC
Staphylococcus aureus						
226	3.13	3.13	100	<0.09	0.28	1.8
T-5	1.25	1.25	50	1.78	0.19	>6.0
STP	0.31	0.1	⩽0.05	0.53	0.13	0.53
204	3.13	3.13	>100	<0.09	<0.09	0.26
213	1.56	3.13	>100	0.18	0.30	0.75
235	6.25	6.25	>100	0.55	0.12	2.59
Diplococcus pneumoniae						
III	0.2	0.1	0.1	2.73	0.39	0.58
Escherichia coli						
T-16	3.13	6.25	6.25	0.44	0.29	0.48
T-15	3.13	6.25	6.25	2.15	1.11	1.31
2-E-5	12.5	6.25	12.5	0.56	<0.2	0.34
2-E-6	6.25	6.25	25	3.02	<0.2	1.54
2-E-7	12.5	6.25	12.5	3.42	4.06	1.64
312	3.13	12.5	6.25	3.63	1.11	0.93
323	12.5	50	100	0.78	3.15	0.88
324	3.13	6.25	6.25	3.60	⩾12.0	8.51
Proteus mirabilis						
519	6.25	6.25	3.13	5.20	2.20	6.30
522	6.25	12.5	3.13	3.60	5.10	8.60
524	3.13	3.13	0.78	4.28	1.55	0.40
523	6.25	6.25	1.56	2.31	1.27	1.05

[a] Administered by the subcutaneous route.
[b] CEZ = cefazolin; CER = cephaloridine; AB-PC = ampicillin.

Drug concentrations in serum and urine of healthy volunteers. The concentrations of cefazolin and cephaloridine after a single intramuscular dose were determined in the serum of five healthy volunteers (Fig. 3). When a single dose of 250 or 500 mg of cefazolin was given, a mean peak concentration of 29.8 or 44.6 μg per ml of serum was attained at 1 hr after administration. When cephaloridine was similarly given to the same subjects as a single dose of 500 mg, a mean peak concentration of 17.2 μg/ml was reached within 30 min. The peak concentration of cefazolin was therefore two or three times as high as that of cephaloridine. The mean concentrations of cefazolin in serum were higher than those of cephaloridine whenever they were determined.

Urinary excretion was simultaneously studied in the same volunteers (Fig. 4). The amounts recovered in the 24-hr urine samples were 95.9 and 82.4%, respectively, for doses of 250 and 500 mg of cefazolin and 70.2% for 500 mg of cephaloridine. With cefazolin, the maximal concentrations in urine, which exceeded 1,000 μg/ml, were recorded in the 3-hr urine samples. Therapeutically effective levels were maintained for at least 8 to 10 hr.

Identification of active compounds in human urine. The active material recovered in the urine of the volunteers was identified as cefazolin by thin-layer chromatography. As shown in Fig. 5, most of the cefazolin administered was excreted in the urine.

Biliary excretion. Biliary excretion of cefazolin was compared with that of other antibiotics in dogs. Biliary excretion of antibiotics

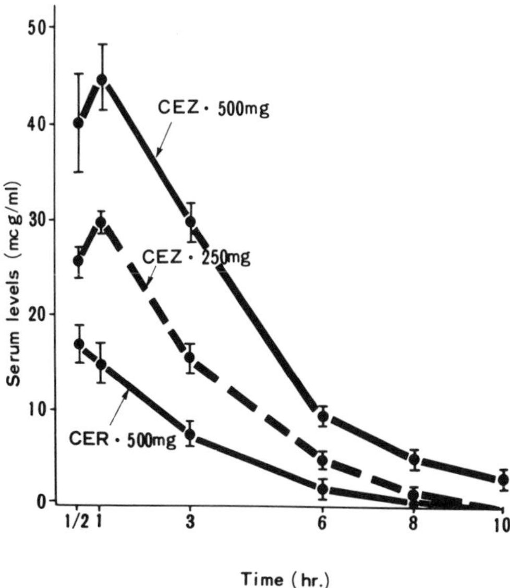

Fig. 3. *Mean concentrations of cefazolin (CEZ) and cephaloridine (CER) in serum after intramuscular administration to the same five healthy volunteers. The subjects, who were in the fasting state, weighed approximately 60 to 70.5 kg. The drug was assayed by the disc method with Bacillus subtilis ATCC 6633 as the test organism.*

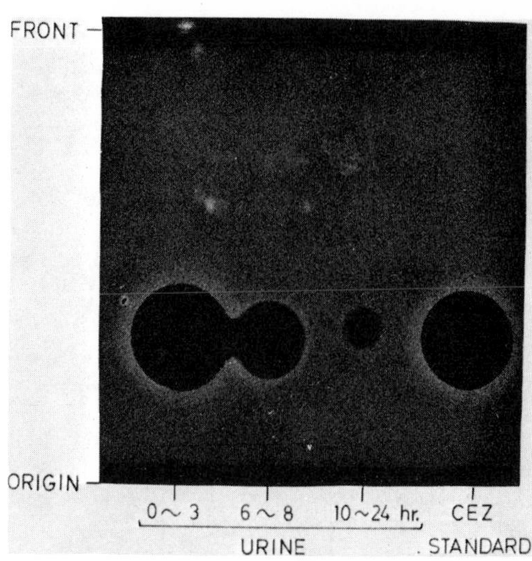

Fig. 5. *Bioautograms of urine after the intramuscular injection of a single 250-mg dose of cefazolin to two healthy adult volunteers. The urine collected over a 24-hr period after drug administration was examined by thin-layer chromatography and bioautography. The adsorbent used was Eastman chromagram 6061, and the solvent was n-butyl alcohol-acetic acid-water (4:1:5). The test organism was Bacillus subtilis ATCC 6633.*

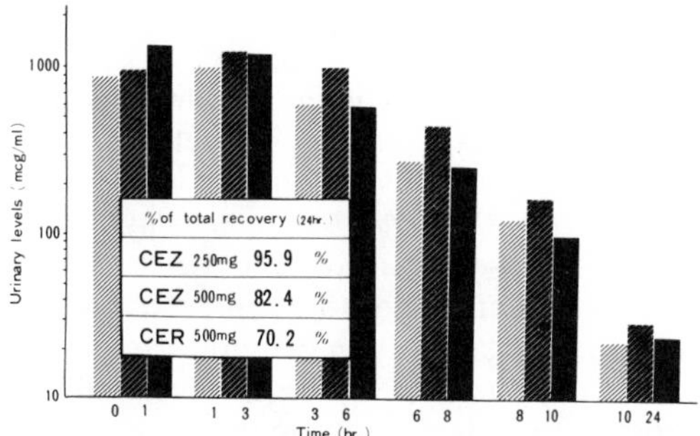

Fig. 4. *Concentrations of cefazolin (CEZ) and cephaloridine (CER) in urine after intramuscular administration to the same five healthy volunteers. The first column in each group represents 250 mg of CEZ; the second, 500 mg of CEZ; the third, 500 mg of CER.*

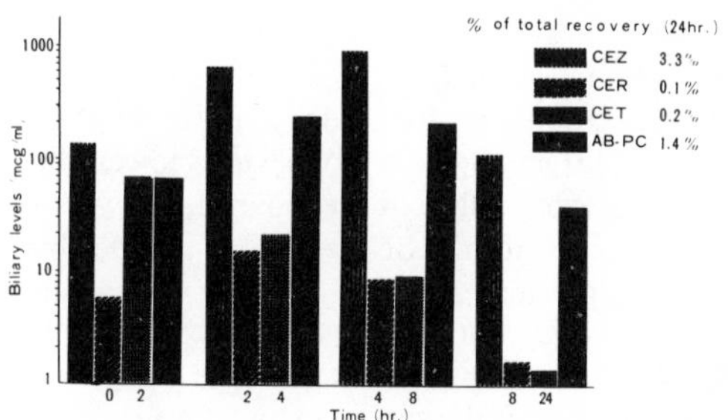

Fig. 6. *Concentrations of cefazolin (CEZ), cephaloridine (CER), cephalothin (CET), and ampicillin (AB-PC) after intramuscular administration of 20 mg/kg to dogs (three dogs per group). The first column in each group represents CEZ (3.3%), the second column CER (0.1%), the third column CET (0.2%), and the fourth column AB-PC (1.4%), expressed as per cent of total recovery in 24 hr.*

generally occurs to only a limited extent, as shown in Fig. 6, because most of the antibiotics administered are excreted by the urinary route. However, the present study revealed that cefazolin is excreted into the bile to a greater extent than is cephaloridine or cephalothin. With a single intramuscular dose of 20 mg of cefazolin per kg, the therapeutically effective levels in the bile (120 to 923 μg/ml) were maintained for 8 hr. The recovery of cefazolin in the 24-hr bile was 3.3% of the administered dose. The results indicated that the rate of biliary excretion is of an order similar to that of ampicillin, and higher than that of cephaloridine or cephalothin.

Tissue distribution. Tissue distribution of cefazolin was compared with that of related antibiotics in rats, after a single intramuscular dose of 20 mg/kg (Fig. 7). When administered

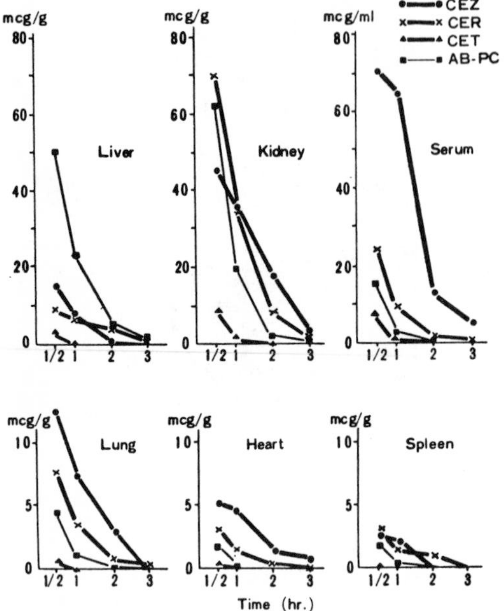

Fig. 7. *Concentrations of cefazolin (CEZ), cephaloridine (CER), cephalothin (CET), and ampicillin (AB-PC) in tissues and serum after intramuscular administration of 20 mg/kg to Sprague-Dawley rats (three rats per group).*

intramuscularly to rats, cefazolin was well distributed in various tissues tested. The maximal concentrations in the kidney (45.2 μg/g) and liver (14.0 μg/g) were somewhat lower than those of ampicillin or cephaloridine, whereas the concentrations of cefazolin in the lung (12.5 μg/g) and heart (5.2 μg/g) were higher than those of the other antibiotics. A similar tendency was observed when the drugs were administered by the subcutaneous route.

DISCUSSION

As is well known, cephaloridine is considered by some to be the most useful of the broad-spectrum antibiotics, because of its high in vitro activity (3, 13), its stability (10), and its very low toxicity, except for damage to the kidney (4, 14). Cephalothin is less stable in the human body (1, 12), because it is easily converted into a deacetyl-compound of relatively lower activity; however, its toxicity is lower than that of cephaloridine.

The in vitro activity of cefazolin is almost comparable to that of cephaloridine, and is definitely higher than that of other cephalosporin C derivatives. Its protective activity in mice experimentally infected with *S. aureus* and *E. coli* was also confirmed to be nearly equal to that of cephaloridine, with its ED_{50} parallelling its effectiveness in vitro (13). These results indicate that protein binding of cefazolin is not so firm as to reduce its antimicrobial activity in vivo (5, 6). Cefazolin has very low toxicity, and is quite well absorbed into the serum and various tissues when given intramuscularly to animals and human volunteers. The high rate of recovery of cefazolin in the urine and bile was suggestive to a great extent of a high degree of stability in the body. Furthermore, the high concentrations of cefazolin in urine make it quite satisfactory for the treatment of urinary-tract infections. Cefazolin concentrations in bile were far higher than that of cephaloridine (2, 11) or cephalothin (7) and as high as that of ampicillin (9). Accordingly, cefazolin was considered as effective as ampicillin for the treatment of biliary infections.

It might be assumed that the higher concentrations of cefazolin in serum are inevitably produced by the inversely lower concentrations in the tissues. This assumption, however, is obviously inconsistent with the results with cefazolin.

Our present series of experiments have suggested the potential clinical usefulness of this new antibiotic. Furthermore, cefazolin has proved to have extremely low toxicity in animals *(unpublished data).* Consequently, cefazolin should be considered for use in clinical trials. In addition to the above studies, its further investigation as an oral drug (8, 15) will be of a great interest, because cefazolin is absorbed gastrointestinally to a certain extent.

ACKNOWLEDGMENTS

We thank H. Nakano and S. Kumada for encouragement. We are indebted to T. Takano and K. Kariyone for a supply of cephalosporin antibiotics and for helpful suggestion.

LITERATURE CITED

1. Boniece, W. S., W. E. Wick, D. H. Holmes, and C. E. Redman. 1962. In vitro and in vivo laboratory evaluation of cephalothin, a new broad spectrum antibiotic. J. Bacteriol. 84:1292–1296.
2. Dennis, M., J. R. Rasch, and H. K. Hastings. 1966. Clinical evaluation of cephaloridine. Antimicrob. Agents Chemother.–1965, p. 724–727.
3. Goto, S., and S. Kuwahara. 1965. Antibacterial activity of cephaloridine. J. Antibiot. (Tokyo) Ser. B 18: 306–309.
4. Gower, P. E. 1967. The effect of cephaloridine on renal function in patients with renal failure. Postgrad. Med. J. 43:92–94.

5. Hofsten, B. V., and S. O. Falkbring. 1960. A simple arrangement for the concentration of protein solutions. Anal. Biochem. **1**:436–439.
6. Kunin, C. M. 1965. Inhibitors of penicillin binding to serum proteins. Antimicrob. Agents and Chemother.–1964, p. 338–343.
7. Lee, C.-C., and R. C. Anderson. 1963. Blood and tissue distribution of cephalothin. Antimicrob. Agents Chemother.–1962, p. 695–701.
8. Perkins, R. L., G. E. Glontz, and S. Saslaw. 1969. Cephaloglycin: crossover absorption studies and clinical evaluation. Clin. Pharmacol. Ther. **10**:244–249.
9. Quinn, E. L., F. Cox, D. Jones, and L. Zarins. 1965. Clinical experience with parenteral ampicillin. Antimicrob. Agents Chemother.–1964, p. 226–232.
10. Sabath, L. D., M. Jago, and E. P. Abraham. 1965. Cephalosporinase and epnicillinase activities of a β-lactamase from *Pseudomonas pyocyanea*. Biochem. J. **96**: 739–752.
11. Stewart, G. T. 1964. Laboratory and clinical results with cephaloridine. Lancet **2**:1305–1309.
12. Sullivan, H. R., and R. E. McMahn. 1967. Metabolism of oral cephalothin and related cephalosporins in the rat. Biochem. J. **102**: 976–982.
13. Thomson, M., D. Barrett, S. Madden, and M. Ridley. 1967. *In vitro* activity of cephaloridine against *Staphylococci* and *Gonococci*. Postgrad. Med. J. **43**:36–39.
14. Welles, J. S., W. R. Gibson, P. N. Harris, R. M. Small, and R. C. Anderson. 1966. Toxicity, distribution, and excretion of cephaloridine in laboratory animals. Antimicrob. Agents Chemother.–1965, p. 863–869.
15. Wick, W. E. 1967. Cephalexin, a new orally absorbed cephalosporin antibiotic. Appl. Microbiology. **15**:765–769.

Antimicrobial Agents and Chemotherapy—1969

Printed in USA

Laboratory Studies with a New Cephalosporanic Acid Derivative

D. R. CHISHOLM, F. LEITNER, M. MISIEK, G. E. WRIGHT, and K. E. PRICE

Research Division, Bristol Laboratories, Division of Bristol-Myers Co., Syracuse, New York 13201

In preliminary experimental studies, the laboratory performance of BL-P 1322, sodium 7-(pyrid-4-yl-thioacetamido)cephalosporanate, compared favorably with that of cephalothin. The antimicrobial spectrum of the two compounds was similar except that BL-P 1322 was found to be significantly more effective against strains of *Diplococcus pneumoniae, Enterobacter* sp., and *Mycobacterium tuberculosis.* The minimal inhibitory concentrations of BL-P 1322 were not markedly affected by changes in inoculum size, and the compound was bound to human serum proteins only to the extent of 44 to 50%. The concentrations of BL-P 1322 in blood after its parenteral administration to mice were at least comparable to those of cephalothin. The therapeutic efficacy of the new cephalosporin in experimental infections of mice proved to be outstanding; its activity against both gram-positive and gram-negative organisms was of the same order as that of cephalothin. Infections studied included ones caused by penicillinase-producing and nonproducing strains of *Staphylococcus aureus*, as well as strains of *D. pneumoniae, Streptococcus pyogenes, Escherichia coli, Klebsiella pneumoniae,* and *Proteus mirabilis.*

BL-P 1322, sodium 7-(pyrid-4-yl-thioacetamido)cephalosporanate, is a new semisynthetic derivative of 7-aminocephalosporanic acid that has been selected from a cephalosporin screening program as an interesting candidate for clinical use. The screen was designed to detect compounds that have broad-spectrum antimicrobial properties and possess, in addition, acceptable pharmacological characteristics. This report presents results from a series of in vitro and in vivo experiments which show that BL-P 1322 readily satisfies these criteria.

MATERIALS AND METHODS

Compounds. The sodium salt of 7-(pyrid-4-yl-thioacetamido)cephalosporanic acid (BL-P 1322) was originally synthesized by the Organic Chemistry Research Department at Bristol Laboratories (L. B. Crast, Jr., U.S. Patent 3,422,100). Larger quantities were prepared by the Chemical Development Department. The studies described in the present report were carried out with one of the latter lots. This material was a white crystalline solid with an estimated purity of 95%. It was soluble in water to the extent of at least 50 mg/ml. Commercially available cephalothin (Keflin, Eli Lilly & Co., Indianapolis, Ind.) was utilized as the control compound.

In vitro tests. The minimal inhibitory concentration (MIC) of the drugs for numerous clinical isolates of gram-positive and gram-negative organisms was determined by an agar-dilution method in which the multiple inoculator apparatus described by Steers, Foltz, and Graves (3) was used. *Streptococcus pyogenes* and *Diplococcus pneumoniae* were added as a 10^{-1} dilution of an overnight culture to plates containing Trypticase Soy Agar (BBL) plus 2% defibrinated sheep blood. *Haemophilus influenzae* and *Neisseria gonorrhoea* were tested in a similar manner except that the medium used was GC Medium Base (BBL) supplemented with Iso-VitaleX Enrichment (BBL) and 2% Hemoglobin Powder (BBL).

The MIC for all other microorganisms except *Mycobacterium tuberculosis* H37Rv was determined by adding a 10^{-2} dilution of an overnight culture in Antibiotic Assay Broth (Difco) to Nutrient Agar (Difco) plates containing various concentrations of the antibiotics. *M. tuberculosis* was grown for 5 to 7 days at 37 C in a liquid Tween-albumin medium and then diluted to 2% (v/v) in sterile medium for a working inoculum. Various concentrations of the test compound in the same medium were added in 0.5-ml volume to 3.5-ml portions of this inoculum. The MIC was determined after incubation at 37 C for 5 to 7 days.

Serum binding and drug concentrations in blood. The extent to which BL-P 1322 and cephalothin are bound to human serum proteins was determined by measuring the relative potency of the two compounds in *p*H 7.2, 0.001 M phosphate buffer and in 95% human serum (2). The concentrations in blood were determined by bleeding male, Swiss-Webster mice from orbital sinuses at various intervals after the compounds had been administered by the intravenous, intramuscular, or subcutaenous route. The techniques employed were those described by Price et al. (1).

Experimental mouse infections. The curative dose, 50% (CD_{50}), for BL-P 1322 and cephalothin was determined in a series of mouse infections produced by gram-positive and gram-negative bacteria. Tests were conducted in 18 to 22-g male, Swiss-Webster mice. In each case, the animals were infected by the intraperitoneal route with sufficient bacterial cells to kill all nontreated mice within 72 hr. The *Proteus mirabilis, Escherichia coli,* and *Staphylococcus aureus* (A9606 and A9537) strains were injected in 5% mucin. No mucin was required to produce infections with *D. pneumoniae, S. pyogenes,* and *Klebsiella pneumoniae.* Compounds were administered subcutaneously at 0 and 4 hr or at 0, 2, 4, and 6 hr postinfection. The percentage of dead animals versus the dose in milligrams per kilogram per treatment was plotted on log-probit paper to obtain the CD_{50}.

Effect of inoculum size on MIC. Serial twofold dilutions of cephalothin and BL-P 1322 were made in Nutrient Broth (Difco). Appropriate dilutions (10^{-2}, 10^{-4}, 10^{-6}) of an overnight broth culture of the test organism were added to tubes containing different concentrations of the test compound. All tubes were incubated at 37 C for 18 hr. The MIC was the lowest concentration causing complete inhibition of growth.

Bactericidal studies. Both BL-P 1322 and cephalothin were diluted in twofold increments in Nutrient Broth. Portions of a 10^{-4} dilution of an overnight culture of *S. aureus* A9537 were introduced into tubes containing various concentrations of the two drugs. Viable-cell counts were determined on each drug concentration after incubation for 3, 6, and 24 hr at 37 C.

RESULTS AND DISCUSSION

Cephalothin has been shown to be effective in vitro against most gram-positive cocci, including penicillin-resistant staphylococci. Substantially higher concentrations are required to inhibit gram-negative bacteria. That BL-P 1322 behaved similarly to cephalothin in vitro is clear from the data presented in Table 1. Against *D. pneumoniae, Enterobacter* sp., and *M. tuberculosis* H37Rv, however, BL-P 1322 was effective at concentrations somewhat lower than those found with cephalothin.

The influence of inoculum size on in vitro activity was examined with penicillin-sensitive and penicillin-resistant staphylococci, as well as with several gram-negative species. Results of these studies indicate that inhibitory concentrations of BL-P 1322 and cephalothin are not influenced significantly by differences in the size of the inoculum.

Table 1. *Comparative in vitro activity of cephalothin and BL–P 1322*

Organism	No. of strains tested	Median MIC (μg/ml)	
		Cephalothin	BL–P 1322
Staphylococcus aureus (P–)[a]	13	0.1	0.1
S. aureus (P+)	18	0.1	0.1
Diplococcus pneumoniae	14	0.1	0.03
Streptococcus pyogenes	18	0.01	0.01
Escherichia coli	56	4	3
Proteus mirabilis	26	1	1
P. morganii	16	500	500
P. vulgaris	9	4	2
Klebsiella pneumoniae	10	4	4
Enterobacter sp.	10	133	38
Serratia marcescens	6	>500	>500
Shigella sp.	9	2	1
Salmonella sp.	20	2	1
Haemophilus influenzae	22	2	2
Neisseria gonorrhoea	15	3	8
N. meningitidis	2	0.4	0.4
Mycobacterium tuberculosis	1	100	25

[a] (P–) = penicillinase nonproducer; (P+) = penicillinase producer.

The effect of several different concentrations of the two compounds on the viable count of *S. aureus* A9537 after 3, 6, and 24 hr at 37 C is shown in Fig. 1. At 0.25 μg/ml, BL-P 1322 and

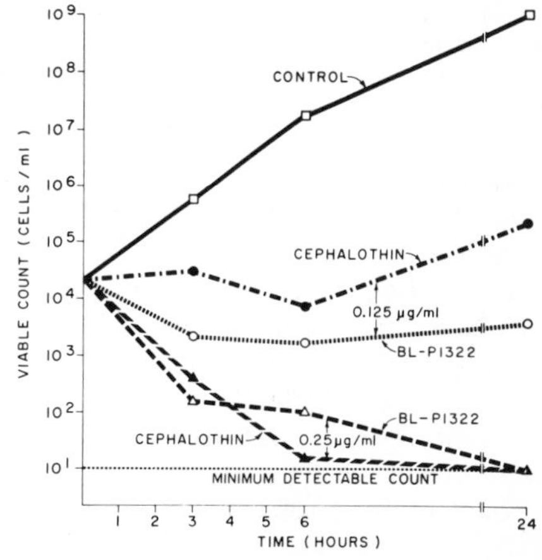

Fig. 1. *Number of viable Staphylococcus aureus A9537 cell units present in Nutrient Broth cultures containing various concentrations of BL-P 1322 and cephalothin. The cultures, which had an initial count of 3 × 10⁴ cells units/ml, were incubated at 37 C and sampled for enumeration of viable cells at the indicated times.*

Table 2. *Concentrations of BL–P 1322 and cephalothin in the blood of mice*

Compound	Dose (mg/kg)	Route[a]	Concn in blood (μg/ml) at selected time intervals after administration of the antibiotics				
			10 min	20 min	30 min	40 min	60 min
BL–P 1322	5	iv	3.6[b]	3.2	1.5	0.9	–
Cephalothin	5	iv	4.5	2.9	1.4	0.5	–
BL–P 1322	10	im	–	5	–	1.3	0.2
Cephalothin	10	im	–	3.7	–	1	0–0.4
BL–P 1322	10	sc	–	3.7	–	2.2	0.8
Cephalothin	10	sc	–	3.7	–	1.4	0–0.6

[a] Intravenous (iv), intramuscular (im), or subcutaneous (sc).
[b] Average value of 12 mice per compound at each time interval.

Table 3. *Comparative* CD_{50} *of cephalothin and BL–P 1322 in experimental bacterial infections of mice*[a]

Infecting organism	No. of treat-ments[b]	CD_{50} (mg/kg)	
		Cephalo-thin	BP–P 1322
Diplococcus pneumoniae A9585 .	2	7.0	5
Streptococcus pyogenes A9604 ..	2	6	6
Staphylococcus aureus A9537 (P–)[c]	2	0.7	0.7
S. aureus A9606 (P+)................	2	3	2
Escherichia coli A15119........	4	28	56
Klebsiella pneumoniae A9977 ...	4	60	110
Proteus mirabilis A9900	4	4	2

[a] Ten animals/dose level.
[b] Treated by the subcutaneous route at 0 and 4 hr or at 0, 2, 4, and 6 hr postinfection.
[c] (P–) = penicillinase nonproducer, (P+) = penicillinase producer.

cephalothin reduced the number of viable cells from an initial level of approximately 10^4 to a 24-hr level of less than 10^1/ml. Both compounds inhibited bacterial multiplication at 0.125 μg/ml and were without appreciable effect at 0.063 μg/ml.

The extent to which the compounds are bound to human serum proteins was determined by the technique of Scholtan and Schmid (2). The amount of BL-P 1322 bound ranged from 44 to 50%, as compared with about 65% for cephalothin.

The concentrations of BL-P 1322 and cephalothin in blood after their intravenous, intramuscular, or subcutaneous administration to mice are presented in Table 2. In general, for any given route of administration, peak levels attained with the two antibiotics were comparable. The length of time that detectable levels persisted was also found to be similar for the two compounds.

The relative effectiveness of BL-P 1322 and cephalothin in the treatment of mice infected with various gram-positive and gram-negative bacteria is shown in Table 3. It is readily apparent that the CD_{50} of BL-P 1322 against the four gram-positive organisms was low and compared favorably with the CD_{50} of cephalothin.

Infections produced by *E. coli* and *K. pneumoniae* also responded similarly to the two antibiotics, although the CD_{50} was considerably higher than with *P. mirabilis* and the gram-positive species.

LITERATURE CITED

1. Price, K. E., J. A. Bach, D. R. Chisholm, M. Misiek, and A. Gourevitch. 1969. Preliminary microbiological and pharmacological evaluation of 6-(R-α-amino-3-thienylacetamido) penicillanic acid (BL-P 875). J. Antibiot. (Tokyo) **22:**1–11.
2. Scholtan, W., and J. Schmid. 1962. Die Bindung der Penicilline an die Eiweisskorper des Serums und des Gewebes. Arzneimittel-Forschung **12:**741–750.
3. Steers, E., E. L. Foltz, and B. S. Graves. 1959. An inocula replicating apparatus for routine testing of bacterial susceptibility to antibiotics. Antibiot. Chemotherapy 9:307–311.

Antimicrobial Agents and Chemotherapy—1969

Siccanin, a New Antifungal Antibiotic

I. In Vitro Studies

MAMORU ARAI, KEIJIRO ISHIBASHI, and HIROSHI OKAZAKI

Fermentation Research Laboratories, Sankyo Co., Ltd., Tokyo, Japan

Siccanin was effective in vitro against various human pathogenic fungi, especially against *Trichophyton, Epidermophyton,* and *Microsporum.* The minimal inhibitory concentrations (MIC) of siccanin against these organisms were 0.4 to 6.3 μg/ml, even after 2 weeks of incubation. Activity of a lesser degree was demonstrated against gram-positive bacteria, including *Mycobacterium,* but neither gram-negative bacteria nor yeasts were susceptible to the antibiotic. Addition of serum to the test medium reduced the antibiotic activity to 30% of that without serum. Upon heating siccanin solution at 100 C for 2 hr, complete recovery of the initial activity was noted at *p*H 3 to 9. Development of siccanin resistance in some strains of *Trichophyton* was moderate (a fourfold decrease in susceptibility). The MIC effective against the original strain generally remained effective even after 20 transfers of the organism in the presence of the antibiotic.

Siccanin, an antifungal antibiotic produced by *Helminthosporium siccans,* was discovered in 1962 (3). The antibiotic was first isolated from the culture filtrate by solvent extraction, but more recently it was accumulated mainly in the mycelial fraction from which it was extracted with methanol or acetone. Siccanin was characterized as a compound with the molecular formula $C_{22}H_{30}O_3$; melting point, 139 to 140 C; $[\alpha]_D^{20}$,–136° (*c*=2, $CHCl_3$); *p*K, 10.9. The ultraviolet-absorption spectrum in ethyl alcohol showed maxima at 210.3 nm (ϵ=4.569 × 10^4) and 285.6 nm (ϵ=1.717 × 10^3) with a shoulder at 278.0 nm (ϵ=1.538 × 10^3). Infrared absorption ($CHCl_3$) was observed at 3,460, 1,630, 1,570, 1,360, 1,350, 1,170, 1,060, and 830 cm^{-1}. It was soluble in *n*-hexane, benzene, chloroform, ethyl acetate, and methanol, but was insoluble in water. The chemical structure of siccanin was established by X-ray crystallographic analysis of the *p*-bromobenzenesulfonate ester (2). A planar representation of the structure is shown in Fig. 1.

MATERIALS AND METHODS

Assay methods. Both biological and chemical procedures were applied to the quantitative determination of siccanin. Antibiotic activity was assayed by the conventional cylinder-plate method with the use of *Penicillium chrysogenum* Q176. The spore suspension was added to Sabouraud glucose-agar (300,000 spores per ml), and 8 ml of this seeded agar was poured into each petri dish without the base layer. Siccanin was dissolved in ethyl alcohol or dimethylformamide (DMF) and was diluted with sterile water. Final concentrations of the solvents were adjusted to 25 and 15% for ethyl alcohol and DMF, respectively. Siccanin concentrations of 10 and 2.5 μg/ml were used as high and low doses of the standard preparation. The antibiotic was evaluated over a range of 0.5 to 40 μg/ml, concentrations which gave zones of inhibition ranging in diameter from 14.0 to 29.0 mm.

A chemical determination of siccanin based on the diazo-coupling reaction of the phenolic group in the antibiotic on thin-layer chromatography was conducted as follows. Amounts of 0.5 to 3 μliters of methanol solutions containing siccanin at concentrations of 1 to 5 mg/ml were applied on chromatographic films (Eastman Chromagram Sheet 6061) by use of a 10-μliter microsyringe. The films were developed with either of two solvent systems, benzene or *n*-hexane-ethyl alcohol

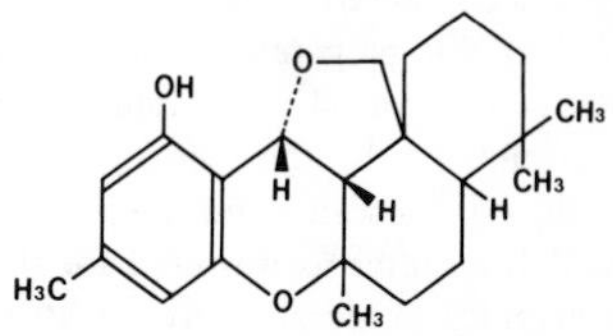

OH O CH3 H H H CH3 H3C O CH3

Fig. 1. *Structure of siccanin $C_{22}H_{30}O_3$; molecular weight, 342.*

(9:1). After removal of the residual solvent, the films were dipped into a mixture of 0.5% benzidine in 0.164 N HCl, 10% $NaNO_3$ in water, and acetone (2:2:1), in which they developed a red color; they were then dipped into 0.5 N HCl-acetone (1:1). The excess reagent on the films was blotted with filter paper at each step of dipping. The instrument used to scan the films was an Atago Densitometer (model 180–2).

Antimicrobial spectrum. The antifungal and antibacterial spectra of siccanin were determined by the standard agar-dilution assay method, with the use of Sabouraud glucose-agar and potato-sucrose-agar for fungi and glycerol-bouillon-agar for bacteria. Being sparingly soluble in water, siccanin in DMF (10 mg/ml) was diluted with water or 10% DMF to prepare a serial twofold dilution with the range of 0.5 to 1,000 μg/ml. The final concentration of DMF in the solution was adjusted to 10%. To 1 ml of these dilutions was added 9 ml of the melted agar medium in a petri dish. The test organisms were previously grown at 26 C for 2 days for yeasts and for 1 week for fungi, or at 37 C for 2 days for bacteria, on slants of the same media mentioned above. The agar plates were streaked with one loopful of the cell suspension, which had been washed off with water from the slants, and were incubated for 2 to 14 days at 26 C for fungi and at 37 C for bacteria.

Effect of serum on activity. The MIC against six strains of *Tricophyton* on Sabouraud glucose-agar containing 10 to 20% horse serum was determined by the agar-dilution method. Repression of siccanin activity by serum was also observed in shaken cultures. *T. interdigitale* F 62–3 was inoculated into 20 ml of Sabouraud glucose medium in 50-ml L tubes and was cultured with shaking at 26 C for 15 days. Siccanin and serum were added on the third day of incubation, and the weight of mycelia, after drying at 100 C for 2 to 6 hr, was measured at 3-day intervals.

Effect of pH on activity. The MIC of siccanin against *T. interdigitale* and *T. mentagrophytes* on media with various *p*H values was determined by the agar-dilution method on Sabouraud glucose-agar buffered with 0.02 M phosphate buffer to a final *p*H of 5, 6, 7, or 8.

Stability of siccanin. The heat stability of siccanin in solution was tested by use of 50% ethyl alcohol-buffer with various *p*H values. Siccanin (2 mg/ml) in ethyl alcohol was added to an equal volume of 0.05 M phosphate buffer or to the same buffer with the *p*H adjusted to 1 to 11 with HCl or NaOH. After being heated at 100 C for 2 hr, the solution was neutralized with 50% ethyl alcohol-buffer and then diluted with water or ethyl alcohol to prepare solutions containing 10 and 2.5 μg of siccanin per ml (estimated) in 25% ethyl alcohol for determination by the cylinder-plate method. A standard solution of siccanin was prepared with the same amount of the buffer as was used for the sample solution. The stability of siccanin in a crystalline state was also tested by storing siccanin crystals at 40 and 60 C and at 38 C with 80% relative humidity. The residual activity was assayed by both thin-layer chromatography and cylinder-plate methods.

Development of resistance to siccanin. Four strains of *Trichophyton* were successively transferred every 2 weeks on slants of Sabouraud glucose-agar in the presence of twofold dilutions of the highest concentrations of the antibiotic on which the growth of the organism was detected within 2 weeks. The MIC against the transferred organisms was determined by the agar-dilution method after 2-week incubation, and this was compared with the MIC against the original strains which had been successively transferred in the absence of siccanin at the same time intervals.

RESULTS

Antimicrobial spectrum. The antimicrobial activity of siccanin was apparent against parasitic fungi, especially against *Trichophyton, Epidermophyton,* and *Microsporum* (Table 1). The MIC against these organisms was as low as 0.4 to 6.3 μg/ml, even after 2 weeks of incubation. Strains of *Trichophyton* freshly isolated from patients were more susceptible to siccanin than were strains from laboratory stock cultures (MIC, 0.8 to 1.6 μg/ml at the 14th day). Most other fungi, including yeasts, were not susceptible to the antibiotic. A concentration of 100 μg/ml did not inhibit *Acremonium potronii* IAM 5074, *Phialophora verrucosa* MTU 589, *Allescheria boydii* NI 2053, *Scopulariopsis* sp. NHL-MR 109–3, *Aspergillus niger* ATCC 9142, *Penicillium notatum* NI 6233, *P. chrysogenum* IAM 7106, *Helminthosporium zizaniae* IAM 8, *Ophiobolus miyabeanus* AES O–1, *Macrosporium bataticola* AES M–1, *Alternaria kikuchiana* F42–5, *Fusarium moniliforme* USDA 1004.1, *Gibberella fujikuroi* F14–6, *Botrytis cinerea* IAM 5126, *Gloeosporium kaki* KYU 438, *Ceratostomella fimbriata* KYU 851, *Trichoderma* T–1 ATCC 9645, *Candida albicans* YU 1200, *Cryptococcus neoformans* WH–15–4, and *Torulopsis glabrata* IFO 0622. Gram-positive bacteria and *Mycobacterium* were inhibited by 25 to 50 μg/ml, but gram-negative bacteria, such as *Escherichia coli* NIHJ and *Proteus vulgaris* OX19, were not affected by 100 μg of siccanin per ml.

Effect of serum on activity. When tested by the agar-dilution method, the activity of siccanin was reduced to one-fourth to one-eighth of the original values by the addition of serum to the medium (Table 2). To evaluate stimulation of the growth of *Trichophyton* by serum, the effect of siccanin on the growth curve of *T.*

Table 1. *Minimal inhibitory concentrations of siccanin against various microorganisms*

Microorganism	Medium[a]	Minimal inhibitory concn (μg/ml)			
		2 days	4 days	7 days	14 days
Trichophyton interdigitale F62–3	S	0.8–1.6	1.6–3.1	1.6–3.1	3.1–6.3
T. interdigitale F62–8	S	0.1–0.2	0.4–0.8	0.8	0.8–1.6
T. interdigitale (freshly isolated)[b]	S	0.1	0.8	1.6	1.6
T. asteroides F62–1	S	0.2–0.8	0.8	0.8–1.6	0.8–1.6
T. mentagrophytes IFO 5809	S	0.2–0.8	1.6–3.1	3.1–6.3	3.1–6.3
T. mentagrophytes (freshly isolated)	S	0.1	0.8	1.6	1.6
T. rubrum IFO 5467	S	0.05–0.8	0.8	0.8	0.8–1.6
T. rubrum (freshly isolated)	S	–	0.05	0.4	0.8
T. cerebriforme IFO 5930	S	–	0.1	0.4	0.4
T. concentricum IFO 5972	S	–	0.2	0.8	1.6
T. ferrugineum IFO 5832	S	–	0.1–0.2	0.2–0.4	0.4
Epidermophyton floccosum ATCC 11146	S	0.05	0.05	0.4	0.4
E. floccosum (freshly isolated)	S	0.05	0.05	0.4	0.4
Microsporum gypseum IFO 5948	S	0.05	0.8	3.1	6.3
M. gypseum IFO 6076	S	0.8	3.1	3.1	3.1
M. gypseum IFO 6077	S	0.8	1.6	3.1	6.3
M. gypseum IFO 6078	S	0.8	1.6	3.1	6.3
M. audouini IFO 6074	S	–	0.1	0.4	0.8
Blastomyces brasiliensis OUT 4210	P	–	0.4	0.8	–
Hormodendrum pedrosoi IAM 5108	P	–	1.6	1.6	–
Sporotrichum schenckii IFO 5984	S	6.3	12.5	12.5	12.5
Coccidioides immitis IFO 5960	S	–	0.2	1.6	1.6
Geotrichum candidum IFO 6454	S	12.5	12.5	12.5	12.5
Aspergillus fumigatus IAM 2034	S	–	6.3	6.3	–
A. flavus ATCC 9463	S	12.5	25	25	–
A. oryzae NRRL 2160	S	3.1	>100	>100	>100
A. oryzae IAM 2625	S	0.8	12.5	>100	>100
Penicillium chrysogenum Q176	S	3.1	6.3	6.3	6.3
Piricularia oryzae AES	P	3.1	6.3	6.3	–
Bacillus subtilis PCI 219	G	25	25	25	–
Staphyloccocus aureus 209P	G	25	25	25	–
S. aureus 52–34[c]	G	25	25	25	–
Mycobacterium smegmatis 607	G	50	50	50	–

[a] P = Potato-sucrose-agar; S = Sabouraud glucose-agar; G = glycerol-bouillon-agar.
[b] Freshly isolated strains from the patients at Juntendo Hospital, in Tokyo.
[c] Resistant to chloramphenicol, tetracycline, and erythromycin.

interdigitale in medium with or without serum was tested as indicated in Fig. 2. The mycelial weight obtained with serum was approximately 1.5 times higher than that without serum at the stationary phase on the 12th day of incubation. Growth inhibition caused by 0.2 and 0.6 μg of siccanin per ml was reduced in the presence of serum to 25 and 50%, respectively, of the inhibition in the absence of serum at the same incubation time.

Effect of pH on activity. The MIC of siccanin was lower at *p*H 5.0 than at *p*H 6.0 or above (Fig. 3). In consideration of the growth retardation of *Trichophyton* in Sabouraud glucose-agar

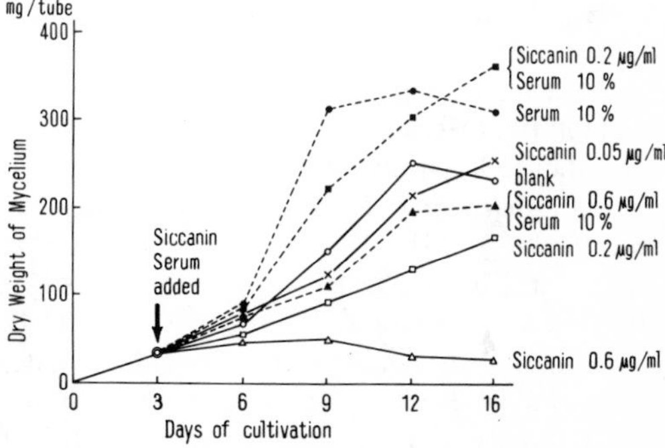

Fig. 2. *Effect of serum on the inhibition of growth of Trichophyton interdigitale F 62–3 by siccanin.*

Table 2. *Effect of serum on the activity of siccanin as determined by the agar dilution method.*

Test organism	Serum concn (%)	Minimal inhibitory concn (μg/ml)			
		2 days	5 days	7 days	14 days
Trichophyton asteroides F 62–1	0	0.2	0.8	0.8	0.8
	10	1.6	6.3	6.3	6.3
	20	1.6	6.3	6.3	6.3
T. interdigitale F 62–3	0	0.8	1.6	1.6	3.1
	10	6.3	12.5	12.5	12.5
	20	6.3	12.5	>12.5	>12.5
T. mentagrophytes IFO 5809	0	0.8	3.1	3.1	3.1
	10	6.3	12.5	12.5	12.5
	20	6.3	>12.5	>12.5	>12.5
T. interdigitale F62–8	0	0.1	0.4	0.8	1.6
	10	0.4	3.1	6.3	6.3
	20	0.8	6.3	12.5	12.5
T. rubrum IFO 5467	0	–	0.8	0.8	0.8
	10	–	3.1	6.3	6.3
	20	–	3.1	3.1	3.1
T. ferrugineum IFO 5832	0	–	0.2	0.4	0.4
	10	–	1.6	1.6	3.1
	20	–	3.1	3.1	3.1

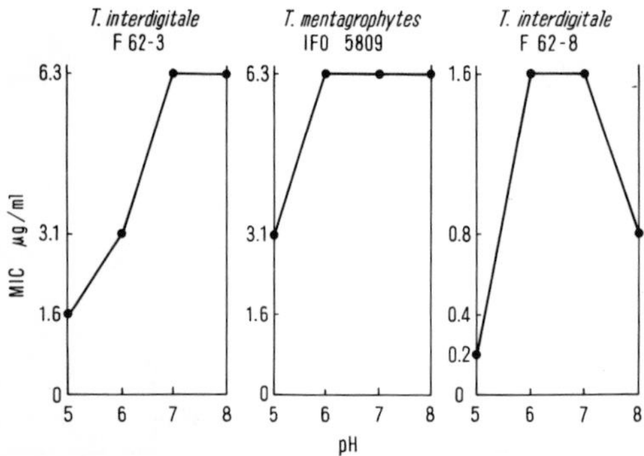

Fig. 3. *Effect of pH of the medium on the minimal inhibitory concentrations of siccanin.*

Table 3. *Stability of siccanin in 50% ethyl alcohol at various pH levels to heating at 100 C for 2 hr*

*p*H	Residual activity (%)
1	90.6
3	99.9
5	104.6
7	101.8
9	101.7
11	94.3

at *p*H 5.0, even in the absence of the antibiotic, the lower MIC at *p*H 5.0 might be partly due to the acidity of the medium.

Stability of siccanin. Siccanin was found to be very stable. Recovery of the initial activity was complete between *p*H 3 and 9, 90.6% at *p*H 1.0, and 94.3% at *p*H 11.0, even after heating at 100 C for 2 hr in a sealed tube (Table 3). Slight coloration was noted at *p*H 1.0 and 11.0. Siccanin was also stable in the crystalline state. As shown in Table 4, more than 90% of the initial activity still remained after 6 months of storage at 60 C, and 83.4% remained after storage at 38 C and a relative humidity of 80%.

Development of resistance to siccanin. Neither *T. interdigitale* F 62–3 nor *T. mentagrophytes* IFO 5809 exhibited a loss of susceptibility to siccanin after 20 serial transfers (Fig. 4). *T. interdigitale* F 62–8 and *T. rubrum* IFO 5467 showed a fourfold increase in the highest concentration of siccanin permitting growth.

DISCUSSION

Siccanin was found to be highly effective against *Trichophyton, Epidermophyton,* and *Microsporum,* but the MIC of the antibiotic for these dermatophytes changed significantly between 2 and 14 days of incubation. The effective concentrations at the 14th day were four-

Table 4. *Stability of siccanin in crystals*

Conditions of storage	Residual activity (%)				
	1 week		2 weeks		6 months, bioassay
	TLC[a]	Bioassay	TLC	Bioassay	
40 C	99.8	95.2	99.5	92.8	90.4
60 C	98.9	94.8	98.5	95.1	93.0
38 C, 80% RH	99.0	92.3	99.1	95.1	83.4

[a] Thin-layer chromatography.

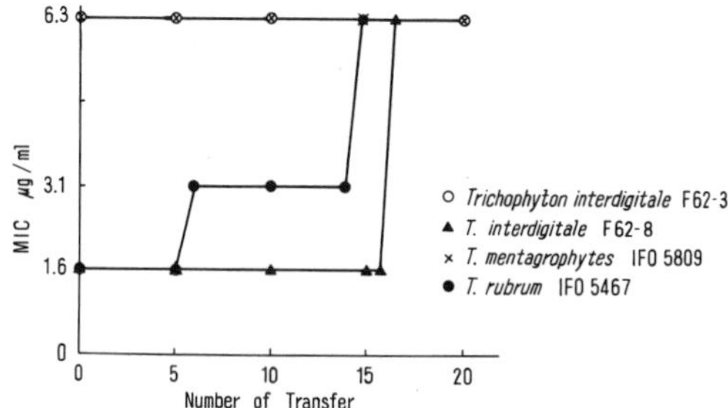

Fig. 4. *Development of resistance to siccanin.*

to 16-fold higher than those at the 2nd day. Furthermore, the growth of *Trichophyton* was inhibited by a very low concentration of siccanin in shaken culture (Fig. 2). *T. interdigitale* F 62–3 was completely inhibited by 0.6 μg of siccanin per ml, even after 15 days of incubation. It appears that the in vitro antifungal concentrations of siccanin were considerably affected by the difference in experimental procedures.

The antimicrobial activity was influenced by the addition of serum to the medium, as is the case with many other antibiotics (5, 7). The effect of serum on siccanin activity also varied with the experimental conditions. The growth of dermatophytes was enhanced by serum, which in turn increased the MIC of siccanin against these organisms. From the results in Fig. 2, the growth inhibition rates on the 12th day were plotted against the siccanin concentration to estimate the real effect of serum on the activity. The growth inhibition caused by a siccanin concentration of 0.6 μg/ml was equal to that caused by 0.2 μg/ml in the absence of serum. These results suggested that the actual reduction of siccanin activity with serum (to one-third) was less than the apparent reduction obtained in the agar-dilution method (to one-fourth to one-eighth).

Rosenthal and Wise (6) developed strains of *T. rubrum* and *M. canis* that were fivefold more resistant in vitro to griseofulvin than were parent strains. Gordee and Matthews (1) induced a fourfold decrease in susceptibility of *T. mentagrophytes* to pyrrolnitrin after eight weekly transfers. The present studies revealed that after 20 transfers no decrease in susceptibility to siccanin was acquired by *T. interdigitale* F 62–3 and *T. mentagrophytes* IFO 5809, and only a fourfold decrease in the susceptibility of *T. interdigitale* F 62–8 and *T. rubrum* IFO 5467 occurred. These observations indicate that dermatophytes may develop in vitro resistance to siccanin at a very slow rate. In addition, it may be significant that all four strains of *Trichophyton* were inhibited by 6.3 μg/ml after 20 transfers in the presence of the antibiotic. This finding suggests that 6.3 μg/ml might be a critical concentration of siccanin for inhibition of the growth of *Trichophyton* in general.

Ishibashi (4), one of the present authors, reported that endogenous respiration of *T. mentagrophytes* was inhibited by 60% at a siccanin concentration of 0.5 μg/ml. Studies on the mechanism of action of siccanin are now in progress, and inhibition of the respiratory system in *T. mentagrophytes* by siccanin has been further confirmed. The details of these investigations will be published elsewhere.

LITERATURE CITED

1. Gordee, R. S., and T. R. Matthews. 1968. Evaluation of the in vitro and in vivo antifungal activity of pyrrolnitrin. Antimicrob. Agents Chemother.–1967, p. 378–387.
2. Hirai, K., S. Nozoe, Y. Iitaka, K. Ishibashi, and M. Shirasaka. 1967. The structure of siccanin. Tetrahedron Lett. 23:2177–2179.
3. Ishibashi, K. 1962. Studies on antibiotics from *Helminthosporium* sp. fungi. VII. Siccanin, a new antifungal antibiotic produced by *Helminthosporium siccans*. J. Antibiot. (Tokyo) Ser. A 15:161–167.
4. Ishibashi, K. 1962. Studies on antibiotics from *Helminthosporium* sp. fungi. Part IX. Effects of ophiobolin, zizanin, pyrenophorin, and siccanin on respiration and phosphorous

incorporation of *Trichophyton mentagrophytes.* J. Agr. Chem. Soc. Jap. **36**:649–652.
5. Moriguchi, I., S. Wada, and T. Nishizawa. 1968. Protein bindings. III. Binding of sulfonamides to bovine serum albumin. Chem. Pharm. Bull. (Tokyo) **16**:601–605.
6. Rosenthal, S. A., and R. S. Wise. 1960. Studies concerning the development of resistance to griseofulvin by dermatophytes. Amer. Med. Ass. Arch. Dermatol. **81**:681–689.
7. Tompsett, R., S. Shultz, and W. McDermott. 1947. The relation of protein binding to the pharmacology and antibacterial activity of penicillins X, G, dihydro F, and K. J. Bacteriol. **53**:581–595.

Antimicrobial Agents and Chemotherapy—1969

Siccanin, a New Antifungal Antibiotic

II. In Vivo Studies

SHINICHI SUGAWARA

Central Research Laboratories, Sankyo Co., Ltd., Tokyo, Japan

Siccanin, an antibiotic derived from *Helminthosporium siccans*, is specifically effective against human pathogenic dermatophytes. The toxicity of siccanin was found to be very low. Tests on various pharmacological activities of siccanin gave practically negative results. Topically applied formulations of siccanin were very effective in improving the condition of lesions and in preventing fungal growth in experimental dermatophytic infections of guinea pigs. Oral treatment with siccanin powder failed to cure the disease in animals. Clinical trials by topical applications proved the effectiveness of siccanin against superficial fungal infections. The tolerance was found to be excellent.

Siccanin was discovered in the fermentation broth of *Helminthosporium siccans*, a parasitic fungus of Italian rye-grass, by Ishibashi (3). The antibiotic was isolated from mycelia by solvent extraction followed by carbon chromatography. The compound has the molecular formula of $C_{22}H_{30}O_3$ (melting point, 139 to 140 C), and the structure (1) was established by X-ray diffraction study by Hirai et al. (2). The antibiotic properties in vitro of siccanin were studied extensively by Arai et al. (1). They found siccanin to be highly effective against human pathogenic dermatophytes such as *Trichophyton, Epidermophyton,* and *Microsporum* sp. (minimal inhibitory concentrations, 0.4 to 6.3 μg/ml). Gram-positive bacteria and mycobacteria were inhibited by 25 to 50 μg/ml. Gram-negative bacteria and yeasts were not susceptible to 100 μg of siccanin per ml. The development of resistance to siccanin in *Trichophyton* sp. was hardly observed after 20 serial transfers at 2-week intervals.

In this report, some aspects of the activity of siccanin in vivo will be described.

MATERIALS AND METHODS

Male albino guinea pigs weighing about 350 g were infected superficially with a clinical isolate of *T. mentagrophytes* (granulare). Their backs were depilated with electric clippers and abraded with a sheet of sandpaper in four or six places. A sample from a heavy spore suspension (10^8 to 10^9 spores/ml) in saline prepared from a Sabouraud agar slant (14 days old) was applied to the area. Topical treatments applied once daily commenced at the third, fifth, and eighth days postinfection and continued for 8, 10, and 14 days, respectively, excepting on Sundays. These treatment schedules were designated day-3, day-5, and day-8 methods. Oral treatment once a day was started on the day of infection and lasted for 14 days. Lesions were graded on a basis of – to ++, depending on the degree of scaling, crusting, erythema, and hair growth. At intervals, scales were removed from the lesion, and, at the termination of the treatment, the skin was excised. These materials were cultured for 2 weeks at room temperature on plates of Sabouraud agar containing cycloheximide (0.4 mg/ml) and chloramphenicol (0.05 mg/ml). The results of the cultured lesion tissue were expressed as the number of positive cultures/total number of cultures.

For topical use, siccanin was formulated into ointments and tinctures (0, 1, and 2%) with glycol salicylate, di-*iso*-propyl adipate, and some minor ingredients. Each dose of ointment or solution was approximately 0.2 g or 0.2 ml. For oral use, siccanin fine powder (ca. 1.5 μm in diameter) was suspended in saline with a small amount of tragacanth powder. The in vivo activity of siccanin was compared with that of griseofulvin, pyrrolnitrin, tolnaftate, and some other commercially available preparations. Toxicological and pharmacological studies were conducted by usual methods.

RESULTS AND DISCUSSION

Toxicology. Acute toxicity of the antibiotic was estimated in mice and rats after administration by various routes (Table 1).

The subacute and chronic toxicity of the drug was studied in rabbits by daily topical applications of the antibiotic preparations for 1 month at 20, 40, and 80 mg per kg per day and for 6 months at 10, 30, and 60 mg per kg per day, respectively. There was no reduction of the rate of growth even at the highest doses. Histological and hematological observations of various organs and tissues revealed that the antibiotic is practically nontoxic. The precise results of these studies will be published separately by Suzuki et al.

Table 1. *Acute toxicity of siccanin*

Route of administration	Sex	LD_{50} (mg/kg)	
		Mouse	Rat
Intraperitoneal	♂	1,720	> 600[a]
	♀	1,590	> 600[a]
Oral	♂	>6,000[a]	>1,000[a]
	♀	>6,000[a]	>1,000[a]
Subcutaneous	♂	>3,000[a]	> 600[a]
	♀	>3,000[a]	> 600[a]

[a] None of the animals died at the highest dose tested.

Pharmacology. Studies on the effects of the antibiotic on the central nervous and cardiovascular systems and on blood sugar levels, and determination of such activities as antispasmodic, analgesic, anti-inflammatory, antitussive, and diuretic, gave practically negative results. Siccanin formulations were nonirritating to the skin and mucous membranes in both animals and humans.

Animal infection studies. Effects of siccanin against experimental dermatophytosis in guinea pigs evaluated by the day-3, day-5, and day-8 methods are presented in Tables 2, 3, and 4, respectively.

Table 2. *Effect of siccanin in animal experiments evaluated by the day-3 method (i.e., drug therapy starting at day 3 and administered eight times)*

Drug	Sample				Final lesion score		
	Scales after four treatments		Skin after eight treatments				
	1 week[a]	2 weeks	1 week	2 weeks	Scale	Erythema	Appearance
Untreated control	8/8[b]	8/8	8/8	8/8	++	+	Very poor
Ointment, 1%	0/16	0/16	0/16	0/16	±	–	Good
Tincture, 1%	0/16	0/16	3/16	6/16	±	–	Good

[a] Time for which samples were cultured.
[b] Number of positive cultures/total number of cultures.

Table 3. *Effect of siccanin in animal experiments evaluated by the day-5 method (i.e., drug therapy starting at day 5 and administered 10 times)*

Drug	Sample				Final lesion score		
	Scales after 5 treatments		Skin after 10 treatments				
	1 week[a]	2 weeks	1 week	2 weeks	Scale	Erythema	Appearance
Untreated control	16/16[b]	16/16	16/16	16/16	++	+	Very poor
Ointment							
0%	9/12	12/12	10/12	10/12	+	+	Poor
1%	0/20	0/20	1/20	3/20	–	–	Good
2%	0/20	0/20	2/20	4/20	–	–	Good
Tincture							
0%	12/12	12/12	12/12	12/12	++	+	Poor
1%	1/20	1/20	12/20	15/20	–	–	Good
2%	0/20	0/20	1/20	8/20	–	–	Good

[a] Time for which samples were cultured.
[b] Number of positive cultures/total number of cultures.

Table 4. *Effect of siccanin in animal experiments evaluated by the day-8 method (i.e., drug therapy starting at day 8 and administered 14 times)*

Drug	Sample				Final lesion score		
	Scales after 6 treatments		Skin after 14 treatments				
	1 week[a]	2 weeks	1 week	2 weeks	Scale	Erythema	Appearance
Untreated control	12/12[b]	12/12	12/12	12/12	++	±	Poor
Ointment							
1%	0/20	0/20	0/20	3/20	–	–	Good
2%	0/20	0/20	3/20	3/20	–	–	Good
Tincture							
1%	0/20	0/20	2/20	5/20	–	–	Good
2%	0/20	0/20	0/20	3/20	–	–	Good

[a] Time for which samples were cultured.
[b] Number of positive cultures/total number of cultures.

Placebo-treated and untreated but infected controls retained typical symptomatic appearances throughout the test periods, and all cultures of scales and skin of these groups gave a very high percentage of positive results. In contrast, after a few days of topical applications the cultures of scales of all treated groups became essentially negative and lesion scores were lowered. At the termination of treatment, both 1 and 2% siccanin formulations had significantly reduced the skin culture scores, and the general appearances of the infected areas on the backs of guinea pigs were highly improved, appearing as almost normal skin. Regrowth of hair was noted in some cases.

The cure rate (percentage) for siccanin formulations is tabulated in Table 5, together with the results obtained simultaneously with some commercially available preparations. The in vivo effectiveness of siccanin compared favorably

Table 5. *Comparison of the cure rate (per cent) with various preparations*

Drug[a]	Treatment method					
	Day-3		Day-5		Day-8	
	1 week[b]	2 weeks	1 week	2 weeks	1 week	2 weeks
Siccanin, O						
1%	100	100	95	85	100	85
2%	–	–	90	80	85	85
Siccanin, T						
1%	80	60	40	25	90	75
2%	–	–	95	60	100	85
Decanohydroxamate, O	50	–	–	–	–	–
Diamthazole, O	–	–	95	95	–	–
Griseofulvin, O	100	100	–	–	100	100
Haloprogin, O	65	–	–	–	–	–
Pyrrolnitrin, T	90	80	70	50	100	95
Thimerosal, T	30	–	–	–	–	–
Tolnaftate, O	85	50	50	35	100	90
Tolnaftate, T	95	45	80	70	100	100
Undecynate–I, O	95	75	–	–	75	60

[a] O = ointment; T = tincture.
[b] Time at which skin culture was read.

Table 6. *Clinical results with siccanin preparations*

Prepn used	Result	No. of infections						Effective rate (%)	No. of side reactions[a]
		Tinea cruris	Tinea pedis	Tinea corporis	Tinea ungium	Tinea versi-color	Total		
Ointment, 1%	Excellent	108	24	7			139 }	79.7	
	Good	56	84	5		3	148 }		
	Fair	6	16				22		
	Poor	8	39	2	1	1	51		
	Total	178	163	14	1	4	360		13 (3.6%)
Tincture, 1%	Excellent	61	27	8	1	2	99 }	77.4	
	Good	36	89	7		3	135 }		
	Fair	8	20				28		
	Poor	3	31		3	2	40[b]		
	Total	108	167	15	4	7	302		6 (2.0%)

[a] Skin irritation.
[b] Includes one *Candida* infection treated with tincture with poor results.

with that of griseofulvin, pyrrolnitrin, diamthazole, tolnaftate, and iodoundecynate, and was somewhat superior to results with variotin, haloprogin, decanohydroxamate, and thimerosal.

Oral treatment with siccanin powder in daily doses up to 100 mg/kg, starting on the day of infection and continuing for 14 days thereafter, failed to cure the disease in guinea pigs, whereas griseofulvin powder in daily doses of 100 mg/kg for the same period resulted in almost complete cure.

There was no change in the susceptibility to siccanin of strains isolated from cultures of the scales and skin of animals in the siccanin-treated groups.

Clinical studies. Preliminary clinical trials were conducted in more than 600 patients at 13 hospitals (Table 6). The effectiveness of topical applications of siccanin against fungal infections such as tinea cruris, tinea pedis, and tinea corporis was demonstrated. The incidence of side reactions was very low, and slight skin irritation was noted in only 19 of 662 patients (2.9%).

As described above, siccanin showed outstanding antifungal properties and should serve as an effective agent for treatment of superficial fungal infections in man.

ACKNOWLEDGMENTS

I express my sincere thanks to Takashi Okonogi for his comments and encouragement. The technical assistance of Isamu Igarashi, Harui Enokida, and Reiko Matoba is greatly appreciated.

LITERATURE CITED

1. Arai, M., K. Ishibashi, and H. Okazaki. 1970. Siccanin, a new antifungal antibiotic. I. In vitro studies. Antimicrob. Agents Chemother.–1969, p. 247–252.
2. Hirai, K., S. Nozoe, K. Tsuda, Y. Iitaka, K. Ishibashi, and M. Shirasaka. 1967. The structure of siccanin. Tetrahedron Lett. **23**:2177–2179.
3. Ishibashi, K. 1962. Studies on antibiotics from *Helminthosporium* sp. fungi. VII. Siccanin, a new antifungal antibiotic produced by *Helminthosporium siccans*. J. Antibiot. (Tokyo) Ser. A **15**:161–167.

Antimicrobial Agents and Chemotherapy—1969

Tinidazole, a Potent New Antiprotozoal Agent

M. W. MILLER, H. L. HOWES, and A. R. ENGLISH

Pfizer Medical Research Laboratories, Groton, Connecticut 06340

A series of 2-methyl-5-nitroimidazoles was prepared with substitution in the 1-position by short aliphatic side chains incorporating electron-attracting groups. Several sulfones were shown to be potent, well-tolerated, orally active antiprotozoal agents. One of these, ethyl[2-(2-methyl-5-nitro-l-imidazolyl) ethyl]sulfone, is in clinical trial under the nonproprietary name tinidazole.

A variety of nitroaromatic structures show systemic antiprotozoal activity. For example, **1** (Fig. 1) is a commercial coccidiostat (11), **2** and **3** are antihistomonal agents (6, 13), and **4**, metronidazole, is effective in the treatment of both trichomoniasis (1, 5) and amebiasis (15). Chloramphenicol, **5**. and the nitrofurans, **6**, are antibacterial (3, 14), and **8** shows both antibacterial and antiprotozoal efficacy (2). Niridazole, **7** (16), is used in the treatment of both schistosomiasis and amebiasis (12). [Chloramphenicol also suppresses molluscan schistosomiasis, as shown by Warren and Weisberger (17).]

The low toxicity of the 2-methyl-5-nitroimidazoles encouraged us to attempt to augment their antiprotozoal potency while maintaining a satisfactory therapeutic index. This effort resulted in the synthesis of ethyl[2-(2-methyl-5-nitro-1-imidazolyl)ethyl]sulfone, **9** (nonproprietary name tinidazole), a potent, orally effective agent against trichomoniasis and amebiasis (9). As with **8**, some spectrum expansion was noted in **9** and related structures.

MATERIALS AND METHODS

The 1-substituted 2-methyl-5-nitroimidazoles listed in Table 1 were prepared by the general method described below for tinidazole or by minor variants of this technique.

Ethylsulfonylethyl p-toluenesulfonate. To 69 g (0.5 mole) of ethylsulfonylethanol in 150 ml of pyridine at 0 C was added 95 g (0.5 mole) of *p*-toluenesulfonyl chloride. The *p*-toluenesulfonyl chloride was added in several portions so that the temperature remained between 0 and 10 C. After addition was complete (10 min), the reaction mixture was stirred at 0 to 10 C for 2 hr. Then 250 ml of water was added slowly, and the mixture was extracted with $CHCl_3$. The extract was washed with 2 N HCl until the aqueous phase remained acidic, and then was washed once with water. Drying over Na_2SO_4 followed by concentration yielded an oil which crystallized to give 113.2 g (77.5% of theoretical) of product (melting point, 57 to 58 C).

Ethyl[2-(2-methyl-5-nitro-1-imidazolyl)ethyl] sulfone. A mixture of 58.4 g (0.2 mole) of the above tosylate and 12.7 g (0.1 mole) of 2-methyl-5-nitroimidazole was heated at 145 to 150 C under nitrogen with stirring for 4 hr. The reaction mixture was extracted with 500 ml of hot water. The aqueous solution was adjusted to *p*H 9 with 10% Na_2CO_3, and then was extracted with $CHCl_3$. The $CHCl_3$ extract was washed with water, dried over Na_2SO_4, and concentrated to a gummy solid. Recrystallization from benzene yielded 4.36 g (18% of theoretical) of colorless crystals (melting point, 127 to 128 C).

The details of the biological evaluation procedure have been published elsewhere (4, 9).

The octanol-water distribution coefficients were determined according to techniques described by Hansch and his co-workers (7, 8, 10). The extinction coefficients of the ultraviolet absorptions were used to determine the amount of compound in each layer.

RESULTS AND DISCUSSION

Some of the 1-substituted 2-methyl-5-nitroimidazoles prepared are listed in Table 1 together with their minimal effective doses. The minimal effective dose is defined as the lowest oral dose (milligrams per kilogram of the drug) which, when administered daily for 3 days, commencing 24 hr after infection, completely prevented the development of trichomoniasis in 100% of the treated mice. In this case the minimal effective dose of a reference drug, metronidazole, **4**, is 100 mg/kg.

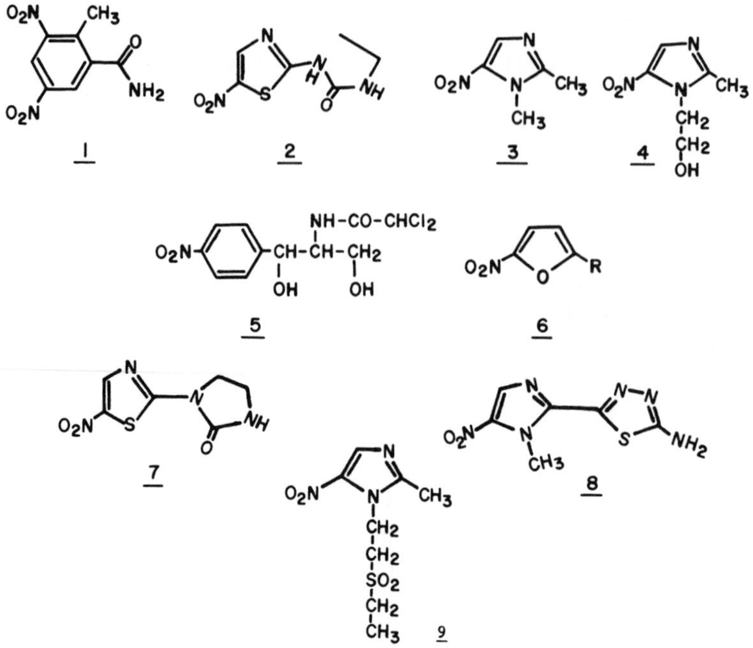

Fig. 1. *Nitroaromatic structures with systemic antiprotozoal activity.*

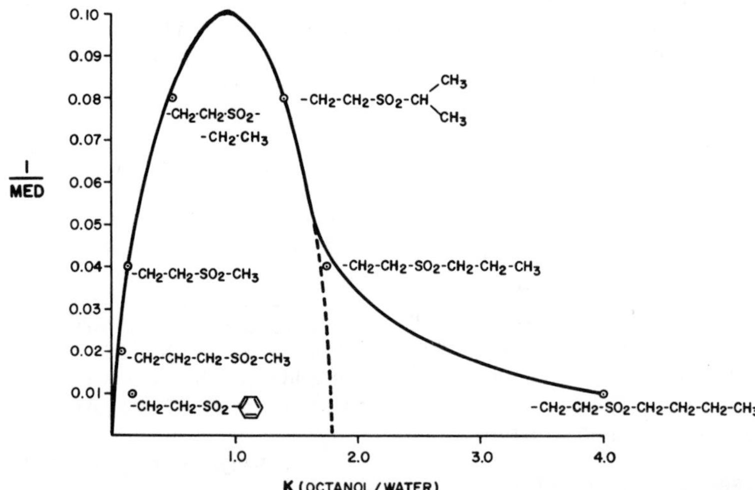

Fig. 2. *Relationship between antitrichomonal potency of 1-substituted 2-methyl-5-nitroimidazoles and the octanol-water distribution coefficient.*

Potency was improved by electron-attracting groups situated in the 1 side chain and separated from the 1-nitrogen atom by one, two, or three methylene groups. A series in which sulfone was the electron-attracting center was particularly active. It produced the most efficacious antitrichomonal agents of this series, **9** and **10**, each of which was eightfold more potent than the control in our model mouse infection.

Within narrow structural limits antitrichomonal potency was directly proportional to the octanol-water distribution coefficient. As shown in Fig. 2, a clean parabolic curve was obtained over much of the series without recourse to logarithms or other mathematical manipulations when distribution coefficients were plotted against the reciprocals of the minimal effective doses.

Table 1. *1-Substituted 2-methyl-5-nitroimidazoles*

N
O_2N N CH_3
R

No.	R	Minimal effective dose[a]
		mg/kg
9	$-CH_2CH_2SO_2CH_2CH_3$	12.5
10	$-CH_2CH_2SO_2CH(CH_3)_2$	12.5
10	$-CH_2CH_2SO_2CH_2CH_2CH_3$	25
12	$-CH_2CH_2SO_2CH_3$	25
13	$-CH_2CH_2SO_2CH_2CH_2CH_2CH_3$	100
14	$-CH_2CH_2CH_2SO_2CH_3$	50
15	$-CH_2CH_2CH_2SO_2-C_6H_5$	100
16	$-CH_2CH_2C{\equiv}CH$	25
17	$-CH_2C{\equiv}CH$	100
18	$-CH_2C{\equiv}CCH_2OH$	200
19	$-CH_2CH_2CH{=}CH_2$	100
20	$-CH_2CH_2-C_6H_5$	200
21	$-CH_2CHCl_2$	50
22	$-CH_2CF_3$	200
23	$-CH_2CH_2SCH_2CH_3$	–

[a] Determined in mice infected with *Trichomonas foetus*. See references 4 and 9 for a detailed description of the evaluation technique.

Toxicity. The metronidazole control had an acute oral mouse toxicity of >2,000 mg/kg, and tinidazole was similar. The oral LD_{50} of a 10% suspension was >3,600 mg/kg in mice and >2,000 mg/kg in rats. The intraperitoneal LD_{50} was >2,300 mg/kg in mice and >2,000 mg/kg in rats. Tinidazole administered orally as a 150 mg/kg dose twice daily for 30 days caused no adverse changes observable clinically or at necropsy in rats and in monkeys. The drug is currently under clinical investigation.

Spectrum. In vivo and in vitro studies have shown that, in addition to tinidazole's high degree of potency against *Trichomonas foetus* and *T. vaginalis*, it is also active against *Eimeria tenella* and *Histomonas meleagridis* and is as effective as metronidazole against *Entamoeba histolytica*.

The in vivo antibacterial activity of tinidazole was determined against experimental systemic infection in mice produced by the intraperitoneal inoculation of test organisms. Against an experimental *Streptococcus pyogenes* C203 infection, the PD_{50} was 25 mg/kg for the oral route and 33 mg/kg for the subcutaneous route. In contrast, tinidazole failed to protect mice against infection produced by *Pasteurella multocida*, *Staphylococcus aureus* (antibiotic-susceptible), and a multiply resistant (penicillin, streptomycin, tetracyclines) strain of *S. aureus* at dosage concentrations up to 100 mg/kg.

ACKNOWLEDGMENTS

We are grateful to Robert Martingano, Annette Silva, and John Kivlin for technical assistance. We appreciate reviews of the manuscript by John Lynch and by Richard Koch. Information on the toxicity of tinidazole was contributed by E. Gralla and the toxicology section at these laboratories.

LITERATURE CITED

1. Beckman, H. 1963-64. Vaginal trichomoniasis and moniliasis. Year B. Drug Ther., p. 383-384.
2. Berkelhammer, G., and G. Asato. 1968. 2-Amino-5-(1-methyl-5-nitro-2-imidazolyl)-1,2,4-thiadizole: A new antimicrobial agent. Science (Washington) **162**:1146.
3. Brock, T. D. 1964. Chloramphenicol, p. 119-169. *In* R. J. Schnitzer and F. Hawking (ed.), Experimental chemotherapy, vol. 3. Academic Press Inc., New York.
4. Butler, K., H. L. Howes, J. E. Lynch, and D. K. Pirie. 1967. Nitroimidazole derivatives. Relationship between structure and antitrichomonal activity. J. Med. Chem. **10**:891-897.
5. Cosar, C., L. Julou, and M. Bonazet. 1959. Activité de l'(hydroxy-2-ethyl)-1-methyl-2-nitro-5-imidazole (8.823 R.P.) vis-a-vis des infections expérimentales a *Trichomonas vaginalis*. Ann. Inst. Pasteur (Paris) **96**:238-241.
6. Cuckler, A. C., C. M. Malanga, A. J. Basso, R. C. O'Neill, and K. Pfister. 1956. Nithiazide. I. Chemical and biological studies on 1-ethyl-3-(5-nitro-2-thiazolyl)urea and related compounds. Proc. Soc. Exp. Biol. Med. **92**:483-485.
7. Fujita, T., J. Iwasa, and C. Hansch. 1964. A new substituent constant, π, derived from partition coefficients. J. Amer. Chem. Soc. **86**:5175-5180.
8. Hansch, C., and S. M. Anderson. 1967. The effect of intramolecular hydrophobic bonding on partition coefficients. J. Org. Chem. **32**:2583-2586.
9. Howes, H. L., Jr., J. E. Lynch, and J. L. Kivlin. 1970. Tinidazole, a new antiprotozoal agent: effect on *Trichomonas* and other protozoa. Antimicrob. Agents Chemother.–1969, p. 261-266.
10. Iwasa, J., T. Fujita, and C. Hansch. 1965. Substituent constants for aliphatic functions obtained from partition coefficients. J. Med. Chem. **8**:150-153.
11. Joyner, L. P. 1960. Coccidiostatic activity of 3,5-dinitro-*ortho*-toluamide against *Eimeria tenella*. Res. Vet. Sci. **1**:363-370.
12. Lambert, C. R. 1966. Nouveau traitement des schistosomiases et de l'amibiase, le CIBA 32644-Ba. Acta Trop. **23**:1-80.

13. Lucas, J. M. S. 1961. 1,2-Dimethyl-5-nitroimidazole, 8.595 R.P. I. Prophylactic activity against experimental histomoniasis in turkeys. Vet. Rec. **73**:465-467.

14. Paul, H. E., and M. F. Paul. 1964. The nitrofurans—chemotherapeutic properties, p. 307-359. *In* R. J. Schnitzer and F. Hawking (ed.), Experimental chemotherapy, vol. 2. Academic Press Inc., New York.

15. Powell, S. J., I. MacLeod, A. J. Wilmot, and R. Elsdon-Dew. 1966. Metronidazole in amoebic dysentery and amoebic liver abscess. Lancet **2**:1329-1331.

16. Schmidt, P., and M. Wilhelm. 1966. A new group of antischistosomal compounds. Angew. Chem. Int. Ed. Engl. **5**:857-862.

17. Warren, K. S., and A. S. Weisberger, 1966. Suppression of schistosomiasis in snails by chloramphenicol. Nature (London) **209**:422-423.

Antimicrobial Agents and Chemotherapy—1969

Tinidazole, a New Antiprotozoal Agent: Effect on *Trichomonas* and Other Protozoa

H. L. HOWES, Jr., J. E. LYNCH, and J. L. KIVLIN

Chas. Pfizer & Co., Inc., Groton, Connecticut 06340

Tinidazole, 1-[2-(ethylsulfonyl)ethyl)-2-methyl-5-nitroimidazole, is the most potent member of a series of compounds possessing a wide spectrum antiprotozoal activity. Antitrichomonal studies were conducted in vivo with mice infected with *Trichomonas foetus,* and in vitro activity against *T. foetus* and *T. vaginalis* was determined. In vivo, the minimal effective dose of tinidazole, whether administered orally or subcutaneously, was 12.5 mg/kg; that of metronidazole was 100 mg/kg. In vitro cidal studies showed that tinidazole is 4 to 16 times more potent than metronidazole against both *T. foetus* and *T. vaginalis.* However, when inhibitory activity was measured, the two drugs were of equal potency. The four- to eightfold difference in the calculated ratios of cidal activity to inhibitory activity accounts for the superior in vivo potency of tinidazole. The minimal effective dose of tinidazole against *Entamoeba histolytica* in rats was 50 mg/kg, as is that of metronidazole. No differences in cidal or inhibitory potencies of the two drugs were detectable in vitro. Studies in chickens showed tinidazole to be active against *Eimeria tenella* and *Histomonas meleagridis.* However, no activity was detected against *Trypanosoma brucei, T. congolense, T. cruzi,* or *Plasmodium berghei* in mice.

The chemotherapy of clinical trichomoniasis was significantly improved by the discovery of metronidazole in 1959 (3). Since that time, other workers (1, 2, 9, 10) have had considerable success in finding other potent, broad-spectrum antiprotozoal agents among nitroimidazole derivatives. Tinidazole, 1-[2-(ethylsulfonyl)ethyl]-2-methyl-5-nitroimidazole, is the most potent member of a new series of nitroimidazoles. The laboratory evaluation of its efficacy against a variety of protozoa is the subject of this report.

MATERIALS AND METHODS

Therapeutic antitrichomonal activity was studied in 1 CR female mice (18 to 20 g) with peritoneal cavity infections caused by *Trichomonas foetus.* The inoculum was prepared from 48-hr cultures of *T. foetus* grown in Standard Trypticase Serum Base (STS) medium (BBL) plus 6% human serum. Mice, in groups of four to six, were inoculated intraperitoneally with 5×10^5 organisms. Drug, dissolved in 1% methyl cellulose, was administered orally or subcutaneously in a 0.5-ml volume once a day for 3 days, commencing 24 hr after infection. Mice were examined 24 hr after the third treatment. If no viable organisms were detected by a microscopic examination of a peritoneal wash with a portion of STS, they were considered "cleared" of infection.

The minimal inhibitory (MIC) and cidal (MCC) concentrations against *T. foetus* and *T. vaginalis* were determined in either STS or Diamond's (4) medium. In the MIC studies, the number of organisms per milliliter at the beginning (zero hour) of the incubation period (37 C) was 4×10^4 to 10×10^4; for the MCC studies, it was 5×10^5 to 20×10^5. Counts of viable (external or internal motion, or both) organisms per milliliter were made, and the ratio of organisms after incubation to organisms at zero hour was calculated. The MIC was defined as the lowest concentration (micrograms per milliliter) which produced a ratio $\leqslant 0.5$. The MCC was defined as the lowest concentration in which no viable organisms ($<1.25 \times 10^3$/ml) were detected. Ratios of cidal activity to static activity were calculated by dividing the MCC by the MIC.

Therapeutic activity against amoebiasis was studied in 35- to 45-g male albino rats (five or six per group) by use of a previously described method (7). Briefly, rats were inoculated intracecally with approximately 2×10^5 *Entamoeba histolytica* trophozoites obtained from 48-hr

Locke's egg slant-Locke's overlay cultures. Drugs were administered orally once a day for 4 days, commencing 48 hr after infection. Efficacy was evaluated, both macroscopically and microscopically, 24 hr after the fourth dose. The number of rats cleared of infection and the average degree of infection (ADI) were determined. The ADI was calculated by summing the pathology scores of individual rats and dividing the total by the number of rats. The scoring system was as follows: 0, no amoebae or gross pathology; 1, few amoebae; 2, many amoebae, no cecal inflammation; 3, many amoebae, cecal lesions or inflammation; 4, many amoebae, cecal lesions, inflammation, and mucus.

Locke's egg slant-Locke's overlay cultures were used to determine the MIC, which was defined as the lowest concentration in which no organisms ($<1.25 \times 10^3$) were detected after 48 hr of incubation (37 C) in the presence of drug. Cidal studies were conducted by incubating approximately 9×10^4 trophozoites/ml in the presence of 80 μg of drug per ml in Locke's solution and comparing the number of organisms per milliliter to that of drug-free controls.

Prophylactic anticoccidial activity was studied in 1-day-old Barred Rock Cross cockerels (five per group) infected with *Eimeria tenella.* Medicated feed was administered to chickens commencing 24 hr before their oral inoculation with 2×10^5 sporulated oocysts. Medication was continued until the eighth day postinfection, at which time the percentage of normal weight gain and ADI were determined. The ADI was calculated as described above, and the scoring system (6) was as follows: 0, no cecal lesions; 1, light cecal lesions; 2, moderate cecal lesions; 3, severe cecal lesions; 4, death.

Prophylactic antihistomonal activity was studied in 10-day-old Barred Rock Cross cockerels infected with *Histomonas meleagridis* in a previously described manner (8). Briefly, immediately after intramuscular vaccination with a Newcastle's disease vaccine (Vipol 717 strain, Vineland Poultry Laboratories), the chickens (eight per group) were infected orally with 550 embryonated *Heterakis gallinae* ova. As a further stress, feed was withheld from all the chickens for 24 hr after inoculation with ova. Drug dissolved in 1% methyl cellulose was administered once a day for 5 days, commencing 2 hr before ova inoculation on the day of infection. All the chickens were necropsied 11 days postinfection, and the percentage of normal weight gain and ADI, calculated as described above, were determined.

Therapeutic antimalarial activity was studied in CF 1, male, albino mice (17 g) infected with *Plasmodium berghei* (NYU strain). Mice (10 per group) were inoculated intraperitoneally with sufficient parasitized red blood cells to produce 100% mortality in 6 to 8 days. Efficacy was based on a significant delay (>2 standard deviations) in the mean day of death after a single subcutaneous treatment 72 hr postinfection.

Therapeutic antitrypanosomal activity was studied in CF 1 male albino mice (17 to 20 g) infected with *Trypanosoma brucei, T. congolense,* or *T. cruzi.* The methods, which have been previously described (5), essentially involved the oral or subcutaneous administration of drug twice a day for 3 days, commencing 1 hr postinfection, and the determination of efficacy on the basis of delay of the mean day of death.

RESULTS

In a series of in vivo studies tinidazole was found to be highly effective against *T. foetus* in mice. Its minimal effective dose by oral and subcutaneous routes was 12.5 mg/kg (Table 1). The minimal effective dose of metronidazole was 100 mg/kg. Both drugs were well tolerated

Table 1. *Therapeutic activity against Trichomonas foetus in mice (four to six per group)*

Route	Dose	Tinidazole			Metronidazole		
		No. of trials	Total no. infected	Per cent cleared	No. of trials	Total no. infected	Per cent cleared
	mg/kg						
Oral	200	1	5	100	7	33	100
	100	2	10	100	7	33	100
	50	4	20	100	7	33	56
	25	9	44	100	5	25	4
	12.5	9	44	100	2	12	0
	6.25	9	44	12			
Subcutaneous	100				1	5	100
	50				1	5	20
	25				1	5	0
	12.5	1	5	100			
	6.25	1	5	0			

in these studies at the 200 mg/kg level orally, and tinidazole, like metronidazole, was subsequently found to be tolerated at much higher doses by both mice and rats (>2,000 mg/kg produced no toxic symptoms).

In vitro studies were conducted with trichomonads in STS and Diamond's medium. Initially, STS medium was used both for in vitro studies and as the source of inoculum for in vivo experiments. However, Diamond's medium is clearer than STS medium, and therefore easier to examine microscopically, and it has the capacity to support three times as many organisms per milliliter (Table 2). Therefore, all of the in vitro studies reported were conducted in Diamond's medium. *T. foetus* and *T. vaginalis* had similar generation times in the two media, but the extended log growth period in Diamond's medium resulted in greater numbers of organisms being obtained (Table 2). Maximal numbers of organisms per milliliter were reached in from 30 to 40 hr. Thus, it was concluded that MIC or MCC data from long-term (>24 hr) incubation studies were difficult to interpret, in that the control cultures were close to or in the log death phase, and that attention should be focused on data from short-term in vitro studies.

In studies with *T. foetus* and *T. vaginalis* in Diamond's medium, the MIC of metronidazole was only one to two times that of tinidazole over a range of incubation periods (Table 3). However, tinidazole was cidal at much lower concentrations than metronidazole, and the tinidazole MCC to MIC ratios ranged from 2 to 4, whereas the ratios for metronidazole ranged from 4 to 32. An estimate of the magnitude of tinidazole's greater cidal potency (four- to eightfold) was obtained by dividing the MCC to MIC ratios of metronidazole by those of tinidazole (Table 3). After 48 hr of incubation, the *T. vaginalis* MCC to MIC ratios differed by only twofold. This may have been partially due to the approach of the log death phase during which cidal effects may be potentiated.

Results from additional cidal studies, in which trichomonads were exposed to a 20 μg/ml concentration of metronidazole and tinidazole, clearly reflected the superior cidal potency of the latter (Fig. 1 and 2). After only 3 hr of exposure to tinidazole, there was a significant

Table 2. *Growth of Trichomonas foetus and T. vaginalis in STS and Diamond's medium*

Species	Medium	Generation time	End of log phase	Time to maximal no. of organisms/ml	Maximal no. of organisms/ml
		hr	*hr*	*hr*	
T. foetus	STS	4.0	25	40	1.7×10^6
	Diamond's	4.0	32	40	5.9×10^6
T. vaginalis	STS	3.5	20	35	1.8×10^6
	Diamond's	3.2	25	30	5.0×10^6

Table 3. *Minimal inhibitory concentration (MIC) and minimal cidal concentration (MCC) against Trichomonas foetus and T. vaginalis in Diamond's medium*

Incubation time	Species	Tinidazole			Metronidazole			Metronidazole ratio/tinidazole ratio
		MCC	MIC	Ratio (MCC/MIC)	MCC	MIC	Ratio (MCC/MIC)	
hr		μg/ml	μg/ml		μg/ml	μg/ml		
6	*T. foetus*	40	10	4	320	10	32	8
24		5	2.5	2	20	2.5	8	4
6	*T. vaginalis*	40	10	4	>80	20	>8	>2
12		5	2.5	2	80	5	16	8
24		2.5	1.25	2	20	2.5	8	4
48		1.25	1.25	2	10	2.5	4	2

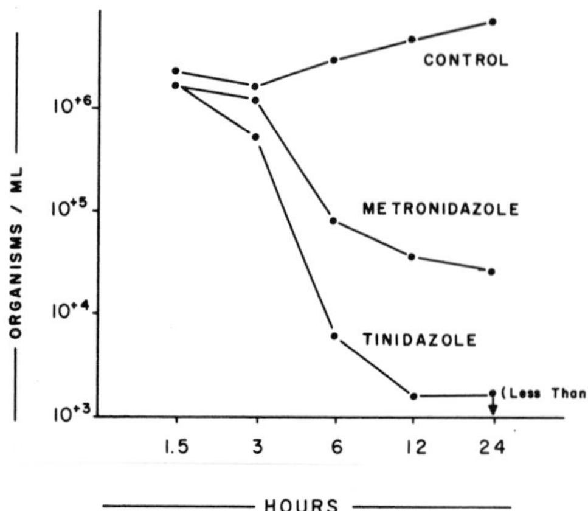

Fig. 1. *Cidal activity against Trichomonas foetus in Diamond's medium. Drug concentration: 20 μg/ml.*

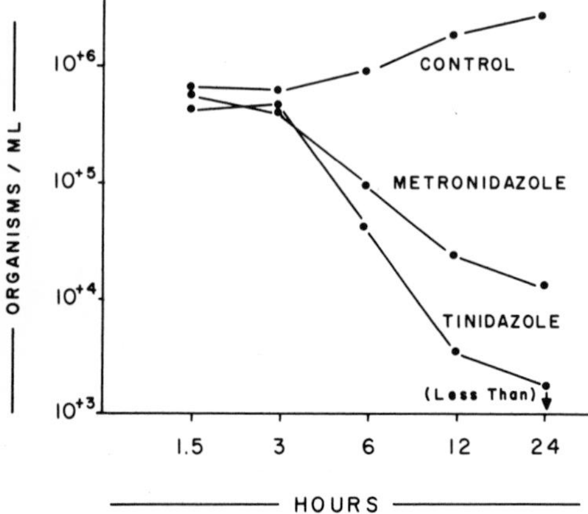

Fig. 2. *Cidal activity against Trichomonas vaginalis in Diamond's medium. Drug concentration: 20 μg/ml.*

reduction in the *T. foetus* counts (Fig. 1). The log reduction in counts by 12 hr was >3 for tinidazole and <2 for metronidazole. Against *T. vaginalis* (Fig. 2), the differences were of a similar order of magnitude.

When compared in vivo in rats infected with *E. histolytica,* the minimal effective dose of both drugs was 50 mg/kg (Table 4). After 48 hr of incubation, the MIC of both drugs against *E. histolytica* trophozoites was also the same (40 μg/ml) and, not surprisingly, a cidal rate study with 80 μg of each drug per ml did not distinguish between the two compounds (Fig. 3).

Metronidazole and tinidazole were effective at relatively high concentrations in feed in controlling cecal coccidiosis (Table 5). The minimal

Table 4. *Therapeutic activity against Entamoeba histolytica in rats (five or six per group)*

Treatment	Dose	No. of rats cleared/no. infected	Avg degree of infection
	mg/kg		
Tinidazole	200	9/10	0.10
	50	7/10	0.30
	25	2/6	2.00
	6.25	13/24	1.02
	3.125	3/9	2.00
Metronidazole	200	5/6	0.17
	50	7/9	0.22
	25	3/6	1.33
	6.25	11/23	1.28
	3.125	4/9	1.56
Infected control	–	8/24	1.94

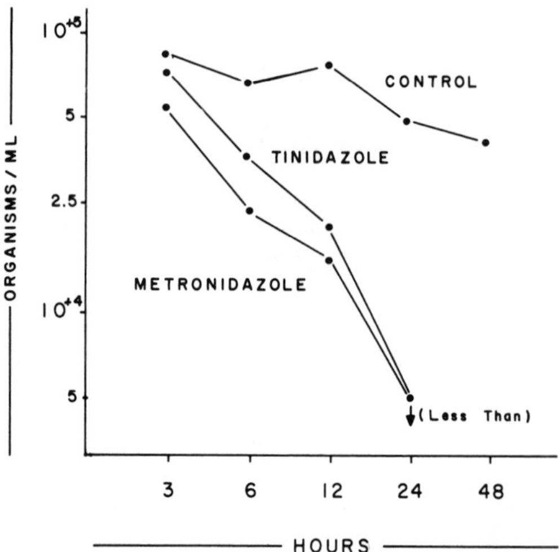

Fig. 3. *Cidal activity against Entamoeba histolytica trophozoites in Locke's solution. Drug concentration: 80 μg/ml.*

Table 5. *Prophylactic activity against Eimeria tenella in 10-day-old cockerels (five per group)*

Treatment	Per cent in feed	Per cent wt gain	Avg degree of infection
Tinidazole	0.10	102	0.8
	0.05	72	2.8
Metronidazole	0.40	75	1.0
	0.20	57	2.4
Infected control	–	37	3.4

effective concentration of tinidazole was 0.10%, a level which permitted the chickens to grow at a normal rate and which all but completely suppressed cecal pathology. Metronidazole at 0.40% controlled cecal pathology to a similar degree; however, there was some weight suppression which may have been due to drug toxicity.

In a limited prophylactic study with *H. meleagridis*, tinidazole and metronidazole were effective at 100 and 200 mg/kg, respectively. However, the minimal effective doses were not determined.

Metronidazole and tinidazole were ineffective against *P. berghei* (600 mg/kg subcutaneously), *T. cruzi, T. brucei*, and *T. congolense* (200 mg/kg orally and subcutaneously) in mice.

DISCUSSION

Although the term "broad-spectrum antiprotozoal" may occasionally be used rather loosely, with 5-nitroimidazoles in general and tinidazole in particular, it is almost an understatement. In the studies reported herein, tinidazole was shown to be active against a potpourri of parasitic protozoa (*(T. foetus, T. vaginalis, E. histolytica, E. tenella*, and *H. meleagridis)* from three of the four subphyla (Mastigophora, Sarcodina, Sporozoa, and Ciliophora) that make up the phylum Protozoa. Since tinidazole was not tested against a ciliophoran, e.g. *Balantidium coli*, the question of whether or not the fourth subphylum can be included in its spectrum remains unanswered.

Although tinidazole was inactive against one sporozoan, *P. berghei*, it effectively controlled cecal coccidiosis induced by another sporozoan, *E. tenella*, at concentrations in feed in excess of 0.05%. It was at least four times as potent as metronidazole, but it is not as potent as some of the more popular anticoccidials currently used (Amprolium, Zoalene, Coyden, Bonaid). However, its potency compares rather favorably with some of the older anticoccidials, e.g., Nitrosal, Polystat, Unistat, and Sulquin, all of which have been used in the feed at concentrations of 0.1% or higher.

Tinidazole was inactive against species of a mastigophoran genus *(Trypanosoma)* which produce blood infections in mice. However, mastigophorans in the peritoneal cavity of mice *(T. foetus)* and the ceca of chickens *(H. meleagridis)* were susceptible to tinidazole. The minimal effective concentration of tinidazole in the chicken-*H. meleagridis* test model was not determined. However, since histomonads and trichomonads are close relatives in the class Zoomastigophorea, one might predict that, just as tinidazole was more potent than metronidazole as an antitrichomonal, tinidazole would also be the more potent antihistomonal.

Tinidazole and metronidazole were equipotent in vitro as static antitrichomonals, but tinidazole was 4 to 16 times more potent as a cidal agent. The difference in cidal potency manifested itself in the mouse-*T. foetus* test model in which the minimal effective doses of tinidazole and metronidazole were 12.5 and 100 mg/kg, respectively. The promising nature of these data stimulated the undertaking of clinical studies in humans, and the results obtained to date indicate that relatively low doses of tinidazole have been effective (J. R. Migliardi, *personal communication*).

Perhaps the most notorious species of the phylum Sarcodina is *E. histolytica*, and the need for better chemotherapeutic agents in the treatment of human amoebiasis is well known. Encouraging reports have appeared in the literature which describe the effectiveness of 5-nitroimidazoles, namely, niridazole (11) and metronidazole (12), against both the intestinal and the hepatic forms of the disease. In our laboratory studies, tinidazole was at least as effective as metronidazole and therefore is being considered for the treatment of amoebiasis.

ACKNOWLEDGMENTS

We are pleased to acknowledge the technical assistance of G. Smith and J. Drury.

LITERATURE CITED

1. Berkelhammer, G., and G. Asato. 1968. 2-Amino-5-(1-methyl-5-nitro-2-imidazolyl)-1,3,4-thiadiazole: a new antimicrobial agent. Science (Washington) **162**:1146.
2. Butler, K., H. L. Howes, J. E. Lynch, and D. K. Pirie. 1967. Nitroimidazole derivatives. Relationship between structure and antitrichomonal activity. J. Med. Chem. **10**:891-897.
3. Cosar, C., S. Julou, and M. Bonazet. 1959. Activité de l'(hydroxy-2'éthyl)-1-méthyl-2-nitro-5-imidazole (8.823 R.P.) vis-a-vis des infections expérimentales a *Trichomonas vaginalis*. Ann. Inst. Pasteur (Paris) **96**:238-241.
4. Diamond, L. S. 1957. The establishment of various trichomonads of animals and man in axenic cultures. J. Parasitol. **47**:488-490.
5. Goble, F. C. 1950. Chemotherapy of experimental trypanosomiasis. I. Trypanocidal activity of certain bis(2-methyl-4-amino-6-quinolyl) amides and ethers. J. Pharmacol. **98**:49-60.
6. Lynch, J. E. 1961. A new method for the primary

evaluation of anticoccidial activity. Amer. J. Vet. Res. **22**:324-326.

7. Lynch, J. E., B. J. Bamforth, and D. Goeckeritz. 1956. The laboratory evaluation of antiamebic activity. The comparative results obtained by the use of *in vitro* and *in vivo* methods. Antibiot. Chemother. **6**:337-350.
8. McGuire, W. C., M. W. Moeller and N. F. Morehouse. 1964. The effect of dimetridazole ongrowth and the prevention of histomonosis in poultry. Poultry Sci. **43**:864-871.
9. Mitrovic, M., M. Hoffer, and E. G. Schildknecht. 1969. Antihistomonal activity of 1,2-disubstituted 5-nitroimidazoles. Antimicrob. Agents Chemother.–1968, p. 445-448.
10. Peterson, E. H. 1968. The efficacy of 1-methyl-2-carbamoyloxymethyl-5-nitroimidazole against enterohepatitis in experimental poults. Poultry Sci. **47**:1245-1250.
11. Powell, S. J., I. MacLeod, A. J. Wilmot, and R. Elsdon-Dew. 1966. Ambilhar in amoebic dysentery and amoebic liver abscess. Lancet **2**:20-22.
12. Powell, S. J., I. MacLeod, A. J. Wilmot, and R. Elsdon-Dew. 1966. Metronidazole in amoebic dysentery and amoebic liver abscess. Lancet **2**:1329-1331.

Antimicrobial Agents and Chemotherapy—1969

Tinidazole and Metronidazole Pharmocokinetics in Man and Mouse

JAMES A. TAYLOR, JR., JOSEPH R. MIGLIARDI, and M. SCHACH VON WITTENAU

Medical Research Laboratories, Chas. Pfizer & Co., Inc., Groton, Connecticut 06430

Tinidazole (1-[2-(ethylsulfonyl)-ethyl]-2-methyl-5-nitroimidazole) was found to be effective against *Trichomonas foetus* in mice, and had significantly greater in vivo potency and in vitro cidal activity than metronidazole (1-β-hydroxyethyl-2-methyl-5-nitroimidazole). The disposition of both drugs was studied in mice and in healthy adult human volunteers. In mice, tinidazole and metronidazole were rapidly absorbed ($A_{1/2}$ <1.0 hr) and showed similar plasma half-lives ($T_{1/2}$ = 1.7 hr). In man, the concentrations of apparent drug in plasma were comparable after administration of equal doses of the two drugs and decreased at similar rates. However, whereas unchanged drug appeared to be the only nitroimidazole in plasma and urine after administration of tinidazole, several nitro-containing derivatives were present in those body fluids after ingestion of metronidazole. The urinary recovery of unchanged drug within 24 hr was about 20% of the administered dose of tinidazole and 15% of that of metronidazole. The superior in vivo potency of tinidazole in mice cannot be explained on a pharmacokinetic basis but must be due to higher intrinsic activity. By analogy, tinidazole may be therapeutically effective in man at a significantly lower dose than metronidazole.

A new synthetic antimicrobial agent, tinidazole (structure I, Fig. 1), showed an in vivo potency against *Trichomonas foetus* in mice eightfold greater than that of metronidazole (structure II, Fig. 1). A study with both drugs was conducted in mice to determine whether this potency difference could be explained on a pharmacokinetic basis. The pharmacokinetics of tinidazole and metronidazole were also investigated in man during phase I human toleration studies with single and multiple oral doses.

MATERIALS AND METHODS

Studies in mice. Male albino mice weighing 18 to 20 g received metronidazole (100 mg/kg) or tinidazole (12.5 or 100 mg/kg) as a single oral dose in aqueous solution. At regular time intervals, 10 mice per dose group were sacrificed, blood samples were pooled, and plasma was collected for assay.

Studies in humans. Thirty healthy male volunteers from a prison inmate population were divided into three equal groups: group I was maintained as a placebo control; group II received tinidazole in capsules; and group III received metronidazole in tablet form. On day 6, the oral dosage of metronidazole was increased from 250 mg initially to 250 mg three times daily, and was maintained at this level through day 35, the last day of the trial. The tinidazole dosage was increased more slowly up to 250 mg three times daily on day 18, and was also maintained at this level until day 35.

Plasma and urine samples were obtained from subjects at specific time intervals during single- and multiple-dose studies. During continuous administration of 250 mg three times daily, plasma samples were obtained from the metronidazole and tinidazole groups on days 22 and 29. On these latter days, samples were collected just prior to each 250-mg dose (0.8:30, 14:00, and 18:30 hr), 3 hr after the first and second doses (11:30 and 17:00), and 14 hr after the last daily dose (08:30 hr of next day).

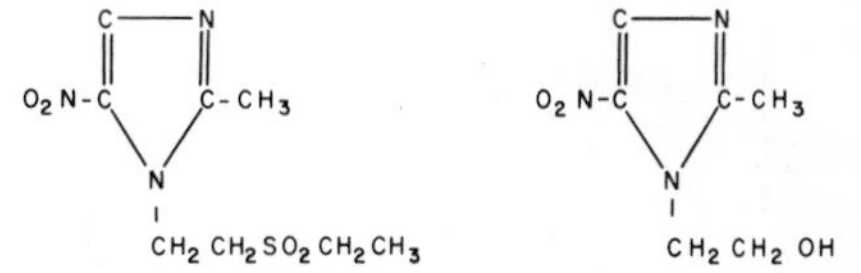

C——N, ‖ ‖, O_2N-C C-CH_3, N, $CH_2CH_2SO_2CH_2CH_3$ — I

C——N, ‖ ‖, O_2N-C C-CH_3, N, CH_2CH_2OH — II

Fig. 1. *Structures of tinidazole (I) and metronidazole (II).*

The chemical assay procedure used to measure apparent tinidazole and metronidazole concentrations in plasma or urine was a polarographic method similar to that employed by Kane (1). This assay is based on the electrolytic reduction of the nitro group and measures the total nitroimidazole concentration. The resultant increase in diffusion current in the reduction potential is proportional to the drug concentration. A dropping mercury electrode was used, and polarograms (recordings of diffusion current versus voltage) were obtained with a Beckman Electroscan 30. Plasma and urine samples were assayed directly, without prior extraction or dilution. By this method, nitroimidazole concentrations above 0.5 μg/ml in plasma and above 5 μg/ml in urine could be measured with a standard deviation of ±10%.

Plasma protein binding of tinidazole and metronidazole was measured by the method of Toribara (3). Drug distribution between chloroform and *p*H 9 borate buffer was determined by an eight-step countercurrent procedure beginning with a spiked urine standard and moving the low phase. Both layers in all tubes were assayed for nitroimidazole content. The organic layer was blown to dryness under a stream of nitrogen, and the residue was redissolved in *p*H 9 borate buffer. Distribution of urinary nitroimidazoles in drug-treated individuals was also investigated to determine possible nonreductive biotransformation.

RESULTS AND DISCUSSION

Studies in mice. Nitroimidazole concentrations in plasma of mice after single oral doses tinidazole (12.5 or 100 mg/kg) or metronidazole (100 mg/kg) are shown in Fig. 2. On similar oral doses (100 mg/kg), mice given tinidazole and metronidazole showed rapid drug absorption (<1.0 hr) and similar apparent drug half-lives in plasma (1.7 hr). The drug concentrations in plasma were higher by a factor of 3:2 after administration of tinidazole. The highest concentrations observed (4.5 μg/ml after 12.5 mg of tinidazole per kg, 77.5 μg/ml after 100 mg of tinidazole per kg, and 55.0 μg/ml after 100 mg of metronidazole per kg) in all cases were those obtained at 0.5 hr after oral administration. The apparent tinidazole concentrations after a 12.5 mg/kg dose were lower than expected on the basis of the concentrations observed after a 100 mg/kg dose. These data show that the eightfold potency superiority of tinidazole over metronidazole in mice cannot be explained by absorption or plasma drug kinetics, but is probably due to differences in intrinsic potencies.

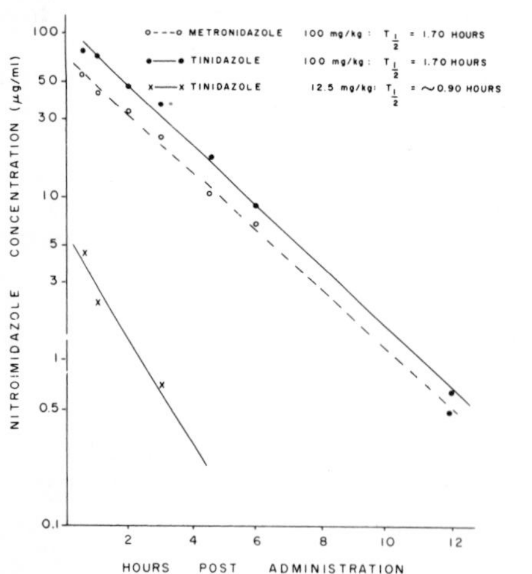

Fig. 2. *Nitroimidazole concentrations in plasma of mice after single oral doses of tinidazole or metronidazole.*

Studies in humans. An investigation of tinidazole and metronidazole binding to human plasma proteins showed that neither drug was significantly bound (12 and 20%, respectively). This suggests that in man plasma protein binding probably has little effect on the pharmacokinetics of these compounds.

Nitroimidazole concentrations in human plasma after administration of a single oral 125-mg capsule of tinidazole or 250-mg tablet of metronidazole are shown in Fig. 3. After tinidazole administration, apparent drug concentrations increased, with an absorption half-life ($A_{1/2}$) of 2.4 hr, to a maximum at 6 hr, and decreased, thereafter, with a half-life ($T_{1/2}$) of 9.4 hr. Apparent metronidazole concentrations

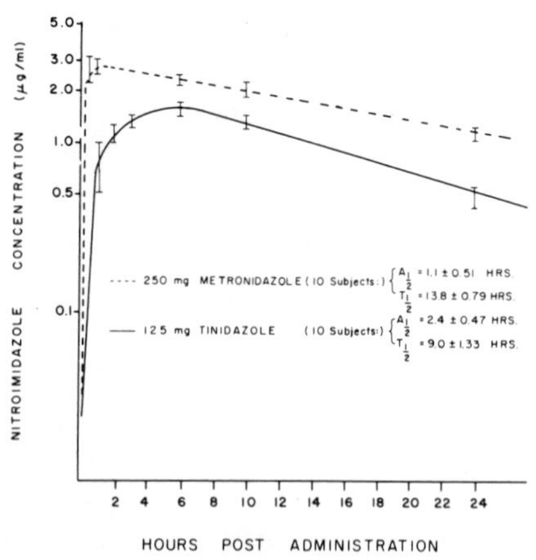

Fig. 3. *Nitroimidazole concentrations in human plasma after single oral doses of tinidazole or metroindazole.*

in human plasma increased more rapidly ($A_{1/2}$ = 1.1 hr) to a maximum at 1 hr, and then decreased, with a half-life of 13.8 hr. Differences in absorption and plasma half-lives were significant at the 95 and 99% confidence levels, respectively. Absorption half-life differences may reflect variation between tablet and capsule dissolution rates.

Concentrations of apparent drug in plasma increased in proportion to the dosage of metronidazole and tinidazole. After a period on the dosage of 250 mg three times daily, apparent drug concentrations reached equilibrium levels, as shown in Fig. 4. A pharmacokinetic similarity is noted. The difference between apparent tinidazole and metronidazole concentrations in plasma at equilibrium after administration of the same daily oral dose was not significant at the 95% confidence level.

Nitroimidazole excretions in urine were determined after single and multiple oral doses of tinidazole or metronidazole (Fig. 5). After similar oral doses, twice as much drug-related material was measured in the urine of subjects given metronidazole as in the urine of subjects receiving tinidazole.

Urine from metronidazole-dosed male volunteers and urine spiked with standard metronidazole were partitioned between chloroform and pH 9 borate buffer in an eight-step countercurrent distribution. This procedure was employed to differentiate between drug and metabolites. The presence in human urine of at least one major metabolite more polar than metronidazole was indicated (Fig. 6). Thin-layer

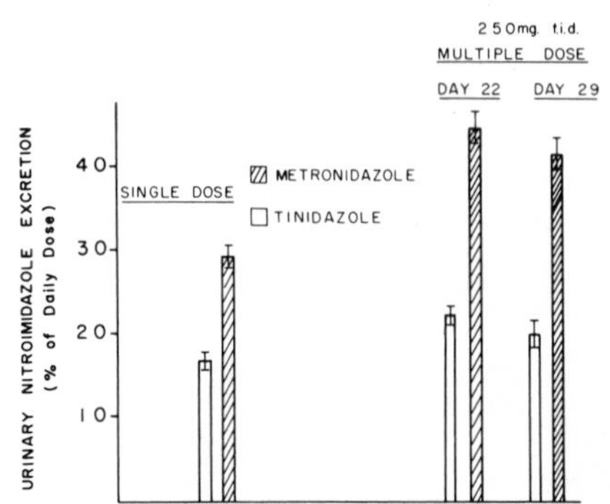

Fig. 5. *Percentage urinary recovery of nitroimidazole within 24 hr after single or multiple oral doses of tinidazole and metronidazole in humans.*

chromatography of an n-butyl alcohol extract of urine from this group showed at least five drug-related zones, two of which predominated. Stambough et al (2) reported similar findings, indicating that the major metabolite of metronidazole in man is the 2-hydroxymethyl derivative. This metabolite together with unchanged drug comprises 70% of the total nitro-containing compounds excreted in human urine. On administration of 250 mg three times daily, approximately 15% of a total daily dose may be excreted as unchanged drug. The presence of metronidazole metabolites was indicated in human plasma also because only 7 to 9% of nitroimidazole present was extractable with chloroform, wheras 16 to 20% of standard drug was removed from plasma spiked at similar drug levels.

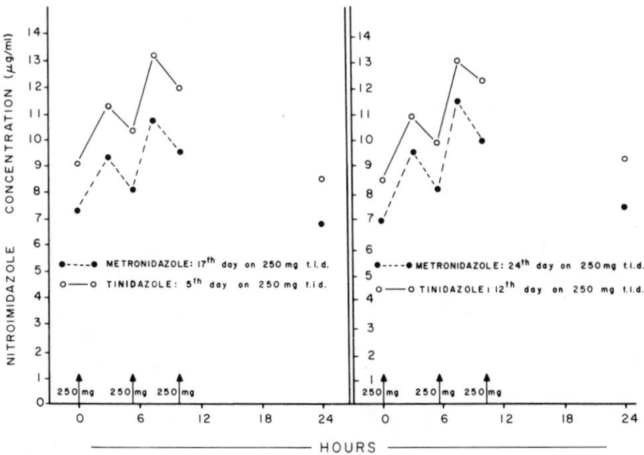

Fig. 4. *Nitroimidazole concentrations in plasma of humans during a daily oral regimen of 250 mg of tinidazole or metronidazole three times daily.*

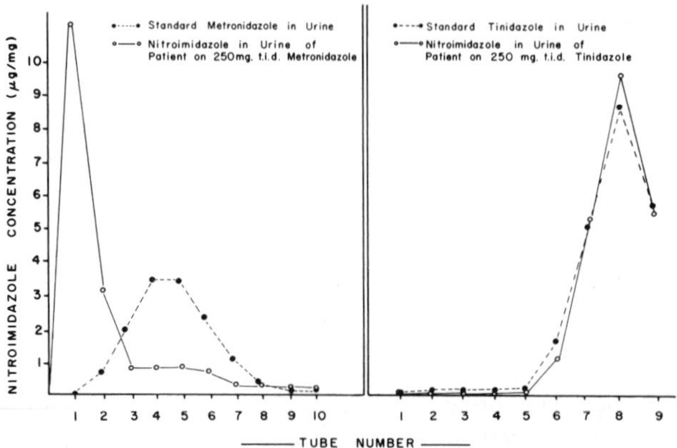

Fig. 6. *Countercurrent distribution (between pH 9 borate buffer and chloroform) of urinary nitroimidazoles from subjects maintained on tinidazole or metronidazole (250 mg three times daily).*

Similar countercurrent distribution studies with urine collected from humans on tinidazole did not indicate the presence of other nitroderivatives (Fig. 6). Thin-layer chromatography of urine extract showed only one spot corresponding to unchanged drug. Over 40% (42 to 45%) of total nitroimidazole was extracted with chloroform from plasma of the tinidazole-treated group, and the same amount was removed by chloroform from plasma spiked with tinidazole standard. These studies indicate that tinidazole is more resistant to nonreductive biotransformation.

Plasma pharmacokinetics of tinidazole and metronidazole are similar in mice and also in man. In spite of this similarity, in mice tinidazole is more potent than metronidazole. By extrapolation, in man tinidazole may be therapeutically effective at a significantly lower dose than the 250 mg three times daily regimen presently recommended for metronidazole.

ACKNOWLEDGMENTS

We are grateful to Roberta Tanner for valuable technical assistance and to H. L. Howes and G. A. Forcier for their cooperation during this investigation.

LITERATURE CITED

1. Kane, P. O. 1961. Polarographic methods for the determination of two anti-protozoal nitroimidazole derivatives in materials of biological and non-biological origin. J. Polarographic Sci. **8**:73–78.
2. Stambough, J. E., L. G. Feo, and R. W. Manthei. 1967. Isolation and identification of the major urinary metabolite of metronidazole. Life Sci. **6**:1811–1819.
3. Toribara, T. Y. 1953. Centrifuge type of ultrafiltration apparatus. Anal. Chem. **25**:1286.

Antimicrobial Agents and Chemotherapy—1969

BAY b 5097, a New Orally Applicable Antifungal Substance with Broad-Spectrum Activity

M. PLEMPEL, K. BARTMANN, K. H. BÜCHEL, and E. REGEL

Farbenfabriken Bayer, Wuppertal, Germany

In vitro, BAY b 5097 was found to have antifungal activity against dermatophytes corresponding to the spectrum of the activity of griseofulvin; against yeasts, dimorphic fungi, and chromomycetes, its activity corresponded to that of amphotericin B and nystatin. BAY b 5097 was also active in vitro against some molds. No primary resistance was found among 72 clinical isolates of *Candida* and 40 strains of *Trichophyton.* No secondary resistance was induced in *T. mentagrophytes* and *Aspergillus nidulans* by more than 15 serial passages. At concentrations attainable in vivo, BAY b 5097 was fungistatic. Systemic infections of mice produced by *C. albicans, Histoplasma capsulatum, A. fumigatus,* and *A. nidulans* were treated orally with good results. Preliminary pharmacokinetic and metabolic studies showed that the drug was quickly absorbed after oral administration, but practically no absorption occurred when it was given subcutaneously or intraperitoneally. The distribution into organs and tissues was good. In man, administration of 20 mg/kg three times daily—a dosage justified by toxicity studies—provided concentrations in the serum which seem to be adequate for trials of the drug in systemic mycoses such as candidiosis, coccidiodomycosis, histoplasmosis, South American blastomycosis, cryptococcosis, some types of chromoblastomycosis and phycomycosis, aspergillosis, and deep dermatophytoses. Furthermore, the drug was active and well tolerated when applied topically to mice and guinea pigs with experimental infections produced by *T. mentagrophytes* or *T. quinckeanum.* Therefore, its trial as local therapy in epidermophytoses seems worthwhile.

BAY b 5097 is a chlorinated tritylimidazole (Fig. 1) synthesized by Büchel and Regel in 1967. It is a weak base which is poorly soluble in water but is soluble in organic solvents such as acetone, chloroform, and dimethylformamide.

EXPERIMENTAL

In vitro activity. The in vitro activity of BAY b 5097 was determined in liquid media (Table 1).

The minimal inhibitory concentration (MIC) of BAY b 5097 was not higher than 4 μg/ml except for *Madurella* species and one strain of *Nocardia.* Thus, the compound has good activity against dermatophytes, yeasts, blastomycetes, and chromomycetes. Its activity against dermatophytes corresponds to the spectrum of activity of griseofulvin, and its activity against yeasts, blastomycetes, and chromomycetes covers the spectrum of amphotericin B and nystatin. It was also active against *Aspergillus* species and molds.

Among 72 strains (freshly isolated from humans) and among 40 strains of *Trichophyton* species, none showed primary resistance to BAY b 5097. Resistance beyond the range of normal susceptibility was not acquired by *T. mentagrophytes, Candida albicans,* and *A. nidulans* during 14 to 50 serial passages.

In vivo activity. The in vivo activity of BAY b 5097 was tested against experimental candidiasis. The curves in Fig. 2 represent the average survival rates observed in eight experiments with a total of 160 animals per group. After 5 days, only 5% of the animals in the control group survived. Animals treated orally with increasing dosages (highest dosage was 150 mg/kg of body weight) showed a survival rate of 40 to 100%. The treatment was administered 1 hr preinfection and 7 hr postinfection.

With a treatment course consisting of two oral applications daily for 5 days the ED_{95} was calculated to be 54 mg/kg of body weight twice daily; the ED_{50} was 20 mg/kg twice daily.

The effectiveness of BAY b 5097 in the treatment of experimental candiasis was also measured by counting the number of viable cell units in kidney homogenates. Fig. 3 shows that the number of cell units in untreated mice was

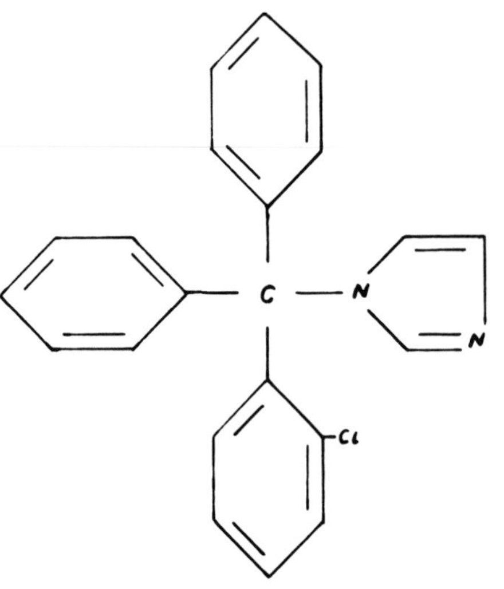

Fig. 1. *Structure of BAY b 5097 [bis-phenyl-(2-chlor-phenyl)-1-imidazolylmethane].*

Table 1. *Activity of BAY b 5097 against various species of fungi*

Species	No. of strains tested	Minimal inhibitory concn (µg/ml)				
		<1	1	4	10	>20
Trichophyton spp.	40	7[a]	23	2	–	–
Epidermophyton floccosum	3	3	–	–	–	–
Microsporum spp.	12	4	8	–	–	–
Aspergillus spp.	6	–	6	–	–	–
Penicillium commune	1	–	1	–	–	–
Mucor mucedo	3	–	–	3	–	–
Cladosporium carrioni	1	–	1	–	–	–
Madurella spp.	3	–	–	–	1	2
Candida albicans	72	4	61	7	–	–
C. tropicalis	7	–	6	1	–	–
Candida spp.	10	2	7	1	–	–
Histoplasma capsulatum	4	–	4	–	–	–
Cryptococcus neoformans	3	–	2	2	–	–
Coccidioides immitis	7	–	7	–	–	–
Paracoccidioides brasiliensis	1	–	1	–	–	–
Sporotrichum schenkii	2	–	2	–	–	–
Chromomycetes (*Allescheria* and *Phialophora*)	10	–	6	4	–	–
Nocardia spp.	4	–	–	3	1	–

[a] Number of strains susceptible to the indicated concentration.

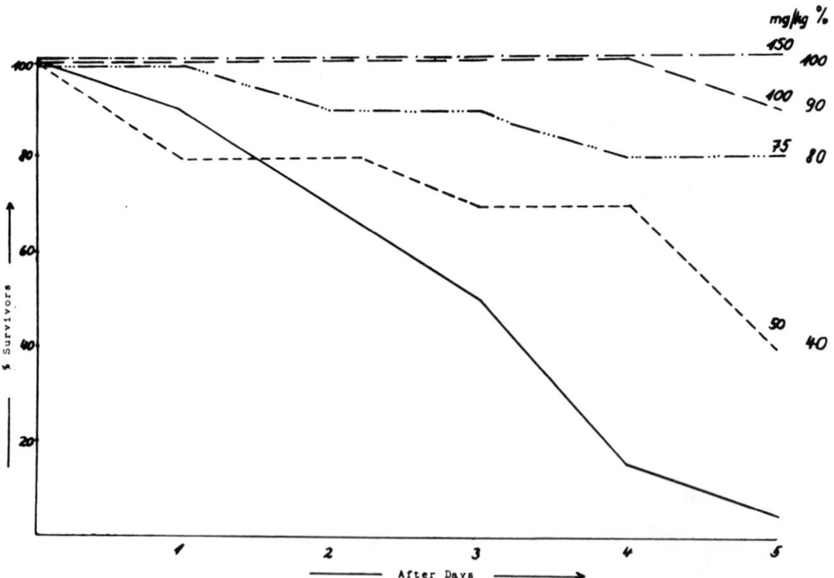

Fig. 2. *Mortality curves for Candida-infected mice treated with BAY b 5097. The drug was administered 1 hr before and 7 hr after intravenous infection in dosages of 50, 75, 100, or 150 mg/kg. The survival of an untreated control group is shown also. The number of mice used for each dose level was 160. The values plotted are mean values from eight experiments. The solid line represents the control.*

200 to 500 times higher than that in animals treated twice daily with 40 mg of BAY b 5097 per kg of body weight.

The systemic antimycotic activity of BAY b 5097 was also demonstrated against experimental histoplasmosis, aspergillosis, and trichophytosis. The compound was very effective when administered orally in doses of 50 to 100 mg/kg twice daily for a total treatment period of 1 to 8 days. The compound was ineffective when administered parenterally, probably because it is poorly absorbed after parenteral administration.

The development of trichophytosis was suppressed in guinea pigs by topical application of different formulations containing 1% BAY b 5097 once a day. If the treatment lasted from the 3rd to the 12th days after infection, the relapse rate was 60 to 80%; the action of BAY b 5097 is only fungistatic. If the treatment was carried out for 1 month, the relapse rate dropped to 5%. Skin irritation was not observed.

Pharmacodynamic and pharmacokinetic properties. The pharmacological screening procedures did not reveal any exceptional activity. On oral administration of BAY b 5907, the acute LD_{50} ranged from 750 to 1200 mg/kg of body weight in various animal species. Higher doses administered in subacute toxicity studies resulted in some cellular enlargement in the liver and adrenals.

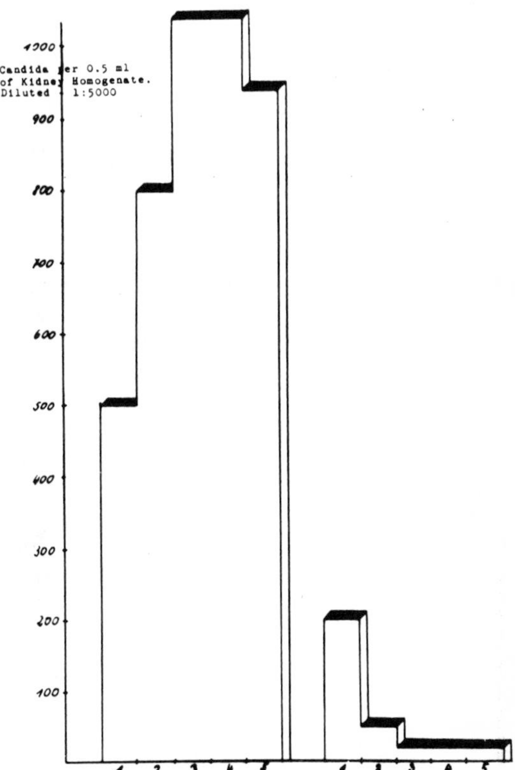

Fig. 3. *Viable-cell counts in the kidneys of Candida-infected mice. Kidneys were homogenized and diluted 1:5,000; counts were made on 0.5-ml amounts of the diluted homogenate. The counts in untreated control mice are shown at the left. The counts on the right are for mice treated orally with 40 mg of BAY b 5097 per kg of body weight twice daily for 5 days. The numbers of the absissa represent days after infection.*

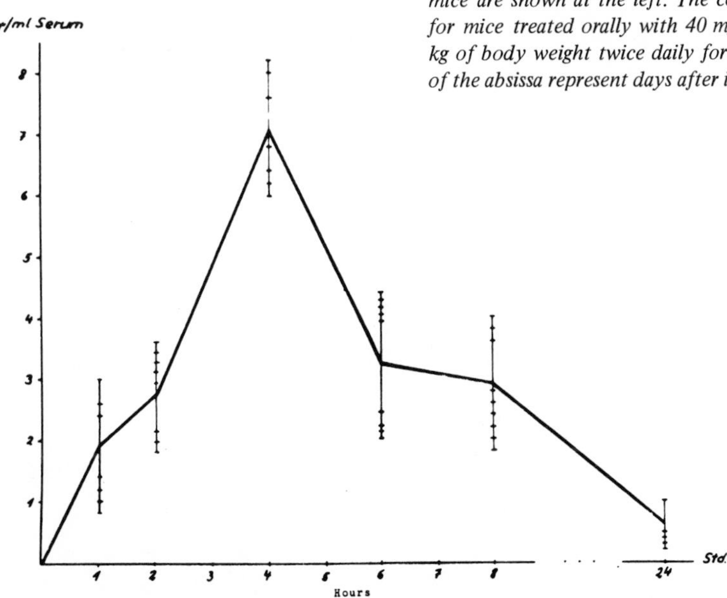

Fig. 4. *Concentrations of BAY b 5097 in the blood of mice and rats after a single oral dose of 100 mg/kg.*

To get some preliminary information about the kinetics, we worked out an assay procedure which was sufficient for these studies. Biological material was extracted with petroleum ether, and the extract was subjected to thin-layer chromatography. After extraction from the chromatogram, the eluate was finally analyzed by microbiological or colorimetric methods.

Figure 4 shows the drug concentrations in the serum of mice and rats after a single oral dose of 100 mg/kg. Maximal concentrations were obtained after 4 hr. The apparent half-life amounted to 3 to 5 hr.

Drug concentrations in lungs, livers, kidneys, and hearts of dogs were about two-thirds of those in serum. In the urine of mice, we detected several metabolites, but none of them showed antimicrobial activity. It was possible to extract the active compound together with inactive metabolites from the feces. Obviously, the drug was excreted mainly via the bile and only to a small extent by the kidneys. For chemical determinations the material was extracted with butylacetate. The addition of perchloric acid caused the development of a yellow color which was measured at 475 nm.

From the curves obtained with animal sera, one may conclude that a therapeutic effect in man can be expected when the dosage used yields drug concentrations in the serum which lie just above the MIC.

The results to date allow the conclusion that BAY b 5097 should be effective in the systemic treatment of many fungal diseases such as dermatomycoses, candidiasis, histoplasmosis, North and South American blastomycosis, cryptococcosis, aspergillosis, and mucor mycosis. The compound is an antimycotic agent with a broad spectrum of activity and possesses a satisfactory degree of effectiveness both in vitro and in vivo.

Antimicrobial Agents and Chemotherapy—1969

4-(1-Adamantyl)-3-Thiosemicarbazones as Potential Chemotherapeutic Agents

B. PRESCOTT, G. LONES, C. L. PEACOCK, and G. CALDES

Laboratory of Microbiology, National Institute of Allergy and Infectious Diseases, Bethesda, Maryland 20014

Forty-seven 4-(1-adamantyl)-3-thiosemicarbazones were prepared and tested as potential antifungal, antiparasitic, and antitumor agents. Among the 47 compounds, 17 preparations were found to suppress the growth of *Histoplasma capsulatum.* Four derivatives–salicylaldehyde-4-(1-adamantyl)-3-thiosemicarbazone, 5-chlorosalicylaldehyde-4-(1-adamantyl)-3-thiosemicarbazone, 5-bromosalicylaldehyde-4-(1-adamantyl)-3-thiosemicarbazone, and 5-bromoindole-3-carboxaldehyde-4-(1-adamantyl)-3-thiosemicarbazone–exhibited high in vitro activity against *H. capsulatum* in concentrations as low as 4 μg/ml. Three derivatives–salicylaldehyde-4-(1-adamantyl)-3-thiosemicarbazone, 5-bromoindole-3-carboxaldehyde-4-(1-adamantyl)-3-thiosemicarbazone, and 3-ethoxy-4-hydroxybenzaldehyde-4-(1-adamantyl)-3-thiosemicarbazone–displayed moderate activity against *Cryptococcus neoformans* at 500 μg/ml, and one, 5-bromosalicylaldehyde-4-(1-adamantyl)-3-thiosemicarbazone, in a concentration of 100 μg/ml. The compounds were also studied for antitumor activity against Walker 256 (intramuscular) carcinosarcoma and leukemia L-1210 in the screening program of the Cancer Chemotherapy National Service Center. In preliminary studies, the salicylaldehyde-4-(1-adamnatyl)-3-thiosemicarbazone was found to possess antitumor activity against the Walker 256 tumor system, whereas none of the compounds exhibited any activity in the leukemia L-1210 mouse tumor system. The compounds were also tested against *Plasmodium berghei* in experimentally infected mice. None of the derivatives displayed any appreciable activity against this parasite. In acute toxicity studies, the highest tolerated dose of this series of compounds in DBA mice by intraperitoneal injection was 2 g/kg.

The discovery of Tibione (4-acetylaminobenzaldehyde thiosemicarbazone) by Domagk (2) as an effective clinical chemotherapeutic antimycobacterial agent prompted investigators to synthesize numerous thiosemicarbazones. 3-Indolecarboxaldehyde thiosemicarbazone has been investigated as a potential antituberculosis agent (14), 4-aminobenzaldehyde-3-thiosemicarbazone and isatin-β-thiosemicarbazone have been studied as antiviral chemotherapeutic agents (1, 6), and isoquinoline-1-carboxaldehyde thiosemicarbazone has been shown to possess antitumor activity (4). During the past several years, we have synthesized and studied the effects of a number of thiosemicarbazones as potential antibacterial (9), antifungal (11), antiviral (10), and antitumor agents (8). The results of the studies stimulated our interest in the preparation of additional thiosemicarbazones as potential atoxic antimicrobial agents.

The recent discovery of the antiviral activity of adamantanamine and derivatives (7, 12) and of the effectiveness of the adamantyl group in compounds used as medicinals (3, 5) prompted us to extend our studies to thiosemicarbazones such as 4-(1-adamantyl)-3-thiosemicarbazones to determine the potential of these compounds as chemotherapeutic agents. This report concerns studies with these thiosemicarbazones. The synthesis of 47 compounds is described, together with the results of analyses and tests for acute toxicity in mice and for in vitro antifungal activity against *Histoplasma capsulatum* no. 6633 and *Cryptococcus neoformans* no. 3769. The compounds were also studied for antitumor activity against Walker 256 carcinosarcoma (intramuscular) and leukemia L-1210, and for antimalarial activity in experimentally infected animals.

MATERIALS AND METHODS

The 1-adamantyl isothiocyanate intermediate was synthesized from 1-adamantanamine hydrochloride according to the method of Seligman et al. (13). The crude product was crystallized from toluene. The crystals melted at 165 to 167 C. *Analysis.* Calculated for $C_{11}H_{15}NS$: C, 68.34; H, 7.82; N, 7.25. Found: C, 68.17; H, 7.19; N, 7.27. The isothiocyanate was converted into the corresponding thiosemicarbazide by reaction with 95% hydrazine hydrate according to the following procedure. A 20-g amount of 1-adamantyl isothiocyanate was dissolved in 50 ml of dioxane; the mixture was stirred, and 10 g of hydrazine hydrate was added. A heavy white solid precipitated from the warm solution. The mixture was cooled to room temperature and the insoluble product was filtered on a Büchner funnel, washed with cold water and petroleum ether, and air-dried. Crystallization of the thiosemicarbazide from a large volume of 50% ethyl alcohol gave a colorless crystalline compound with a 90% yield; melting point, 218 to 219 C. *Analysis.* Calculated for $C_{11}H_{19}N_3S$: C, 58.62; H, 8.49; N, 18.65. Found: C, 58.85; H, 8.43; N, 18.66. All of the aldehydes employed were commercial preparations. The synthetic route of the 4-(1-adamantyl)-3-thiosemicarbazones is shown in Fig. 1.

The new thiosemicarbazones were prepared by condensation of the thiosemicarbazide with various aromatic and heterocyclic aldehydes. Condensation proceded with ease, and the subsequent refluxing of the mixtures gave yields of 80 to 90% of the expected 4-(1-adamantyl)-3-thiosemicarbazones with the following procedure. A warm solution of 1-adamantylthiosemicarbazide (0.1 mole) in 95% ethyl alcohol (100 ml) was mixed with a solution of the aldehyde in (25 ml) 95% ethyl alcohol, and the resulting mixture was refluxed for 30 min on a steam bath. In numerous instances, the crystalline condensation product precipitated from the warm reaction mixture. The mixture was allowed to cool overnight at 4 C, and the insoluble reaction product was filtered, washed with cold 50% ethyl alcohol and petroleum ether, and air-dried. Analytical samples were prepared by three successive crystallizations from 50% ethyl alcohol, yielding white, yellow, and orange colored compounds. Table 1 gives a summary of the aldehydes used and a comparison of the analytical results with the calculated composition.

NH2 + CSCl2 → N=C=S + NH2 NH2 → N(H)–C(=S)–N(H)–NH2

I II III IV V

N(H)–C(=S)–N(H)–NH2 + R–C(H)=O → N(H)–C(=S)–N(H)–N=C(H)–R + H2O

V VI VII

Fig 1. *Preparation of 4-(1-adamantyl)-3-thiosemicarbazones. (I) 1-Adamantanamine. (II) Thiocarbonyl chloride. (III) 1-Adamantyl isothiocyanate. (IV) Hydrazine. (V) 1-Adamantylthiosemicarbazide. (VI) Aldehyde, R = aliphatic, aromatic or heterocyclic group. (VII) 4-(1-Adamantyl)-3-thiosemicarbazone.*

The series of 4-(1-adamantyl)-3-thiosemicarbazone derivatives was tested in our in vitro antifungal screening program. The following procedure employed in our laboratory for several years was used to test the potential antifungal activity of the compounds against *H. capsulatum* no. 6633 and *C. neoformans* no. 3769. Weighed amounts of the compounds were dissolved in dimethylsulfoxide (DMSO), and fivefold dilutions were prepared with sterile 2% glucose in 1% Neopeptone (Difco) broth to give test solutions containing 0.8, 4, 20, 100, and 500 μg of compound per ml. The final concentrations of DMSO was 1% in all tests, including the controls. Volumes of 5 ml of the test solutions were dispensed in duplicate in sterile tubes (20 × 150 mm). Each tube was inoculated with 5×10^7 *H. capsulatum* yeast-form cells or 5×10^6 *C. neoformans* cells in 0.1 ml of broth (as determined by direct microscopic count) and was incubated at 30 C. The *H. capsulatum* cells were from 72-hr glucose-cysteine-blood-agar slants, and the *C. neoformans,* from 72-hr glucose-Neopeptone-agar slants incubated at 37 C. After 72 hr, the cultures were examined microscopically for evidence of growth. Absence of a distinct increase in the number of yeast cells in the *C. neoformans* cultures or outgrowth of mycelium from the yeast cells in the *H. capsulatum* was accepted as evidence of inhibition. Broth cultures in which inhibition occurred were subcultured to glucose-Neopeptone-agar slants, incubated at 30 C, and examined at intervals thereafter. Slants were considered negative when no colonies developed in 30 days.

Pharmacological studies. Acute toxicity studies in the DBA strain of mice maintained at the National Institutes of Health (Bethesda, Md.) revealed that these thiosemicarbazone derivatives are of relatively low or no toxicity. The amount of the various preparations tolerated by all of the DBA mice was 2 g/kg. The procedure employed in the study has been described previously (11).

RESULTS

Antifungal studies. In vitro antifungal studies were performed on the 47 compounds with *H. capsulatum* and *C. neoformans.* Table 2 summarizes the antifungal activity of the compounds against *H. capsulatum.* Among the 47 compounds, 17 were found to possess in vitro

Table 1. *Chemical and physical properties of 4-(1-adamantyl)-3-thiosemicarbazones*

Derivative of aldehyde	Melting point[a]	Empirical formula	Analysis					
			Calculated (%)			Found (%)		
			C	H	N	C	H	N
Pentafluorobenzaldehyde	258[c]	$C_{18}H_{18}F_5N_3S$	53.59	4.49	10.42	53.74	4.45	10.73
2-Chlorobenzaldehyde	221	$C_{18}H_{22}ClN_3S$	62.14	6.37	12.08	62.24	6.49	12.03
3-Iodobenzaldehyde	216	$C_{18}H_{22}IN_3S$	49.20	5.04	9.57	49.79	5.18	9.94
4-Iodobenzaldehyde	230	$C_{18}H_{22}IN_3S$	49.20	5.04	9.57	49.59	5.63	9.94
2-Chloro-6-fluorobenzaldehyde	203	$C_{18}H_{21}FClN_3S$	59.15	5.79	11.49	59.26	5.74	11.29
2,4-Dichlorobenzaldehyde	240	$C_{18}H_{21}Cl_2N_3S$	56.54	5.53	10.99	56.31	5.72	11.11
3,4-Dichlorobenzaldehyde	245	$C_{18}H_{21}Cl_2N_3S$	56.54	5.53	10.99	56.95	5.71	11.56
3,5-Dichlorobenzaldehyde	250	$C_{18}H_{21}Cl_2N_3S$	56.54	5.53	10.99	56.44	5.65	10.59
3-Nitrobenzaldehyde	223-226	$C_{18}H_{22}N_4O_2S$	60.31	6.19	15.63	60.31	6.37	15.61
4-Nitrobenzaldehyde	253	$C_{18}H_{22}N_4O_2S$	60.31	6.19	15.63	60.36	6.16	15.39
2-Methylbenzaldehyde	176	$C_{19}H_{25}N_3S$	69.68	7.69	12.83	69.75	7.66	12.80
Cinnamaldehyde	202-204	$C_{20}H_{25}N_3S$	70.75	7.42	12.37	70.61	7.22	12.34
α-Methylcinnamaldehyde	203	$C_{21}H_{27}N_3S$	71.34	7.69	11.89	71.53	7.55	11.77
α-Pentylcinnamaldehyde	164	$C_{25}H_{35}N_3S$	73.29	8.61	10.26	73.22	8.67	10.70
2-Nitrocinnamaldehyde	224-226	$C_{20}H_{24}N_4O_2S$	62.47	6.29	14.58	62.43	6.09	14.45
4-Dimethylaminocinnamaldehyde	190-192	$C_{22}H_{30}N_4S$	69.06	7.90	14.66	68.70	7.56	15.00
1-Naphthaldehyde	196	$C_{22}H_{25}N_3S$	72.68	6.93	11.56	72.38	7.02	11.70
4-Chloro-3-nitrobenzaldehyde	247	$C_{18}H_{21}ClN_4O_2S$	55.02	5.38	14.26	55.16	5.58	14.28
5-Chloro-2-nitrobenzaldehyde	228	$C_{18}H_{21}ClN_4O_2S$	55.02	5.38	14.26	55.03	5.52	14.00
2-Chloro-4-dimethylaminobenzaldehyde	230	$C_{20}H_{27}ClN_4S$	61.44	6.96	14.33	61.52	6.85	14.32
Salicylaldehyde	201	$C_{18}H_{23}N_3OS$	65.62	7.03	12.75	65.91	6.67	12.40
2-Methoxybenzaldehyde	186	$C_{19}H_{25}N_3OS$	66.44	7.33	12.23	66.70	7.42	12.47
2-Ethoxybenzaldehyde	217	$C_{20}H_{27}N_3OS$	67.19	7.62	11.76	67.20	7.30	11.86
5-Chlorosalicylaldehyde	224	$C_{18}H_{22}ClN_3OS$	59.41	6.09	11.55	59.02	5.86	11.41
5-Bromosalicylaldehyde	222	$C_{18}H_{22}BrN_3OS$	52.93	5.44	10.29	52.59	5.40	10.11
3,5-Dichlorosalicylaldehyde	215	$C_{18}H_{21}Cl_2N_3OS$	54.27	5.31	10.55	54.73	5.27	10.46
3,5-Dibromosalicylaldehyde	230	$C_{18}H_{21}Br_2N_3OS$	44.37	4.34	8.63	44.21	4.13	8.43
3,5-Diiodosalicylaldehyde	210	$C_{18}H_{21}I_2N_3OS$	37.19	3.64	7.23	37.37	3.51	7.04
3,4-Dimethoxybenzaldehyde	160	$C_{20}H_{27}N_3O_2S$	64.31	7.29	11.25	64.11	7.84	11.78
2,4,6-Trimethoxybenzaldehyde	165	$C_{21}H_{29}N_3O_3S$	62.50	7.25	10.41	62.07	7.19	9.92
3,4-Diethoxybenzaldehyde	130	$C_{22}H_{31}N_3O_2S$	65.79	7.78	10.46	65.98	7.77	10.54
2,4,5-Triethoxybenzaldehyde	180	$C_{24}H_{35}N_3O_3S$	64.69	7.92	9.43	64.60	7.82	9.44
4,6-Dimethoxysalicylaldehyde	243-246	$C_{20}H_{27}N_3O_3S$	61.67	6.99	10.79	61.89	6.97	10.43
2-Hydroxy-1-naphthaldehyde	208	$C_{22}H_{25}N_3OS$	69.62	6.64	11.07	69.71	6.91	11.48
3-Ethoxy-4-hydroxybenzaldehyde	178	$C_{20}H_{27}N_3O_2S$	64.31	7.29	11.25	64.70	7.17	11.03
4-Dimethylaminobenzaldehyde	192-194	$C_{20}H_{28}N_4S$	67.35	7.92	15.71	67.75	8.02	15.82
4-Diethylaminobenzaldehyde	177-178	$C_{22}H_{32}N_4S$	68.71	8.39	14.57	68.48	8.58	14.73
3-Benzyloxybenzaldehyde	206	$C_{25}H_{29}N_3OS$	73.31	4.69	10.23	73.14	4.81	9.95
4-Benzyloxybenzaldehyde	188	$C_{25}H_{29}N_3OS$	73.31	4.69	10.23	73.84	4.94	9.92
Piperonal	212-213	$C_{19}H_{23}N_3O_2S$	63.83	6.48	11.76	63.91	6.38	11.66
6-Nitropiperonal	215	$C_{19}H_{22}N_4O_4S$	56.69	5.51	13.92	56.79	5.37	13.97
Indole-3-carboxaldehyde	208	$C_{20}H_{24}N_4S$	68.14	6.86	15,89	68.55	6.43	15.69
5-Bromoindole-3-carboxaldehyde	180	$C_{20}H_{23}BrN_4S$	55.68	5.37	12.99	55.93	5.67	12.95
5-Chloro-2-thiophenecarboxaldehyde	220	$C_{16}H_{20}ClN_3S_2$	54.29	5.69	11.87	54.31	5.93	11.71
1-Pyrenecarboxaldehyde	245-247	$C_{28}H_{27}N_3S$	76.85	6.22	9.60	77.04	6.47	9.42
Isatin	287	$C_{30}H_{39}N_7S_2$	64.14	6.99	17.45	64.35	6.41	17.48
9-Anthraldehyde	230-234	$C_{26}H_{27}N_3S$	75.50	6.59	10.16	75.79	6.98	10.16

[a] All melting points are uncorrected and were determined on a Fisher-Johns melting-point apparatus.

Table 2. *In vitro antifungal activity of certain 4-(1-adamantyl)-3-thiosemicarbazones against Histoplasma capsulatum*

Derivative of aldehyde	Concn (μg/ml)	
	A[a]	B[b]
4-Iodobenzaldehyde	500	>500
3-Nitrobenzaldehyde	500	>500
2-Hydroxy-1-napthaldehyde	500	>500
Salicylaldehyde	0.8	4
5-Chlorosalicylaldehyde	4	4
3,5-Dichlorosalicylaldehyde	20	20
4,6-Dimethoxysalicylaldehyde	500	>500
5-Bromosalicylaldehyde	4	4
3,5-Dibromosalicylaldehyde	500	>500
3,4-Dimethoxybenzaldehyde	500	>500
3,4-Diethoxybenzaldehyde	500	>500
3-Ethoxy-4-hydroxybenzaldehyde	20	20
4-Dimethylaminobenzaldehyde	500	>500
6-Nitropiperonal	100	500
5-Bromoindole-3-indolecarboxaldehyde	4	4
5-Chloro-2-thiophenecarboxaldehyde	100	500
Isatin	100	100

[a] Minimal concentration tested causing inhibition of growth in broth with a fivefold dilution starting with 500 μg/ml and decreasing to 0.8 μg/ml.

[b] Minimal concentration tested resulting in negative culture when subcultured to medium containing no drug. Lower concentrations of drug gave positive cultures when subcultured.

activity against *H. capsulatum*, and 4 of the 17 also exhibited a low order of activity against *C. neoformans*. Four derivatives—salicylaldehyde-4-(1-adamantyl)-3-thiosemicarbazone, 5-chlorosalicylaldehyde-4-(1-adamantyl)-3-thiosemicarbazone, 5-chlorosalicylaldehyde-4-(1-adamantyl)-3-thiosemicarbazone, and 5-bromoindole-3-carboxaldehyde-4-(1-adamantyl)-3-thiosemicarbazone—exhibited in vitro activity against *H. capsulatum* in concentrations as low as 4 μg/ml. Two others, 3,5-dichlorobenzaldehyde-4-(1-adamantyl)-3-thiosemicarbazone and 3-ethoxy-4-hydroxybenzaldehyde-4-(1-adamantyl)-3-thiosemicarbazone, in a concentration of 20 μg/ml, inhibited the growth of *H. capsulatum* for the period studied, and three derivatives—6-nitropiperonal, 5-chloro-2-thiophenecarboxaldehyde, and isatin—were slightly effective at a concentration of 100 μg/ml. Eight of the derivatives—4-iodobenzaldehyde, 3-nitrobenzaldehyde, 3,4-dibromosalicylaldehyde, 3,4-dimethoxybenzaldehyde, 3,4-diethoxybenzaldehyde, 4,6-dimethoxysalicylaldehyde, 4-dimethylaminobenzaldehyde, and 2-hydroxyl-1-naphthaldehyde—were inhibitory in a concentration of 500 μg/ml. Four of the 17 compounds which were active against *H. capsulatum* displayed moderate activity against *C. neoformans*—one, 5-bromosalicylaldehyde, in a concentration of 100 μg/ml, and three derivatives, salicylaldehyde, 3-ethoxy-4-hydroxybenzaldehyde, and 5-bromoindole-3-carboxaldehyde, in a concentration of 500 μg/ml. It is perhaps significant that three of these compounds are those that were the mose effective (4 μg/ml) against *H. capsulatum*. None of the aldehydes used in these studies was antifungal in previous tests in the fivefold concentrations of the derivatives tested.

Antitumor activity. The compounds listed in Table 1 were also tested for antitumor activity against Walker 256 (intramuscular) carcinosarcoma and leukemia L-1210 in the screening program of the Cancer Chemotherapy National Service Center. The testing procedures employed have been described previously (Protocols 1.502 and 1.303, Cancer Chemotherapy Rep. No. 25, 1962). Preliminary experiments with the Walker tumor system show that the salicylaldehyde-4-(1-adamantyl)-3-thiosemicarbazone may possess potential antitumor activity. No activity was indicated for any of the compounds in the leukemia L-1210 mouse tumor system.

Antimalarial activity. The series of compounds was also studied for potential antimalarial activity in mice experimentally infected with *Plasmodium berghei* by Leo Rane of the University of Miami Medical School. Test solutions were administered to the mice in single subcutaneous doses of 160, 320, and 640 mg/kg. None of the compounds exhibited any antimalarial activity against this organism.

DISCUSSION

The thiosemicarbazones reported here represent a new series of compounds in which certain derivatives possess potential antifungal activity. The activity of the active preparations may be ascribed to the presence of the adamantyl group in the molecule, since it has been shown that certain compounds which are effective as medicinal agents contain this group (3, 7, 12). In addition, the antifungal screening data indicate that only certain supporting groups increase the activity of the thiosemicarbazone radical. For example, salicylaldehyde, inactive per se, is very effective as a suitable supporting moiety in the synthesis of an active thiosemicarbazone. No toxic side reactions were observed which might be attributed to the test substances in the animals receiving 2 g of compound per kg.

LITERATURE CITED

1. Bauer, D. G., and F. W. Sheffield. 1959. Antiviral chemotherapeutic activity of isatin-β-thiosemicarbazone in mice infected with rabbit-pox virus. Nature (London) **184**:1496.
2. Domagk, G., R. Behnisch, F. Mietzsch, and H. Schmidt. 1946. Über eine neue, gegen Tuberkelbazillen in vitro wirksame Verbindungsklasse. Naturwissenschaften **33**:315.
3. Fieser, L. F., and M. Z. Nazer, 1967. Naphthoquinone antimalarials. XXX. 2-Hydroxy-3[w-(1-adamantyl)-alkyl]-1,4-naphthoquinones. J. Med. Chem. **10**:517-521.
4. French, F. A., and E. J. Blanz. 1965. The carcinostatic activity of α-(N)-heterocyclic carboxaldehyde thiosemicarbazones. I. Isoquinoline-1-carboxaldehyde thiosemicarbazone. Cancer Res. **25**:1454-1458.
5. Gerzon, K., E. U. Krumkalns, R. L. Brindle, F. L. Marshall, and M. A. Root. 1963. The adamantyl group in medicinal agents. I. Hyopglycemic N-arylsulfonyl-N′-adamantylureas. J. Med. Chem. **6**:760-763.
6. Hamre, D., K. A. Brownlee, and R. Donovick. 1951. Studies on the chemotherapy of vaccinia virus. II. The activity of some thiosemicarbazones. J. Immunol. **67**:305-312.
7. McGahen, J. W., and C. E. Hoffmann. 1968. Influenza infections in mice. I. Curative activity of amantadine HCl. Proc. Soc. Exp. Biol. Med. **129**:678-681.
8. Prescott, B. 1967. 4-Hydroxy-2-butanone thiosemicarbazone. A potential anticancer agent. J. Med. Chem. **10**:484.
9. Prescott, B., and G. Caldes. 1965. Étude de quelques nouveaux dérivés de la 4,4′-diaminodiphenylsulfone en tant qu'agents antimicrobiens potentials. II. Thiosemicarbazones. Med. Hyg. **23**:158-164.
10. Prescott, B. and C. P. Li. 1964. Long chain thiosemicarbazones as potential anticancer and antiviral agents. J. Med. Chem. **7**:383-385.
11. Prescott, B., C. P. Li, W. R. Piggott, W. B. Hill, and E. C. Martino. 1963. Some new thiosemicarbazones as potential chemotherapeutic agents. Thymolthiosemicarbazones. Proc. Int. Soc. Chemother., p. 1358-1362. Georg Thieme Verlag, Stuttgart.
12. Schulman, J. L. 1968. Effect of 1-amantanamine hydrochloride (Amantadine HCl) and methyl-1-adamantanethylamine hydrochloride (Rimantadine HCl) on transmission of influenza virus infection in mice. Proc. Soc. Exp. Biol. Med. **128**:1173-1178.
13. Seligman, R. B., R. W. Bost, and R. L. McKee. 1953. Some new derivatives of p-aminosalicylic acid. J. Amer. Chem. Soc. **75**:6334-6335.
14. Weller, L. E., H. M. Sell, and R. Y. Gottshall. 1959. 3-Indolecarboxaldehyde thiosemicarbazone. A new antitubercular compound. J. Amer. Chem. Soc. **76**:1959.

Antimicrobial Agents and Chemotherapy—1969

Antimicrobial Activity of 3-Substituted 5-Amino-1, 2, 4-Oxadiazoles

HANS H. GADEBUSCH, HERMAN BREUER, GENNARO MIRAGLIA, HAROLD I. BASCH, and RICHARD SEMAR

The Squibb Institute for Medical Research, New Brunswick, New Jersey 08903, and Chemische Fabrik von Heyden, Regensburg, Germany

The synthesis of 3-substituted 5-amino-1,2,4-oxadiazoles has produced several new broad-spectrum antimicrobial agents. The most active of these, *trans*-5-imino-3-[2-(5-nitro-2-furyl)vinyl]-Δ^2-1,2,4-oxadiazoline (SQ 18,506), possesses in vitro antibacterial activity, and is also effective against certain fungi and against a strain of *Trichomonas foetus.* Preliminary chemotherapeutic studies have suggested that the compound is also effective in vivo.

Recently, one of us reported a novel synthesis for the preparation of 5-substituted 3-amino-1,2,4-oxadiazoles (2). The promising antimicrobial properties of these compounds prompted us to prepare a number of 3-substituted 5-amino-1,2,4-oxadiazoles and to investigate them for antimicrobial activity. Some of these substances were shown to exist in the tautomeric imino form, but, for purposes of clarity, only the amino form is illustrated.

MATERIALS AND METHODS

Synthesis. The general approach to the synthesis of these compounds is presented in Fig. 1. Compounds of the type illustrated as I (where *n* represents the presence or absence of a vinyl bridge) react directly with primary and secondary amines to produce secondary and tertiary amines of type II. Reaction of I with ammonia yields the primary amine III, which may be acylated by reaction with acid anhydrides to provide the corresponding amides (IV). These amides are acidic in nature, so that treatment with a base such as sodium methoxide, followed by an alkyl halide, produces the substituted amides (V). These compounds may be used as intermediates for the alternative synthesis of secondary amines (VI) by reaction with an alcoholic solution of hydrogen chloride.

Biological methods. The microbiological and chemotherapeutic methods used in this study were those commonly used by the pharmaceutical industry. All compounds were solubilized with the aid of dimethylsulfoxide (DMSO) prior to being tested by the conventional, twofold serial dilution assay, with double-strength Penassay (Difco) broth or STS (BBL) medium (1). Bacteria and *Trichomonas* were incubated at 37 C; fungi were cultured at 25 to 28 C. Protective activity against systemic infection was studied in 18- to 20-g CF1-S (Carworth Farms) mice. The intraperitoneal challenge consisted of a 100 LD_{50} dose of *Salmonella schottmuelleri* SC 3850 suspended in 5% gastric mucin (female mice), or a 4 LD_{50} dose (ca. 2×10^6 cells) of *T. foetus* BrM grown for 48 hr in STS medium containing 10% rabbit serum (male mice). Compounds were administered subcutaneously (solubilized in 10% DMSO) in divided doses at 1 and 4 hr after infection, or were given orally, suspended in 5% gum acacia, once daily for 5 days. In both instances, the protective dose, 50% end point (PD_{50}), was determined by the method of Reed and Muench (3).

RESULTS

The in vitro antibacterial properties of some of the new nitrofuryl-substituted 5-amino-1,2,4-oxadiazoles are presented in Table 1. Although the overall activities were similar, derivatives containing the vinyl bridge (n=1) were, in each instance, more active than the corresponding compounds without the vinyl bridge (n=0). SQ 18,506 was the most active compound in either series, demonstrating, among others, potent activity against *Pseudomonas aeruginosa.* Table 2 illustrates the potent antitrichomonal activity of both groups of compounds and the almost complete lack of antifungal activity (at 50 μg/ml) for those compounds that lack the vinyl bridge (n=0). In those compounds where n=1, an increase in length of the carbon chain in the R_2 substituent likewise reduced or eliminated antifungal activity; anticandidal activity was the most labile. Again SQ 18,506 showed the greatest activity. The results of chemothera-

Table 1. *In vitro antimicrobial activity of nitrofuryl-substituted 5-amino-1,2,4-oxadiazoles*

NO_2–(2,5-furylene)–$(CH{=}CH)_n$–C(=N–O–C(=N)–)–$N(R_1)(R_2)$

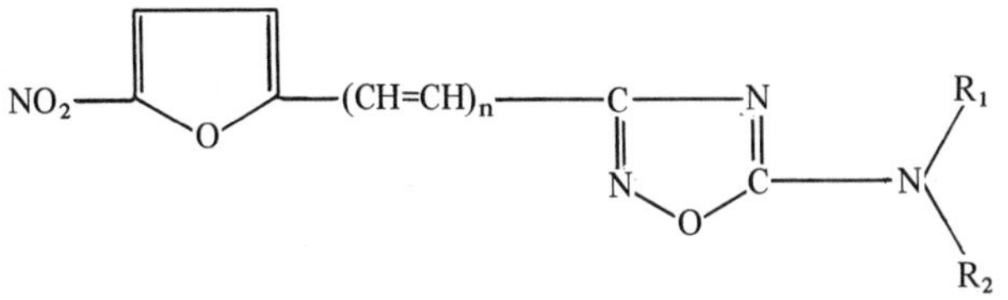

Compound	n	R_1	R_2	Melting point (C)	Minimal inhibitory concn (μg/ml)			
					Staphylococcus aureus P209	*Salmonella schottmuelleri* 3850	*Escherichia coli* 2975	*Pseudomonas aeruginosa* 3840
SQ 18,646	0	H	H	231–233	9.4	0.12	0.24	37.5
SQ 19,883	0	H	CH_3	240–242	4.3	0.3	0.6	>50
SQ 18,648	0	CH_3	CH_3	171–172	9.4	1.1	1.8	37.5
SQ 18,647	0	H	$(CH_2)_2OH$	135–137	0.4	0.77	1.2	37.5
SQ 19,105	0	H	$COCH_3$	202–203	1.2	1.2	4.7	>50
SQ 18,506	1	H	H	290[a]	0.15	0.05	0.05	7.8
SQ 18,983	1	H	CH_3	191–192	0.28	0.39	0.69	>50
SQ 18,707	1	CH_3	CH_3	177–178	4.7	0.6	1.5	37.5
SQ 65,350	1	H	$(CH_2)_2OH$	168–170	0.1	0.1	0.28	25.0
SQ 19,104	1	H	$COCH_3$	208–209	0.19	0.6	0.6	>50
SQ 20,027	1	H	$COCH_2CH_3$	234–236	0.22	1.0	1.0	>50
SQ 20,019	1	H	$COCH(CH_3)_2$	205–206	0.07	1.4	9.4	>50

Table 2. *In vitro antifungal and antitrichomonal activity of nitrofuryl-substituted 5-amino-1,2,4 oxadiazoles*

Compound	n	R_1[a]	R_2[a]	Minimal inhibitory concn (μg/ml)			
				Candida albicans 1539	*Trichophyton mentagrophytes* 2637	*Fusarium bulbigenum* 5273	*Trichomonas vaginalis* 8560
SQ 18,646	0	H	H	>50	>50	>50	3.1
SQ 19,883	0	H	CH_3	>50	>50	>50	9.4
SQ 18,648	0	CH_3	CH_3	37.5	>50	>50	3.1
SQ 18,647	0	H	$(CH_2)_2OH$	>50	>50	>50	6.2
SQ 19,105	0	H	$COCH_3$	>50	>50	>50	12.5
SQ 18,506	1	H	H	10.9	9.4	12.5	1.5
SQ 18,983	1	H	CH_3	6.3	1.6	12.5	2.3
SQ 18,707	1	CH_3	CH_3	6.3	5.5	12.5	2.3
SQ 65,350	1	H	$(CH_2)_2OH$	>50	31.2	1.19	6.3
SQ 19,104	1	H	$COCH_3$	>50	>50	>50	12.5
SQ 20,027	1	H	$COCH_2CH_3$	>50	37.5	–	3.5
SQ 20,019	1	H	$COCH(CH_3)_2$	>50	37.5	–	0.6

[a] See structure in Table 1.

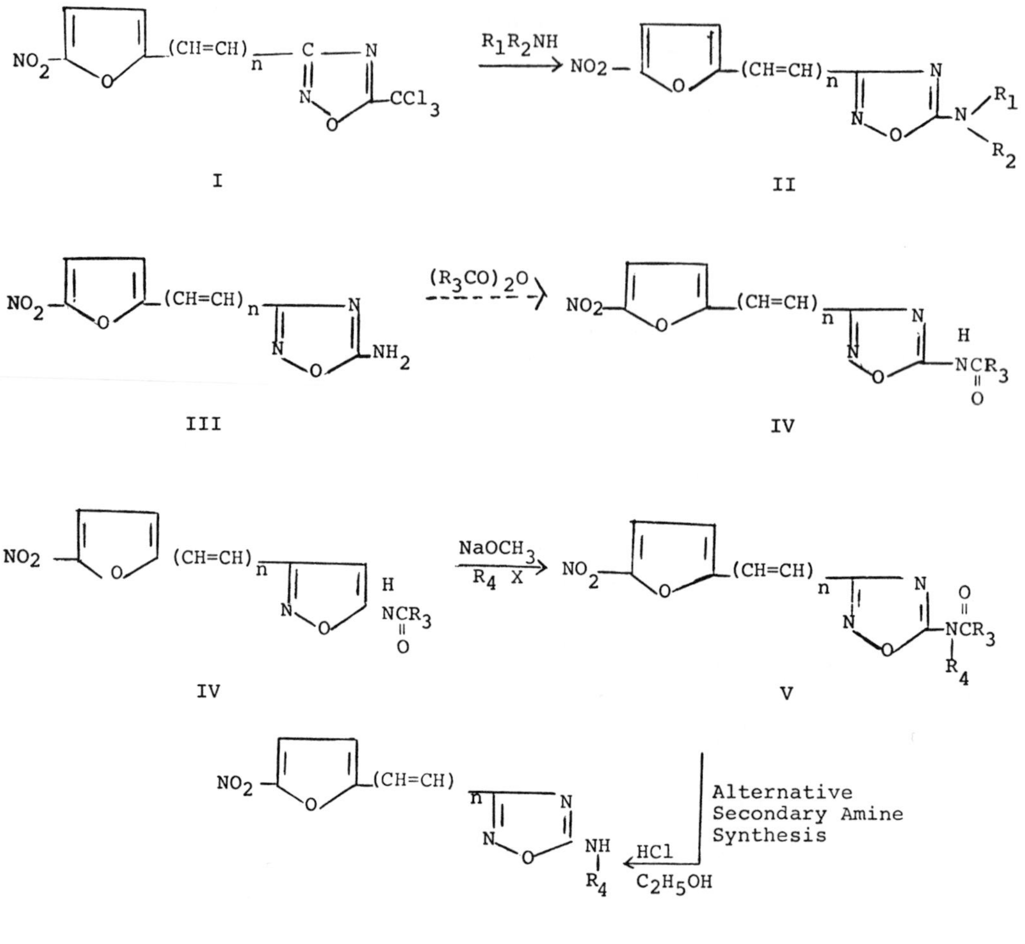

R_1R_2NH ; $(R_3CO)_2O$; $NaOCH_3$, R_4X ; HCl, C_2H_5OH

I II III IV IV V VI

Alternative Secondary Amine Synthesis

Fig. 1. *General synthesis of 3-substituted 5-amino-1,2,4-oxadiazoles.* R_1, R_2 = *hydrogen, alkyl, hydroxyalkyl;* R_3, R_4 = *alkyl.*

Table 3. *Chemotherapeutic activity of nitrofuryl-substituted 5-amino-1,2,4 oxadiazoles in mice*

Compound	*n*	R_1[a]	R_2[a]	PD_{50} (mg/kg)[b]	
				S. schottmuelleri	*T. foetus*
SQ 18,646	0	H	H	157	7.7
SQ 19,883	0	H	CH_3	400	–
SQ 18,648	0	CH_3	CH_3	156	8.4
SQ 18,647	0	H	$(CH_2)_2OH$	>400	18.2
SQ 19,105	0	H	$COCH_3$	58	–
SQ 18,506	1	H	H	400	18.0
SQ 18,983	1	H	CH_3	>400	18.0
SQ 18,707	1	CH	CH_3	>400	34.5
SQ 19,104	1	H	$COCH_3$	200	25.0

[a] See structure in Table 1.
[b] Administered subcutaneously in *S. schottmuelleri* infection and orally in *T. foetus* infection.

peutic experiments with *S. schottmuelleri* and *T. foetus* (Table 3) suggest that the broad spectrum of activity demonstrated in vitro by some of these compounds may eventually be translatable into meaningful in vivo efficacy.

LITERATURE CITED

1. Basch, H., and H. H. Gadebusch. 1968. In vitro antimicrobial activity of dimethylsulfoxide. Appl. Microbiol. **16**:1953–1954.
2. Breuer, H. 1969. Nitroheterocycles. I. Nitrofuryl-substituted 3-amino-1,2,4-oxadiazoles and 5-amino-1,2,4-oxadiazoles. J. Med. Chem. **12**:708–709.
3. Reed, L. J., and H. Muench. 1938. A simple method of estimating fifty percent end points. Amer. J. Hyg. **27**:495–499.

Antimicrobial Agents and Chemotherapy—1969

Phosphonomycin

I. Discovery and In Vitro Biological Characterization

E. O. STAPLEY, D. HENDLIN, J. M. MATA, M. JACKSON, H. WALLICK, S. HERNANDEZ, S. MOCHALES, S. A. CURRIE, and R. M. MILLER

Merck Institute for Therapeutic Research, Rahway, New Jersey 07065, and Compania Espanola de la Penicilina y Antibioticos, Madrid, Spain

Streptomycetes isolated from soil and identified as strains of *Streptomyces fradiae, S. viridochromogenes,* or *S. wedmorensis* have been found to produce phosphonomycin, an interesting new broad-spectrum antibiotic. Submerged growth of these cultures produced a substance which was differentiated from known antibiotics on the basis of antibacterial spectrum, cross-resistance, and physical-chemical characteristics. Phosphonomycin was shown to inhibit a wide variety of bacteria, including both gram-positive and gram-negative species. Its action is bactericidal and involves interference with cell wall synthesis as evidenced by the fact that it causes spheroplast formation by susceptible bacteria.

In the course of a program directed toward the isolation and evaluation of new broad-spectrum antibiotics, we isolated from soil a number of streptomycetes which were found to produce the new antibiotic phosphonomycin (2). This new antibiotic proved to be of considerable interest because of its broad antibacterial spectrum and low toxicity (5). This unique antibiotic, which represents a new type of molecule with many distinctive characteristics, has been identified chemically as (−) *cis*-1, 2-epoxypropylphosphonic acid (1).

In this report, we present biological data relevant to the discovery of the antibiotic, its description, the characterization of some of the organisms which produce it, and the procedures employed to identify the crude antibiotic present in the broth of those cultures.

The discovery of phosphonomycin is an example of the ubiquitous nature of microorganisms, in that it has been possible to isolate phosphonomycin-producing streptomycete strains from soil samples obtained in such widely separated areas as the state of Ohio and the provinces of Alicante, Madrid, and Valencia in Spain.

MATERIALS AND METHODS

Taxonomic studies. The taxonomic characteristics of the cultures which produce phosphonomycin were determined by use of the media and methods described by Waksman (11), Pridham, Hesseltine, and Benedict (7), Pridham and Gottlieb (6), and the International Committee on Bacterial Nomenclature (10).

Assay procedures. The antibiotic potency of broth or of purified samples of phosphonomycin was determined by disc-plate agar-diffusion assays performed with *Proteus vulgaris* MB-838. Plates 100 mm in diameter were used; each plate contained 5 ml of Nutrient Agar plus 0.2% yeast extract which was seeded with 5 ml of diluted (optical density, 0.22) 18-hr broth culture per 150 ml of medium. A slope of approximately 4.5 and inhibition zones of 30 mm were observed when a concentration of 2 μg of pure phosphonomycin per ml was used and plates were incubated for 18 hr at 37 C. Tris(hydroxymethyl)aminomethane buffer of *p*H 8.0 at 0.05 M concentration was used as the standard diluent.

Identification studies. The biological characteristics of phosphonomycin were investigated by the use of standardized antibacterial spectrum and cross-resistance assays and by evaluation of the effect of selected agents on antibacterial activity (special effects spectrum). The procedures used have been discussed in detail previously (8).

The presence of antibiotic on paper-strip chromatograms or paper electrophoresis strips was determined by bioautography with the use of thin-agar plates prepared in the same manner as the assay plates.

Paper-strip electrophoresis was performed in a refrigerated unit operated for 2.5 hr at 600 v with 0.165 M phosphate buffer at *p*H 7.0 on strips of Schleicher & Schuell SS-598 filter paper 52 cm in length. Paper-strip chromatography was performed by the decending technique with Whatman 3M filter paper. The following solvents were used: (A) isopropanol-0.01 M phosphate buffer, *p*H 6.0 (7:3), and (B) methanol-2% sodium chloride solution (7.5:2.5). The mobilities were recorded as the R_F of the center of the zone of inhibition observed after overnight incubation of bioautograph plates.

The spheroplast induction test was performed by the procedure described by Lederberg in 1956 (4).

RESULTS AND DISCUSSION

Taxonomy. The microorganisms which produce phosphonomycin have been classified in the genus *Streptomyces.* Most of the detailed studies of this antibiotic were performed with an isolate identified as *Streptomyces fradiae* MA-2898 (NRRL-B-3357) and with subisolates made from this culture. *S. fradiae* MA-2898 is a unique strain of the species, differing in one or more characteristics from all members of the species described in standard reference works. The original isolate of this culture, obtained as a single colony from soil, has proved to be variable. Single-colony subisolates exhibited significant variations in pigmentation of aerial mycelium, extent of sporulation, and fermentation of carbohydrates. Each of the streptomycete variants produces phosphonomycin. In addition to the sporulating variants of the original isolate, the parent culture degenerates with a significant frequency to a nonsporulating form which does not produce the antibiotic.

For the taxonomic studies, the parent culture and the single-colony isolates were stabilized by the process of lyophilization of spore stocks to insure reproducible results. Cultures grown from these stabilized stocks were used for examination of morphological and physiological characteristics. Some of the single-colony isolates prepared from this initial strain of *S. fradiae* (MA-2898) differ from the standard descriptions of this species to the extent that, standing alone, they might be considered as new species. The fact that all single-colony isolates originated from a single stock, as well as the high order of variability shown by the parent culture, justifies the inclusion of the culture and all of its variants as strains of *S. fradiae.* Waksman (11) defined *S. fradiae* broadly as follows: "the characteristics of the species are that it is non-chromogenic, strongly proteolytic, and produces the characteristic sea-shell pink aerial mycelium on various synthetic media; on organic media, orange-colored growth is produced without any aerial mycelium." The strains of *S. fradiae* obtained from isolate MA-2898 fit this general description with the exception that aerial mycelium is often observed on organic media. The listing of cultures which produce phosphonomycin (see Table 1) includes *S. fradiae* strains MA-2911, MA-2912, and MA-2913, which represent typical subisolates from strain MA-2898. Most of our detailed fermentation studies, which are reported separately (3), were performed with *S. fradiae* MA-2913.

A number of other isolates from soil have produced various *Streptomyces* cultures capable of elaborating phosphonomycin. Conclusions on taxonomic studies with nine such cultures are reported in Table 1. Included in Table 1 is one other isolate of *S. fradiae* MA-2915, as well as a

Table 1. *Streptomyces cultures which produce phosphonomycin*

Merck no.	Source	Taxonomic identity	No.
MA–2898	Soil from Alicante, Spain	*S. fradiae*	NRRL B–3357
MA–2911	Subisolate of MA–2898	*S. fradiae*	NRRL B–3358
MA–2912	Subisolate of MA–2898	*S. fradiae*	NRRL B–3359
MA–2913	Subisolate of MA–2898	*S. fradiae*	NRRL B–3360
MA–2867	Soil from Valencia, Spain	*S. viridochromogenes*	NRRL 3414
MA–2903	Soil from Madrid, Spain	*S. viridochromogenes*	NRRL 3413
MA–2916	Soil from Madrid, Spain	*S. viridochromogenes*	NRRL 3415
MA–2917	Soil from Ohio	*S. viridochromogenes*	NRRL 3416
MA–2915	Soil from Alicante, Spain	*S. fradiae*	NRRL 3417
MA–3269	Soil from Pennsylvania	*S. wedmorensis*	NRRL 3426
MA–3270	Soil, specific source unknown	*S. viridochromogenes*	NRRL 3427
MA–3271	Soil, specific source unknown	*S. viridochromogenes*	NRRL 3720
MA–3272	Soil, specific source unknown	*S. viridochromogenes*	NRRL 3721

series of seven isolates which were identified as *S. viridochromogenes* and one isolate identified as *S. wedmorensis*. This last culture was found to differ in some aspects from all previously described species of *Streptomyces*. It is most closely related to *S. wedmorensis*. Its relatively rapid peptonization of milk and production of a soft coagulum were differences noted, but they are not considered sufficient to establish a new species.

The taxonomic studies performed indicate, therefore, that phosphonomycin is a product of a variety of different species of *Streptomyces*. Isolates have been obtained from soils collected at widely separated points around the world and under different geographical conditions. Thus, the occurrence of cultures with the capacity for making this antibiotic appears to be widespread.

Assay studies. Phosphonomycin was produced by submerged fermentation in shaken Erlenmeyer flasks or stainless-steel fermentors with the strains described above (3). The activity of the antibiotic was determined by disc-plate assay against *P. vulgaris* MB-838. An example of the standard curve is presented in Fig. 1. The response was linear when plotted as a function of the log of the drug concentration over a range from 0.2 to 10.0 μg/ml. The slope of the curve varied from 4.0 to 5.0, which indicates that the antibiotic diffuses readily in agar. This property is consistent with the behavior of neutral or acidic substances of low molecular weight.

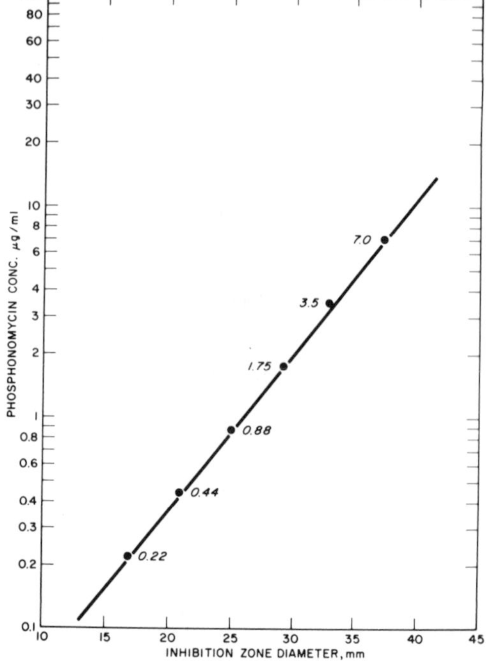

Fig. 1. *Phosphonomycin diffusion plate assay. This assay was performed versus Proteus vulgaris MB-838 in Nutrient Agar + 0.2% yeast extract with 13-mm filter-paper discs soaked in 0.05* M, *pH 7.0 tris(hydroxymethyl)aminomethane buffer solutions.*

Biological characterization. The antibacterial spectrum of phosphonomycin was determined by the agar-diffusion procedure. The results of such a test for the pure disodium salt of phosphonomycin and for a crude broth extract are presented in Table 2. It is apparent from these data that the antibiotic component of the crude preparation was identical with that prepared as a pure, crystalline salt. The 15 cultures included in this study represent a variety of species, including both gram-positive and gram-negative bacteria. Although phosphonomycin was not active against all of the strains tested, it is of interest that the degree of activity or lack of activity was not divided along the lines of the Gram-stain reaction of the microorganisms. That is to say, the range of activities against the gram-positive organisms was similar to that against the gram-negative organisms. A further point of interest is the fact that *Serratia marcescens*, an organism quite frequently found

Table 2. *Antibacterial spectrum of phosphonomycin*

Organism	Inhibition zone diam[a]	
	Crude prepn, 4 mg/ml	Pure disodium salt, 250 μg/ml
	mm	*mm*
Escherichia coli MB–60	25	26
Bacillus sp. MB–633	7	7
Proteus vulgaris MB–1012	42	40
Pseudomonas aeruginosa MB–979	7	8
Serratia marcescens MB–252	15	15
Staphylococcus aureus MB–108	17	13
B. subtilis MB–964	29	27
Sarcina lutea MB–1101	20	21
S. aureus MB–698	29	40
Streptococcus faecalis MB–753	12	14
Alcaligenes faecalis MB–10	13	12
Brucella bronchiseptica MB–965	7	7
Salmonella gallinarum MB–1287	35	35
Vibrio percolans MB–1272	34	28
Xanthomonas vesicatoria MB–815	7	11

[a] Agar-diffusion assays performed with 7-mm paper discs.

to be very resistant to antibiotics, demonstrated some susceptibility in these tests.

The pattern of cross-resistance of phosphonomycin with a series of known antibiotics is presented in Table 3. These tests were performed against *Escherichia coli* MB-60 and against a series of antibiotic-resistant cultures prepared by in vitro exposure of *E. coli* MB-60 to specific antibiotics. As has been pointed out in previous publications, the purpose of such tests is characterization of the antibiotics rather than evaluation of cross-resistance from the standpoint of therapeutic significance (9). In support of this observation, the result here indicated, that phosphonomycin was cross-resistant with chloramphenicol and that two of three tetracycline-resistant isolates were resistant to phosphonomycin, turned out to be a specific characteristic of these strains in vitro. Thus, it did not indicate that cross-resistance between phosphonomycin and tetracycline or chloramphenicol is a general occurrence. Reference to the report on antibiotic susceptibility testing (12) shows that there was no correlation between in vitro resistance of clinical isolates to tetracycline or chloramphenicol and resistance to phosphonomycin. As with the data on the antibacterial spectrum, these results with the crude preparation and the pure disodium salt indicate that the same antibiotic substance was present in both preparations.

In addition to determining the antimicrobiai spectrum and cross-resistance spectrum, tests were performed to detect the effect of certain additives on the activity of phosphonomycin in agar-diffusion assays. It is apparent from the results of these tests (Table 4) that the addition of blood plasma reduced the activity of phosphonomycin, whereas the addition of a soluble cation-exchange resin had no effect or an opposite tendency. Phosphate buffer at a concentration of 0.1 M caused a sharp reduction in apparent antimicrobial activity, and phosphonomycin was found to be somewhat more active at *p*H 5 than at 7 or 9. It has been found upon experience that different antibiotics react differently to the presence of these materials in the assay agar.

The effects noted with resin, blood plasma, and *p*H were consistent with those observed for acidic antibiotics. However, the effect of plasma was attributed to glucose repression of an L-α-glycerophosphate transport system (2). The dramatic reduction in inhibition zone size observed with addition of 0.1 M phosphate buffers is unusual and helps to distinguish this antibiotic from some of the others which have been examined in the same tests. Again in these tests, the response of the crude preparation and the purified salt indicated that a similar antibiotic substance is present in both.

Table 3. *Cross-resistance pattern of phosphonomycin*

Escherichia coli w strain	Diam of inhibition zones[a]	
	Crude prepn, 4 mg/ml	Pure disodium salt, 250 μg/ml
	mm	*mm*
Susceptible parent	25	26
Streptomycin-resistant	23	24
Streptothricin-resistant	18	14
Cycloserine-resistant	18	21
Pleocidin-resistant	39	31
Chloramphenicol-resistant	12	14
Chlortetracycline-resistant	17	14
Oxytetracycline-resistant	7	13
Neomycin-resistant	45	40
Tetracycline-resistant	33	27
Viomycin-resistant	17	18
Polymyxin-resistant	15	13
Grisein-resistant	24	19

[a] Tests were performed by agar-diffusion assays with 7-mm paper discs. The series of antibiotic-resistant *E. coli* strains were isolated from a single parent strain after exposure to the specific antibiotics in vitro.

Table 4. *Special effects spectrum of phosphonomycin*

Escherichia coli w test assay	Inhibition zone diam[a]	
	Crude prepn, 4 mg/ml	Pure disodium salt, 250 μ/ml
	mm	*mm*
Control, no additive	25	26
Blood plasma, 20%	16	21
Dowex soluble cation exchange resin ET91, 1%	24	30
Phosphate buffer, 0.1 M, *p*H 5	9	10
Phosphate buffer, 0.1 M, *p*H 7	7	7
Phosphate buffer, 0.1 M, *p*H 9	7	7

[a] Tests performed by agar-diffusion assay with 7-mm paper discs. Nutrient Agar plus 0.2% yeast extract was used with medium additive noted.

The data from all three of the foregoing series of tests were entered into a profile comparison computer program which calculated the similarity of the antibiotic potency spectrum in the tests cited. This comparison demonstrated that phosphonomycin is distinct from all antibiotics previously studied by these methods in our laboratories, and that the crude substances from the several cultures discussed in this report are identical with purified phosphonomycin.

In addition to the foregoing system for identification based on agar-diffusion plate assays for antibacterial spectrum, cross-resistance, and the effect of selected agents on activity, several other procedures can be used to check the identity of crude or purified samples of phosphonomycin. Although paper-strip chromatography is not as reliable as might be desired with crude samples of small, acidic, water-soluble compounds such as phosphonomycin, it is possible to get some data from such tests. Results of paper-strip chromatography trials with crude samples from several of the cultures discussed in this report are presented in Table 5. The R_F values in the two systems reported here, especially system A, are affected by impurities in the crude samples. For this reason, several control trials were incorporated, and mixed chromatograms were performed to verify the fact that variations in mobility resulted from impurities rather than from differences in the antibiotics. Thus, the R_F of pure phosphonomycin varied in the examples presented here from 0.21 to 0.27 in solvent system A. A crude preparation from the culture of *S. viridochromogenes* MA-2867 presented an R_F of 0.42 in solvent system A. However, a mixture of this preparation plus pure phosphonomycin resulted in a single spot with an R_F of 0.44. Somewhat less variation was observed with solvent system B, and all of the observations reported here might be considered to be within experimental error for this type of solvent system.

Table 5. *Comparison of pure and crude phosphonomycin by paper-strip chromatography*

Culture sample	R_F in solvent system[a]	
	A	B
S. viridochromogenes MA–2867		
Extract	0.42	0.79
Above extract + phosphonomycin	0.44	0.78
Control, phosphonomycin	0.25	0.74
S. viridochromogenes MA–2903		
Broth	0.27	0.73
Above broth + phosphonomycin	0.27	0.74
Control, phosphonomycin	0.27	0.75
S. viridochromogenes MA–2916		
Extract	0.28	0.82
Above extract + phosphonomycin	0.28	0.81
Control, phosphonomycin	0.24	0.81
S. viridochromogenes MA–2917		
Broth	0.24	0.79
Above broth + phosphonomycin	0.22	0.77
Control, phosphonomycin	0.21	0.78
S. fradiae MA–2915		
Broth	0.26	0.77
Above broth + phosphonomycin	0.24	0.77
Control, phosphonomycin	0.23	0.73

[a] System A = 70% isopropyl alcohol–30% 0.01 M phosphate buffer, *p*H 6.0. System B = 75% methyl alcohol–25% of 2% NaCl solution. Antibiotics were demonstrated by bioautography versus *Proteus vulgaris* or *Erwinia atroseptica* in Nutrient Agar + 0.2% yeast extract.

Another analytical method which has proven to be very useful in the identification of phosphonomycin samples is paper-strip electrophoresis. Table 6 presents a comparison of pure and crude samples of the antibiotic based on paper-strip electrophoresis under standard conditions. Phosphonomycin proved to be an extremely mobile material when tested in this system. Indeed, acidic antibiotics which move as rapidly as phosphonomycin are very rare, and this test alone is sufficient to raise suspicion of the presence of this compound in a crude broth preparation. It is clear from the results presented in Table 6 that all of the cultures tested contained an antibiotic which presented the characteristic fast-moving anionic spot. As in the paper chromatography experiments, mixed spots were employed and were found to give single spots of the expected mobility.

A further test which can be used to establish the identity of antibiotics in crude broth samples is specific cross-resistance with phosphonomycin. By exposure of susceptible microorganisms through serial passage in vitro in the presence of phosphonomycin, followed by selection of pure cultures, resistant strains can be obtained which prove to be highly resistant to phosphonomycin and very specific in their resistance. Such a culture, selected from *P. vulgaris* MB-838 which was used as an assay organism in these studies, was used to check the identity of the antibiotic produced by a number of these cultures. It is clear from the data in Table 7 that the resistant strain *P. vulgaris* MB-2146 shows normal susceptibility to a selec-

Table 6. *Comparison of pure and crude phosphonomycin by paper-strip electrophoresis*

Sample	Movement toward anode[a]
	cm
MA–2867	
Extract	13.0
Extract + phosphonomycin	12.4
MA–2903	
Extract	11.4
Extract + phosphonomycin	11.7
MA–2916	
Extract	12.9
Extract + phosphonomycin	13.3
MA–2917	
Broth	13.0
Broth + phosphonomycin	12.9
MA–2915	
Extract	11.7
Extract + phosphonomycin	13.0
MA–3269	13.4
MA–3270	12.1
MA–3271	13.1
MA–3272	13.0
Phosphonomycin trial 1	12.2
Phosphonomycin trial 2	13.5
Phosphonomycin trial 3	12.1
Phosphonomycin trial 4	13.0

[a] Paper-strip electrophoresis results were demonstrated by bioautography versus *Proteus vulgaris* or *Erwinia atroseptica* after development for 2.5 hr at 600 v with 0.165 M, *p*H 7.0 phosphate buffer.

Table 7. *Cross-resistance to phosphonomycin*

Antibiotic sample	Inhibition zone diam at 37 C		
	Disc size[a]	MB–838 (susceptible)	MB–2146 (resistant)
	mm	*mm*	*mm*
MA–3269, broth	7	26	7
MA–3270, broth	7	24	7
MA–3271, broth	7	32	7
MA–3272, broth	7	27	7
Phosphonomycin (10 μg/ml)	7	31	7
Streptomycin (100 μg/ml)	13	23	23
Chloramphenicol (50 μg/ml)	13	29	30
Cycloserine (200 μg/ml)	13	21	20
Penicillin (4 μg/ml)	13	30	32
Phosphonomycin (100 μg/ml)	13	35	13

[a] Assay performed by agar-diffusion method with discs soaked in antibiotic solution and set on plates seeded with *Proteus vulgaris* MB–838 and a phosphonomycin-resistant isolate (MB–2146) obtained by exposure of MB–838 to phosphonomycin in vitro.

Table 8. *Effect of temperature on phosphonomycin activity as determined by agar-diffusion assay*

Antibiotic Sample	Inhibition zone diam[a]	
	37 C	25 C
MA–3269 culture broth	26	7[b]
MA–3270 culture broth	24	7
MA–3271 culture broth	32	7
MA–3272 culture broth	27	7
Phosphonomycin, 10 μg/ml	31	7

[a] Assay performed by agar diffusion versus *Proteus vulgaris* MB–838.
[b] The disc size was 7 mm; thus, no inhibition zone was detectable.

tion of other antibiotics including streptomycin, chloramphenicol, cycloserine, and penicillin, but that it is highly resistant to phosphonomycin and to the antibiotic in the broths of the four cultures under study here.

One further test which is distinctive for phosphonomycin and can be applied to check the identity of unknown antibiotics in crude broth culture is reported in Table 8. We found that the incubation temperature of the assay, under the specific conditions and with the specific organism utilized in our test, was very important for the demonstration of phosphonomycin activity. In the example presented here, with a 10 μg/ml solution of phosphonomycin at 37 C, a 31-mm zone was observed after overnight incubation of the assay plates. In contrast, an identical plate incubated overnight at 25 C did not reveal any inhibition zone whatsoever. This test can be used with broth cultures of organisms which are suspected of being producers of phosphonomycin. In many of our antibiotic studies and screening assays we have used temperatures of 25 or 28 C for assays so that the highest degree of susceptibility would be obtained. In tests of a wide variety of antibiotics, we have observed that plate assays incubated at 25 C result in larger zones of inhibition than those incubated at 37 C. Thus, the result described here, for this specific assay of phosphonomycin, is unusual and provides another distinctive test which can be used to check the identity of the antibiotic present in crude preparations of unknown antibiotics from broths.

The mode of action of phosphonomycin in inhibiting bacteria can be deduced from the fact that it induces the formation of spheroplasts by susceptible microorganisms in liquid culture media under the conditions described by Lederberg (4). With pure phosphonomycin, a concentration of 12.5 μg/ml was sufficient to convert all of the bacteria in a *P. vulgaris* MB-838 culture to spheroplasts. Thus, it is apparent that this antibiotic interferes with cell wall synthesis.

In summary, the data described in this report characterize phosphonomycin as an acidic, water-soluble, electrophoretically mobile, cell wall-active, phosphate-antagonized substance with unique antibacterial and cross-resistance spectra. On the basis of our tests, it was possible to characterize crude phosphonomycin as identical with the purified substance and it was possible to distinguish it from all antibiotics previously studied in our laboratories.

ACKNOWLEDGMENTS

We acknowledge the assistance of Tomas Cubillo, Ann Germain, Evelyn Cross, Maria-Rosa Casado, and the many technicians whose work made this report possible.

LITERATURE CITED

1. Christensen, B. C., W. J. Leanza, T. R. Beattie, A. A. Patchett, B. H. Arison, R. E. Ormond, F. A. Kuehl, G. Albers-Schonberg, and O. Jardetzky. 1969. Phosphonomycin: Structure and Synthesis. Science (Washington) **166**:123–125.
2. Hendlin, D., E. O. Stapley, M. Jackson, H. Wallick, A. K. Miller, F. J. Wolf, T. W. Miller, L. Chaiet, F. M. Kahan, E. L. Foltz, H. B. Woodruff, J. M. Mata, S. Hernandez, and S. Mochales. 1969. Phosphonomycin, a new antibiotic produced by strains of *Streptomyces*. Science (Washington) **166**:122–123.
3. Jackson, M., and E. O. Stapley. 1970. Phosphonomycin. II. Fermentation studies. Antimicrob. Agents Chemother.–1969, p. 291–296.
4. Lederberg, J. 1956. Bacterial protoplasts induced by penicillin. Proc. Nat. Acad. Sci. U.S.A. **42**:574–577.
5. Miller, A. K., B. M. Frost, M. E. Valiant, H. Kropp, and D. Hendlin. 1970. Phosphonomycin. V. Evaluation in mice. Antimicrob. Agents Chemother.–1969, p. 310–315.
6. Pridham, T. G., and D. Gottlieb. 1948. The utilization of carbon compounds by some Actinomycetales as an aid for species determination. J. Bacteriol. **56**:107–114.
7. Pridham, T. G., C. W. Hesseltine, and R. G. Benedict. 1958. A guide for the classification of streptomycetes according to selected groups. Appl. Microbiol. **6**:52–79.
8. Stapley, E. O. 1958. Cross-resistance studies and antibiotic identification. Appl. Microbiol. **6**:392–398.
9. Stapley, E. O., D. Hendlin, J. M. Mata, S. Hernandez, A. K. Miller, M. Jackson, and H. Wallick. 1969. Antibiotic MSD-819. I. Microbial production and biological characteristics. Antimicrob. Agents Chemother.–1968, p. 249–254.
10. Subcommittee on Taxonomy of the Actinomycetes. 1963. Recommendation of the International Committee on Bacterial Nomenclature. Int. Bull. Bacteriol. Nomencl. Taxon. **13**:169–170.
11. Waksman, S. A. 1961. The actinomycetes, vol. 2. The Williams & Wilkins Co., Baltimore.
12. Zimmerman, S. B., E. O. Stapley, H. Wallick, and R. Baldwin. 1970. Phosphonomycin. IV. Susceptibility testing method and survey. Antimicrob. Agents Chemother.–1969, p. 303–309.

Antimicrobial Agents and Chemotherapy—1969

Phosphonomycin

II. Fermentation Studies

M. JACKSON and E. O. STAPLEY

Merck Institute for Therapeutic Research, Rahway, New Jersey 07065

Studies on phosphonomycin were hampered by low potencies in the initial liquid production medium. Nutrition and culture studies were undertaken to improve fermentation yields. Phosphonomycin production was studied concurrently in both complex and semisynthetic media. In the semisynthetic medium, with corn starch as the carbon source, L-asparagine supported adequate growth but DL-methionine and monosodium glutamate were required for antibiotic production. The addition of sodium citrate gave a marked increase in potency. Phosphorus, added in the form of inorganic or organic compounds, was necessary at a minimal concentration of 0.006 M. Inorganic salts of calcium, magnesium, iron, and cobalt were required for antibiotic production. In addition, trace elements were added in the seed stage to promote growth. The complex medium had ground oats, soybean meal, and distiller's solubles as the basic nutrients. The addition of cobalt and sodium citrate increased the antibiotic yield. These studies resulted in a 20-fold increase in potency in both complex and semisynthetic media, from 2 to 41 μg of phosphonomycin-free acid per ml.

Phosphonomycin is a new antibiotic of unusual structure (1) and interesting biological properties (2). It has been demonstrated to afford protection against a variety of bacterial infections and to be low in toxicity (3). Initial studies of this new agent were severly limited by the fact that it was produced in very low yields (1 to 2 μg/ml). Accordingly, fermentation studies were initiated to raise the potency of fermentation broth enough to permit preparation of purified antibiotic for detailed studies of the substance in vitro and in vivo.

For use in studies of the biosynthesis of phosphonomycin, and to evaluate the effect of medium changes on phosphonomycin production, we undertook the development of two types of media: a practical medium for production of the antibiotic (complex organic medium) and a semisynthetic medium for study of biosynthetic pathways and the effect of various agents on the phosphonomycin fermentation.

MATERIALS AND METHODS

Organism. The organisms used in this investigation were MA-2898 (NRRL B-3357) and its natural isolate MA-2913 (NRRL B-3360). The cultures have been identified as strains of *Streptomyces fradiae* (4). All cultures were maintained in the lyophilized state.

Fermentation conditions. Laboratory fermentations were run in 250-ml Erlenmeyer flasks at 28 C on a 220 rev/min shaker with a 2-inch (5-cm) throw. Baffled Erlenmeyer flasks, containing 40 ml of medium for semisynthetic medium experiments and 50 ml for complex medium experiments, were used for development of vegatative inoculum. Seed flasks were shaken for 1 to 2 days, until good growth was observed. Inoculum was added to production flasks at 2 to 3%. Production flasks were unbaffled and, except when indicated otherwise, contained a volume of 30 ml of semisynthetic media or complex organic media. Semisynthetic media were autoclaved at 120 C for 20 min, and complex organic media, at 120 C for 25 min. Peak antibiotic potencies were obtained after 3 to 4 days of fermentation.

Assay. Assays of the supernatant fluid from centrifuged broth samples (6,000 rev/min for 10 min) were run as described by Stapley et al. (4) and are recorded as phosphonomycin free acid (micrograms per milliliter).

Media. Two types of experiment were conducted. One series of experiments was performed with semisynthetic media and the other with media containing complex organic ingredients.

For the semisynthetic media, reagent-grade salts and corn starch from good commercial grades were used. Monosodium glutamate was obtained from Merck & Co.,

Inc., Rahway, N.J., L-asparagine, from Difco; and DL-methionine, from Mann Fine Chemicals, Inc., New York, N.Y., or Matheson, Coleman & Bell, East Rutherford, N.J. Trace elements were prepared in a solution which, when added 10 ml/liter of medium, resulted in the following final concentrations (milligrams per liter): $FeSO_4 \cdot 7H_2O$, 10.0; $MnSO_4 \cdot 4H_2O$, 10.0; $CuCl_2 \cdot 2H_2O$, 0.25; $CaCl_2$, 1.0; H_3BO_3, 0.56; $(NH_4)_6Mo_7O_{24} \cdot 4H_2O$, 0.19; and $ZnSO_4 \cdot 7H_2O$, 2.0.

The vitamin mix solution contained: calcium pantothenate, 40 mg; riboflavine, 40 mg; pyridoxine, 40 mg; pyridoxal, 40 mg; niacin, 40 mg, thiamine, 40 mg; *p*-aminobenzoic acid, 4 mg; biotin, 0.3 mg; B_{12}, 0.08 mg; and distilled water, 200 ml. This solution was added in an amount of 5 ml/liter of medium.

For the complex organic media, standard grades of distiller's solubles (i.e., Hiram Walker & Sons, Peoria, Ill., and Brown-Forman Distillers Corp., Louisville, Ky.) were used. The soybean meal was Staley's 4S, micropulverized. Several types of oat products were used, but the one which was generally employed, and which was used for large-scale fermentations was Crescent Brand ground oats (Fruen Milling Co., Minneapolis, Minn.).

RESULTS AND DISCUSSION

The initial production medium, I, was composed of: tomato paste (Contadina Brand), 20.0 g; Gerber's baby food oatmeal, 20.0 g; and distilled water, 1,000 ml. Seed medium contained: Difco yeast extract, 10.0 g; dextrose, 10.0 g; phosphate buffer, 2.0 ml (91.0 g of KH_2PO_4 plus 95.0 g of Na_2HPO_4 in 1,000 ml of distilled water); $MgSO_4 \cdot 7H_2O$, 0.05 g; and distilled water, 1,000 ml. When the original culture, MA-2898, was used in these media, activities of 2 μg/ml were obtained.

Early in the investigation, it was found that this culture tended to "degenerate" to nonproducing, asporogenous forms when transferred through two or more stages of the above seed medium. Several natural isolates were obtained and tested. One of these, MA-2913, when developed in the above seed medium with corn starch substituted for dextrose, gave improved potencies without "degenerate" forms.

Since the tomato paste medium was not easily adapted to large-scale fermentations and because increased potencies were desirable, the development of a complex organic medium was undertaken. In the initial experiments with culture MA-2898, medium II (composed of ground oatmeal, 20.0 g; 4S soybean meal, 20.0 g; distiller's solubles, 10.0 g; sodium ascorbate, 0.5 g; sodium citrate, 2.0 g; and distilled water, 1,000 ml; *p*H 6.5), when used in an amount of 50 ml per 250-ml flask, gave yields of 4 μg/ml, and this became the basis for a development program. An early modification, III, of the medium (i.e., ground oatmeal, 30.0 g; 4S soybean meal, 25.0 g; distiller's solubles, 10.0 g; sodium ascorbate, 0.5 g; sodium citrate, 4.0 g; and distilled water, 1,000 ml; *p*H 6.5) yielded potencies of 6 μg/ml. When medium III was used with the stable culture MA-2913, potencies of approximately 11 μg/ml were achieved.

Culture MA-2913 was used for subsequent experiments. The sodium citrate concentration in medium III (see Table 1) was arrived at by testing concentrations varying from 0 to 8 g/liter. Phosphonomycin yields of 6.5, 7.2, 8.0, 10.3, and 11.5 μg/ml were obtained with sodium citrate concentrations of 0, 1, 2, 4, and 8 g/liter, respectively. On the basis on these results, 4 g/liter appeared to be the most practical concentration and was retained in subsequent studies.

Using medium III (see Table 1) and culture MA-2913, commercial corn starch and a variety of oat samples were tested for production potential. Phosphonomycin yields of 11 to 12 μg/ml were obtained with all samples except one, Crescent Brand Pulverized Oats (Fruen Co.), which gave 14.5 μg/ml. Because of a 10% increase in potency, low cost, and ready availability, the Crescent Brand oats from Fruen Co. were selected for production and were used in subsequent experiments. In addition, a variety of other carbon sources were tested for their effect on phosphonomycin production. Several (dextrin, galactose, glycogen, glucose) gave potencies at least 80% of those obtained with ground oats, but none was superior.

Variations in agitation and aeration were studied in the next series of experiments. Results of two experiments are shown in Table 2. The 30-ml volume, with the addition of Polyglycol 2000 (Dow Chemical Co., Midland, Mich.), was selected for subsequent experiments, and potencies of 28 to 32 μg/ml were usually obtained. In view of the fact that several oil sources were capable of increasing the yield of phosphonomycin, it would appear that the physical effect of the oil, rather than a nutritional effect, was involved. An advantage to the selection of Polyglycol 2000 rests in the fact that it is commonly employed as a defoaming agent in large-scale fermentors, and would give less problem in scale-up. The most obvious explanation for the effect of Polyglycol 2000 is

Table 1. *Summary of development studied on culture and complex organic media for phosphonomycin-producing cultures of Streptomyces fradiae*[a]

Medium	Ingredients per liter of distilled water										Culture	Vol/250-ml flask	Phosphonomycin potency
	Tomato paste	Gerber's Baby Food Oatmeal	Ground oatmeal	Crescent Brand oats	Staley's 4S soybean meal	Distiller's solubles	Sodium ascorbate	Sodium citrate	$CoCl_2 \cdot 6H_2O$	Polyglycol 2000			
	g	*g*	*g*	*g*	*g*	*g*	*g*	*g*	*g*	*ml*		*ml*	*μg/ml*
I	20.0	20.0	–	–	–	–	–	–	–	–	2898	50	2
II*	–	–	20.0	–	20.0	10.0	0.5	2.0	–	–	2898	50	4
III*	–	–	30.0	–	25.0	10.0	0.5	4.0	–	–	2898	50	6
III	–	–	30.0	–	25.0	10.0	0.5	4.0	–	–	2913*	50	11
III	–	–	30.0	–	25.0	10.0	0.5	4.0	–	–	2913	30*	16
IV	–	–	–	30.0*	25.0	10.0	0.5	4.0	–	5.0*	2913	30	31
V*	–	–	–	20.0	15.0	5.0	–	4.0	–	5.0	2913	30	31
VI	–	–	–	20.0	15.0	5.0	–	4.0	0.1*	5.0	2913	30	41

[a] The asterisks indicate factors varied from preceding basal formulas to effect the improved potency. The *p*H of medium I was 5.5 without adjustment. The *p*H of all other media was adjusted to 6.5 with NaOH.

Table 2. *Effect on phosphonomycin yield of changes in volume and addition of oil to complex organic medium*[a]

Vol 250 ml flask	Presterile oil addition (0.5 ml/flask)	Phosphonomycin (μg/ml, free acid)
50 (control)	None	11.0
40	None	14.6
30	None	16.0
40	Corn oil	19.6
40	Soybean oil	22.4
40	Polyglycol 2000	21.0
30	Polyglycol 2000	28.6

[a] The basic composition of the medium is given as medium III in Table 1.

improved aeration, which also results from the reduced volumes in shake-flask experiments.

The new fermentation conditions were used in a reevaluation of the concentrations of the various ingredients. It was found that sodium ascorbate was unnecessary and that a balance of oats, soybean meal, and distiller's solubles was important. Thus, a considerable simplification of the formula was possible. The final selection (V) was as follows: Crescent Brand oats, 20.0 g; Brown & Forman distiller's solubles, 5.0 g; Staley's 4S soybean meal, ground, 15.0 g; sodium citrate, 4.0 g; Polyglycol 2000, 5 ml; and distilled water, 1,000 ml; the *p*H was adjusted to 6.5. In a series of experiments, medium IV averaged 31.1 μg/ml and medium V, 30.7 μg/ml. The reduced solids content of medium V, as compared with IV (Table 1), results in greater ease of purification without any significant reduction in yield.

In experiments conducted in semisynthetic media, it had been found that $CoCl_2 \cdot 6H_2O$ significantly increased the yield. When it was added to the complex medium, V, at 0.1 g/liter, the average yield in a series of experiments was raised from 29.9 to 41.5 μg/ml. This medium including $CoCl_2 \cdot 6H_2O$ (medium VI) was successfully scaled up to 1,200-gal (4,536-liter) fermentations with potencies equivalent to those observed in shake flasks.

Calculations based on the phosphorus content of the ingredients and an analysis of the medium showed that the concentration of phosphorus was equivalent to 1.3 to 1.5 g/liter as K_2HPO_4. Satisfactory results with this concentration of phosphorus are consistent with the requirement shown in semisynthetic medium for this level of broth potency.

Table 1 shows a summary of these studies. The effect of culture selection, various organic nutrients and their balance, agitation-aeration, oil addition, and $CoCl_2$ addition can be seen in the stepwise improvement of potencies from 2 to 41 μg/ml.

Semisynthetic media. Initial experiments on culture MA-2913, used for all experiments in semisynthetic media, showed that growth and

Table 3. *Basal media employed in studied of semisynthetic medium*[a]

Medium	Ingredients per liter of distilled water													
	Corn starch	Asparagine	DL-Methionine	Monosodium glutamate	Vitamin mix	Sodium ascorbate	Sodium citrate	K_2HPO_4	NaCl	$CaCL_2 \cdot 2H_2O$	$MgSO_4 \cdot 7H_2O$	$FeSO_4 \cdot 7H_2O$	Trace element mix #2	$CoCl_2 \cdot 6H_2O$
	g	*g*	*g*	*g*	*ml*	*g*	*g*	*g*	*g*	*g*	*g*	*g*	*ml*	*g*
S-1	20.0	5.0	–	–	–	0.5	1.0	0.5	0.5	0.5	0.2	0.03	10	–
S-2	20.0	5.0	1.0	1.0	5	0.5	1.0	0.5	0.5	0.5	0.2	0.03	10	–
S-3	20.0	5.0	1.0	1.0	5	0.5	4.0	0.5	0.5	0.5	0.2	0.03	10	0.1
S-4	20.0	5.0	1.0	1.0	–	–	4.0	0.5	–	–	–	–	–	0.1
S-5	20.0	5.0	1.0	1.0	–	–	4.0	1.0	–	0.5	0.2	–	–	0.1
S-6	20.0	5.0	1.0	1.0	–	–	4.0	–	–	0.5	0.2	0.2	–	0.1

[a] The *p*H of all media was 7.0. The media were dispensed in amounts of 30 ml per 250-ml flask and were autoclaved at 120 C for 20 min.

Table 4. *Effect of the addition of* DL*-methionine and monosodium glutamate to a semisynthetic medium*

Additions to basal medium S-1[a]	*p*H	Phosphonomycin (μg/ml, free acid)
None	8.1	<0.3
Monosodium glutamate	8.5	0.81
DL-Methionine	7.9	<0.3
DL-Methionine and monosodium glutamate	8.4	1.4

[a] The composition of medium S-1 is given in Table 3. Both monosodium glutamate and DL-methionine were added in amounts of 1.0 g/liter.

Table 5. *Effect of the addition of sodium citrate and cobalt chloride to a semisynthetic medium*

Addition to basal medium S-2[a]		Total sodium citrate	Phosphono-mycin
Compound	Amt		
	g/liter	*g/liter*	*μg/ml*
None	–	1.0	1.6
Sodium citrate	1.0	2.0	7.6
Sodium citrate	3.0	4.0	11.2
$CoCl_2 \cdot 6H_2O$	0.1	1.0	10.4

[a] The composition of medium S-2 is given in Table 3.

sporulation were satisfactory on a medium of: corn starch, 10.0 g; L-asparagine, 1.0 g; K_2HPO_4, 1.0 g; agar, 20.0 g; and tap water, 1,000 ml. Slant cultures developed on this medium were used as the source of inoculum for all production studies in semisynthetic media. Initial studies employed seed flasks of this medium (without agar).

In the initial experiment on production medium, basal medium S-1 (Table 3) was used. When DL-methionine and monosodium glutamate were added to this medium, growth levels were unchanged, but final *p*H values increased and potencies were increased from less than 0.3 to 1.5 μg/ml (Table 4). Later experiments indicated that concentrations of 1.0 g each of DL-methionine and monosodium glutamate per liter, together with 5.0 g of L-asparagine per liter, were within the optimal range, and they were adopted for subsequent experiments. Addition of other amino acids was tested but did not result in any increases in potency.

Tests were run to determine the optimal concentration of sodium citrate and the effect of the addition of $CoCl_2 \cdot 6H_2O$ on production (Table 5). The basal medium used for this experiment was S-2 (Table 3). The seed medium had the same formula (S-2). The results indicated that at least 4 g of sodium citrate per liter was required and that $CoCl_2 \cdot 6H_2O$ gave a significant potency increase.

Additional experiments were done to determine whether all of the remaining ingredients in the medium were necessary. NaCl was eliminated because these ions were furnished by sodium citrate and $CaCl_2$. Activities in medium S-3 (Table 3), both with and without sodium ascorbate and the vitamin mix, were 26 μg/ml. Since the omission of sodium ascorbate and the vitamin mix did not reduce growth or potency significantly, they were eliminated from both seed and production media.

The requirements for $CaCl_2 \cdot 2H_2O$ and $MgSO_4 \cdot 7H_2O$ were evaluated with S-3 as the seed medium and S-4 as the basal production medium (Table 3). If either or both of these salts were eliminated, phosphonomycin potencies were reduced from 21 to <3 μg/ml. Culture growth was reduced slightly by the elimination of $CaCl_2 \cdot 2H_2O$ and was markedly reduced when $MgSO_4 \cdot 7H_2O$ was omitted.

The next step was to determine the effect of the trace elements. Growth in the seed flask of medium S-5, which lacked the trace elements, was poor but sufficient for use as inoculum. The trace elements tested were those listed in the media section of Materials and Methods and were added at the concentrations shown. The results, as shown in Table 6, establish $FeSO_4$ as an obvious requirement for activity. When it was found that $FeSO_4$ alone would not give optimal seed growth, the trace elements were added to both the seed and production media.

Media containing 0.5 g of K_2HPO_4 per liter had given erratic results, especially when the higher potencies were obtained. Consequently, an experiment was run to determine the optimal level. The basal medium used was S-6 (Table 3). The seed medium was also S-6 but with the addition of trace elements solution and 0.3 g of K_2HPO_4 per liter. The maximal carry-over of K_2HPO_4 from the seed would be 0.01 g/liter. The results (Table 7) showed that at least 1.0 g of K_2HPO_4 per liter was required for this level of phosphonomycin production. The potency increase from the additional K_2HPO_4 resulted from the phosphate radical rather than potassium, as shown by the failure of KCl to replace K_2HPO_4.

With the addition of KCl to supply the potassium necessary for growth, other phosphorus sources were tested as substitutes for K_2HPO_4. Na_2HPO_4 addition gave results similar to K_2HPO_4. $CaHPO_4$, when added at 5.0 g/liter, gave the highest potency, 41.0 μg/ml. Phosphorus-containing organic compounds which would substitute for K_2HPO_4, when added on an equivalent molar basis, included 2-aminoethyl phosphonic acid, fructose-1,6-diphosphate, phosphoglyceric acid, glucose-1- or glucose-6-phosphate, and disodium inosinate.

With the formula established, an experiment was run to determine whether vitamin B_{12}

Table 6. *Effect of the addition of trace elements to a semisynthetic medium*

Omitted salts[a]	*p*H	Estimated growth	Phosphonomycin (μg/ml, free acid)
All	7.2	+1	<3.0
None	9.0	+3	24.6
$FeSO_4 \cdot 7H_2O$	8.9	+3	<3.0
$MnSO_4 \cdot 4H_2O$	9.1	+3	22.1
$CuCl_2$	9.1	+3	25.2
H_3BO_3	9.0	+3	24.4
$(NH_4)_6Mo_7O_{24} \cdot 4H_2O$	9.0	+3	25.5
$ZnSO_4 \cdot 7H_2O$	9.0	+3	24.9

[a] The basal medium used was S-5 (Table 3 with all trace elements added except as noted. Growth estimate and *p*H determination were made after 3 days of incubation. Potencies are the maximum observed on the 3rd or 4th day.

Table 7. *Effect of the addition of K_2HPO_4 to a semisynthetic medium*[a]

Flask	Amt of K_2HPO_4	*p*H	Estimated growth	Phosphonomycin, free acid
	g/liter			*μg/ml*
1	0	8.4	+2	3.0
2	0.1	8.3	+3	3.0
3	0.2	8.0	+3	3.0
4	0.5	8.8	+3	8.1
5	1.0	9.1	+3	27.5
6	2.0	9.0	+3	26.5
7	0.5[b]	9.0	+3	5.6

[a] The basic medium used was S-6 (Table 3).
[b] Flask 7 also received 0.45 g of KCl per liter.

could satisfy the requirement for $CoCl_2$ on an equivalent molar basis. The basal medium was S-6 (Table 3) with $CoCl_2 \cdot 6H_2O$ removed. $CoCl_2 \cdot 6H_2O$ concentrations of 0, 10, and 100 mg/liter gave phosphonomycin potencies of <3.0, 22.5, and 27 μg/ml, respectively. B_{12} could not satisfy this requirement. Even when it was added at a level (57.0 μg/ml) which provided a cobalt concentration equivalent to that obtained from 10 mg of $CoCl_2 \cdot 6H_2O$ per liter, the phosphonomycin potency was only 3.3 μg/ml.

An experiment was also run to determine whether vitamin B_{12} could supply the requirement for DL-methionine, first shown in one of the initial experiments (Table 4). The basal medium for this experiment was S-5 (Table 3) with trace element solution added and DL-

Table 8. *Summary of the development of semisynthetic media for phosphonomycin-producing cultures of Streptomyces fradiae*

Medium	Ingredients per liter of distilled water															Phosphonomycin potency
	Corn starch	Asparagine	DL-Methionine	Monosodium glutamate	Vitamin mix	Sodium ascorbate	Sodium citrate	K_2HPO_4	$CaHPO_4$	NaCl	$CaCl_2 \cdot 2H_2O$	$MgSO_4 \cdot 7H_2O$	$FeSO_4 \cdot 7H_2O$	Trace element mixture	$CoCl_2 \cdot 6H_2O$	
	g	*g*	*g*	*g*	*ml*	*g*	*g*	*g*	*g*	*g*	*g*	*g*	*g*	*ml*	*g*	*μg/ml*
1	20.0	5.0	–	–	5	0.5	1.0	0.5	–	0.5	0.5	0.2	0.03	10	–	<0.3
2	20.0	5.0	1.0*	1.0*	5	0.5	1.0	0.5	–	0.5	0.5	0.2	0.03	10	–	1.5
3	20.0	5.0	1.0	1.0	5	0.5	4.0*	0.5	–	0.5	0.5	0.2	0.03	10	–	11.2
4	20.0	5.0	1.0	1.0	5	0.5	1.0	0.5	–	0.5	0.5	0.2	0.03	10	0.1*	10.4
5	20.0	5.0	1.0	1.0	5	0.5	4.0*	0.5	–	0.5	0.5	0.2	0.03	10	0.1*	12.3
6	20.0	5.0	1.0	1.0	–	–	4.0	1.0*	–	–	0.5	0.2	–	10	0.1	27.5
7	20.0	5.0	1.0	1.0	–	–	4.0	–	5.0*	–	0.5	0.2	–	10	0.1	41.0

[a] The asterisks indicate factors varied from preceding basal formulas to effect the improved potency. The strain used in testing all of these media was 2913.

methionine removed. Phosphonomycin potency of the medium without DL-methionine was 10 μg/ml, and with 1.0 g of DL-methionine per liter it was 27 μg/ml. This confirms the stimulatory effect of this amino acid. The addition of 0.1 μg of B_{12} per ml to the basal medium as a substitute for DL-methionine gave only 10.6 μg/ml, which indicates that the stimulatory effect of the amino acid cannot be supplied by B_{12}.

A summary of the key factors in the stages of development is given in Table 8. Through the addition and balance of amino acids and salts, potencies equivalent to those obtained with complex medium (41 μg/ml) were achieved in a semisynthetic medium.

ACKNOWLEDGMENTS

We express our appreciation for the assistance of S. A. Currie for culture studies, W. Maiese for performance of antibiotic assays, P. Fiorello for fermentation studies, and B. L. Wilker, K. Prescott, and A. Barreto for studies on scale-up of fermentation.

LITERATURE CITED

1. Christensen, B. G., W. J. Leanza, T. R. Beattie, A. A. Patchett, B. H. Arison, R. E. Ormond, F. A. Kuehl, G. Albers-Schonberg, and O. Jardetzky. 1969. Phosphonomycin: structure and synthesis. Science (Washington) **166**:123-125.
2. Hendlin, D., E. O. Stapley, M. Jackson, H. Wallick, A. K. Miller, F. J. Wolf, T. W. Miller, L. Chaiet, F. M. Kahan, E. L. Foltz, H. B. Woodruff, J. M. Mata, S. Hernandez, and S. Mochales. 1969. Phosphonomycin: a new antibiotic produced by strains of *Streptomyces*. Science (Washington) **166**:122-123.
3. Miller, A. K., B. M. Frost, M. E. Valiant, H. Kropp, and D. Hendlin. 1970. Phosphonomycin. V. Evaluation in mice. Antimicrob. Agents Chemother.–1969, p. 310-315.
4. Stapley, E. O., D. Hendlin, J. M. Mata, M. Jackson, H. Wallick, S. Hernandez, S. Mochales, S. A. Currie, and R. M. Miller. 1970. Phosphonomycin. I. Discovery and in vitro biological characterization. Antimicrob. Agents Chemother.–1969, p. 284-290.

Antimicrobial Agents and Chemotherapy—1969

Phosphonomycin

III. Evaluation In Vitro

D. HENDLIN, B. M. FROST, E. THIELE, H. KROPP, M. E. VALIANT, B. PELAK, B. WEISSBERGER, C. CORNIN, and A. K. MILLER

Merck Institute for Therapeutic Research, Rahway, New Jersey 07065

Phosphonomycin, a new, broad-spectrum antibiotic, is bactericidal in action. Younger cells appeared to be more susceptible to its action than older cells. Exposure of a 4-hr culture to the antibiotic for 30 min decreased the bacterial population 99.9%. The activity of phosphonomycin was found to be dependent upon the test medium. Of a number of media tested, Nutrient Broth allowed the greatest activity. Size of inoculum also had a significant effect on antibiotic activity; increasing the inoculum from 10^4 to 10^6 cells per ml increased the minimal inhibitory concentration eightfold. In selected organisms, resistance to phosphonomycin developed rapidly on serial transfer in increasing concentrations of antibiotic. Analysis of bacterial populations indicated that resistance to the antibiotic was due to spontaneous mutation. Studies with several cultures resistant to phosphonomycin in vitro indicated that they grew poorly in complex media, and in the two instances studied the cultures had lost their virulence for mice.

The discovery of phosphonomycin, a new broad-spectrum antibiotic, and the elucidation of its structure were reported recently (1, 4). Its production and isolation are described in a separate communication (10). This paper describes in vitro observations on the antibacterial activity and bactericidal action of phosphonomycin. Some studies on the development of resistance to phosphonomycin also are described.

MATERIALS AND METHODS

Phosphonomycin. Synthetic disodium phosphonomycin, which is a highly water-soluble salt, was used in all experiments unless otherwise indicated. The activities are reported as total weight of the salt, which is 76% free acid.

Preparation of inoculum. The cultures used in this study were laboratory cultures maintained in the lyophilized state. Inoculum was prepared from cultures regenerated in Brain Heart Infusion (BHI, Difco or BBL).

Antibacterial activity. Minimal inhibitory and minimal bactericidal concentrations were determined by the conventional twofold serial dilution method in test tubes (16 × 125 mm) containing a total volume of 2.5 ml. Tubes were incubated for 48 hr at 37 C, and the minimal inhibitory concentration (MIC) was defined as the lowest concentration of antibiotic that suppressed visible growth. The minimal bactericidal concentration (MBC) was determined by inoculating a series of tubes containing 9.5 ml of BHI (Difco) with 0.5 ml from the tube containing the MIC and higher concentrations of phosphonomycin, and also from at least two tubes showing growth in the MIC test. The subculture end points were read after 48 hr of incubation at 37 C, and the MBC was defined as the lowest concentration of antibiotic which gave no visible growth on subculture.

Bactericidal activity. The rate of killing was determined with a 3-hr broth culture diluted to contain about 10^7 cells per ml when added to various concentrations of antibiotic. Growth in the presence and absence of antibiotic was followed by plating samples from the tubes at various time intervals. The effect of the age of the culture on the bactericidal action of phosphonomycin was studied by use of 4- and 16-hr Nutrient Broth (BBL) cultures diluted with medium or with antibiotic solution to contain about 10^6 cells per ml. Survivors in the 4- and 16-hr cultures were determined by plating samples at various time intervals.

Resistance development. The twofold broth-dilution test was used to study the development of resistance to phosphonomycin. After 24 hr of incubation, growth in tubes containing the highest concentration of antibiotic was used to inoculate the next series of tubes. In each instance, the inoculum was diluted so that the final concentration of cells was approximately 10^4 per ml. (The actual counts by plating varied between 10^4 and 10^5.) The procedure was repeated four times, and the MIC was determined each time.

Induction of resistance. A 4-hr shaken culture of *Salmonella schottmuelleri* 3010 grown in BHI (BBL) was subdivided into three portions, to each of which phosphonomycin (fermentation material of 70% purity) was added to give a final concentration of 0, 0.1, or 1.0 μg/ml. The flasks, which contained approximately 10^9 cells per ml, were incubated on a shaker at 37 C for 2 hr. The contents of each flask were then diluted 100-fold in BHI, and 9-ml portions of each were added to cuvettes containing 1 ml of various concentrations of antibiotic. The cuvettes were incubated for 6 hr without shaking, and optical density readings were made at various time intervals with a Coleman Junior spectrophotometer at a wavelength of 610 nm.

Fluctuation tests. The method of Demerec (2) was followed. The experiment with *S. schottmuelleri* 3010 was carried out in BHI (BBL). An overnight culture of the organism was diluted with medium to contain about 640 cells per ml. A 20-ml portion of this dilution was dispensed in a large tube, and 1-ml portions were placed in each of 20 small tubes. After overnight incubation at 37 C, twenty 0.5-ml samples from the single culture containing 2.7×10^8 cells per ml were plated in BHI Agar (Difco) containing 20 μg of phosphonomycin per ml. Similarly, 0.5-ml samples from each of the 20 small tubes containing about 3×10^8 cells per ml also were plated in antibiotic-supplemented medium. The plates were incubated at 37 C, and counts were made 72 hr later.

The procedure for *Escherichia coli* 2017 was essentially the same as for *S. schottmuelleri* 3010, except that Nutrient Broth (Difco) and Nutrient Agar (Difco) were employed, and the growth vessels were 125-ml Erlenmeyer flasks containing 22 ml of an overnight culture diluted to contain 1,060 cells per ml. After incubation, twenty 1-ml samples, each containing about 5×10^8 cells per ml, from one flask, and a 1-ml sample containing about 3×10^8 cells per ml from each of the 20 individual flasks were plated in Nutrient Agar containing 300 μg of phosphonomycin per ml.

RESULTS

Antibacterial studies. In preliminary experiments with fermentation concentrates, it was found that high concentrations of phosphonomycin were required to inhibit a number of microorganisms in the broth-dilution test. Yet, infections in mice caused by some of these same microorganisms were well-controlled by lower concentrations of antibiotic. In these instances, the amount of phosphonomycin required to protect 50% of the infected mice by the intraperitoneal route (7) was 2 to 20% of the MIC determined in BHI. The presence of in vivo activity was sufficient incentive for continued effort on the isolation and the evaluation of the compound.

In an attempt to determine the reason(s) for the relatively poor in vitro activity of phosphonomycin, the effect of medium composition and size of inoculum on antibiotic activity was investigated. Such experiments demonstrated that medium composition had a marked effect on antibiotic activity. Tests with five microorganisms in four media indicated that the greatest susceptibiltiy to phosphonomycin in almost all instances was obtained in Nutrient Broth. The data in Table 1 indicate that with some microorganisms the MIC varied as much as 32-fold. Preliminary experiments with concen-

Table 1. *In vitro activity of phosphonomycin in several media*[a]

Organism[b]	Medium							
	Brain Heart Infusion		Nutrient Broth		Typticase Soy		Mueller-Hinton	
	MIC	MBC	MIC	MBC	MIC	MBC	MIC	MBC
Escherichia coli 2017	1,000	1,000	250	250	1,000	1,000	125[c]	125
Klebsiella pneumoniae B 3265	>4,000	>4,000	>4,000	>4,000	>4,000	>4,000	>4,000	>4,000
Proteus mirabilis 3201	250	250	125	125	500	500	>4,000	>4,000
Salmonella schottmuelleri 3010	16[c]	16	<8	<8	31	31	<8	<8
Staphylococcus aureus 2949	1,000	1,000	31	31	62	62	62	62

[a] Tubes were inoculated so that they contained 10^4 cells per ml. Minimal inhibitory and minimal bactericidal concentrations (MIC and MBC) are in micrograms per milliliter.

[b] The numbers of the cultures refer to specific strains carried in the Merck Sharp & Dohme Laboratories.

[c] Skip tubes.

trates of phosphonomycin indicated that the addition of inorganic phosphate, which is present in appreciable quantities in many bacteriological media, was capable of decreasing susceptibility to the antibiotic. More extensive studies on some of the factors affecting antibiotic susceptibility in broth and agar assays are described in a separate paper (12).

Drifts in end points in the broth assay were noted with some bacteria when the incubation time was increased from 24 to 48 hr. For this reason, the MIC was determined after 48 hr of incubation. Furthermore, size of inoculum also affected the activity of phosphonomycin against six of seven organisms studied (Table 2). Increasing the inoculum from 10^2 to 10^6 cells per ml resulted in as much as a 30-fold increase in the MIC. The MIC was increased as much as eightfold by increasing the inoculum from 10^4 to 10^6 cells per ml.

Bactericidal activity. Determination of the MBC showed that there was little significant difference between the 48-hr MIC and MBC for the test organisms, indicating that phosphonomycin is bactericidal in action. A more detailed study was carried out on the rapidity with which bacteria are killed by phosphonomycin. Figure 1 demonstrates the rapid killing observed with the antibiotic. Exposure of *S. schottmuelleri* 3010 in Nutrient Broth to as little as 1 μg of phosphonomycin per ml resulted in a 3-log drop in viable bacteria in 1 hr. No viable organisms were recovered when 5×10^7 cells per ml were incubated with 10 μg of antibiotic per ml for 6

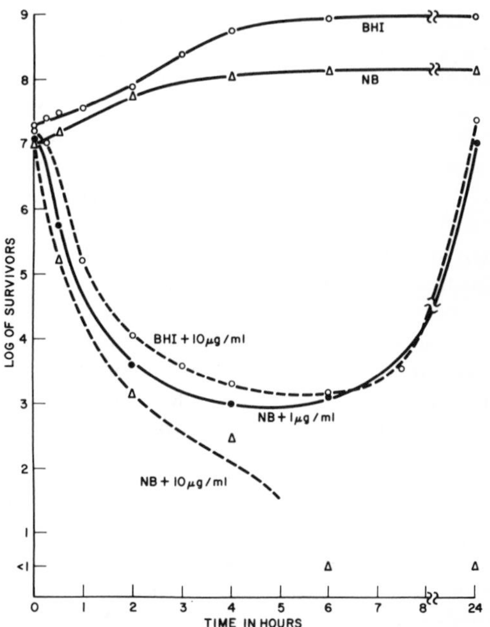

Fig. 1. *Effect of medium on the bactericidal activity of phosphonomycin against Salmonella schottmuelleri 3010 (mean of two tests). BHI = Brain Heart Infusion; NB = Nutrient Broth.*

hr. Phosphonomycin at 10 μg per ml in BHI markedly reduced the bacterial population, but, like the 1-μg level of antibiotic in Nutrient Broth, it did not eliminate the bacteria completely; heavy growth occurred at 24 hr. These data correlate well with the results obtained in studies on the MIC and MBC in which it was observed that phosphonomycin is more effective against *S. schottmuelleri* 3010 in Nutrient Broth than in BHI.

Preliminary experiments also indicated that age of the culture had a marked effect on the bactericidal action of phosphonomycin. Data from a representative experiment with *S. schottmuelleri* 3010 are presented in Table 3. It can be seen that killing of a 4-hr culture (log phase) occurred much more rapidly than killing of a diluted 16-hr culture (lag phase). Whereas a 99.9% kill occurred in 30 min with the younger cells, it took 4 hr to attain a comparable decrease in cell numbers with the diluted 16-hr culture. Thus, it appears that exponentially growing cells are more susceptible than lag-phase cells to the bactericidal action of phosphonomycin. This is what one might expect of an antibacterial agent which was shown to inhibit cell wall synthesis (4).

Table 2. *Effect of inoculum size on the minimal inhibitory concentration of phosphonomycin*

Organism[a]	Minimal inhibitory concn (μg/ml)		
	10^2[b]	10^4	10^6
Escherichia coli 2017	16	250	500
Klebsiella pneumoniae B 3265	250	>4,000	>4,000
Proteus mirabilis 3201	125	125	1,000
Salmonella schottmuelleri 3010	≤8	≤8	≤8
Staphylococcus aureus 2949	≤8	31	250
Pasteurella multocida 1590	39	78	625
Streptococcus pyogenes 3009	312	625	2,500

[a] Nutrient Broth was used with all organisms except *P. multocida* and *S. pyogenes*. With these fastidious organisms, Brain Heart Infusion supplemented with 10% horse serum was used.

[b] Approximate numbers of bacteria per milliliter of medium.

Development of resistance. Several observations pointed to the presence of phosphonomycin-resistant cells in a given population. These were (i) drift in end point with incubation time, (ii) effect of inoculum size and the appearance of skips in the broth-dilution tests, and finally (iii) isolation of resistant cells during the course of bactericidal tests in which large populations were exposed to subinhibitory concentrations of phosphonomycin.

More extensive studies were carried out on resistance development in vitro. Representative data presented in Table 4 demonstrate the rapidity with which several selected microorganisms developed resistance to phosphonomycin on successive transfer through Trypticase Soy Broth containing increasing concentrations of antibiotic. After four serial transfers, the susceptibility to phosphonomycin decreased 4- to 256-fold, depending on the test organism.

Table 3. *Effect of age of Salmonella schottmuelleri 3010 on the bactericidal activity of phosphonomycin*[a]

Time[b] (hrs)	No. of surviving cells (per ml)			
	16-hr diluted culture (lag phase)		4-hr culture (log phase)	
	Control	Phosphonomycin[c]	Control	Phosphonomycin[c]
0	1.1×10^6	9.0×10^5	1.2×10^6	5.2×10^5
0.25	–	–	1.5×10^6	1×10^3
0.5	1.1×10^6	1.8×10^5	1.6×10^6	5×10^2
1.0	1.3×10^6	1.1×10^4	3.1×10^6	–
2.0	3.1×10^6	1.3×10^3	1.3×10^7	–
4.0	–	1.5×10^2	6.2×10^7	–
6.0	7.5×10^7	–	–	–

[a] Growth in Nutrient Broth.
[b] Time after addition of antibiotic.
[c] Phosphonomycin concentration 10 μg/ml.

Resistant isolates of *S. schottmuelleri* 3010 retained their tolerance to phosphonomycin even after 20 serial passages in antibiotic-free media, indicating that resistance to phosphonomycin developed in vitro is a stable characteristic. It should be noted that these experiments were done with Trypticase Soy Broth, which is a less favorable medium than Nutrient Broth for demonstration of phosphonomycin activity. Furthermore, the strains of *E. coli* and *Proteus* used in these experiments were less susceptible than most clinical isolates studied. This accounts for the initial high MIC of phosphonomycin for the microorganisms studied.

The isolation of resistant bacteria from antibiotic-containing media posed the question: Is resistance induced as a result of interaction of bacteria with antibiotic or does resistance originate spontaneously by mutation? Two experimental models were employed to examine these possibilities: (i) induction experiments and (ii) a fluctuation test.

Attempts were made to induce resistance to phosphonomycin by exposing cells for a given time to two concentrations of antibiotic and then determining whether they became insusceptible to phosphonomycin. The procedure used was similar to that employed by Weaver and Pattee (11) to establish the inducible nature of erythromycin resistance of *Staphylococcus aureus.*

A 4-hr broth culture of *S. schottmuelleri* was exposed to 0.0, 0.1, or 1.0 μg of phosphono-

Table 4. *Development of resistance to phosphonomycin on exposure to increasing concentrations of antibiotic*

Organism	No. of exposures					Increase in MIC
	One	Two	Three	Four	Five	
Escherichia coli 2017	625[a]	2,500	2,500	2,500	5,000	8-fold
Klebsiella pneumoniae B3265	625	>5,000	>20,000	>20,000	>20,000	>32-fold
Proteus vulgaris 1810	39	39	39	156	2,500	64-fold
Salmonella schottmuelleri 1814	156	156	156	312	625	4-fold
S. schottmuelleri 3010	2.4	9.8	9.8	156	625	256-fold
Staphylococcus aureus 2949	39	78	312	2,500	5,000	128-fold
Streptococcus pyogenes 3009	19.5	4.8	156	312	312	16-fold

[a] Minimal inhibitory concentration (micrograms per milliliter) determined in Trypticase Soy Broth with an inoculum of 10^4 to 10^5 cells per ml.

mycin per ml in BHI for 2 hr at 37 C. At the end of the 2-hr incubation period, the number of bacteria in the flasks with and without antibiotic ranged from 5.2×10^8 to 5.6×10^8 per ml, indicating that the antibiotic had failed to significantly decrease the number of viable organisms. The organisms from antibiotic and control flasks diluted 100-fold were used to inoculate a series of tubes containing various amounts of antibiotic, and their growth was then monitored turbidimetrically. The data obtained indicated that pre-exposure of *S. schottmuelleri* 3010 to subinhibitory concentrations of phosphonomycin had no apparent effect on the susceptibility of the organism to the antibiotic. Similar results were obtained when a 16-hr culture was used as the initial inoculum. These results indicate that resistance to phosphonomycin, unlike resistance to erythromycin (11), is apparently not an inducible phenomenon.

Luria and Delbruck (6), studying the origin of bacterial resistance to bacteriophages, devised a simple experimental model, the fluctuation test, to distinguish between an inductive process and spontaneous mutation. Demerec (2) adapted the procedure to his studies on the mechanism of the development of resistance to penicillin and streptomycin, and we employed his modification to study the development of resistance to phosphonomycin. The method assumes that, if resistance is acquired through the interaction of bacterium and antibiotic, then similar numbers of resistant organisms should be obtained regardless of the previous history of the culture. If, however, resistance occurs by prior mutation, which is random, then some mutations will occur early and others late in the growth period. Therefore, the number of resistant cells would fluctuate from sample to sample, depending upon when the mutation occurred. If it occurred early, there would be a large number of resistant cells. If mutation occurred late, the resistant population would be small. Thus, variation in numbers of resistant organisms would be greater among samples from separate cultures than from the same culture (2).

Data obtained with *S. schottmuelleri* 3010 and *E. coli* 2017 showed that the variance of the independent cultures was large (3,155 and 334) compared with the variance of the single cultures (30 and 22). The probability that the variation observed among the independent cultures of *S. schottmuelleri* and *E. coli* was not due to chance was statistically significant (P = much less than 0.001 in both cases). These results indicate that resistance to phosphonomycin originates through mutation. Thus, the mechanism of in vitro development of resistance to phosphonomycin appears to be the same as that reported for penicillin, streptomycin, and a number of other antibiotics.

Phosphonomycin-resistant clones of several microorganisms isolated from antibiotic-supplemented agar plates and clones obtained by plating from antibiotic-containing broths were examined in greater detail. It was found that these resistant isolates grew on antibiotic-free solid media as very small colonies. A number of these resistant cultures—*S. aureus, E. coli,* and *S. schottmuelleri*—grew very poorly in liquid media (BHI or Nutrient Broth) which supported luxuriant growth of the antibiotic-susceptible parent (Table 5). When resistant *E. coli* isolates were grown in BHI on a shaker, they grew as well as the susceptible parent but retained their high resistance to phosphonomycin.

Phosphonomycin-resistant isolates of *S. schottmuelleri* 3010 and *E. coli* 2017 were examined for their virulence in white Swiss mice (A. K. Miller, H. Kropp, and D. Hendlin, *unpublished data*). None of the five antibiotic-resistant isolates of *E. coli* was virulent even when the number of organisms injected was 20 times the LD_{50} of the parent strain. The in vitro resistant *S. schottmuelleri* cells showed reduced virulence which was regained after two passages through mice. Mouse passage did not restore the virulence of the phosphonomycin-resistant strains of *E. coli* 2017. Additional studies with organisms whose phosphonomycin resistance was developed in vitro are in progress.

Numerous reports in the literature indicate that antibiotic resistance among the *Enterobacteriaceae* is a significant clinical problem. Resistance among microorganisms isolated from patients is frequently extrachromosomal and is transferable by conjugation (3, 5, 8, 9). Extrachromosomal, or R factor-mediated resistance, is unlike the chromosomal type normally obtained in the laboratory by serial transfer of cultures in media of increasing antibiotic concentration. We were unable to demonstrate transfer of phosphonomycin resistance from isolates of *Sal-*

Table 5. *Growth of phosphonomycin-resistant organisms and their susceptible parent strains*[a]

Time (hr)	*Salmonella schottmuelleri* 3010		*Staphylococcus aureus* 2949		*S. aureus* 2949		*Escherichia coli* 2017	
	Parent (1.5×10^7)	Resistant[b] (5×10^6)	Parent (9×10^6)	Resistant[c] (1×10^7)	Parent (6.3×10^6)	Resistant[c] (2.7×10^6)	Parent (2.4×10^6)	Resistant[c,d] (1.2×10^6)
0	0.07	0.05	0.08	0.08	0.01	0.01	0.01	0.01
1	0.07	0.07	0.08	0.08	0.01	0.01	–	–
2	0.10	0.07	0.09	0.09	0.02	0.02	–	–
3	0.20	0.07	0.13	0.09	0.02	0.02	–	–
4	0.38	0.07	0.26	0.12	0.03	0.02	–	–
5	0.47	0.07	0.38	0.10	0.06	0.02	–	–
6	0.50	0.08	0.53	0.17	0.11	0.02	0.37	0.09
7	0.55	0.09	0.77	0.24	0.19	0.03	–	–
8	0.56	0.09	0.77	0.28	0.30	0.03	–	–
9	–	–	0.80	0.35	0.38	0.04	–	–
24	0.71	0.68	0.75	0.85	0.62	0.14	0.41	0.35

[a] Results are given as the optical density at 610 nm. Organisms were grown in Brain Heart Infusion except that *E. coli* was grown in Nutrient Broth. The size of the inoculum (cells per milliliter) is given parenthetically for each organism.

[b] Resisters selected from broth supplemented with phosphonomycin.

[c] Resisters selected from agar supplemented with phosphonomycin.

[d] Optical density readings are the averages of five isolates.

monella and *Proteus* to a recipient *E. coli* strain by standard procedures.

The significance of the in vitro resistance encountered with phosphonomycin in our studies as it relates to therapy in man is not clear. The importance that should be attached to the in vitro resistance observed to date with phosphonomycin will depend on the clinical experience with this drug.

ACKNOWLEDGMENTS

We are indebted to Mary A. Parsons and William York for technical assistance with some of the experiments.

LITERATURE CITED

1. Christensen, B., W. J. Leanza, T. R. Beattie, A. A. Patchett, B. H. Arison, R. E. Ormond, F. A. Kuehl, Jr., G. Albers-Schonberg, and O. Jardetzky. 1969. Structure and synthesis of phosphonomycin. Science (Washington) **166**:123–125.
2. Demerec, M. 1948. Origin of bacterial resistance to antibiotics. J. Bacteriol. **56**:63–74.
3. Gill, F. A., and E. W. Hook. 1966. *Salmonella* strains with transferable antimicrobial resistance. J. Amer. Med. Ass. **198**:1267–1269.
4. Hendlin, D., E. Stapley, J. M. Mata, S. Hernandez, S. Plates, M. Jackson, H. Wallick, A. K. Miller, F. J. Wolf, T. W. Miller, L. Chaiet, F. M. Kahan, H. B. Woodruff. 1969. Phosphonomycin, a new antibiotic produced by strains of *Streptomyces*. Science (Washington) **166**:122–123.
5. Kabins, S. A., and S. Cohen. 1966. Resistance-transfer factor in Enterobacteriaceae. N. Engl. J. Med. **275**:248–252.
6. Luria, S. E., and M. Delbruck. 1943. Mutations in bacteria from virus sensitivity to virus resistance. Genetics **28**:491–511.
7. Miller, A. K., B. M. Frost, M. E. Valiant, H. Kropp, and D. Hendlin. 1970. Phosphonomycin. V. Evaluation in mice. Antimicrob. Agents Chemother.–1969, p. 000–000.
8. Salzman, T. C., and L. Klemm. 1967. Transferable drug resistance (R factors) in *Enterobacteriaceae:* relationship to nosocomial infections. Antimicrob. Agents Chemother.–1966, p. 212–220.
9. Smith, D. H., and S. E. Armour. 1966. Transferable R factors in enteric bacteria causing infection of the genitourinary tract. Lancet **2**:15–18.
10. Stapley, E., D. Hendlin, J. M. Mata, M. Jackson, H. Wallick, S. Hernandez, S. Mochales, S. A. Currie, and R. M. Miller. 1970. Phosphonomycin. I. Discovery and in vitro biological characterization. Antimicrob. Agents Chemother.–1969, p. 284–290.
11. Weaver, J. R., and P. A. Pattee. 1964. Inducible resistance to erythromycin in *Staphylococcus aureus*. J. Bacteriol. **88**:574–580.
12. Zimmerman, S. B., E. O. Stapley, H. Wallick, and R. Baldwin. 1970. Phosphonomycin. IV. Susceptibility testing method and survey. Antimicrob. Agents Chemother.–1969, p. 303–309.

Antimicrobial Agents and Chemotherapy—1969

Phosphonomycin

IV. Susceptibility Testing Method and Survey

S. B. ZIMMERMAN, E. O. STAPLEY, H. WALLICK, and R. BALDWIN

Merck Institute for Therapeutic Research, Rahway, New Jersey 07065

An extensive study of media was undertaken to develop a satisfactory susceptiblilty test for the assay of phosphonomycin. Nutrient Agar and Nutrient Broth were found to be the best media among the wide variety investigated. Addition of fresh, defibrinated blood (5 to 10%) rendered the medium more suitable for the growth of fastidious pathogenic bacteria and markedly potentiated the activity of phosphonomycin against some cultures. In other experiments, inorganic phosphate or sodium chloride decreased in vitro phosphonomycin activity against some of the test organisms. Susceptibility of several hundred clinical isolates of human pathogenic strains of bacteria to phosphonomycin was determined in disc-plate tests with the use of Nutrient Agar containing 5% defibrinated sheep blood. Although many isolates were resistant to one or more antibiotics, over 80% were susceptible to phosphonomycin.

Phosphonomycin, a new antibiotic (3) which was found to be active in mice against a wide variety of both gram-positive and gram-negative bacteria, presented a problem for in vitro susceptibility tests. Initial antibiotic susceptibility tests failed to correlate with the in vivo test results (2, 4). Cultures tested in agar-diffusion and liquid-dilution susceptibility tests, done with media commonly employed in clinical laboratories, were found relatively insusceptible to phosphonomycin when compared with the results of protection tests against experimental infections in mice. Consequently, an extensive study of media was undertaken to develop satisfactory susceptibility test methods for demonstrating the activity of phosphonomycin. A wide variety of bacteria, including both gram-positive and gram-negative organisms, representing a broad range of susceptibility to known antibiotics, were used as inocula for the various test media. Emphasis was placed on the development of a disc agar-diffusion assay and its application to a representative series of pathogenic clinical isolates.

MATERIALS AND METHODS

Comparison of media for demonstration of susceptibility. The following solid media were obtained from Difco Laboratories: Nutrient Agar, Nutrient Agar containing 0.2% yeast extract, SR Medium Base (sulfonamide resistance test medium) containing 1.5% agar, Brain Heart Infusion Agar, Antibiotic Medium No. 3 (Penassay Broth), Mueller-Hinton Agar, and Nutrient Agar containing 0.5% Proteose Peptone No. 3. Trypticase Soy Agar and horse serum were obtained from Baltimore Biological Laboratories. The horse serum was added (5%) to autoclaved and cooled (45 C) Nutrient Agar. Oxoid Sensitivity Agar (Oxo Ltd., London, England) was also used.

Based on results in other reports (2, 3, 5), modifications of some of the above-mentioned media were made in experiments designed to study the effect of phosphate on susceptibility to phosphonomycin. SR Medium Base Agar was prepared with tris(hydroxymethyl)aminomethane (Mann Research Laboratories, New York, N.Y.) replacing inorganic phosphate (P_i). Reduction of the P_i content of media was achieved by precipitation of P_i as the magnesium-ammonium salt; the methods used were similar to those described by Countryman and Volkin (1). In these experiments, reduction of the P_i content of Nutrient Agar was carried out without the prescribed preliminary acid precipitation. Phosphate-reduced supernatant fluids were adjusted to final *p*H values of 7.5 to 8.0 with 3 N HCl.

For media containing blood, freshly drawn sheep blood was defibrinated by mechanical stirring with sterile glass beads immediately after withdrawal by venipuncture. Within 1 hr after defibrination, the blood was added (5%) to appropriate autoclaved and cooled (45 C) agar media. When hemolyzed blood was required, whole defibrinated sheep blood was mixed with an equal volume of distilled water and permitted to stand for 0.5 hr before incorporation into appropriate agar media. Ten per cent of the 1:1 blood-water mixture was added to agar to achieve a final content of 5% hemolyzed blood. Liquid media were prepared in basically the same manner as described above except that blood and serum were added after the autoclaved media had cooled to room temperature.

Preparation of inocula. The cultures used in the study of media were obtained from the Merck culture collection in a lyophilized state and were inoculated into Nutrient Agar slants containing 0.2% yeast extract. The slant cultures were stored at 5 C after overnight incubation at 37 C. A loopful of cells from a slant culture was transferred to Nutrient Broth or Brain Heart Infusion and incubated overnight without shaking at 37 C. The overnight cultures were diluted with Nutrient Broth to an optical density of 0.22 at 660 nm. For media lacking blood, 4 ml of the diluted overnight culture was added to 100 ml of agar at 45 C; 5-ml amounts of seeded agar were poured into 15 X 100 mm plates. For media containing blood, inoculations were made by uniformly covering the surface of agar plates (10 ml in 15 X 100 mm petri dishes) by means of sterile cotton swabs that had been dipped into undiluted overnight cultures of the test organisms. Broth-dilution tests were inoculated by adding to each tube containing 2 ml of test medium 0.04 ml of diluted overnight culture. Our standard cell suspension (optical density, 0.22) was further diluted 1:50 with phosphate-reduced Nutrient Broth (1). This procedure yielded a final cell concentration in each tube of ~25,000/ml.

Disc-plate susceptibility tests were performed by placing antibiotic filter-paper discs (diameter, 0.25 inch, 6.3 mm) on the surface of freshly inoculated agar. The plates were examined for zones of inhibition after 16 to 18 hr of incubation at 37 C. Phosphonomycin discs were prepared with the aid of a Hamilton syringe equipped with a repeating dispenser. Discs containing 30 and 5 μg were prepared by dispensing on each disc 20 μliters of distilled water solutions of phosphonomycin at concentrations of 1,500 and 250 μg/ml, respectively. Commercially prepared 30- and 5-μg antibiotic discs (BBL Sensi-discs) were used to test chloramphenicol, tetracycline, and nalidixic acid.

Liquid-dilution assays were performed by preparing serial twofold dilutions of phosphonomycin in appropriate test media, after which inoculations were made as described above. Minimal inhibitory concentrations were determined visually after 24 hr of incubation at 37 C.

Survey of susceptibility of pathogenic clinical isolates. Nutrient Agar containing 5% defibrinated sheep blood was the medium used throughout the survey and was prepared as described above. The majority of the cultures tested were obtained on agar slants within 1 month of isolation from infected patients at the University of Pennsylvania Graduate Hospital, Philadelphia. The remaining test organisms were in the form of drug susceptibility plates obtained from St. Joseph's and Morrisania Hospitals, New York, N.Y., and from Southwest Medical School, University of Texas, Dallas, or were lyophilized cultures available in the culture collection at the Merck Institute for Therapeutic Research, Rahway, N.J. All test cultures were inoculated into Brain Heart Infusion and were grown on a reciprocal shaker at 37 C; lyophilized cultures were grown overnight, whereas cultures available on agar were grown for 4 hr before inoculation to susceptibility test plates. Antibiotic-impregnated filter-paper discs were placed on the surface of the agar immediately before incubation for 16 to 18 hr at 37 C, as described above.

RESULTS

Influence of medium composition on culture susceptibility. The comparison of several standard culture media frequently used in clinical laboratories for antibiotic susceptibility tests indicated that Nutrient Agar produced the best overall susceptibility to phosphonomycin (Table 1).

The addition of either peptone or horse serum to Nutrient Agar resulted in no appreciable difference in demonstrating susceptibility to phosphonomycin. Of all the combinations of organisms and media tested, only Trypticase Soy Agar with the two *Shigella* strains and Mueller-Hinton Agar with *Staphylococcus aureus* were superior to Nutrient Agar for the detection of susceptibility to phosphonomycin. The addition of 0.2% yeast extract to Nutrient Agar decreased phosphonomycin activity against *Salmonella gallinarum, Shigella* sp. 113-57, and *Proteus vulgaris,* but increased the susceptibility of *S. aureus.* The decrease in susceptibility in the presence of the yeast extract was demonstrable either by the presence of a haze of resistant growth within the zone of inhibition or by a decrease in zone diameter.

Since several of the media in which the organisms were poorly susceptible contained appreciably more phosphate than Nutrient Agar contains, and because previous studies had indicated that phosphates antagonized phosphonomycin activity (2, 3), media were designed to study the effect of phosphate on microbial susceptibility to phosphonomycin. As shown in Table 1, the addition or removal of inorganic phosphate influenced the degree of susceptibility of most of the organisms tested. *S. gallinarum* and, to a lesser extent, *P. vulgaris* and

Table 1. *Comparison of phosphonomycin activity in various agar culture media*[a]

Medium	Test organism					
	P. vulgaris MB-1012	*Shigella* sp. 113-57	*Shigella* sp. 122-57	*S. gallinarum* MB-1287	*S. aureus* MB-210	*S. faecalis* MB-753
Nutrient Agar (NA)	5	10	10	32	18.9	1,000
NA, P_i removed[b]	2.5	14.6	35.2	4.8	20	1,000
NA + 0.2% yeast extract (NAY)	5.6	16.8	28	28	6.4	>1,000
NAY, P_i removed	1.5	2.4	64	10	>500	>1,000
NAY, P_i added[c]	–	100	90	15	750	>1,000
NA + 5% horse serum	5	16	20	48	>400	>400
NA + 0.5% peptone (NAP)	3.2	40	22	24	20	>1,000
NAP, P_i removed	48	10	8	16	240	>1,000
SR Agar	160	16	16	480	72	100
SR Agar, Tris replacing P_i	36	12.4	19.2	400	800	1,000
Trypticase Soy Agar	340	3	4.4	400	>1,000	>1,000
Mueller-Hinton Agar	340	240	224	272	10	1,000
Brain Heart Infusion Agar	1,200	300	>1,500	>1,500	1,500	1,500
Oxoid Sensitivity Agar	248	68	12	>400	>450	1,000
Antibiotic Medium No. 3	>400	32	40	300	>400	1,000

[a] Results are expressed as the amount of phosphonomycin (micrograms per milliliter) required to produce a zone of inhibition about 20 mm in diameter. Zones of inhibition around 0.25-inch filter-paper discs (7 mm when wet), impregnated with phosphonomycin (ammonium salt), were measured after 16 to 18 hr of incubation at 37 C.

[b] P_i = inorganic phosphate, removed by precipitation as the Mg-NH_4 salt.

[c] Inorganic phosphate was added as 2 g of K_2HPO_4 plus 1 g of KH_2PO_4 per liter.

Shigella sp. 113-57 were more susceptible when the phosphate content was low. On the other hand, *S. aureus* and, to a lesser extent, *Shigella* sp. 122-57 appeared to lose susceptibility to phosphonomycin when the inorganic phosphate content of the media was low.

The addition of 0.2% yeast extract (Difco) to Nutrient Agar tended to result in a decrease in phosphonomycin activity against those organisms that showed a gain in susceptibility in low phosphate media, e.g., *S. gallinarum, Shigella* sp. 113-57, and *P. vulgaris.* On the other hand, *S. aureus,* which displayed increased susceptibility to phosphonomycin when the phosphate content was increased similarly demonstrated an increase in susceptibility when yeast extract was added to Nutrient Agar.

The data in Table 2 show that adding defibrinated sheep blood to media had a marked effect on phosphonomycin activity. Blood, when added to Nutrient Agar, strongly potentiated the susceptibility of *Shigella* sp. 118-57 and 122-57, *E. coli* MB-1418, and, to a lesser extent, *P. vulgaris* and *Shigella* sp. 113-57. Potentiation of the susceptibility of the latter two organisms by blood was demonstrated by clarification of the zone of inhibition, rather than by an increase in zone diameter. *S. aureus* showed a loss of susceptibility in the presence of blood in Nutrient Agar, again demonstrating a response opposite to that of *Shigella* sp. and *P. vulgaris.*

The susceptibility-potentiating effect of adding blood to Brain Heart Infusion Agar and to Trypticase Soy Agar was generally less apparent than with Nutrient Agar, except for *Shigella* sp. 113-57 and 118-57; these two organisms demonstrated marked increases in susceptibility to phosphonomycin when blood was present in Trypticase Soy Agar.

Effect of NaCl and hemolyzed blood on disc-plate susceptibility. Experiments were performed to determine whether a concentration of NaCl sufficient to prevent hemolysis in Nutrient Agar would affect the susceptibility of assay organisms to phosphonomycin. The results (Table 3) showed that with *Escherichia coli* MB-1418, and to a lesser extent with *E. coli* MB-2596 and *Shigella* 118-57, the addition of NaCl to Nutrient Agar markedly decreased the clarity or the diameter, or both, of the zones of inhibition. The data also showed that in media with or without previously hemolyzed blood NaCl itself contributed to a reduction in the size and clarity of the zones of inhibition. In

Table 2. *Effect of blood on susceptibility to phosphonomycin*[a]

Medium	Test organism							
	P. vulgaris MB-1012	*Shigella* sp. 113-57	*Shigella* sp. 118-57	*Shigella* sp. 122-57	*S. gallinarum* MB-1287	*S. aureus* MB-210	*S. faecalis* MB-753	*E. coli* MB-1418
Nutrient Agar (NA)	42	38	23	16	—[c]	37	18[c]	13
NA + 5% sheep blood ...	38[b]	39[b]	32	33	39	25	19	36
Brain Heart Infusion Agar (BHA)	21	20	9	7	14	22	20	7
BHA + 5% sheep blood ..	25	21	7	7	10	27	18	7
Trypticase Soy Agar (TSA)	25	18	18	12	24	23	15	7
TSA + 5% sheep blood ..	19	44	38	13[b]	21	23[b]	13[b]	7

[a] Results are expressed as the diameter (millimeters) of the zone of inhibition. Susceptibility was determined in agar-diffusion tests by use of 0.25-inch filter-paper discs impregnated with 30 μg of phosphonomycin (ammonium salt). Zones of inhibition were measured after 16 to 18 hr of incubation at 37 C.

[b] Clearer zone of inhibition was observed than on the corresponding medium without blood.

[c] Growth of the test organism was minimal.

Table 3. *Effect of sodium chloride and hemolyzed blood on phosphonomycin activity*[a]

Organism	Diam (mm) of zone of inhibition					
	No blood added		Unhemolyzed blood added		Hemolyzed blood added	
	Without NaCl	With NaCl	Without NaCl	With NaCl	Without NaCl	With NaCl
E. coli MB-1418	13	11H[b]	19	≤7	21	15
E. coli MB-2596	35	22	35	35H	36	24
Shigella sp. 118-57	13	≤7	19	13	20	13

[a] Nutrient Agar (Difco) plates were used to determine susceptibility. When indicated, 5% defibrinated sheep blood and 0.5% NaCl were added. Antibiotic assay discs (0.25 inch, 7 mm when wet) were impregnated with 5 μg of phosphonomycin (disodium salt). Plates were incubated for 16 to 18 hr at 37 C.

[b] H = hazy zone of inhibition.

addition to its effect on phosphonomycin activity against some of the organisms, the addition of blood rendered Nutrient Agar more suitable for the growth of fastidious test organisms, e.g., *Salmonella gallinarum* and *Streptococcus faecalis* (Table 2).

Liquid-dilution assay in tubes. The results of liquid-dilution assays are summarized in Table 4. The results indicate that, as was the case with solid media, the addition of 5% defibrinated sheep blood to Nutrient Broth vastly increased the susceptibility of many of the test organisms to phosphonomycin. The potentiating effect was more striking in liquid than in solid media. Among media without blood, Nutrient Broth was superior to Brain Heart Infusion (with or without 10% horse serum) and to SR Medium Base as a susceptibility test medium.

Disc-plate susceptibility survey of human pathogens. The assay medium used in the survey was the one allowing demonstration of the greatest overall activity, namely, Nutrient Agar containing 5% defibrinated sheep blood. Evaluation of the susceptibility of each culture tested was based on the following definitions: "susceptible" indicates a distinct zone of inhibition around both the 30- and 5-μg antibiotic-impregnated discs; "moderately susceptible" represents a minimal, if any, detectable zone of inhibition around the 5-μg disc and a distinct zone of inhibition around the 30-μg disc; "resistant" represents the absence of a zone of inhibition around both 30- and 5-μg discs.

Based on the above criteria, phosphonomycin showed a markedly greater disc-plate activity against 105 randomly selected pathogenic clinical isolates than did chloramphenicol, tetracycline, or nalidixic acid (Table 5). The comparison showed that 89.3% of the 105 strains tested were susceptible to phosphonomycin,

Table 4. *Comparision of phosphonomycin activity in various liquid culture media*[a]

Microorganism	Media				
	Nutrient Broth (NB)	NB + 5% DSB[b]	Brain Heart Infusion (BH)	BH + 10% horse serum	SR Broth
Aerobacter aerogenes MB-835	75.0	0.78	500	500	250
Escherichia coli MB-1418	75.0	3.12	125	500	250
Klebsiella pneumoniae MB-1264	250.0	9.32	250	250	62.5
Proteus vulgaris MB-838	75.0	50	125	125	62.5
P. vulgaris MB-1012	3.7	0.11	250	250	250
Pseudomonas aeruginosa MB-979	250.0	250	500	>1,000	>1,000
Salmonella gallinarum MB-1287	7.5	1.56	125	62.5	15.6
Shigella sp. 118-57	60.0	0.78	250	250	125
Shigella sp. 122-57	30.0	1.56	125	250	125
Staphylococcus aureus MB-210	125.0	1.56	125	>1,000	62.5
Streptococcus faecalis MB-753	125.0	62.5	250	250	62.5

[a] Results are expressed as the minimal inhibitory concentration of phosphonomycin (micrograms per milliliter). Phosphonomycin activity (ammonium salt) was determined in liquid-dilution assays by visual estimations of minimal inhibitory concentrations in serial twofold dilutions of phosphonomycin in appropriate media. Initial cell concentrations were ~25,000/ml. Tubes were incubated for 24 hr at 37 C.

[b] Defibrinated sheep blood.

Table 5. *Relative antibiotic susceptibility of pathogenic clinical isolates*[a]

Clinical test strains[b]	No. of susceptible strains				No. of moderately susceptible strains				No. of resistant strains			
	PHOS	CLM	TET	NA	PHOS	CLM	TET	NA	PHOS	CLM	TET	NA
Aerobacter spp. (8)	6	1	2	4	2	1	1	2	0	6	5	2
Citrobacter sp. (1)	0	0	0	0	1	0	0	1	0	1	1	0
Enterococcus spp. (4)	0	0	0	1	3	4	2	0	1	0	2	3
Escherichia coli (16)	16	11	3	12	0	2	4	2	0	3	9	0
Klebsiella-Aerobacter (2)	2	2	2	2	0	0	0	0	0	0	0	0
Paracolobactrum sp. (1)	1	0	0	0	0	0	0	0	0	1	1	1
Proteus mirabilis (7)	7	7	0	5	0	0	0	2	0	0	7	0
Pseudomonas aeruginosa (3)	1	1	0	0	1	1	1	1	1	1	2	2
Pseudomonas spp. (5)	2	2	0	1	1	1	2	3	2	2	3	1
Serratia sp. (1)	1	1	1	0	0	0	0	1	0	0	0	0
Shigella sp. (1)	0	0	0	0	1	0	0	0	0	1	1	1
Staphylococcus aureus (54)	53	34	8	1	1	13	2	50	0	7	44	3
Streptococcus pyogenes (1)	1	1	1	0	0	0	0	0	0	0	0	1
Salmonella schottmuelleri (1)	1	1	1	1	0	0	0	0	0	0	0	0
No. of strains	91	61	18	27	10	22	12	62	4	22	75	14
Percent	89.3	59.2	17.5	27.7	7.8	20.4	11.7	60.4	2.9	20.4	70.8	11.9

[a] Susceptibility wad determined by disc-plate agar-diffusion assays with Nutrient Agar plus 5% defibrinated sheep blood as the plating medium. Antibiotic filter-paper discs, 0.25 inch in diameter, containing 30 and 5 μg of each antibiotic, were placed on agar previously inoculated by the swab method. Zones of inhibition were measured after 16 to 18 hr of incubation at 37 C. Evaluations of susceptibility were based on criteria described for the use of 30- and 5-μg Sensi-discs (BBL). PHOS = phosphonomycin (ammonium salt); CLM = chloramphenicol Sensi-discs (BBL); TET = tetracycline Sensi-discs (BBL); NA = nalidixic acid Sensi-discs (BBL).

[b] Numbers in parentheses show the number of strains tested.

whereas 59.2% were susceptible to chloramphenicol, 27.7% to nalidixic acid, and 17.5% to tetracycline. On the basis of these favorable results, a subsequent survey of phosphonomycin activity against 409 additional human pathogens was performed (Table 6). The results indicated that 82.9% of the total of 514 cultures tested were susceptible to phosphonomycin, 12.8% were moderately susceptible, and only 4.3% were resistant. Particularly susceptible were strains of nonpigmented *Serratia, Aerobacter, E. coli, Proteus,* coliforms, and *S. aureus.* Most of the 50 strains of *Pseudomonas* tested were either susceptible or moderately susceptible to phosphonomycin. Of the wide variety of bacteria studied, the only genera not exhibiting marked susceptibility to phosphonomycin were *Pseudomonas, Enterococcus, Streptococcus,* and *Enterobacter.* However, of these four genera, only 12 strains of the 92 tested were evaluated as resistant.

DISCUSSION

Our results clearly indicate that Nutrient Agar and Nutrient Broth are the best media for demonstrating phosphonomycin activity and that the presence of 5% defibrinated sheep blood not only markedly enhances susceptibility to phosphonomycin, but also improves the growth of fastidious organisms such as *Sal-*

Table 6. *Susceptibility of pathogenic clinical isolates to phosphonomycin*[a]

Organism	Total no. tested	No. susceptible	No moderately susceptible	No. resistant
Gram-negative Organisms				
Aerobacter aerogenes	2	2	0	0
Aerobacter spp.	15	13	2	0
Bacteroides spp.	2	2	0	0
Citrobacter sp.	1	1	0	0
Enterobacter	5	1	4	0
Escherichia coli	58	52	6	0
Coliforms	38	38	0	0
Klebsiella spp.	2	2	0	0
Klebsiella-Aerobacter spp.	3	3	0	0
Paracolobactrum spp.	3	3	0	0
Proteus mirabilis	20	20	0	0
P. vulgaris	2	1	1	0
Proteus spp.	50	46	4	0
Pseudomonas aeruginosa	7	2	3	2
Pseudomonas spp.	43	22	13	8
Salmonella spp.	5	5	0	0
Serratia spp.	41	41	0	0
Shigella spp.	24	17	3	4
Totals (gram-negative)	321	271 (84.4%)	36 (11.2%)	14 (4.4%)
Gram-positive Organisms				
Enterococcus spp.	6	1	3	2
Pneumococcus spp.	1	1	0	0
Staphylococcus albus	1	1	0	0
S. aureus	154	132	16	6
Streptococcus pyogenes	3	1	2	0
Streptococcus spp.	28	19	9	0
Totals (gram-positive)	193	155 (80.3%)	30 (15.5%)	8 (4.2%)
Combined totals (gram-negative and gram-positive)	514	426 (82.9%)	66 (12.8%)	22 (4.3%)

[a] Susceptibility was determined by disc-plate agar-diffusion assays with Nutrient Agar plus 5% defibrinated sheep blood as the plating medium. Antibiotic-impregnated filter-paper discs, 0.25 inch in diameter, were placed on agar previously inoculated by the swab method. Zones of inhibition were measured after 16 to 18 hr incubation at 37 C. Evaluations of susceptibility were based on criteria described for the use of 30- and 5-μg Sensi-discs (BBL).

monella gallinarum and *Streptococcus faecalis*. A survey of phosphonomycin activity against more than 500 human pathogens, representing more than 15 genera, indicated that over 80% of the strains were susceptible to phosphonomycin when tested on nutrient agar containing 5% blood.

The presence of inorganic phosphate in test media has been shown to antagonize phosphonomycin activity (2, 3, 5). The present study indicated that, although the overall result of the presence of phosphate is to decrease susceptibility, the effect can vary with the organism tested. It is possible that the low phosphate content of Nutrient Agar is one of the factors that render it the most suitable medium for testing bacterial susceptibility to phosphonomycin. It is also possible, however, that the loss of susceptibility observed when yeast extract was added to Nutrient Agar may be attributable to factors other than the phosphate content. Such effects may have something in common with the lower degree of susceptibility observed in other test media such as Brain Heart Infusion and Oxoid Sensitivity Agar.

The mode of action of the potentiation of phosphonomycin activity by blood is presently under study (F. M. Kahan, P. J. Cassidy, and J. S. Kahan, *unpublished data*). Observations to date suggest that enzymes in blood generate glucose-6-phosphate (G6P) from substrates present in Nutrient Broth, and that the addition of G6P to blood-free Nutrient Agar results in increases in zone size and clarity similar to those obtained with the addition of blood. Hemolysis, which undoubtedly occurs in Nutrient Agar, may contribute to the increase in activity. Presumably, the presence of 0.5% NaCl is sufficient to prevent hemolysis. The results in Table 5 show that the presence of 0.5% NaCl in Nutrient Agar-blood plates sharply reduces phosphonomycin activity, possibly as a result of the prevention of hemolysis. This could, in part, explain the relative insusceptibility to phosphonomycin in standard blood-agar media such as Brain Heart Infusion Agar and Trypticase Soy Agar, both of which contain 0.5% NaCl.

The survey of the susceptibility of clinical pathogens to phosphonomycin in Nutrient Agar containing 5% sheep blood indicates that phosphonomycin has a broad spectrum of activity. The susceptible organisms tested included strains of *Serratia* (nonpigmented), *Proteus, E. coli, Aerobacter,* and *S. aureus*. Phosphonomycin compared favorably with chloramphenicol, tetracycline, and nalidixic acid when tested against 105 randomly chosen gram-negative and gram-positive pathogens. Although phosphonomycin showed only moderate activity against *Pseudomonas* strains in the original survey of 105 cultures, when the survey was extended, over 50% of the *Pseudomonas* strains demonstrated susceptibility to phosphonomycin. Phosphonomycin activity against *Pseudomonas, Enterococcus, Enterobacter,* and *Streptococcus* was not as pronounced as against the other genera tested; however, only 12 of the 92 strains included in these four genera were found to be resistant.

In general, the in vitro data presented here indicate that phosphonomycin is a potentially useful antibiotic with a broad spectrum of activity. The criteria chosen for evaluating susceptibility, though arbitrary, consisted of recognized procedures for the relative evaluation of a new antibiotic. When compared with currently available in vivo data in mice (4), the in vitro data presented here seem reasonable. The ultimate significance of these evaluations must await clinical studies.

ACKNOWLEDGMENTS

We express our appreciation to A. Germain, J. A. Bauer, and S. Czajkowski for able technical assistance. We are also indebted to B. Frost and B. Shidlovsky of the Merck Institute for Therapeutic Research, Rahway, N.J., and to I. E. L. Foltz of the Graduate Hospital, University of Pennsylvania, Philadelphia, for supplying many of the clinical isolates tested in the susceptibility survey.

LITERATURE CITED

1. Countryman, J. L., and E. Volkin. 1959. Nucleic acid metabolism and ribonucleic acid heterogeneity in *Escherichia coli*. J. Bacteriol. 78:41-48.
2. Hendlin, D., B. M. Frost, E. Thiele, H. Kropp, M. E. Valiant, B. Pelak, B. Weissberger, C. Cornin, and A. K. Miller. 1970. Phosphonomycin. III. Evaluation in vitro. Antimicrob. Agents Chemother.–1969, p. 297-302.
3. Hendlin, D., E. O. Stapley, M. Jackson, H. Wallick, A. K. Miller, F. J. Wolf, T. W. Miller, L. Chaiet, F. M. Kahan, E. L. Foltz, H. B. Woodruff, J. M. Mata, S. Hernandez, and S. Mochales. 1969. Phosphonomycin, a new antibiotic produced by strains of *Streptomyces*. Science (Washington) **166**:122-123.
4. Miller, A. K., B. M. Frost, M. E. Valiant, H. Kropp, and D. Hendlin. 1970. Phosphonomycin. V. Evaluation in mice. Antimicrob. Agents Chemother.–1969, p. 000-000.
5. Stapley, E. O., D. Hendlin, J. M. Mata, M. Jackson, H. Wallick, S. Hernandez, S. Mochales, S. Currie, and R. M. Miller. 1970. Phosphonomycin. I. Discovery and in vitro biological characterization. Antimicrob. Agents Chemother.–1969, p. 284-290.

Antimicrobial Agents and Chemotherapy—1969

Phosphonomycin

V. Evaluation in Mice

A. KATHRINE MILLER, BETTINA M. FROST, MARY E. VALIANT, HELMUT KROPP, and DAVID HENDLIN

Merck Institute for Therapeutic Research, Rahway, New Jersey 07065

Phosphonomycin is a relatively nontoxic antibiotic. In mice, the toxicity noted with high doses of the sodium and calcium salts of the antibiotic was ascribed to the cation. Phosphonomycin was rapidly absorbed from the mouse gut, and peak concentrations in the plasma were attained within 0.5 to 1.0 hr. The antibiotic was excreted rapidly in the urine, approximately 50% of the orally administered dose being recovered during the first 8 hr. The disodium and the calcium salts of the antibiotic were essentially identical in their therapeutic activity. When therapy was given by gavage, phosphonomycin compared favorably with tetracycline and chloramphenicol in tests against gram-negative organisms; it was effective also against clinical isolates which were multiply drug-resistant. Phosphonomycin protected mice against infection with *Staphylococcus aureus* and was more effective than oxacillin against the penicillinase-producing staphylococci tested. It was not so active as tetracycline or chloramphenicol against infection with *Diplococcus pneumoniae* or *Streptococcus pyogenes.* Mice were protected even when therapy was delayed 4 hr after infection with *Salmonella schottmuelleri* or *Pasteurella multocida.*

Phosphonomycin is a broad-spectrum antibiotic recently described (3) and identified as (−)-cis-1,2,-epoxypropylphosphonic acid (1). It is a bactericidal agent that acts by affecting the integrity of the cell wall. Although its in vitro activity is influenced by constituents of the culture media (3), it is an effective chemotherapeutic agent in vivo. In this paper, we report some of the pharmacological properties of the antibiotic and its antibacterial activity against a variety of systemic infections in mice.

MATERIALS AND METHODS

Antibiotic agents. Pure disodium or calcium phosphonomycin, prepared by chemical synthesis, was used in all experiments except those concerned with chronic toxicity. Aqueous solutions were used except when large doses of the calcium salt were to be administered; then suspensions were prepared in water with the aid of a few drops of Tween 20 or Tween 80 (Mann Research Laboratories, New York, N.Y.) and grinding. Commercial preparations of chloramphenicol (Parke, Davis & Co., Detroit, Mich.; sodium succinate, for injection), tetracycline-HCl (Roerig, for intravenous injection), sodium penicillin G (The Upjohn Co., Kalamazoo, Mich.), and oxacillin (Bristol Laboratories, Syracuse, N.Y.) were dissolved in water.

Antibiotic assay. The activity of body fluids was estimated by a cylinder-plate agar-diffusion assay with *Proteus vulgaris* MB 838 as the test organism (5). Urine samples usually were diluted with *p*H 8 tris(hydroxymethyl)aminomethane buffer, and blood samples and standards were diluted in the appropriate biological fluids.

Bacterial cultures. The test cultures included "antibiotic-susceptible" strains from the Merck, Sharp & Dohme stock culture collection as well as clinically isolated strains showing multiple-drug resistance. *Staphylococcus aureus* 2949 commonly is called the Smith strain, and *Streptococcus pyogenes* 3009 is known generally as C-203. None of the other cultures have designations other than those of our collection. The cultures are maintained in a lyophilized state. They were restored for each test, were allowed to grow, and were transferred once into broth to prepare the challenge culture.

In vivo tests: efficacy. White Swiss female mice (Charles River CD1, average weight 20 to 23 g, or Carworth Farms CF_1, average weight 18 to 20 g) were used in groups of six for each of the fourfold drug concentrations studied. In general, antibiotic-susceptible organisms were tested in CD1 mice, and antibiotic-resistant organisms, in CF_1 mice. Infection was by the intraperitoneal route. Appropriate broth dilutions of the test culture were used except with *P. vulgaris* 1810, for which the infecting dose was suspended in 5% hog gastric mucin. In most tests, therapy was given by the indicated route at the time of infection (0 hr) and again 6 hr later, but in tests against penicillinase-producing staphylococci therapy was given only at 0 hr. Virulence controls were included in each experiment to determine that the infections used were 100% lethal. Seven days after infection, the experiments were terminated, and the amounts of antibiotic required to protect 50% of the infected animals (ED_{50}) were calculated by the method of Knudson and Curtis (4). Tests were repeated at least once and usually twice. Approximate 95% confidence limits of the geometric means of the ED_{50} values were calculated by the following method suggested by J. L. Ciminera. The approximate 95% confidence limits of the geometric mean ED_{50} are given by antilog ($m + Qw$) where Q is a quantity depending on the number of assays combined (two assays, $Q = 1.25$; three, $Q = 0.68$; four, $Q = 0.49$; five, $Q = 0.38$; six, $Q = 0.32$; seven, $Q = 0.28$) and w is the range of the individual estimates of m (logs of the individual ED_{50} values included in the mean).

Toxicity. Two doses of twofold increments of the Ca or the Na salts of phosphonomycin were given 6 hr apart so that the dosage schedule and duration of the observation period corresponded with that used in the efficacy tests. The toxicities of Ca^{++} as $CaCl_2 \cdot 2H_2O$ and Na^+ as NaCl given intraperitoneally were determined by this same schedule. In chronic toxicity tests, a phosphonomycin preparation of 70% purity was used. Five mice were given intraperitoneal doses of the drug three times a day, at 4-hr intervals, for 10 consecutive days. Each dose was equivalent to 7.9 mg of the pure disodium salt for a total dosage of 23.7 mg per day. A second group of mice received an equivalent number of injections of saline, as controls. All mice were sacrificed the day after the last injection. The tissues were removed, fixed in 10% Formalin, embedded in paraffin, sectioned, and stained with hematoxylin and eosin for examination.

Blood samples. Randomized groups of 10 mice (average weight, 18.5 g) were given two doses by gavage, 6 hr apart, of fourfold increments of phosphonomycin disodium. At stated intervals, groups of mice were bled from the heart by use of heparinized needles and syringes. The blood from each group was pooled and centrifuged, and the plasma was stored frozen until assayed.

Urine samples. Mice weighing 20 g were placed in metabolism cages in groups of 10. Each mouse was given phosphonomycin disodium or water by gavage in 0.5-ml volume, and each received an additional 1 ml of water, 0.5 ml at the time of the drug administration and 0.5 ml 4 hr later. Food and water were withheld for 8 hr but were given *ad libitum* between 8 and 24 hr. The pooled urine from each group of mice was collected at stated intervals, the volume was recorded, and the samples were kept cold until assayed.

RESULTS AND DISCUSSION

Efficacy studies. Both the calcium and the sodium salts of phosphonomycin were effective orally in protecting mice against infection. Because their activities were essentially identical, only end points obtained with preparations of the disodium salt are given in this paper.

In addition to the oral route of therapy, the intraperitoneal and subcutaneous routes also were studied. Data obtained from tests in which 17 organisms were used showed the following ratios: oral to intraperitoneal, 4:5; oral to subcutaneous, 2:3; and subcutaneous to intraperitoneal, 3. The antibiotic, therefore, is well absorbed.

Table 1 shows the ED_{50} of phosphonomycin disodium, tetracycline-HCl, and chloramphenicol given by gavage to mice infected with antibiotic-susceptible strains of bacteria. Phosphonomycin compared favorably with tetracycline and chloramphenicol in these tests against the gram-negative organisms and against *S. aureus* 2949. It was not so active as the other antibiotics against *Diplococcus pneumoniae* I-37 or against either strain of *S. pyogenes* tested. Table 2 lists the ED_{50} of the same three antibiotics against clinically isolated strains of gram-negative multiply drug-resistant bacteria. Phosphonomycin was able to protect mice against most of these strains. Table 3 gives the ED_{50} of these three antibiotics and also of oxacillin against five multiply antibiotic-resistant, clinically isolated staphylococci. In these tests, phosphonomycin was more active than oxacillin.

The duration of phosphonomycin protection also was studied. In these experiments, mice were given single doses of antibiotic at intervals prior to infection with *Salmonella schottmuelleri* 3010. Comparison with the ED_{50} when treatment was given at the time of infection showed that about 20 and 2 times more antibiotic was required when the mice were treated 2 and 1 hr, respectively, prior to infection. The sharp increase in the ED_{50} with increased pretreatment time may indicate that a rapid loss of antibiotic follows the administration of a single dose.

Table 1. *Activity of phosphonomycin, tetracycline, and chloramphenicol in mice infected with antibiotic-susceptible bacteria*

Infecting organism	Geometric mean of oral ED_{50}[a] (μg/dose)		
	Phosphonomycin, disodium	Tetracycline-HCl	Chloramphenicol
Escherichia coli 2017	530 (240–1,170)	224 (110–445)	205 (126–336)
Klebsiella pneumoniae 3068	723 (395–1,360)	1,390 (602–3,210)	279 (160–488)
K. pneumoniae B	2,760 (1,780–4,270)	712 (175–2,900)	212 (132–340)
Paracolobactrum arizonae 3270	165 (149–183)	826 (408–1,670)	384 (240–615)
Pasteurella multocida 1590	921 (574–1470)	821 (534–1260)	
Proteus mirabilis 3201	256 (195–386)	>10,000	250 (163–335)
P. morganii 3202	430 (310–597)	283 (283)	396 (292–619)
P. vulgaris 1810	327 (125–853)	8,000 (4,630–13,800)	319 (230–442)
Pseudomonas aeruginosa 2616	1,830 (1,040–3,220)	>10,000	4,490 (2,730–7,380)
P. aeruginosa 3210	881 (341–2,280)	>7,250	2,370 (882–6,360)
Salmonella schottmuelleri 1814	118 (63–225)	1,850 (1,070–3,210)	615 (248–1,540)
S. schottmuelleri 3010	5 (4–7)	617 (321–1,190)	220 (154–315)
S. typhosa 2866	58 (42–80)	284 (91–884)	394 (127–1,230)
Diplococcus pneumoniae I–37	4,550 (2,060–10,000)	936 (444–1,970)	1,370 (467–4,020)
Staphylococcus aureus 2949	93 (75–116)	269 (232–312)	771 (351–1,700)
Streptococcus pyogenes 1685	2,770 (625–12,300)	284 (234–345)	560 (281–1,120)
S. pyogenes 3009	1,030 (413–2,570)	114 (84–155)	638 (476–855)

[a] Infection intraperitoneally. Therapy by gavage at 0 hr and again 6 hr after infection. Geometric mean of at least two and usually three or four tests; 95% confidence limits in parentheses.

To determine the therapeutic activity of phosphonomycin, the compound was given as a single dose 4 or 6.5 hr after infection with *S. schottmuelleri* 3010. Under these conditions, 10 and 100 times more antibiotic was required at the 4- and 6.5-hr dose period, respectively, than when the drug was given immediately after infection. A therapeutic trial also was conducted with *Pasteurella multocida* 1590. In this test, delaying therapy by 4 hr increased the ED_{50} 20-fold.

This increase in ED_{50} with delayed therapy may reflect the rapid increase in numbers of microorganisms and the extent to which the host defense mechanisms were overwhelmed. These observations were extended by determining the effect of the size of the infecting dose of *P. multocida* 1590 or of *S. pyogenes* 3009 on the ED_{50} of phosphonomycin. In these experiments, infecting doses of each organism were prepared to contain 200,000, 2,000, and 20 LD_{50} (the dose required to kill 50% of the infected control mice). With *P. multocida* 1590, 100- and 10,000-fold increases in the LD_{50} resulted in 4- and 25-fold increases in the ED_{50}, respectively. The latter increase is comparable to the increase in the ED_{50} when therapy was delayed 4 hr.

With the *S. pyogenes* 3009 infection, increasing the challenge 100-fold resulted in a threefold increase in ED_{50}; the heaviest challenge required 10 times more antibiotic than the lightest one.

Increases in the ED_{50} were also observed to accompany increased challenge doses when penicillin was used as the therapeutic agent in these infections.

Experiments described in a separate report (2) showed that resistance to phosphonomycin could be developed in vitro by transferring microorganisms through antibiotic-containing broth. Attempts to demonstrate the development of resistance in vivo with *S. schottmuelleri* 3010 have so far failed. Cultures of this organism, recovered after four serial passages through mice treated with phosphonomycin, have remained susceptible to the antibiotic. These preliminary studies are being extended.

Toxicity. In the two-dose test schedule, both salts of phosphonomycin were relatively nontoxic for mice by all three routes of administration. Data presented in Table 4 show that the LD_{50} of the pure calcium salt given intraperitoneally was 19.6 mg per dose, equivalent to 5.9 mg of Ca^{++} ion per dose. Since at this concentration the salt was not in solution, the Ca^{++} content tolerated as the antibiotic salt was

Table 2. *Activity of phosphonomycin, tetracycline, and chloramphenicol in mice infected with antibiotic-resistant gram-negative bacteria*

Infecting organism	Geometric mean of oral ED_{50}[a] (μg/dose)		
	Phosphonomycin, disodium	Tetracycline-HCl	Chloramphenicol
Aerobacter sp.			
3285	1,560 (1,040–2,340)	>10,000	>5,000
3286	309 (245–390)	>10,000	>5,000
3287	399 (180–883)	>10,000	>5,000
3288	>16,000	1,920 (1,200–3,080)	389 (138–1,090)
3289	3,470 –>16,000	>10,000	>5,000
3290	606 (251–1,460)	>10,000	2,660 (2,150–3,300)
Escherichia coli			
3291	1,030 (498–2,130)	>10,000	476 (318–713)
3292	6,370 (3,630–11,200)	>10,000	1,180 (268–5,200)
3293	6,400 –ca 16,000	>10,000	1,720 (902–3,280)
3294	421 (99–1,790)	>10,000	197 (123–316)
3295	3,690 (2,310–5,900)	ca 7,380 (3,970–13,700)	1,610 (625–4,150)
3296	1,080 (994–1,170)	>10,000	466 (403–539)
Proteus mirabilis			
2919	593 (215–1,630)	>10,000	1,010 (1,010–1,010)
3011	119 (107–132)	>10,000	1,040 (509–2,130)
3255	624 (133–2,930)	>10,000	302 (118–776)
3299	15 (8–28)	>10,000	237 (171–328)
Proteus sp.			
3300	66 (62–70)	>10,000	172 (93–317)
3306	269 (232–311)	6,930 (5,960–8,060)	613 (248–1,520)
Pseudomonas			
3254	3,850 (3,110–4,770)	3,940 (2,170–7,160)	2,200 (1,010–4,810)
3301	3,880 –>20,000	>10,000	2,400 (2,300–2,500)
Shigella sp.			
3297	19 (5–68)	>10,000	125 (125–125)
3298	3,310 (2,020–5,420)	>10,000	>5,000
3302	46 (25–86)	>10,000	464 (270–797)
3303	492 (140–1,720)	5,110 –>10,000	466 (377–576)
3304	1,710 (861–3,390)	929 (442–1,950)	308 (192–494)

[a] Infection intraperitoneally. Therapy by gavage at 0 hr and again 6 hr after infection. Geometric mean of at least two and usually three or four tests; 95% confidence limits in parentheses.

comparable to the 3.5 mg of Ca^{++} shown to be toxic when given as $CaCl_2 \cdot H_2O$. Given subcutaneously or orally, the Ca salt suspension was not toxic for mice even at 50 mg per dose. The intraperitoneal toxicity of the sodium salt, given as a solution, also can be ascribed to its cation content.

No gross abnormalities were observed at autopsy in mice that survived treatment with the sodium salt. However, mice injected intraperitoneally with the calcium salt showed extensive fusing of the mesentery tissues with the abdominal organs. White deposits, presumably insoluble calcium phosphonomycin, were noted on the intestines and some of the spleens. Similar white deposits were noted at the site of the subcutaneous injection of the 50-mg doses. No grossly visible changes in the tissues or organs of mice receiving the calcium salt by gavage were detected.

During the 10-day treatment period of the chronic toxicity test, no untoward effects were noted in mice treated with the equivalent of 23.9 mg of pure disodium phosphonomycin per day given in three divided doses. Weight gain in the treated animals was comparable to that of saline-injected control animals. The mice were sacrificed on the 11th day, 16 hr after receiving the 30th intraperitoneal injection. No gross abnormalities were noted during the removal of

Table 3. *Ability of several antibiotics to protect mice against infection with antibiotic-resistant staphylococci of clinical origin*[a]

Infecting organism	Oral ED_{50}[b] (μg/dose)			
	Phosphonomycin disodium	Tetracycline-HCl	Chloramphenicol	Oxacillin
S. aureus 2957	72 (69–76)	493 (229–1,060)	1,440 (1,320–1,570)	1,290 (964–1,730)
S. aureus 3036	925 (459–1,860)	>10,000	742 (496–1,110)	2,290 (1,230–4,250)
S. aureus 3089	453 (176–1,170)	>10,000	322 (159–651)	1,830 (987–3,390)
S. aureus 3106	198 (109–361)	>10,000	511 (484–539)	3,710 (1,380–9,990)
S. aureus 3147	516 (188–1,410)	>10,000	975 (734–1,290)	3,530 (1,480–8,400)

[a] All of these multiple-resistant cultures were penicillinase producing, and four of the five were also resistant to tetracycline. Resistance to other antibiotics and phage types varied from strain to strain.

[b] Infection given intraperitoneally. Therapy by gavage as a single dose at the time of infection. Geometric mean of the ED_{50} values of at least two and usually three tests; 95% confidence limits in parentheses.

Table 4. *Toxicity of salts of phosphonomycin in mice*

Compound	LD_{50}(mg/dose)[a]		
	Intraperitoneal	Subcutaneous	Oral
Calcium salt	19.6 (5.9)[b]	>50	>50
Sodium salt	80.3 (24)	80.3	>100
$CaCl_2 \cdot 2H_2O$ ...	8.8 (3.5)	–	–
NaCl	70.7 (28)	–	–

[a] Compounds administered in two doses 6 hr apart. High concentrations of the calcium salt of phosphonomycin were not in solution, but were given as a suspension.

[b] Figures in parentheses indicate content of the cation in milligrams.

tissues to be fixed in Formalin. Examination of the following tissues revealed no histopathology: bone marrow, striated muscle, various segments of the large and small intestine, stomach, mesentery of the small intestine (including lymph nodes), pancreas, liver, spleen, kidney, adrenal, thymus, lung, heart, aorta, and brain. There was a mild diffuse peritonitis that, according to the pathologist, is found after the intraperitoneal injection of most materials.

Concentrations in plasma and urinary excretion. Phosphonomycin was rapidly absorbed from the mouse gut. Maximal concentrations in the plasma occurred within 0.5 to 1 hr after the first oral dose and also after a second dose given 6 hr later. The second drug peak was, on the average, 40% higher than the initial peak, probably reflecting residual antibiotic in the blood and other tissues from the first dose of drug. As shown in Fig. 1, the plasma levels of phosphonomycin are dose-related.

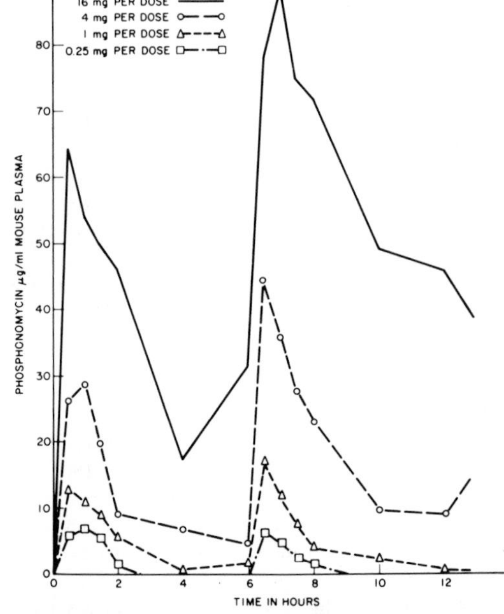

Fig. 1. *Phosphonomycin concentration in plasma of mice that had received oral doses at 0 hr and again at 6 hr.*

The antibiotic is rapidly excreted in the urine. Approximately 30 to 45% of the orally administered dose was recovered in the urine as active antibiotic within the first 4 to 6 hr, and another 2 to 5% was excreted during the next 18 to 20 hr; collections were not made after 20 hr (Table 5). After administration of a single oral dose of 1 or 5 mg of disodium phosphonomycin, the concentration of antibiotic in the urine reached a peak during the 2- to 4-hr collection period.

Table 5. *Urinary recovery of phosphonomycin disodium from mice*

Time after dose	Recovery after 1.0 mg[a]				Recovery after 5.0 mg[a]			
	Amt of urine	Drug/ml	Total drug	Per cent	Amt. of urine	Drug/ml	Total drug	Per cent
hr	*ml*	*μg*	*μg*		*ml*	*μg*	*μg*	
0–2	10	164	1,640	16 (16)[b]	8.0	223	1,784	4 (4)
2–4	1.6	817	1,307	13 (29)	2.0	3,545	7,090	14 (18)
4–6	6.5	226	1,469	15 (44)	6.2	1,070	6,634	13 (31)
6–8	0.5	114	57	1 (45)	0.8	430	344	1 (32)
8–24	5.3	107	567	6 (51)	1.1	168	184	0.4 (32.4)

[a] Urine pooled from 10 mice, each receiving 1.0 or 5.0 mg of phosphonomycin disodium in 0.5-ml volume by gavage at 0 hr; 0.5 ml of water was given each mouse at 0 hr and again at 4 hr.

[b] Numbers in parentheses show the accumulative percentage recovery.

Peak concentrations in the urine of mice were 82 μg/ml with the 1-mg dose and 354 μg/ml with the 5-mg dose.

ACKNOWLEDGMENTS

We are indebted to Joseph Brown for preparing the tissues and to Henry Siegel for examining the sections and reporting on the histopathology. We thank H. Wallick and his associates for bioassays and Carolyn Cornin, Barbara Pelak, Gail Owens, Barbara Weissberger, and Jon Sundelof for laboratory assistance. The statistical formula for confidence limits of the in vivo test was prepared by Joseph Ciminera.

LITERATURE CITED

1. Christensen, B. G., W. J. Leanza, T. R. Beattie, A. A. Patchett, B. H. Arison, R. E. Ormond, F. A. Kuehl, Jr., G. Albers-Schonberg, and O. Jardetzky. 1969. Structure and synthesis of phosphonomycin. Science (Washington) **166**:123–125.
2. Hendlin, D., B. M. Frost, E. Thiele, H. Kropp, M. E. Valiant, B. Pelak, B. Weissberger, C. Cornin, and A. K. Miller. 1970. Phosphonomycin. III. Evaluation in vitro. Antimicrob. Agents Chemother.–1969, p. 297–302.
3. Hendlin, D., E. O. Stapley, M. Jackson, H. Wallick, A. K. Miller, F. J. Wolf, T. W. Miller, L. Chaiet, F. M. Kahan, E. L. Foltz, and H. B. Woodruff. 1969. Phosphonomycin, a new antibiotic produced by strains of *Streptomyces.* Science (Washington) **166**:122–123.
4. Knudson, L. F., and J. M. Curtis. 1947. The use of angular transformation in biological assays. J. Amer. Statist. Ass. **42**:282–296.
5. Stapley, E. O., D. Hendlin, J. M. Mata, M. Jackson, H. Wallick, S. Hernandez, S. Mochales, S. A. Currie, and R. M. Miller. 1970. Phosphonomycin. I. Discovery and in vitro biological characterization. Antimicrob. Agents Chemother.–1969, p. 284–290.

Antimicrobial Agents and Chemotherapy—1969

Pharmacodynamics of Phosphonomycin After Intravenous Administration in Man

E. L. FOLTZ and H. WALLICK

Section of Clinical Pharmacology, Department of Medicine, Graduate Hospital, University of Pennsylvania, Philadelphia, Pennsylvania 19146, and Merck Sharp & Dohme Research Laboratories, Rahway, New Jersey 07065

Phosphonomycin, a new antimicrobial agent which inhibits bacterial cell wall formation, was studied in normal, healthy male volunteers for pharmacokinetic properties after intravenous administration of the sodium salt. With single doses of 250 mg of the sodium salt administered over a period of 10 to 15 min, peak concentrations of 12.6 μg/ml in serum were observed 15 min after completion of injection; after the administration of 500 mg, the peak concentrations were 31.5 μg/ml. The concentrations in serum declined in a biphasic manner, suggesting an early rapid equilibration with extracellular and perhaps intracellular fluid compartments; a later slower decline was associated with a steady rate of renal clearance. Measurable concentrations in the serum extended through 8 to 12 hr after single doses. Urinary recovery approximated a first-order rate of elimination, with approximately 95% recovery in 24 hr after administration. Calculations on urinary recovery after the first 2 hr suggested clearance approximating the rate of glomerular filtration. This was subsequently checked against endogenous creatinine clearance by conventional clearance techniques. Calculations of volume of distribution suggested that phosphonomycin is distributed in greater than extracellular fluid volume. Evidence for modest cumulative effects was obtained by repeat doses at 2-, 4-, and 6-hr intervals. No toxicity or local irritation was observed in these trials.

Since the discovery and isolation of phosphonomycin, its bactericidal activity against gram-positive and gram-negative bacteria has been demonstrated both in vitro and in vivo (2, 3, 5, 6). These studies clearly indicated the potential clinical usefulness of this drug in the treatment of selected infectious diseases. Clinical pharmacological trials were begun shortly after completion of animal safety trials. This report describes our initial experience with the intravenous administration of the sodium salt of phosphonomycin.

MATERIALS AND METHODS

Subjects for the trials were selected from male prisoners who volunteered after they had been informed of the nature of the agent and of the studies to be performed. The subjects were screened to ensure that they had taken no other antimicrobial agent during the preceding week. They reported on the morning of the test days in the postabsorptive state and were permitted food and liquids *ad libitum.*

Injections of the sodium salt of phosphonomycin were carried out with Lyovac preparations reconstituted with 5% dextrose water and diluted to a volume of 25 to 30 ml. Doses of 250 and 500 mg were injected over periods of 10 to 15 min. In renal clearance studies, a calculated maintenance dose was administered in 400 ml of dextrose water over a period of 2 hr, starting approximately 2 hr after the initial "stat" injection of 250 mg of the drug.

Blood samples were obtained by venipuncture prior to administration of the drug, and at 0.25, 0.5, 1, 1.5, 2, 4, 6, and 8 hr after injection. A 12-hr blood sample was obtained during the initial intravenous trial with the 250-mg dose, and more frequent intermediate samplings were obtained when 500-mg doses were administered. Serum was immediately harvested and frozen until time of bioassay. Periodically, the entire urinary output was collected, generally in the intervals of 0 to 2, 2 to 4, 4 to 8, 8 to 12, and 12 to 24 hr. Samples were collected for bioassay and were held in the frozen state until time of analysis. All urinary volumes were recorded.

During the estimation of renal clearance of the sodium salt of phosphonomycin, blood samples were obtained at 0.5-hr intervals through the first 4 hr postinjection and subsequently at 5, 6, 8, and 10 hr. Urine collections were made by voiding at 2, 3, 4, 6, 8, and 12 hr after the initial injection, and also by collecting all urine during the period from 12 to 24 hr after injection. Serum and urine samples from 2 through 4 hr were also assayed for endogenous creatinine by a modification of the Folin-Wu chemical method (1).

Bioassay was carried out by a standard cup-plate method with either *Proteus vulgaris* ATCC 21100 or *Erwinia atroseptica* as the test organism.

RESULTS

All subjects tolerated the single and multiple intravenous doses of phosphonomycin with no pain or sequellae. Minimal irritation and some venospasm in the antebrachial veins were noted in the multiple-dose study, since these same veins were used for multiple blood aspirations as well as for injections. No thromboses or phlebitis resulted during these studies.

At 15 min after the completion of the injection, peak concentrations in serum were obtained with both 250- and 500-mg doses. The average peak concentration for six subjects, each of whom received a 250-mg dose, was 12.6 μg/ml, whereas 31.5 μg/ml was assayed for the six subjects receiving 500-mg doses (Table 1).

During the first 60 min, drug concentrations in the serum appeared to decline at a relatively rapid rate with both drug dosages; this probably represented a period of rapid tissue equilibration as well as renal excretion. Thereafer, the serum decay curve approximated a first-order reaction at a rate somewhat slower than that noted during the first 60 min. At 8 hr postinjection, the concentrations in serum averaged 0.7 and 1.7 μg/ml with the 250- and 500-mg doses, respectively (Fig. 1).

Urinary excretion occurred promptly, and approximately half of each dose was excreted in the first 2 hr after injection. Concentrations in the urine generally exceeded 100 μg/ml during the first 8 hr in the subjects receiving the smaller of the two doses. Excretion appeared to be fairly complete within the first 24 hr. Recovery under maximal control approached 90% by bioassay methods, and ranged from a low of 75% to greater than 100% (Table 2).

When doses of 500 mg were repeated at 6-hr intervals, the first peak concentration averaged 28.0 μg/ml, but after subsequent doses, it ranged from 32.2 to 36.0 μg/ml, suggesting some cumulative activity. "Trough" concentrations at 6 hr after the first dose averaged 3.3 μg/ml subsequently ranged from 2.8 to 4.8 μg/ml (Table 3, Fig. 2).

Table 1. *Concentrations of phosphonomycin in the serum after intravenous administration to healthy volunteers*[a]

Dose (mg)	Subject	Concn in serum (μg/ml)									
		15 min	30 min	1 hr	1.5 hr	2 hr	3 hr	4 hr	5 hr	6 hr	8 hr
250	1	12.2	10.9	7.6	6.4	5.1	–	2.4	–	1.3	0.8
	2	12.7	15.5	8.5	8.0	8.9	–	3.2	–	1.8	0.8
	3	12.7	9.3	6.2	5.4	5.1	–	1.7	–	1.1	0.3
	4	10.5	8.6	6.4	5.4	5.3	–	2.3	–	1.3	0.6
	5	14.7	11.4	6.6	5.9	6.0	–	2.9	–	1.8	1.0
	6	13.0	10.9	7.5	6.2	5.9	–	2.9	–	2.0	0.8
	Avg	12.6	11.1	7.1	6.2	6.05	–	2.6	–	1.5	0.7
500	1	27.4	24.8	18.9	21.4	11.7	8.2	6.3	4.0	2.9	1.8
	2	26.0	20.3	16.1	11.9	9.8	6.0	4.6	3.7	2.9	1.6
	3	32.8	20.7	15.0	11.2	10.7	7.4	5.2	3.9	2.8	1.8
	4	36.0	23.4	14.3	13.1	10.7	7.5	5.5	3.8	2.9	1.6
	5	35.8	25.6	18.8	13.5	11.2	7.7	6.0	4.6	3.3	1.9
	6	31.0	19.6	16.5	10.1	8.2	5.7	5.1	3.3	2.5	1.5
	Avg	31.5	22.4	16.6	13.5	10.4	7.1	5.5	3.9	2.9	1.7

[a] With both doses, the concentration at 0 min was less than 0.3 μg/ml. In subjects receiving the 250-mg dose, the concentration had returned to less than 0.3 μg/ml at 12 hr. Concentrations in the serum of these subjects were not measured at 3 or 5 hr.

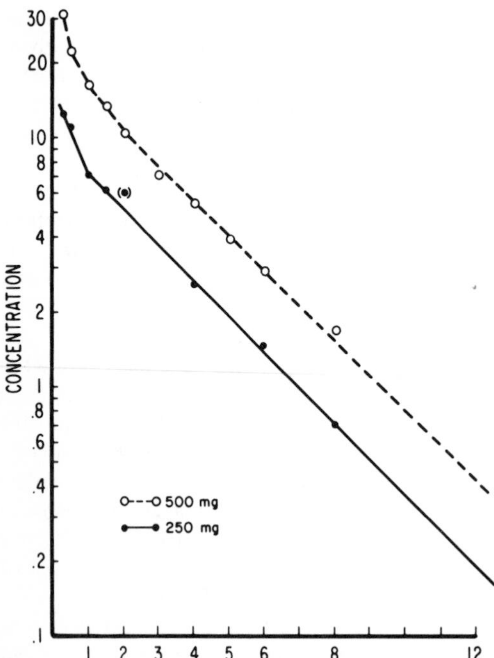

Fig. 1. *Concentrations of phosphonomycin in serum (micrograms per milliliter) after intravenous administration of single doses in two dosage levels to different subjects.*

Table 2. *Average urinary recovery of phosphonomycin after single intravenous doses of the sodium salt*[a]

Dose (mg)	Collection periods					24-hr total	Percentage of dose
	0–2 hr	2–4 hr	4–8 hr	8–12 hr	12–24 hr		
250	139.3	50.2	39.4	15.3	6.7	250.9	100.0
500	155.9	174.6	88.8	21.2	16.8	457.3	91.4

[a] Each drug dosage was administered to six normal subjects in the fasting state through the 4th hr. Recovery is given in milligrams per collection period.

Conventional clinical biochemical tests of the blood were performed before the study and after its completion. Determination of blood-urea nitrogen, creatinine, bilirubin, alkaline phosphatase, and serum transaminases revealed no abnormalities or significant shifts for any of these biochemical parameters.

Calculations on the basis of serum decay curves and urinary recoveries suggested that renal clearance approximated glomerular filtration. A conventional clearance study was then

Table 3. *Drug concentrations in serum after repeated intravenous doses of phosphonomycin at 6-hr intervals in healthy volunteers*

Concn in serum (μg/ml)[a]

Subject	15 min	1 hr	2 hr	6 hr	6 hr 15 min	12 hr	12 hr 15 min	18 hr	18 hr 15 min	24 hr	24 hr 15 min
1	26.0	13.7	9.0	7.0	31.0	3.2	30.3	2.7	29.0	6.0	30.6
2	31.6	17.6	10.4	2.9	37.9	2.5	38.1	3.5	32.6	5.0	35.3
3	31.0	15.0	8.2	2.6	37.2	3.1	34.4	2.6	35.4	4.4	32.5
4	30.6	15.0	10.6	3.1	34.1	3.4	35.5	3.5	35.7	4.6	34.4
5	23.6	10.2	6.8	1.8	27.8	1.9	25.8	1.6	30.9	3.6	33.5
6	25.0	13.3	8.8	2.5	30.5	2.9	29.3	3.2	33.0	5.3	36.6
Avg	28.0	14.1	9.0	3.3	33.1	2.8	32.2	2.9	32.8	4.8	33.8

Subject	30 hr	30 hr 15 min	36 hr	36 hr 15 min	37 hr	38 hr	40 hr	42 hr	42 hr 15 min	48 hr
1	4.3	31.9	4.3	34.8	13.6	10.4	5.7	4.6	34.2	3.3
2	3.8	42.0	3.6	34.2	20.0	12.4	5.7	3.8	40.4	2.2
3	4.0	43.1	3.6	44.5	20.7	12.9	6.8	4.1	38.6	2.8
4	4.1	34.1	5.0	42.0	24.9	15.0	7.6	4.9	37.0	2.9
5	2.7	29.5	2.7	29.5	13.6	8.4	5.2	2.7	30.0	2.1
6	4.3	34.5	3.9	30.8	18.1	12.9	6.2	4.0	28.6	3.8
Avg	3.9	35.9	3.9	36.0	18.5	12.0	6.2	4.0	34.8	2.9

[a] In all subjects, treatment was started on 6 March 1969, and the concentration at 0 min was less than 0.3 μg/ml.

planned in which the estimation of endogenous creatinine clearance was compared with the clearance of the sodium salt of phosphonomycin.

On the basis of the above results with single doses and additional unreported experience with the 250-mg doses, it appeared that the concentrations in serum were approximately 5 μg/ml 2 hr after the injection. Hence, at 2 hr after administration of a 250-mg intravenous dose, a constant drip of the sodium salt of phosphonomycin in a total volume of 400 ml of 5% dextrose water was started. Doses of 70 to 80 mg, depending on the body weight, were administered. It was hoped that a constant concentration could be maintained in serum for a 2-hr period by approximating a replacement of 580 to 660 μg/min.

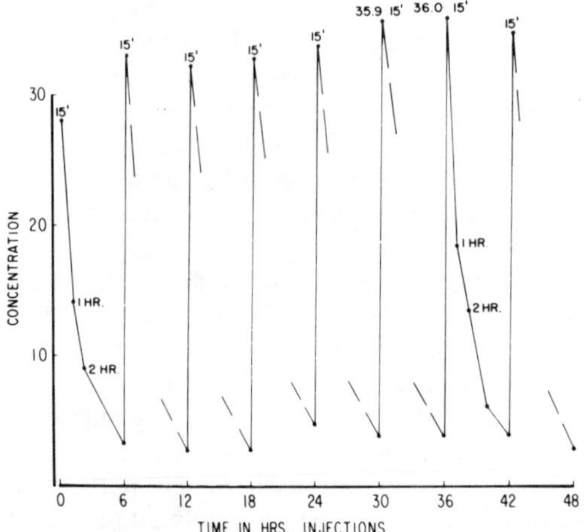

Fig. 2. *Concentrations of phosphonomycin in serum (micrograms per milliliter) after intravenous administration of 500-mg doses of phosphonomycin sodium at 6-hr intervals.*

The results of this study (Tables 4 and 5) show that the concentration in the serum of each subject was approximately constant during the "steady-state" period. Bioassay did not reveal any variation greater than 0.6 μg/ml. During these two urine collection periods of 1 hr each (2 to 3 and 3 to 4 hr), approximately 23 to 38 mg of the sodium salt of phosphonomycin was recovered per hr. Calculations of the clearance indicated that these men averaged approximately 113 ml per min per 1.73 square meters for the sodium salt as compared with 130 ml per min per 1.73 square meters for endogenous creatinine. The average urinary recovery of the sodium salt from five subjects during the 24-hr postinjection period was 99%; one subject did not complete the 12- to 24-hr urine collection satisfactorily.

DISCUSSION

The sodium salt of phosphonomycin can readily be prepared in a stabile sterile state of lyophilization. This material was easily reconstituted into sterile solution for parenteral injection by the addition of dextrose solution or sterile water.

In our initial studies, single doses of 250 and 500 mg were administered to healthy volunteers. Administration of these doses of the drug over

Table 4. *Concentrations of phosphonomycin in serum after an intravenous loading dose and constant infusion*[a]

Subject	Day	Date, 1969	Concn in serum (μg/ml)[b]											
			0.5 hr	1 hr	1.5 hr	2 hr	2.5 hr	3 hr	3.5 hr	4 hr	5 hr	6 hr	8 hr	10 hr
1	1	28 May	11.0	7.5	6.2	5.6	5.8	5.2	5.5	5.3	3.4	2.1	1.5	1.0
2	1	28 May	9.2	6.5	5.3	4.0	4.4	4.3	4.5	4.6	2.4	1.9	1.1	<0.3
Avg			10.1	7.0	5.8	4.8	5.1	4.8	5.0	5.0	2.9	2.0	1.3	0.5
3	2	5 June	10.3	6.5	4.5	4.0	4.6	4.0	4.1	4.1	2.1	1.5	0.7	<0.3
4	2	5 June	7.6	5.1	4.2	3.6	3.4	3.7	3.7	3.3	2.4	1.6	0.9	<0.3
Avg			9.0	5.8	4.4	3.8	4.0	3.9	3.9	3.7	2.3	1.6	0.8	<0.3
5	3	12 June	10.3	7.0	5.6	4.6	4.7	5.2	5.3	5.0	3.2	2.0	0.8	<0.3
6	3	12 June	10.1	6.7	6.1	4.4	4.6	5.0	4.7	5.2	3.3	2.2	0.8	<0.3
Avg			10.2	6.9	5.9	4.5	4.7	5.1	5.0	5.1	3.3	2.1	0.8	<0.3

[a] Each subject received 250 mg intravenously in a single dose at 0 hr and then a variable dose as a constant infusion from 2 to 4 hr.
[b] In all subjects, the concentration at 0 hr was less than 0.3 μg/ml.

Table 5. *Comparison of renal clearances of phosphonomycin and endogenous creatinine*

Subject	Maintenance dose (mg)	2- to 3-hr collections						3- to 4-hr collections						Avg 2-hr clearance		Avg total clearance (ml per min per 1.73 square meters)	
		Phosphonomycin			Creatinine			Phosphonomycin			Creatinine						
		Serum[a]	Urine[b]	Clearance	Serum[c]	Urine[d]	Clearance	Serum[a]	Urine[b]	Clearance	Serum[c]	Urine[d]	Clearance	Phosphonomycin	Creatinine	Phosphonomycin	Creatinine
1	80	5.5	597	90	10.7	1,687	158	5.3	553	104	9.2	1,312	143	97	150	84	130
2	75	4.2	599	143	10.7	1,185	111	4.5	613	136	10.5	1,832	174	139	143	134	137
3	75	4.2	646	154	10.4	1,668	160	4.1	589	144	10.4	1,438	138	149	149	129	129
4	70	3.6	509	141	10.7	1,674	156	3.6	530	147	9.3	1,490	160	144	156	131	142
5	70	4.8	554	115	10.2	1,188	116	5.2	548	105	10.3	1,388	135	110	126	106	121
6	75	4.7	561	119	11.0	1,492	136	5.0	468	94	10.7	1,377	129	106	132	97	120
Avg														124	143	113.5	130

[a] Average concentration in serum (micrograms per milliliter).
[b] Urinary recovery (micrograms per minute).
[c] Average serum creatinine (micrograms per milliliter).
[d] Urinary creatinine (micrograms per minute).

an interval of 10 to 15 min in 25 to 30 ml of 5% dextrose water was uneventful and produced no immediate or delayed discomfort. No untoward effects were noted with a multiple-dose schedule of eight doses of 500 mg each injected at 6-hr intervals; however, minimal evidence of local venospasm was noted at the antebrachial sites of injections and multiple venipunctures for the pharmacokinetic studies. Conventional biochemical studies of the serum did not show any abnormalities in those parameters analyzed before and after the performance of the study.

The drug concentrations in serum were at their peak 15 min after injection, and phosphonomycin was identified in active form in the serum for more than 8 hr after injection. Although comparative data are not available for the administration of 250- and 500-mg doses to the same subjects, the average peak concentration in serum of men receiving the higher dose was slightly more than twice that reached with the lower dose.

After injection of the single doses, the serum decay curves showed a biphasic pattern, with rapid decline during the first hour and a slower decline through the next 8 to 12 hr. The decay curves were almost parallel for the two doses in different subjects.

Urinary excretion occurred promptly, and during the first 2 hr approximately 30 to 45% of each dose was eliminated. At the end of 4 hr, the urinary recovery of the drug amounted to 60 to 65% of the amount administered. These data confirm the observation that, after equilibration, half of the remaining activity in the serum was lost in slightly more than 100 min. At the end of 24 hr, the urinary recovery was practically complete.

From these data, volumes of distribution were calculated according to the method recommended by Riegelman, Loo, and Rowland for a two-compartment open model (4). With data from both the 250- and 500-mg doses, volumes of distribution in central and peripheral compartments were estimated to total from 18.5 to 26.8 liters. These exceed extracellular fluid volumes for these subjects and indicate that a large portion of the drug must be distributed intracellularly.

Multiple injections of the sodium salt of phosphonomycin produced some evidence of cumulative activity. Just prior to the second injection of 500 mg, "trough" concentrations averaged 3.3 μg/ml. Hence, an additive effect from the second and subsequent doses was anticipated. Peak values following these doses were approximately 4.2 to 8.0 μg/ml greater than the average peak value following the first dose. However, the effect was not constantly cumulative, but demonstrated a plateau of peak concentration not exceeding 36 μg/ml. There is little likelihood that this minimal cumulative effect will increase after the administration of serial doses to approach toxic concentrations.

Clearance studies were designed to be accomplished with a minimum of disturbance to the subject. Instead of comparing rates of excretion of the drug with an exogenous substance such as inulin, urinary clearance of endogenous creatinine was measured. In this way, the "maintenance infusion" of the sodium salt was not complicated by a concomitant inulin infusion.

Although the merits of using endogenous creatinine clearance in such a manner are debatable, the values obtained in these subjects compared favorably with data for estimated glomerular filtration rates in normal males. Phosphonomycin was cleared at a somewhat slower rate than endogenous creatinine; however, the rates were sufficiently close to allow the assumption that in man there is not a significant excretion of the drug by tubular activity. The possibility of some tubular reabsorption cannot be excluded.

The high concentrations of phosphonomycin easily achieved in the serum and in the urine, and its apparent lack of toxicity, suggest that a clinical trial of this compound in bacterial infections, especially those of the urinary tract, is warranted.

ACKNOWLEDGMENTS

We acknowledge the assistance of King Chiu Kwan for calculations referable to distribution of phosphonomycin. We also thank William Maiese, Lorraine Leidy, and Shirley Czajkowski for technical assistance in the performance of bioassays and chemical tests.

LITERATURE CITED

1. Hawk, P. B., B. L. Oser, and W. H. Summerson. 1954. Practical physiological chemistry, 13th ed.
2. Hendlin, D., B. M. Frost, E. Thiele, H. Kropp, M. E. Valiant, B. Pelak, B. Weissberger, C. Cornin, and A. K. Miller. 1970. Phosphonomycin. III. Evaluation in vitro. Antimicrob. Agents Chemother.–1969, p. 297–302.
3. Miller, A. K., B. M. Frost, M. E. Valiant, H. Kropp, and D. Hendlin. 1970. Phosphonomycin. V. Evaluation in mice. Antimicrob. Agents Chemother.–1969, p. 310–315.
4. Riegelman, S., J. Loo, and M. Rowland. 1968. Concept of a volume of distribution and possible errors in evaluation of this parameter. J. Pharm. Sci. **57**:128.
5. Stapley, E. O., D. Hendlin, J. M. Mata, M. Jackson, H. Wallick, S. Hernandez, S. Mochales, S. A. Currie, and R. M. Miller. 1970. Phosphonomycin. I. Discovery and in vitro biological characterization. Antimicrob. Agents Chemother.–1969, p. 284–290.
6. Zimmerman, S. B., E. O. Stapley, H. Wallick, and R. Baldwin. 1970. Phosphonomycin. IV. Susceptibility testing method and survey. Antimicrob. Agents Chemother.–1969, p. 303–309.

Antimicrobial Agents and Chemotherapy—1969

Pharmacodynamics of Phosphonomycin After Oral Administration in Man

E. L. FOLTZ, H. WALLICK, and CHARLES ROSENBLUM

Section of Clinical Pharmacology, Department of Medicine, Graduate Hospital, University of Pennsylvania, Philadelphia, Pennsylvania 19146, and Merck Sharp & Dohme Research Laboratories, Rahway, New Jersey 07065

The absorption and excretion of the calcium salt of phosphonomycin were studied in man. Drug concentrations were measured in serum after single oral doses ranging from 250 to 2,000 mg. Absorption began during the first 30 min after ingestion, and peak concentrations occurred in the serum between 1.5 and 2 hr after ingestion. With the largest doses, peak concentrations tended to occur somewhat later. The drug was present in serum in amounts that were measurable by bioassay methods through 12 hr, but not at 24 hr. Approximately 30 to 40% of the oral dose was identified in the urine in the first 24 hr. A smaller portion could be detected by bioassay during the second day, but the total recovery was generally less than 50%. In subsequent studies with tritium-labeled compound, approximately one-third of the dose was not absorbed and could be identified in the stool within 72 hr. A fraction of the dose was eliminated more slowly by both fecal and urinary routes. Repeat oral doses showed early cumulative effects which reached a plateau after an interval that appeared to be related to frequency of dosage. No significant toxicity was encountered, but minimal gastrointestinal effects were noted when sustained multiple-dose oral regimens were used.

The discovery of the antimicrobial substance phosphonomycin, which is produced by several species of *Streptomyces,* was followed by intensive in vitro and in vivo trials for antibacterial activity (1-4). Because these studies indicated a bactericidal action of phosphonomycin against organisms, its potential clinical application was readily apparent. Safety trials in animals have indicated that this compound has a low order of toxicity.

As an initial step in the evaluation of therapeutic efficacy, clinical pharmacological trials were planned to determine dosage, route of administration, resulting antibacterial activity in blood and urine, and disposition of the antibiotic. This report is concerned with such studies with the calcium salt of phosphonomycin.

MATERIALS AND METHODS

Subjects for the trials were selected from male volunteers in either a prison or a penal rehabilitation center. The subjects were informed of the nature of the studies and the compound to be administered. They were selected after review indicated that no other antimicrobial agent had been taken during the preceding 4 to 5 days. All subjects reported early on the morning of the test day in a fasting state unless otherwise stated.

The calcium salt of phosphonomycin was administered in gelatin capsules, each containing the equivalent of 250 mg of the free acid. Single oral doses from 250 to 2,000 mg were administered, followed by the ingestion of 100 to 120 ml of water. Food and fluids were permitted *ad libitum* after 4 hr. Multiple-dose studies were carried out in similar fashion, except that the fasting state was observed only for the initial dose on the first test day.

Blood samples were obtained by venipuncture just prior to administration of the drug and at suitable intervals thereafter, but generally included sampling at 0.5, 1, 1.5, 2, 4, 6, 8, and 12 hr postadministration. Serum was promptly harvested and frozen. The entire urinary output was collected, generally for the intervals of 0 to 2, 2 to 4, 4 to 8, 8 to 12, and 12 to 24 hr after administration of the drug. Samples of each of the specimens to be used for bioassay were immediately frozen. All urine volumes were measured and recorded.

Serum and urine samples were maintained in the frozen state until time of bioassay. Bioassay was carried out by a standard cup-plate method with either *Proteus vulgaris* ATCC 21100 or *Erwinia atroseptica* as the test organism.

RESULTS

A dose-response trial was completed in eight subjects, each of whom received doses of 250, 1,000, and 2,000 mg. Individual and average results are shown in Table 1. Two subjects (no. 4 and 8) were unable to complete the rotation because of changes in prison status. In most subjects, concentrations after all doses occurred at 2 hr but in three subjects peak concentrations with the 2,000-mg dose were observed at 4 hr. The average peak concentrations were 2.8, 5.2, and 6.9 μg/ml after administration of doses of 250, 1,000, and 2,000 mg, respectively (Table 1).

Although the serum decay curve fell below 1 μg/ml at 6 hr after administration of the 250-mg dose, average concentrations with the larger doses exceeded 1 μg/ml at 12 hr. There was an increase in total antimicrobial activity with each of the higher doses, but this was not proportional to the increment in dosage.

Urinary recovery of the active phosphonomycin (Table 2) began during the first 2 hr, regardless of the size of the dose, and reached a peak rate during the interval from 2 to 4 hr after drug administration. By the end of the 24-hr urine collection period, the total recovery of active drug in the urine averaged 38, 33, and 20%, respectively, of the 250-, 1,000-, and 2,000-mg doses. Hence, the percentage of the doses excreted in the urine decreased as dose size increased.

Because urinary recovery after oral administration of the calcium salt was considerably lower than that observed after intravenous

Table 1. *Concentrations of phosphonomycin in the serum of healthy subjects after oral administration of three different single doses of the calcium salt*

Dose (mg)	Subject	Day	Concn (μg/ml)							
			0.5 hr	1 hr	1.5 hr	2 hr	4 hr	6 hr	8 hr	12 hr
250	1	1	<0.3	<0.3	1.0	3.0	2.0	0.8	0.5	0.3
	2	1	<0.3	1.6	1.9	1.9	1.1	1.0	0.7	0.3
	3	1	<0.3	1.5	3.2	5.5	3.2	1.7	1.1	0.5
	5	2	<0.3	1.7	1.7	1.3	0.7	0.5	<0.3	<0.3
	6	2	<0.3	0.8	1.4	2.0	1.2	<0.3	<0.3	<0.2
	7	2	<0.3	0.7	2.0	2.3	1.3	0.5	<0.3	<0.3
	9	3	<0.3	1.5	4.1	5.0	3.1	2.2	1.1	0.6
	10	3	<0.3	1.6	1.9	1.7	0.8	0.8	0.5	<0.3
	Avg		<0.3	1.2	2.2	2.8	1.7	0.9	0.5	<0.3
1,000	1	3	0.3	2.3	4.2	4.5	3.2	2.6	2.1	1.8
	2	3	0.3	3.6	4.8	4.7	3.2	2.3	1.6	1.5
	3	3	<0.3	2.2	4.1	4.8	4.3	2.5	2.2	1.7
	5	1	0.9	4.0	6.5	6.8	4.3	3.1	2.3	1.2
	6	1	<0.3	2.8	7.5	7.8	3.8	2.9	1.4	<0.3
	7	1	0.5	2.9	3.8	4.4	2.1	1.6	0.9	0.7
	9	2	<0.3	1.1	1.5	1.7	1.9	1.4	1.2	1.5
	10	2	0.4	2.6	5.6	6.7	4.2	3.3	2.1	1.5
	Avg		0.3	2.7	4.8	5.2	3.4	2.5	1.7	1.2
2,000	1	2	<0.3	2.9	4.0	6.7	5.6	3.1	2.6	1.7
	2	2	<0.3	0.5	4.4	9.8	8.1	4.3	2.4	1.3
	3	2	<0.3	0.3	0.8	3.3	7.9	4.1	3.2	2.5
	5	3	0.5	4.0	6.6	8.1	7.0	5.0	3.4	2.3
	6	3	<0.3	3.7	5.2	5.0	3.0	2.3	2.1	1.4
	7	3	<0.3	3.7	7.6	8.0	7.0	4.3	2.6	1.4
	9	1	<0.3	0.8	1.7	3.7	9.1	6.2	4.3	3.0
	10	1	0.6	2.9	6.3	7.0	7.6	3.8	3.0	2.0
	Avg		<0.3	2.4	4.6	6.5	6.9	4.1	3.0	2.0

Table 2. *Average urinary recovery of phosphonomycin after various single oral doses of the calcium salt*[a]

Dose (mg)	Collection periods 0-2 hr	2-4 hr	4-8 hr	8-12 hr	12-24 hr	24-hr total	Percentage of dose
250	16.1	28.8	23.9	14.6	10.9	94.3	37.7
1,000	29.4	140.7	57.8	47.4	57.9	333.2	33.3
2,000	49.2	94.7	99.8	78.7	82.6	405.0	20.3

[a] Each drug dosage was administered to eight normal subjects in the fasting through the 4th hr. Recovery is given in milligrams per collection period.

administration of the sodium salt, and because drug concentrations in the serum were not comparable, it was obvious that part of the oral dosage was either unabsorbed or degraded. Hence, the fate of an orally administred dose of labeled phosphonomycin was studied.

After an oral dose of 500 mg of the calcium salt of phosphonomycin, which contained 25 μc of tritium-labeled drug, radioactivity appeared promptly in the serum and reached a peak within 1.5 hr. By bioassay, peak activity was observed at 1.5 hr and was sustained through 2 hr. The average peak concentration observed by bioassay was 3.2 μg/ml; by radioactive estimate, it was 4.1 μg/ml (Fig. 1). The urinary recovery in 48 hr by bioassay averaged 38% for four subjects. The tritium label permitted an estimate of 33.8% average recovery in the urine for the same period, and an additional 1.3% was identified by radioactive assay during the third 24-hr period. Bioassay did not permit an accurate estimate of the urinary content of phosphonomycin during the third day.

By assay of radioactivity, the stools collected during the first 72 hr after administration of a single labeled dose were found to contain approximately 32.3% of the administered dose. An additional 2 to 3% was identified in those subjects who completed stool collections through the seventh day after drug administration. The portion of the dose recovered in the first 3 days still left approximately 30 to 35% of the administered dose either unidentified or unrecovered, but analysis of incidental urine samples during the sixth and seventh days suggested that radioactively labeled material was present there as well as in the stoool.

After oral administration of 500 mg of the calcium salt of phosphonomycin every 6 hr for 6 days, concentrations in serum showed cumulative effects which reached a plateau at approximately 12 hr (Fig. 2). Average peak concentrations ranged from 3.5 to 6.7 μg/ml after the third dose (Table 3).

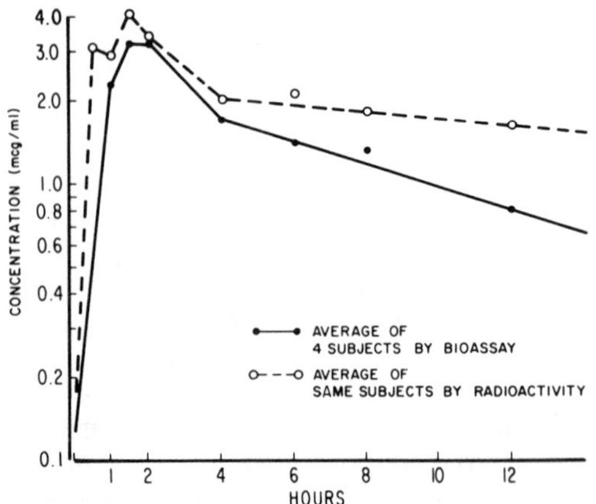

Fig. 1. *Concentrations of phosphonomycin in serum as estimated by bioassay and radioactivity of the same blood samples.*

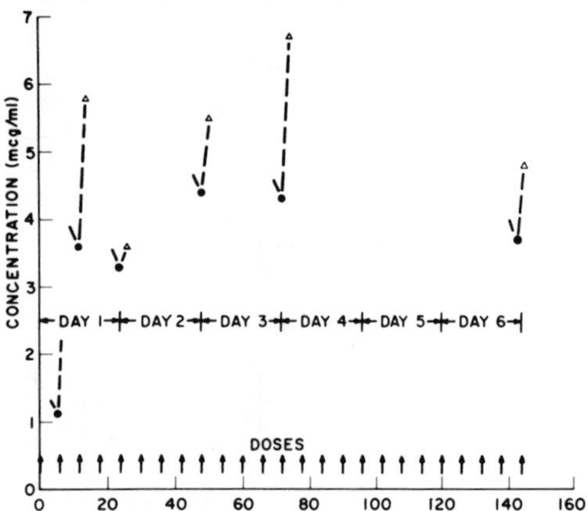

Fig. 2. *Drug concentrations in serum after oral doses of 500 mg of phosphonomycin calcium every 6 hr for 6 days. Values are the average for eight subjects and were obtained by bioassay.*

Laboratory tests before and after drug administration, including hemoglobin, hematocrit, white cell count and differential cell count, urinalyses, blood urea nitrogen, creatinine, bilirubin, alkaline phosphatase, and serum transaminases, showed no abnormalities or significant trends to indicate toxicity.

In a subsequent double-blind trial for safety assessment, 20 volunteers received 500 mg of phosphonomycin four times daily for 28 days and 10 volunteers received a placebo on a similar dosage schedule. Sixteen men in the treatment

Table 3. *Drug concentrations in serum after multiple oral doses of phosphonomycin (500 mg every 6 hr)*

Subject	Concn (μg/ml)										
	6 hr	12 hr	14 hr	24 hr	26 hr	48 hr	50 hr	72 hr	74 hr	144 hr	146 hr
1	1.5	5.3	9.6	3.8	4.5	4.8	5.1	4.5	8.9	3.2	4.1
2	1.5	2.7	6.6	2.4	3.0	4.9	6.8	4.8	5.5	4.4	4.9
3	1.7	3.2	7.3	4.2	4.7	4.9	6.3	4.3	3.8	2.9	4.8
4	1.1	2.5	1.9	2.5	2.8	2.9	5.1	4.0	6.0	2.8	4.6
5	2.4	2.6	4.9	2.6	3.0	4.9	4.9	3.7	3.9	2.8	6.2
6	<0.4	5.2	3.8	5.3	4.4	5.8	4.9	5.4	9.3	5.5	4.1
7	0.8	4.0	8.1	3.0	2.6	3.2	3.0	3.3	9.0	3.2	5.2
8	<0.4	3.5	4.2	2.8	3.0	3.9	7.8	5.1	6.8	4.5	4.2
Avg	1.1	3.6	5.8	3.3	3.5	4.4	5.5	4.4	6.7	3.7	4.8

group and 10 in the placebo group completed the study; none of the subjects was dropped from the study because of side effects or toxicity. Hematologic studies, urinalyses, and selected blood chemistry studied did not indicate any deleterious effects of the chronic drug administration to these subjects. Minor gastrointestinal side effects were encountered in the treatment group, whose members experienced an increase in frequency of stools and a softening of the stool. Thirteen of 16 subjects on active therapy who completed the study commented on this change in stool habits, but it was only noteworthy in 4 subjects during the first 10 days of the trial. By the beginning of the third week of the trial, few subjects commented upon any change in bowel habit or gastrointestinal symptomatology. None of the subjects discontinued the study because of changes in stool habit. Bacteriological studies of the stools will be reported elsewhere.

DISCUSSION

Because of the hygroscopic nature of the sodium salt of phosphonomycin, suitable solid dosage forms for oral administration were not available. The calcium salt was chosen for oral administration because its physical properties permitted the production of suitable capsular or tablet preparations. The oral administration of the calcium salt of phosphonomycin resulted in antibacterial activity in blood and urine in clinical pharmacological trials. Approximately one-third of an oral dose was absorbed from the gastrointestinal tract in the first 2 hr after dosage, as measured by bioassay. Concentrations in serum rose during the first 2 hr to a peak concentration that was related to the dose. Average peak concentrations of 3.5 to 4.0 μg/ml were attained in these as well as other trials after single oral doses of 500 mg. Evidence of modest cumulative effects were apparent after multiple oral doses.

Urinary excretion occurred promptly after appearance of the drug in the blood. Serum decay curves approximated a first-order rate of elimination, but with some deviations presumably related to absorption and gastric emptying. Antibiotic activity in excess of 1 μg/ml was observed through 8 hr after a single oral dose of 500 mg and was slightly lower than 1 μg/ml at 12 hr.

Urinary recovery of the drug approximated one-third to one-fourth of a single oral dose in the first 24 hr. Approximately 5% appeared in the urine during the first 2 hr, and excretion increased to approximately 10% or more in the 2 to 4 hr collections. Proportionally smaller percentages of the doses were recovered as the dose was increased from 250 to 2,000 mg; however, concentrations in the 12 to 24-hr specimens for the 1,000- and 2,000-mg doses were considerably higher than for the 250-mg dose, and suggested that excretion was not complete in this period of collection.

Radioactively labeled doses suggested that 35% of the dose was excreted in the feces within the first several days after single dose. This material presumably was never absorbed, although a small amount may have been excreted by this route after cycling in the enterohepatic circulation.

Approximately 30% of the dose did not appear in either the urine or feces during the first 72 hr. Drug concentrations in serum dropped to low levels detectable by radioactive assay after 24 hr. Hence, it seems likely that a part of the dose was trapped in the intestinal wall in transport from lumen to the enteric circulation. Small amounts in both urine and fecal samples between the fifth and seventh days suggested a slow elimination of this unaccounted residual of the single oral dose.

After repeated doses of phosphonomycin, modest cumulative effects occurred in the serum. The drug appeared to be eliminated in the urine in increasing amounts after the first two doses. The concentrations in serum did not continue to increase after the third dose of this regimen; hence, potentially toxic cumulative concentrations are unlikely, except with extreme impairment of renal blood flow and function.

All oral doses in single- and multiple-dose sutdies were well tolerated, and no significant laboratory or clinical evidence of toxicity was encountered. Some side effects were observed, as with other orally administered antibiotics which are effective against the normal intestinal flora. These side effects were related to change in stool habit and in consistency of the stool. Serious, persistent diarrhea was not encountered in these trials, and only 20 to 25% of subjects complained of the change in stool habits. Several subjects who were constipated viewed this effect as beneficial. None of the men abandoned the study because of the side effects.

Since the drug concentrations in serum after oral dosage exceeded minimal inhibitory concentration for many susceptible organisms, and since the concentrations in urine were generally in excess of 100 μg/ml 12 hr after a single oral dose of 500 mg, clinical therapeutic trials in urinary-tract infections have been initiated.

ACKNOWLEDGMENTS

We acknowledge the assistance of Irwin H. Breslow and William Kenny in carrying out the studies with the volunteers. Appreciation is also extended to the Radioactive Assay Laboratories, Merck Institute for Therapeutic Research, Rahway, N.J. The technical assistance of the following people in the biological assay of the samples is also acknowledged: William Maiese, Shirley Czajkowski, Christine Hushion, Patricia McCloskey, and Brenda Hunt.

LITERATURE CITED

1. Hendlin, D., B. M. Frost, E. Thiele, H. Kropp, M. E. Valiant, B. Pelak, B. Weissberger, C. Cornin, and A. K. Miller. 1970. Phosphonomycin. III. Evaluation in vitro. Antimicrob. Agents Chemother.–1969, p. 297-302.
2. Miller, A. K., B. M. Frost, M. E. Valiant, H. Kropp, and D. Hendlin. 1970. Phosphonomycin. V. Evaluation in mice. Antimicrob. Agents Chemother.–1969, p. 310-315.
3. Stapley, E. O., D. Hendlin, J. M. Mata, M. Jackson, H. Wallick, S. Hernandez, S. Mochales, S. A. Currie, and R. M. Miller. 1960. Phosphonomycin. I. Discovery and in vitro biological characterization. Antimicrob. Agents Chemother.–1969, p. 284-290.
4. Zimmerman, S. B., E. O. Stapley, H. Wallick, and R. Baldwin. 1970. Phosphonomycin. IV. Susceptibility testing method and survey. Antimicrob. Agents Chemother.–1969, p. 303-309.

Antimicrobial Agents and Chemotherapy—1969

Preliminary Clinical Trials with Phosphonomycin

WILLIAM J. HOLLOWAY, JANET CLARK, and ROSEMARY ROCCO

Infectious Disease Research Laboratory, Wilmington Medical Center, Wilmington, Delaware 19899

Phosphonomycin is a new antibiotic active against a broad spectrum of gram-positive and gram-negative microorganisms. Strains of *Staphylococcus aureus, Escherichia coli, Proteus,* and *Serratia* appeared to be particularly susceptible to this antibiotic. In vitro susceptibility testing was complicated by the appearance of resistant clones in the antibiotic zone on solid media and by the skip-tube phenomenon when drug susceptibility was determined by the broth-dilution technique. In this study, 22 patients with urinary-tract infection and 8 patients with soft-tissue and bone infections were treated orally with phosphonomycin. Most of the urinary-tract infections were chronic, and the cure rate was very low. However, phosphonomycin appeared to be effective in eradicating susceptible pathogens from the urine in acute infections. The patients with staphylococcus infection were more difficult to evaluate, but it appeared that phosphonomycin did have some effect against staphylococci in vivo.

Phosphonomycin (MK-955) is a new broad-spectrum antibiotic produced by several strains of *Streptomyces* which was developed in the Research Laboratories of Merck, Sharp & Dohme (1, 2). Its action is bactericidal, affecting the integrity of the bacterial cell wall by interfering with an enzyme step in the production of cell wall precursors. Phosphonomycin has been shown to be effective in preventing the development of a variety of gram-negative and gram-positive infections in experimentally infected animals and has appeared to be as potent as tetracycline and chloramphenicol in these studies. It has been particularly effective against staphylococci in vitro and has produced good results in systemic, kidney, and eye infections in laboratory animals. Short-and long-term toxicity studies have shown this antibiotic to be well tolerated.

In this paper, we report the results of a preliminary clinical investigation of the effectiveness of phosphonomycin in the treatment of various infections in humans.

MATERIALS AND METHODS

Phosphonomycin was supplied in capsules, each containing 250 mg, for oral administration and as a solution containing 1 mg of free acid per ml for laboratory use. Antibiotic discs containing 5 and 30 μg of phosphonomycin were supplied for use in screening laboratory isolates for susceptibility to this antibiotic.

The 30 patients selected for inclusion in this study were from the Medical and Surgical Services of the Wilmington Medical Center, the Pyelonephritis Clinic of the Wilmington Medical Center, and the out-patient population of the Brandywine Medical Center; 16 of the patients were female and 14 were male, and their ages ranged from 18 to 86 years. Of the 30 patients, 22 had urinary-tract infections, and the remaining eight had infection of bone or soft tissue.

Urinary-tract infection. Amont the 22 patients with urinary-tract infections treated with phosphonomycin, 16 had chronic, recurrent urinary-tract infection, and 6 had acute, uncomplicated infection. The 16 patients with chronic urinary-tract infection attended the Pyelonephritis Clinic of the Wilmington Medical Center and were comprised of a group of patients with highly resistant infecting microorganisms who had had therapeutic trials on a great number of antibiotics. The six patients with acute urinary-tract infection were selected from the out-patient population of the Brandywine Medical Center.

Three of the patients with acute urinary-tract infection suffered from acute pyelonephritis, two patients had acute cystitis, and one patient had asymptomatic bacteriuria. The infecting organism was *Escherichia coli* in two instances, *Klebsiella-Enterobacter* in two instances, and a *Proteus* species in two instances. Among the 16 patients with chronic urinary-tract infection, 14 had chronic pyelonephritis and 2 patients had chronic cystitis. The pathogens in this group of chronic patients consisted of *Klebsiella-Enterobacter* in three, *Proteus* species in four, *E. coli* in four, *Pseudomonas* species in four, and in one instance an enterococcus.

The dosage of phosphonomycin generally used in the treatment of urinary-tract infection was 500 mg every 6 hr; if this dosage schedule was not feasible in outpatients, 500 mg four times daily was used. In three instances, the dose was reduced to 250 mg every 6 hr or four times daily. The usual duration of therapy was 10 to 14 days, although in three patients therapy was continued as long as 6 months.

Bone and soft tissue infections. Four patients with osteomyelitis and four patients with soft-tissue infection were selected for inclusion in this study. These patients had clinical indications for the utilization of a systemic antibiotic in a situation which did not appear to be life-threatening.

Two of the four patients with osteomyelitis were infected with a strain of *Staphylococcus aureus* (multiply antibiotic-resistant). In the remaining two patients, the pathogen isolated repeatedly from the sinus tract in pure culture was *Serratia marcescens* or *Pseudomonas aeruginosa*.

Two of the four patients with soft tissue infection were suffering from extensive cellulitis, one patient had a pilonidal abscess, and one patient had an infected stasis ulcer. The patient with the pilonidal abscess had a mixed infection with *S. aureus* and several gram-negative rods. The patient with the stasis ulcer and the two patients with cellulitis were suffering from infections due to *S. aureus*.

The patients with bone and soft tissue infection were given a loading dose of 1 g of phosphonomycin followed by 500 mg every 6 hr.

Toxicity studied. All patients receiving phosphonomycin were monitored with the following studies before, during, and after therapy: complete blood count with platelet estimation, urinalysis, blood-urea nitrogen, serum glutamic oxalacetic transaminase, alkaline phosphatase, and serum bilirubin. Serum and urine were obtained from all patients in the study for determination of antibiotic levels at various intervals after dosage with phosphonomycin.

Microbiological data. All pathogens isolated from patients treated in this study were tested for susceptibility to phosphonomycin by the disc agar-diffusion technique and by the broth-dilution technique. Agar-diffusion tests were carried out on Nutrient Agar with and without blood and on Mueller-Hinton agar with and without glucose-6-phosphate added. In serial dilution susceptibility studies, Nutrient Broth plus blood or glucose-6-phosphate was used. Wild strains of various organisms isolated in the clinical laboratories of the Wilmington Medical Center were tested for susceptibility to phosphonomycin by the disc agar-diffusion technique. Representative numbers of these strains were also tested by the broth-dilution technique.

RESULTS

Four of the six patients with acute urinary-tract infection treated with phosphonomycin were considered to have a successful outcome and one patient failed to respond to therapy. The remaining patient was judged to have an indeterminate result because diarrhea required. discontinuing phosphonomycin before sufficient therapy was given to evaluate the efficacy of the drug. For the purposes of this study, a patient was considered to have a successful outcome if there was a disappearance of symptoms and the elimination of infecting microorganism from the urine for at least 1 week after cessation of antibiotic therapy. Sufficient time has not elapsed to allow long-term follow-up of the majority of these patients to be included in this report.

Nine of the 16 patients with chronic urinary-tract infection failed to show clinical or microbiological improvement after therapy with phosphonomycin. In one patient with chronic infection, the result of therapy was considered indeterminate because of the concurrent administration of a second antibiotic agent. Three patients with chronic infection responded satisfactorily to phosphonomycin therapy. In these patients, there was improvement in clinical symptoms and eradication of the infecting organism from the urine for at least 1 week after cessation of therapy, but in all three instances microbiological and clinical relapse occurred within 3 weeks of cessation of phosphonomycin therapy. Three patients with chronic infection were considered to have had a qualified success from phosphonomycin therapy. In these patients, the clinical symptoms were improved and the urine was maintained in a sterile condition for at least 6 months by maintenance therapy with phosphonomycin. Two of these patients were receiving a dosage of 250 mg four times daily, and one patient received 500 mg four times daily. It should be noted that these three patients previously had persistent bacteriuria in spite of therapy with a number of other antibacterial agents. Table 1 lists the results of therapy with phosphonomycin in relation to the infecting organism in each instance. From this small number of patients, it is impossible to

Table 1. *Results of phosphonomycin therapy of urinary-tract infections*

Organism	Success	Failure[a]	Indeterminate
Klebsiella-Enterobacter	3	2	1
Proteus mirabilis	4	2	–
Escherichia coli	2	3	–
Pseudomonas species	–	3	1
Enterococcus	1	–	–

[a] In 8 of the 10 failures, a susceptible organism was replaced by a resistant organism.

predict which urinary pathogen is most likely to respond to this new antibacterial agent.

Bone and soft tissue infection. Four patients with osteomyelitis were treated with phosphonomycin, and in no instance was there an unqualified success. A 48-year-old female with *Pseudomonas* osteomyelitis of the tibia which appeared after the successful treatment of *Aspergillus fumigatus* osteomyelitis showed considerable improvement during the first 3 weeks of phosphonomycin therapy. Cessation of the drainage from the sinus tracts and improvement in the sense of well-being occurred. Subsequently, although this patient continued to show some clinical improvement, the sinus tracts again began to drain and culture revealed reappearance of the *Pseudomonas* species.

A 43-year-old male patient with metarsal osteomyelitis due to *Serratia marcescens* was treated with phosphonomycin after he failed to improve on gentamicin therapy. There was no evidence of improvement during therapy with this new antibiotic agent.

Two patients with osteomyelitis due to *S. aureus* were treated with phosphonomycin. In one, there was no evidence of any response to this agent; in the second patient, the results were considered indeterminate because some improvement had occurred in the first 72 hr of therapy but severe explosive diarrhea required cessation of treatment at that time.

Four patients with soft tissue infection (*S. aureus*, three patients; *S. aureus* associated with gram-negative rods, one patient) were treated with phosphonomycin, and in each instance appeared to have a satisfactory result. Admittedly, these particular patients were difficult to evaluate because other modalities of therapy used in soft tissue infection, such as warm moist compresses, drainage when necessary, and inactivity of the part, were included in the treatment of these patients.

Toxicity data. Eight of the 30 patients receiving phosphonomycin therapy experienced diarrhea of a moderate to severe degree. In one patient there was diarrhea and vomiting, and in another patient severe rectal burning occurred without associated diarrhea. Therefore, one-third of the patients in this study experienced significant gastrointestinal side effects. In 3 of the 30 patients, the diarrhea was severe enough that the patient voluntarily discontinued therapy. No abnormalities were noted in the various toxicity studies carried out in this group of patients.

Laboratory data. The concentrations of phosphonomycin in serum and urine were measured in a majority of the patients in this study. Table 2 lists a representative number of these determinations. On an oral dose of 500 mg every 6 hr, the concentrations in serum ranged from 4.5 to 14.5 μg/ml 2 hr after dosage, and averaged 3.7 μg/ml at 4 hr. In the few patients receiving 250 mg every 6 hr, the concentrations in serum and urine were proportionately lower than in those receiving the 500-mg dosage. At 6 hr, no detectable phosphonomycin remained in the blood.

Microbiological data. A representative number of wild strains of microorganisms isolated in the clinical laboratories of the Wilmington Medical Center were tested by the disc agar-diffusion technique for susceptibility to phosphonomycin (Table 3). The agar used was Nutrient Agar with blood added, and the disc utilized contained 30 μg of phosphonomycin. A zone greater than 15 mm in diameter was considered to indicate susceptibility. As can be seen in Table 3, 96% of

Table 2. *Concentrations of phosphonomycin in serum and urine*

Patient	Dose (every 6 hr)	Concn in serum		Concn in urine
		2 hr	4 hr	
		μg/ml	*μg/ml*	*μg/ml*
P. T.	500	4.5	–	246
P. T.	500	8.4	3.1	334
G. L.	500	10.2	4.7	383
E. M.	500	14.5	–	437
S. S.	500	7.2	3.5	–
S. S.	500	8.8	–	–
J. F.	250	–	1.1	234
J. F.	250	–	1.0	43

the strains of *S. aureus,* 59% of the strains of enterococcus, 98% of the strains of *E. coli,* 95% of the strains of *Klebsiella* species, 97% of the strains of *Proteus* species, 65% of the strains of *Pseudomonas,* and 94% of the 17 strains of *Serratia marcescens* were considered susceptible in vitro to phosphonomycin. The third column of Table 3 indicates that resistant colonies were found frequently in the clear zone surrounding the antibiotic disc. This was particularly true with the strains of *S. aureus* tested (77%) and the strains of *Klebsiella* species tested (70%), and the presence of these resistant colonies suggests that potential for the development of in vitro resistance, particularly in the instance of urinary-tract infection. When Mueller-Hinton agar with glucose-6-phosphate was used, fewer of these resistant variants were found in the antibiotic disc zone; however, this special medium did not completely prevent their appearance.

It is possible that these resistant colonies account for the results noted in Table 4. In testing 10 strains of each of the pathogens by a broth-dilution technique, considerable variation in susceptibility was noted. The values reported in Table 4 are all bacteriostatic concentrations, as we have found it difficult to obtain in vitro bactericidal concentrations of phosphonomycin in our laboratory.

Table 3. *Susceptibility of 100 bacterial strains to phosphonomycin as determined by the agar-diffusion test with 30-μg discs*

Organism	Resistant	Susceptible	Variants
	%	%	%
Staphylococcus aureus	4	96	77
Enterococcus	41	59	24
Escherichia coli	2	98	25
Klebsiella	5	95	72
Proteus	3	97	45
Pseudomonas	35	65	48
Serratia (17 strains)	6	94	6

DISCUSSION

This brief preliminary experience with the clinical utilization of phosphonomycin has not been extensive enough for us to draw definite conclusions concerning its potential as a therapeutic agent in clinical medicine.

In a small number of acute urinary-tract infections, the results appeared to be satisfactory, but the results in a larger number of chronic urinary infections were much less promising. However, it should be noted that, in a difficult patient population, six patients with infection resistant to other antibiotics were treated successfully with phosphonomycin, although three of these have required maintanance therapy with small doses of the antibiotic.

A disturbing in vitro phenomenon is the finding of resistant variants in the zones of inhibition surrounding the antibiotic discs. These resistant variants cannot be eliminated even when blood or glucose-6-phosphate is added to the Nutrient Agar used as a base medium. It is conceivable that these resistant variants could act as persisters in vivo, and they might then play a role in promoting the development of solid resistance to phosphonomycin as the susceptible microorganisms are eliminated from the urine.

No serious toxicity with phosphonomycin occurred in this small group of patients, but gastrointestinal disturbances were significant in 30% of the patients and required cessation of therapy in 10% of the patients.

Table 4. *Minimal inhibitory concentrations of phosphonomycin*[a]

Organism	Bacteriostatic concn (μg/ml)									
	0.39	0.78	1.56	3.12	6.25	12.5	25	50	100	>100
Escherichia coli	0	4	0	3	3	0	0	0	0	0
Enterobacter	1	0	0	0	1	1	2	2	1	2
Klebsiella	0	0	0	0	0	3	6	1	0	0
Pseudomonas	0	0	0	0	0	0	0	0	1	9
Serratia	0	0	2	0	0	4	3	0	0	1
Proteus	0	0	0	0	0	1	0	2	4	3

[a] Broth media contained 25 μg of glucose-6-phosphate per ml. Ten strains of each pathogen were tested, and the results show the number of strains with the indicated susceptibility.

Since phosphonomycin exhibits in vitro and in vivo activity against gram-negative pathogens and *S. aureus,* further evaluation of this new antibiotic in the treatment of infection due to these organisms seems justified. More experience is needed with both oral and intravenous administration of the drug.

ACKNOWLEDGMENTS

This investigation was supported by a grant-in-aid from Merck, Sharp & Dohme Laboratories, Inc.

LITERATURE CITED

1. Christensen, B. G., W. J. Leanza, T. R. Beattie, A. A. Patchett, B. H. Arison, R. E. Ormond, F. A. Kuehl, G. Albers-Schonberg, and O. Jardetzky. 1969. Phosphonomycin: structure and synthesis. Science (Washington) **166**:123-124.
2. Hendlin, D., E. O. Stapley, M. Jackson, H. Wallick, A. K. Miller, F. J. Wolf, T. W. Miller, L. Chaiet, F. M. Kahn, H. B. Foltz, H. B. Woodruff, J. M. Mata, S. Hernandez, and S. Mochales. 1969. Phosphonomycin, a new antibiotic produced by strains of *Streptomyces.* Science (Washington) **166**:122-123.

Antimicrobial Agents and Chemotherapy—1969

Clinical Pharmacology and In Vitro Activity of Phosphonomycin

DONALD G. KESTLE and WILLIAM M. M. KIRBY

Department of Medicine, University of Washington School of Medicine, Seattle, Washington 98105

Pharmacological studies were performed with oral and intravenous preparations of phosphonomycin in 10 healthy volunteers. Average peak drug concentrations in plasma after oral administration of 0.5-, 1.0-, and 2.0-g doses were 3.2, 5.3, and 7.1 μg/ml, respectively. Rapid intravenous injection of 250 mg resulted in a peak plasma concentration of 16 μg per ml of plasma, and an infusion of 125 mg per hr gave a constant level of about 15 μg/ml when the steady state was reached. Urinary recovery was virtually complete after intravenous administration, but less than one-third of an oral dose appeared in the urine within 24 hr. The drug was excreted by glomerular filtration and had a plasma half-life of approximately 1.5 hr. Concentrations in the urine were mostly above 100 μg/ml for 12 to 24 hr after single oral doses. Protein binding in 100% serum was 0%. In vitro activity in nutrient broth or agar was greater with 5% defibrinated blood than without. The drug was less active in Brain Heart Infusion, Trypticase Soy Broth, and Mueller-Hinton broth with or without blood. Phosphonomycin was active against *Staphylococcus aureus, Escherichia coli,* and some *Proteus, Pseudomonas,* and *Serratia* strains. Bactericidal and bacteriostatic end points were the same, or varied by no more than one tube, in most instances. Disc-diffusion susceptibility tests did not correlate well with minimal inhibitory concentrations, and many inner colonies frequently were present within the zones of inhibition. The addition of glucose-6-phosphate to Mueller-Hinton medium caused a marked lowering of the minimal inhibitory concentration of phosphonomycin for *E. coli* and *S. aureus,* and a striking decrease in the number of inner colonies around phosphonomycin susceptibility discs.

Phosphonomycin (MK–955) is a new antibiotic which has several unique characteristics. Its in vitro and pharmacological properties constitute the scope of this report.

MATERIALS AND METHODS

Phosphonomycin was kindly supplied by the Merck Sharp & Dohme Research Laboratories as 30-μg susceptibility discs, as standard powder (ethylenediammonium salt), as 250-mg capsules (calcium salt), and as powder for injection (disodium salt).

Broth-dilution susceptibility tests. The antibacterial activity of phosphonomycin was measured in four broth media against the following 181 pathogens recently isolated in the microbiology laboratory of the University Hospital: *Staphylococcus aureus,* 25 strains; *Escherichia coli,* 25 strains; *Klebsiella,* 25 strains; *Enterobacter,* 25 strains; *Pseudomonas aeruginosa,* 25 strains; *Proteus mirabilis,* 25 strains; indole-positive *Proteus* species *(P. morganii, P. vulgaris,* and *P. rettgeri),* 25 strains; and *Serratia marcescens,* 6 strains. All isolates were tested in Mueller-Hinton broth and Nutrient Broth (Difco), with and without 5% difibrinated human blood. For a few strains, phosphonomycin activity was also determined in Trypticase Soy Broth (BBL) and Brain Heart Infusion (Difco) with and without blood.

A few colonies of each organism to be tested were seeded into Mueller-Hinton broth. After at least two overnight passages in broth, 0.5-ml amounts of 10^{-4} dilutions of an overnight culture were pipetted into rows of tubes containing 0.5 ml of broth into which serial twofold dilutions of phosphonomycin had been incorporated. After the addition of the bacterial inoculum, the concentration of antibiotic in the tubes ranged from 0.20 to 100 μg/ml. For staphylococci, a 100-fold greater inoculum (10^{-2} dilution of an overnight culture) was also used.

The minimal inhibitory concentration (MIC) in Mueller-Hinton broth and Nutrient Broth without blood was defined as the lowest concentration of phosphonomycin preventing turbidity as observed visually after overnight incubation at 37 C. In Mueller-Hinton broth with blood, the MIC was regarded as the lowest concentration of antibiotic resulting in the absence of changes in the color, and the absence of discrete colonies on the surface, of the sedimented red blood cells. The red blood cells were hemolyzed by Nutreint Broth, which made the reading of the MIC more difficult in this medium. The end point for staphylococci was the lowest concentration of antibiotic that prevented the appearance of discrete colonies when the tubes were shaken gently. Turbidity by itself could not be used, as all tubes, including the negative control tubes (without bacteria), were slightly turbid. The growth of gram-negative bacteria was associated with a brown color, and for them the MIC was the lowest concentration of antibiotic that prevented this change in color.

The minimal bactericidal concentration (MCB) was determined by subculturing from the tubes showing no growth in the MIC test onto Trypticase Soy Agar with a calibrated loop delivering 0.01 ml of broth, and noting the lowest concentration of antibiotic that prevented growth of more than five colonies of staphylococci and of the gram-negative organisms (10^{-4} dilution). For tests involving the larger inoculum of *S. aureus* (10^{-2} dilution), prevention of the growth of more than 20 colonies was used as the end point. When *P. mirabilis* and *P. vulgaris* were tested, 0.5% sodium taurocholate was incorporated into the agar to prevent swarming. An overnight culture of *S. aureus* diluted 10^{-2} and 10^{-4} contained approximately 2×10^6 to 5×10^6 and 2×10^4 to 5×10^4 organisms/ml, respectively; a 10^{-4} dilution of the gram-negative bacilli contained about 2×10^5 to 5×10^5 bacteria/ml. Thus, the MBC, as defined here, was responsible for killing at least 99% of the organisms exposed to the antibiotic.

Agar-dilution susceptibility tests. The agar-dilution method of determining the MIC was used with the following organisms: *S. aureus,* 26 isolates; *E. coli,* 25 isolates; *Klebsiella,* 16 isolates; *Enterobacter,* 5 isolates; and *Pseudomonas,* 18 isolates. Nutrient agar with 5% heparinized human blood was used for all isolates, and the staphylococci were also tested on Mueller-Hinton agar with 5% blood. Agar plates containing twofold dilutions of phosphonomycin were inoculated by use of a Steers-Foltz (6) replicator with 10^{-2} dilutions of overnight broth cultures; these contained 10^6 to 10^7 organisms/ml. The MIC was defined as the lowest concentration of antibiotic completely inhibiting any visible growth after overnight incubation at 37 C.

Disc-diffusion susceptibility tests. A standardized single-disc method used in our laboratories for a number of years was employed (1), with a 30-μg phosphonomycin disc. The 90 isolates referred to in the preceding section were tested with Nutrient Agar plus blood, and zone sizes for 30 of the isolates were also determined on Mueller-Hinton agar containing blood. Before applying the discs, the plates were streaked with the same 10^{-2} dilutions of overnight broth cultures that were used for the agar-dilution tests described above. The zone size was measured after overnight incubation and was correlated with the MIC obtained by the agar-dilution method.

Protein binding. The degree of serum protein binding of phosphonomycin was determined by a modified ultrafiltration method in 100% pooled human serum (3). The filtrate was obtained by use of negative pressure at 37 C, *p*H 7.4, and a phosphonomycin concentration of 20 μg/ml. Three ultrafiltration units were used for each experiment, and the experiment was performed twice.

Pharmacological studies. Absorption of phosphonomycin after oral administration of single 0.5-, 1.0-, and 2.0-g doses was determined in 10 healthy, fasting volunteers. Drug concentrations in plasma were measured at 1, 2, 4, 6, and 8 hr by a previously described agar well diffusion method (3), with *Sarcina lutea* as the assay organism. Complete urine collections were obtained for periods of 0 to 2, 2 to 4, 4 to 8, and 8 to 24 hr. Phosphonomycin concentrations in urine were measured by the same assay method used with plasma, except that *P. vulgaris* (MB–838) was used as the test organism because it gave more distinct zones of inhibition with urine specimens than did *S. lutea.*

Four volunteers were given 250 mg of the disodium salt of phosphonomycin intravenously in 5 min, and blood was obtained for antibiotic assay at 0.25, 0.5, 0.75, 1, 1.5, 2, 3, 4, 5, and 6 hr. Urine was collected for 24 hr and was assayed as described above.

An intravenous infusion of 125 mg of phosphonomycin per hr was given to four volunteers with a constant infusion pump (Harvard Apparatus Co., Millis, Mass.) for 2.5 to 4 hr to achieve a steady level of the antibiotic in the plasma. In two of the subjects, a loading dose of 250 or 125 mg was given by rapid intravenous injection (5 min) prior to the start of the constant infusion so that the steady state was reached more rapidly. Antibiotic concentrations in plasma were measured every 30 min during the infusion and every hour for 4 hr after the infusion was discontinued. Urine was collected for 24 hr and was also assayed for phosphonomycin.

RESULTS AND DISCUSSION

Broth-dilution tests. For the 181 clinical isolates tested, the MIC was usually the same as the MBC, or differed from it by no more than one tube. Because of this similarity in end points, and the difficulties in reading the MIC in Nutrient Broth with blood (owing to hemolysis), only the MBC will be reported here. Table 1 shows the percentage of strains having an MBC of 6.25 μg or less per ml in Mueller-Hinton broth

Table 1. *In vitro susceptibility of 181 clinical isolates to phosphonomycin as determined in two broth media with and without blood*

Organism	No. of strains	Percentage of strains with an MBC of 6.25 μg or less per ml			
		Mueller-Hinton	Mueller-Hinton with blood	Nutrient	Nutrient with blood
Staphylococcus aureus (10^{-2} dilution) . .	25	0	0	0	32
S. aureus (10^{-4} dilution)	25	20	24	40	84
Escherichia coli	25	0	16	4	92
Klebsiella	25	0	0	8	16
Enterobacter	25	0	0	16	20
Pseudomonas	25	8	4	8	8
Proteus mirabilis	25	28	32	60	64
Other *Proteus* species	25	8	16	48	48
Serratia	6	0	0	17	17

Table 2. *Susceptibility of clinical isolates to phosphonomycin in Nutrient Broth with 5% defibrinated human blood*

Organism	No. tested	Minimal bactericidal concn (μg/ml)					
		⩽1.5	3.1	6.2	12.5	25	⩾50
Staphylococcus aureus (10^{-2} dilution) . . .	25	1[a]	1	6	8	5	4
S. aureus (10^{-4} dilution)	25	11	4	5	3	2	
Escherichia coli	25	16	5	2		1	1
Klebsiella	25	1	2	1	4	4	13
Enterobacter	25	4	1		4	3	13
Pseudomonas	25	1	1		2	7	14
Proteus mirabilis	25	6	4	6	3	4	2
Other *Proteus* species	25	6	4	2	2	7	4
Serratia	6			1	1	4	

[a] Number of strains.

and Nutrient Broth with and without blood. This concentration was chosen as a representative peak level attainable in plasma with oral administration of phosphonomycin (*see below*, section on Pharmacology). The bactericidal activity of phosphonomycin was consistently greatest in Nutrient Broth with blood; in this medium, 92, 84, and 64%, respectively, of strains of *E. coli, S. aureus* (lighter inoculum), and *P. mirabilis* were killed. It has been found at the Merck, Sharp & Dohme Research Laboratories that hexokinase released when red blood cells are hemolyzed by nutrient broth causes the formation of glucose-6-phosphate (G6P), and that the G6P thus formed is responsible for the increased antibacterial activity noted in Nutrient Broth with blood (E. L. Foltz, *personal communication*). Except with the *Proteus* strains, less than half the organisms were killed in Nutrient Broth without blood. Phosphonomycin was much less active in Mueller-Hinton broth, and the presence of red blood cells, which were not hemolyzed by this medium, caused little or no enhancement of antibacterial activity. The results in Trypticase Soy Broth and Brain Heart Infusion, with and without blood, were similar to those obtained with Mueller-Hinton broth. A more detailed presentation of MBC in Nutrient Broth with blood is given in Table 2 to indicate the number of strains killed by various concentrations of the antibiotic.

Agar-dilution and disc-diffusion tests. A poor correlation was observed between the results of agar-dilution and disc-diffusion tests, in contrast to the good correlation that occurs with most other antibiotics for which the approximate MIC can be estimated from knowledge of the zone size. With strains susceptible to phosphonomycin, there was usually a large (greater than 20 mm), somewhat indistinct zone of inhibition, with many colonies growing inside this zone. The number of inner colonies was frequently large enough to permit the recording of an inner as well as an outer zone, but neither correlated well with the results of the agar-dilution tests. The inner colonies appeared to represent resistant mutants, as the MIC for these colonies (determined by the broth-dilution method) was higher than that for the parent culture. Initial studies showed that the number of inner colonies was greatest with Mueller-Hinton agar with or without blood, and the 90 strains examined were therefore tested with Nutrient Agar containing 5% blood, by both the agar-dilution and disc-diffusion tests. Table 3 shows representative results for 10 of the strains tested. Large zones of inhibition occurred with strains susceptible to both low and high phosphonomycin concentrations, and this variability probably reflected the number and degree of resistance of the mutants present in each individual culture. On the other hand, for all of the 22 strains that gave no zone of inhibition around the 30-μg disc, the MIC was 50 μg/ml or higher, and with 17 strains the MIC was 100 μg/ml or more. Thus, the absence of any zone indicated resistance, but when a zone of inhibition was present, it was associated with an MIC ranging from quite low to quite high.

When it was learned that G6P was responsible for the increased antibacterial activity noted with hemolyzed red blood cells, agar-dilution tests were performed with and without this substance added to Mueller-Hinton agar in a concentration of 25 μg/ml. It can be seen in Table 4 that adding G6P to Mueller-Hinton agar caused a marked lowering of the MIC for 9 of 10 strains of *S. aureus* and for 7 of 10 strains of *E. coli*. For strains showing this reduction in MIC, there was also a marked decrease in the number of inner colonies around the 30-μg phosphonomycin susceptibility disc when G6P was added to Mueller-Hinton agar. This was especially striking with *E. coli*. With some strains of *E. coli*, there was no zone of inhibition without G6P in the agar, and a large clear zone when it was present. With staphylococci, the difference was never so striking, but there was a marked reduction in the number of inner colonies with strains for which the agar-dilution test showed an appreciable decrease in the MIC. When G6P was incorporated in the discs rather than in the agar, there was clearing centrally, but further away from the discs the number of inner colonies was little different than on plates where

Table 3. *Sizes of zones of inhibition and minimal inhibitory concentrations (MIC) of phosphomycin for 10 clinical isolates grown on Nutrient Agar with 5% heparinized human blood*

Organism	Zone size	MIC[a]
	mm	*μg/ml*
Staphylococcus aureus	38	12.5
	38	1.5
Escherichia coli	27	100
	30	3.1
Klebsiella	14	100
	6	100
Enterobacter	6	100
	6	100
Pseudomonas	31	25
	31	3.1

[a] Determined by the agar-dilution method.

Table 4. *Reduction of the minimal inhibitory concentrations of phosphonomycin by the addition of glucose-6-phosphate (G6P) to Mueller-Hinton agar*

Organism	Strain no.	Minimal inhibitory concn (μg/ml)[a]	
		Mueller-Hinton agar	Mueller-Hinton agar plus G6P[b]
Staphylococcus aureus	1	1.56	<0.20
	11	50	0.78
	16	6.25	<0.20
	17	6.25	0.78
	18	6.25	0.39
	44	6.25	0.78
	118	25	1.56
	169	6.25	6.25
	172	12.5	3.12
	178	1.56	<0.20
Escherichia coli	34	100	1.56
	200	>100	>100
	200	>100	100
	213	50	6.25
	215	>100	6.25
	216	100	0.78
	219	>100	50
	220	>100	>100
	223	25	0.39
	226	50	3.12

[a] Determined by the agar-dilution method.
[b] Added at a concentration of 25 μg/ml.

G6P was not present either in the discs or in the agar.

In contrast to these results, the addition of G6P to Mueller-Hinton agar did not cause a lowering of the MIC, or a decrease in the number of inner colonies around phosphonomycin discs, with any of the *Proteus* strains, either indole-positive or indole-negative.

Protein binding. Binding of phosphonomycin by serum proteins, as studied by a modified ultrafiltration method in 100% pooled human serum, was 0% in all six determinations.

Pharmacology. Average concentrations of phosphonomycin in plasma after oral administration of the calcium salt to 10 fasting volunteers are shown in Fig. 1. Average peak concentrations of 3.2 and 5.3 μg/ml were achieved at 2 hr with single 0.5- and 1.0-g doses, respectively. The 2-g dose gave a peak concentration of 7.1 μg/ml at 4 hr. The concentrations in blood gradually declined, and at 6 hr concentrations of 0.8, 2.2, and 4.0 μg/ml were measured with the 0.5-, 1.0-, and 2.0-g doses, respectively.

Average 24-hr urinary excretion of phosphonomycin after oral administration of 0.5, 1.0, and 2.0 g was 27.5, 29.0, and 24.3%, respectively. Urinary concentrations of phosphonomycin with all three dosages were 73 μg/ml or higher for the four collection periods (Table 5). The decline in the curves for the concentration in plasma suggests that much less phosphonomycin was excreted during the second than the first 12 hr, and this undoubtedly accounts for the relatively small amounts recorded for the 8- to 24-hr period.

Concentrations of phosphonomycin in plasma after a rapid intravenous injection of 250 mg of the disodium salt are shown in Fig. 2. The average half-life of the drug in plasma for the four subjects, as calculated by the method of least squares, ranged from 85 to 103 min, with an average of 92 min, or approximately 1.5 hr.

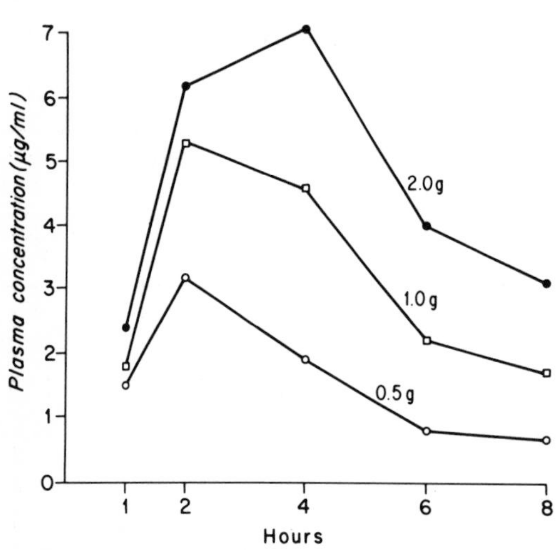

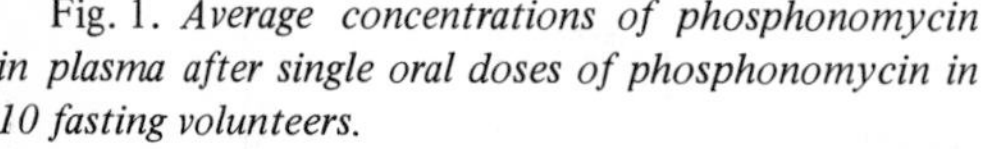
Fig. 1. *Average concentrations of phosphonomycin in plasma after single oral doses of phosphonomycin in 10 fasting volunteers.*

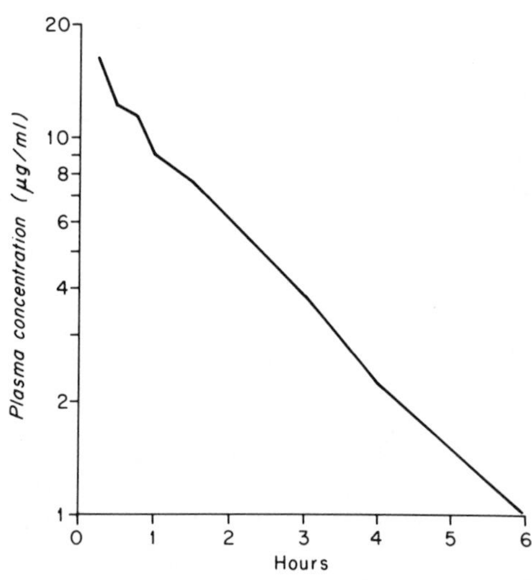

Fig. 2. *Average concentrations of phosphonomycin in plasma after a rapid intravenous injection of 250 mg in four healthy volunteers.*

Table 5. *Average urinary excretion of phosphonomycin after oral administration to 10 fasting volunteers*

Dose	Concn of antibiotic in pooled urine specimen (μg/ml)				Total excretion for 24 hr[a]
	0–2 hr	2–4 hr	4–8 hr	8–24 hr	
g					%
0.5	77 (3.9%)[a]	118 (6.3%)	100 (6.3%)	73 (12.2%)	27.5
1.0	101 (3.6%)	148 (5.5%)	254 (6.9%)	149 (12.5%)	29.0
2.0	179 (1.8%)	189 (4.2%)	353 (6.7%)	234 (11.1%)	24.3

[a] Percentage of administered dose excreted in urine.

Ninety per cent of the dose injected was recovered in the urine in 24 hr, indicating that the low urinary recovery after oral administration largely reflects limited absorption from the intestinal tract.

A constant concentration of phosphonomycin in plasma was achieved in four volunteers with a continuous intravenous infusion of 125 mg per hr. The steady state in plasma was reached at a level of about 15 μg/ml in two volunteers after 2.5 to 3 hr of infusion, and within 30 to 40 min in the two subjects who were given a loading dose of 125 or 250 mg by rapid intravenous injection prior to the start of the continuous infusion. Clearance and volume of distribution results obtained during a 1-hr period at the steady state are shown for the four volunteers in Table 6. Plasma clearance, calculated by dividing the dose administered (micrograms per minute) by the concentration in plasma (5), averaged 125.9 ml/min. Renal clearance was determined by the usual formula $RC = UV/P$, where U and P are urine and plasma concentrations, respectively, and V is the urine volume. The average renal clearance was 92.8 ml/min, whereas creatinine clearances determined simultaneously averaged 112.2 ml/min.

The apparent volume of distribution was determined in two ways. The first utilized the standard procedure of dividing the amount of phosphonomycin appearing in the urine during a 24-hr period after stopping the intravenous infusion by the antibiotic concentration in plasma at the steady state; this method gave an average value of 15.53 liters. The apparent volume of distribution was also measured by use of the plasma decay curve after an intravenous injection of the antibiotic over a 5-min period. The declining curve for the concentration in plasma was converted to the theoretical best line by the method of least squares and was extended back to the time of the injection (4). The plasma concentration at time zero was then divided into the total infused dose to obtain the apparent volume of distribution, and the average volume, 15.57 liters, was almost identical with the value obtained with the first method. Thus, phosphonomycin appears to be distributed in a volume approximately the size of the extracellular fluid compartment.

Table 6. *Steady-state data obtained with a constant intravenous infusion of phosphonomycin*

Subject	Plasma clearance	Renal clearance	Creatinine clearance	Apparent volume of distribution
	ml/min	*ml/min*	*ml/min*	*liters*
B. A.	122.3	79.8	106.6	15.34
S. K.	129.5	95.9	115.1	15.35
L. A.	127.8	104.9	117.4	15.68
K. N.	124.0	90.6	109.7	15.74
Average	125.9	92.8	112.2	15.53

ACKNOWLEDGMENTS

We are grateful to Rita Cavanaugh and Stephanie Kohl for valuable technical assistance.

LITERATURE CITED

1. Bauer, A. W., W. M. M. Kirby, J. C. Sherris, and M. Turck. 1966. Antibiotic susceptibility testing by a standardized single disk method. Amer. J. Clin. Pathol. **45**:493–496.
2. Bennett, J. V., J. L. Brodie, E. J. Benner, and W. M. M. Kirby. 1966. Simplified, accurate method for antibiotic assay of clinical specimens. Appl. Microbiol. **14**:170–177.
3. Bennett, J. V., and W. M. M. Kirby. 1965. A rapid, modified ultrafiltration method for determining serum protein binding and its application to new penicillins. J. Lab. Clin. Med. **66**:721–732.
4. Kunin, C. M., A. C. Dornbush, and M. Finland. 1969. Distribution and excretion of 4 tetracycline analogues in normal young men. J. Clin. Invest. **38**:1950–1963.
5. Smahel, O., O. Schuck, Q. Modr, and R. Dvoracek. 1967. Distribution, plasmatic and renal clearances of penicillin G, oxacillin, and cephaloridine. Proc. Int. Congr. Chemother., 5th, Vienna, p. 89–92.
6. Steers, E., E. L. Foltz, and B. S. Graves. 1959. Inocula replicating apparatus for routine testing of bacterial susceptibility to antibiotics. Antibiot. Chemother. **9**:307–311.

Antimicrobial Agents and Chemotherapy—1969

Evaluation of Phosphonomycin, a New Cell Wall-Active Antibiotic

H. CLARK, N. K. BROWN, J. F. WALLACE, and M. TURCK

Department of Medicine, University of Washington School of Medicine, and U.S. Public Health Service Hospital, Seattle, Washington 98114

Phosphonomycin (MK-955), an antibiotic unrelated to existing antimicrobial agents, inhibits cell wall synthesis of susceptible bacteria. The activity of the drug in vitro is influenced by the type of medium; nutrient broth plus 5% blood is suitable for testing most bacteria, and this medium was used in determining the susceptibility of 169 gram-negative isolates. With an inoculum of 10^5 organisms/ml, over 90% of *Escherichia coli* and *Proteus mirabilis* isolates were inhibited by 10 μg of drug per ml of medium. At this concentration, 75% of *Klebsiella* strains and only 30% of other *Enterobacteriaceae* and *Pseudomonas* strains were inhibited. However, at 100 μg/ml, a concentration readily obtainable in urine, more than 80% of all *Enterobacteriaceae* and *Pseudomonas* strains were inhibited. Increasing the inoculum produced a diminution in both bacteriostatic and bactericidal activity. The drug was well absorbed after oral administration of 2 g/day to 27 patients with recurrent bacteriuria. In general, phosphonomycin was effective in the treatment of bacteriuria caused by *E. coli* and *P. mirabilis,* but showed little activity against *Klebsiella* in vivo. In addition, three of four patients with *Pseudomonas* infections developed sterile urine during therapy. Emergence of resistant strains and relapse after cessation of therapy were relatively frequent. However, because of its apparent low toxicity and good toleration, further clinical trials of phosphonomycin may be warranted.

Phosphonomycin (MK-955), an antibiotic unrelated to existing antimicrobial agents, is characterized by its low molecular weight and its ability to inhibit cell wall synthesis of susceptible bacteria. Preliminary studies of its in vitro activity indicated that phosphonomycin has a broad antimicrobial spectrum and apparently has low toxicity. In the present study, the antibacterial activity of phosphonomycin was tested in vitro against gram-negative bacteria, and its effect in 27 patients with infections of the urinary tract was determined.

MATERIALS AND METHODS

Laboratory studies. Minimal inhibitory and minimal bactericidal concentrations (MIC and MBC) were determined by a dilution technique in Nutrient Broth with 5% sheep blood. Approximately 30 clinical isolates each of *Escherichia coli, Proteus mirabilis,* indole-producing strains of *Proteus, Klebsiella, Enterobacter,* and *Pseudomonas aeruginosa* were used in these tests. The lowest concentration of antibiotic in which fewer than 10 viable colonies were recovered when approximately 0.005 ml of broth from each tube was subcultured onto antibiotic-free agar was designated the bactericidal end point (MBC). An 18-hr broth culture of each isolate was tested at both 10^{-2} and 10^{-4} dilutions, which contained approximately 10^7 and 10^5 organisms per ml, respectively. The susceptibility of these same isolates to phosphonomycin was also determined in Nutrient Broth without blood but with the addition of sheep serum, and in Nutrient Broth alone. In general, the addition of defibrinated sheep blood to Nutrient Broth increased the susceptibility of most test organisms, and results of dilution tests reported here are based upon the activity of phosphonomycin in the presence of sheep blood. In addition, inhibitory zones around discs containing 30 μg of phosphonomycin were measured on Nutrient Agar with 5% sheep blood.

Clinical studies. There were adequate clinical and bacteriological data for analysis from 27 patients with significant bacteriuria who were treated with phosphonomycin. All but one patient had received previous antimicrobial therapy with other agents for urinary-tract infection, but either bacteriuria had recurred with the same strain (relapse) or a new organism (reinfection) had appeared. All patients were initially treated with a short course of phosphonomycin (500 mg four times a day for 7 days). This brief duration of therapy was chosen to assess the toleration and toxicity of phosphonomycin in selected patients with recurrent bacteriuria and to establish the frequency of emergence of resistant strains. Patients who relapsed with the same strain subsequently were treated with the same daily dosage of phosphonomycin for 6 weeks. Of the total group of 27 patients, 26 were women. The average age of the study population was 57 years. Although the majority did not have structural abnormalities of the excretory system or marked diminution in renal function, three patients had azotemia (serum creatinine >2 mg/100 ml), three had renal stones, and one had diabetes.

Urine for quantitative cultures was collected from each patient at least twice before initiation of therapy, on the last day of treatment, and 2 and 6 weeks after cessation of treatment. The methods employed for selection of patients, collection and quantitation of bacteriological specimens, and performance of serological typing have been described in previous publications (1, 2). In selected patients and in normal volunteers, concentrations of phosphonomycin in serum and urine were determined by a cylinder-plate assay method with *P. vulgaris* as the test organism.

RESULTS OF LABORATORY STUDIES

Susceptibility of E. coli and P. mirabilis to phosphonomycin. The cumulative percentage of 29 isolates each of *E. coli* and *P. mirabilis* susceptible to increasing concentrations of phosphonomycin is shown in Fig. 1, which also summarizes the effects of inoculum size on the antibacterial activity of this antibiotic. When tested with an inoculum of approximately 10^5 organisms per ml, all 29 isolates of *E. coli* were inhibited and 28 of the 29 (97%) were killed by phosphonomycin in concentrations of 10 μg or less per ml. Increasing the inoculum size 100-fold, from 10^5 to 10^7 bacterial cells per ml, resulted in only a slight decrease in susceptibility of these *E. coli* isolates to phosphonomycin, and at a concentration of 100 μg/ml (readily attainable in urine) all 29 isolates were inhibited and killed. Similarly, a high degree of antibacterial activity against 29 isolates of *P. mirabilis* was observed; 28 of the 29 cultures were inhibited by 10 μg of phosphonomycin per ml when the antibiotic was tested against an inoculum of 10^5 bacterial cells per ml. However, unlike the results observed with *E. coli,* increasing the size of the inoculum 100-fold resulted in a marked decrease in the susceptibility of *P. mirabilis,* and less than 25% of the isolates were inhibited or killed in the presence of 10 μg of phosphonomycin per ml. At a concentration of 100 μg/ml, all but one of these isolates of *P. mirabilis* were both inhibited and killed, even when a large inoculum of bacterial cells (10^7/ml) was used.

Susceptibility of Klebsiella and Enterobacter to phosphonomycin. Figure 2 depicts the antibacterial activity of phosphonomycin against 29 isolates of *Klebsiella* and 25 isolates of *Enterobacter.* When an inoculum of 10^5 bacterial cells per ml was used, 22 of 29 (76%) isolates of *Klebsiella* were inhibited by 10 μg or less of phosphonomycin per ml, whereas only 4 of 29 (14%) of these same strains were killed at that concentration of drug. Furthermore, increasing the size of the inoculum resulted in a decrease in susceptibility of *Klebsiella* to phosphonomycin and in a disparity between the MIC and MBC for susceptible organisms. *Enterobacter* isolates, differentiated from *Klebsiella* in this study by their motility and positive ornithine decarboxylase reaction, were found to have a lower degree of susceptibility to phosphonomycin than was observed with *E. coli, P. mirabilis,* or *Klebsiella.* For example, when an inoculum of 10^5 organ-

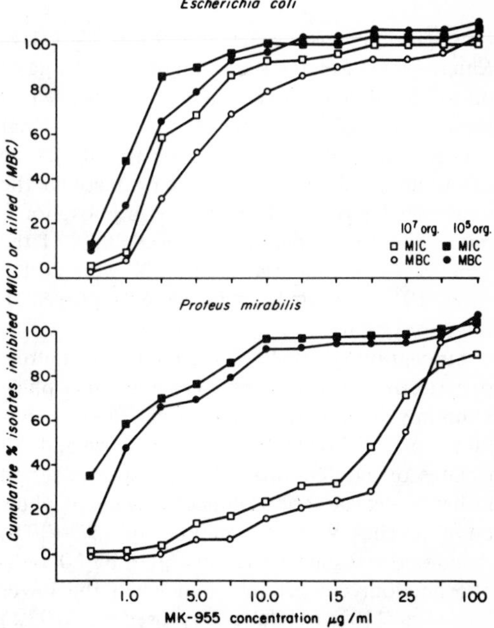

Fig. 1. *Cumulative percentage of 29 isolates each of Escherichia coli and Proteus mirabilis inhibited (MIC) or killed (MBC) by increasing concentrations of phosphonomycin tested in broth medium with bacterial inocula of two different sizes.*

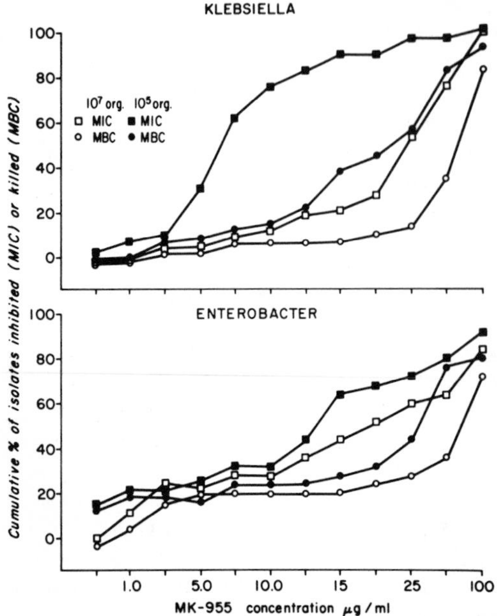

Fig. 2. *Cumulative percentage of 29 isolates of Klebsiella and 25 isolates of Enterobacter inhibited (MIC) or killed (MBC) by increasing concentrations of phosphonomycin tested in broth medium with bacterial inocula of two different sizes.*

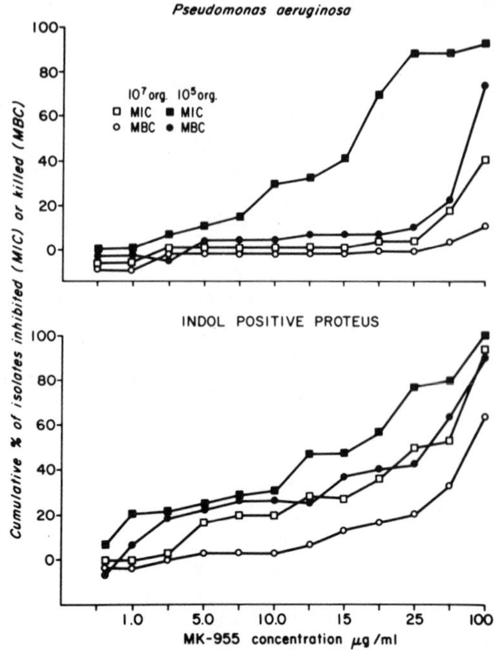

Fig. 3. *Cumulative percentage of 27 isolates of Pseudomonas aeruginosa and 30 isolates of indole-positive Proteus species inhibited (MIC) or killed (MBC) by increasing concentrations of phosphonomycin tested in broth medium with bacterial inocula of two different sizes.*

isms per ml was used, only 9 of 25 (32%) *Enterobacter* isolates were inhibited by 10 µg of phosphonomycin per ml, and only 6 (24%) of these same 25 isolates were killed by that concentration of drug. Increasing the size of the inoculum resulted in a further decrease in the susceptibility of *Enterobacter.* At a phosphonomycin concentration of 100 µg/ml, 85% of the isolates were inhibited and 72% were killed when 10^7 organisms per ml were employed in the test system.

Susceptibility of P. aeruginosa and indole-producing species of Proteus to phosphonomycin. Figure 3 summarizes the susceptibility of 27 isolates of *P. aeruginosa* and 30 isolates of indole-positive *Proteus* species tested in broth against various concentrations of phosphonomycin. Whereas only 8 of 27 (30%) *Pseudomonas* isolates were inhibited by 10 µg of phosphonomycin per ml, even when the lower inoculum (10^5 cells/ml) was used, 25 (93%) isolates were inhibited by 100 µg/ml, and 20 (74%) were killed by this concentration of antibiotic. However, when tested against 10^7 organisms per ml, a concentration of 100 µg of phosphonomycin per ml inhibited only 11 (41%) isolates of *Pseudomonas,* and killed only 4 (11%) of these strains. Similarly, phosphonomycin exerted much less activity against indole-positive *Proteus* species than against *P. mirabilis.* However, 28 of 30 indole-positive isolates (95%) were inhibited and 19 (63%) were killed by 100 µg/ml when tested against an inoculum of 10^5 organisms per ml.

RESULTS OF CLINICAL STUDIES

Effect on bacteriuria. The effect of treatment with 2 g of phosphonomycin per day administered for 7 days to 27 patients with bacteriuria is summarized in Table 1. Sixteen courses of treatment were given for *E. coli* infections, and the urine was free from bacteriuria during treatment in all but one of the patients. In this patient whose urinary pathogen was initially susceptible to 7.5 µg of phosphonomycin per ml in vitro, the original strain of *E. coli* O16 was replaced during therapy by a resistant strain (MIC, 250 µg/ml) of the same serogroup. By 6 weeks after cessation of therapy, an additional

Table 1. *Effect of phosphonomycin on bacteriuria*

Organism	No.	No. persistent during treatment	No. eradicated after treatment
Escherichia coli	16	1	8
Proteus mirabilis	4	0	0
Klebsiella	3	3	0
Pseudomonas aeruginosa .	4	1	2
Total	27	5	10

seven patients relapsed with the same strain of *E. coli.* However, no apparent change in susceptibility to phosphonomycin in vitro was seen among these strains.

Four courses of treatment were given for *P. mirabilis* infection, and all four specimens cultured during therapy were sterile. However, significant *Proteus* bacteriuria recurred shortly after cessation of treatment in all four patients. Similarly, when studied at the completion of treatment with phosphonomycin, none of three patients with *Klebsiella* infection was free from bacteriuria. In fact, all had positive urine cultures *during* treatment. Persistent *Klebsiella* infection in these patients was related to high initial resistance, as well as to an increase in resistance in two of the three isolates during therapy. Finally, four patients were treated for *P. aeruginosa* bacteriuria, and three who were believed to have localized bladder infection were cleared of bacteriuria during therapy with phosphonomycin. Subsequently, after cessation of treatment, only two patients remained free from infection. The occurrence of persistent or relapsing *Pseudomonas* infection in the remaining two patients was associated with increased resistance in vitro to phosphonomycin.

Overall, in only 10 of the total group of 27 patients with bacteriuria treated for 1 week with phosphonomycin was there evidence on follow-up examination at 6 weeks that the initial strain had been eradicated.

MK-955 concentrations in urine and serum. Figure 4 summarized the cumulative percentage of antibiotic recovered from the urine of four normal volunteers and three patients with renal insufficiency, after the ingestion of 500 mg of phosphonomycin. It can be seen that there was a diminution in the excretion of phosphonomycin in patients with impaired renal function, and less than 5% of the administered drug was recovered

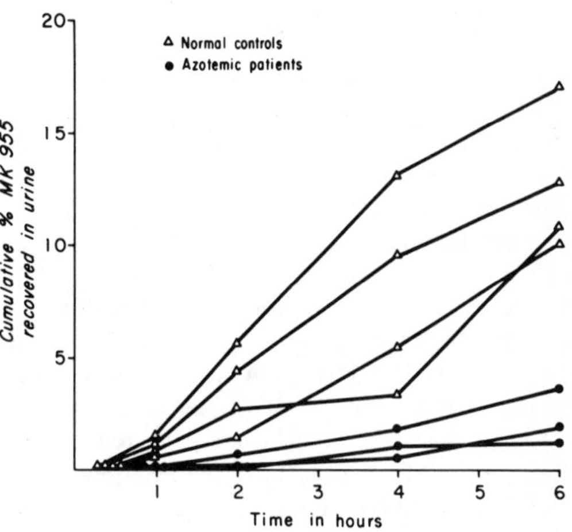

Fig. 4. *Concentrations of phosphonomycin in urine assayed by a cylinder-plate method in three patients with azotemia and in four normal controls.*

in the urine within 6 hr. On the other hand, more than 10% of the antibiotic was recovered in the urine from normal individuals. Although not shown in Fig. 4, the concentrations in serum were higher in the three patients with renal insufficiency than in the normal subjects. For example, a mean peak concentration of 4.6 μg/ml, with a range of 2.8 to 6.8 μg/ml, was observed in the serum of azotemics, whereas peak concentrations of 2.5 μg/ml, with a range of 1.7 to 3.9 μg/ml, were observed in normal volunteers.

Tolerance and toxicity. In general, the drug appeared to be well tolerated. Side effects noted during therapy included six complaints of diarrhea or loose stools, two episodes of vaginal pruritus, and single complaints of weakness, headache, and drowsiness. No 7-day course of therapy was interrupted because of side effects attributed to phosphonomycin. A survey for possible renal, hepatic, and hematologic toxicity revealed elevations of alkaline phosphatase and serum transaminase, and eosinophilia appeared in one patient. This patient had recently undergone major surgery with methoxyflurane anesthesia, and the role of phosphonomycin in these derangements was uncertain. Therefore, after resolution of the chemical abnormalities, the patient was again challenged with phosphonomycin under close observation. No detectable change in total eosinophile count, alkaline phosphatase, or serum transaminase was demonstrated with the second course.

DISCUSSION

Because of the increasing occurrence of drug-resistant strains, there has been a continued search for new antimicrobial agents effective in the treatment of gram-negative bacterial infections of the urinary tract. One such agent, phosphonomycin, has been shown to possess in vitro activity against some species of gram-negative organisms commonly encountered in patients with bacteriuria, and in the present study it was effective in eliminating bacteriuria *during* therapy in 22 of 27 patients. In five patients, the initial pathogen persisted during therapy and four isolates developed increasing resistance, whereas an additional 12 patients relapsed after cessation of treatment with no change in susceptibility of their strains. Overall, only 10 of 27 patients with bacteriuria still were free from their initial pathogen 6 weeks after discontinuing treatment. Furthermore, phosphonomycin was effective primarily against *E. coli* infections and, in this regard, performed no better than many other drugs already available for the treatment of gram-negative infections.

The relatively poor results reported in this study in patients treated with phosphonomycin for 1 week are not surprising. First, all but one of the patients previously had received treatment with other drugs but infection had persisted or recurred. Second, three patients had renal stones, and relapsing infection is frequent in such patients regardless of the antimicrobial employed. Finally, many of the patients in this study had a renal source for their bacteriuria which had been documented by ureteral catheterization. Previous studies from our laboratory have shown that renal bacteriuria is more refractory to short-term treatment than is infection confined to the bladder (3, 4). Whether prolongation of treatment with phosphonomycin in patients with renal bacteriuria will result in more permanent eradication of infection is not known. In this regard, only one of six patients who had completed 6 weeks of treatment with phosphonomycin is still free from infection. Furthermore, emergence of resistant organisms in the urine of three of six patients treated with the second course of phosphonomycin occurred, whereas no change in susceptibility in vitro was noted among these same strains during the initial challenge. In addition, increasing resistance to phosphonomycin developed in vitro when these strains were passed serially in broth in increasing concentrations of antibiotic. These observations suggest that step-wise resistance occurring during treatment with phosphonomycin may be a problem of considerable magnitude.

Finally, although results of susceptibility tests performed in vitro correlated well with responses observed in the urine of patients, the need to employ special media containing blood will further restrict the usefulness of phosphonomycin in clinical practice.

ACKNOWLEDGMENTS

This investigation was supported by Public Health Service training grant AI146-09 from the National Institute of Allergy and Infectious Diseases, and by Merck, Sharp & Dohme Research Laboratories, West Point, Pa. We gratefully acknowledge the assistance and cooperation of Merck, Sharp & Dohme for performing the cylinder-plate assays for phosphonomycin in blood and urine.

LITERATURE CITED

1. Lindemeyer, R. I., M. Turck, and R. G. Petersdorf. 1963. Factors determining the outcome of chemotherapy in infections of the urinary tract. Ann. Intern. Med. **58**:201–216.
2. Ronald, A. R., M. Turck, and R. G. Petersdorf. 1966. A critical evaluation of nalidixic acid in urinary-tract infections. N. Engl. J. Med. **275**:1081–1089.
3. Turck, M., A. R. Ronald, and R. G. Petersdorf. 1967. The correlation between site of infection and pattern of recurrence in chronic bacteriuria. Trans. Ass. Amer. Physicians Philadelphia **80**:227–235.
4. Turck, M., A. R. Ronald, and R. G. Petersdorf. 1968. Relapse and reinfection in chronic bacteriuria. II. The correlation between site of infection and pattern of recurrence in bacteriuria. N. Engl. J. Med. **278**:422–427.

Antimicrobial Agents and Chemotherapy—1969

Acute Gonococcal Urethritis: Failure of Response to Phosphonomycin Therapy

PAUL M. SOUTHERN, JR.,[1] JACK A. BARNETT, JAMES P. LUBY, JAMES W. SMITH, and JAY P. SANFORD

Department of Internal Medicine, The University of Texas (Southwestern) Medical School at Dallas, Dallas, Texas 75235, and Veterans Administration Hospital, Dallas, Texas 75216

Twenty-three individuals with acute urethritis due to *Neisseria gonorrhoeae* were treated with phosphonomycin (500 mg orally four times daily for 4 days). Seventeen were available for final evaluation. All 17 were classified as treatment failures, with positive urethral cultures at follow-up. In vitro antimicrobial susceptibility studies revealed a median minimal inhibitory concentration of 40 μg/ml, with a range of 2.5 to >40 μg/ml. Twenty-three patients were available for evaluation of adverse side effects of phosphonomycin. Mild to moderate gastrointestinal symptoms occurred in 11 patients, but none was severe enough to warrant discontinuation of the drug. No hematological abnormalities were observed. Modest elevations of serum glutamic oxalacetic transaminase and of alkaline phosphatase after therapy were observed in two individuals. These data suggest that phosphonomycin is not indicated in therapy of gonococcal infections.

Phosphonomycin (MK-955) is a new broad-spectrum antimicrobial agent produced by streptomycetes (2, 3). It is a low molecular weight acid which exerts its bactericidal action by virtue of interference with bacterial cell wall synthesis at the level of the nucleotide muramyl peptides that serve as cell wall precursors in all bacteria (3). Antimicrobial activity has been demonstrated after oral administration, and protection of mice against infection with gram-positive and gram-negative bacteria has been achieved (3).

Recent experience has indicated increasing resistance of *Neisseria gonorrhoeae* to penicillin G (1, 4, 6, 8-10), necessitating the use of larger doses for effective therapy of gonococcal urethritis (4, 7). For this reason, newer antimicrobial agents have been periodically evaluated for efficacy in the treatment of gonnorhea. In addition, alternative agents are necessary in individuals who are sensitive to penicillin. These facts, coupled with the knowledge regarding the mode of action of phosphonomycin, prompted a study of the efficacy of this agent in treating men with acute gonococcal urethritis.

[1] Work performed during tenure of Veterans Administration Research Associate program.

MATERIALS AND METHODS

Male subjects who presented for treatment of acute urethritis at the City of Dallas Health Department venereal disease clinic were entered into the study. Urethral exudate was obtained for bacterial smear and for culture on Thayer-Martin medium. Therapy with phosphonomycin was instituted if gram-negative intracellular diplococci were seen in smears of urethral exudate. If gonococci were not subsequently isolated on culture, the individuals were dropped from the study. Therapy consisted of 500 mg of phosphonomycin administered orally every 6 hr for 4 days. At the completion of therapy, patients were re-evaluated to determine symptomatic response, and urethral smear and culture were repeated. Laboratory studies were performed prior to and at the completion of therapy to detect possible drug toxicity. These included hematocrit, hemoglobin, total and differential leukocyte counts, blood-urea nitrogen, serum glutamic oxalacetic transaminase, alkaline phosphatase, serum bilirubin, serum lactic dehydrogenase, serum cholesterol, serum calcium, serum inorganic phosphorus, serum glucose, total serum proteins, and serum albumin. The in vitro susceptibility to phosphonomycin of all gonococci isolated was tested by a method previously described (5).

RESULTS

Twenty-nine patients were entered into the study; 18 were black and 11 white. Their ages ranged from 15 to 45 years. Six failed to return for follow-up and were excluded from evaluation. An additional six individuals had negative initial urethral cultures and were excluded on this basis. The remaining 17 patients were all classified as treatment failures, with positive urethral cultures after completion of therapy. Twenty-three patients were available for evaluation of side effects caused by phosphonomycin. Ten reported no adverse symptoms. Gastrointestinal symptoms occurred in 11. These consisted of three to six loose stools per day, occasionally associated with abdominal cramping. In none were the symptoms severe enough to warrant discontinuation of therapy. Dry mouth and dizziness were each reported by one patient during therapy. The significance of these symptoms is uncertain. No hematological derangements were noted. Blood chemistries were normal with the exception that one patient each showed modest elevations of serum glutamic oxalacetic transaminase (59 units) and alkaline phosphatase (30 King-Armstrong units). It was not possible to re-evaluate either of these individuals.

Results of in vitro susceptibility tests of the *N. gonorrhoeae* isolates are shown in Table 1. The median minimal inhibitory concentration (MIC) of phosphonomycin was 40 μg/ml; for only three isolates was the MIC below 40 μg/ml. There was no apparent tendency for the gonococci to develop greater resistance to phosphonomycin during the course of therapy. In vitro susceptibility tests of eight additional *N. gonorrhoeae* strains (isolated from patients with gonococcal arthritis being treated at Parkland Memorial Hospital) revealed an MIC of 40 μg/ml in every instance.

Table 1. *In vitro susceptibility of Neisseria gonorrhoeae to phosphonomycin*

Source of isolates	MIC
	μg/ml
Pretreatment isolates (23)[a]	
Median MIC	40
Range of MIC	10–>40
Post-treatment isolates (20)[a]	
Median MIC	40
Range of MIC	2.5–>40

[a] Six patients failed to return for follow-up evaluation. Some of the patients had more than one post-treatment culture.

DISCUSSION

Recently, evidence has accumulated emphasizing the decreasing susceptibility of *N. gonorrhoeae* to penicillin G (1, 4, 6, 8-10). Thus, larger doses of penicillin G have been necessary for successful treatment of individuals with acute gonococcal urethritis. This, in addition to the number of persons with penicillin hypersensitivity, has led to the evaluation of other therapeutic agents in this clinical setting. Because of the mode of action of phosphonomycin, its known effectiveness in a variety of experimental gram-negative and gram-positive infections, and its demonstrated absorption in active form after oral administration, the present study was undertaken. Unfortunately, the data clearly show that, from the standpoint of both treatment failure and lack of in vitro effectiveness, phosphonomycin is not indicated in therapy of gonococcal infections.

ACKNOWLEDGMENTS

We gratefully acknowledge the cooperation and assistance of Ray Vowell, Lee J. Alexander, and Hal J. Dewlett, City of Dallas Health Department.

This investigation was supported by a Grant-in-Aid from Merck, Sharp and Dohme, Inc.

LITERATURE CITED

1. Amies, C. R. 1967. Development of resistance of gonococci to penicillin: an eight-year study. Can. Med. Ass. J. **96**:33–35.
2. Christensen, B. G., W. J. Leanza, T. R. Beattie, A. A. Patchett, B. H. Arison, R. E. Ormond, F. A. Kuehl, Jr., G. Albens-Schonberg, and O. Jardetzky. 1969. Phosphonomycin: structure and synthesis. Science (Washington) **166**:123–125.
3. Hendlin, D., E. O. Stapley, M. Jackson, H. Wallick, A. K. Miller, F. J. Wolf, T. W. Miller, L. Chaiet, F. M. Kahan, E. L. Foltz, H. B. Woodruff, J. M. Mata, S. Hernandez, and S. Mochales. 1969. Phosphonomycin, a new antibiotic produced by strains of streptomyces. Science (Washington) **166**:122–123.
4. Holmes, K. K., D. W. Johnson, T. M. Floyd, and P. A. Kvale. 1967. Studies of venereal disease. II. Observations on the incidence, etiology, and treatment of postgonococcal urethritis syndrome. J. Amer. Med. Ass. **202**:467–473.
5. Kutscher, E., P. M. Southern, Jr., and J. P. Sanford. 1969. Clinical significance of lincomycin-resistant *Neisseria gonorrhoeae*. Antimicrob. Agents Chemother.–1968, p. 331–334.
6. Martin, J. E., Jr., S. B. Samuels, W. L. Peacock, Jr., and J. D. Thayer. 1965. *Neisseria gonorrhoeae* and *Neisseria menin-*

gitidis sensitivity to spectinomycin, lincomycin, and penicillin G. Antimicrob. Agents Chemother.–1964, p. 437–439.
7. Minkin, W. 1968. Treatment of gonorrhea by penicillin in a large single dose. Mil. Med. **133**:382–386.
8. Ronald, A., A. H. B. Pedersen, and J. C. Sherris. 1967. Antibiotic susceptibilities of *Neisseria gonorrhoeae* isolates. Northwest Med. **66**:352–356.
9. Thayer, J. D., F. W. Field, M. I. Perry, J. E. Martin, and W. Garson. 1961. Surveillance studies of *Neisseria gonorrhoeae* sensitivity to penicillin and nine other antibiotics. Bull World Health Organ. **24**:327–331.
10. Thayer, J. D., S. B. Samuels, J. E. Martin, Jr., and J. B. Lucas. 1965. Comparative antibiotic susceptibility of *Neisseria gonorrhoeae* from 1955 to 1964. Antimicrob. Agents Chemother.–1964, p. 433–436.

Antimicrobial Agents and Chemotherapy—1969

Printed in USA

Activity of Phosphonomycin in Nasal Carriers of Coagulase-Positive Staphylococci

JAMES W. SMITH[1] and JAY P. SANFORD

University of Texas (Southwestern) Medical School, Dallas, Texas 75235, and Veterans Administration Hospital, Dallas, Texas 75216

Phosphonomycin was demonstrated to be effective in vitro against coagulase-positive staphylococci, including strains susceptible and resistant to benzyl penicillin. Among 80 strains tested, 96% were susceptible to 2.5 μg or less per ml. Hospital personnel who were persistent nasal carriers of coagulase-positive staphylococci were treated with phosphonomycin in a dosage of 2 g daily by mouth. Evaluation of effectiveness was based upon quantitative cultures obtained from the nasal vestibule. The pretreatment cultures from 10 patients contained a mean of 4.1 $\log_{10}$ staphylococci per sample. Seven of the 10 had two or more cultures that became negative during treatment, and in the other three the number of staphylococci decreased by $\geqslant 2.0 \log_{10}$ during treatment. All strains of staphylococci isolated from the anterior nares before, during, and after treatment were susceptible in vitro to 2.5 μg or less of phosphonomycin per ml. The only side effects consisted of mild gastrointestinal complaints in three patients during treatment. These studies demonstrate that phosphonomycin is effective in vitro against staphylococci and in the treatment of nasal carriers of staphylococci.

Phosphonomycin (MK–955) is a new antibiotic which was derived from a fermentation broth of *Streptomyces fradiae* and which is not related to other known antibiotics (3). In vitro activity against coagulase-positive staphylococci has been demonstrated (2), and it has also been effective in the prevention and treatment of experimental infections with coagulase-positive staphylococci (3).

The present studies were initiated to evaluate the effectiveness of phosphonomycin in humans who were persistent nasal carriers of coagulase-positive staphylococci by determining its effect on quantitative nasal cultures for staphylococci.

MATERIALS AND METHODS

Cultures were obtained from the nasal vestibules of nursing personnel at Parkland Memorial Hospital three times within 1 week. The number of staphylococci per sample was determined quantitatively by the technique described by White and associates (12). Patients were classified as "carriers" if all three cultures contained coagulase-positive staphylococci. A representative colony from each positive culture was submitted for bacteriophage typing, and its susceptibility to penicillin G, tetracycline, erythromycin, chloramphenicol, kanamycin, streptomycin, methicillin, and phosphonomycin was tested by an agar-dilution method (5, 11). All phosphonomycin susceptibility tests were performed on Nutrient Agar (Difco) with 5% sheep blood.

Nasal carriers were treated orally with 500 mg of phosphonomycin every 6 hr for 7 days. No other antibiotic was administered during therapy. At least two nasal cultures were obtained during treatment, and cultures were followed for at least 10 days after discontinuation of therapy.

Laboratory studies performed prior to and at the completion of treatment to detect possible toxicity included: hematocrit, hemoglobulin, total and differential leukocyte counts, urinalyses, blood-urea nitrogen, serum creatinine, serum glutamic oxalacetic transaminase, alkaline phosphatase, serum bilirubin, and serum lactic dehydrogenase.

RESULTS

In vitro susceptibility to phosphonomycin was determined for 80 strains of coagulase-positive staphylococci obtained from the clinical bacteriology laboratory at Parkland Memorial

[1] Work performed during a Veterans Administration Clinical Investigatorship.

Hospital. The minimal inhibitory concentrations were 2.5 μg/ml or lower for 96% of the strains (Fig. 1).

Ten persistent nasal carriers of coagulase-positive staphylococci were treated with phosphonomycin (0.5 g orally four times daily). In 8 of the 10 carriers, the staphylococci isolated before treatment were resistant to benzyl penicillin, and 1 other carrier had staphylococci which were resistant to another single antibiotic. Five individuals carried staphylococci before treatment which were bacteriophage type III and five carried nontypable organisms. No staphylococci of 80/81 phage type were isolated.

During treatment with oral phosphonomycin, the number of staphylococci fell to less than 20 in seven individuals, and a decrease of >2 logs of bacteria occurred in the other three (Table 1). Only five of the carriers reacquired coagulase-positive staphylococci during the period of follow-up, which lasted for at least 10 days after completion of the course of treatment. All strains of staphylococci isolated from the anterior nares before, during, and after treatment were susceptible in vitro to 2.5 μg of phosphonomycin or less per ml.

The only side effects consisted of mild gastrointestinal complaints (loose stools) in three patients during treatment. No abnormalities were noted in hematological, biochemical, and renal function tests performed during the course of treatment.

DISCUSSION

Our results confirm the effectiveness of phosphonomycin in vitro against coagulase-positive staphylococci. Based upon the technique of quantitative suppression of staphylococci in anterior nares of chronic staphylococcal carriers, which affords a controlled method for clinical evaluation (12), our results demonstrate that phosphonomycin is as effective as nafcillin, methicillin, or oxacillin in eradicating staphylococci from the nasal vestibule (7, 10, 13). Although treatment was successful in suppressing staphylococci during treatment and for a certain period after treatment in one-half of the individuals treated, permanent eradication of staphylococci from carrier sites is not anticipated because most persistent carriers eventually reacquire staphylococci regardless of the antibiotic employed (8).

The emergence of drug-resistant organisms during treatment, which is a major concern with any new antimicrobial agent, was not observed. All staphylococcal isolates obtained during and after treatment remained susceptible in vitro to phosphonomycin. Previous studies have shown that the early emergence of resistant organisms can be demonstrated during treatment of nasal carriers with new antimicrobial agents (6).

Phosphonomycin is effective in vitro against staphylococci, and in patients it is effective against both penicillin G-susceptible and -resistant staphylococcal infections, as determined by the technique of quantitative suppression of

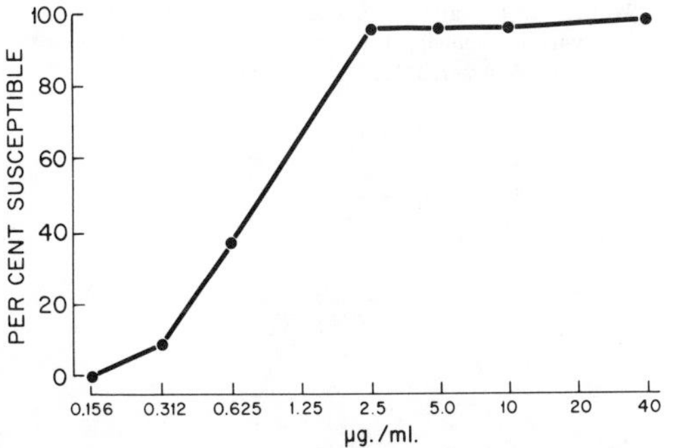

Fig. 1. *In vitro susceptibility of coagulase-positive staphylococci to phosphonomycin expressed as minimal inhibitory concentrations (micrograms per milliliter).*

Table 1. *Effect of 500 mg of phosphonomycin every 6 hr on coagulase-positive staphylococci from nasal carriers*

Patient	No. of organisms (mean $\log_{10}$ of positive cultures)		
	Pretreatment	During treatment[a]	After treatment[a]
L.A.	4.0	0.7	2.9
L.B.	4.1	0	0
P.B.	3.1	1.1	3.5
J.B.	3.8	0	4.4
E.J.	4.9	2.7	3.7
T.G.	5.0	0	0
E.P.	4.1	0	0
S.D.	3.4	0	0
B.M.	3.3	0	0
A.D.	4.3	0	5.5

[a] Cultures "during treatment" were obtained on the third or fourth day and the seventh day of treatment; those "after treatment" were obtained 4 to 40 days after treatment was discontinued.

nasal carriage. It also appears to have little toxicity. Its potential role as an antistaphylococcal agent should be considered not only in terms of its own effectiveness and toxicity but also in comparison with the alternative agents available. Penicillin G or the synthetic penicillins appear to remain the agents of choice unless patients have become hypersensitive to them. In the patient with hypersensitivity to the penicillins, the cephalosporins have been used, but some degree of cross-reactivity between the penicillins and cephalosporins can be demonstrated experimentally and occurs in patients (1, 9). Hence, cephalothin must be used with caution in treatment of patients with a history of allergic reactions to penicillin and cannot be considered as a uniformly safe substitute for penicillin in such patients (9). Kanamycin, gentamicin, bacitracin, and vancomycin remain relatively effective antistaphylococcal agents, but each has potentially serious toxicity (4). The same holds for chloramphenicol, and a high proportion of staphylococci are resistant to the tetracyclines. Although it bears no structural relationship and its mode of action is totally dissimilar, phosphonomycin would appear logically to be considered with the macrolide class of antistaphylococcal agents (erythromycin and triacetyloleandomycin) and lincomycin. The present studies were not designed to produce comparative data from which conclusions as to efficacy or lack of toxicity of phosphonomycin relative to the macrolides or lincomycin could be drawn. The studies do suggest that, as an antistaphylococcal agent, phosphonomycin would be most useful in patients who are allergic to the penicillins and that it should be considered in comparison with the macrolides.

ACKNOWLEDGMENTS

We acknowledge the excellent technical assistance of Earline Kutscher, Martha J. Adkins, and Benita Mays.

This investigation was supported by a Grant-in-Aid from Merck, Sharp & Dohme, Inc.

LITERATURE CITED

1. Brandriss, M. W., J. W. Smith, and H. G. Steinman. 1965. Common antigenic determinants of penicillin G, cephalothin and 6-aminopenicillanic acid in rabbits. J. Immunol. **94**:696–704.
2. Hendlin, D., B. M. Frost, E. Thiele, H. Kropp, M. E. Valiant, B. Pelak, B. Weissberger, C. Cornin, and A. K. Miller. 1970. Phosphonomycin. III. Evaluation in vitro. Antimicrob. Agents Chemother.–1969, p. 297–302.
3. Hendlin, D., E. O. Stapley, M. Jackson, H. Wallick, A. K. Miller, F. J. Wolf, T. W. Miller, L. Chaiet, F. M. Kahan, E. L. Foltz, H. B. Woodruff, J. M. Mata, S. Hernandez, and S. Mochales. 1969. Phosphonomycin, a new antibiotic produced by strains of streptomyces. Science (Washington) **166**:122–123.
4. Hoeprich, P. D. 1969. Gentamicin versus Staphylococcus aureus. J. Infec. Dis. **119**:391–392.
5. Jackson, G. G., and M. Finland. 1951. Comparisons of methods for determining sensitivity of bacteria to antibiotics. A.M.A. Arch. Intern. Med. **88**:446–460.
6. Smith, J., and A. White. 1963. Development of resistance to fusidic acid during treatment of nasal carriers of staphylococci. Antimicrob. Agents Chemother.–1962, p. 155–159.
7. Smith, J., and A. White. 1963. Activity of sodium nafcillin [6-(2-ethoxy-1-napthamido-) penicillanic acid] against staphylococci in vivo. Antimicrob. Agents Chemother.–1962, p. 354–361.
8. Smith, J., and A. White. 1963. Activity of 3 penicillins against staphylococci. J. Lab. Clin. Med. **61**:129–137.
9. Thoburn, R., J. E. Johnson, and L. E. Cluff. 1966. Studies on the epidemiology of adverse drug reactions. IV. The relationship of cephalothin and penicillin allergy. J. Amer. Med. Ass. **198**:345–348.
10. Varga, D. T., and A. White. 1961. Suppression of nasal, skin, and aerial staphylococci by nasal application of methicillin. J. Clin. Invest. **40**:2209–2214.
11. White, A., F. Foster, and V. Knight. 1959. Propagation of staphylococcal phages in liquid medium. Antibiot. Chemother. **9**:81–86.
12. White, A., T. Hemmerly, M. P. Martin, and V. Knight. 1959. Studies on the origin of drug-resistant staphylococci in a mental hospital. Amer. J. Med. **25**:26–39.
13. White, A. C., and J. Smith. 1962. Antistaphylococcal activity of penicillin P-12 (5-methyl-3-phenyl-4-isoxazolyl penicillin). Amer. J. Med. Sci. **241**:202–208.

Antimicrobial Agents and Chemotherapy—1969

Efficacy of Phosphonomycin in Treatment of Urinary-Tract Infections

JACK A. BARNETT, PAUL M. SOUTHERN, JR.,[1] JAMES P. LUBY, and JAY P. SANFORD

Department of Internal Medicine, The University of Texas (Southwestern) Medical School at Dallas, Dallas, Texas 75235

Twenty-five patients with urinary-tract infections were treated orally with phosphonomycin in a dosage of 2.0 g per day for 8 days. Fifteen patients had acute, uncomplicated urinary-tract infections, seven patients had chronic, asymptomatic bacteriuria, and three patients had urinary-tract disease requiring catheter drainage. Failure to eradicate bacteriuria by therapy occurred in two, one, and two patients in the respective groups. Bacteriological cure or failure correlated well with in vitro drug susceptibility as determined by the agar-dilution technique. Only three failures occurred in patients infected with organisms inhibited by concentrations of phosphonomycin ⩽10 μg/ml. Drug infidelity clearly accounted for one of these and was suspected in another. The third failure related to a patient with prostatism requiring an indwelling catheter throughout the period of phosphonomycin therapy. In vitro studies demonstrated that all of 60 isolates of *Escherichia coli* and 95 of 103 isolates of *Serratia marcescens* were inhibited by concentrations ⩽10 μg/ml. In contrast, only 12 of 40 *Pseudomonas aeruginosa* isolates and 4 of 12 *Klebsiella* isolates were inhibited at that concentration. Thus, in the dosage program evaluated in this study, phosphonomycin appears to hold promise in the treatment of urinary-tract infections caused by *E. coli* and *S. marcescens* and would be expected to be ineffective in most instances involving *Pseudomonas* or *Klebsiella.*

Phosophonomycin, an antimicrobial agent derived from streptomycetes, has been shown to inhibit cell wall synthesis in a variety of bacteria (1, 2). In vitro studies demonstrated that the agent is effective against certain organisms commonly involved in urinary-tract infections. This study was designed principally to evaluate the efficacy of phosphonomycin in the treatment of patients with uncomplicated urinary-tract infections.

MATERIALS AND METHODS

Patients. Initial efforts were directed toward determining the efficacy of the agent in patients with acute, uncomplicated urinary-tract infections. Initially, patients presenting to the emergency room of Parkland Memorial Hospital were selected for possible inclusion in the study. Minimal criteria for the establishment of a presumptive diagnosis of acute, uncomplicated urinary-tract infection included a brief history (⩽1 week) of dysuria and frequency, plus the presence of pyuria (⩾20 polymorphonuclear cells per low-power field), in a clean-voided urine specimen. Patients who were toxic or were known to have structural abnormality of the urinary tract were not accepted into this phase of the study.

At the time of entrance into the study, a clean-voided urine specimen was obtained for culture, and blood specimens were obtained for determination of hemoglobin, hematocrit, complete blood count, and differential count. Serum was also tested for cholesterol, calcium, inorganic phosphorus, total bilirubin, albumin, total protein, uric acid, urea nitrogen, lactic dehydrogenase, and glutamic oxalacetic transaminase (SMA-12).

Therapy with phosphonomycin (MK-957, calcium salt) was initiated by administration of an oral dose of 500 mg four times daily. A 4-day supply was issued, and the patient was instructed to return for reevaluation 48 to 72 hr after initiation of therapy. If the pretreatment urine culture was positive (>100,000 colonies per ml), and the patient had experienced symptomatic relief without adverse effects attributable to the drug, an additional urine culture was obtained and therapy was continued for a total of 8 days. At the time of final

[1] Work performed during tenure of Veterans Administration Research Associate program.

evaluation, 48 to 96 hr after completion of drug therapy, another clean-voided urine specimen was obtained for culture, and blood specimens were obtained hematological and chemical determinations.

In addition to the above patients who had actute, uncomplicated urinary-tract infections, a similar protocol was followed with seven patients known to have long-standing asymptomatic bacteriuria and with three hospitalized patients having urinary-tract infections complicated by instrumentation of the genitourinary tract.

Bacteriological studies. Organisms in urine were isolated and identified by standard techniques. The organisms were quantitated either by the pour plate method or by utilization of a calibrated loop (0.01 ml) and surface colony counting.

In vitro susceptibility testing was performed by the agar-dilution technique with the use of final concentrations of phosphonomycin of 0.312, 0.625, 2.5, 10, and 40.0 μg/ml, and by the disc susceptibility technique. In the latter system, 5- and 30-μg discs were used, and were considered to be inhibited if the zone size exceeded 10 mm in diameter. Nutrient Agar (Difco) with 5% sheep blood was used in both test systems.

RESULTS

The in vitro susceptibility of certain gram-negative bacilli to phosphonomycin as determined by the agar-dilution technique is shown in Table 1. All *Escherichia coli* isolates and 92% of 103 *Serratia marcescens* isolates were susceptible to 10 μg or less per ml. In contrast, only 12 of 40 isolates of *Pseudomonas aeruginosa* and 4 of 12 isolates of *Klebsiella pneumoniae* were susceptible to 10 μg or less per ml.

A total of 44 patients with acute, uncomplicated urinary-tract infections volunteered to participate in the study. Of these, 29 were excluded from final evaluation: 13 had sterile urine cultures before initiation of therapy, 2 had adverse reactions possibly related to the drug, and 14 failed to return for final evaluation after completion of therapy. Thus, 15 patients completed this phase of the study. The patients were all women, ranging in age from 17 to 62 years with a mean age of 25 years. All patients had dysuria, frequency, pyuria, and, on urine culture, ⩾100,000 organisms per ml. In addition, five patients had an oral temperature of ⩾100 F (⩾37.8 C) at the time of initial examination and four patients had costovertebral angle tenderness.

In each instance, the infecting organism was an *E. coli* strain which was susceptible in vitro to ⩽10 μg of phosphonomycin per ml. All patients noted relief from symptoms within 24 to 48 hr after institution of therapy. Thirteen patients had sterile urine cultures during therapy and at the time of final evaluation. One bacteriological failure was clearly related to drug infidelity; in the other instance there was no definitive explanation.

One 13-year-old boy and six women ranging in age from 26 to 74 years comprised the group of patients with asymptomatic bacteriuria. Infecting organisms were *K. pneumoniae* in one, *Alcaligenes faecalis* in one, and *E. coli* in five instances. Post-therapy urine cultures were sterile in six of these patients. The infecting organism in the patient whose bacteriuria persisted was a *K. pneumoniae* strain which was resistant to 40 μg/ml in agar-dilution testing and to the 30-μg disc.

Three patients with complicated urinary-tract infection were treated with phosphonomycin. An 18-year-old boy had a heminephrectomy as a consequence of a gunshot wound. He developed fever, and urine obtained from the nephrostomy tube and urethral catheter yielded *S. marcescens* repeatedly. After institution of therapy with phosphonomycin the patient defervesced within 48 hr. The urine cultures continued to yield *Serratia,* however, until the fourth day of therapy when the nephrostomy tube and urethral catheter were withdrawn. Cultures became sterile by the sixth day and remained sterile through final evaluation 2 weeks after therapy was completed.

The other two patients were elderly men with prostatism requiring urethral catheters throughout the period of therapy with phosphonomycin. In one patient, the infecting organism was *K. pneumoniae* resistant to 40 μg/ml, and in the other patient, a *S. marcescens* strain susceptible to 2.5 μg/ml. In both instances, bacteriuria persisted through the treatment period.

Table 1. *In vitro susceptibility of gram-negative bacteria to phosphonomycin* [a]

Organism	No. of Isolates	Cumulative percentage of isolates inhibited			
		0.625 μg/ml	2.5 μg/ml	10 μg/ml	40 μg/ml
Escherichia coli	60	15	80	100	100
Serratia marcescens	103	4	30	92	99
Pseudomonas aeruginosa	40	–	5	30	90
Klebsiella pneumoniae	12	8	8	33	75

[a] Agar-dilution method.

Adverse reactions. Phosphonomycin was well tolerated by 19 of the 25 patients entered into the final evaluation. Diarrhea of mild or moderate degree was noted by three patients, and one patient experienced explosive diarrhea 12 hr after initiation of therapy. Stool culture revealed no pathogens in the latter instance. The drug was discontinued and the diarrhea gradually subsided within 48 hr. One patient tolerated the primary course of therapy well but developed urticaria when she independently reinstituted phosphonomycin therapy without medical advice for an undefined febrile illness. After 36 hr of therapy with phosphonomycin, one patient developed a severe pharyngitis with clinical features of herpangina. The drug was discontinued and the patient recovered within 5 days on symptomatic therapy. In no instance were there adverse changes in hemoglobin, hematocrit, white blood cell count, differential count, or serum chemistries.

DISCUSSION

The in vitro efficacy of phosphonomycin against *E. coli* (all strains inhibited by concentrations $\leqslant 10$ μg/ml) correlated well with the clinical responsiveness of patients with urinary-tract infections involving this species. Of 20 patients having either acute, symptomatic urinary-tract infections or asymptomatic bacteriuria caused by *E. coli,* 18 achieved sterile urine cultures which were maintained through the final post-therapy evaluation. Further, symptomatic patients gained relief from dysuria and frequency within 48 hr after initiation of therapy. One of the two bacteriological failures in this group was accounted for by drug infidelity and, since this phase of the study was performed in out-patients, the same factor would well account for the other failure.

Further correlation between in vitro drug susceptibility and clinical responsiveness was demonstrated by the two patients with *Klebsiella* infections. In each instance, the organism was resistant to phosphonomycin concentrations $\geqslant 40$ μg/ml and both patients remained bacteriuric throughout therapy. Aside from the two failures in the *E. coli* group, the only bacteriological failure involving a susceptible organism (*S. marcescens* inhibited by 2.5 μg/ml) occurred in a patient with prostatism requiring a urethral catheter throughout the period of therapy.

Thus, phosphonomycin has demonstrated efficacy in eradicating organisms from urine when susceptible species are involved. In vitro studies predict the usefulness of phosphonomycin in infections involving *E. coli* and *S. marcescens.* The agent, in the dose range evaluated in this study, would be predicted to be ineffective in most instances of infection with *K. pneumoniae* or *P. aeruginosa.*

The emergence of resistant strains was not encountered in these short-term studies. In treatment failures, the organisms were initially resistant. Although our observations did not provide evidence that emergence of resistant strains is an important clinical problem with phosphonomycin, the limited number and type of patients do not justify broad conclusions in regard to this problem.

ACKNOWLEDGMENT

This investigation was supported by a Grant-in-Aid from Merck, Sharp & Dohme Research Laboratories.

LITERATURE CITED

1. Christensen, B. G., W. J. Leanza, T. R. Beattie, A. A. Patchett, B. H. Arison, R. E. Ormand, F. A. Kuehl, Jr., G. Albers-Schonberg, and O. Jardetsky. 1969. Phosphonomycin: Structure and synthesis. Science (Washington) **166**:123–125.
2. Hendlin, D., E. O. Stapley, M. Jackson, H. Wallic, A. K. Miller, F. J. Wolf, T. W. Miller, L. Chaiet, F. M. Kahan, E. L. Flotz, H. B. Woodruff, J. M. Mata, S. Hernandez, and S. Mochales. 1969. Phosphonomycin, a new antibiotic produced by strains of streptomyces. Science (Washington) **166**:122–123.

Antimicrobial Agents and Chemotherapy—1969

Clinical Studies with the Cendehill Strain of Attenuated Rubella Vaccine

V. E. KILPE, R. M. SABUNDAYO, A. R. SCHWARTZ, Y. TOGO, and R. B. HORNICK

University of Maryland School of Medicine, Baltimore, Maryland 20201

Three clinical studies designed to evaluate the Cendehill strain of rubella vaccine are presented. The first was a closed study in which nine seronegative children were immunized with rubella vaccine and seven children served as susceptible contacts. Rubella virus shedding occurred from the nose and throat of the vaccinees, but the vaccine virus was not transmitted to any of the susceptible contacts. The second study was a double-blind study in which 10 seronegative women were immunized with rubella vaccine and 8 women were given saline placebo injections. One vaccinee had transient arthritis on the 20th postvaccination day, and another vaccinee had transient neck stiffness between the 17th and 22nd postvaccination days. All vaccinees developed rubella hemagglutination-inhibiting (HI) antibodies. In the third study, 6,371 children were immunized with the Cendehill rubella vaccine, and 98.7% of the susceptible vaccinees developed rubella HI antibodies 6 to 8 weeks after vaccination.

The Cendehill strain of rubella virus was originally isolated from a clinical case of rubella and was serially propogated in primary rabbit kidney cells. At high passage level, the virus has been shown to be effective in evoking an antibody response in animals and humans (3). This report describes three clinical studies which were designed to evaluate communicability, antibody response, and reactions to the Cendehill rubella vaccine in children and adult women.

STUDY POPULATION AND METHODS

Closed study in children. Participants in the closed study were mentally retarded children aged 4 to 10 years at the Rosewood State Hospital, Owings Mills, Md. After permission to administer rubella vaccine was obtained from parents of each child, 16 seronegative children were confined to a cottage for 45 days. Nurses and attendants were screened for rubella hemagglutination-inhibiting (HI) antibodies, and only the seropositive staff was allowed to work with the children. Nine children were given 0.5 ml of the vaccine subcutaneously and seven children served as susceptible controls. There was intimate contact between the vaccinees and controls for 45 days. Temperatures were taken four times daily, and the children were examined once daily by a physician. Nose, throat, stool, and blood specimens were obtained from all children for virus isolation. About 2 months after the initial vaccination, the seronegative contacts were also given rubella vaccine.

Trial in adult women. Eighteen seronegative student nurses ranging in age from 21 to 23 years volunteered for the study, which was conducted in a double-blind fashion. Ten seronegative women were immunized with 0.5 ml of the vaccine subcutaneously, and eight women were given saline placebo injections. All women were examined three times weekly for reactions for 28 days. Placebo subjects were immunized with the same lot of rubella vaccine after the initial double-blind study was over. Follow-up blood samples were obtained between the 34th and 92nd postvaccination days. The second part of this study was conducted in 29 adult female volunteers at the Maryland House of Correction for Women, Jessup, Md. This was done to evaluate clinical reaction to the Cendehill rubella vaccine as well as immune responses in adult women without having prior knowledge of their serological status. The women volunteers ranged in age from 19 to 50 years. A blood sample was drawn before rubella immunization. The women were examined by a physician three times weekly for 28 days. Postvaccination blood samples were obtained on day 70.

Open field trial in parochial school children. Participants in this study were children in kindergarten and grades 1 through 3 in the Baltimore Parochial schools. Parents were requested to enter their children in the study after reading an informational letter sent home. The ages of the children ranged from 2 to 14 years with a mean age of 7 years. A total of 3,636 children were immunized with the vaccine subcutaneously, and 257 children given saline placebo injections served as controls. The seronegative placebo controls were given rubella vaccine at the time of the second postvaccination bleeding. Each vaccinee and placebo control was given a card, and the parents were asked to note any adverse reactions on this card over a 21-day period. Housecalls by physicians participating in the vaccine study were made on request by parents or when a telephone call reported a child with fever or rash.

Open field trial on military bases. Participants in this study were the dependent children of active duty and retired military personnel who receive their primary medical care either at the U.S. Kimbrough Army Hospital, Fort George G. Meade, Md. or the U.S. Kirk Army Hospital, Aberdeen Proving Grounds, Md. The children ranged in age from 2 to 14 years with a mean of 5 years. The children entered the study after an informational letter was distributed to their parents. The opportunity for rubella vaccination was provided during the period provided for routine preschool physical examinations at the outpatient clinics at these two Army Hospitals. A total of 2,539 children received a single dose from one of five production lots of the vaccine, and 196 children received saline placebo injections.

At the time of vaccination, each parent received a card on which to report any adverse reactions during the next 21-day period. The seronegative vaccinees and placebo controls were requested to return in 30 days so that a postvaccination blood sample could be obtained. At this time, each seronegative placebo control received the vaccine and was given another adverse reaction card to report any sequelae to the vaccine over the subsequent 21 days.

Vaccine. The Cendehill strain of live attenuated rubella vaccine was used in all children. Contact children and placebo control subjects received 0.5 ml of normal saline.

Serological tests. Rubella antibody titrations were performed by the hemagglutination-inhibition technique (5) in microplates. Serum samples were treated with 25% kaolin and rooster erythrocytes. Eight hemagglutinating antigen units were employed. Antigen was prepared in this laboratory from virus (Gilchrist strain) propagated in BHK 21 cell cultures. The antigen was treated with Tween 80 and ether. Duplicate serum samples were also assayed at the Smith, Kline and French Laboratories for rubella HI antibody titers.

RESULTS

Closed study in children. No clinical reactions were observed which could be directly attributed to the rubella vaccine. However, on the 21st postvaccination day a brief febrile illness occurred among the vaccinees and three contacts. Temperatures ranged from 101 to 104 F (38.3 to 40 C) and abated within 24 hr. Pharyngeal injection and vessicles with surrounding erythema were observed in some subjects. Echovirus 3 was isolated from all febrile children and from seven children without fever. The febrile illness was attributed to the echovirus 3 infection and not to the rubella vaccine.

The pattern of virus excretion in the vaccinees is shown in Fig. 1. Rubella virus shedding occurred from the nose and throat in eight of nine vaccines from the 9th to the 17th postvaccination days. In this group of children, 84% of the rubella virus isolates were obtained from the nose, 16% were obtained from the throat, and no rubella virus was recovered from the blood or stools. Rubella virus was not recovered from any of the contact children. In the second group of six vaccinees, rubella virus was recovered from the nose and throat of four vaccinees from the 14th through 17th days. In addition, echovirus 7 was also isolated from nose, throat, and stool specimens on the 6th through 18th days; however, all children were asymptomatic. Although the vaccinees shed rubella virus, it was not transmitted to any of the susceptible contacts.

The rubella HI antibody responses of the children in the closed study are shown in Fig. 2. The rubella HI antibody began to appear at the beginning of the 3rd week and reached the peak

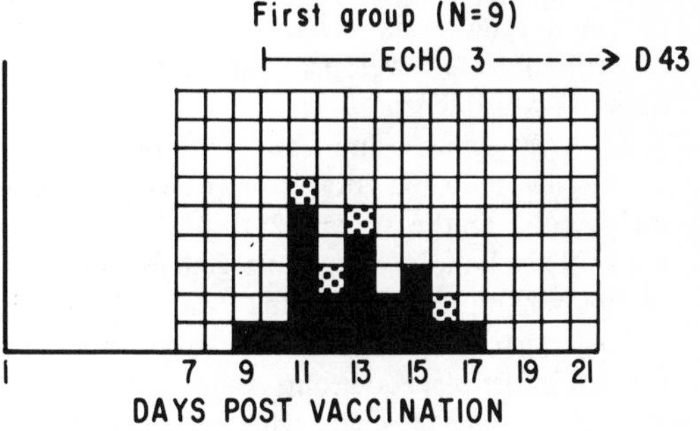

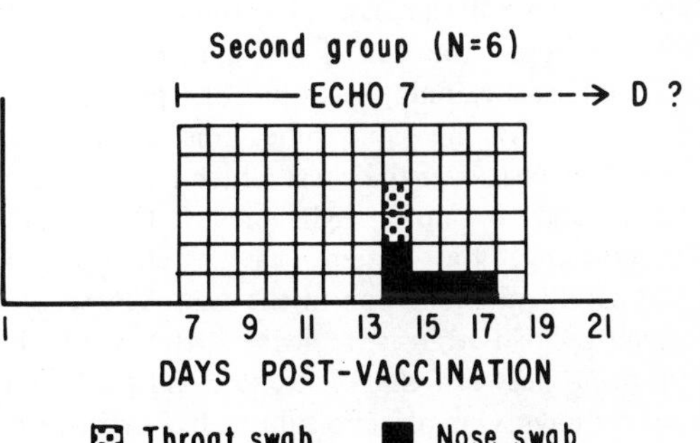

Fig. 1. *Excretion of rubella virus by 15 children in the closed study.*

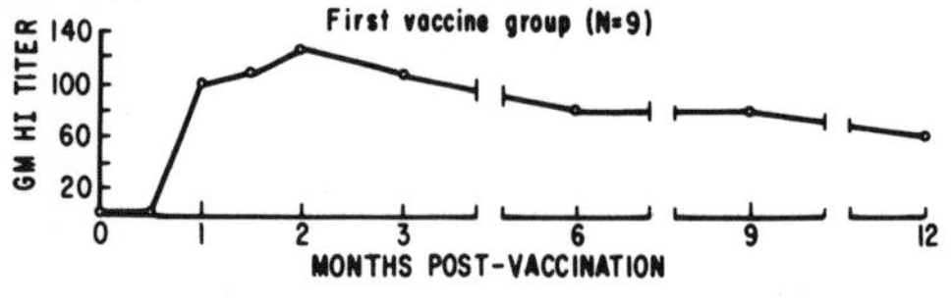

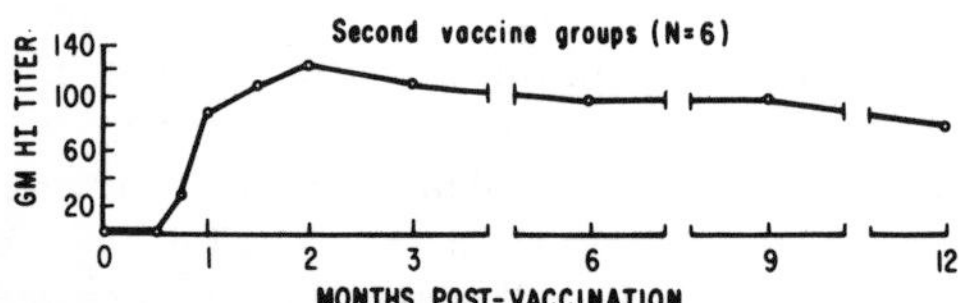

Fig. 2. *Serological response to Cendehill rubella vaccine in 15 children in the closed study.*

of approximately 1:130 on the 65th day. The HI titer then gradually declined to about 1:70 one year after vaccination.

Trial in adult women (nursing students). The evaluation of clinical reactions to the rubella vaccine was difficult because of an intercurrent outbreak of A_2 influenza among the vaccinees and placebo subjects between the 15th and 38th postvaccination days. Seven of 10 vaccinees and 6 to 8 placebo subjects had influenza or upper respiratory tract infections, or both. A_2 influenza virus was isolated from the nasal secretions of one vaccinee. Six vaccinees and six placebo control subjects developed significant antibody rises to A_2 influenza.

Seven vaccinees and four placebo subjects developed palpable posterior cervical lymph nodes between the 8th and 24th postvaccination days. The lymph node enlargement in both groups was minimal, averaging 1 cm in diameter.

Two women in the vaccinee group and two women in the placebo group complained of joint symptoms. One woman who received rubella vaccine developed transient arthritis (lasting 24 hr) involving the proximal interphalangeal joints of the hands, the right knee, and questionably the ankles, beginning on the 20th postvaccination day. At the same time, this woman had transient rash over the chest which lasted several hours and a painful right biceps. On further questioning, the patient gave a history of Raynaud's phenomenon in the past. The second vaccinee had transient neck stiffness in the morning between the 17th and 22nd postvaccination days. One placebo subject had arthritis of the left second metacarpophalangeal joint lasting 2 days on day 45. She had preceding beta-hemolytic streptococcal infection of the throat and influenza on day 23. The second placebo subject had transient arthralgia on the 8th day.

After the initial observation period, the placebo subjects were also given rubella vaccine. All 18 women who received rubella vaccine developed rubella HI antibodies ranging in titer from 1:40 to 1:320 with a geometric mean titer of 1:141.

Trial in seropositive women (inmate volunteers). Only 23 of the 29 vaccinated women remained in the study until its completion. Twenty-eight women had pre-existing rubella HI antibodies ranging in titer from 1:10 to 1:5,120. No rises in HI antibody titer were detected in 22 paired sera. There were no significant objective reactions to the rubella vaccine in this group of seropositive women.

Open field trials in children. Among the 3,636 parochial school children immunized, 2,001 or 55% of the vaccinees were found to be seronegative. The reactions to the vaccine as reported by parents are illustrated in Fig. 3. Reaction cards were returned by 1,393 seronegative vaccinees, 1,054 seropositive vaccinees, and 200 placebo control subjects. The low incidence of symptoms or signs that patients would become aware of was significant as a measure of the vaccine's acceptability. Absence of a reaction to the rubella vaccine was reported by 81% of the

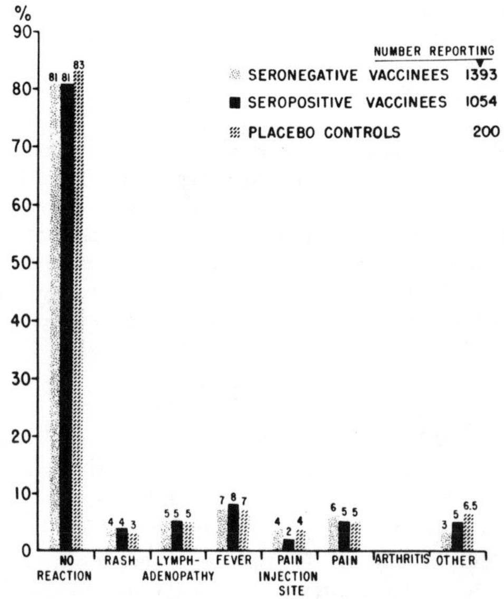

Fig. 3. *Reactions to Cendehill rubella vaccine and placebo injections as reported by parents of parochial school children.*

seronegative and seropositive vaccinees and by 83% of the placebo control subjects. Rash was reported in 4% of the vaccinees and 3% of the placebo subjects. Lymphadenopathy, a difficult evaluation for parents to make, was reported in 5% of the vacinees and 5% of the placebo subjects; these figures were obviously inaccurate. Fever was reported in 7% of seronegative vaccinees, 8% of the seropositive vaccinees, and 7% of the placebo subjects. Pain at the injection site was reported in 4% of the seronegative vaccinees, 2% of the seropositive vaccinees, and 4% of the placebo subjects. Pain in other locations or unspecified was reported in 6% of the seronegative vaccinees, 5% of the seropositive vaccinees, and 5% of the placebo subjects. Arthritis was not reported by any of the vaccinees. Unrelated symptoms, such as ear infections, indigestion, nausea, stomach ache, etc., were reported in 3% of the seronegative vaccinees, 5% of the seropositive vaccinees, and 6.5% of the placebo subjects. Only a small percentage of the parents reported the date when the reactions occurred, but it appears that most of them occurred shortly after vaccination (Fig. 4). The reactions were reported in the vaccinees as well as the placebo control subjects. A number of the children reporting rash, fever, and lymphadenopathy were seen at home by a vaccination team physician and none of these children was thought to have a reaction to the rubella vaccine. Several of the children reporting rash had chickenpox and one had scarlet fever. Several children with fever and lymphadenopathy had upper respiratory infections.

The incidence of clinical reactions in the children on military bases was comparable to that noted above for the group of Baltimore parochial school children. A report of no adverse reaction to the vaccine was registered by 89% of the seronegative vaccinees, 94% of the seropositive vaccinees, and 91% of the placebo controls. Rash was noted in 3.5% of the seronegative vaccinees, 3.1% of the seropositive vaccinees, and 2.1% of the controls. Fever was observed in 5.1% of the seronegative vaccinees, and 2.3% of the seropositive vaccinees, and 7% of the controls. Lymphadenopathy was reported in 3.3% of the seronegative vaccinees, 1.4% of the seropositive vaccinees, and 1.4% of the control subjects. Pain at the site of injection occurred in 1.2% of the seronegative vaccinees, 1.1% of the seropositive vaccinees, and 1.4% of the placebo subjects. Other reactions reported included sore throat, vomiting, and diarrhea in a very small number in each group.

Of particular interest was the reporting of transient arthralgias in four seronegative and two seropositive vaccinees and in one recipient of the placebo saline control. There were also four possible allergic reactions to the vaccination, two each in the seropositive and seronegative vaccine groups. These children experienced urticaria, pruritus, and facial or periorbital edema within the first 24 hr after receiving vaccine. These symptoms were not serious enough for the parents to seek medical assistance. Unfortunately, additional details of the arthritis and possibly allergic reactions are not available.

The onset of symptoms after vaccination of

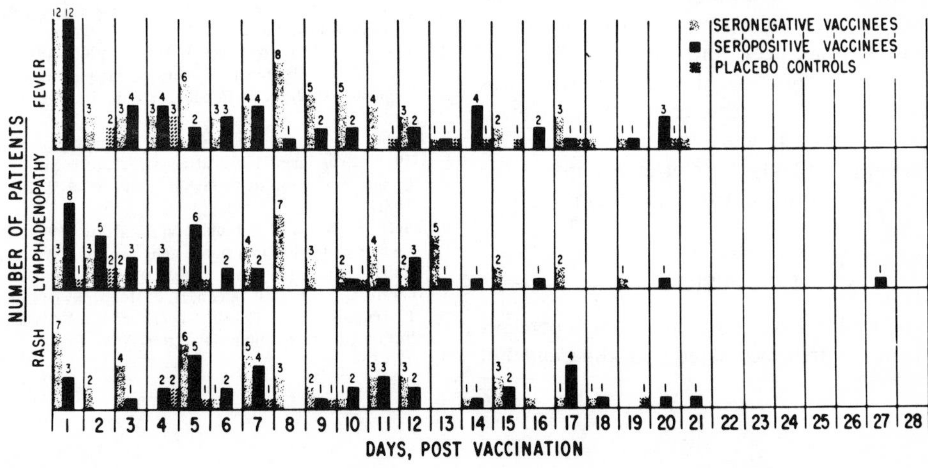

Fig. 4. *Onset of symptoms after vaccination with Cendehill rubella vaccine as reported by parents of parochial school children.*

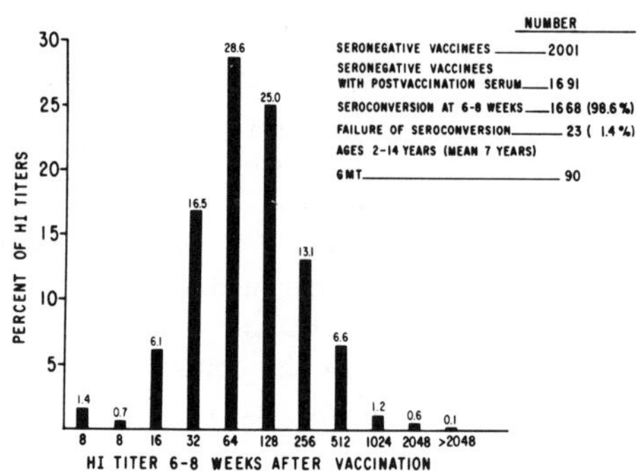

Fig. 5. *Antibody response to Cendehill rubella vaccine in parochial school children.*

the children on military bases was similar to that shown in Fig. 4. As with the parochial school children, the majority of the reactions occurred shortly after vaccination.

Antibody responses to the rubella vaccine in the parochial school children are shown in Fig. 5. There were 2,001 seronegative vaccinees, and the postvaccination sera of 1,691 of these were tested 6 to 8 weeks after vaccination. HI antibodies had developed in 1,668 children (98.6%); the remaining 23 (1.4%) failed to develop rubella HI antibodies. In the seroconvertor group, the geometric mean titer was 1:90. HI antibody titers ranged from 1:8 to more than 1:2,048, and 96% of the children had HI titers ranging between 1:16 and 1:512.

Among the total group of 2,539 children on military bases who received the vaccine, 1,371 or 54% were susceptible to rubella at the time of vaccination. the HI antibody responses to the vaccine were determined on 1,144 of the 1,371 seronegative vaccinees who returned for postvaccination testing. A rise in HI titer was observed in 98.9% of this group at the end of the 30-day period. Only 12 (1.0%) failed to develop any antibody titer after receipt of the vaccine. The range in titer was from 1:16 to 1:4,096.

DISCUSSION

These studies have shown that a high percentage of the children vaccinated with the Cendehill rubella vaccine shed virus from the nose and throat; however, the virus was not transmitted to susceptible contacts. Prinzie et al. (3) have described similar findings. A majority of the rubella virus isolates were obtained from the nose; nasal swabs and nasal washings were the best specimens for investigating rubella virus shedding in vaccinees. Intercurrent infections with echoviruses 3 and 7 did not interfere with antibody response to rubella vaccine.

Only 2 of 47 women who received rubella developed joint symptoms. The arthritis and arthralgia in both women was mild and of brief duration. The lymphadenopathy in the seronegative women may have been related to the rubella vaccine or to influenza or upper respiratory infection. These results were similar to those reported by Farquhar et al. (1) and Gold et al. (2).

Children tolerated the Cendehill rubella vaccine well. A small percentage of the vaccinees reported rash, fever, and lymphadenopathy. However, these symptoms occurred with almost equal frequency among the placebo subjects. Therefore, many of the reactions reported by parents may represent intercurrent illnesses and do not necessarily represent reaction to the rubella vaccine. The Cendehill rubella vaccine was highly effective in inducing serum antibodies in 98.7% of the children vaccinated. Our experience in children is similar to that reported by Schiff et al. (4).

LITERATURE CITED

1. Farquhar, J. D., and J. E. Corretjer. 1969. Clinical experience with Cendehill rubella vaccine in mature women. Amer. J. Dis. Child. **118**:266–268.
2. Gold, J. A., A. Prinzie, and J. McKee. 1969. Adult women vaccinated with rubella vaccine. A preliminary report on controlled studies with Cendehill strain. Amer. J. Dis. Child. **118**:264–265.
3. Prinzie, A., C. Huygelen, J. Gold, J. Farquhar, and J. McKee. 1969. Experimental live attenuated rubella virus vaccine. Clinical evaluation of Cendehill strain. Amer. J. Dis. Child. **118**:172–177.
4. Schiff, G. M., J. L. Rauh, and T. Rotte. 1969. Rubella vaccine evaluation in a public school system. Amer. J. Dis. Child. **118**:203–208.
5. Stewart, G. L., P. D. Parkman, H. E. Hopps, R. D. Douglas, J. P. Hamilton, and H. M. Meyer, Jr. 1967. Rubella-virus hemagglutination-inhibition test. N. Engl. J. Med. **276**:554–557.

Antimicrobial Agents and Chemotherapy—1969

Clinical Trials with Cendehill Strain Attenuated Rubella Virus Vaccine

JAMES D. CHERRY, FRANCES L. HORVATH, GEORGE D. COMERCI, URSULA T. ROLFE, JOHN E. BOBINSKI, JEROME A. HIRSCHFELD, KENNETH S. SHEPARD, and HELEN L. BRUCE

Infectious Disease Unit, Cardinal Glennon Memorial Hospital for Children, and Department of Pediatrics, St. Louis University School of Medicine, St. Louis, Missouri 63104

Since April 1968, a closed trial, a family study, and two open trials with Cendehill strain rubella vaccine have been conducted. Over 7,000 doses of vaccine have been administered and no early allergic reactions have been noted. In the family study, 97% of the seronegative vaccinees developed rubella hemagglutination-inhibiting antibody and none of the 180 seronegative contact subjects demonstrated serological evidence of rubella virus infection. During the open trials, the occurrence of "wild" rubella made clinical evaluation difficult, but, since the occurrence of symptoms was less in vaccinees than in seronegative control subjects, it appears that little or no clinical illness was due to immunization. Of the 3,648 seronegative vaccinees, 98% demonstrated seroconversion. Vaccinated children appeared to be protected when they were later exposed to natural disease.

Since the advent of the isolation of rubella virus in tissue culture, several candidate attenuated rubella virus vaccines have been developed (11, 16, 20, 21). One of these vaccines (Cendehill strain) has been extensively evaluated in several centers throughout the world (1, 2, 6-9, 13, 18, 21, 23). Since April 1968, our group has conducted a closed trial, a family study, and two open trials with Cendehill strain rubella vaccine. The latter three trials are the subject of this report; the closed trial has been published elsewhere (2).

MATERIALS AND METHODS

Vaccine. The origin and passage history of Cendehill strain rubella virus vaccine have been described by others (12, 18). In the present studies, vaccine was supplied in single-dose vials of lyophilized material with a titer of $10^{3.8}$ tissue culture infectious doses fifty ($TCID_{50}$) per vial as assayed in primary rabbit kidney cells. Five different vaccine lots were used in the studies.

Family study population. Participating families were enlisted from the outpatient clinic and mothers' clubs of local church parishes. A parent in each family was given a complete description of the study. Only families in which the mothers were shown to have rubella hemagglutination-inhibiting (HAI) antibody titers $\geqslant 8$ or who were practicing artificial contraception were admitted to the study.

Open trial 1 population. This study was conducted in the hospital clinic at Scott Air Force Base and was open to children 1 to 13 years of age (a small number of older children also participated). The subjects were children of military personnel, as well as children from the surrounding civilian communities.

Open trial 2 population. In this study, all children in the public and parochial kindergartens of St. Louis, Mo., were invited to participate.

In addition to these three studies, 262 other children in two parochial schools were administered Cendehill strain rubella vaccine.

In all studies, the parents or guardians of the children were given a complete description of the program, and informed consent was obtained for all participants. Children who were known to be allergic to neomycin, who had received immunizations during the preceding month, who were acutely or chronically ill, or who were receiving corticosteroids were omitted from the studies.

Vaccination and procedure for the family study. From July to December 1968, 126 families with two or more children were studied. Following the collection of blood, at least one child, and in larger families two or three children, were inoculated with 0.5 ml ($10^{3.8}$ $TCID_{50}$) of vaccine subcutaneously in the right deltoid region. The remaining children and the mother served as control and contact subjects. If the initial serum was seropositive (rubella HAI antibody titer $\geqslant 8$), the uninoculated child was considered a "control," and if seronegative (rubella HAI antibody titer <8), a "contact" subject. After inoculation, the vaccinated children were observed for early aberrant reactions for approximately 20 min, during which time the study program was reviewed with the mothers. During the 28-day period following immunization, the mother recorded daily temperatures on herself and all participating children and examined the children for exanthem and other untoward signs. On or around the 13th study day, the vacccinee was examined by one of the authors, and throat, nasal, and rectal swabs were collected. During the latter part of the study, in addition to examining the vaccinee on the 13th day, other children in the family were also examined.

All parents were urged to report to the vaccination center any unusual symptoms, such as fever or rash, in uninoculated subjects as well as in vaccinees. Most of these reported illnesses were seen by one of us, and specimens for viral studies were obtained. Convalescent-phase sera were obtained in approximately 6 to 8 weeks.

Vaccination and procedure for open trial 1. Immunization clinics were conducted on 27 through 30 January 1969. Prior to inoculation, blood was obtained from all subjects. The vaccinees were inoculated with 0.5 ml ($10^{3.8}$ $TCID_{50}$) of vaccine subcutaneously in the right deltoid region; every tenth child registered was used as a control and was similarly inoculated with 0.5 ml of saline. After inoculation, the children were observed for early aberrant reactions for approximately 20 min, and during this time the study program was reviewed with the parents.

A clinical surveillance card was given to the parents for each child participating in the study. These cards were completed by the parents and were returned to the center 3 weeks after entry into the study. All parents were urged to report by phone any unusual symptoms, such as rash. Frequently, when a reported illness was suggestive of rubella, the child was seen by a physician and specimens for viral studies were obtained.

Four weeks after the onset of the study, all parents were contacted by letter and urged to report any additional illnesses in their families that were thought to be rubella. Eight weeks after the onset of the study, all children whose initial rubella HAI antibody titers were <8 were asked to return for the collection of convalescent-phase specimens. At this time, control subjects who were initially seronegative were inoculated with rubella vaccine and were observed for another 3-week period.

Vaccination and procedure for open trial 2. Immunization teams visited the kindergartens during the week of 24 March 1969. All participants had been preregistered and each child had been assigned a coded subject number, indicating whether the child was to be a "vaccinee" or a "control." The remaining procedure was similar to that of open trial 1. Convalescent-phase sera were collected 8 weeks after vaccination.

On 1 June 1969, a surveillance form was sent to the parents of all kindergarten children who had been absent from school during the month of May, regardless of whether the children had participated in the vaccine program, inquiring whether the reason for the child's absence was natural rubella infection; it required only a "yes" or "no" answer.

Virologic techniques. Virus isolation techniques have been previously described (2). In brief, all specimens were inoculated into African green monkey kidney tissue culture, blind-passed once, and tested for interference by echovirus 11 challenge. Rubella virus isolation was presumptively diagnosed by the demonstration of interference in the passage culture. In the family study, most specimens were also inoculated into human embryonic lung diploid cells (WI-38). Enteroviruses were isolated and identified by standard methods.

During the periods of the reported studies, specimens were frequently collected from children seen in the outpatient department of Cardinal Glennon Memorial Hospital, and also from other patients referred to us with exanthematous illnesses suggestive of rubella.

Serological techniques. Samples of all sera for serological study were shipped frozen to Smith, Kline & French Laboratories, and the remainder of the samples were stored at –20 C. All sera were examined for HAI antibody at Smith, Kline & French Laboratories, and HAI titers on selected sera were also performed in our laboratory (2).

RESULTS

Analysis of study population. The population of the family study (Table 1) consisted of 126 families with 546 subjects. Of this group, serological follow-up was obtained in 540 (99%) and clinical surveillance was completed on 512

Table 1. *Distribution of study population during family study with Cendehill strain rubella vaccine*

Subject category	No.	Median age	No. with serological follow-up	No. with clinical surveillance
Seronegative vaccinees	120	3	119	111
Seropositive vaccinees	24	6	23	23
Seronegative contacts	179	7	177	163
Seropositive controls	97	9	95	95
Seropositive mothers	123	–	123	117
Seronegative mothers	3	–	3	3
Totals	546	–	540	512

(94%). There were 120 seronegative vaccinees and a total of 182 seronegative contact subjects. The median ages were 3 years for seronegative vaccinees, 6 years for seropositive vaccinees, 7 years for contacts, and 9 years for controls.

The populations of open trials 1 and 2 have been combined in Table 2. Initially, 6,961 children were entered into these studies; acute-phase serum in sufficient quantity for rubella antibody determinations were collected from 6,870 children and, henceforth, this figure will be considered the total study group. Of the total group, 4,197 (61%) were seronegative. Clinical observation cards were returned on 63% of the subjects (93% in trial 1 and 50% in trial 2), and convalescent-phase serum was obtained in 87% of the initially seronegative children (83% in trial 1 and 88% in trial 2).

Clinical findings. Just prior to the onset of the Scott Air Force Base study, there were reports of scattered rubella cases in the community. On the day following the period of vaccine administration, an assistant in the program developed clinical rubella, proven by the recovery of rubella virus from his nose and throat. It is estimated that about one-twentieth of the total Scott Air Force Base study population would have had exposure to this worker.

Immediately prior to and throughout the 8-week period of the kindergarten study, "wild" rubella cases were reported in St. Louis and within the school system. Several cases were seen by the authors and some were confirmed virologically.

The overall clinical findings reported by parents in the open trials are listed in Table 3. Illness was noted in 14% of the seropositive controls, 15% of the seropositive vaccinees, 19% of the seronegative vaccinees, and 21% of the seronegative controls. Overall illness and fever in seronegative vaccinees occurred significantly more commonly than in seropositive vaccinees and seropositive controls; seronegative controls had fever and rash more frequently than seropositive controls.

An analysis of the reported exanthems is presented in Table 4. Sixty-eight episodes of rash occurred in seropositive vaccinees. Except for the occurrence of hives in three children, the illnesses were quite nonspecific, and none was suggestive of rubella. Of the seronegative vaccinees, eight probably had varicella, four had hives, 1 had roseola infantum, and 18 had illnesses highly suggestive of rubella. Eighty (67%) of the exanthems in seronegative vac-

Table 2. *Distribution of study population during open trials with Cendehill strain rubella vaccine*

Subject category	No.	No. with serological follow-up	No. with clinical follow-up
Seronegative vaccinees	3.741	3,265	2,345
Seronegative controls	456	383	277
Seropositive vaccinees	2,403	–	1,560
Seropositive controls	270	–	181
Totals	6,870	3,648 (87%)[a]	4,363 (63%)

[a] Convalescent-phase sera only collected on subjects initially seronegative.

Table 3. *Clinical findings in 4,363 study subjects during open trials with Cendehill strain rubella vaccine*

Clinical category	Subject categories			
	Seronegative vaccinees	Seronegative controls	Seropositive vaccinees	Seropositive controls
Total subjects	2,345	277	1,560	181
Illness reported	443[a] (19%)	57[b] (21%)	226 (15%)	26 (14%)
Fever	182[c] (8%)	27[c] (10%)	98 (6%)	7 (4%)
Swollen nodes	144 (6%)	21 (8%)	78 (5%)	7 (4%)
Rash	148 (6%)	26[a,c] (9%)	66 (4%)	7 (4%)
Pain at site of inoculation	69 (3%)	8 (3%)	23 (1%)	3 (2%)
"Other"[d]	134 (6%)	15 (5%)	69 (4%)	9 (5%)

[a] Significant at $P < 0.005$ when compared with seropositive vaccinees.
[b] Significant at $P < 0.01$ when compared with seropositive vaccinees.
[c] Significant at $P < 0.05$ when compared with seropositive controls.
[d] Includes complaints such as headache, cough, coryza, vomiting, diarrhea, etc.

Table 4. *Characteristics of exanthems in study subjects during open trials with Cendehill strain rubella vaccine*

Clinical category	Subject categories			
	Seronegative vaccinees	Seronegative controls	Seropositive vaccinees	Seropositive controls
Total rashes	148	26	68[a]	7
Date of rash not recorded	29	7	9	3
Onset of rash before day 12	80 (67%)	11 (58%)	35 (59%)	3 (75%)
Findings highly suggestive of rubella[b]	18	7	0	0
Prior "wild" rubella exposure . .	8	1	0	0
Probably varicella	8	0	0	0
Probably urticaria	4	1	3	0
Probably roseola infantum	1	0	0	0

[a] Includes two children who had two separate occurrences of rash.
[b] Generalized rash of 2- to 5-days' duration; lymphadenopathy; temperature $<$101.5 F (38.6 C).

cinees occurred before the 12th study day, whereas 11 (58%) similarly occurred in seronegative controls.

After the initial 3-week observation period, no further exanthems in Scott Air Force Base study participants were reported to the center until after the collection of convalescent-phase bloods.

In Table 5 the results of the kindergarten rubella survey for the month of May are reported. Absences reported by the parents to be due to rubella were significantly more frequent in children not participating in the study than in study participants.

Clinical observation cards were returned on 204 of the 408 initially seronegative control children who were vaccinated at the time of the convalescent-phase blood collection. Of this group, 24 reported illnesses and 7 exanthems were noted. All of the exanthems occurred prior to the 12th postvaccination day.

Including these vaccinated controls, the previous closed clinical trial, and school children immunized without serological study, over 7,000 doses of vaccine have been administered and no early allergic reactions have been noted.

Virus isolation studies. In the family study routine specimens on or about day 13 were collected from all but one vaccinee, and 52 rubella strains were recovered from 44 seronegative vaccinees (37%); these included 32 nasal, 17 throat, and 3 rectal isolates. None of the seropositive vaccinees shed virus. In addition, specimens were collected from vaccinees and other family members at the time of intercurrent illnesses; 10 rubella strains were recovered from seronegative vaccinees but no interfering agents were recovered from specimens collected from "contacts," "controls," or seropositive vacinees.

Table 5. *Kindergarten absences during May 1969 due to "rubella" as reported by 3,190 patients*

Subject category	Total	Rubella absences
Study participants	1,221	31[a] (2.5%)
Nonparticipants	1,969	89 (4.5%)

[a] $P < 0.005$ when compared with nonstudy children.

Thirty-nine of the original family study virus-positive specimens and 57 similar specimens from the closed clinical trial (2) were assayed for virus concentration. These results are recorded in Fig. 1. The majority of titers in vaccine infections were low, as 48 of the 96 originally positive specimens failed to yield virus after storage with its associated freezing and thawing. Whereas 64% of the nasal specimens had titers of $10^{1.5}$ or greater, only 20% of throat swabs had similar titers.

During the study period of the open trials, specimens from 14 Scott Air Force Base subjects were submitted for virus isolation studies. Twelve rubella viral strains were recovered from six patients—four seronegative controls and two seronegative vaccinees. Two seropositive vaccinees were studied and neither yielded an isolate. In the kindergarten study, specimens from four seronegative vaccinees were submitted for viral isolation. These four patients yielded five rubella viral strains.

Serology. Convalescent-phase serum was ob-

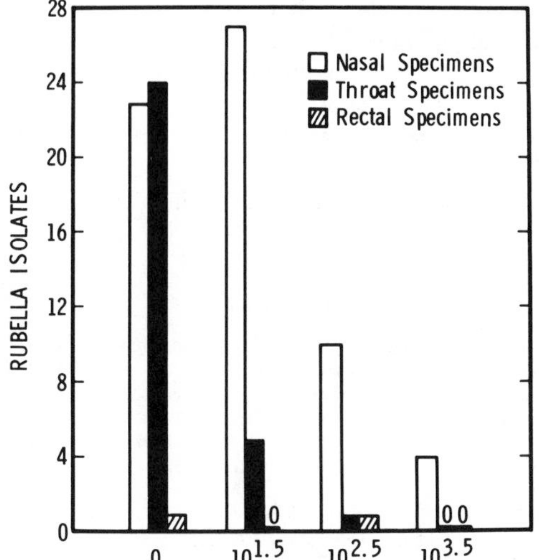

Fig. 1. *Concentration of rubella virus in 96 virus-positive primary specimens from children immunized with Cendehill strain rubella vaccine. All primary specimens were frozen (−80 C) for 2 to 8 months following original isolation and prior to these titrations.*

tained from 540 of the 546 family study participants. There were 180 seronagative contact subjects with available serum specimens and none developed HAI antibody to rubella virus. Of the seronegative vaccinees, all but three developed HAI antibody to rubella, with a geometric mean titer of 61. Patients from whom rubella virus was recovered had a geometric mean antibody titer of 68, whereas virus-negative patients had a geometric mean titer of 57. One child who failed to develop HAI antibody had received measles vaccine and immune globulin (0.01 ml/lb) 5 days prior to rubella immunization.

In the open trials, there were 4,197 initially susceptible children, and convalescent-phase serum was collected from 3,648 (87%). Seroconversion was demonstrated by 98% of the seronegative vaccinees, with a geometric mean antibody titer of 77. Seroconversion was noted in 35 (9%) of the seronegative controls. It is of interest that only seven (20%) of these children were reported to have had rubella-like illnesses.

Continued surveillance of family study subjects. In the spring of 1969, four seronegative contact subjects and a 15-year-old sibling, who had not participated in the study, in another study family experienced clinical rubella. Four of these children were studied and rubella virus was recovered from each. None of the vaccinees became ill. In three instances, the vaccinees were seen 2 weeks after the sibling's illness, and nose and throat swabs were collected for rubella studies. Rubella virus was not recovered from these specimens.

DISCUSSION

An acceptable rubella vaccine should cause no illness or minimal illness, it should not be transmissible, it should be highly immunogenic, it should prevent disease with natural challenge, and it should contain no adventitious agents. In our studies to date, over 7,000 doses of Cendehill strain rubella vaccine have been administered and no early allergic-type reactions have occurred. In comparison, Detels et al.(5) noted that 3 children of 900 who received HPV-77 vaccine (with 12 dog kidney passages) had severe immediate reactions. In the open trials, seven children who received vaccine had mild urticaria (Table 4) during the observation period. This may represent an allergic reaction, but since similar findings were noted in a seronegative control the possibility of another etiology must be considered. During the period of these trials, similar urticarial illnesses in children not participating in the trials were not infrequently seen in the outpatient clinic.

In the open trials, illnesses with fever, swollen nodes, and rash were more commonly reported in seronegative vaccinees and controls than in seropositive subjects (Table 3). As the incidence of these clinical findings was greater in seronegative controls, the symptomatology may have been due to natural rubella infection and not vaccine-induced. Many of the seronegative vaccinees were probably already infected with "wild" rubella at the time of immunization. The occurrence of the majority of the rubella-like illnesses prior to the 12th study day supports this view. In the study reported by Detels et al.(4), HPV vaccine was evaluated during epidemic rubella. The attack rate in vaccine and placebo recipients was similar for the first 12 days after inoculation; then the occurrence of illness in vaccinees fell until the 17th day, and thereafter only scattered cases were reported.

When volunteers have been inoculated with virulent rubella virus (10, 19), the earliest noted appearance of rash has been 12 days after administration. This suggests that even if vaccine administration did cause rash it would be unlikely to occur before the 12th postinoculation day.

The occurrence of natural rubella during the periods of the open trials makes the evaluation of vaccine transmissibility difficult. However, the family study was conducted during the summer and fall when natural rubella was not known to be present in the community, and none of the 180 seronegative contact subjects acquired infection that could be detected by the occurrrence of serological conversion.

Dudgeon et al. (6) reported one instance of a seronegative unvaccinated subject who developed rubella antibody after contact with an individual vaccinated with Cendehill strain, and Wilkins and associates (24) noted rubella infection in a control patient that they attributed to spread of HPV-80 vaccine virus from a vaccinee. Although it seems possible that these infections in susceptible subjects could be the results of wild natural infections or study errors, they are certainly cause for concern.

Other closed trials have demonstrated no transmission (2, 3, 7, 11, 14-21). The low concentrations of virus in the noses of vaccinees (Fig. 1) as compared with those noted in natural rubella cases are reassuring (2, 17).

The isolation rate of rubella virus from seronegative vaccinees is similar to that noted in other studies (2, 3, 14, 15, 17). It is important to emphasize that the majority of isolates were recovered from the nose and that these tended to be in higher primary concentration than isolates from the throat. Multiplication of virus in the nose and throat with resulting secretory antibody may be important in rubella immunity. However, it has been demonstrated that later intranasal challenge of vaccinated subjects with virulent virus is associated with some local replication of virus (22, 24).

The geometric mean HAI antibody titers of 68 in the family study and 77 in the open trials compare favorably with those noted in other studies (2, 13, 23). The lack of serconversion in 2% of seronegative subjects is also similar to the results with other rubella vaccines (11, 13, 16, 20). It seems probable that some of these failures are due to the initial presence of specific antibody, but at levels lower than the present test procedures can measure.

Although the observation period following our trials has not been long, it would appear that immunized children have been protected from natural disease. As noted in Table 5, the reporting of school absences due to rubella was significantly greater in the unvaccinated seronegatives than in vaccinees. The lack of clinical illness and virus infection in immunized family study subjects after natural challenge is also encouraging.

ACKNOWLEDGMENTS

We are indebted to the many participating physicians, nurses, technicians, and secretaries who made this study possible. We are also particularly indebted to John Bell of Smith, Kline & French Laboratories, to Curtis Johnson, Cleo Hollinshed, and Sue Hagan for technical assistance, and to Ronald Schoengold of Smith, Kline & French Laboratories for performing the rubella antibody titers.

This investigation was supported by the Cardinal Glennon Research Fund and by a grant from Smith, Kline & French Laboratories.

LITERATURE CITED

1. Byrne, E. B., J. M. Ryan, M. F. Randolph, and D. M. Horstmann, 1969. Live attenuated rubella virus vaccines in young adult women. Trials of Cendehill and $HPV_{77}DE_5$. Amer. J. Dis. Child. **118**:234–236.
2. Cherry, J. D., J. E. Bobinski, and G. D. Comerci. 1969. A clinical trial with live attenuated rubella virus vaccine (Cendehill 51 strain). J. Pediat. **75**:79–86.
3. Cooper, L. Z., J. P. Giles, and S. Krugman. 1968. Clinical trial of live attenuated rubella virus vaccine, HPV-77 strain. Amer. J. Dis. Child. **115**:655–657.
4. Detels, R., J. T. Grayston, K. S. W. Kim, K. P. Chen, J. L. Gale, R. P. Beasley, and L. Gutman. 1969. Prevention of clinical and subclinical rubella infection. Efficacy of three HPV-77 derivative vaccines. Amer. J. Dis. Child. **118**:295–300.
5. Detels, R., J. T. Grayston, K., S. W. Kim, K. P. Chen, L. Gutman, J. L. Gale, and R. P. Beasley. 1969. The efficacy of HPV-77 rubella vaccine in prevention of disease. Symp Ser. Immunobiol. Standard. **11**:365–370.
6. Dudgeon, J. A., W. C. Marshall, and C. S. Peckham, 1969. Rubella vaccine trials in adults and children. Comparison of three attenuated vaccines. Amer. J. Dis. Child. **118**:237–242.
7. DuPan, R. M., C. Huygelen, J. Peetermans, and A. Prinzie. 1968. Clinical trials with a live attenuated rubella virus vaccine. Cendehill 51 strain. Amer. J. Dis. Child. **115**:658–662.
8. Farquhar, J. D., and J. E. Corretjer. 1969. Clinical experience with Cendehill rubella vaccine in mature women. Amer. J. Dis. Child. **118**:266–268.
9. Gold, J. A., A. Prinzie, and J. McKee. 1969. Adult women vaccinated with rubella vaccine. A preliminary report on controlled studies with Cendehill strain. Amer. J. Dis. Child. **118**:264–265.
10. Green, R. H., M. R. Balsamo, J. P. Giles, S. Krugman, and G. S. Mirick. 1965. Studies of the natural history and prevention of rubella, Amer. J. Dis. Child. **110**:348–365.
11. Hilleman, M. R., E. B. Buynak, J. E. Whitman, R. W. Weibel, and J. Stokes. 1969. Live attenuated rubella virus vaccines. Experiences with duck embryo cell preparations. Amer. J. Dis. Child. **118**:166–171.
12. Huygelen, C., and J. Peetermans. 1967. Attenuation of

rubella virus by serial passage in primary rabbit kidney cell cultures. II. Experiments in animals. Arch. Gesamte Virusforsch. **21**:357–365.

13. Karchmer, A. W., K. L. Herrmann, J. P. Friedman, T. C. Shope, E. E. Page, M. S. Dressler, W. H. Armes and J. J. Witte. 1969. Comparative studies of rubella vaccines. Amer. J. Dis. Child. **118**:197–202.
14. Lepow, M. L., J. A. Veronelli, D. D. Hostetler, and F. C. Robbins, 1968. A trial with live attenuated rubella vaccine. Amer. J. Dis. Child. **115**:639–647.
15. Meyer, H. M., P. D. Parkman, T. E. Hobbins, and F. A. Ennis. 1968. Clinical studies with experimental live rubella virus vaccine (strain HPV-77). Evaluation of vaccine-induced immunity. Amer. J. Dis. Child. **115**:648–654.
16. Meyer, H. M., P. D. Parkman, T. E. Hobbins, H. E. Larson, W. J. Davis, J. P. Simsarian, and H. E. Hopps. 1969. Attenuated rubella viruses. Laboratory and clinical characteristics. Amer. J. Dis. Child. **118**:155–165.
17. Meyer, H. M., P. D. Parkman, and T. C. Panos. 1966. Attenuated rubella virus. II. Production of an experimental live-virus vaccine and clinical trial. N. Engl. J. Med. **275**:575.
18. Peetermans, J., and C. Huygelen. 1967. Attenuation of rubella virus by serial passage in primary rabbit kidney cell cultures. I. Growth characteristics in vitro and production of experimental vaccines at different passage levels. Arch. Gesamte Virusforsch. **21**:133.
19. Plotkin, S. A., D. Cornfeld, and T. H. Ingalls. 1965. Studies of immunization with living rubella virus. Trials in children with a strain cultured from an aborted fetus. Amer. J. Dis. Child. **110**:381–389.
20. Plotkin, S. A., J. D. Farquhar, M. Katz, and F. Buser. 1969. Attenuation of RA 27/3 rubella virus in WI-38 human diploid cells. Amer. J. Dis. Child. **118**:178–185.
21. Prinzie, A., C. Huygelen, J. Gold, J. Farquhar, and J. McKee. 1969. Experimental live attenuated rubella virus vaccine. Clinical evaluation of Cendehill strain. Amer. J. Dis. Child. **118**:172–177.
22. Schiff, G. M., R. Donath, and T. Rotte. 1969. Experimental rubella studies. I. Clinical and laboratory features of infection caused by the Brown strain rubella virus. II. Artificial challenge studies of adult rubella vaccinees, Amer. J. Dis. Child. **118**:269–274.
23. Schiff, G. M., J. L. Rauh, and T. Rotte, 1969. Rubella vaccine evaluation in a public school system. Amer. J. Dis. Child: **118**:203–208.
24. Wilkins, J., J. M. Leedom, B. Portnoy, and M. A. Salvatore. 1969. Reinfection with rubella virus despite live vaccine induced immunity. Trials of HPV-77 and HPV-80 live rubella virus vaccines and subsequent artificial and natural challenge studies. Amer. J. Dis. Child. **118**:275–294.

Antimicrobial Agents and Chemotherapy—1969

Antibody Response and Reactions to Cendehill Rubella Vaccine in Adult Women

SUZANNE DesROSIERS, TE-WEN CHANG, and LOUIS WEINSTEIN

Infectious Disease Service, New England Medical Center Hospitals and Department of Medicine, Tufts University School of Medicine, Boston, Massachusetts 02111

The incidence of joint involvement and other untoward effects following immunization with Cendehill strain (51) rubella vaccine was determined in 108 adult women, ranging in age from 16 to 61. Of these, 52 were rubella-susceptible and 56 were immune to this agent prior to vaccination. Eighty per cent of the seronegative vaccinated subjects were over 20 years of age. Forty-five women, in two-thirds of whom rubella hemagglutinin-inhibiting (HI) antibody was not demonstrable, were matched for age and residence and served as controls. Determination of HI antibody levels 6 weeks after vaccination revealed a good response in those receiving the vaccine. No change in antibody titer was detected in the control subjects. Only one vaccinated patient had vague arthralgia, suggestive of very mild joint involvement. Among the other reactions noted in those receiving the vaccine were transient, faint, macular rash (two cases) and local discomfort at the site of injection. Lymphadenopathy developed in both immunized and unimmunized individuals. However, enlargement of the postauricular and epitrochlear nodes was considerably more common in rubella-susceptible women given the virus. Cendehill rubella vaccine appears to be a highly effective immunizing agent in adult women. The incidence of reactions accompanying its use in such individuals is lower than that which follows injection of the HPV–77 strain of rubella virus.

The primary aim of immunization against rubella is the prevention of the disease in pregnant women and the elimination of its profound and often devastating effects on the babies. Rubella vaccine has proved to be effective in young children, and the main emphasis of programs of vaccination at present is on this age group. By thus decreasing the pool of virus available for transmission, the risk to the older population, including those that are pregnant, should be sharply reduced or eliminated (1, 5, 9, 13, 15). However, there still exists an appreciable number of females of child-bearing age who may not benefit immediately from such a program and who, therefore, should be immunized. One of the important drawbacks to this is the high frequency of joint involvement in people in this age group given rubella vaccine (4, 7). Although this manifestation is common (20 to 25%) in patients infected by the wild strain of the virus, its incidence is often higher after exposure to the vaccine strain, exceeding 40% in some studies (17). The purpose of the present study was to determine the level of antibody response and the rate of reactions in adult women given the Cendehill rubella virus vaccine.

MATERIALS AND METHODS

The total number of women included in the study was 478. Of these, 153 were medical students, nurses, or other hospital personnel engaged in their usual daily activities, and 325 were mentally retarded individuals residing in one institution (Fernald School, Waltham, Mass.). Screening for the presence of rubella hemagglutinin-inhibiting (HI) antibody was carried out 48 hr before vaccination except in 50 persons in whom this was performed on the same day that the vaccine was given. All of the subjects or their legal guardians were informed of the potential hazards of the procedure; consent was obtained in every instance before immunization. A total of 108 women were given Cendehill vaccine; of these, 52 were seronegative and 56 were seropositive before vaccination. Forty-five individuals (30 with, and 15 without rubella antibody prior to injection) matched for age and place of residence served as controls. The age distribution of all of these individuals is presented in Table 1. Since the risk of joint involvement appears to be age-related, it is important to point out that over 80% of the nonimmune subjects were over 20 years of age (the group with the greatest susceptibility to arthritic manifestations), and 46% were more than 23 years of age.

Prior to vaccination, all of the experimental subjects underwent a physical examination, including measurement and functional evaluation of every joint in the mentally retarded group. The medical records of all those residing at the Fernald State School were reviewed, with special attention to cause of retardation, medical and surgical history, medication, intercurrent diseases, and abnormal concentrations of serum lipids and proteins. The Fernald group was examined for joint manifestations almost every day. The others were seen three times a week. The presence or absence of lymphadenopathy, rash, fever, or other side effects was recorded.

Part of the study was carried out from November 1968 to January 1969, a period during which upper respiratory infections were prevalent. The clinical observations were continued for 4 weeks after vaccination. Titrations of serum HI antibody titers were carried out 6 weeks after the vaccine was administered. No attempt was made to isolate the vaccine virus from any of the subjects.

Screening for the presence of rubella antibody prior to immunization was carried out on fresh serum samples. After storage at –20 C for 6 weeks, these specimens were retitrated simultaneously with those obtained after vaccination. The titrations were performed by a modification of the method of Mann et al. (11). Serial twofold dilutions of each serum were made in dextrose-gelatin-Veronal buffer (*p*H 7.0). The lowest dilution employed was 1:8; all specimens exhibiting agglutination of chick erythrocytes at this dilution in the presence of 4 hemagglutinating units of rubella antigen (Flow Laboratories, Inc., Baltimore, Md.) were considered to be devoid of HI antibody.

The Cendehill vaccine (51) was a lyophilized preparation containing $10^{3.8}$ plaque-forming units. It was reconstituted with 0.5 ml of diluent and was injected subcutaneously (deltoid area in 99 subjects and anterior aspect of the forearm in 9 subjects).

Table 1. *Distribution by age group of vaccinated and control subjects*

Age group (years)	No. of vaccinated women	Percentage	No. of controls	Percentage
15–19	29	26.8	1	2.2
20–29	59	54.6	13	28.8
30–39	12	11.1	14	31
40–49	4	3.7	7	15.5
50–59	3	2.8	6	13.3
60–69	1	0.926	3	6.6
>80	–	–	1	2.2
Total	108	–	45	–

RESULTS

The relationship between age and HI antibody to rubella virus is illustrated in Fig. 1. This antibody could not be demonstrated in 85 (17.6%) of the 478 subjects studied. This finding is in general agreement with those of other observers (3, 16).

Laboratory investigations. The levels of HI antibody reached after vaccination are presented in Table 2. The seroconversion rate in individuals with no antibody prior to vaccination was over 98%. The HI geometric mean titer (GMT) in this group was 1:94 (Table 3). Some degree of relation of the antibody response to age was noted in susceptible vaccinees. The mean age of subjects exhibiting a titer of 1:256 was under 30 years; that for levels of 1:512 was up to 32 years.

Table 2. *Serological response (HI) to Cendehill vaccine*

Initial condition	Seroconverted	Total	Seroconversion rate (%)	Geometric mean titer	
				Before	After[a]
Initially seronegative women	51	52	98.07	<8	94[b]
Contact controls					
Seronegative	0	30	0	<8	<8
Seropositive	–	15	–	56	37
Initially seropositive women	–	56	–	218	315[c]

[a] Six weeks after vaccination.
[b] Details are given in Table 3.
[c] Details are given in Table 4.

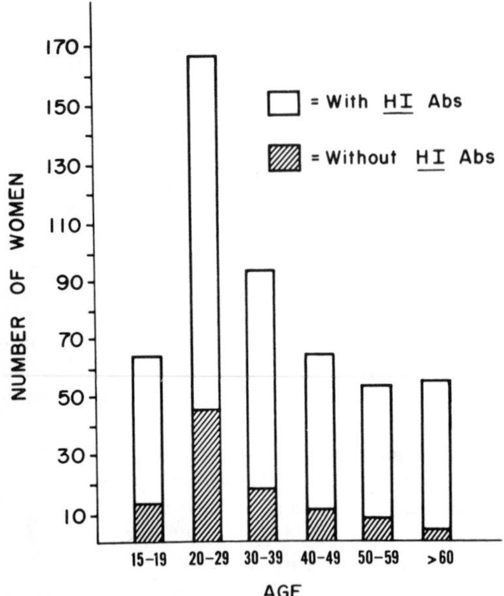

Fig. 1. *Age distribution of HI antibody to rubella virus in 478 adult women.*

Table 3. *Serological response of 52 women initially susceptible to rubella*

No. of vaccinees	HI titer 6 weeks postvaccination[a]
1	<8
4	16
9	32
10	64
17	128
7	256
2	512
2	1,024

[a] The geometric mean titer for the 52 vaccinees was 94.

Prior to vaccination, the GMT of HI antibody to rubella virus in the "immune" individuals was 1:218; after immunization, it rose to 1:315 (Table 4). No change in titer followed injection of the vaccine in 25 subjects. In 6 other instances, antibody titers decreased to one-half of the levels present prior to vaccination; in 17, administration of the vaccine produced only a twofold increase in the quantity of HI antibody. An appreciable "booster" effect (fourfold or greater increment) was noted in only eight (14.3%) of the persons found to have antibody before they were given the vaccine. There appeared to be no correlation between the preimmunization titer and the degree of response to the vaccine. Unvaccinated control subjects showed no change in HI antibody titer during the period of observation.

Table 4. *Rubella HI antibody response in 56 initially seropositive women*[a]

Before vaccination		After vaccination	
No. of women	HI titer	No. of women	HI titer
1	8	1	8
2	16	1	16
1	32	1	32
7	64	4	64
17	128	11	128
10	256	9	256
8	512	17	512
6	1,024	8	1,024
2	2,048	1	2,048
2	4,096	3	4,096

[a] The geometric mean titer for the 56 women was 218 before vaccination and 315 after vaccination.

Table 5. *Comparison between normal and mentally retarded women of the previous antibody titer (HI) and the antibody response after rubella vaccination*

Determination	Normal women	Mentally retarded women	Together
Number initially seronegative	28	24	52
Mean age (years)	21	28	24
HI titer 6 weeks after vaccination (GMT)	107	73	94
Number initially seropositive	47	9	56
Mean age	21	31	26
Prevaccination	261	64	218
Postvaccination	404	87	315
Number with "booster effect" (⩾fourfold increase in HI antibody)	8	0	8

Very striking was the fact that the serological response to Cendehill rubella vaccine was lower in both seronegative and initially seropositive mentally retarded persons than in normal persons (Table 5). The greatest difference was noted in those in whom HI antibody was detectable prior to vaccination. The GMT for normal women in this group 6 weeks after vaccine was given was 1:404; in the mentally retarded ones, it was 1:87.

Clinical observations. True arthritis did not occur in any of the individuals involved in this study. However, a 20-year-old nurse, seronegative prior to immunization, complained of pain on movement of the right elbow 12 days after receiving the vaccine; the joint was not red or swollen and was freely movable. The right epitrochlear nodes were markedly enlarged and tender. Although this may have been responsible for the discomfort, the possibility that mild synovitis or tendonitis was present could not be ruled out.

Cervical and suboccipital lymphadenopathy was common in both immunized and unimmunized individuals. Although enlargement of the postauricular and epitrochlear nodes occurred in both groups, it was observed much more frequently in those who had been vaccinated (Table 6). Generalized lymphadenopathy developed in two of the women, in neither of whom HI antibody had been detected prior to injection of the Cendehill strain; some of the nodes remained enlarged for as long as 7 weeks after they first appeared. The peripheral white blood counts in these subjects ranged from 5,000 to 9,000 with a predominance of lymphocytes, some of which were "atypical" (13 and 30% on the 9th and 16th days after immunization, respectively). Heterophile agglutination studies for infectious mononucleosis were negative.

Four of the women developed reactions at the site of injection of the vaccine; two were seronegative and two were seropositive prior to immunization. In those with detectable HI antibody before vaccination, an area of erythema without induration, measuring approximately 4 X 6 cm was observed on the 2nd and 3rd days after vaccination. The others exhibited an erythematous, pruritic lesion at the site of injection 11 days after inoculation. There appeared to be no correlation between the local reaction and the pre- and postimmunization HI antibody titers. Among other complaints were pharyngitis, low back pain, abdominal cramps, and anorexia; these were as common in the vaccinated as in the unvaccinated group. Fever (over 37.8 C) was recorded in one control and five immunized subjects. Two individuals, seronegative before receiving the vaccine, reported a transient, faint, pink macular rash; this was not observed by us.

Table 6. *Reactions to Cendehill vaccine*

Clinical feature	Vaccinated (108)		Controls (45)
	Susceptible (52)	Nonsusceptible (56)	
Rash			
No. of occurrences	2 (3.85%)	0	0
Time of onset (mean)	day 11	–	–
Duration (mean)	24 hr	–	–
Reaction at site of vaccination			
No. of occurrences	2 (3.8%)	2 (3.6%)	0
Type of reaction	Erythema and pruritis	Erythema, no induration	–
Time of onset (mean)	day 11	day 2	–
Duration (mean)	1.5 days	2 days	–
Fever (over 37.8 C)			
No. of occurrences	4 (7.7%)	1 (1.8%)	1 (2.2%)
Time of onset (mean)	day 10	day 10	day 15
Lymphadenopathy			
No. of occurrences	35 (67.3%)	18 (32.1%)	25 (55.5%)
Time of onset (mean)	day 14	day 16	day 17
Generalized	2 (4%)	0	0
Pre-or postauricular, or both	23 (44.2%)	5 (8.8%)	12 (26.6%)
Epitrochlear	5 (9.8%)	1 (1.78%)	0
Arthralgia			
No. of occurrences	1 (right elbow)	0	0
Time of onset	day 12	–	–
Duration	4 days	–	–

DISCUSSION

The most striking feature of this study was the almost total absence of arthralgia or arthritis following injection of the Cendehill rubella vaccine. This is in sharp contrast to the frequency with which joint manifestations have appeared with the use of other attenuated strains of the virus. Arthritis has been observed in 33 to 40% of individuals given the HPV–77 vaccine (4, 17). Arthralgia or arthritis, or both, have been reported to occur in 20 to 25% of those receiving the Cendehill strain (4, 10). However, the significance of arthralgia in relation to the immunization procedure is open to considerable question because of the highly subjective nature of this complaint. This is pointed out by the observations of Gold and his co-workers (8), who reported an incidence of arthralgia in 7% of adult women given Cendehill vaccine and in 11.4% of those injected with a placebo. Since 46% of the subjects immunized in the present study were mentally defective, it is very likely that they could not or would not complain of joint pain. This may have been a factor in the paucity of this symptom in this group. On the other hand, only one person in the normal group presented this difficulty, and, as pointed out above, there was probably an explanation for this which did not involve disease of joint structures. The possibility may also be raised that no arthritis was observed in the mentally defective women because they were physically inactive; only one of these individuals was completely bed-ridden, and five were partially active. The present study, as well as those of others in which both the HPV–77 and Cendehill strains were used (4, 10), indicate no definite relation between the degree of antibody response and the frequency of postimmunization joint disorders.

The antibody responses observed in this investigation are, in general, comparable in degree to those recorded by others (7, 8, 14). The somewhat lower levels observed in other studies (2) may be related to the fact that immune globulin was administered concurrently with the vaccine. A possible explanation for discrepancy in some instances may be the use of different methods of treating the serum prior to titration for the presence of HI antibody (6, 11). Most interesting is the observation that levels of HI antibody reached after vaccination were appreciably lower in mentally retarded subjects than in normal persons; this has also been reported by others (2). Although there is no clear-cut explanation for this difference, the possibility that age (mentally deficient group averaged 31 and the normal individuals 21 years), low protein diet (institutionalized patients), or opportunity for contact with rubella viruses (nurses) may be involved cannot be ruled out.

The incidence of lymphadenopathy observed in the present study was higher than that reported by others (7, 12). This was probably related to treatment with diphenylhydantoin, frequency of dental caries and infections of the skin and scalp in the mentally defective group, and respiratory-tract infections in the others, since the immunization was carried out during the winter months. It is important, in this regard, to point out that enlargement of the cervical and suboccipital lymph nodes was equally common in the vaccinated and unvaccinated groups. However, postauricular and epitrochlear lymphadenopathy occurred about five times more often in those who were rubella-susceptible prior to vaccination than in vaccinated subjects with detectable HI rubella antibody before immunization.

Reactions at the site of injection of the vaccine remain unexplained. They could not be produced by the intradermal instillation of 0.1 ml of the vaccine inactivated by heating at 56 C for 30 min. The possibility that the local reaction was due to the neomycin present in the vaccine was excluded.

The results of this study indicate that the Cendehill strain of rubella virus is an effective immunizing agent and that its use in adult women is accompanied by a very low incidence of side effects. No instances of arthritis and only one questionable episode of arthralgia occurred in the group of individuals tested, whereas the administration of other vaccine preparations appears to have produced a fairly high incidence of joint disorders in similar groups of individuals.

ACKNOWLEDGMENTS

We are indebted to H. Moser, M. Farrell, A. Bill, P. Abbott, and B. Meister of the Fernald State School, Waltham, Mass., to A. McCarthy of the St. Elizabeth Hospital School of Nursing, and to M. M. Osborne, Jr., of the Tufts University, for their invaluable help and cooperation.

The technical assistance of Catherine Nelson is appreciated.

This investigation was supported by a grant from the Smith, Kline & French Laboratories, Philadelphia, Pa., and by Public Health Service Training Grant AI–276 from the National Institute of Allergy and Infectious Diseases.

LITERATURE CITED

1. Advisory Committee on Immunization Practices. 1969. Recommendations of the Public Health Service Advisory Committee on Immunization Practices. Amer. J. Dis. Child. **118**:397–399.
2. Cherry, J. D., J. E. Bobinski, and G. D. Commerci. 1969. A clinical trial with live attenuated rubella virus vaccine (Cendehill 51 strain). J. Pediat. **75**:79–86.
3. Cockburn, W. C. 1969. World aspects of the epidemiology of rubella. Amer. J. Dis. Child. **188**:112–122.
4. Cooper, L. Z., P. R. Ziring, H. J. Weiss, D. A. Matters, and S. Krugman. 1969. Transient arthritis after rubella vaccination. Amer. J. Dis. Child. **118**:218–225.
5. Du Pan, M. R., C. Huygelen, J. Peetermans, and A. Prinzie. 1968. Clinical trials with a live attenuated rubella virus vaccine. Cendehill 51 strain. Amer. J. Dis. Child. **115**: 658–662.
6. Enders-Ruckle, G. 1969. Seroepidemiology of rubella and reinfection. Amer. J. Dis. Child. **118**:139–142.
7. Farquhar, J. D., and J. E. Corretjer. 1969. Clinical experience with Cendehill rubella vaccine in mature women. Amer. J. Dis. Child. **118**:266–268.
8. Gold, J. A., A. Prinzie, and J. McKee. 1969. Adult women vaccinated with rubella vaccine. Amer. J. Dis. Child. **118**:264–265.
9. Hilleman, M. R., E. B. Buynak, R. E. Weibel, and J. Stokes, Jr. 1968. Live attenuated rubella virus vaccine. N. Engl. J. Med. **279**:300–303.
10. Horstmann, D. M., E. B. Byrne, J. M. Ryan, M. F. Randolph, H. Liebhaber, and R. W. McCollum. 1969. Comparison of HPV–77/DE5 and Cendehill strain vaccines in adult women. Proc. 23rd Symp. Microbiological Standardization: Rubella Vaccines, London, S. Karger, Basel. 1968, vol. 2, p. 429–435.
11. Mann, J. J., R. D. Russen, J. R. Lehrich, and J. A. Kasal. 1967. The effect of kaolin on immunoglobulins: An improved technique to remove the non-specific serum inhibitor of reovirus hemagglutination. J. Immunol. **98**:1136–1142.
12. Marshall, W. C., J. A. Dudgeon, and C. F. Peckham. 1969. Clinical studies of rubella vaccines in adults. 23rd Symp. Microbiological Standardization: Rubella Vaccines, London, 1968, p. 423–428. S. Karger, Basel.
13. Meyer, H. M., Jr., P. D. Parkman, and T. C. Panos. 1966. Attenuated rubella virus. II. Production of an experimental live virus vaccine and clinical trials. N. Engl. J. Med. **275**:575–580.
14. Monto, A. S., J. J. Cavallaro, and G. C. Brown. 1969. Attenuated rubella vaccination in families: Observations on the lack of fluorescent antibody response and on the use of blood collection filter paper discs in the hemagglutination-inhibition test. J. Lab. Clin. Med. **74**:98–102.
15. Prinzie, A., C. Huygelen, J. Gold, J. Farquhar, and J. McKee. 1969. Experimental live attenuated rubella virus vaccine. Clinical evaluation of Cendehill strain. Amer. J. Dis. Child. **118**:172–177.
16. Rawls, W. E., J. L. Melnick, C. M. P. Bradstreet, M. Bailey, A. A. Ferris, M. I. Lehman, F. P. Nagler, J. Furesz, R. Kono, M. Ohthawara, P. Halonen, J. Stewart, J. M. Ryan, J. Strauss, J. Zdrazilek, J. Leerhoy, H. VanMagnus, R. Sohier, and W. Ferreira. 1967. WHO collaborative study on the sero-epidemiology of rubella. Bull. World Health Organ. **37**:79.
17. Weibel, R. E., J. Stokes, Jr., E. B. Bunyak, and M. R. Hilleman. 1969. Rubella vaccination in adult females. N. Engl. J. Med. **280**:682–685.

Antimicrobial Agents and Chemotherapy—1969

Amantadine Therapy of Epidemic Influenza A_2/Hong Kong

VERNON KNIGHT, DAVID FEDSON, JAMES BALDINI, R. GORDON DOUGLAS, and ROBERT B. COUCH

Baylor College of Medicine, Houston, Texas 77025, Laboratory of Clinical Investigation, National Institute of Allergy and Infectious Diseases, Bethesda, Maryland 20014, and E. I. du Pont de Nemours & Co., Wilmington, Delaware 19898

In a double-blind comparison of the therapeutic effect of amantadine in a natural outbreak of Hong Kong influenza in January 1969 near Houston, Tex., the titers of virus in throat swabs from 12 treated patients decreased appreciably more during the first 10 hr of treatment than similar titers of 16 untreated patients ($P = 0.06$). The titer of shed virus decreased significantly more rapidly ($P<0.05$) among amantadine-treated patients ill more than 48 hr before treatment than among five similar placebo patients. Cough, sore throat, and nasal obstruction cleared more rapidly in treated patients ($P<0.05$), and decline of fever in six treated patients sick for less than 48 hr before treatment was more rapid than among 13 similar untreated patients. These findings are considered to be consistent with a limited therapeutic effect of the drug.

The therapeutic effects of amantadine hydrochloride against A_2/Hong Kong/68 influenza were evaluated during an outbreak of illness in a Texas prison in January 1969. In a double-blind study, 13 patients received amantadine hydrochloride (100 mg every 12 hr for 6 days) and 16 control patients were given placebo.

MATERIALS AND METHODS

The methods employed have been described in a more detailed report of this study (1). Participants were adult male inmates of the Ramsey I and II units of the Texas Department of Corrections. The study was arbitrarily limited to 29 of 37 ill volunteers who shed the Hong Kong strain of virus and who showed a fourfold or greater neutralizing antibody response to the agent. The average age of patients in the treated and placebo groups was 27 and 39 years, respectively. In other respects, the differences were not significant. During the course of the study, patients were examined twice daily, and severity of the signs and symptoms was recorded. For virus isolation, throat swabs were taken before treatment, 10 hr later, and at three subsequent 24-hr intervals. Quantitative viral titrations were done in rhesus monkey kidney cells.

RESULTS

Recovery from illness was rapid in both groups, and no complications or side effects of therapy were noted. In general, signs and symptoms were less severe in the amantadine-treated patients, and nasal stuffiness, dry or productive cough, and sore throat were significantly reduced ($P<0.05$). There was a tendency toward earlier reduction in the severity of signs and symptoms in the drug-treated group, and fever also fell more rapidly. The average time required by the amantadine-treated patients to reach persisting levels of 99 F (37.2 C) or less was 44.5 hr, compared with 71.3 hr for the placebo group ($P<0.05$).

Amantadine-treated patients tended to have fewer positive cultures and also tended to shed less virus (Table 1). Despite these general trends

Table 1. *Virological findings in patients with A_2/Hong Kong/68 influenza treated with amantadine or placebo*

Time after beginning of treatment (hr)	Amantadine		Placebo	
	Geometric mean titer	Per cent positive specimens	Geometric mean titer	Per cent positive specimens
0 3	.46[a]	92	2.97	94
10 1	.50	67	2.28	88
34 0	.77	62	0.94	75
58 0	.39	62	0.53	44
82 0	.076	8	0.13	13

[a] Virus titer, $\log_{10}$ per 0.1 ml of swab fluid.

in drug-treated patients, the differences approached significance only in the reduction in titer during the interval from before treatment to 10 hr after the start of treatment ($P = 0.06$). In addition, it was found that five amantadine-treated patients ill for longer than 48 hr before therapy had a significantly greater reduction in virus titer in the first 10 hr than five similar patients who received placebo ($P<0.05$). Among patients ill less than 48 hr, these differences were not significant.

Neutralizing antibody responses were similar in both groups, with a geometric mean increase of 32-fold in the amantadine-treated group and 64-fold in the placebo group.

Further studies of amantadine in clinical influenza are needed, particularly in patients with influenzal pneumonia. Increased doses of drug might also be tried. The clinical, virological, and serological findings in this study are consistent with a limited the therapeutic effect of amantadine in Hong Kong influenza.

LITERATURE CITED

1. Knight, V., D. Fedson, J. Baldini, R. G. Douglas, and R. B. Couch. 1970. Amantadine therapy of epidemic influenza A_2 (Hong Kong). Infec. Immun. 1:200–204.

Antimicrobial Agents and Chemotherapy—1969

Treatment of Congenital Cytomegalic Inclusion Disease with Antiviral Agents

STANLEY A. PLOTKIN and HARRISON STETLER[1]

The Wistar Institute of Anatomy and Biology, Philadelphia, Pennsylvania 19104, and The Children's Hospital of Philadelphia, Philadelphia, Pennsylvania 19146

In view of the poor prognosis for normal growth and development in congenital cytomegalovirus infection, antiviral chemotherapy was attempted in six patients. The drugs used included 5-fluorodeoxyuridine, pyran copolymer (an interferon inducer), and cytosine arabinoside. Pyran copolymer failed to induce significant interferon synthesis in infected infants, suggesting that the experimentally observed reticuloendothelial blockade was also present clinically. 5-Fluorodeoxyuridine caused improvement in one patient with cytomegalovirus pneumonia but otherwise did not seem effective. Cytosine arabinoside appeared to produce clinical benefits in three patients with cytomegalovirus infection. In one patient virus excretion was abolished permanently, in one patient temporarily, but in a third patient not at all.

The cytomegaloviruses of man are members of the herpes group of viruses. They contain deoxyribonucleic acid (DNA) cores, and therefore their replication is subject to inhibition by substances that interfere with DNA synthesis. The treatment of herpes simplex keratitis and encephalitis with 5-iododeoxyuridine are well-known examples of the clinical usefulness of antiviral chemotherapy for herpesviruses (1, 6). Leukemics with cytomegalovirus pneumonia have been given 5-fluorodeoxyuridine (FUDR) with apparently good results (2), although the effect of this treatment must be evaluated against the high natural remission rate of cytomegalovirus pneumonia.

Congenital cytomegalovirus infection in its most severe form manifests a disseminated sepsis syndrome during the newborn period, with hepatosplenomegaly, thrombocytopenia, and anemia. Later in life, frank microcephaly and mental retardation commonly develop; the prognosis for normality in a child who survives the disseminated disease is generally considered to be poor (15).

In the disseminated stage, the infant excretes large amounts of virus in the urine and may have positive throat and leukocyte cultures. In view of the poor prognosis and the continued presence of significant multiplication of virus, we have attempted to treat congenital cytomegalic inclusion disease with antiviral chemotherapy. Conchie et al. (4) have previously reported on the use of idoxuridine in one such patient with what they believe to have been favorable results.

[1] Present address: Alaska Native Medical Center, Anchorage, Alaska.

MATERIALS AND METHODS

Virus isolation. All virus isolations were performed by inoculation of confluent cultures of WI-38 human fibroblasts that had been drained dry. After adsorption for 0.5 hr, the cultures were covered with Eagle's basal medium with 2% fetal calf serum. Penicillin, streptomycin, or gentamicin was used in the medium.

Urine was inoculated in 1-ml volumes, without filtration if the specimen had been obtained by suprapubic puncture, or after filtration through a 450-nm filter if the specimen was naturally voided.

Throat swabs were swirled in Hanks medium, which was then inoculated into tissue culture.

Leukocytes were collected by first allowing the erythrocytes to sediment by gravity and then collecting the supernatant plasma. The leukocytes were washed in saline before inoculation.

The identification of cytomegalovirus was based on the following criteria: (i) typical local cytopathic effect (CPE); (ii) intranuclear inclusion bodies in stained cells; (iii) lack of CPE in monkey kidney, rabbit kidney, or other cell types; (iv) in some cases, preparation of a complement-fixation (CF) antigen by sonic treatment of infected cells, with demonstration of antigenic specificity against known positive and negative sera.

Serology. Two serological tests were used, the CF test (13) with one of the isolates from patient 3 as the antigen, and a new immunodiffusion test which is described elsewhere (F. C. Jensen, S. A. Plotkin, and H. Stetler, *unpublished data*).

Administration of drugs. All drugs were given intravenously, in 5% dextrose and 0.25% saline solutions, by infusion over a 2-hr period. The patients were all admitted to the Children's Hospital of Philadelphia for the duration of their treatment.

RESULTS

Three antiviral agents were tested for their action in congenital cytomegalovirus infection: FUDR, which had been used in the postnatally acquired disease; pyran copolymer, an interferon inducer; and cytosine arabinoside.

FUDR. Treatment with intravenous infusion of FUDR was administered to three infants with congenital cytomegalovirus infection.

The first patient was treated at 13 days of age. This infant was a female who showed hepatosplenomegaly, periventricular intracranial calcifications, jaundice, and inclusion body-bearing cells on liver biopsy. At 2 weeks of age her CF titer was 1:64, and at 7 and 11 months of age the immunodiffusion test was strongly positive. As summarized in Table 1, therapy was followed by a reduction in the size of liver and spleen and a temporary lack of virus excretion. However, the infant became markedly microcephalic and retarded.

The second patient was a 3-month-old boy with hepatosplenomegaly, chorioretinitis, jaundice, and giant-cell hepatitis shown by liver biopsy. This infant also had a ventricular septal defect, but was not in cardiac failure. At the time of therapy, he was doing poorly because of respiratory insufficiency accompanied by pulmonary infiltrations. Virus was isolated when the infant was first seen at 3 months of age. The CF titer was 1:32 at that age, and at 21 months of age the immunodiffusion test was positive. Treatment was followed by prompt improvement in respiratory function (Fig. 1), but there was little change in other clinical measurements or in virus excretion (Table 2). At 2 years of age, the infant was retarded in growth and was functioning at a 5-month-old level. He also showed typical infantile spasms.

The third patient was a 15-day-old boy with hepatosplenomegaly, petechiae, and thrombocytopenia. He was excreting large amounts of virus, and had a CF titer of 1:128. Treatment with FUDR was followed by a disappearance of petechiae and a decrease in the hepatosplenomegaly (Table 3). Virus excretion was unaffected. At 2 years of age, the infant had a left

Table 1. *Treatment with 5-FUDR:*[a] *patient 1*

Determination	Pretreatment (age: 11 days)	Post-treatment	
		38 days of age	2 years of age
Head circumference, cm	30.5	32	41
Third percentile for age, cm[b]	34	35.5	45.8
Intracranial calcification	Yes	Yes	Yes
Chorioretinitis	No	No	No
Liver size, cm[c]	5.5	2	2
Spleen size, cm[c]	3	1	Tip
Petechiae	No	No	No
Platelets/mm^3	205,000	180,000	–
Bilirubin, total, mg/100 ml	13.8	5.4	<1
Bilirubin, direct, mg/100 ml	8.3	3.6	–
Serum glutamic oxalacetic transaminase, units	148	148	–
Neurological status	General spasticity	General spasticity	General spasticity, myclonic jerks
Functional level[b]	Normal	Birth	3 months
Virus in urine, TCD_{50}/ml	10^3-10^4	None found	Positive[d]

[a] Intravenous administration of 45 mg (15 mg/kg) daily for 5 days started at 11 days of age.

[b] Normal values obtained from *Textbook of Pediatrics*, 9th ed., edited by Nelson, Vaughan, and McKay, W. B. Saunders, Philadelphia, 1969.

[c] Below costal margin.

[d] Virus again detected 3 months post-treatment.

hemiparesis and was deaf, but appeared to have motor functions of an 18-month-old child.

Pyran copolymer. To induce endogenous interferon, pyran copolymer was given to two patients in single doses of 15 mg/kg. One of the patients is described as the first patient above (Table 1). The pyran copolymer was given to this infant at 33 days of age after FUDR had failed to affect virus excretion. No fever developed after administration of the pyran copolymer, and no interferon was detected in the infant's blood.

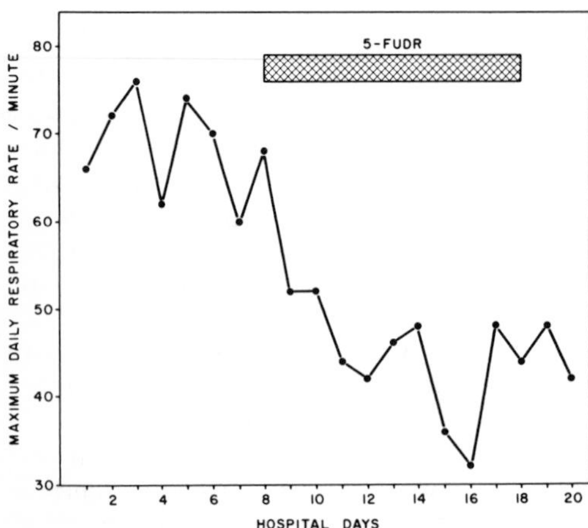

Fig. 1. *Respiratory rate of patient 2, treated with 5-fluorodeoxyuridine (5-FUDR).*

The second patient treated with pyran copolymer (patient 4) had hepatosplenomegaly and jaundice, and received pyran copolymer at 3 months of age. (This patient had been cured of viruria with cytosine arabinoside, as described in detail immediately below.) This patient had one fever spike at 48 hr postinjection, and a 1:10 titer of interferon was demonstrated in serum obtained at that time. Other serum samples failed to show interferon. No clinical effect was demonstrated.

Cytosine arabinoside. Three patients were given cytosine arabinoside, a drug which was chosen because of its in vitro activity against cytomegalovirus.

Patient 4 was the firstborn son of a 21-year-old father and a 20-year-old mother. The pregnancy and delivery were apparently uncomplicated, but the infant became jaundiced and developed petechiae 2 hr after birth. His birth weight was 2,970 g and his head circumference was 34.5 cm. Hepatosplenomegaly was noted.

Laboratory studies during the first weeks of life showed normal blood counts except that the platelet count fell to 23,000 per mm^3. The serum bilirubin rose, at 8 days of age, to 27 mg/100 ml, of which 40 to 50% was conjugated.

Table 2. *Treatment with FUDR:[a] patient 2*

Determination	Pretreatment (age: 3 months)	Post-treatment	
		4 months of age	2 years of age
Head circumference, cm	35.3	36	42
Third percentile for age, cm[b]	38.7	40	45.8
Intracranial calcifications	No	No	No
Chorioretinitis	Yes	Yes	Yes
Liver size, cm[c]	5	5	3.5
Spleen size, cm[c]	1.5	1.5	1.5
Petechiae	No	No	No
Platelets, mm^3	638,000	247,000	–
Bilirubin, total, mg/100 ml	10.6	9.6	0.9
Bilirubin, direct, mg/100 ml	5.7	4.5	–
Serum glutamic oxalacetic transaminase, units	325	330	140 (at 1 year)
Neurological status	Irritable	High-pitched cry	Infantile spasms
Functional level[b]	2 months	3 months	5 months
Virus in urine	Positive[d]	Positive[d]	Positive[d]

[a] Intravenous administration of 45 mg (15 mg/kg) daily for 10 days started at 3 months of age.
[b] Normal values obtained from *Textbook of Pediatrics,* 9th ed., edited by Nelson, Vaughan, and McKay, W. B. Saunders, Philadelphia, 1969.
[c] Below costal margin.
[d] No titration performed, but development of cytopathic effect in culture occurred at a similar interval after inoculation of all specimens.

Table 3. *Treatment with FUDR:*[a] *patient 3*

Determination	Pretreatment (age: 15 days)	Post-treatment	
		33 days of age	2 years of age
Head circumference, cm	33.5	35.8	48
Third percentile for age, cm[b]	34	35.3	45.8
Intracranial calcifications	No	No	No
Chorioretinitis	No	No	No
Liver size, cm[c]	5	4	Not palpable
Spleen size, cm[c]	6	2	Not palpable
Petechiae	Yes	No	No
Platelets/mm^3	86,000	179,000	–
Bilirubin, total, mg/100 ml	1.2	<1	<1
Serum glutamic oxalacetic transaminase, units	47	80	–
Neurological status	Normal	Normal	Left hemiparesis, central deafness
Functional level[b]	2 weeks	1 month	18 months
Virus in urine, TCD_{50}/ml	$10^{6.5}$-10^7	10^5	10^4

[a] Intravenous administration of 45 mg (14 mg/kg) daily for 5 days started at 15 days of age.

[b] Normal values obtained from *Textbook of Pediatrics,* 9th ed., edited by Nelson, Vaughan, and McKay, W. B. Saunders, Philadelphia, 1969.

[c] Below costal margin.

Table 4. *Cytosine arabinoside*[a] *treatment: patient 4*

Determination	Pretreatment (age: 7 weeks)	Post-treatment	
		10 weeks of age	15 months of age
Head circumference, cm	35	36	44.6
Third percentile for age, cm[b]	36.5	37.5	45.6
Intracranial calcifications	No	No	No
Chorioretinitis	No	No	No
Liver size, cm[c]	5	4	Not palapable
Spleen size, cm[c]	9	8	Not palpable
Petechiae	Yes	No	No
Bilirubin, total, mg/100 ml	18	16.3	1
Bilirubin, direct, mg/100 ml	8	8.9	–
Serum glutamic oxalacetic transaminase, units	950	720	–
Neurological status	Irritable	Perhaps improved	Normal
Functional level[b]	1 month	2 months	1 year

[a] Intravenous administration of 57 mg (15 mg/kg) daily for 5 days started at 7 weeks of age.

[b] Normal values obtained from *Textbook of Pediatrics,* 9th ed., edited by Nelson, Vaughan, and McKay, W. B. Saunders, Philadelphia, 1969.

[c] Below costal margin.

The IgM globulin concentration was elevated at 35 mg/100 ml.

Upon transfer to Children's Hospital of Philadelphia at 7 weeks of age, the child weighed 3,800 g, had a length of 53 cm, and had a head circumference of 35 cm (Table 4). Temperature, pulse, and respiration were normal, but there was deep jaundice and numerous petechiae of the skin. The abdomen was distended; the liver edge was 5 cm below the right costal margin, and the spleen was descended to the iliac crest. Chorioretinitis was absent.

The hemoglobin was 10 g/100 ml, with a reticulocyte count of 5.3%. There were 100,000 platelets/mm^3. The serum bilirubin was 18 to 19.3 mg/100 ml, with 8.9 to 9.3 mg/100 ml conjugated. Studies of liver functions showed serum glutamic oxalacetic transaminase of 950 units, serum glutamic pyruvic transaminase of 370 units, and alkaline phosphatase of 19.3 units. Liver biopsy revealed severe biliary cirrhosis with giant-cell formation. Normal results were obtained for urinalysis, electrolytes, calcium and phosphorus, blood-urea nitrogen, and serum proteins. X-ray studies failed to reveal calcifications of the brain or bone abnormalities.

Virological studies confirmed the presence of cytomegalovirus in a titer of $10^{4.5}$ to $10^{5.0}$ TCD_{50} per ml. The CF test was positive at 1:64, and the immunodiffusion test was positive when later tested at 11 months of age.

Cytosine arabinoside was given intravenously in quantities of 15 mg/kg each day for 5 days, from the 9th to 13th hospital days.

No dramatic clinical change occurred after therapy. Liver disease continued to be evident. However, the patient appeared to be in better general condition. Thrombocytopenia (as low as 18,000/mm^3) began 10 days after the first day of treatment with cytosine arabinoside, and, although asymptomatic, caused sufficient concern to warrant treatment with several platelet transfusions. These had little effect on the platelet count, which rose spontaneously on the 15th day.

Despite the nonspecific clinical effect, virus excretion could not be detected within 1 week and was not observed on repeated examinations thereafter (Table 5). When the child was 15 months old, he weighed 8,600 g and was no longer jaundiced. Hepatosplenomegaly persisted, although both liver and spleen had become smaller. The head circumference was 44.6 cm, 1 cm below the third percentile for the child's age.

Neurological examination has not revealed specific abnormalities. The child stands, is cruising, and says "mama" and dada." He appears alert and responds to simple commands.

His platelet count ranges between 150,000 and 200,000/mm^3 with normal hemoglobin and white blood count. The values for his liver function tests (bilirubin, transaminase, alkaline phosphatase) have returned to normal.

Patient 5 (Table 6) was a Negro boy admitted

Table 5. *Cytomegalovirus excretions of patient 4, treated with cytosine arabinoside*

Age	Cytomegalovirus isolated ($\log_{10}$ TCD_{50}/ml)
Pretreatment	
4 weeks	$10^{5.0}$
7 weeks	$10^{4.5}$
Post-treatment	
8 weeks	None
10 weeks	None
5 months	None
6 months	None
8 months	None
1 year	None

Table 6. *Cytosine arabinoside[a] treatment: patient 5*

Determination	Pretreatment (age: 6 weeks)	Post-treatment	
		8 weeks of age	7 months of age
Head circumference, cm	32	33	39
Third percentile for age, cm[b]	36	36.8	42.5
Intracranial calcifications	No	No	No
Chorioretinitis	No	No	No
Liver size, cm[c]	3	2	Not palpated
Spleen size, cm[c]	Not palpated	Not palpated	Not palpated
Petechiae	No[d]	No	No
Platelets/mm^3	339,000	264,000	–
Bilirubin, total, mg/100 ml	2.0	1.0	–
Bilirubin, direct, mg/100 ml	1.1	–	–
Serum glutamic oxalacetic transaminase, units	140	118	–
Neurological status	Normal	Normal	Normal
Functional level[b]	1 month	2 months	5 months

[a] Intravenous administration of 24 mg (10 mg/kg) daily for 3 days started at 6 weeks of age.

[b] Normal values obtained from *Textbook of Pediatrics*, 9th ed., edited by Nelson, Vaughan, and McKay, W. B. Saunders, Philadelphia, 1969.

[c] Below costal margin.

[d] Present at birth.

to Children's Hospital on the day of birth. He was the third child of a 24-year-old mother who had had no prenatal care but who denied illness during pregnancy. On physical examination, the infant weighed 2,400 g and had a head circumference of 28 cm. His cry was weak and he appeared ill and irritable with obvious jaundice and petechiae. The liver and spleen were enlarged, with their edges reaching 3 cm below the costal margins, but there was no chorioretinitis or intracranial calcification. Blood counts were normal except for a platelet count of 104,000/mm^3. The total bilirubin was 17.7 mg/100 ml, and the serum transaminase, 400 units. The IgM concentration was elevated at 43 mg/100 ml. During the first day of life, two exchange transfusions were performed for bilirubin approaching 20 mg/100 ml; on the following day, partition of serum bilirubin showed that 25% was conjugated. Cytomegalovirus was isolated at 2 days and at 3 weeks of age. CF, fluorescent macroglobulin, and immunodiffusion tests all showed negative results during the first 2 weeks of life, perhaps because of the exchange transfusions. A CF titer of 1:16 was found at 2 weeks, as well as a weak positive immunodiffusion test.

Jaundice gradually decreased, but at 1 month of age the bilirubin was still 4.6 mg/100 ml. The serum transaminase fell to 140 units during the same period. An interstitial pneumonia, visible by X-ray, resolved spontaneously, but the infant did not feed well, and at 40 days of age he had gained only 470 g since birth, or an average of 10.3 g/day.

Cytosine arabinoside was administered for 3 days, in a daily dosage of 10 mg/kg. After treatment, the infant's general state appeared to be improved, and he began to gain weight at a rate of 31.5 g/day (Fig. 2). No bone marrow depression was observed.

Virus disappeared from the infant's urine after treatment and could not be recovered for at least 1.5 months. Cytomegalovirus reappeared in urine collected 3 months after treatment (Table 7).

Upon examination at 7 months of age, the infant was microcephalic (head circumference, 39 cm) but otherwise healthy and thriving (weight, 6.4 kg). His functional level was that of a 5-month-old infant.

Recently, a third infant was treated with cytosine arabinoside. This child had hepato-

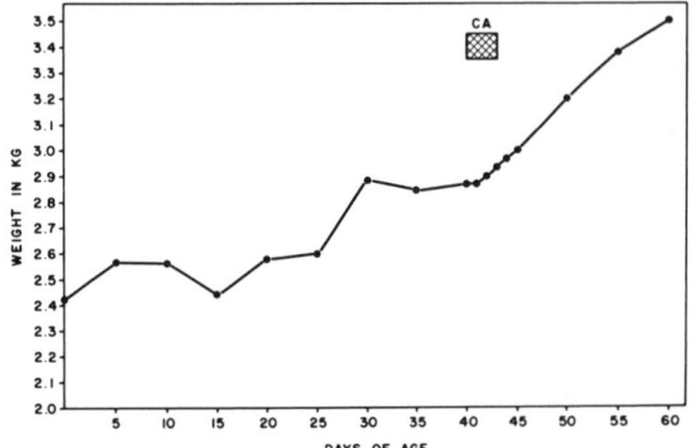

Fig. 2. *Weight gain of patient 5, treated with cytosine arabinoside (CA).*

Table 7. *Viruria in patient 5, treated with cytosine arabinoside*

Age	Cytomegalovirus isolated
Pretreatment	
2 days	Yes
3 weeks	Yes
4 weeks	Yes
Post-treatment	
7 weeks	No
3 months	No
4.5 months	Yes
7.5 months	Yes

splenomegaly, thrombocytopenia, and respiratory distress in the newborn period. During the first 22 months of life, he showed extremely poor physical and mental development. At that age, he could not sit up and was functioning at a level of about 4 months. Microcephaly and chorioretinitis were present. He had repeated attacks of diarrhea and vomiting, and on two occasions needed to be admitted to the hospital for intravenous fluids. He weighed only 6.7 kg and he appeared emaciated. Because the infant was doing so poorly and because virus excretion had continued for 22 months, intravenous cytosine arabinoside was tried.

The infant received a dose of 9 mg/kg daily for 5 days. No reaction was seen except that the platelets dropped to 70,000/mm^3, 12 days after the first infusion, but spontaneously returned to normal.

Virologically, the results were unremarkable, as cytomegalovirus continued to be present in the urine. Clinically, however, there may have been an effect. When seen 10 weeks post-treatment, the infant had gained 1,200 g of weight, 5.5 cm in length, and, most remarkable, had an increase of 1.5 cm in head circumference. The mother reported improvement in appetite and absence of gastrointestinal symptoms.

DISCUSSION

In evaluating our results, at least two questions must be considered. What is the prognosis for central nervous system function in cytomegalic inclusion disease, and does continued infection influence this prognosis? While the prognosis for mental normality in congenital cytomegalovirus infection is poor, it may not be totally hopeless. In recently reported series, as many as 40% of infants with neonatal cytomegalovirus infection ended up with normal intelligence (8, 10). We cannot, therefore, determine from our experience with cytosine arabinoside whether antiviral treatment improved the chance for normal intelligence. However, since the results were favorable, further studies appear justified. With regard to the question of whether infants with cytomegalic inclusion disease are affected by infection after birth, we would draw an analogy with congenital rubella in which the virus is also excreted for long periods. After birth, cataracts may develop and both encephalitis and pneumonia may worsen (9). We believe that attempts to eradicate cytomegalovirus in symptomatic infants are desirable, at least in early infancy when the infection is disseminated.

The failure of FUDR to accomplish this purpose is surprising in view of the clinical success of this drug in the treatment of cytomegalovirus pneumonia (2). Although clinical improvement in cytomegalovirus pneumonia after treatment is striking, there are inadequate virological data concerning the effect of FUDR on virus excretion in this condition.

Conchie et al. (4) reported the treatment of one congenitally infected infant with idoxuridine, a related drug inhibitor. They observed a pronounced drop in virus excretion, accompanied by clinical improvement after treatment. However, neither effect was long-lasting, and a second patient failed to respond at all.

Two of our subjects were given pyran copolymer in a dosage which normally evokes pyrexia and interferon production (11). One subject failed to respond with either fever or interferon. The second, who had been freed from virus excretion by previous treatment with cytosine arabinoside, had one fever spike and a concomitant appearance of interferon. These results parallel the results of the studies of Osborne and Medearis (12) and Glasgow et al. (7), who found that CMV infection removed the normal interferon response of mice and of human tissue cultures. The failure to produce interferon response may be related to reticuloendothelial blockade by cytomegalovirus.

The effect of cytosine arabinoside on virus excretion in two of the patients reported here was striking. Whereas FUDR acts as an enzyme inhibitor, and idoxuridine is incorporated into DNA as a false thymidine, cytosine arabinoside largely blocks the synthesis of deoxycytidine, a precursor of DNA (3). Studies in vitro showed that cytosine arabinoside is more effective than other pyrimidine nucleosides in inhibiting cytomegalovirus (R. W. Sidwell et al., Bacteriol. Proc., p. 191, 1969). We do not know the optimal dosage of cytosine arabinoside; our dosage was based on the experience of others treating neoplasms (5, 14). At doses of 15 mg/kg daily for 5 days, the antiviral effect was marked, but thrombocytopenia was a problem. At 9 to 10 mg/kg for 3 to 5 days, there was no toxicity but the antiviral effect was temporary. An intermediate dosage may be desirable–or perhaps the risks of toxicity should be accepted for the sake of therapeutic effect, provided one has facilities to support the patient through a period of bone marrow depression.

In the future, we will use cytosine arabinoside in the treatment of other patients with congenital cytomegalovirus infection, and hope to develop a protocol which will permit a controlled evaluation of chemotherapy in this disease.

ACKNOWLEDGMENTS

We are grateful to Thomas Merigan for supplying us with pyran copolymer and for the performance of the interferon assays.

This work was supported by Pennsylvania Department of Health contract 69-59301, ME-561 from the Commonwealth of Pennsylvania.

LITERATURE CITED

1. Breeden, C. J., T. C. Hall, and H. R. Tyler. 1966. Herpes simplex encephalitis treated with systemic 5-iodo-2′ deoxyuridine. Ann. Intern. Med. **65**:1050-1056.
2. Cangir, A., M. P. Sullivan, W. W. Sutow, and G. Taylor. 1967. Cytomegalovirus syndrome in children with acute leukemia. Treatment with floxuridine. J. Amer. Med. Ass. **201**:612-615.

3. Cardeilhac, P. T., and S. S. Cohen. 1964. Some metabolic properties of nucleotides of 1-beta-d-arabino-furanosyl-cytosine. Cancer Res. **24**:1595-1603.

4. Conchie, A. F., B. W. Barton, and J. O'H. Tobin. 1968. Congenital cytomegalovirus infection treated with idoxuridine. Brit. Med. J. **4**:162-163.

5. Ellison, R. R., J. F. Holland, M. Weil, C. Jacquillat, M. Boiron, J. Bernard, A. Sawitsky, F. Rosner, B. Gussoff, R. T. Silver, A. Karanas, J. Cuttner, C. L. Spurr, D. M. Hayes, J. Blom, L. A. Leone, F. Haurani, R. Kyle, J. L. Hutchison, R. J. Forcier, and J. H. Moon. 1968. Arabinosyl-cytosine, a useful agent in the treatment of acute leukemia in adults. Blood **32**:507-523.

6. Evans, A. D., O. P. Gray, M. H. Miller, E. R. Verrier Jones, R. D. Weeks, and C. E. C. Wells. 1967. Herpes simplex encephalitis treated with intravenous idoxuridine. Brit. Med. J. **2**:407-410.

7. Glasgow, L. A., J. B. Hanshaw, T. C. Merigan, and J. K. Petralli. 1967. Interferon and cytomegalovirus *in vivo* and *in vitro*. Proc. Soc. Exp. Biol. Med. **125**:843-849.

8. Jack, I., E. K. Turner, D. M. Danks, T. G. Maddison, and J. H. Colebatch. 1967. Cytomegalovirus infection in Melbourne children. Aust. Pediat. J. **3**:61-69.

9. Lindquist, J. M., S. A. Plotkin, L. Shaw, R. F. Gilden, and M. L. Williams. 1965. Congenital rubella as a systemic disease. Brit. Med. J. **2**:1401-1406.

10. McCracken, G. H., Jr., H. R. Shinefield, K. Cobb, A. R. Rausen, M. R. Dische, and H. F. Eichenwald. 1969. Congenital cytomegalic inclusion disease. Amer. J. Dis. Child. **117**:522-539.

11. Merigan, T. C., and W. Regelson. 1967. Interferon induction in man by a synthetic polyanion of defined composition. New Engl. J. Med. **277**:1283–1297.

12. Osborn, J. E., and D. N. Medearis, Jr. 1967. Suppression of interferon and antibody and multiplication of Newcastle disease virus in cytomegalovirus infected mice. Proc. Soc. Exp. Biol. Med. **124**:347-353.

13. Rowe, W. P., J. W. Hartley, S. Waterman, H. C. Turner, and R. J. Huebner. 1956. Detection of human salivary gland virus in the mouth and urine of children. Proc. Soc. Exp. Biol. Med. **92**:418-424.

14. Talley, R. W., R. M. O'Bryan, W. G. Tucker, and R. V. Loo. 1967. Clinical pharmacology and human antitumor activity of cytosine arabinoside. Cancer **20**:809-816.

15. Weller, T. H., and J. B. Hanshaw. 1962. Virologic and clinical observations on cytomegalic inclusion disease. N. Engl. J. Med. **266**:1233-1244.

Antimicrobial Agents and Chemotherapy—1969

Topical Gentamicin in Burns

C. F. T. SNELLING, A. R. RONALD, D. A. KERNAHAN, W. R. WATERS, and L. M. VISTNES
University of Manitoba and Winnipeg General Hospital, Winnipeg 3, Manitoba, Canada

Twenty-seven patients with burns involving more than 10% of the body surface were treated with a daily application of 0.1% gentamicin sulfate cream. During the first postburn week, most patients received systemic penicillin as prophylaxis against group A streptococci; thereafter, systemic antibiotics were administered only for specific infection. Parenteral gentamicin was not used in any patient. Serial biopsies of full-thickness burn wounds were obtained twice weekly for quantitative bacterial culture. With uninterrupted topical gentamicin prophylaxis, burn-wound colonization with *Pseudomonas aeruginosa* occurred in only two patients and no burns were colonized with *Staphylococcus aureus*. In the first 11 patients gentamicin applications were interrupted or irregular during the debridement and grafting period, resulting in colonization with *P. aeruginosa* in eight instances. In subsequent patients, uninterrupted daily application of gentamicin during this period did not interfere with successful graft take and colonization with *Pseudomonas* was prevented. In the 5-year period (1964–1968) prior to the use of topical antimicrobial therapy in the Winnipeg General and Children's Hospitals, the mortality rate in 50 patients with burns involving more than 25% of the body surface was 48%. In the present study, mortality decreased to 15% in 20 patients with burns involving a comparable percentage of the body surface.

The introduction of topical antimicrobial agents in burn-wound management has created cautious optimism in the efforts to prevent burn-wound infection. The topical antimicrobial agents mafenide and gentamicin have been shown to curtail surface colonization and subsequent invasive infection of burn wounds and adjacent unburned tissue. Results obtained with the use of combined topical and systemic gentamicin in the therapy of established *Pseudomonas* infection of burn wounds were reported by Stone et al. (9–11). A comparison of results obtained with the topical agents silver nitrate, mafenide, and gentamicin in a burn unit was reported by Altemeier and MacMillan (1), MacMillan (5), and MacMillan, Hill, and Altemeier (6).

Until recently, the conventional open or closed method of burn-wound care without topical therapy was used in the Winnipeg General and Children's Hospitals. The rate of mortality was high in patients with burns involving more than 25% of the body surface. In this report, we describe our clinical experience with topical gentamicin in 27 patients with burns of more than 10% of the body surface.

MATERIALS AND METHODS

The ages of the 27 patients treated ranged from 3 to 88 years, and the extent of burns ranged from 11 to 75% of the total body surface (Table 1).

On admission, 0.1% gentamicin sulfate cream was applied with a gloved hand to the burn wound. All areas with the exception of the face and perineum were dressed with multilayered gauze occlusive dressings. The dressings were removed daily, the wound was cleansed with saline (either on the ward or in a Hubbard tank), and gentamicin cream and dressings were reapplied.

The initial 11 patients were treated with alternate forms of topical therapy during the debridement and grafting phases. These included dry dressings, saline, Eusol, and 2% streptomycin compresses. However, subsequent patients were continuously treated with topical gentamicin applications until grafting had been completed.

A patient's course within the study was completed when less than 3% of the body surface remained to be autografted, when the patient died, or when a break occurred in the regimen of daily gentamicin application before either of the preceding end points had been reached.

Systemic penicillin was administered throughout the first postburn week to 21 of the 27 patients. Thereafter, systemic antibiotics were given only for specific infections. Systemic gentamicin was not used in any patient.

Wound infection was monitored by culturing skin swabs and full-thickness burn-wound biopsies. Quantitative bacterial counts on the burn-wound biopsies were made twice weekly throughout the patient's course. A swab culture rated 2+ or greater or a burn wound biopsy with a bacterial count greater than 100,000 organisms per g of burn-wound tissue was accepted as evidence of colonization. This is the minimal concentration cited by Teplitz and Moncrief in their definition of burn wound sepsis (7), an entity which also involves invasion of adjacent unburned tissue. Wound infection was defined as colonization plus a clinical state characterized by wound exudate, pyrexia, and leukocytosis requiring specific systemic antibiotic therapy.

Systemic absorption of gentamicin was determined by weekly measurements of the gentamicin concentration in serum. The effect of topical gentamicin on both partial- and full-thickness burn wounds was also observed.

Rates of mortality were compared with our own previous experience and with current burn mortality expectation tables.

RESULTS

Wound infection. Treatment commenced within 12 hr of burn in 24 patients. Treatment was initiated in the other three patients by the fifth postburn day (after transfer from outlying hospitals).

Initial wound cultures were negative in 25 patients. *Enterobacter* sp. and *Aeromonas* sp. were each cultured initially in one patient but disappeared with commencement of topical gentamicin.

Twenty-seven patients received a total of 1,057 days of uninterrupted topical gentamicin therapy. Wound colonization and infection during this period are tabulated in Table 1.

Gram-negative colonization occurred in 13 patients, and progressed to clinical infection in 5 patients. *Pseudomonas aeruginosa* colonized two patients' wounds. One of these patients (no. 7) had deep perineal burns, with full-thickness burns involving 33% of the body surface. On the 55th postburn day, his wounds were colonized with a type 5 *P. aeruginosa* which was susceptible to 6.25 μg of gentamicin per ml. He was treated successfully with a 5-day course of carbenicillin. The second patient (no. 27), who was 68 years of age and had a 45% burn and a tracheotomy, inoculated his wound with drainage from the tracheotomy on the 44th postburn day. Initially, the organism cultured was *P. aeruginosa* type 10 for which the minimal inhibitory concentration (MIC) of gentamicin was 3.1 μg/ml. This patient died 10 days later because of advanced malnutrition, and the organism found in postmortem biopsies was *P. aeruginosa* type 31 for which the MIC of gentamicin was 12.5 μg/ml. No systemic therapy had been given. *P. maltophilia* colonization occurred in three patients. In two of them (no. 19 and 22), the organism disappeared spontaneously. In the third (no. 24), a 40-year-old female patient with 75% burn, colonization occurred on the 7th postburn day and the patient died on the 10th postburn day. Colonization with the *Enterobacteriaceae* was observed in only five instances. Less common gram-negative burn wound pathogens were isolated in 11 instances. Clinical wound infections with these gram-negative organisms occurred in only two patients and were successfully treated.

Gram-positive colonization occurred in 15 patients. Colonization with *Staphylococcus aureus* did not occur in any patient. Group A streptococci colonized the wounds of five patients, in all of whom colonization occurred during the first week. None of these patients had received prophylactic penicillin. Of 21 patients who received penicillin during the first week, none was colonized with group A streptococci. Gram-positive clinical wound infections occurred in eight patients, and all were successfully treated with systemic antibiotics.

Fungal colonization occurred in 25 patients. *Candida* species were the most common, and *Aspergillus* was present in four patients. Although yeast concentrations as high as 10^9 organisms/ml were observed, no clinically recognized infections developed.

The use of systemic antibiotics during the period of gentamicin therapy was reviewed. Wound infection was treated for 118 days, and respiratory- and urinary-tract infections were treated for 145 days. Prophylactic penicillin was given for 176 days. Parenteral gentamicin was not used in any patient. Systemic antibiotics were not required for 569 days or 54% of the treatment period.

In 14 patients, daily gentamicin applications were continued until less than 3% of the body

Table 1. *Extent of burn, colonization, and treatment of 27 patients*

Patient no.	Age (years)	Total burn (%)/ full thickness (%)	Days of continuous gentamicin	Gram-negative colonization	Gram-positive colonization	Prophylactic penicillin	Yeast colonization	Duration of topical gentamicin[a]
1	3	19/12	45	None	Group A streptococci[b]	No	*Candida* sp.	A
2	21	20/9	20	None	None	Yes	*Candida* sp.	A
3	44	13/7	26	None	None	Yes	*Candida* sp.	C
4	56	24/16	40	*Acetobacter anitratum*[b]	None	Yes	*Candida* sp.	C
5	65	17/14	30	*Alcaligenes faecalis*	Viridans streptococci	No	*Acremonium* sp.	C
6	72	21/8	102	None	Group A streptococci[b]	No	*Candida* sp.	A
7	88	11/11	7	None	Group A streptococci[b]	No	None	C
8	4	35/35	10	None	None	Yes	*Candida* sp.	C
9	10	27/24	100	None	Enterococci[b] and Viridans streptococci[b]	Yes	*Candida* sp.	A
10	11	35/14	45	None	None	Yes	*Candida* sp. *Aspergillus* sp.	A
11	13	28/10	39	*Flavobacterium*	None	Yes	*Candida* sp. and *A. fumigatus*	A
12	17	27/12	26	None	None	Yes	*Candida* sp.	A
13	20	39/20	13	None	Group A *streptococci*[b]	No	*Candida* sp.	C
14	27	35/25	24	*A. faecalis*	Enterococci	Yes	*Candida* sp.	C
15	31	30/5	38	None	None	Yes	None	A
16	41	33/33	60	*Pseudomonas aeruginosa*[b] and *Klebsiella* sp.[b]	Group A streptococci,[b] Viridans streptococci, and enterococci	No	*Candida* sp.	A
17	50	30/3	29	None	None	Yes	*Candida* sp.	A
18	71	33/17	18	None	None	Yes	*Candida* sp.	C
19	12	50/24	60	*A. faecalis, Flavobacterium,* and *P. maltophilia*	None	Yes	*Candida* sp. and *Aspergillus*	A
20	16	61/57	41	*Escherichia coli*	Viridans streptococci	Yes	*Candida* sp.	C
21	19	45/36	86	None	Enterococci[b] and *Sarcina*[b]	Yes	*Candida* sp.	A
22	21	52/9	32	*Proteus, A. faecalis,* and *P. maltophilia*	Enterococci	Yes	*Candida* sp.	A
23	36	42/18	47	*A. faecalis*[b]	Enterococci	Yes	*Aspergillus*	A
24	40	75/66	6	*P. maltophilia*[b]	Enterococci	Yes	*Candida* sp.	B
25	43	55/28	40	*A. anitratum*	Enterococci[b]	Yes	*Candida* sp.	C
26	58	52/34	18	*A. faecalis* and *Aeromonas* sp.	None	Yes	*Candida* sp.	C
27	68	45/39	55	*P. aeruginosa,*[b] *Serratia,*[b] and *E. coli*[b]	Viridans streptococci and enterococci[b]	Yes	*Candida* sp.	B

[a] A indicates topical gentamicin daily until less than 3% of the body surface remained to be grafted. B indicates death during period of daily gentamicin application. C indicates interruption or cessation of topical gentamicin when greater than 3% of body surface remained to be grafted. Course in these patients continues in Table 2.

[b] Colonization progressed to clinical wound infection.

surface remained to be autografted. Two patients died during treatment. In the remaining 11 patients, all of whom were treated in the early phases of the study, there was a break in the regimen of daily applications. In some, gentamicin was applied irregularly at 3- to 5-day intervals, and a few were treated with gentamicin and nystatin on alternate days because of initial concern with fungal colonization. In others, the administration of gentamicin was stopped completely to allow the wound to be prepared for grafting. Colonization occurring in these 11 patients is tabulated in Table 2. *P. aeruginosa* colonized the wounds of 8 of the 11 patients. *Escherichia coli* and *S. aureus* colonized two patients each. Table 2 also shows the *P. aeruginosa* pyocine types, the susceptibility to gentamicin, and the treatment course followed. All patients responded to the treatment given. In most patients, topical gentamicin was again started on a daily basis and subsequent colonization with *Pseudomonas* did not occur.

Systemic absorption. The concentrations of gentamicin in serum were measured in most patients. The maximal level observed was 5.0 μg/ml. Transient elevations of blood-urea nitrogen (>25 mg/100 ml) and serum creatinine (>1.0 mg/100 ml) were observed in the early postburn period, but the levels returned to normal despite continued application of topical gentamicin. No patient demonstrated vestibular toxicity.

Burn-wound behavior. Topical gentamicin altered the traditional behavior of full-thickness burn wounds. Wound eschar, although mature at 14 days, remained firmly adherent, often for 1 to 2 months, and had to be electively debrided under general anesthetic. Wound infection, which normally aids in separation, played little role in these burns.

Deep partial-thickness wounds, including some initially diagnosed as full thickness, showed spontaneous regeneration of epithelium. Islands of epithelium appeared after about 3

Table 2. *Colonization in 11 patients whose topical gentamicin therapy was interrupted*

Patient no.	Reason for stopping gentamicin therapy	Gram-negative colonization	*Pseudomonas* pyocine type	MIC of gentamicin (μg/ml)	Drug used for treatment of *Pseudomonas*
3	To prepare for grafting	None	–	–	–
4	To prepare for grafting	*Pseudomonas aeruginosa*	10	>100	Carbenicillin
5	To prepare for grafting	*Klebsiella* and *P. aeruginosa*	10	>100	Carbenicillin
7	To prepare for grafting	None	–	–	–
8	To prepare for grafting	*P. aeruginosa*	Not done	Not done	Carbenicillin
13	Alternating topical gentamicin and topical nystatin	*Escherichia coli*	–	–	–
14	To prepare for grafting	*P. aeruginosa*	1	3.1	Topical neomycin
18	To prepare for grafting	*P. aeruginosa*	U/C	25	None
20	To prepare for grafting	*P. aeruginosa*	10	>100	Carbenicillin
25	To prepare for grafting	*P. aeruginosa*	5	3.1	Topical gentamicin
26	Alternating topical gentamicin and nystatin	*E. coli* and *P. aeruginosa*	10	>100	Carbenicillin

weeks, enlarged, and coalesced. This was most evident in extensive burns where areas were left undebrided long after the original injury, owing to a lack of donor sites. The ultimate area grafted was often much less than originally anticipated.

Mortality. In 27 patients treated to date, there have been 3 deaths. All occurred in patients with burns involving more than 40% of the body surface. One death (patient 26) was due to myocardial infarction occurring in a 58-year-old man on the 92nd day after complete wound coverage had been achieved. The other two deaths, referred to above, were due to burn wound sepsis (no. 24) and severe malnutrition (no. 27).

Mortality expectation was calculated from two tables based on probit analysis. Bull and Fisher's (2) figures derived from experience in Birmingham between 1942 and 1952 predicted a mortality of 13.5 for this group of patients. Pruitt et al. (8), whose figures reflect experience at the Surgical Research Unit of Brooke Army Medical Center between 1950 and 1960, predicted a mortality of 9.7. Unfortunately, no comparable figures are available for burn mortality in the past decade, a period during which topical antimicrobial therapy has been widely used.

Table 3 presents a comparison of our recent experience with topical therapy and the preceding 5-year period in the Winnipeg General and Children's Hospitals during which topical therapy was not used. In burns involving from 11 to 40% of the body surface, there was no mortality in 18 patients treated with gentamicin. In burns involving more than 40% of the body surface, mortality was reduced from 82 to 33% by application of gentamicin. However, the number of patients treated in this series was too small to allow any definite conclusions regarding the effect of topical gentamicin on burn mortality.

Table 3. *Burn mortality*

Extent of burn (% of body surface)	Present study		1964–1968	
	No. of patients	Mortality	No. of patients	Mortality
		%		%
11 to 40	18	0	107	11
41 or more	9	33	22	82

DISCUSSION

This study set out to assess the value of topical gentamicin as prophylaxis against burn-wound colonization and infection. Stone et al. (11) first reported on the use of gentamicin in the treatment of *Pseudomonas* sepsis. Recognizing that toxins absorbed from the burn wound were a prelude to septicemia, they advocated simultaneous use of topical and systemic gentamicin and successfully treated nine consecutive cases of *Pseudomonas* burn wound sepsis. With this therapy, Stone (10) noted a decrease in the mortality caused by *Pseudomonas* septicemia from 100 to 20%. MacMillan (5) compared mafenide, silver nitrate, and gentamicin in 161 burned patients in Cincinnati. Mortality figures took into account the extent of body surface burned, but not patient age. In 70 patients treated with topical and systemic gentamicin, the mean total burn area was 32%. This compares with 35% in the present series. The extent of full-thickness burn was virtually equal in both groups of patients. MacMillan reported six deaths in the gentamicin group, a mortality of 9%, compared with three deaths or 11% in this series. Four of the deaths in the patients treated with gentamicin were attributed by MacMillan to *Pseudomonas* infection. The mortality was 26% for 61 patients treated with silver nitrate and 23% for 30 patients treated with mafenide. The extent of burn was similar in all three groups.

Lindberg et al. (4), who used topical mafenide in 490 patients with burns at the U.S. Army Surgical Research Unit, Fort Sam Houston, Tex., reported a dramatic decrease in mortality among patients whose burns involved 30 to 60% of the body surface. Whereas with conventional therapy the mortality in this group was 59%, with topical mafenide therapy the mortality decreased to 22%. In the present series, 2 of the 13 patients with this extent of burn expired.

Each of these topical regimens has been associated with undesirable side effects. Silver nitrate is esthetically offensive because of its staining characteristics. It can also cause severe electrolyte depletion. Mafenide is a carbonic anhydrase inhibitor and may produce life-threatening metabolic acidosis. Skin sensitivity develops in 5% of patients. Parenteral gentamicin has resulted in renal and vestibular derangements, but this has not been noted with topical therapy. However, the concentrations of gentamicin in serum should be monitored in patients with large burns.

The emergence of gentamicin-resistant *P. aeruginosa* during topical therapy may become a significant problem. MacMillan (5) reported 12 patients with resistant isolates. In the present series, five isolates appeared for which the MIC of gentamicin was 25 μg/ml or more. Four of the five were pyocine type 10. In retrospect, this may have been due to cross infection. Uninterrupted daily topical gentamicin in this series has not been associated with resistant *Pseudomonas*. It may be that intermittent, irregular therapy permits *Pseudomonas* to colonize the burn and topical gentamicin then selects out the resistant mutants. Further study is required.

The initial reports on another topical therapeutic agent in burns, silver sulfadiazine, are promising (3). Further comparative studies of all of these agents with patients controlled for extent of burn and age are needed to determine the efficacy and role of each in the prevention of burn wound sepsis.

LITERATURE CITED

1. Altemeier, W. A., and B. G. MacMillan. 1968. Comparative studies of topical silver nitrate, sulfamylon and gentamicin. Ann. N.Y. Acad. Sci. **150**:966–978.
2. Bull, J. P., and A. J. Fisher. 1954. A study of mortality in a burns unit: A revised estimate. Ann. Surg. **139**:269–274.
3. Fox, C. L., B. W. Rappole, and W. Stanford. 1969. Control of Pseudomonas infection in burns by silver sulfadiazine. Surg. Gynecol. Obstet. **128**:1021–1026.
4. Lindberg, R. B., J. A. Moncrief, and A. D. Mason, Jr. 1968. Control of experimental and clinical burn wound sepsis by topical application of sulfamylon compounds. Ann. N.Y. Acad. Sci. **150**:950–960.
5. MacMillan, B. G. 1969. Gentamicin in the management of thermal injuries. J. Infec. Dis. **119**:492–503.
6. MacMillan, B. G., E. O. Hill, and A. W. Altemeier. 1967. Use of topical silver nitrate, mafenide and gentamicin in the burn patient. Arch. Surg. **95**:472–481.
7. Moncrief, J. A., and C. Teplitz. 1964. Changing concepts in burn sepsis. J. Trauma **4**:235–245.
8. Pruitt, B. A., W. T. Tumbusch, A. D. Mason, and E. Pearson. 1964. Mortality in 1,100 consecutive burns treated at a burns unit. Ann. Surg. **159**:396–401.
9. Stone, H. H. 1966. Review of Pseudomonas sepsis in thermal burns. Verdoglobin determination and gentamicin therapy. Ann. Surg. **163**:279–305.
10. Stone, H. H. 1969. The diagnosis and treatment of Pseudomonas sepsis in major burns. J. Infec. Dis. **119**:504–505.
11. Stone, H. H., J. D. Martin, W. E. Huger, and L. Kolb. 1965. Gentamicin sulfate in the treatment of Pseudomonas sepsis in burns. Surg. Gynecol. Obstet. **120**:351–352.

Antimicrobial Agents and Chemotherapy—1969

Therapy of Infections with the Combination of Carbenicillin and Gentamicin

VICTORIO RODRIGUEZ, JOHN P. WHITECAR, JR., and GERALD P. BODEY[1]

Department of Developmental Therapeutics, The University of Texas M. D. Anderson Hospital and Tumor Institute, Houston, Texas 77025

Carbenicillin and gentamicin were used in the treatment of 32 infections occurring in cancer patients. The antibiotic combination was effective in all of the 5 infections caused by *Pseudomonas* sp. and *Proteus* spp., but was ineffective against 3 of the 4 infections caused by *Escherichia coli* and 6 of the 12 infections caused by organisms of the *Klebsiella-Enterobacter-Serratia* group. Superinfections with *Klebsiella* sp., *E. coli,* and *Candida* sp. occurred in three patients. The in vitro susceptibility of the organisms to gentamicin did not correlate with the clinical response; however, the failures were not due to resistance of the infecting organisms. Many of the patients had severe granulocytopenia, and the response rate was lowest in this group of patients. The intravenous administration of both antibiotics was well tolerated with minimal toxicity.

Gram-negative infections have substantially increased in hospitalized patients with chronic debilitating disease (1, 18). This is especially true in individuals with malignancies and particularly in patients with acute leukemia (3, 4). *Pseudomonas aeruginosa* has been responsible for the largest number of fatal episodes of septicemia in these patients (2). However, since the introduction of carbenicillin, about 70% of *Pseudomonas* sp. infections have been cured in patients with metastatic cancer and leukemia (5). Carbenicillin was uniformly efficacious in these patients regardless of the degree of granulocytopenia. Superinfections, however, occurred in 20% of the patients treated with carbenicillin alone. The organisms most frequently causing superinfections were members of the *Klebsiella-Enterobacter-Serratia* group (5).

Gentamicin is an aminoglycoside antibiotic which is effective against most gram-negative bacteria (19, 20). It is bactericidal in vitro and is synergistic with carbenicillin against *Pseudomonas* sp. (7, 15). Good clinical results have been obtained with gentamicin alone and in combination with other antibiotics (11, 12, 16). However, experience with this antibiotic in the treatment of infections occurring in patients with seriously impaired host defenses has been limited.

The combination of carbenicillin and gentamicin provides broad-spectrum activity against most gram-positive cocci and gram-negative bacteria. Thus, the addition of gentamicin might reduce the incidence of superinfection associated with the administration of carbenicillin alone. Consequently, this combination was studied as a means of treating infections occurring in cancer patients. The results of therapy of 32 infectious episodes are described in this report.

MATERIALS AND METHODS

The combination of carbenicillin and gentamicin was used for treatment of 32 infections occurring in 23 patients. All patients had acute leukemia or metastatic cancer. Their median age was 57 years (range, 13 to 68 years). Eight patients were treated for more than one infectious episode. The antibiotic combination was used as initial therapy for 25 infections. In the other seven infections, it was administered after the patients had failed to respond to other antibiotics (tetracycline, chloramphenicol, and the polymyxins).

When utilized as initial therapy, the combination was instituted promptly after the onset of fever. Fever was defined as a temperature greater than 101 F (38.3 C) not associated with the transfusion of blood products. Cultures of blood and urine, and of material from the

[1] Scholar of the Leukemia Society of America, Inc.

throat and other appropriate sites were obtained from all patients prior to the initiation of antibiotic therapy. Only patients with documented infection were included in the study. Most organisms cultured from sites of infection were tested in vitro for susceptibility to carbenicillin and gentamicin, by use of the serial dilution technique.

Both antibiotics were given for a minimum of 2 weeks or for 5 days after the patients became afebrile, whichever was longer. Both drugs were administered in 200 ml of dextrose solution over a 2-hr period. The dose of carbenicillin was 4 g every 4 hr, and the dose of gentamicin was 30 mg/m^2 (0.75 mg/kg) every 6 hr, after an initial dose of 40 mg/m^2 (1 mg/kg). The carbenicillin used in this study was supplied as Pyopen by Beecham Pharmaceuticals, Division of Beecham Inc., Clifton, N.J. Gentamicin was supplied as Garamycin by Schering Corp., Bloomfield, N.J.

The results were evaluated as follows. Patients were considered to have achieved a complete response if they became afebrile and all clinical and laboratory signs of infection disappeared. Those who died of superinfection or of their malignancy were considered to have responded completely if the original infection had been resolved and no evidence of infection was found at postmortem examination. Patients who responded to the antibiotic combination but relapsed within 1 week after cessation of therapy were considered to have had a partial response. Infections caused by new organisms arising during treatment of the original infection were considered to be superinfections.

Daily blood counts and serial determinations of blood urea nitrogen (BUN), creatinine clearance, and serum glutamic oxalacetic and pyruvic transaminases (SGOT, SGPT) were performed in most of the patients during antibiotic therapy.

RESULTS

The types of infections treated with the combination of carbenicillin and gentamicin are listed in Table 1. Septicemia accounted for 47% of all infections. The site of origin of the septicemia was the lungs in nine cases, the skin in one case, and the urinary tract in one case. The site of origin could not be determined in four cases. The mixed infections were one case of pneumonia and peritoneal abscess and one of pyelonephritis, pneumonia, and meningitis.

Table 1. *Types of infections treated with carbenicillin-gentamicin*

Type	Episodes
Septicemia	15
Pneumonia	8
Cellulitis	4
Sinusitis	2
Myositis	1
Mixed	2
Total	32

The etiological agents in 38% of these infections were organisms of the *Klebsiella-Enterobacter-Serratia* group (Table 2). The remaining gram-negative infections were caused by *Pseudomonas* sp., *Proteus* spp., and *Escherichia coli.* Infections caused by multiple gram-negative organisms (*Klebsiella* sp., *E. coli,* and *Pseudomonas* sp.) occurred in three patients. There were only two episodes of *Staphylococcus aureus* infection. No organisms were identified in six patients, despite clinical and radiological evidence of infection.

The combination of carbenicillin and gentamicin was effective in 56% of the therapeutic trials (Table 3). Of the 18 patients who responded, 16 had a complete response and 2 had a partial response.

Table 2. *Organisms causing infection in patients treated with carbenicillin-gentamicin*

Organism	Episodes
Klebsiella sp.	10
Escherichia coli	4
Pseudomonas sp.	3
Proteus sp.	2
Enterobacter sp.	1
Serratia sp.	1
Multiple gram-negative bacteria	3
Staphylococcus aureus	2
Unknown	6

Table 3. *Therapeutic results with carbenicillin-gentamicin combination*

Organism	Episodes	Complete or partial responses	
		No.	Per cent
Klebsiella-Enterobacter-Serratia	12	6	50
Escherichia coli	4	1	25
Peeudomonas sp.	3	3	100
Proteus sp.	2	2	100
Multiple gram-negative bacteria	3	0	0
Staphylococcus aureus	2	1	50
Unknown	6	5	83
Total	32	18	56

Of the patients with septicemia, 53% failed to respond and eventually died of their infections. Carbenicillin and gentamicin were efficacious in eradicating all infections caused by *Pseudomonas* sp. and *Proteus* spp. Also, the majority of infections in which no organism was identified responded to this therapy. The antibiotics were effective against 50% of the infections caused by organisms of the *Klebsiella-Enterobacter-Serratia* group. However, five of seven patients with *Klebsiella* sp. septicemia failed to respond, and died of their infection. The combination of carbenicillin and gentamicin was ineffective in the three patients infected with multiple gram-negative bacteria. Also, one of two patients with *S. aureus* infection failed to respond.

Superinfections occurred in three patients while they were receiving therapy with this combination. The infecting organisms were *Klebsiella* sp., *E. coli,* and *Candida albicans.*

The majority of the patients in this study had granulocytopenia (less than 1,500/mm^3), and 23 of the 32 patients had severe granulocytopenia (less than 500/mm^3; Table 4). Ten of these 23 patients had infections caused by the *Klebsiella-Enterobacter-Serratia* group, and only 3 of the 10 responded to therapy. In contrast, all of the patients with *Pseudomonas* sp. and *Proteus* spp. infections who were severely granulocytopenic responded to therapy.

The in vitro susceptibility to carbenicillin and gentamicin was determined for the infecting organisms from 15 patients (Table 5). There was no correlation between the in vitro susceptibility of these organisms and the therapeutic results. The organisms causing infections which failed to respond were as susceptible to gentamicin as the organisms causing infections which responded. All of the organisms isolated from patients who failed to respond were susceptible to 3.12 μg or less of gentamicin per ml.

Serial BUN determinations were performed on 20 patients who received carbenicillin and gentamicin for at least 7 days. Six patients developed azotemia (Table 6). Their median highest BUN was 34 mg/100 ml (range, 26 to 70 mg/100 ml) and occurred on day 9 (range, days 7 to 17). The BUN returned to normal in

Table 4. *Results with carbenicillin-gentamicin related to absolute granulocyte count*

Granulocyte count/mm^3	Complete or partial response	Failure	Total
>1,000	5	3	8
500–1,000	1	0	1
100–500	4	2	6
<100	8	9	17
Total	18	14	32

Table 5. *Clinical results with carbenicillin-gentamicin related to the in vitro drug susceptibility of the infecting organisms*

Patient	Organism	Minimal inhibitory concn (μg/ml)		Clinical results
		Carbenicillin	Gentamicin	
G.P.	*Klebsiella*	400	0.78	Complete response
N.G. #1	*Klebsiella*	>400	0.39	Complete response
P.S.	*Klebsiella*	>400	0.20	Complete response
L.T.	*Klebsiella*	50	0.39	Failure
G.R.	*Klebsiella*	>400	0.78	Failure
G.T.	*Klebsiella*	>400	0.78	Failure
N.G. #2	*Klebsiella*	>400	3.12	Failure
A.K.	*Klebsiella*	400	0.39	Failure
	E. coli	6.25	1.56	
P.S.	*E. coli*	12.5	1.56	Complete response
T.S.	*E. coli*	200	1.56	Failure
B.J.	*E. coli*	>400	1.56	Failure
H.L.	*Pseudomonas*	400	0.78	Complete response
B.C.	*Pseudomonas*	400	1.56	Complete response
G.P.	*Serratia*	25	1.56	Complete response
B.S.	*S. aureus*	1.56	0.10	Failure

Table 6. *Nephrotoxicity from carbenicillin-gentamicin*

Blood urea nitrogen		No. of patients
Initial	During therapy	
Normal	Normal	11
Normal	Elevated	6
Elevated	Normal	3

Table 7. *Creatinine clearances in patients receiving carbenicillin-gentamicin*

Initial creatinine clearance (ml/min)	During therapy	No. of patients
>85	Unchanged	6
>85	Decreased	5
<85	Increased	2

one patient; the other five patients died of their infection.

Serial creatinine clearance was determined for 13 patients (Table 7). The creatinine clearance decreased in five patients during therapy. The median lowest determination was 67 ml/min (range, 32 to 71 ml/min) and occurred on day 8 (range, days 3 to 19). The creatinine clearance returned to greater than 85 ml/min in one patient; the other four patients died of their infection.

Transitory elevations of SGOT and SGPT were observed in six patients. The highest values were 204 and 550 units, respectively. All of these patients, however, also received antitumor therapy known to alter liver function studies. Urticaria which necessitated discontinuation of the antibiotics was observed in one patient after 13 days of therapy. He had no history of penicillin allergy or prior exposure to gentamicin. No symptoms of auditory or vestibular dysfunction were observed in these patients, although specific tests were not performed.

DISCUSSION

The combination of carbenicillin and gentamicin was effective against 56% of 32 infectious episodes occurring in cancer patients. This response rate is similar to that obtained in a group of patients with acute leukemia treated with methicillin and colistin (6). However, the incidence of *Klebsiella* sp. infections was much lower in the latter group. The combination of carbenicillin and gentamicin was effective against all of the infections caused by *Pseudomonas* sp. and *Proteus* spp. However, equally good results have been obtained with carbenicillin alone (5, 13, 17). The response rate was only 44% in patients whose infections were caused by *E. coli, Klebsiella* sp., *Enterobacter* sp., and *Serratia* sp. With the exception of *E. coli,* these organisms are usually resistant to carbenicillin. However, gentamicin is effective against over 85% of isolates of these organisms in vitro (13).

There was no correlation between the in vitro susceptibility of the infecting organisms and the clinical results. A similar lack of correlation has been observed previously with carbenicillin (5). The inefficacy of gentamicin was not due to resistant organisms. Organisms isolated from infections that failed to respond were as susceptible to gentamicin as organisms isolated from infections that responded.

The poor response rate was not due to inadequate drug concentrations in serum following the intravenous administration of gentamicin. Peak levels above 4 μg of gentamicin per ml of serum are generally achieved when the drug is administered by this route and in the dosage employed herein (14). Concentrations over 100 μg of carbenicillin per ml of serum generally can be maintained when carbenicillin is administered at a dose of 30 g/day (6). The dose of carbenicillin was reduced in this study because of its synergism with gentamicin in vitro.

The response rate was lowest in patients who had granulocytopenia. It has been reported that patients with granulocytopenia usually respond poorly to treatment (3). Some antibiotics are known to be less effective in patients with impaired host defenses and granulocytopenia (8–10), and in our experience gentamicin has not been very effective against *Serratia* sp. infections occurring in patients with granulocyte counts below 1,500 mm^3 (G. P. Bodey, V. Rodriguez, and J. P. Smith, Cancer, *in press*). Other investigators have also found that gentamicin failed to be effective in cancer patients with leukopenia (21). However, carbenicillin has been effective against *Pseudomonas* sp. infections, regardless of the patient's granulocyte count (5).

The administration of carbenicillin and gentamicin was well tolerated by all patients. No localized phlebitis or generalized reactions occurred that could be attributable to intravenous gentamicin. One patient developed urticaria which was most likely caused by carbenicillin. Azotemia occurred in 30% of the patients. Several patients with abnormal renal function initially improved while on therapy. The infection rather than antibiotic administration may have been the cause of azotemia in some patients. Transient elevations of serum transaminases in these patients may have been due to carbenicillin, although antitumor chemotherapeutic agents were given simultaneously.

The results of this study indicate that the combination of carbenicillin and gentamicin is effective against only 50% of bacterial infections occurring in cancer patients. The response rate was high for those infections which would be expected to respond to carbenicillin and the response rate was low for those infections which would be expected to respond only to gentamicin. This suggests that gentamicin is less effective in patients with granulocytopenia than in patients with normal granulocyte levels.

LITERATURE CITED

1. Altemier, W. A., J. C. Todd, and W. W. Inge. 1967. Gram-negative septicemia: a growing threat. Ann. Surg. **166**:530–542.
2. Bodey, F. P. 1966. Infectious complications of acute leukemia. Medical Times **94**:1076–1085.
3. Bodey, G. P., M. Buckley, Y. S. Sathe, and E. J. Freireich. 1966. Quantitative relationships between circulating leukocytes and infection in patients with actue leukemia. Ann. Intern. Med. **64**:328–340.
4. Bodey, G. P., B. A. Nies, N. R. Mohberg, and E. J. Freireich. 1965. The effect of adrenal corticosteroid therapy on infections in acute leukemia. Amer. J. Med. Sci. **250**:162–167.
5. Bodey, G. P., V. Rodriguez, and J. K. Luce. 1969. Carbenicillin therapy of gram-negative bacilli infections. Amer. J. Med. Sci. **257**:408–414.
6. Bodey, G. P., V. Rodriguez, and D. Stewart. 1969. Clinical pharmacological studies of carbenicillin. Amer. J. Med. Sci. **257**:185–190.
7. Brumfitt, W., A. Percival, and D. A. Leigh. 1967. Clinical and laboratory studies with carbenicillin. A new penicillin active against Pseudomonas pyocyanea. Lancet **1**:1289–1293.
8. Frei, E., III, R. H. Levin, G. P. Bodey, E. E. Morse, and E. J. Freireich. 1965. The nature and control of infections in patients with acute leukemia. Cancer Res. **25**:1511–1515.
9. Freid, M. A., and K. L. Vosti. 1968. The importance of underlying disease in patients with gram-negative bacteremia. Arch. Intern. Med. **121**:418–423.
10. Hersh, E. M., G. P. Bodey, B. A. Nies, and E. J. Freireich. 1965. Causes of death in acute leukemia. J. Amer. Med. Ass. **193**:105–109.
11. Jao, R. L., and G. G. Jackson. 1964. Gentamicin sulfate, new antibiotic against gram-negative bacilli. J. Amer. Med. Ass. **189**:817–822.
12. Martin, C. M., A. J. Cuomo, M. J. Geraghty, J. R. Zager, and T. C. Mandes. 1967. Gentamicin sulfate in the treatment of extraurinary infections due to gram-negative bacteria. J. Infec. Dis. **119**:506–517.
13. Richardson, A. E., K. W. James, C. R. Spittle, and O. P. W. Robinson. 1968. Experiences with carbenicillin in the treatment of septicemia and meningitis. Postgrad. Med. J. **44**:844–847.
14. Rodriguez, V., G. P. Bodey, and D. Stewart. 1969. Clinical pharmacological studies of carbenicillin. Amer. J. Med. Sci. **257**:185–190.
15. Standiford, H. C., A. C. Kind, and W. M. M. Kirby. 1969. Laboratory and clinical studies of carbenicillin against gram-negative bacilli. Antimicrob. Agents Chemother.–1968, p. 286–291.
16. Stone, H. H., and L. Kolb. 1967. Gentamicin sulfate in the treatment of extraurinary infections due to gram-negative bacteria. S. Med. J. **60**:142–171.
17. Stratford, B. C. 1968. The treatment of infections due to Pseudomonas aeruginosa with carbenicillin (Pyopen). Med. J. Aust. **2**:890–895.
18. Turck, M. 1967. The problem of infections due to gram-negative organisms. Antimicrob. Agents Chemother.–1966, p. 265–273.
19. Waitz, J. A., and M. J. Weinstein. 1969. Recent microbiological studies with gentamicin. J. Infec. Dis. **119**:355–360.
20. Weinstein, M. J., G. M. Luedemann, E. M. Oden, G. H. Wagman, J. P. Rosselet, J. Marquez, C. T. Coniglio, W. Charney, H. Herzog, and J. Black. 1963. Gentamicin, a new antibiotic complex from Micromonospora. J. Med. Chem. **6**:463–464.
21. Young, L. S., D. B. Louria, and D. Armstrong. 1967. Gentamicin in the treatment of severe hospital-acquired gram-negative infections. Trans. N.Y. Acad. Sci. **29**:579–588.

Antimicrobial Agents and Chemotherapy—1969

Emergence of Resistance in *Pseudomonas* During Carbenicillin Therapy

K. K. HOLMES, H. CLARK, F. SILVERBLATT, and M. TURCK

Department of Medicine, University of Washington School of Medicine, and U. S. Public Health Service Hospital, Seattle, Washington 98114

Although carbenicillin is active against many strains of *Pseudomonas aeruginosa*, it has been reported that development of resistance may restrict its clinical usefulness. Previous studies from our laboratory demonstrated the emergence of resistance to carbenicillin in three of nine patients with *Pseudomonas* infection. Carbenicillin has now been employed in the treatment of 35 episodes of *Pseudomonas* infection occurring in 31 patients. *Pseudomonas* persisted during therapy in 16 of 20 infections occurring outside of the urinary tract, and a fourfold or greater increment in resistance developed in eight isolates. In contrast, *Pseudomonas* was eradicated during therapy in 14 infections of the urinary tract. Of nine recurrences, only one was associated with increased resistance to carbenicillin. These findings, coupled with other in vitro observations, indicate that rapid emergence of resistance during carbenicillin treatment will limit its usefulness in deep-seated *Pseudomonas* infection.

Carbenicillin may be valuable when used alone (1, 3, 5, 12, 16, 18) or in combination with gentamicin (13, 14) in the treatment of serious *Pseudomonas aeruginosa* infections. However, the minimal inhibitory concentration (MIC) of carbenicillin for most clinical isolates of *P. aeruginosa* is only slightly less than the concentrations which can be achieved in serum, even by daily administration of intravenous doses of 24 to 30 g of antibiotic (4). In many patients, suboptimal levels of carbenicillin are undoubtedly maintained at the site of skin infection in burns or wounds, and at the surface of the bronchial mucosa and in sputum in bronchopulmonary infections, particularly when smaller doses of carbenicillin, of the order of 4 to 6 daily, are employed. Exposure of *P. aeruginosa* in vitro to subinhibitory concentrations of carbenicillin regularly results in the rapid emergence of resistant variants in a stepwise fashion characteristic of resistance to the penicillins produced in the laboratory (2, 5, 12). Therefore, it is not surprising that the development of resistance in *P. aeruginosa* during therapy with carbenicillin has been noted in several clinical reports (6, 10, 12, 15).

The present communication, which is an extension of previous studies reported from this laboratory (12), describes the results of 33 separate courses of carbenicillin administered to 31 patients with *P. aeruginosa* infection. The frequent emergence of resistant variants during treatment of extraurinary infections is contrasted to the infrequent development of resistance to carbenicillin during treatment of urinary-tract infections.

MATERIALS AND METHODS

Patient population. Carbenicillin was administered to 20 hospitalized patients with extraurinary *P. aeruginosa* infections. The sites of infection in these patients were bronchopulmonary, soft tissue, peritoneal, parotitis with bacteremia, and perirectal phlegmon with bacteremia. Thirteen hospitalized patients with *P. aeruginosa* urinary-tract infections received carbenicillin. Two patients received a second course of therapy when the initial short course was unsuccessful in eradicating bacteriuria. In addition, two of the patients with extraurinary infection had concomitant *P. aeruginosa* bacteriuria, allowing a comparison of the effect of carbenicillin in different foci of infection in the same patient.

Treatment regimens. Patients with urinary-tract infection received 1 g of carbenicillin intramuscularly every 6 hr for 7 to 14 days. One patient received 1 g every 8 hr for 6 weeks after an initial 7-day course was unsuccessful. Patients with extraurinary infections received doses ranging from 4 to 24 g daily.

Laboratory studies. The susceptibility of clinical isolates of *P. aeruginosa* to carbenicillin was determined by a standardized disc method (17) with the use of a 30-μg disc, and by a serial broth-dillution method described previously (12).

RESULTS OF CLINICAL STUDIES

Carbenicillin in treatment of urinary-tract infections. The pertinent clinical features and results of studies in patients with bacteriuria treated with carbenicillin are summarized in Table 1. The initial siolates of *P. aeruginosa* were eradicated from the urine *during* therapy in all but one patient. This patient, a 50-year-old woman with probable medullary cystic disease and unilateral upper tract infection, documented by ureteral catheterization studies, had a few colonies of *P. aeruginosa* recovered from her urine during treatment. The isolate of *Pseudomonas* cultured from the urine of this patient after cessation of treatment with carbenicillin had developed increasing resistance, and the MIC changed from 5 to 100 μg/ml. Subsequently, she received a more protracted course of carbenicillin over a 6-week period. Although the urine became sterile during treatment, she again relapsed when therapy was discontinued. The isolate recovered at the completion of the second course of treatment with carbenicillin also was less susceptible than at the onset of therapy (MIC increased from 100 to 250 μg/ml). Although relapse of *Pseudomonas* bacteriuria occurred with seven additional courses of carbenicillin therapy, the isolates of Pseudomonas recovered from these patients had remained susceptible to essentially the same concentrations of drug as the microorganisms cultured prior to treatment.

Overall, only one of nine unsuccessful courses of therapy for *Pseudomonas* urinary-tract infections was associated with significant emergence of resistance, defined as a fourfold or greater increase in MIC. However, reinfection with *Klebsiella* or *Streptococcus faecalis* occurred in four additional patients, and only two patients, both with infections which were thought to be localized to the bladder, were still free from significant bacteriuria on follow-up examination.

Carbenicillin in treatment of extraurinary infections. A total of 20 treatment courses with carbenicillin were administered to 19 patients with *Pseudomonas* infection arising from foci outside the urinary tract (Table 2). *Pseudomonas* was recovered during therapy from the

Table 1. *Treatment of Pseudomonas aeruginosa urinary-tract infections with carbenicillin*

Age (years)	Sex	Predisposing factors	Cultures: Before treatment	Cultures: During treatment	Cultures: After treatment	Comment
50	F	Probably medullary cystic disease	*Pseudomonas* (5.0)[a]	*Pseudomonas*	*Pseudomonas* (100)	*Pseudomonas* persisted with increased resistance after 7 days of therapy
50	F	Probably medullary cystic disease	*Pseudomonas* (100)	Sterile × 3	*Pseudomonas* (250)	Relapse in same patient after 6 weeks of therapy
59	M	Benign prostatic hypertrophy, acute pyelonephritis	*Pseudomonas* (50)	Sterile	*Klebsiella*	Reinfection after treatment
59	F	Foley catheter (removed)	*Pseudomonas* (50)	Sterile	*Pseudomonas* (100)	Relapse after 6 days of treatment
59	F	Foley catheter (removed)	*Pseudomonas* (100)	Sterile	Sterile	Cured after 15 days of therapy
77	M	Prostatic carcinoma	*Pseudomonas* (50)	Sterile	Sterile	Cured
34	F	Foley catheter (removed)	*Pseudomonas* (50)	*Klebsiella*	*Klebsiella*	Superinfection during therapy
57	M	Foley catheter (removed)	*Pseudomonas* (100)	Sterile	*Pseudomonas* (100)	Relapse after therapy
42	F	Recurrent bladder bacteriuria	*Pseudomonas* (50)	Sterile	*S. faecalis*	Reinfection after therapy
77	M	Benign prostatic hypertrophy	*Pseudomonas* (7.5)	Sterile	*Pseudomonas* (7.5)	Relapse after therapy
51	M	Foley catheter (removed)	*Pseudomonas* (15)	Sterile	*Pseudomonas* (15)	Relapse after therapy
80	M	Bilateral ureteral obstruction	*Pseudomonas* (100)	Sterile	*Pseudomonas* (100)	Relapse after therapy
66	M	Foley catheter (in place)	*Pseudomonas* (100)	Sterile	*Klebsiella*	Reinfection after therapy
51	M	Foley catheter (removed)	*Pseudomonas* (50)	–	*Pseudomonas*	Relapse after therapy
44	F	Nephrostomy	*Pseudomonas* (50)	*Klebsiella*	*Pseudomonas*	Relapse after therapy

[a] Minimal inhibitory concentration in micrograms per milliliter is given in parentheses.

Table 2. *Treatment of Pseudomonas aeruginosa infections with carbenicillin*

Age (years)	Sex	Type of infection	Cultures: Before treatment	Cultures: After treatment	Carbenicillin: Dose (g/day)	Carbenicillin: Duration (days)	Comment
		Bronchopulmonary					
64	M	Pneumonia with effusion	*Pseudomonas* (50)[a]	*Pseudomonas* (100)	6	7	Persistent *Pseudomonas* despite clinical improvement
44	M	Myasthenia gravis with pneumonia	*Pseudomonas* (50)	*Pseudomonas* (250)	6	4	*Pseudomonas* persisted with increased resistance; patient died
53	M	Empyema with bacteremia	*Pseudomonas* (25)	*Pseudomonas* (100)	24	6	*Pseudomonas* persisted with increased resistance in empyema, but bacteremia cleared
53	M	Bronchitis	*Pseudomonas* (2.5)	*Pseudomonas*[b]	6	10	Persistent *Pseudomonas* with no clinical improvement
51	M	Bronchiectasis	*Pseudomonas* (100)	*Pseudomonas*	8	10	Persistent *Pseudomonas* with no clinical improvement
77	M	Pneumonia	*Pseudomonas*	*Pseudomonas* (50)	12	14	Persistent *Pseudomonas* with no clinical improvement
66	M	Bronchitis	*Pseudomonas* (50)	*Pseudomonas* (100)	4	8	Persistent *Pseudomonas* despite clinical and radiographic improvement
52	M	Bronchitis	*Pseudomonas* (25)	Sterile	6	7	Cure
61	M	Pneumonia	*Pseudomonas*	Sterile	24	7	Tracheostomy aspirate sterilized during treatment; patient died
80	M	Decubitus ulcer	*Pseudomonas* (50)	*Pseudomonas* (250)	6	6	*Pseudomonas* persisted with increased resistance and no clinical improvement
59	F	Stasis ulcer	*Pseudomonas* (50)	Sterile	4	7	Cure
83	F	Infected wound	*Pseudomonas* (100)	*Pseudomonas* (500)	8	18	*Pseudomonas* persisted with increased resistance despite clinical improvement
46	F	Ecthyma gangrenosum during chemotherapy for choriocarcinoma	*Pseudomonas*[c]	*Pseudomonas* (250)	12	9	*Pseudomonas* persisted with increased resistance; no improvement until neutropenia resolved
51	M	Open fracture wound	*Pseudomonas* (50)	*Pseudomonas* (250)	12	5	*Pseudomonas* persisted with increased resistance and no clinical improvement
		Peritonitis					
82	F	Peritonitis and enterocolitis	*Pseudomonas* (50)	*Pseudomonas* (500)	6	6	*Pseudomonas* persisted in stool with increased resistance; peritonitis controlled but enterocolitis was not
48	F	Peritonitis	*Pseudomonas*	*Pseudomonas* (250)	24	8	Persistent *Pseudomonas* despite clinical improvement
21	M	Peritoneal abscesses	*Pseudomonas* (100)	*Pseudomonas* (100)	12	8	Persistent *Pseudomonas* despite clinical improvement
50	M	Peritonitis	*Pseudomonas* (25)	*Pseudomonas* (50)	24	4	Persistent *Pseudomonas* despite clinical improvement
		Miscellaneous					
53	M	Parotitis with bacteremia	*Pseudomonas* (100)	*Pseudomonas* (500)	24	8	*Pseudomonas* persisted with increased resistance in parotid drainage but bacteremia cleared
17	M	Acute myelogenous leukemia with bacteremia	*Pseudomonas* (100)	Sterile	24	7	Cured; probenecid given also

[a] MIC in micrograms per milliliter given in parentheses.
[b] MIC not retested, but no change in diameter of disc zone.
[c] MIC not determined on initial isolate, but disc zone decreased from 18 to 6 mm.

initial site of infection in 16 of 20 (80%) courses of therapy in extraurinary infections. Furthermore, unlike the strains of *Pseudomonas* cultured from the urine, which generally were equally susceptible to carbenicillin both before and at the completion of treatment, 8 of 13 (62%) *Pseudomonas* isolates which persisted during therapy in sites outside of the urinary tract, and for which in vitro tests of susceptibility to carbenicillin were conducted both before and after treatment, developed at least a fourfold increase in MIC. However, satisfactory clinical improvement often occurred during treatment with carbenicillin despite persistence of infection and emergence of resistance of *P. aeruginosa* in most patients. Furthermore, carbenicillin was effective in controlling three separate episodes of *Pseudomonas* bacteremia even though the initial focus of infection was not eradicated.

RESULTS OF LABORATORY STUDIES

Susceptibility of Pseudomonas to carbenicillin. Figure 1 depicts the activity of carbenicillin against 30 initial isolates of *P. aeruginosa* recovered from patients in this study, and also shows the effect of inoculum size on determination of both the MIC and the minimal bactericidal concentration. When tested with an inoculum of 10^5 bacterial cells, a carbenicillin concentration of 25 μg/ml, which is a concentration that can be achieved in the blood with a 1-g parenteral dose, inhibited the growth of only 30% of the strains of *Pseudomonas.* Furthermore, increasing the inoculum size 100-fold, from 10^5 to 10^7 bacterial cells, resulted in an apparent further diminution in susceptibility of these isolates, and less than 5% were inhibited by 25 μg or less of carbenicillin per ml. In addition, although more than 90% of the *Pseudomonas* isolates were inhibited by 100 μg of carbenicillin per ml when tested against an inoculum of 10^5 organisms, only 29% of these same strains were susceptible to that concentration of drug when the higher inoculum was employed. It should be noted, however, that more than 75% of the *Pseudomonas* strains were inhibited by 250 μg or less of carbenicillin per ml (a concentration which can readily be achieved in the urine) regardless of the inoculum size. Finally, although carbenicillin was bactericidal against the majority of strains, there frequently was a disparity between the minimal inhibitory and minimal bactericidal end point of carbenicillin against *P. aeruginosa;* this was most marked with the higher inoculum.

Comparison of antibiotic-disc and broth-dilution tests of susceptibility to carbenicillin. Inhibitory zones about discs containing 30 μg of carbenicillin were measured for 30 *Pseudomonas* isolates and were compared with the results of broth-dilution studies performed with an inoculum of 10^5 bacterial cells (Fig. 2). It is apparent that the correlation between the two tests used to determine antimicrobial susceptibility was poor, and recognition of isolates susceptible to

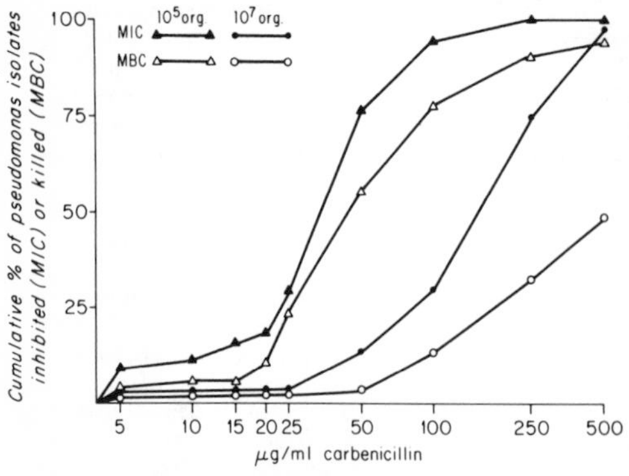

Fig. 1. *Cumulative percentage of 30 clinical isolates of Pseudomonas aeruginosa inhibited (MIC) or killed (MBC) by increasing concentrations of carbenicillin test in broth medium with bacterial inocula of two different sizes.*

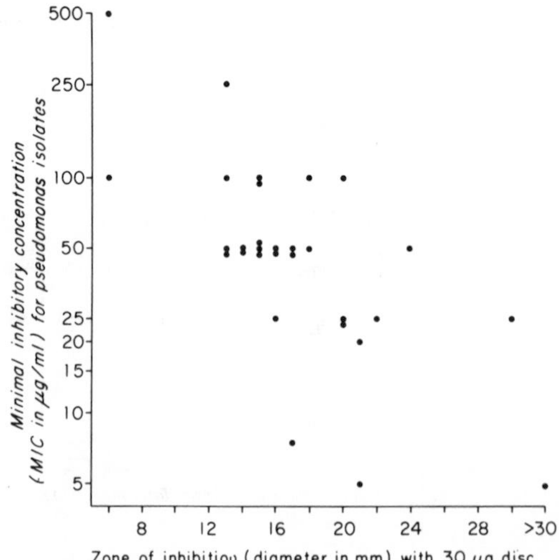

Fig. 2. *Comparison of antibiotic disc (30-μg content) and broth-dilution tests of susceptibility to carbenicillin tested against an inoculum of approximately 10^5 organisms/ml.*

low concentrations of carbenicillin was unreliable by the disc technique alone. For example, some isolates for which carbenicillin concentrations of 100 μg/ml were required to inhibit growth displayed a zone of inhibition of the same size as that of organisms which were inhibited by 25 μg of antibiotic per ml. Although not shown in Fig. 2, many additional isolates of *Pseudomonas* have been compared by means of the two techniques for determining in vitro susceptibility, and no strain for which the MIC was greater than 250 μg/ml showed any zone of inhibition when tested with 30-μg carbenicillin discs. Since peak antibiotic concentrations of 250 μg/ml can be achieved in serum by means of intermittent infusions of large doses of carbenicillin, a strain of *P. aeruginosa* which gives any measurable zone of inhibition may be considered amenable for initial treatment with carbenicillin.

DISCUSSION

Although carbenicillin is active in vitro against *P. aeruginosa,* the concentration of antibiotic necessary for inhibition of most strains generally exceeds 25 μg/ml. Peak concentrations of carbenicillin achieved in serum after a 1-g intramuscular dose approximate 25 μg/ml, whereas concentrations greater than 600 μg/ml regularly are obtained in the urine (12). Therefore, although most clinical isolates of *P. aeruginosa* present in the urine would be inhibited or killed by the levels achieved with the 1-g dose, infections with *P. aeruginosa* emanating from extraurinary foci would not be expected to respond. However, higher doses of carbenicillin are well tolereated, and Bodey et al. (4) demonstrated peak concentrations in serum and lymph just over 300 μg/ml after the rapid injection of 5 g of carbenicillin. When this 5-g dose was given in a slow infusion administered every 4 hr, concentrations higher than 100 μg/ml of serum were maintained. On the other hand, peak concentrations of carbenicillin reached in the sputum, in the peritoneal fluid, and in purulent wound or burn exudates after administration of comparable amounts of drug are not known.

It is clear from these data that the margin between the concentrations of carbenicillin achievable in serum (and presumably tissue) and the MIC for most clinical isolates of *P. aeruginosa* is quite small. Therefore, the persistence of extraurinary infection is predictable when doses of carbenicillin of less than 24 to 30 g per day are employed. However, even when these large doses were used in our patients, persistence during therapy was observed in four of six courses of treatment for deep-seated *Pseudomonas* infection. On the other hand, persistence of *P. aeruginosa* in the urinary tract was of a different nature, in that microbial growth was completely suppressed during treatment by the high levels of carbenicillin in the urine in all but one instance.

It is not known why relapse of *P. aeruginosa* urinary infection occurred in eight patients after cessation of treatment despite complete suppression of this organism during carbenicillin therapy. In this regard, persistence of urinary-tract infection during antibiotic therapy has been associated with the presence of viable L-forms in some patients (7), and this phenomenon has been observed in a patient with *P. aeruginosa* bacteriuria, from whom *P. aeruginosa* L-forms, but not classical forms, were recovered during antibiotic therapy (L. Gutman, *personal communication*). Although pyocine or phage typing of individual isolates of *Pseudomonas* was not performed during this study, and no serological identification of the isolates was made, the likelihood was great that persistent or relapsing infection was due to the initial infecting strain in most cases. This is particularly true of relapsing urinary infections, for *P. aeruginosa* invariably reappeared in the urine within a few days of discontinuing treatment, and no genitourinary instrumentation had been undertaken in the interim. Darrell and Waterworth (6) did carry out pyocine typing of *P. aeruginosa* strains isolated from extraurinary sites during antibiotic therapy, and they found that strains which developed increased resistance to carbenicillin during therapy were of the same pyocine type as isolates initially obtained from the same site of infection prior to treatment.

The different modes of persistence of *P. aeruginosa* in extraurinary and in urinary infections helps to explain why a moderate but significant increase in carbenicillin resistance was seen only with extraurinary infection. Moderate resistance to the penicillins usually occurs in a stepwise fashion, and requires the continuous replication of the bacterial genome, with selection of mutants of increasing resistance. *P. aeruginosa* apparently is capable of multiplication, and thereby of giving rise to more resistant variants, in the presence of levels of carbenicillin which are achieved at extraurinary sites. On the other hand, *P. aeruginosa* cannot multiply in the urine during carbenicillin therapy, because the concentration of the drug far exceeds the MIC for most isolates. Since the opportunity for mutation does not exist, when relapse occurs after treatment is stopped, no further increase in resistance would be expected. Pertinent to this point are the results of carbenicillin treatment in two patients who were colonized with *Pseudomonas* both in the urine and in extraurinary foci. Treatment of one patient resulted in eradication of *P. aeruginosa* in the urine, whereas *P. aeruginosa* which persisted in the sputum showed a twofold increase in resistance to carbenicillin. In the second patient, although relapse of *P. aeruginosa* bacteriuria occurred after treatment, there was no change in susceptibility of the urinary isolate to carbenicillin, whereas the strain present in the sputum persisted and the MIC increased from 50 to 250 μg/ml.

In vitro passage of *P. aeruginosa* in increasing concentrations of carbenicillin has been shown to result in selection of variants with a fivefold or greater increase in resistance to carbenicillin (2, 5, 6, 8, 10, 12). Although initial experiments of this sort suggested that the resulting variants were avirulent (8) or unstable (5) in their resistance, more recent studies have demonstrated resistant variants which were both stable (2, 6, 10) and virulent (2, 10) for mice. In addition, three strains which had developed resistance during therapy were retested in vitro after they had been stored on nutrient agar slants for 16 to 19 months, and all three retained their resistance to cerbenicillin. From the foregoing discussion, these in vitro experiments seem quite analogous to the in vivo situation in which extraurinary *P. aeruginosa* isolates are exposed to subinhibitory concentrations of carbenicillin during therapy. This stepwise and usually limited increase in resistance, similar to that seen with the other penicillins, is not likely to be due to a de novo mutation to penicillinase production. Although it is conceivable that a mutation in vitro from inducible to constitutive production of a carbenicillinase might result in some increased resistance to carbenicillin, it has not been satisfactorily demonstrated that the resistance of *Pseudomonas* variants produced in vitro is related to destruction of carbenicillin. The most likely explanation for resistance to the drug is that populations of *P. aeruginosa* are heterogeneous in susceptibility to carbenicillin, and there are occasional resistant clones. During treatment, or during performance of in vitro studies with large inocula of bacterial cells, susceptible organisms are eradicated, leaving the resistant clones to emerge. The mechanism of resistance to the penicillins which accounts for this stepwise increase in resistance in vitro remains biochemically obscure, and, until recently, was primarily a laboratory phenomenon. However, current problems with methicillin-resistant staphylococci, increasing resistance of gonococci to penicillin G, and the moderate levels of resistance of *P. aeruginosa* to carbenicillin seen in this study fall into this general category.

Similarly, the gradual and moderate increase in carbenicillin resistance observed by Lowbury et al. (10) over a 3-year period in the MRC Burns Research Unit was comparable to the moderate increases of resistance seen in individual patients during the present study. The moderately resistant strains isolated by Lowbury et al. from burns (MIC, 256 to 512 μg/ml) were virulent for mice and did not inactivate carbenicillin. In contrast, in March of 1969, these authors isolated two separate strains of *P. aeruginosa,* as characterized by serogroup and phage type, which simultaneously developed high levels of resistance to carbenicillin (MIC of 4,096 μg/ml). These strains were also virulent for mice. Moreover, both were found to inactivate carbenicillin in vitro, suggesting to these workers that these two strains produced a carbenicillinase. The resistance was found to be unstable on subculture, and acriflavine was found to enhance reversion to carbenicillin susceptibility, suggesting that a genome for carbenicillinase production was carried on an extrachromosomal plasmid. Direct evidence has, in fact, been provided for extrachromosomal genetic units in *Pseudomonas* (11). Lowbury et al. also believed that the simultaneous appearance of resistance due to carbenicillinase production in two separate types of *P. aeruginosa* was a result of resistance transfer, possibly by transduction.

Although the degree of resistance to carbenicillin which appeared in persisting strains of *P. aeruginosa* during the present study was less dramatic than the high levels of resistance in the two strains isolated by Lowbury et al., which was thought to be associated with the production of carbenicillinase, the epidemiological implications may be no less ominous. For various reasons, there has been an increase in the frequency of nosocomial infection due to opportunistic *P. aeruginosa* (9), and cross infections with this organism are a particular hazard. The emergence of resistant strains in individual patients during carbenicillin treatment could quite predictably be translated into a hospitalwide increase in carbenicillin resistance of the prevalent strains of *P. aeruginosa,* particularly if carbenicillin is used widely. Such a mechanism undoubtedly accounted for the gradual emergence of resistance in the MRC Burns Research Unit (8, 10) where carbenicillin had been extensively used.

The potential clinical significance in the individual patient of moderately increased levels of carbenicillin resistance lies in the narrow margin which exists between concentrations achievable in blood and the MIC for most clinical isolates of *P. aeruginosa.* At the present time, this margin appears to be just sufficient to allow adequate results in the treatment of *P. aeruginosa* bacteremia (3). Indeed, the clinical improvement seen in several patients in the present study, despite persistence of the organism in the extraurinary site of infection, may indicate that serum levels of carbenicillin were sufficient to prevent new invasion of well-vascularized tissues. However, any further increase in the MIC of carbenicillin against prevalent strains of *P. aeruginosa* could be expected to compromise therapeutic results significantly.

At the least, a policy of restricting the use of carbenicillin in *P. aeruginosa* infection to only significant and serious infection, rather than using it for the indiscriminate treatment of patients who are merely colonized by this organism, should obviously be advocated. When carbenicillin is used alone for extraurinary *P. aeruginosa* infection in patients with normal renal function, it should be used in doses of at least 24 to 30 g daily in conjunction with oral probenecid. Even with such a policy, however, the persistence and development of increased resistance may be unavoidable in some cases. For this reason, the use of carbenicillin along with another agent such as gentamicin may be preferable. This combination, which is synergistic and is bactericidal for the majority of clinical isolates of *P. aeruginosa* (13, 14), requires further clinical evaluation.

ACKNOWLEDGMENTS

This investigation was supported by Public Health Service training grant AT146-09 from the National Institute of Allergy and Infectious Diseases, and by Chas. Pfizer & Co., Inc. Dr. Clark was supported by a Postdoctoral Fellowship Award from the National Institutes of Health.

LITERATURE CITED

1. Acred, P., D. M. Brown, E. T. Knudsen, G. N. Rolinson, and R. Sutherland. 1967. New semi-synthetic penicillin active against *Pseudomonas pyocyanea.* Nature (London) **215**:25-30.
2. Bell, S. M., and D. D. Smith. 1969. Resistance of *Pseudomonas aeruginosa* to carbenicillin. Lancet **1**:753-754.
3. Bodey, G. P., V. Rodriguez, and J. K. Luce. 1969. Carbenicillin therapy of gram-negative bacilli infections. Amer. J. Med. Sci. **257**:408-414.
3. Bodey, G. P., V. Rodriguez, and D. Stewart. 1969. Clinical pharmacological studies of carbenicillin. Amer. J. Med. Sci. **257**:185-190.
5. Brumfitt, W., A. Percival, and D. A. Leigh. 1967. Clinical and laboratory studies with carbenicillin. Lancet **1**:1289-1293.
6. Darrell, J. H. and P. M. Waterworth. 1969. Carbenicillin resistance in *Pseudomonas aeruginosa* from clinical material. Brit. Med. J. **3**:141-143.
7. Gutman, L. T., M. Turck, R. G. Petersdorf, and R. J. Wedgewood. 1965. Significance of bacterial variants in urine of patients with chronic bacteriuria. J. Clin. Invest. **44**:1945-1952.
8. Jones, R. J., and E. J. L. Lowbury. 1967. Prophylaxis and therapy for *Pseudomonas aeruginosa* infection with carbenicillin and with gentamicin. Brit. Med. J. **3**:79-82.
9. Leading Article. 1967. Pseudomonas infections in hospital. Brit. Med. J. **4**:309-310.
10. Lowbury, E. J. L., A. Kidson, H. A. Lilly, G. A. J. Ayliffe, and R. J. Jones. 1969. Sensitivity of *Pseudomonas aeruginosa* to antibiotics: emergence of strains highly resistant to carbenicillin. Lancet **2**:448-452.
11. Mandel, M. 1966. Deoxyribonucleic acid base composition in the genus Pseudomonas. J. Gen. Microbiol. **43**:273-292.
12. Silverblatt, F., and M. Turck. 1969. Laboratory and clinical evaluation of carbenicillin (carboxybenzyl penicillin). Antimicrobial Agents and Chemotherapy–1968, p. 279-285.
13. Smith, C. B., P. E. Dans, J. N. Wilfert, and M. Finland. 1969. Use of gentamicin in combinations with other antibiotics. J. Infec. Dis. **119**:370-377.
14. Sonne, M., and E. Jawetz. 1969. Combined action of carbenicillin and gentamicin on *Pseudomonas aeruginosa* in vitro. Appl. Microbiol. **17**:893-896.
15. Stephenson, J. P. B. 1969. Resistance of *Pseudomonas aeruginosa.* Lancet **1**:1098-1099.
16. Stratford, B. C. 1968. The treatment of infections due to *Pseudomonas aeruginosa* with carbenicillin ("Pyopen"). Med. J. Aust. **2**:890-895.
17. Turck, M., R. I. Lindemeyer, and R. G. Petersdorf. 1963. Comparison of single disc and tube dilution techniques in determing antibiotic sensitivities of gram-negative pathogens. Ann. Intern. Med. **58**:56-65.
18. Van Rooyen, C. E., J. F. Ross, G. W. Bethune, and A. C. MacDonald. 1967. Bacteriological observations on carbenicillin in the control of *Pseudomonas aeruginosa* infection in burns. Can. Med. Ass. J. **97**:1227-1229.

Antimicrobial Agents and Chemotherapy—1969

Clinical and Laboratory Evaluation of Cephalexin in Urinary-Tract Infections

J. F. ACAR, J. G. BAUDENS, and Y. A. CHABBERT

Institut Pasteur, Service d'Etudes de la Sensibilite aux Antibiotiques, I.N.S.E.R.M., Hopital Saint Joseph, Paris, France

Cephalexin is better absorbed orally than other cephalosporins, and appears to be useful in the treatment of urinary-tract infections. Thirty episodes of urinary-tract infection due to gram-negative organisms were treated by administration of 500 or 750 mg of cephalexin four times daily. Evaluation of the treatment was based on the kinetics of urinary bacterial response during and after treatment. In three patients regarded as treatment failures, bacterial elimination did not occur during treatment. In 11 patients, relapse occurred immediately after treatment was stopped. Among the factors which seemed to influence the outcome of treatment was the type of infection. Results were best in patients with urinary-tract infections without any other clinical or radiological abnormalities. Two observations made in tests conducted in vitro may also explain the differences in the effectiveness of cephalexin. The bactericidal effect of the drug varied in the presence of bacterial inocula of different sizes, and susceptilility to cephalexin of strains harboring R factors governing β-lactamase production differed from that of strains without R factors.

Cephalexin, one of the newest members of the cephalosporin family, has interesting pharmacological properties. Its excellent absorption provides high concentrations in serum and urine. In some studies, cephalexin has been reported to have lower in vitro activity than other cephalosporins; however, it has been suggested that the high concentrations of the drug in serum and urine, which are reached because of nearly complete absorption by the oral route, might overcome the low in vitro activity (10, 11, 14). In a previous study of the activity of cephalexin in urinary-tract infections, Clark and Turck (6) reported unexplained bacterial persistence in the urine of some patients during treatment.

In this report, we attempt to correlate in vitro studies of the susceptibility of gram-negative organisms to cephalexin with clinical results in 30 episodes of urinary-tract infection treated with cephalexin.

MATERIALS AND METHODS

Strains. Four groups of bacterial strains were studied comparatively. One group consisted of 31 enterobacteria isolated from patients treated with cephalexin (*Escherichia coli,* 19; *Klebsiella,* 5; *Providencia,* 2; *Proteus,* 5). These strains were found to be susceptible to cephalothin and cephaloridine by routine testing. A second group of 63 strains was from our laboratory collection (*E. coli,* 29; *Klebsiella,* 20; *Proteus,* 14). The third group consisted of one ampicillin-resistant mutant strain of *E. coli* K-12 selected by the Szybalski technique. The fourth group contained 16 substrains of *E. coli* K-12, in each of which a different R factor governed β-lactamase production. The 16 different R factors originated from *E. coli, Salmonella, Shigella, Proteus, Providencia,* and *Pseudomonas.*

Transferable R factors governing β-lactamase production were characterized by methods published previously (2).

Laboratory studies. The susceptibility of the organisms to ampicillin and four cephalosporins—cephalothin, cephaloridine, cephaloglycine, and cephalexin—was determined. The minimal inhibitory concentration (MIC) of each drug was measured by a serial twofold dilution method in Mueller-Hinton agar (Difco). The antibiotic concentrations tested ranged from 0.5 to 128 μg/ml. Agar plates were inoculated with 10^6 bacteria/ml (broth dilution of an 18-hr broth culture) by means of a Steers-like replicator, and were incubated at 37 C for 18 hr.

The bactericidal activity of the drugs was determined by performing viable counts. Inocula of 10^5 and 10^7

bacteria/ml were tested with drug concentrations of 32, 64, 128, and 256 μg/ml. The activity of cephalexin was compared with that of cephaloridine and ampicillin. Viable counts were determined on serial dilutions in agar at the 3rd, 6th, and 24th hr.

Clinical studies. Observations were made on 24 patients treated during 30 episodes of urinary-tract infection. Sixteen of the patients were female and eight were male, and their ages ranged from 22 to 76 years. All of the patients had been treated with other drugs previously, but infection had persisted or recurred. Treatment consisted of the administration 500 mg of cephalexin (in 11 episodes of infection) or 750 mg of cephalexin (in 19 episodes) four times daily for a period varying from 1 to 4 weeks. The duration of treatment was generally 14 days, but in one patient treatment was discontinued on the third day because of digestive intolerance.

All of the patients except one had creatinine values below 1.5 mg per 100 ml, and none had marked debility from other disease. Laboratory and urological evaluation before the study allowed a division of the patients into two groups. The seven patients in group I (nine courses of treatment) had urinary-tract infections recurring with a different bacterial strain or serotype. No renal or urinary-tract abnormalities were found clinically or radiologically in these patients. In the 17 patients in group II (21 courses of treatment), urinary-tract infection was associated with other signs of urinary or renal disease. However, none had obstructive uropathy.

Before treatment was started, the infecting organisms were isolated from a clean-catch midstream specimen of urine obtained first thing in the morning. During treatment, cultures were performed on clean-catch midstream specimens of urine collected 6, 12, 24, and 48 hr after the beginning of treatment and every 2 days thereafter until treatment was stopped. After treatment was completed, specimens were collected on the second and fourth days and then once weekly.

The response to therapy was evaluated on the basis of urinary bacterial response during and after treatment (4, 8, 12). According to our previous studies (1, 5), repeated quantitative urine cultures allowed the expression of the effect of treatment by a curve relating bacterial elimination to time.

Quantitative urine cultures were performed by a loop technique (7), controlled on some occasions by a count of viable bacteria in serial dilution. Urine was considered sterile when the number of viable bacteria was lower than 10 bacteria/ml.

Bacteria isolated before treatment and strains responsible for relapse or subsequent infections were collected. The biochemical and serological characteristics of these strains and their antibiotic susceptibility were determined.

Specimens of serum and urine were collected from 17 patients during treatment for the determination of antibiotic concentrations. Antibiotic assays were performed by a paper-disc method with *Bacillus subtilis* as the test organism.

The results of treatment were classified in four groups. (i) Treatment was considered to have cured the infection if the urine remained sterile for more than 2 months after treatment or became reinfected with a different organism. (ii) Patients in whom the same strain or serotype reappeared within 2 days after the end of treatment were designated as having immediate relapse. (iii) Relapse occurring between 7 and 21 days after the end of treatment was classified as delayed replase. (iv) Failure was established by the persistence of the infecting organisms in the urine during treatment.

RESULTS

The MIC of cephalexin for 31 clinically isolated gram-negative microbial strains ranged from 2 to 16 μg/ml. A concentration of 8 μg/ml or less inhibited 90% of these strains, all of which were considered to be of normal or intermediate susceptibility. On the basis of its MIC, cephalexin did not appear to be less active than the three other cephalosporins tested.

Resistance to ampicillin was present in 30% of the strains for which the MIC of cephalexin was between 8 and 16 μg/ml. This resistance and its relation to the level of susceptibility to cephalosporins was studied in *E. coli* K-12 (Fig. 1). Two groups of ampicillin-resistant strains of *E. coli* were tested. The first is represented by 16 substrains of *E. coli* K-12 harboring different R factors governing β-lactamase production. The second group is represented by a β-lactamase-producing mutant of *E. coli* K-12 (3).

In the first group, some substrains were no more resistant than the original receptor strain or were only slightly more resistant (between 4 and 8 μg/ml required for inhibition). Other substrains in this group were more resistant, and the MIC of cephalexin was 16 μg/ml; these strains might be considered to have an intermediate degree of susceptibility. Differences in the inhibitory concentrations of the four cephalosporins suggest that different β-lactamases with different enzymatic profiles might be involved.

The β-lactamase-producing mutant strain of *E. coli* K-12 was highly resistant to cephalothin and cephalexin, and was relatively less resistant to cephaloridine and cephaloglycine. Three clinically isolated strains whose ability to produce β-lactamase was not transmissible exhibited the same type of resistance.

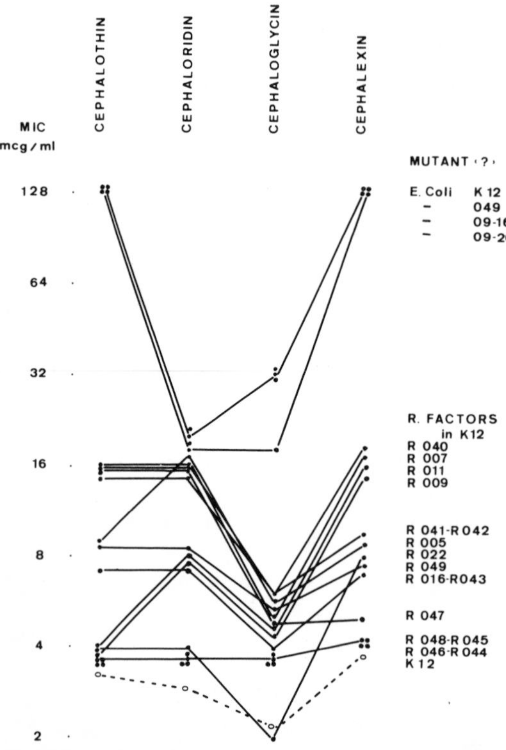

Fig. 1. *Comparative susceptibility to four cephalosporins of Escherichia coli K-12 (dashed line), of E. coli K-12 strains harboring different R factors, of a β-lactamase-producing mutant of E. coli K-12, and of three β-lactamase-producing clinical isolates (049, 09-16, and 09-20).*

The in vitro bactericidal effect of cephalexin (Fig. 2) was influenced by the size of the inoculum. With an inoculum of 10^5 bacteria/ml, the drug was bactericidal after 24 hr. When the effect of cephalexin was compared with that of cephaloridine or ampicillin at the 3rd and 6th hr, the killing activity of cephalexin appeared delayed and lower.

Quite different results were observed when an inoculum of 10^7 bacteria/ml was used. The drug remained bactericidal after 24 hr of contact when used in high concentrations (128 and 256 μg/ml). With 64 or 32 μg of cephalexin per ml, growth resumed after the initial reduction in the number of viable bacteria without any apparent change in the bacterial susceptibility.

A similar effect of the size of inoculum occurred with strains of *E. coli* K-12 harboring R factors.

Clinical results are presented for 29 episodes of urinary-tract infection treated with cephalexin, and three distinct patterns of response are evident.

Rapid elimination of bacteriuria between 6 and 24 hr after the beginning of treatment (Fig. 3A) occurred in 20 patients. Among these were all of the nine patients classified in group I, and seven of the infections in these patients were cured. In group II, this type of response to therapy occurred in 11 patients, and 2 of the infections were cured. The MIC of cephalexin for the bacteria isolated in these 20 infections ranged from 2 to 8 μg/ml (Table 1).

Elimination of bacteria from the urine was delayed in six patients. Urine did not become sterile until 3 to 4 days after the beginning of treatment (Fig. 3B); however, three patients were cured.

The organisms persisted in the urine of three patients. After an initial reduction in the number of viable bacteria, the count remained nearly unchanged during treatment, and immediate relapse occurred after treatment was stopped (Fig. 4).

The MIC of cephalexin for the bacteria isolated from the patients with delayed or incomplete clearing of the urine in most instances was 8 to 16 μg/ml (Table 1). Six of the strains harbored R factors governing β-lactamase production.

Concentrations of the drug in blood and urine of our patients agreed with results reported by others (11). In serum, the peak (range from 15 to 20 μg/ml) was reached 1 hr after drug administration, but at the 4th hr the concentration in serum was generally lower than the MIC for gram-negative bacteria. In urine, mean drug concentrations 6 hr after administration of 500 or 750 mg of cephalexin were 704 and 354 μg/ml, respectively, even in patients whose bacteria persisted during treatment.

Relapses occurred in 17 patients. In 14 of these patients whose relapse occurred immediately after treatment was stopped (on the first or second day), the susceptibility of the bacteria isolated was similar to that of the organisms originally isolated from these patients.

No significant difference between the number of cures and relapses was revealed by a comparison of the group of patients treated with 2 g of cephalexin daily and the group treated with 3 g (Table 2).

Tolerance of cephalexin was excellent. Only one patient complained of nausea and vomiting which made it necessary to stop the treatment. In contrast, three patients received the drug for more than 20 days (one of them for longer than 1 month) without any problem.

DISCUSSION

Cephalexin appeared to be effective in 42% of the episodes of urinary-tract infection studied.

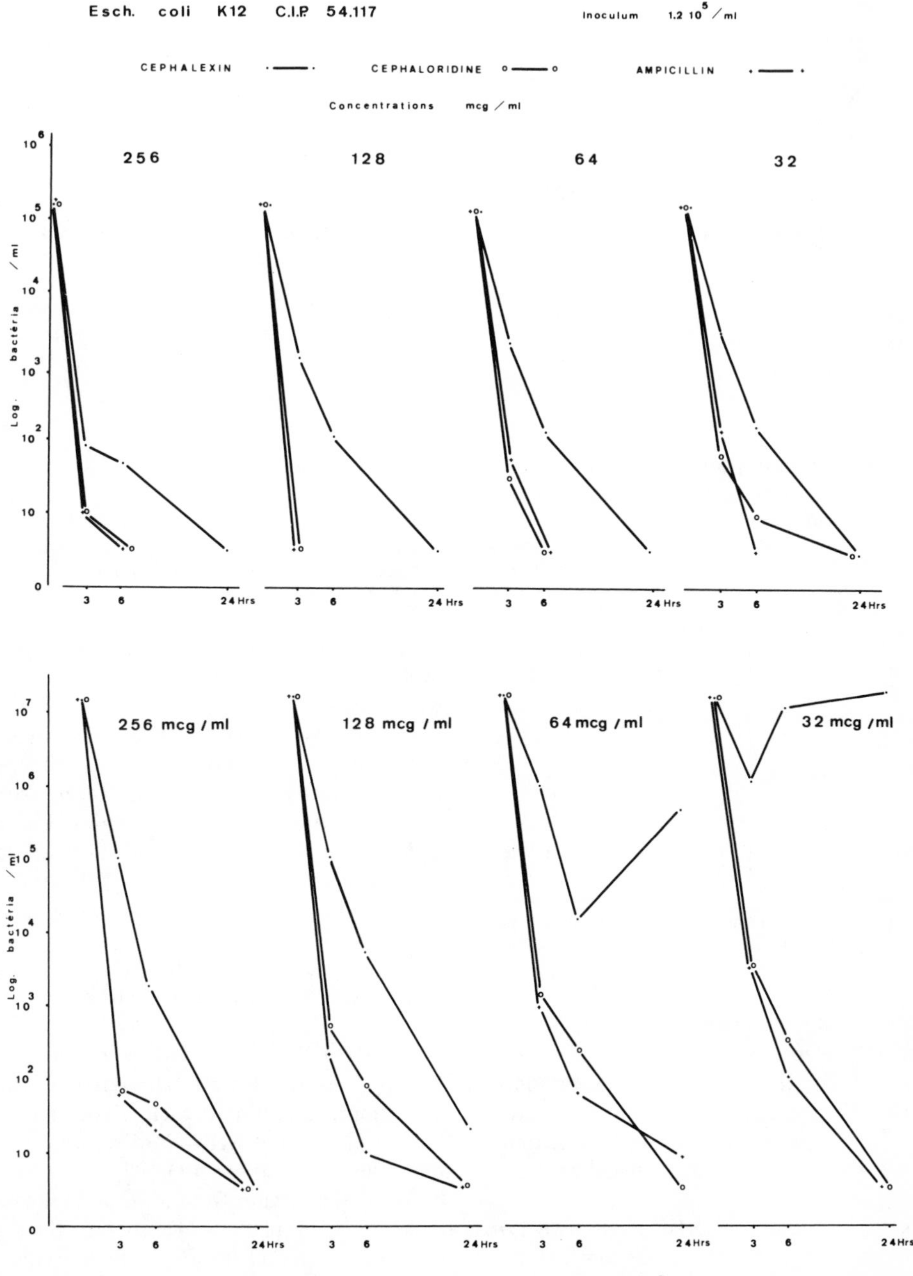

Fig. 2 *Influence of inoculum size on the in vitro bactericidal effect of cephaloridin, ampicillin, and cephalexin.*

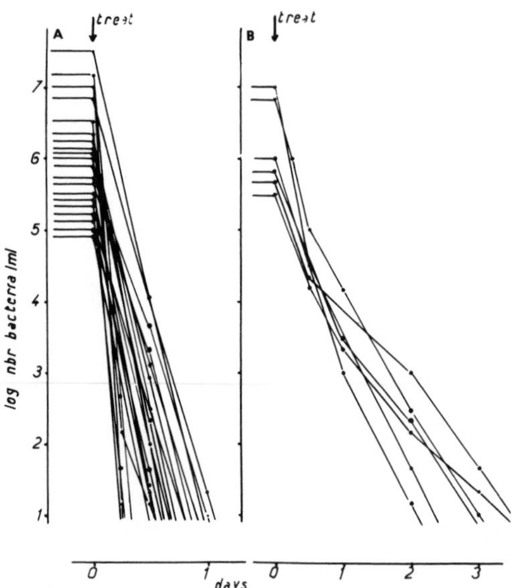

Fig. 3. *Curves of bacterial elimination in urine (A) Rapid elimination. (B) Delayed elimination.*

Table 1. *Minimal inhibitory concentrations (MIC) of cephalexin for bacteria isolated from patients with urinary-tract infections*

Organism[a]	No. of isolates	MIC (µg/ml)			
		2	4	8	16
First group					
Escherichia coli	14	–	4	10	–
Proteus mirabilis	4	–	4	–	–
P. vulgaris	1	1	–	–	–
Klebsiella	2	–	–	2	–
Second group					
E. coli	5	–	–	5	–
Klebsiella	3	–	1	1	1
Providencia	2	–	–	–	2

[a] First group: bacteria eliminated by 24 hr of treatment. Second group: bacteria eliminated with some delay or not eliminated.

Treatment failures were related to a high rate of immediate relapse and to some instances of persistence of the bacteria in urine during treatment. Three factors seem relevant to these results: the type of infection, the susceptibility of the bacteria, and the bactericidal activity of the drug.

Results were quite different in the two types of infections represented by our two groups of patients. In group I, which was made up of patients with acute urinary-tract infections but with no chronic conditions of the kidney or urological abnormalities, 78% of the infections were cured. In group II, made up of patients whose urinary-tract infection was associated with underlying conditions (vesicoureteral reflux, chronic pyelonephritis, recent surgical treatment of renal calculi, chronic cystitis) which cause the infection to be more refractory to drug therapy (13), 25% of the infections were cured. However, the persistence of bacteria in the urine despite high concentrations of drug was unexpected, and the relapses occurred immediately after treatment, without any delay (Fig. 5).

The second factor influencing the outcome of therapy was the susceptibility of the bacteria. The strains harboring R factors governing β-lactamase production were more resistant in vitro than the other strains (9). When the rates of bacterial elimination from urine and the number of relapses in patients whose infections were caused by bacteria harboring R factors governing β-lactamase production were compared with those in patients whose infections were caused

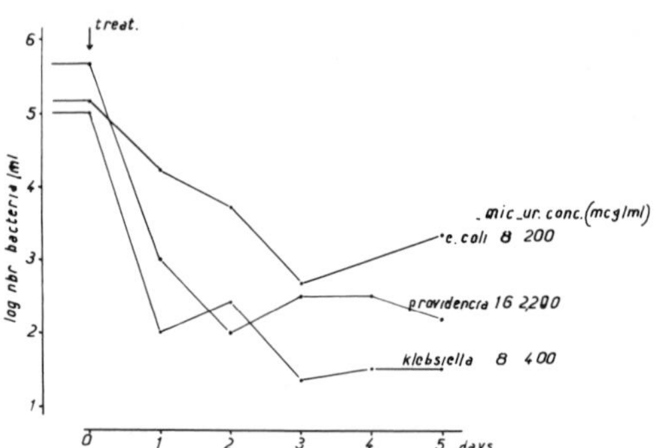

Fig. 4. *Number of viable bacteria in the urine of patients in whom organisms persisted after treatment with cephalexin. The minimal inhibitory concentration and the antibiotic concentration in urine are shown at the right of each curve.*

Table 2. *Comparison of the results of treatment with two different doses of cephalexin*

Daily dose (g)	No. of patients	Result of treatment	
		Cure	Immediate relapse
2[a]	11	4	5
3[b]	18	8	7

[a] Administered as four 500-mg doses per day.
[b] Administered as four 750-mg doses per day.

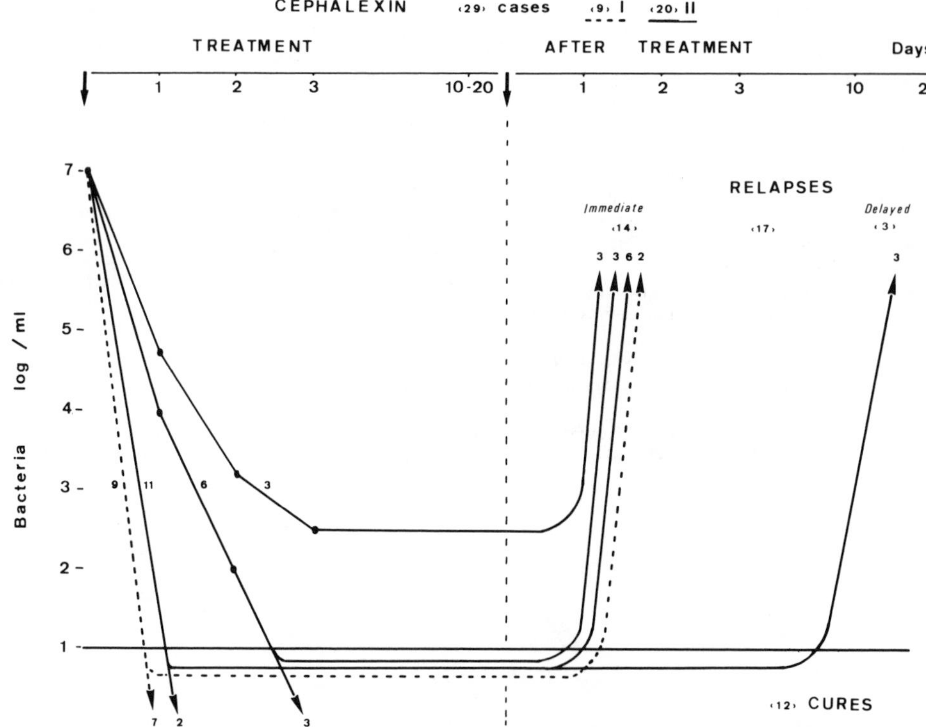

Fig. 5. *Clinical results of treatment according to the type of infection (group I, dashed line; group II, solid line) and the bacterial elimination.*

Table 3. *Correlation between the type of infecting organism and the outcome of treatment with cephalexin*

Type of organism	No. of infections	Bacterial elimination within 24 hr	Bacteria eliminated after 24 hr or not eliminated	Immediate relapse
Strains harboring R factor (resistant to ampicillin)	9 (8 patients)	3	6	7
Strains without R factor (susceptible to ampicillin)	22 (21 patients)	18	4	7

by bacteria without R factors, a significant difference was evident (Table 3). The MIC of cephalexin for the strains harboring R factors was 8 to 16 μg/ml, a level far below the concentrations achieved in urine but higher than the mean concentration in blood. Thus, the antibiotic concentration might have been insufficient at the site of infection. The upper limit of clinical susceptibility of bacteria seems to be around 8 μg/ml.

The third factor which might be involved in the failures and relapses is the reduction in bactericidal activity which occurred when a large inoculum was used, and the regrowth which was observed in vitro. However, further studies are needed on the penetration of the antibiotic into bacteria and on the factors which modified the activity of the drug in urine.

ACKNOWLEDGMENTS

We thank Eli Lilly & Co. for supplying cephalothin, cephaloridine, cephaloglycine, and cephalexin, and Bristol Laboratories for supplying ampicillin.

LITERATURE CITED

1. Acar, J. F. 1969. Dynamique de la bacteriurie dans les infections urinair a bacilles gram negatif traitees par les antibiotiques. Pathol. Biol. **17**:859–864.
2. Baudens, J. G., and Y. A. Chabbert. 1967. Analyse des facteurs de resistence transferables isoles en France. Ann. Inst. Pasteur (Paris) **112**:565–580.
3. Burman, L. G., K. Nordstrom, and H. G. Bowman. 1968. Resistance of *Escherichia coli* to penicillins. V. Physiologi-

cal comparisons of two isogenic strains, one with chromosomally and one with episomally mediated ampicillin resistance. J. Bacteriol. **96**:438–446.

4. Cattell, W. R. J. M. Sardeson, M. B. Sutcliffe, and F. O'Grady. 1968. Kinetics of urinary bacterial response to antibacterial agents, p. 212. *In* Urinary tract infection. Oxford Univ. Pres, London.
5. Chabbert, Y. A. 1966. Correlation between the speed of bactericidal activity of colistin in vitro and in vivo in human urinary infections compared with other antibacterial agents and antibiotics. Advances in antibiotic research, production and clinical use, p. 137.
6. Clark, H., and M. Turck. 1969. In vitro and in vivo evaluation of cephalexin. Antimicrob. agents Chemother.–1968, p. 296–301.
7. Hangen, J., O. Strom, and B. Ostervold. 1968. Bacterial counts in urine. Acta Pathol. Microbiol. Scand. **74**: 391–396.
8. McCabe, W. R., and G. G. Jackson. 1965. Treatment of pyelonephritis. N. Engl. J. Med. **272**:1037–1044.
9. Medeiros, A. A., and T. F. O'Brien. 1968. R factor-mediated increments in levels of resistance to and enzymatic degradation of penicillins and cephalosporins. Antimicrob. Agents Chemother.–1967, p. 271–278.
10. Muggleton, P. W., C. H. O'Callaghan, R. D. Foord, S. M. Kirby, and D. M. Ryan. 1969. Laboratory appraisal of cephalexin. Antimicrob. Agents Chemother.–1968, p. 353–360.
11. Perkins, R. L., H. N. Carlisle, and S. Saslaw. 1968. Cephalexin: in vitro bacterial susceptibility absorption in volunteers and antibacterial activity of sera and urine. Amer. J. Med. Sci. **256**:122–129.
12. Stamey, T. A., D. E. Govan, and J. M. Palmer. 1965. The localisation and treatment of urinary tract infections: the role of bactericidal urine levels as opposed to serum levels. Medicine **44**:1–22.
13. Turck, M., A. R. Ronald, and R. G. Petersdorf. 1968. Relapse and reinfection in chronic bacteriuria. The N. Engl. J. Med. **278**:422–426.
14. Wick, W. E. 1967. Cephalexin, a new orally absorbed cephalosporin antibiotic. Appl. Microbiol. **15**:765–769.

Antimicrobial Agents and Chemotherapy—1969

Therapy with Combinations of Penicillin Analogues in Urinary-Tract Infections

LOUISE RIFF,[1] VERA M. OLEXY, and GEORGE G. JACKSON

Department of Medicine, University of Illinois College of Medicine, Chicago, Illinois 60612

The administration of a penicillinase-resistant penicillin to protect a hydrolyzable penicillin from destruction by β-lactamase has been suggested as one approach to the treatment of gram-negative infections. To determine the contribution to therapy of the penicillinase-resistant component in such a combination, 40 urinary-tract infections were treated sequentially. When a hydrolyzable penicillin (hetacillin) did not eradicate the infection, combination therapy (hetacillin-dicloxacillin) was given. Initial treatment was successful in 23 cases (57%). Addition of dicloxacillin to hetacillin did not alter the results: none of the infections that persisted after treatment with hetacillin alone were cured by the combination. Host factors as well as susceptibility of the organism were important determinants in the outcome of therapy. β-Lactamase was produced by 12 of 13 organisms resistant to hetacillin. In vitro synergism of the combination was demonstrable with only four of the organisms that produced β-lactamases; with two strains, the combination was less than additive. These results indicate that the combination of penicillin analogues is of limited usefulness, and clinically is not more effective than the hydrolyzable penicillin used alone.

It has been shown that the penicillinase-resistant penicillins can act as inhibitors of the β-lactamases from gram-negative organisms and thereby protect hydrolyzable penicillin from inactivation. Prior clinical studies (11–13, 15) with such combinations of penicillin analogues have suggested that they are useful in the treatment of gram-negative infections. However, these studies have infrequently attempted to separate and evaluate in vivo the contribution of each of the penicillin components to therapy.

Reported here are the results of treatment of urinary-tract infections with hetacillin, an amino-penicillin derivative, and dicloxacillin, an isoxazolyl penicillin which is resistant to hydrolysis by β-lactamase. The investigation was designed to determine the benefit from use of the penicillinase-resistant component in combination with hetacillin in comparison with the effectiveness of hetacillin alone. In this application, dicloxacillin was not used as an antibiotic but as a biochemical inhibitor of β-lactamase activity.

[1]U.S. Public Health Service Trainee in Infectious Diseases.

MATERIALS AND METHODS

Quantitative urine cultures were obtained from all patients pre- and post-treatment, and for a minimum of 4 weeks after completion of therapy. Treatment was considered to have resulted in a cure if the infecting organism was eradicated and remained absent for at least 4 weeks. Broth-dilution susceptibility tests were done in tryptose phosphate broth for all urinary isolates. A 10^{-3} dilution of an overnight culture was added to serially diluted antibiotic (hetacillin, dicloxacillin). After overnight incubation, the tubes were read visually to determine the minimal inhibitory concentration (MIC), and then the dilutions were streaked on blood-agar plates to determine the minimal bactericidal concentration (MBC).

The concentrations of antibiotic in body fluids (urine, serum) were measured as described previously (3). For hetacillin, a 10^{-3} dilution of a standard staphylococcal strain, *Staphylococcus aureus* 209P, was added to filtered, serially diluted urine or serum, or to both. After overnight incubation, the results were read visually, and were compared with the end point of a standard antibiotic tested simultaneously. The concentrations of dicloxacillin were determined in the same manner with a strain of *Serratia* that was susceptible to dicloxacillin but resistant to hetacillin.

Production of penicillinase by all organisms was determined by the Gots method (4). For quantitation of the antibiotic-destroying enzymes, filtrates of overnight cultures were reincubated with 100 μg each of penicillin and hetacillin for 18 to 24 hr and were then assayed for drug activity with the standard *S. aureus* 209P. β-Lactamase production was determined by a modification of the iodometric technique described by Perret (9).

Checkerboard. A test for synergy was carried out on all resistant isolates obtained from patients receiving the combination of drugs. In a checkerboard arrangement, tubes in each row contained the same concentration of dicloxacillin, and tubes in each subsequent row contained increasing concentrations. Successive tubes in a given row contained increasing amounts (twofold) of hetacillin. The final volume of the two antibiotics was 1 ml to which 1 ml of a 10^{-3} dilution of the test organism was added. The tubes were incubated overnight and read for both MIC and MBC.

Criteria and treatment. The study consisted of 40 separate episodes of urinary-tract infection in 36 patients. All patients had 10^5 or more organisms per ml of urine prior to initiation of therapy. Most had significant pyuria, although only four were acutely ill.

As the first course of therapy, the patients received hetacillin alone; 1 to 2 g per day was given for an average of 15.7 days (range, 10 to 35 days). If bacilluria persisted after treatment with hetacillin alone, the patient was retreated with hetacillin in the same dose plus dicloxacillin in a dose of 1 to 2 g per day for 14 days.

During treatment, the concentrations of hetacillin in random, single specimens of urine ranged from 50 to 2,000 μg/ml, with an average of 600 μg/ml. Concentrations of hetacillin in serum were 2 to 32 μg/ml, with an average of 12 μg/ml. Dicloxacillin concentrations in urine ranged from 25 to 600 μg/ml, with an average of 150 μg/ml. The highest concentration of dicloxacillin in serum was 6.2 μg/ml; in the majority of patients it was 2 μg or less per ml.

Patient population. Of the 40 infections studied, 15 were in patients who had no detectable anatomical or functional abnormalities of the genitourinary tract. These patients had normal renal function, normal intravenous pyelograms, and normal voiding cystograms; they had no history or present evidence of systemic disease. For purposes of defining host status, this group is designated as "normal."

Twenty-five of the infections were in patients who had either genitourinary disease or systemic disease, or both. The results in patients with disease limited to the genitourinary tract and in patients with systemic diseases did not differ, and these patients are considered as a single group: renal/systemic disease, or the abnormal host.

RESULTS

The initial treatment with hetacillin cured 23 of the 40 infections. In 17 patients, the original organism was present at the end of therapy or the same strain reappeared within 4 weeks.

Organism susceptibility and bacterial etiology. Figure 1 shows the distribution of organisms according to their susceptibility to hetacillin and the results of treatment. The strains distributed themselves into two populations considered here as "susceptible" and "resistant."

The susceptible group was composed of streptococci, *Proteus*, and *Escherichia coli*. Of the *Proteus* strains, six were indole-negative. There was no predominant serotype of *E. coli*; three strains were "rough" and could not be typed. The organisms in the resistant group were *E. coli*, *Klebsiella-Enterobacter*, and *Pseudomonas*.

Cure of infection was more likely with sus-

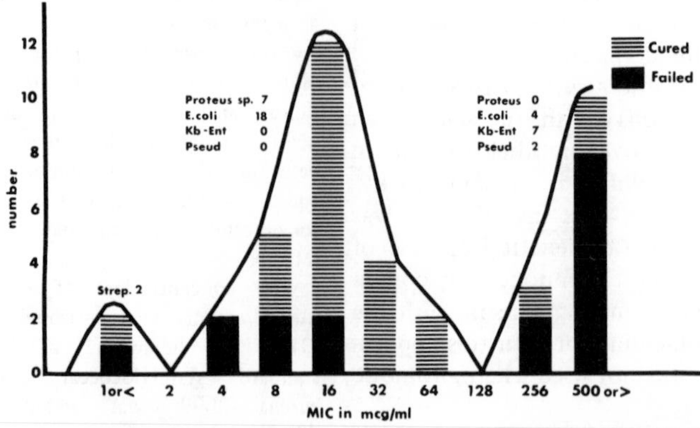

Fig. 1. *Distribution of organisms according to susceptibility to hetacillin.*

ceptible strains and less frequent with resistant strains. Susceptibility to hetacillin could not, however, be used as a single criterion to predict the success or failure of therapy.

Host status. Figure 2 shows the result of treatment according to host status.

In the "normal" group (those patients with a normal intravenous pyelogram, normal voiding cystogram, and no history or laboratory evidence of systemic disease), 10 of 11 patients infected with a strain susceptible to hetacillin were cured. Among four patients in the "normal" group who were infected with strains resistant to hetacillin, two were cured.

In 16 patients with underlying abnormality of the genitourinary tract or with systemic disease whose infections were caused by a susceptible strain, treatment resulted in 10 of the 16 being cured. In nine other patients with abnormal host status but infected with a resistant strain, treatment cured only one.

β-Lactamase production. It was postulated that if the organisms that were resistant to hetacillin were resistant on the basis of β-lactamase production, the addition of a penicillin which inhibits β-lactamase might change their response to that observed with susceptible organisms. Figure 3 shows the relationship between β-lactamase production and the susceptibility of the infecting strains. None of the susceptible strains produced β-lactamase. In the group of resistant strains, 12 of 13 produced β-lactamases.

Hetacillin-dicloxacillin treatment. All but 1 of the 17 patients whose infection failed to clear with hetacillin alone were given a combination of hetacillin in the same dose plus dicloxacillin. Although three-fourths of the infecting organisms produced β-lactamases, the addition of dicloxacillin to hetacillin failed to eradicate any of these infections. Only one organism not eradicated by hetacillin alone changed susceptibility after treatment.

Parenthetically, one patient not included in this study erroneously received hetacillin-dicloxacillin as initial therapy. This was the only treatment success with the combination. The patient was a "normal" host, and was infected with a susceptible strain of *E. coli* that did not produce β-lactamase.

Organisms that produced β-lactamase were studied to determine whether an in vitro advantage of the combination of penicillins was demonstrable. The results of these determinations are shown in Fig. 4. Three patterns of response can be identified: an additive effect (a straight line connecting the MIC of each drug), synergism (concave lines bowing toward the coordinates), and less than addition (convex lines bowing away from the coordinates).

Synergism was shown with the *Pseudomonas* strains and two of the *Enterobacter* group.

The addition of dicloxacillin did not materially alter the susceptibility of the other

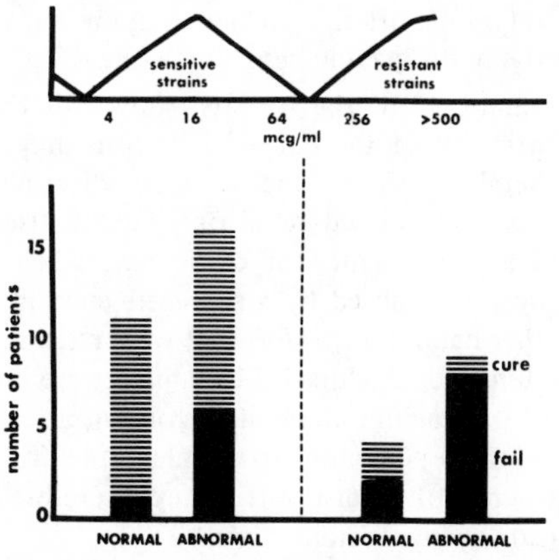

Fig. 2. *Effect of host factors on the outcome of treatment of urinary-tract infections. The small graph at the top refers to the two bacterial populations considered in Fig. 1. The bars represent the result of therapy of infections caused by susceptible and resistant strains as a function of the absence of underlying disease (normal host) or the presence of renal/systemic disease (abnormal host).*

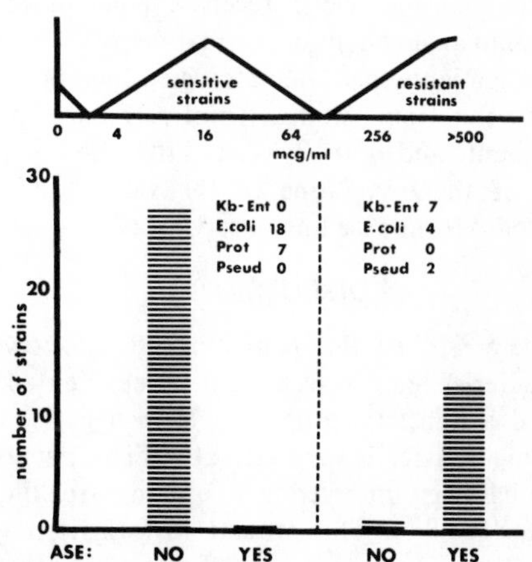

Fig. 3. *Production of β-lactamases by infecting strains according to hetacillin susceptibility.*

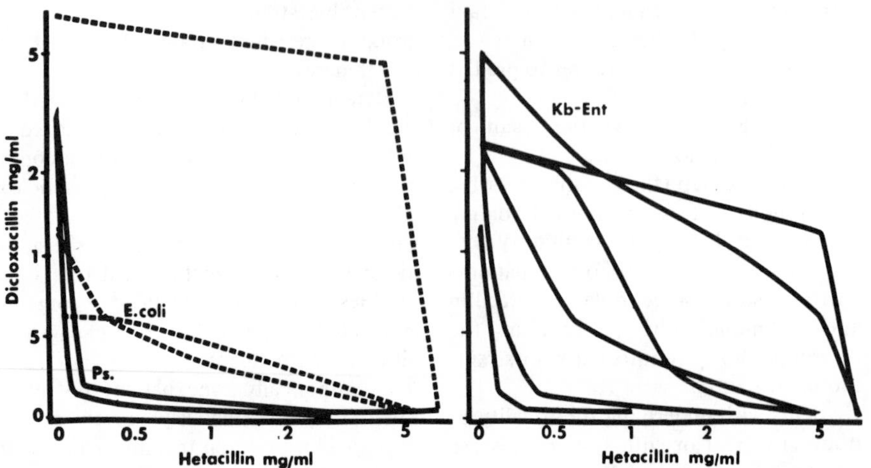

Fig. 4. *Combined action of hetacillin plus dicloxacillin on β-lactamase-producing gram-negative bacteria.*

organims to hetacillin, and with two strains the combination was less than additive.

Toxicity. Both penicillin analogues were tolerated well by most patients. Mild to moderate diarrhea was a frequent complaint which occurred in one-fourth of patients, usually on the second to fourth days of therapy. This was self-limited and was no more severe with the combination than with hetacillin alone. Three patients complained of moderate nausea. Five additional patients could not complete treatment and were excluded from the analysis. Severe diarrhea occurred in three of them, and two discontinued medication because of vomiting.

One patient developed generalized rash and urticaria on the 14th day of hetacillin therapy; this patient had never received penicillin or a penicillin analogue prior to treatment.

All patients had hematologic, hepatic, and renal function studies pretreatment, post-treatment, and 4 to 8 weeks after the completion of therapy. None of the values differed markedly from base line observations.

DISCUSSION

The possibility that penicillin resistance owing to bacterial β-lactamases can be circumvented by use of a nontoxic drug capable of negating the enzyme activity is very attractive. The phenomenon has been observed in several in vitro studies (5, 6, 10, 14). The present investigation was undertaken to translate the meaning of the laboratory observations in terms of its practical application to the treatment of patients with urinary-tract infections. The essential feature of the study relative to those previously reported was the sequential administration of drugs: first, the hydrolyzable penicillin was administered alone; then the same penicillin was administered in combination with a penicillinase-resistant penicillin. Only in this way is it likely that a proper evaluation can be made of the contribution of the second penicillin.

The effect of the combination regimen in the treatment of patients was negligible. Reduction in the number of organisms per milliliter of urine occurred with both treatment regimens, but not more often with the combination than with the hydrolyzable penicillin alone.

Evaluation of the results shows that the susceptibility of the bacterial strain is only one of several significant factors in eradicating an infection. Associated renal or systemic diseases decreased the chance of cure, even when the infection was caused by a susceptible strain. On the other hand, two strains that were resistant to hetacillin and produced β-lactamase were eradicated by hetacillin alone; high concentrations of hydrolyzable penicillin, attainable in the urine in the absence of renal insufficiency, therefore can eradicate some resistant strains.

The addition of the isoxazolyl penicillin resulted in a synergistic effect on the susceptibility of only four strains when measured in vitro. However, the synergistic effect was not necessary for eradication of two of these strains, and the addition of the second penicillin in the doses used was ineffective against the other two strains.

The number of clinical isolates demonstrating synergism of potential clinical significance appears to be small. In a survey of a large number of gram-negative pathogens, McKee and Turck (7) found that only 20% were susceptible to this combination, and others (1, 2, 14) have reported a low incidence of strains responding to mixtures of presently available penicillins and cephalosporins. In vitro studies (8) have suggested that β-lactamase located in the cell wall of the organism is episomally mediated and not susceptible to the action of penicillin combinations. Another possibility is that the β-lactamases from different strains vary in their affinity for inhibitors; it is possible that dicloxacillin was ineffective in inhibiting penicillinase activity, whereas another drug might be effective. These observations suggest that the β-lactamase from each infecting strain must be investigated separately.

In overall view, use of an active hydrolyzable penicillin in the treatment of urinary-tract infections in patients without other renal or systemic disease can be expected to eradicate susceptible strains and some resistant strains. The latter are assumed not to have penicillinase intimately associated with the cell wall. With most other strains, no synergistic effect on penicillin inhibition in vitro was shown by the addition of a penicillinase-resistant penicillin, dicloxacillin. In the doses used, dicloxacillin combined with penicillin was no more effective than penicillin alone in the treatment of patients.

ACKNOWLEDGMENTS

This investigation was supported by Public Health Service research grant AI-1949 and Public Health Service training grant AI-00208 from the National Institute of Allergy and Infectious Diseases, and by a grant from Bristol Laboratories, Syracuse, N.Y.

LITERATURE CITED

1. Bach, J. A., N. Buono, D. Chisholm, K. E. Price, T. A. Purisano, and A. Gourevitch. 1967. In vitro and in vivo synergism of mixtures of penicillins. Antimicrob. Agents Chemother.–1966, p. 328–336.
2. Fraher, M. A., and E. Jawetz. 1968. Combined action of β-lactamase-resistant and β-lactamase-susceptible penicillins on 20 strains of *Pseudomonas aeruginosa*. Antimicrob. Agents Chemother.–1967, p. 711–715.
3. Gonnella, J. S., V. M. Olexy, and G. G. Jackson. 1967. In vitro and clinical effects of cephaloridine, a semisynthetic antibiotic. Amer. J. Med. Sci. **254**:71–82.
4. Gots, J. S. 1945. Detection of penicillinase producing properties of micro-organisms. Science (Washington) **102**:309.
5. Hamilton-Miller, J. M. T., and J. T. Smith. 1964. Inhibition of penicillinases from Gram positive and Gram negative bacteria by substrate analogues. Nature (London) **201**:999–1001.
6. Hamilton-Miller, J. M. T., J. T. Smith, and R. Knox. 1965. Interaction of cephaloridine with penicillinase-producing Gram negative bacteria. Nature (London) **208**:235–237.
7. McKee, W. M., and M. Turck. 1968. Susceptibility of gram negative pathogens to the combination of dicloxacillin and hetacillin. Antimicrob. Agents Chemother.–1967, p. 705–710.
8. Neu, H. C. 1969. Effect of β-lactamase location in *Escherichia coli* on penicillin synergy. Appl. Microbiol. **17**:783–786.
9. Perret, C. J. 1954. Iodometric assay of penicillinase. Nature (London) **174**:1012–1013.
10. Sabath, L. D., and E. P. Abraham. 1964. Synergistic action of penicillins and cephalosporins against *Pseudomonas pyocyanea*. Nature (London) **204**:1066–1069.
11. Sabath, L. D., H. A. Elder, C. E. McCall, and M. Finland. 1967. Synergistic combinations of penicillins in the treatment of bacteriuria. N. Engl. J. Med. **277**:232–238.
12. Sabath, L. D., C. E. McCall, N. H. Steigbigel, and M. Finland. 1967. Synergistic penicillin combinations for treatment of human urinary-tract infections. Antimicrob. Agents Chemother.–1966, p. 149–155.
13. Shirley, R. L., and J. W. Moore, 1965. Pseudomonas urinary tract infection. N. Engl. J. Med. **273**:283.
14. Sutherland, R., and F. R. Batchelor. 1964. Synergistic activity of penicillins against penicillinase-producing Gram negative bacilli. Nature (London) **201**:868–869.
15. Zaidi,, Z. H. 1966. Antibiotics in combination. Lancet **1**:317.

Antimicrobial Agents and Chemotherapy—1969

Novobiocin and Acidification for Treatment of Bacteriuria Due to Gram-Negative Bacilli

JOAN I. CASEY, LEON D. SABATH, STEPHEN H. ZINNER, and MAXWELL FINLAND

Thorndike Memorial Laboratory (Channing Laboratory), Harvard Medical Unit, Boston City Hospital, and Department of Medicine, Harvard Medical School, Boston, Massachusetts 02118

Fourteen patients with well-documented chronic bacteriuria were tested with novobiocin and ammonium chloride to determine whether the increased in vitro activity of novobiocin against gram-negative bacilli in acid media was also demonstrable in patients. In 10 of the 14 patients, the bacterial count of the urine was reduced 99.99% or more during therapy, but in only 8 were the organisms eliminated. Three weeks after therapy was stopped, only two patients remained uninfected. No antibacterial effect was noted in the urine of either of two patients in whom the urine *p*H was not observed to be *p*H 5.5 or lower; the other patients produced more acid urines. The organisms recovered from urine were *Escherichia coli* in seven patients (plus *Proteus* in one of them), *Klebsiella* in five, and *Enterobacter* and *Serratia* each in one patient.

The antibacterial activity of certain antibiotics may be profoundly changed by altering the *p*H of the medium. Streptomycin (1), kanamycin (2), and gentamicin (9) are 100 or more times as active at *p*H 8.5 than at *p*H 5. In contrast, some tetracyclines (4) and mandelic acid (7) are much more active at *p*H 5.0 than at *p*H 8.5. Many physicians, aware of these effects, have appropriately used either acidifying or alkalinizing medications along with the antibacterial substances to increase the therapeutic effect of these antibiotics in urinary-tract infections.

Erythromycin and novobiocin, generally considered to be effective primarily against gram-positive bacteria, are known to be markedly affected in their activity by changes in *p*H. Novobiocin is most active in acid media (6) and erythromycin in alkaline media (3). These effects have recently been restudied in this laboratory in vitro, and these antibiotics have been shown to exhibit considerable activity against most common gram-negative bacillary pathogens at the appropriate *p*H (8, 10, 11). The purpose of the present study was to determine whether this in vitro activity of novobiocin could be applied advantageously in vivo. Because urine is the only body fluid in which marked alteration in *p*H is either possible or desirable, the in vivo effectiveness of novobiocin was studied in patients with bacteriuria.

MATERIALS AND METHODS

Patients. All patients selected for this study had well-documented chronic bacteriuria; that is, cultures of their urines yielded colony counts of 100,000 or more bacteria of the same species per ml of urine on two or more occasions immediately before treatment, with similar bacteriuria previously documented over periods of months to years. Most of these patients had failed earlier to respond to conventional treatment, or infection had recurred after such treatment on one or more occasions. Fourteen patients (10 females and 4 males) ranging in age from 28 to 86 years were studied.

Treatment. The dosage schedule for the first 10 patients was 1 g of novobiocin orally every 12 hr on the first day, and 500 mg every 12 hr on each of 5 subsequent days. The individual doses were doubled for the last four patients. Acidification was accomplished with 1 g of ammonium chloride given orally every 4 hr while the patient was awake. None of the patients had received any antibiotic within 7 days of starting this treatment.

Laboratory studies. Quantitative cultures of the urine were done after the last dose and again 3 days, 3 weeks, and 3 months after therapy had been stopped. The organisms recovered were identified by routine bacteriological methods. Urine *p*H was determined frequently with narrow-range *p*H indicator paper, and in many instances was verified with *p*H meter readings.

Antibiotic susceptibility tests were performed on all isolates. Twofold dilutions of novobiocin sodium in Heart Infusion Agar (Difco) were used, and susceptibility was tested both at *p*H 7.2 to 7.4 and at *p*H 5 (adjusted with concentrated HCl before pouring the plates). An overnight culture was diluted 10^{-1} in distilled water and applied with an inocula replicator (13).

Concentrations of novobiocin in serum and urine were determined by means of a hole-plate, agar-diffusion method, with *Sarcina lutea* SKF 1360 as the indicator organism in Heart Infusion Agar (Difco) that had been adjusted to *p*H 6.6 with HCl. Zones of inhibition were read after incubation for 18 to 24 hr at 37 C; and serum and urine specimens and a standard were dissolved in phosphate buffer (*p*H 6.6).

RESULTS

Clinical and bacteriological response. The urine of 8 of the 14 patients yielded no bacteria at the end of the 6 days of treatment with novobiocin and ammonium chloride (Table 1). In each of two additional patients, the number of *Escherichia coli* colonies in the urine was reduced from 10^8 to 10^4 per ml, but 3 days later the urine again yielded 10^8 colonies/ml.

Three days after treatment ended, the urine of five of the eight patients whose cultures had become negative were still negative (Table 2). At that time, *Proteus* but not *E. coli* was grown from the urine of the patient who originally had a dual infection. At 3 weeks and 3 months, two of the eight patients still had negative urine cultures. One of these two patients has been followed as long as 6 months and has remained uninfected.

In 10 of 12 patients whose urines were maintained at *p*H 5.5 or less, the colony counts of the urine were reduced 4 or more decilogs, and in 8 of the 10 all cultures during therapy yielded no bacterial growth (Table 3). In five of these eight patients, negative urine cultures were obtained after therapy was stopped. Two

Table 1. *Results of cultures at end of treatment*

Organisms	No. of patients	
	Tested	Negative
Escherichia coli	6	3[a]
E. coli + Proteus	1	1[b]
Klebsiella	5	4
Enterobacter	1	0
Serratia	1	0
Totals	14	8

[a] In two additional patients, colony counts were reduced from 10^8 to 10^4/ml.
[b] Negative for both organisms.

Table 2. *Results of follow-up cultures of urine*

Organisms	Patients tested	No. negative after end of therapy			
		3 days	3 weeks	3 months	6 months
Escherichia coli	6	2	1	1	1
E. coli + Proteus	1	1[a]	–[b]	–	–
Klebsiella	5	3	1	1	–
Enterobacter ..	1	0	0	0	–
Serratia	1	0	0	0	–
No. negative ..		6[a]	2	2	1
No. tested	14	14	6	2	1

[a] *E. coli* negative, *Proteus* positive in one patient.
[b] Not tested.

Table 3. *Effect of pH on bacteriuria during novobiocin treatment*

*p*H of urine	No. of patients	No. of patients with	
		Colonies reduced 99.99% or more	Cultures negative
4.5–5.5	12	10	8
>5.5	2	0	0

patients whose urines were regularly less acid did not respond to therapy. All patients with pyuria who responded bacteriologically also had fewer or no pus cells in the bacteria-free urine. Two patients developed rashes shortly after the sixth day of therapy, but no alterations in renal or hepatic function were detected.

Susceptibility tests. Tests for susceptibility to novobiocin were done with organisms isolated from seven patients both before and after therapy. When tested at *p*H 5.5, the minimal inhibitory concentration (MIC) ranged from 1.6 to 6.2 μg/ml for six isolates; the MIC for the other isolate was 12.5 μg/ml. When tested on media at *p*H 7.2 to 7.4, the MIC for all seven isolates was 100 to >800 μg/ml. No change in susceptibility of any of the strains occurred during treatment.

Concentrations of novobiocin in serum and urine. The concentrations of novobiocin in serum ranged from 11 to 210 μg/ml (geometric mean, 29 μg/ml), and those in the urine ranged from 1 to 50 μg/ml (geometric mean, 8 μg/ml).

DISCUSSION

The possible clinical usefulness of treatment with novobiocin plus acidifying medication for bacteriuria was not clearly demonstrated in the present small study. Although some response was seen in 10 of 14 patients, negative urine cultures were achieved in only 8 patients during treatment, and only 2 had negative urine cultures 3 weeks after therapy was stopped. In a group of 24 comparable bacteriuric patients treated with erythromycin and alkalinizing medication (15), 7 had negative urine cultures 3 weeks after therapy was stopped. It is possible that the longer duration of treatment with erythromycin (14 days versus 6 days) may have been a factor.

It was previously shown that most gram-negative bacilli tested (which included *Escherichia, Proteus, Klebsiella, Enterobacter, Serratia,* and *Pseudomonas*) could be inhibited in vitro by concentrations of novobiocin attainable in urine–if the media were sufficiently acid (8). Organisms representing five of those genera were present in the urine of the patients studied here; inhibition of *E. coli, Proteus,* and *Klebsiella* was observed (Table 1), but not of *Enterobacter* or *Serratia.* These results in patients are not surprising, because, in the in vitro study referred to, organisms of the latter two genera were more resistant to novobiocin than were the other organisms.

The concentrations of novobiocin observed in urine specimens in the present study were somewhat lower than those previously reported (12, 14) in subjects who were not acidified. This may represent increased back diffusion of novobiocin from renal tubules resulting from its decreased electrical charge in more acid urine. Such decreased renal excretion of weakly acid molecules in acid urine has been described (5).

ACKNOWLEDGMENTS

We are indebted to Ruth Jones, C. Donald Leaf, and Deborah A. Gerstein for valuable technical assistance, and to The Upjohn Co. for supplying the novobiocin used in this study. This investigation was supported by Public Health Service grants 5 RO1-AI-00023 and 2 TO1-AI-00068 from the National Institute of Allergy and Infectious Diseases.

Dr. Zinner is a recipient of a Fellowship from the Northeast Chapter of the Massachusetts Heart Association, and Dr. Sabath is a recipient of a Research Career Development Award from the National Institute of Allergy and Infectious Diseases.

LITERATURE CITED

1. Abraham, E. P., and E. S. Duthie. 1946. Effect of pH of the medium on activity of streptomycin and penicillin and other chemotherapeutic substances. Lancet **1**:455–459.
2. Garrod, L. P. 1959. Chemotherapy of infections of the urinary tract. Royal College of Physicians of Edinburgh, Publications, No. 11.
3. Haight, T. H., and M. Finland. 1952. Observations on the mode of action of erythromycin. Proc. Soc. Exp. Biol. Med. **81**:188–193.
4. Lorian, V. 1966. Antibiotics and chemotherapeutic agents in clinical and laboratory practice, 1st ed. Charles C Thomas, Publisher, Springfield, Ill.
5. Miline, M. D., B. H. Scribner, and M. A. Crawford. 1958. Non-ionic difusion and the excretion of weak acids and bases. Amer. J. Med. **24**:709–729.
6. Nichols, R. L., and M. Finland. 1957. Novobiocin. A limited bacteriologic and clinical study of its use in forty-five patients. Antibiot. Med. **2**:241–257.
7. Rosenheim, M. L. 1935. Mandelic acid in the treatment of urinary infections. Lancet **1**:1032–1037.
8. Sabath, L. D., D. A. Gerstein, and M. Finland. 1969. Enhanced activity of novobiocin against gram-negative bacilli in acid media. Antimicrob. Agents Chemother.–1968, p. 398–404.
9. Sabath, L. D., D. A. Gerstein, C. D. Leaf, and M. Finland. 1970. Increasing the usefulness of antibiotics: treatment of infections caused by gram-negative bacilli. Clin. Pharmacol. Ther. **11**:161–167.
10. Sabath, L. D., D. A. Gerstein, P. B. Loder, and M. Finland. 1968. Excretion of erythromycin and its enhanced activity in urine against gram-negative bacilli with alkalinization. J. Lab. Clin. Med. **72**:916–923.
11. Sabath, L. D., V. Lorian, D. Gerstein, P. B. Loder, and M. Finland. 1968. Enhancing effect of alkalinization of the medium on the activity of erythromycin against gram-negative bacteria. Appl. Microbiol. **16**:1288–1292.
12. Simon, H. J., R. M. McCune, P. A. P. Dineen, and D. A. Rogers. 1956. Studies on novobiocin, a new antimicrobial agent. Antibiot. Med. **2**:205–218.
13. Steers, E., E. L. Foltz, and B. S. Graves. 1959. Inocula replicating apparatus for routine testing of bacterial susceptibility of antibiotics Antibiot. Chemother. **9**:307–311.
14. Wright, W. W., L. E. Putnam, and H. Welch. 1956. Novobiocin serum concentrations and urinary excretion following oral administration in man. Antibiot. Med. **2**:311–316.
15. Zinner, S. H., L. D. Sabath, J. I. Casey, and M. Finland. 1970. Erythromycin plus alkalinization in treatment of urinary infections. Antimicrob. Agents Chemother.–1969, p. 413–416.

Antimicrobial Agents and Chemotherapy—1969

Erythromycin Plus Alkalinization in Treatment of Urinary Infections

STEPHEN H. ZINNER, LEON D. SABATH, JOAN I. CASEY, and MAXWELL FINLAND

Thorndike Memorial Laboratory (Channing Laboratory), Harvard Medical Unit, Boston City Hospital, and Department of Medicine, Harvard Medical School, Boston, Massachusetts 02118

Twenty-four patients with chronic bacteriuria were treated orally with erythromycin estolate and sodium bicarbonate, usually for 2 weeks. In 22 of the patients (92%) the number of bacteria in urine was reduced during therapy by 99.99% or more, and in 17 patients (71%) the organisms were eliminated. Three weeks after therapy was completed, no organisms were detected in the urine of 29% of the patients. In no instance did the concentration of erythromycin in the patient's serum exceed the minimal inhibitory concentration for the infecting organism, whereas in nearly every instance this concentration was exceeded in the urine when tested at *p*H 8.5. Bacteria that reappeared in the urine of patients after therapy had been discontinued were of the same species as the pretreatment isolates and showed the same susceptibility to erythromycin.

The effects of *p*H on the activity of antibiotics have been known since the observations, by Waksman et al. (10) and by Abraham and Duthie (1), that streptomycin is more active in vitro at alkaline *p*H. In 1947, Harris et al. (5) studied 15 patients with urinary-tract infections and reported that alkalinization of the urine enhanced the activity and therapeutic effect of streptomycin.

In 1952, Haight and Finland (4) reported that erythromycin is most active at alkaline *p*H when tested in broth against *Streptococcus hemolyticus,* and *Sarcina lutea.* In vitro, using dilution tests on agar at *p*H 7.4, these authors showed that the minimal inhibitory concentration (MIC) for most gram-negative organisms was greater than 100 μg/ml, but the possible effect of *p*H on the activity of erythromycin against gram-negative bacteria was not investigated. More recently, Zagar (11) showed that erythromycin at *p*H 8.4 to 8.6 inhibited most of the strains of *Escherichia coli, Bacillus proteus,* and *Pseudomonas aeruginosa* that he tested. He also showed an 11-fold increase in antibacterial activity of urine from patients taking erythromycin when alkali was added to the voided urine (12).

Sabath et al. (7, 8) demonstrated a more marked enhancement of antibacterial activity of erythromycin in urine from volunteers taking the drug plus sodium bicarbonate or acetazolamide. Concentrations of the antibiotic in serum and urine and its renal clearance were not significantly altered by the alkalinization. In vitro, urine specimens from subjects taking both erythromycin and alkalinizing medication inhibited *E. coli, Klebsiella, Proteus, Pseudomonas,* and *Serratia.* However, when the same subjects were taking the same dose of either erythromycin alone or alkali (or acetazolamide) alone specimens of their urine had little or no effect on these organisms. The results of these observations prompted a therapeutic trial.

The present study was designed to determine whether the in vitro observations of enhanced activity of erythromycin at alkaline *p*H could also be demonstrated in patients with urinary-tract infection due to gram-negative organisms.

MATERIALS AND METHODS

Patients and therapy. Erythromycin and alkalinization of the urine was used in the treatment of 24 patients with chronic bacteriuria (20 females, mean age 31 years; 4 males, mean age 75 years). Erythromycin estolate, 500 mg every 8 hr, plus sodium bicarbonate, 1 teaspoonful (5 g) in water three or four times daily, was prescribed for 14 days. Four patients received double this dose of erythromycin. Patients with hypertension, cardiac failure, liver disease, or renal stones were excluded from the study with two exceptions: an 88-year-old man with congestive heart failure received acetazolamide plus potassium bicarbonate, and a patient with cystine stones received the prescribed treatment. None of the patients had received any antibiotic during the 7 days preceding the start of this regimen.

Prior to instituting therapy, at least two and usually three cultures of urine from each patient yielded 10^5 or more colonies of the same bacterial species per ml. Urine was also cultured during therapy, and 3 days, 3 to 4 weeks, and 3, 6, and 12 months after therapy when indicated and feasible. Serum was obtained for tests of renal and hepatic function prior to and at the end of therapy.

Antibiotic susceptibility tests. Organisms were identified by routine bacteriological methods. Tests for erythromycin susceptibility of the pre- and post-therapy organisms were done on Heart Infusion Agar (Difco) by the inocula replicating method of Steers, Foltz, and Graves (9) at *p*H 7.4 and 8.5 by use of a 10^{-1} dilution (in sterile distilled water) of an overnight broth culture. Erythromycin standard (supplied by The Upjohn Co., Kalamazoo, Mich.) was dissolved in methanol (10%, v/v) at 5,000 μg/ml, diluted in water, and added to agar to give final concentrations of erythromycin ranging from 0.5 to 500 μg/ml. The *p*H of the agar was adjusted with NaOH before pouring. Methanol, in concentrations equal to that included in the highest concentration of erythromycin, was incorporated into agar at each *p*H to serve as controls.

Routine disc susceptibility tests to 10 antibiotics (ampicillin, cephalothin, chloramphenicol, erythromycin, gentamicin, kanamycin, nalidixic acid, nitrofurantoin, polymyxin B, and tetracycline) were performed on most of the organisms isolated from the patients before and after erythromycin treatment. These tests were done on nutrient agar at *p*H 7.2 to 7.4

Concentrations of antibiotic in urine and serum. Concentrations of erythromycin in urine and serum were determined for specimens from 21 patients by a previously described modification (7) of the agar-diffusion method of Grove and Randall (3).

RESULTS

Bacteriological results. The bacteriological responses to therapy are summarized in Table 1. The urine became and remained free from the infecting organisms in 17 (71%) of the 24 patients while on the prescribed therapy. In five additional patients, the bacterial counts of the urine were reduced by 4 or more decilogs from the pretreatment numbers while the patients were receiving therapy. Three days after therapy was stopped, the urine of 50% of the treated patients remained uninfected. When cultures were repeated 3 to 4 weeks after therapy was stopped, seven patients (29% of the initial group and 58% of those with sterile urine 3 days after the end of therapy) still showed no evidence of infection.

In the subsequent follow-up, urine specimens from five patients were still free from bacteria at 3 months and specimens from two patients were sterile at 12 months. Thus, an in vivo effect was demonstrated in 22 (92%) of 24 patients with chronic bacteriuria who had received treatment with erythromycin plus alkalinization of the urine.

Susceptibility of the organisms to erythromycin. As shown in Table 2, the mean of the MIC of erythromycin for 38 gram-negative bacilli isolated before and after therapy was 8 to 9 times greater when tested at *p*H 7.4 than at *p*H 8.5. There was no evidence of increased resistance to erythromycin emerging in tests at either *p*H in organisms isolated from patients in

Table 1. *Bacteriological results of treatment of bacteriuria with erythromycin plus alkalinization*

Infecting organism	No. of patients	No. with negative urine cultures: During therapy	3 days after therapy ended	3 to 4 weeks post-therapy
Escherichia coli	14	10	7	3
Klebsiella	6	5	3	3
Enterobacter	1	1	1	1
Proteus mirabilis	1	1	1	0
Klebsiella + *Proteus*	2	0	0	0
Total	24	17	12	7
Percentage of total		71%	50%	29%
Percentage of those negative at previous culture			70%	58%

Table 2. *Susceptibility of organisms cultured from urine*

Organism	No. of isolates	Geometric mean of minimal inhibitory concn (μg/ml): Tested at *p*H 7.4	Tested at *p*H 8.5
Escherichia coli	24	52.5	5.9[a]
Klebsiella-Enterobacter	15	68.2	7.6[a]
Total	39	58.1	6.5

[a] $P<0.01$.

whom the bacteriuria recurred after the prescribed treatment.

Concentrations of erythromycin in serum and urine: pH of urine. Erythromycin concentrations (Table 3) were determined in one or more samples of urine from each of 21 patients; in 14 of these patients, the infecting organisms had been eradicated and in 7 they had not. The geometric mean concentration of erythromycin in the urine of the former was 32 μg/ml (range, 5 to 750 μg/ml) and in the latter it was 36 μg/ml (range, 6 to 340 μg/ml). Concentrations of erythromycin in serum ranged from 0.6 to 15.7 μg/ml; these values did not correlate with the bacteriological results, for none of the infecting organisms was inhibited at *p*H 7.4 at these concentrations. However, in all but two patients on whom data are available, the concentrations of erythromycin attained in the urine were greater than the MIC for the infecting organism when tested at *p*H 8.5 and in some instances at *p*H 7.4. All urine samples during therapy had *p*H values between 7 and 9, usually >8. These data correlate more closely with the results of therapy, for in most instances an effect on the bacterial count was observed.

There was no significant difference in the results of the routine antibiotic disc susceptibility tests done with 10 antibiotics on the organisms isolated before and after treatment with erythromycin plus alkalinization, suggesting that the post-treatment organisms represent recurrences rather than reinfections.

DISCUSSION

Previous studies have shown that the *p*H of the medium in which in vitro susceptibility testing is done is of considerable importance in determining the activity and potential clinical effect of an antibiotic against various organisms (2). The enhanced activity of erythromycin against susceptible organisms at alkaline *p*H in vitro has been known for several years. More recently, however, Zagar (11, 12) and Sabath et al. (7, 8) have shown that erythromycin is also active in alkaline media against gram-negative bacteria usually considered to be resistant to that antibiotic, thus suggesting the possibility of using erythromycin and alkalinization of the urine in the treatment of urinary-tract infections.

The present results indicate that the in vitro enhancement of erythromycin activity at alkaline *p*H can be reproduced in patients with bacteriuria. Concentrations of erythromycin exceeding the MIC at *p*H 8.5 for gram-negative organisms were easily attained in the urine of such patients. Although bacteriuria recurred in many patients treated on this regimen, increased resistance to erythromycin did not develop during 14 days of exposure to the drug. This finding is in sharp contrast to results of treatment of staphylococcal infections with erythromycin alone (6). Differences in the response of patients to erythromycin therapy did not correlate with either the concentration of the drug in the urine or with the *p*H of the urine and therefore may have reflected differences in the infections.

These data suggest that erythromycin and alkalinization of the urine might be added to the therapeutic armamentarium for urinary-tract infections caused by gram-negative organisms. However, its relative value in such infections will not be known until a large, appropriately controlled comparative study is made.

Table 3. *Erythromycin activity in urine*

Bacteriological Effect of therapy	No. of Patients whose urine was tested	Concn of erythromycin in urine (μg/ml)	
		Range	Geometric mean
Organism eliminated . .	14	5-750	32
Organism persisted	7	6-340	36[a]

[a] Not significantly different.

ACKNOWLEDGMENTS

We are indebted to Barbara Roberts for the isolation and identification of the organisms; to Madelyn Stein, Deborah A. Gerstein, and Sarah B. Larabee for technical assistance, and to the physicians of the Boston City Hospital for referring the patients. Erythromycin estolate used in this study was generously supplied as Ilosone by R. S. Griffith, Lilly Laboratories for Clinical Research, Indianapolis, Ind.

The investigation was supported by Public Health Service grants 5R01-AI-00023 and 2T01-AI-00068 from the National Institute of Allergy and Infectious Diseases and by grant FR-76 from the Division of Research Facilities and Resources, National Institutes of Health.

Dr. Zinner is a recipient of a fellowship from the Northeast Chapter, Massachusetts Heart Association, and Dr. Sabath is a recipient of a Career Development Award from the National Institute of Allergy and Infectious Diseases.

LITERATURE CITED

1. Abraham, E. P., and E. S. Duthie. 1946. Effect of pH of the medium on activity of streptomycin and penicillin and other chemotherapeutic substances. Lancet 1:455–459.

2. Brumfitt, W., and A. Percival. 1962. Adjustment of urine pH in the chemotherapy of urinary-tract infections. A laboratory and clinical assessment. Lancet **1**:186–190.
3. Grove, D. C., and W. A. Randall. 1955. Assay methods of antibiotics. Medical Encyclopedia, Inc., New York.
4. Haight, T. H., and M. Finland. 1952. The antibacterial action of erythromycin. Proc. Soc. Exp. Biol. Med. **81**:175–183.
5. Harris, H. W., R. Murray, T. F. Paine, L. Kilham, and M. Finland. 1947. Streptomycin treatment of urinary tract infections with special reference to the use of alkali. Amer. J. Med. **2**:229–250.
6. Jones, W. F., Jr., R. L. Nichols, and M. Finland. 1956. Development of resistance and cross resistance *in vitro* to erythromycin, carbomycin, spiramycin, oleandomycin and streptomycin. Proc. Soc. Exp. Biol. Med. **93**:388–393.
7. Sabath, L. D., D. A. Gerstein, P. B. Loder, and M. Finland. 1968. Excretion of erythromycin and its enhanced activity in urine against gram-negative bacilli with alkalinization. J. Lab. Clin. Med. **72**:916–923.
8. Sabath, L. D., V. Lorian, D. Gerstein, P. B. Loder, and M. Finland. 1968. Enhancing effect on alkalinization of the medium on the activity of erythromycin against gram-negative bacteria. Appl. Microbiol. **16**:1288–1292.
9. Steers, E., E. L. Foltz, and B. S. Graves. 1959. Inocula replicating apparatus for routine testing of bacterial susceptibility of antibiotics. Antibiot. Chemother. **9**:307–311.
10. Waksman, S. A., E. Bugie, and S. Schatz. 1944. Isolation of antibiotic substances from soil micro-organisms, with special reference to streptothricin and streptomycin. Proc. Staff Meetings Mayo Clin. **19**:537–580.
11. Zagar, Z. 1963. Sensitivity of *E. coli, Ps. aeruginosa* and *B. proteus* to erythromycin in various pH culture media. Chemotherapia **6**:82–89.
12. Zagar, Z. 1967. The bacteriologico-clinical aspect of application of erythromycin in the treatment of urinary infections in addition to alkalinization of urine. Proc. 5th Int. Congr. Chemother., Vienna, p. 79–87.

Antimicrobial Agents and Chemotherapy—1969

Renal Damage Associated with Prolonged Administration of Ampicillin, Cephaloridine, and Cephalothin

E. JACK BENNER

Section of Infectious and Immunologic Diseases, Department of Internal Medicine, School of Medicine, University of California, Davis, California 95313, and The Sacramento Medical Center, Sacramento, California 95823

Cephaloridine is known to cause renal tubular damage in rabbits and monkeys, and there have been reports of nephrotoxicity in humans. However, ampicillin and cephalothin are usually considered safe in patients with renal damage or oliguria. These three drugs were given at a dose of 8 g per day for 5 to 15 days to adults with life-threatening infection. The accumulation of antibiotic in the serum was correlated with changes of renal function. In 18 patients whose renal function was normal before institution of therapy, no nephrotoxicity was caused by any of the antibiotics. On the other hand, accumulation of antibiotic and deterioration of renal function occurred in several patients with prerenal azotemia, as well as in patients with primary renal disease. This result was observed with all three of the antibiotics tested, but the accumulation was greater with cephaloridine than with ampicillin, and was least with cephalothin.

The increasing age and frequency of intercurrent diseases of patients with sepsis has been associated with increasing iatrogenic lesions. Serious sepsis requires vigorous antimicrobic therapy. However, the presence of renal disease may promote retention of the antimicrobic agents and subsequent toxicity. It is well known that with such agents as the tetracyclines, kanamycin, streptomycin, gentamicin, vancomycin, polymyxin B, colistin, and amphotericin B, major modifications of the dose schedule are necessary in patients with uremia (3). In addition, cephaloridine has often been incriminated as a nephrotoxic agent, and it has been suggested that ampicillin or cephalothin are "safer" agents in patients with renal dysfunction. Experience with high-dose therapy of patients with serious infection is presented to show that ampicillin and cephalothin can accumulate in the serum of patients with prerenal azotemia as well as in uremic patients. This accumulation of antibiotic was often associated with further deterioration of renal function.

MATERIALS AND METHODS

Patients. The 57 patients were seriously infected and were considered in "critical" condition when treatment was started. The majority were from the U.S. Veterans Administration Hospital, Portland, Ore.; the others were from the internal medicine services of the University of Oregon Medical School Hospitals and the Sacramento Medical Center. Seven patients were infected with *Staphylococcus aureus* in a life-threatening situation, 39 patients had serious *Diplococcus pneumoniae* infection of the lungs, and 10 patients were infected in the lungs or the urinary tract, or both, with *Klebsiella pneumoniae.* The age range was from 42 to 87 years with a mean of 68. The patients frequently had multiple diseases, including one or more of the following: diabetes mellitus, cancer, lymphoma, leukemia, anemia, and gastrointestinal disorders. If there was no history of penicillin allergy, the assignment of drug was random; if penicillin hypersensitivity had previously occurred in the patient, cephaloridine or cephalothin, selected alternately, was given.

Laboratory tests. A complete evaluation of hepatic, renal, and hematopoietic function was made within 24 hr of admission by the clinical laboratories of the appropriate hospital. In addition, clearance of creatinine, 24-hr protein excretion, multiple microscopic examinations of urinary sediment, frequent blood-urea nitrogen determinations, and determinations of the serum creatinine content were made. These tests were always repeated every 3 days and were done more frequently when indicated by the clinical status of the patient. Antibiotic was delivered to the patient as a 2-g bolus by intravenous infusion during a 15- to 30-min period. At hr after completion of the bolus delivery, 10 ml of blood was drawn, and serum was separated and frozen for assay. Approximately 5 hr after completion of the bolus delivery, another serum sample was collected and frozen. This was done one to three times daily for each patient. No change in antibiotic dose was made unless it was the opinion of the consultant in infectious diseases that toxicity was present, as evidenced by deterioration of renal function or evidence of central nervous system penicillin toxicity. All but one patient received therapy for at least 7 days before any reduction in the antibiotic dose occurred. All serum specimens and simultaneously collected specimens of urine were assayed by a large-plate agar-well method with a 95% probability of ±6% accuracy for each specimen (1).

RESULTS

There were 18 patients with normal tests of renal function, 24 with prerenal azotemia (renal function tests became normal with correction of sepsis, heart failure, gastrointestinal bleeding, or fluid and electrolyte balance, or a combination of these), and 15 with documented primary renal disease. One-third of each group received ampicillin, one-third received cephalothin, and one-third received cephaloridine.

Patients with normal renal function. Ampicillin concentrations in the serum ranged from 62 to 154 μg/ml 1 hr after the 2-g bolus was delivered. After 5.7 hr, the concentrations decreased to 7 to 24 μg/ml. Cephaloridine activity was somewhat less in normal patients. Concentrations ranged from 58 to 94 μg/ml 1 hr after the bolus, but rarely decreased to less than 15 μg/ml 6.7 hr after the bolus. In contrast, cephalothin concentrations ranged from 48 to 62 μg/ml 1 hr after the bolus and always returned to 0 to 2 μg/ml 5.7 hr later. There was no evidence of impaired renal function in these 18 patients. The ranges of drug concentrations in the serum are shown as cross-hatched areas in Fig. 2, 3, and 5.

Patients with prerenal azotemia. Of the eight patients who received ampicillin, three had evidence of increasing renal dysfunction during the course of therapy, as shown by a blood-urea nitrogen that increased more than 25 mg/100 ml and by a decrease of 30% or more in the clearance of creatinine (Fig. 1). Each of these patients accumulated ampicillin in the serum to concentrations ranging from 212 to 267 μg/ml 1 hr after the bolus. In addition, 5.7 hr after the dose 68 to 127 μg of ampicillin per ml persisted

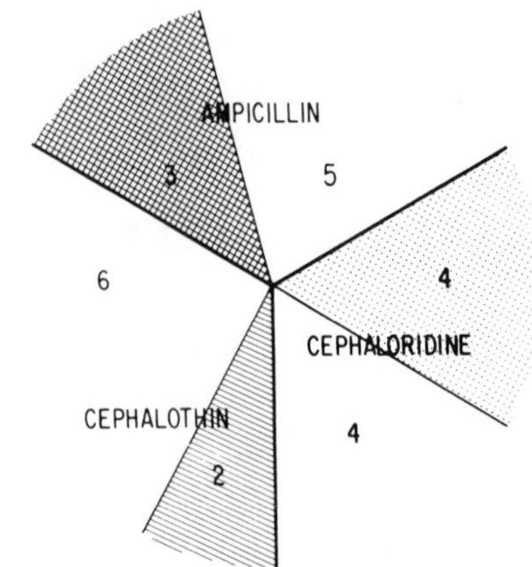

Fig. 1. *Deterioration of renal function (blood-urea nitrogen increased at least 25 mg/100 ml and clearance of creatinine decreased by at least 30%) during therapy with 8 g of the antibiotic per day in 24 patients with prerenal azotemia. Hatched areas represent patients with renal dysfunction.*

in the serum. An additional patient with congestive heart failure had significant accumulation of ampicillin with evidence of central nervous system toxicity, even though the clearance of creatinine increased and the blood-urea nitrogen decreased during therapy (Fig. 2).

Two of the eight patients who received cephalothin also had accumulation of the drug in serum, a significant decrease in the clearance of creatinine, and an increase in the blood-urea nitrogen during therapy (Fig. 1). However, both patients recovered from the azotemic state and from sepsis without other signs of toxicity and with no change in their drug dose.

Cephaloridine, in contrast, was associated

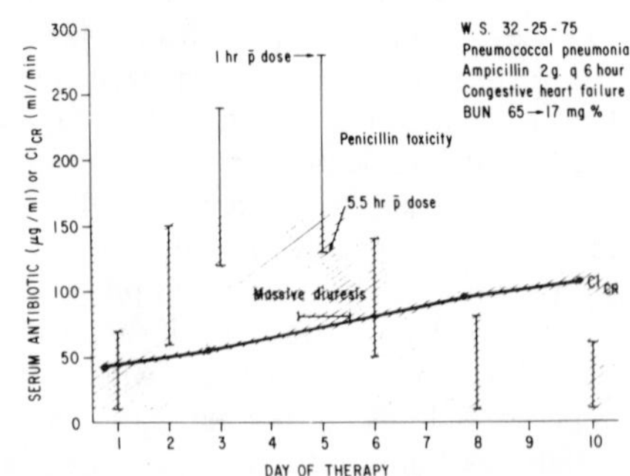

Fig. 2. *Course of a patient who accumulated ampicillin in serum and had neurotoxicity. Hatched area is the range of ampicillin content of serum in six patients with normal renal function: top, peak level; bottom, content 6 hr after dose.*

with increased blood-urea nitrogen content and with a significant decrease in clearance of creatinine in 50% of the patients in this category (Fig. 1). Accumulation of cephaloridine in serum reached toxic levels (200 to 218 μg/ml 1 hr after the dose), and clearance was incomplete (concentrations of more than 100 μg/ml persisted 5.7 hr after the dose). Cephaloridine accumulation also occurred in one patient (Fig. 3), even though renal function improved during therapy.

Patients with primary renal disease. Of the 15 patients with primary renal disease (Fig. 4), 5 had diabetic glomerulosclerosis, 8 had "chronic pyelonephritis and nephrosclerosis," and 2 had chronic glomerulonephritis. Drug accumulation occurred in two patients who received ampicillin. The ampicillin content of the serum exceeded 200 μg/ml and failed to decrease to less than 100 μg/ml 5.7 hr after the intravenous bolus. The blood-urea nitrogen concentration increased significantly, and the clearance of creatinine decreased to less than 20% of the pretreatment value in both of these patients. A reduction in the amount of ampicillin administered was necessary to prevent further toxicity in these two patients.

Although one patient who received cephalothin had a transient rise in the blood-urea nitrogen content and a decrease in clearance of creatinine (Fig. 5), control of sepsis, hyperglycemia, and acidosis of diabetes mellitus was followed by improvement of renal function to the pretreatment values. The accumulated cephalothin in the serum was then cleared to a normal level.

In contrast, in four of five patients treated with cephaloridine, drug accumulated in the serum, renal function decreased, and casts and protein appeared in the urine sediment (Fig. 4). The serum content of cephaloridine 1 hr after the 2-g bolus was 104 to 322 μg/ml. This was much greater than the amounts that occurred in patients with normal renal function, in whom 85 μg/ml was the maximum value (hatched area, Fig. 3). One patient (W. T., 16-04-48), a 52-year-old man with Kimmelsteil-Wilson's disease and staphylococcal pneumonia, died. Autopsy confirmed the renal lesion of diabetic glomerulosclerosis of a chronic severe nature. Whether the deterioration of renal function was due to the infection, the antibiotic, or the primary renal lesion could not be decided by the

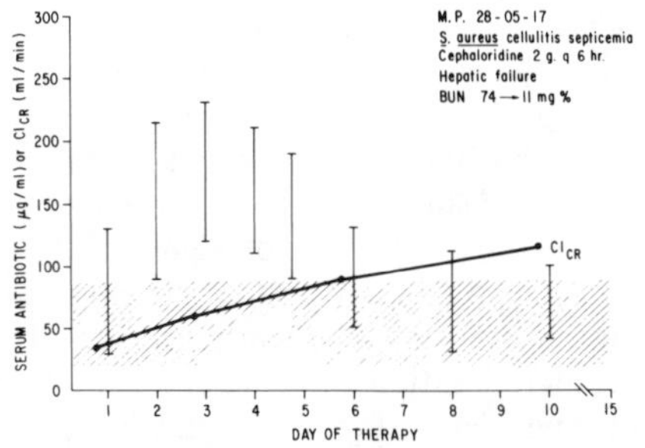

Fig. 3. *Course of a patient who accumulated cephaloridine in serum transiently while renal function was markedly abnormal. Hatched area is the range of cephaloridine content of serum in six patients with normal renal function.*

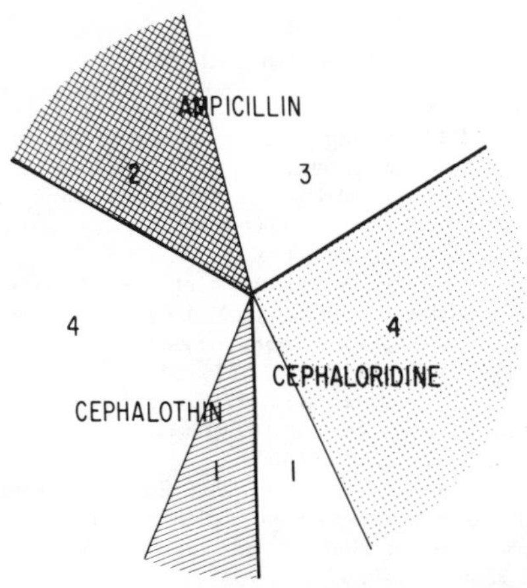

Fig. 4. *Deterioration of renal function (blood-urea nitrogen increased at least 25 mg/100 ml and clearance of creatinine decreased by at least 30%) during therapy with 8 g of the antibiotic per day in 15 patients with primary renal disease. Hatched areas represent patients with renal dysfunction.*

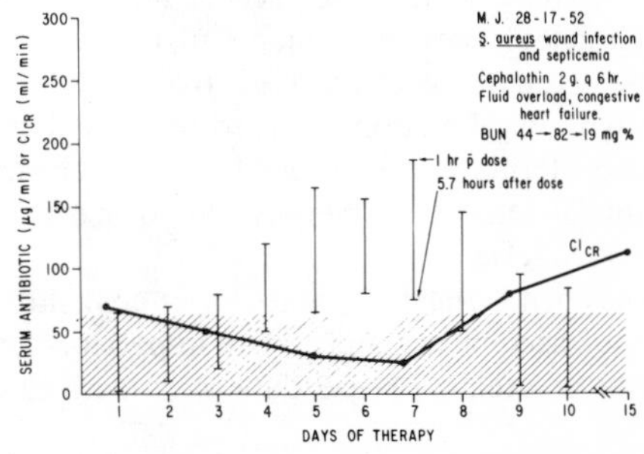

Fig. 5. *Course of a patient who accumulated cephalothin in serum during transient period of renal dysfunction and then recovered. Hatched area is the range of cephalothin content of serum in six patients with normal renal function.*

prosector. Reduction of the dose of cephaloridine to 500 mg every 8 hr was associated with decreasing proteinuria, disappearance of hyaline casts, and return of the blood-urea nitrogen and clearance of creatinine to pretreatment levels in the other three patients. In addition, cephaloridine content in the serum returned to less than 75 μg/ml.

DISCUSSION

It is evident that, in these seriously ill patients, renal dysfunction, whether due to primary renal disease or secondary factors, was often associated with accumulation in the serum of cephaloridine >ampicillin >cephalothin. The simultaneous deterioration of renal function in five patients receiving this large dose of ampicillin clearly indicates a potential hazard. In another group of patients with renal disease who received oral ampicillin, three patients showed deterioration of renal function and other systemic signs of ampicillin hypersensitivity (4). There was, in addition, an 8 to 16-fold increase in ampicillin concentration in the serum and a 9-fold increase in side effects in patients with renal disease who received ampicillin as compared with patients with normal renal function who received ampicillin (4).

Eight seriously ill patients with azotemia or uremia accumulated cephaloridine to high concentrations in the serum; this was associated with further deterioration of renal function. Although seven of the eight patients recovered from the infection and their renal function returned to normal or to its status before cephaloridine therapy, it was necessary to reduce the dose of cephaloridine administered in each of these patients. Linsell et al. (5) noted excretion of excessive numbers of hyaline casts in 14 patients who received 6 g per 24 hr, although renal function returned to normal after the cephaloridine was stopped. It is likely that continued high-dose therapy could have had serious sequelae.

It has been repeatedly stated that cephalothin does not accumulate and is safe in patients with oliguria or uremia. These data were derived on the basis of single or short-term administration of cephalothin, and on the calculation of rates of clearance from the serum. For several years, high concentrations of cephalothin have been observed in my laboratory in serum from patients who have received large doses of cephalothin for several days. It would appear that, although cephalothin can and does accumulate in patients with serious impairment of the clearance mechanism of the kidney, the associated deterioration of renal function is different from that observed with cephaloridine (6). Recovery from sepsis and correction of hemodynamic abnormalities and of fluid and electrolyte balance were associated with return of renal function to normal or to its status before cephalothin treatment in all of these patients and in a previous group of patients who had open-heart surgery (2).

It was concluded that, in the face of impaired clearance mechanisms for these three antibiotics, prolonged administration of significantly large doses, i.e., 8 g per day, led to retention of the antibiotic and was frequently associated with further deterioration of renal function. Careful monitoring of renal function and, when possible, of serum content of these antimicrobial drugs is necessary in seriously ill patients with impaired renal function.

ACKNOWLEDGMENTS

This investigation was supported by a grant from Eli Lilly & Co.

LITERATURE CITED

1. Bennett, J. V., J. L. Brodie, E. J. Benner, and W. M. M. Kirby. 1966. Simplified, accurate method for antibiotic assay of clinical specimens. Appl. Microbiol. **14**:170–177.
2. Benner, E. J. 1969. Metabolism of antibiotics during cardiopulmonary bypass for open-heart surgery. Antimicrob. Agents and Chemother.–1968, p. 373–377.
3. Kunin, C. M. 1967. A guide to use of antibiotics in patients with renal disease. Ann. Intern. Med. **67**:151–158.
4. Lee, H. A., and L. F. Hill. 1968. The use of ampicillin in renal disease. Brit. J. Clin. Pract. **22**:354–357.
5. Linsell, W. D., A. Pines, and J. W. Hayden. 1967. Hyaline cast formation in patients treated with cephaloridine. J. Clin. Pathol. (London) **20**:857–859.
6. Saslaw, S., and H. N. Carlisle. 1968. Studies on therapy of staphylococcal infections in monkeys. III. Comparison of cephalothin, cephaloridine and cephalexin. Amer. J. Med. Sci. **256**:136–149.

Antimicrobial Agents and Chemotherapy—1969

Controlled Prospective Double-Blind Evaluation of a "Prophylactic" Antibiotic (Cephaloridine) in Surgery

J. W. BROWN, N. COOPER, and W. M. RAMBO

Medical College of South Carolina, Charleston, South Carolina 29401

The efficacy of cephaloridine in prophylaxis against postoperative infection was tested in 182 patients. Patients were selected on a random basis if there was neither preexisting renal disease nor other preoperative indication for antibiotics. Cephaloridine (1 g) was given with preoperative medications and 8 hr postoperatively for 5 to 10 doses. A group of 92 patients received a placebo and a group of 90 patients received cephaloridine. The two groups were similar as to age, type and duration of operation, and coexisting diseases. There were 27 postoperative bacterial complications of all types, 21 in the placebo group and 6 in the cephaloridine group. This difference is statistically significant ($P<0.01$). Thirteen wound infections occurred, nine in the placebo group and four in the cephaloridine group. Six pulmonary infections occurred in the placebo group and two in the cephaloridine group. There were six urinary tract infections in the placebo group and none in the cephaloridine group. It is concluded that "prophylactic" cephaloridine is helpful in diminishing the overall incidence of postoperative infections. However, the actual clinical benefit derived from this reduction in postoperative infections is not great enough to warrant the routine use of prophylactic cephaloridine in patients undergoing clean surgery.

The question of whether or not to employ prophylactic antibiotics in surgical patients has still not been answered satisfactorily. The arguments pro and con are legion. Recent interest has centered on the use of prophylactic antibiotics started preoperatively (1-3). In this study, we have attempted a controlled, prospective, double-blind evaluation of cephaloridine begun preoperatively for prophylaxis in clean surgery.

MATERIALS AND METHODS

Patients were eligible for the study if there was no preexisting renal disease or positive indication for antibiotics. Renal disease was evaluated by careful history, preoperative blood urea nitrogen, and urinalysis. As the study was double blind, and approximately half of the patients would receive a placebo, the decision in regard to the eligibility of the patient for the study was left to the patient's surgeon. If a patient was considered eligible for the study, assignment to the cephaloridine or the placebo group was made with the use of a table of random numbers in the hospital pharmacy. The pharmacy maintained the code to control the double-blind aspect of the study, and the code was not broken in any case until all hospital and outpatient charts were carefully evaluated. Clinic follow-up was for at least 4 months. Cephaloridine (1 g) or placebo was administered intramuscularly with the preoperative medication and every 8 hr postoperatively for 5 to 10 doses. If a patient developed a bacterial complication, the study drug was discontinued and appropriate therapy, including antibiotics, was then begun as indicated by the clinical situation. All bacteriological studies were performed by the routine clinical laboratory, and the drug susceptibility of some organisms was based on tests with cephalothin rather than cephaloridine. Infections were defined as follows. Pneumonia was diagnosed only if there was a chest X ray showing a persistent pulmonary infiltrate. (Atelectasis which responded to coughing was excluded.) Wound infection was diagnosed by the presence of pus. Urinary-tract infection was diagnosed only in patients with all of the following findings: a normal preoperative urinalysis, a postoperative urinalysis revealing pyuria and bacilluria, and a urine culture with a colony count in excess of 100,000 colonies per ml. No preoperative urine cultures were obtained on any patients in this study; thus, we cannot be absolutely certain that patients exhibiting symptomatic urinary-tract infections postoperatively, as defined by our criteria, did not have preexisting asymptomatic urinary-tract infections. However, all of these patients had either a clinically significant exacerbation of their preexisting disease or a de novo infection in the postoperative period which required treatment with antibiotics.

RESULTS AND DISCUSSION

The 182 patients in the study were divided into two groups, 92 of whom received the placebo and 90 of whom received cephaloridine. The two groups were similar in regard to age, incidence of obesity, coexisting pulmonary disease, types of operations, use of drains, duration of operations, length of preoperative hospital stay, and incidence of catheterization of the urinary bladder. The patients were divided into five subgroups: (i) exploratory laparotomy with enterotomy, (ii) exploratory laporatomy without enterotomy, (iii) head and neck surgery, (iv) surgery of the parietes (e.g., mastectomies and herniorrhaphies), and (v) miscellaneous surgical procedures requiring the use of the operating room (e.g., breast biopsy, excision of lipomata, large split thickness skin grafts, and surgical procedures for venous insufficiency). The results in terms of bacterial complications for each subgroup are shown in Table 1.

There were 27 postoperative bacterial complications of all types among the 182 patients (Table 2). Twenty-one occurred in the 92 patients receiving the placebo and six occurred in the 90 patients receiving cephaloridine. This difference is statistically significant ($P<0.01$). All organisms cultured are shown in Table 3.

Among the 27 postoperative infections, there were 13 wound infections, 9 in the placebo group and 4 in the cephaloridine group. Two of

Table 2. *Infections in placebo and cephaloridine groups*

Treatment group	No. of patients	No. of infections			
		Wound	Pulmonary	Urinary	Total
Placebo	92	9	6	6	21
Cephaloridine	90	4	2	0	6
Total	182	13	8	6	27

Table 3. *Organisms cultured from patients in both treatment groups*

Organism	No. of patients		
	Placebo	Drug	Total
Escherichia coli	9	2	11
Aerobacter aerogenes	4	0	4
Proteus species	2	1	3
Streptococcus faecalis	3	0	3
Pseudomonas aeruginosa	1	0	1
Staphylococcus aureus	3	0	3
Streptococcus pyogenes	1	0	1
Paracolon group	0	1	1
Gamma-hemolytic *Streptococcus*	2	0	2
Neisseria catarrhalis	2	0	2
Staphylococcus epidermidis	0	2	2
Clostridium perfringens	1	0	1
Klebsiella pneumoniae	0	1	1
Total	28	7	35

Table 1. *Occurrence of infections in five categories of operations*

Category	Treatment group	No. of patients	No. of infections		
			Wound	Pulmonary	Urinary
Laparotomy, gastrointestinal, tract opened	Placebo	15	4	0	1
	Cephaloridine	12	0	0	0
Laparotomy, gastrointestinal, tract closed	Placebo	20	2	0	4
	Cephaloridine	14	2	1	0
Surgery of the head and neck	Placebo	11	0	2	0
	Cephaloridine	7	0	1	0
Surgery of the parietes	Placebo	33	1	3	1
	Cephaloridine	42	2	0	0
Miscellaneous surgical procedures	Placebo	13	2	1	0
	Cephaloridine	15	0	0	0

the wound infections in the cephaloridine group were noted in inguinal herniorrhaphy incisions 8 and 13 weeks postoperatively, suggesting delayed manifestation of this complication due to the use of the antibiotic. Though the number of wound infections was smaller in the cephaloridine group, the groups were too small to achieve statistical significance. Results of bacterial cultures from the infected wounds in the placebo and drug-treated groups are shown in Table 4.

Eight pulmonary infections occurred, six among the 92 patients in the placebo group and two in the 90 patients who received cephaloridine. As was previously noted, the incidence of preexisting pulmonary disease was statistically the same in both groups, and, in fact, only one of the patients in the placebo group and none of the patients in the cephaloridine group who developed pulmonary infections had preexisting pulmonary disease. Once again, although there were fewer pulmonary infections in the patients receiving cephaloridine, the groups were too small to achieve statistical significance.

All of the six urinary-tract infections, or exacerbations of preexisting urinary-tract infection, occurred in the placebo group. Two of the six patients had been catheterized postoperatively, one for 1 day and one for 6 days. The number of patients catheterized postoperatively was statistically the same for both groups. In the absence of preoperative urine cultures on all patients, one can say only that these patients were previously asymptomatic, had normal urinalyses, and experienced either recrudescence of their urinary-tract infection or a de novo infection in the postoperative period for which they required therapy. The difference between the placebo and cephaloridine groups is significant statistically ($P<0.02$) in regard to these episodes of urinary-tract infection. In considering all bacterial complications in the two groups, if one eliminates the urinary-tract infections altogether on the basis that they may not represent new infections, a significant difference is still apparent between the two groups, though the P value is raised somewhat ($0.05>P>0.02$).

Table 4. *Organisms cultured from wound infections in both treatment groups*

Organism	No. of patients		
	Placebo	Drug	Total
Staphylococcus aureus	3	0	3
Streptococcus pyogenes	1	0	1
Paracolon group	0	1	1
Staphylococcus epidermidis	0	2	2
Clostridium perfringens	1	0	1
Escherichia coli	2	0	2
Aerobacter aerogenes	2	0	2
Proteus species	1	0	1
Streptococcus faecalis	1	0	1
Pseudomonas aeruginosa[a]	1	0	1
Total	11	3	15

[a] This organism was resistant to cephalosporin. All other organisms cultured from wounds were susceptible to cephalosporin.

Despite the fact that the overall difference between the two groups in regard to bacterial complications was statistically significant, we did not consider the clinical benefit to the cephaloridine group of corresponding importance. All infections in both groups were readily treated when they occurred, and discovery of two wound infections in the cephaloridine group was delayed until late in the postoperative period. In this study, only one of seven organisms cultured from the patients receiving cephaloridine was resistant to cephalosporin antibiotics, but the possibility of selection of resistant organisms remains a potential problem. No instances of cephaloridine nephrotoxicity were observed in this study, but this type of toxicity is also a hazard to be borne in mind when this antibiotic is used. In view of the other possible problems accompanying the use of an antibiotic, such as allergic or idiosyncratic reactions, we conclude that the use of prophylactic cephaloridine in patients undergoing clean surgery is not warranted.

LITERATURE CITED

1. Bernard, H. R., and W. R. Cole. 1964. The prophylaxis of surgical infection: The effect of prophylactic antimicrobial drugs on the incidence of infection following potentially contaminated operations. Surgery **56**:151-157.
2. Burke, J. F. 1963. Preoperative antibiotics. Surg. Clin. N. Amer. **43**:665-676.
3. Polk, H. C., and J. F. Lopez-Mayor. 1969. Postoperative wound infection: A prospective study of determinant factors and prevention. Surgery **66**:97-103.

Antimicrobial Agents and Chemotherapy—1969

Relationship of Blood Group Antigens of the *Enterobacteriaceae* to Infections in Humans

MARCIA Г. MOODY, VIOLA M. YOUNG, and JOHN E. FABER

National Cancer Institute, Baltimore Cancer Research Center, Baltimore, Maryland 21211, and University of Maryland, College Park, Maryland 20742

A study of 101 bacterial strains of the family *Enterobacteriaceae* recovered from 55 patients with urinary-tract infection or bacteremia, or with both, revealed that only 9 strains had detectable blood group activity. All of the nine strains (six *Escherichia coli,* two *Klebsiella* sp., and one *Proteus mirabilis*) exhibited H(O) activity; no blood group B activity was found. Individuals of blood group A comprised the majority of patients infected with *Enterobacteriaceae,* whereas individuals of blood group O were the most prevalent among the hospital and normal populations. This inversion was significant at the 0.02 level in a two-tailed test. Frequency of infection did not appear to be influenced by the blood group activity of the organism causing infection. The number of patients studied to date is small, and only tentative conclusions may be drawn therefore from the data obtained.

The ecology of infectious diseases. particularly within the hospital environment, has been altered due to the emergence of "normal flora" (12, 21), especially gram-negative microorganisms (12), as etiological agents. Many factors, such as prolonged life span, antibiotic therapy, and other drug therapy, undoubtedly contribute to the increasing prominence of these bacteria as pathogens. Among these pathogens are bacteria of the family *Enterobacteriaceae,* some strains of which have the antigenic characteristic of human blood group-like substances (10, 12, 13, 26, 27). The presence of such blood group antigens in *Enterobacteriaceae* has led to the interesting concept (7) that the sharing of antigens between host and pathogen could affect the pathogenesis (22) and prognosis of some infections by the development of immune tolerance or by the production of an autoimmune state, and, therefore, that the incidence of infections caused by these organisms may be based in part upon blood group distribution within a population.

As the *Enterobacteriaceae* are causative agents of so many infections in the hospital environment, this study was designed to investigate the effect of blood group antigenic relationships between hosts and the *Enterobacteriaceae* as etiological agents and to determine the distribution of such agents among patients of various blood groups.

MATERIALS AND METHODS

Collection of samples. Fifty-five patients, diagnosed as having infection of the urinary tract or bacteremias, or both, caused by genera of the family *Enterobacteriaceae,* were studied. Those patients whose urine samples contained 100,000 or more microorganisms/ml were considered to have urinary-tract infection. Diagnosis of bacteremia caused by the *Enterobacteriaceae* was based on the growth of these microorganisms in blood cultures, and on clinical symptoms consistent with their presence in the blood.

Bacteria. Bacteria recovered from the urine and blood of these patients were identified biochemically and serologically as recommended by Edwards and Ewing (8). The organisms were then lyophilized, sealed under vacuum, and stored at –22 C. As controls, A, B, H(O) active organisms and a nonreactive strain were utilized.

Antisera. Anti-A and anti-B blood sera were obtained from Ortho Diagnostic, Raritan, N.J. Eel sera and plant lectin extracted from *Ulex europaeus* (11) were used as sera which contained H(O) agglutinins.

Bacterial antigens. Cultures grown for 24 hr at 37 C in a blood group reactive-free medium (25) were heated in a water bath at 100 C for 2.5 hr, and the cells were harvested by centrifugation at 1,600 × *g* for 10 min. The sedimented cells were washed three times with 10 volumes of 0.85% saline. The cells were then adjusted with triethanolamine-buffered saline (TBS) photoelectrically standardized to a density approximating 21 × 10^8 bacteria/ml.

Indicator antigens (erythrocyte suspensions). Human A, B, and O erythrocytes were obtained daily by centrifugation of freshly drawn whole blood. The cells were washed three times with TBS and finally were prepared as 1% suspensions (v/v) with TBS.

Determination of blood group activity. Blood group activity was measured by the hemagglutination-inhibition test (HI). Determinations of blood groups A and B were performed by the microtiter method (14), and blood group H(O) activity was measured in glass tubes according to standard blood bank procedures. Tests for each blood group determination were performed in triplicate. Volumes used in the microtiter and tube methods were 0.025 and 0.1 ml, respectively.

Twofold serial dilutions of test antigens were prepared in TBS, and equal volumes of blood group antisera containing 4 hemagglutinating units/volume were added to the dilutions of each system. After incubation at room temperature for 2 hr, the appropriate volumes of 1% erythrocyte suspensions were added to each dilution; the mixtures were reincubated for an additional 1 hr. Tubes were centrifuged at 1,600 × g for 30 sec, gently agitated, and examined for macroscopic hemagglutination. Without disturbing the pattern formation, the microtiter tests were examined for red cell clumping in a mirror.

Blood group activity was expressed in terms of dilution of inhibiting material and serum before the addition of indicator antigen, and the activity level was the highest dilution in which no hemagglutination occurred.

RESULTS

Frequency of occurrence and identification of etiological agents. From blood and urine specimens of 55 patients, 101 bacterial strains of the family *Enterobacteriaceae* were isolated. Of these, 50 were recovered from urine and 51 from blood. The single most prevalent genus was *Escherichia,* which comprised 54.4% of the isolates, followed by *Klebsiella* (18%) and *Proteus* (16.8%). Smaller numbers of *Citrobacter, Enterobacter,* and *Serratia* were also recovered (Table 1).

Of the 55 patients, 72.7% harbored *E. coli* (Table 2). Among these isolates, 18 known serotypes and a group of untypable strains were found. Serotypes O1, O4, and O6 accounted for 50.8% of the *E. coli* isolates and represented 21.8, 14.5, and 14.5%, respectively. No enteropathogenic serotypes were recovered. The predominant serotypes in descending order were *E. coli* O1, O6, and O4 in urine and *E. coli* O1, and O4, and O21 in blood.

Of the other organisms recovered, 19 were from blood and 27 were from urine (Table 2). The most common isolate from blood was

Table 1. *Enterobacteriaceae isolated from 55 patients*

Genus	No. of isolates	Percentage of total isolates
Escherichia	55	54.4
Klebsiella	18	18.0
Proteus	17	16.8
Enterobacter	6	5.9
Citrobacter	3	2.9
Serratia	2	1.9
Total	101	

Table 2. *Incidence of Enterobacteriaceae in 55 patients with bacteremia and urinary-tract infection*

Organism	No. of isolates		Total isolates	No. of patients[a]	Percentage of patients infected
	Urine	Blood			
Escherichia coli	23	32	55	40	72.7
Klebsiella sp.	7	11	18	13	23.5
Citrobacter sp.	3		3	2	3.5
Enterobacter cloacae	2	1	3	2	3.5
E. aerogenes	2	1	3	3	5.4
Serratia sp.		2	2	2	3.5
Proteus mirabilis	10	4	14	11	20.0
P. vulgaris	1		1	1	1.8
P. rettgeri	1		1	1	1.8
P. morganii	1		1	1	1.8
Total	50	51	101		

[a] Some patients had infections caused by multiple organisms.

Klebsiella sp., occurring in 23.5% of the patients. *P. mirabilis* was the most common isolate from urine, occurring in 20% of the patients. Interestingly, 76% of the *Proteus* spp. and all *Citrobacter* strains were recovered from patients with urinary infection, and both *Serratia* strains were isolated from patients with bacteremia.

Frequency of Enterobacteriaceae according to blood groups of patients. The distribution of blood groups in the study patients differed from that found in a normal population and from that of the National Institutes of Health hospital population for the 20-month study period (Table 3). Individuals of blood group A comprised the predominant group among the study patients, whereas individuals of blood group O were the most prevalent among the hospital and normal populations. This inversion was significant at the 0.02 level in a two-tailed test. The frequency of blood group B was the same in the three populations. No blood group AB individual was found among the infected patients. For five patients, blood groups were not recorded.

More blood group B individuals had urinary infection (80%) than bacteremia (20%; Table 4), and individuals of blood group O seemed slightly more prone to develop bacteremia (60%). Although the incidence of urinary infection (52%) and bacteremia (56%) in group A individuals was approximately equal, more of the patients infected with *E. coli* and *Klebsiella* spp. had bacteremia than urinary infection. These two organisms and *Proteus* spp. occurred with approximately the same frequency in urinary infections.

Table 3. *Comparison of approximate frequencies of ABO groups in three populations*

Blood group	Frequency (%)		
	New York Caucasian[a]	NIH Hospital	Study patients
O	45.0	52.5	36.0[c]
A	36.0	31.5	45.0[c]
B	13.0	10.5	9.0
AB	5.0	5.5	0
Unknown[b]			9.0

[a] Reference 31.
[b] Blood group not recorded on patient's chart.
[c] $P < 0.02$ (two-tailed test)

Table 4. *Frequencies of ABO groups in 55 study patients with urinary-tract infection and bacteremia*

Blood group	Frequency (%)		No. of patients
	Blood	Urine	
O	60	40	20
A	56[a]	52[a]	25
B	20	80	5
Unknown	0	100	5

[a] Two patients had bacteremia and urinary infection.

Distribution of the *Enterobacteriaceae* in patients according to their blood types is shown in Table 5. Individuals of blood group A appeared to be more susceptible to infections with *Proteus* spp. and *Klebsiella* spp. than persons of the other blood groups; no individuals of blood group B had an infection with *Proteus* sp., although the latter organism was often isolated from patients of blood groups A and O. *E. coli* was recovered from 90% of the individuals with blood group O, but from only 60 to 66% of other persons. No relationship between blood groups and specific *E. coli* serotypes was established.

Infections with multiple organisms occurred equally among the blood groups (20%). In the 12 incidences of recovery of more than one organism, 10 were found in urinary-tract infection and 2 in bacteremia. The most frequently isolated strains in these infections were *E. coli, P. mirabilis,* and *Klebsiella* spp. in various combinations.

Thirteen (24%) of the 55 study patients had recurring episodes of infection (Table 6). In four of these patients, only the same organism as had been isolated in the original episode was found; in four other individuals, recurring infections yielded both a new etiological agent and the initial organism, and in five patients subsequent infections were caused by an organism different from the original isolate. For example, one patient had four episodes of bacteremia, the first and fourth episodes of which were caused by *P. mirabilis,* whereas the second and third yielded *Klebsiella* sp. and *E. coli* O135. The average length of time between relapses or recurring episodes in the 13 patients was 1 month (range, 6 days to 7 months). The incidence of infectious recurrences among blood groups A and O and among the five patients with unrecorded groups was 7, 5, and 1, respectively, and none occurred in patients of blood group B. Bacteremia recurred more frequently than did urinary infec-

Table 5. *Distribution of the Enterobacteriaceae according to blood group of patient*

Organism	Blood group: A			B			O			Unknown		
	No. of patients	Percentage of group	Percentage of total[a]	No. of patients	Percentage of group	Percentage of total[a]	No. of patients	Percentage of group	Percentage of total[a]	No. of patients	Percentage of group	Percentage of total[a]
Escherichia coli	15	60	27	3	60	5.4	18	90	32.7	4	66.6	7.2
Klebsiella	8	32	14.5	1	20	1.8	4	20	7.2	—	—	—
Proteus	9	36	16	—	—	—	3	15	5.4	2	33.3	3.6
Citrobacter	1	4	1.8	—	—	—	1	5	1.8	—	—	—
Enterobacter	2	8	3.6	1	20	1.8	2	10	3.6	—	—	—
Serratia	1	4	1.8	—	—	—	1	5	1.8	—	—	—

[a]Percentage of total infected patients.

Table 6. *Recurrences of infectious episodes*

Blood group	Date of culture	Source	Organism cultured[a]
A	Patient M. W. 1		
	26 June 1965	Blood	*Escherichia coli* O6
	25 July 1965	Blood	*E. coli* O6
	7 September 1965	Blood	*Klebsiella* sp.
A	Patient E. C.		
	28 September 1965	Blood	*Klebsiella* sp.
	29 October 1965	Blood	*Klebsiella* sp.
	4 November 1965	Blood	*Klebsiella* sp.
A	Patient R. M.		
	3 November 1965	Blood	*Enterobacter cloacae*
	17 November 1965	Nephrostomy wound	*E. cloacae*
A	Patient T. B.		
	15 December 1965	Urine	*E. coli* O1, *Proteus mirabilis*
	28 January 1966	Blood	*E. coli* O1
A	Patient M. D.		
	20 January 1966	Urine	*Klebsiella* sp.
	21 January 1966	Urine	*E. coli* O1
	26 January 1966	Urine	*E. coli* O1, *P. mirabilis*
A	Patient M. J.		
	23 July 1966	Blood	*E. coli* O10
	6 September 1966	Blood	*E. coli* O4
A	Patient M. W. 2		
	30 November 1964	Blood	*P. mirabilis*
	27 December 1964	Blood	*Klebsiella* sp.
	24 May 1965	Blood	*E. coli* O135
	28 June 1965	Blood	*P. mirabilis*
O	Patient F. S.		
	2 October 1964	Blood	*E. coli* O21
	25 November 1964	Blood	*E. coli* O21
	27 December 1964	Blood	*Klebsiella* sp.
	28 December 1964	Blood	*Klebsiella* sp.
O	Patient J. M.		
	22 June 1965	Blood	*E. coli* O117
	27 October 1965	Blood	*E. coli* O91
O	Patient A. P.		
	10 September 1965	Blood	*E. coli* O1
	29 October 1965	Blood	*E. aerogenes*
O	Patient J. P.		
	16 November 1965	Urine	*Citrobacter* sp.
	17 November 1965	Nephrostomy urine	*Citrobacter* sp.
	17 November 1965	Catheterized bladder urine	*E. coli* O1
	6 December 1965	Urine	*E. coli* O1
O	Patient M. G.		
	16 November 1965	Urine	*E. coli* O45, *P. mirabilis*
	26 November 1965	Urine	*P. mirabilis*
	27 November 1965	Blood	*Serratia* sp.
Unknown	Patient B. P.		
	18 November 1965	Urine	*E. coli* O6
	24 January 1966	Urine	*E. coli* O1

[a] In patient J. P., the cultures taken on 16 and 17 November are considered to be from the initial episode. In all other patients, the first culture only represents the initial episode.

tion. All of the different microbial genera were recovered with approximately the same frequency.

Blood group activity of microorganisms. Blood group activity as a property of the bacterium per se was verified by a study of the effect of cultural environment on blood group activity (19). However, the question of whether circulating blood group substances in the patient could coat an inactive organism and thereby impart activity has heretofore remained unanswered. To investigate this problem, an inactive organism was grown in a blood group reactive-free medium to which concentrations of blood group A and B substances varying from 0.05 to 10% had been added. It was found that blood group A substance was capable of coating an inactive organism but only in very high concentrations and that blood group B substance did not coat an inactive organism even at high concentrations. As the amount of circulating blood group substances would not usually approach these high levels, it is not to be expected that blood group activity would be imparted to microorganisms present in the blood stream. Although a negative result in vitro does not preclude a positive result in vivo, it can be reasonably presumed that the blood activity of the test strains was not derived from blood group reactive media or circulating blood group substances.

Blood group activity was demonstrated in only a small percentage of the 101 strains isolated. Nine (8.9%) of the strains had detectable blood group activity (Table 7), and H(O) activity was the only blood group specificity exhibited. Three genera, *Escherichia, Klebsiella,* and *Proteus,* had demonstrable blood group antigens which occurred with approximately the same frequency among isolates of *Klebsiella* and *Escherichia,* 11.0 and 10.9%, respectively, and in only 1 of the 17 *Proteus* strains. No activity was detected in the other genera. The activity levels of the nine strains ranged from 1:4 to 1:16; eight of the active strains were recovered from blood cultures.

Table 7. *Distribution of blood group activity among 101 bacterial strains*

Genus	Strains tested	Blood group activity			Percentage of activity in	
		A	B	O	Genus	Total strains
Escherichia	55	0	0	6	10.9	5.9
Klebsiella	18	0	0	2	11.0	2.0
Proteus	17	0	0	1	5.8	1.0
Enterobacter	6	0	0	0	0	0
Citrobacter	3	0	0	0	0	0
Serratia	2	0	0	0	0	0

The incidence of blood group active bacteria was higher in individuals of blood group A than in individuals of the other blood groups (Table 8). Five of the seven patients from whom such bacteria were recovered were of blood group A, and two were of blood group O.

All isolates from a single patient were not necessarily blood group active. For example, the *E. coli* isolates from urine cultures of patients V. D. and T. B. were inactive, whereas the same serotypes isolated from blood cultures were blood group active. In some instances, the cultures that were taken before and after the recovery of an active strain did not contain blood group active organisms even though the source was the same. Also, inactive and active strains were isolated from the same culture and from cultures taken on the same day. Only individuals of blood group A had such infectious episodes caused by bacterial strains which were blood group active and inactive.

DISCUSSION

Springer and co-workers in 1961 (27) reported that approximately 50% of the members of the family *Enterobacteriaceae* isolated in their study were blood group active. However, the strains were obtained almost exclusively from blood cultures of infants in a general hospital; in a subsequent report, Springer and Williamson (26) stated that the percentage of active strains would probably be less in a more randomly selected collection. As the blood group activity was determined by similar methods in their study and in our (NIH) investigation, a comparison of the two studies seemed indicated. The NIH study group consisted of patients of all ages in a relatively select hospital environment; i.e., the type of patient was predetermined by limitations imposed by the study of specific diseases, some of which could interfere with immune responsiveness (1-3, 15, 23, 24). Furthermore, these infections were not the primary reason for hospitalization. Test strains in this study were recovered both from urine and blood cultures.

Table 8. *Distribution of blood group active organisms in nine patients*

Culture	Patient (sex)	Disease	Blood group	Source	Blood group H(O) active organism	Activity level	Isolation of inactive organisms from same patient
66-212	R. M. (M)	Acute leukemia	O+	Blood	*E. coli* O115	1:16	–
66-218	–			Blood	*E. coli* O115	1:8	–
66-221	–			Blood	*E. coli* O115	1:8	–
66-1192	M. J. (F)	Cancer of bladder	O+	Blood	*E. coli*[a]	1:16	–
66-189	T. B. (F)	Mycosis fungoides, toxoplasmosis	A–	Blood	*E. coli* O1	1:8	*E. coli* O1, urine
65N181	D. B. (F)	Heart disease	A+	Urine	*Klebsiella* sp.	1:4	*Citrobacter* sp.[b], urine *Klebsiella* sp., urine
66-24	V. D. (M)	Hodgkin's disease	A+	Blood	*E. coli* O4	1:4	*E. coli* O4[c], urine
65-1166	S. D. (F)	Acute myelogenous leukemia	A–	Blood	*P. mirabilis*	1:8	*E. coli* O1[b] *Klebsiella* sp., blood
65-1500	M. W. (F)	Lipodystrophy	A+	Blood	*Klebsiella* sp.	1:8	*P. mirabilis* (two isolations), blood *E. coli* O135 (three isolations), blood

[a] Untypable with available antisera.
[b] Isolated from same culture as the active organism.
[c] Cultures taken on same day.

The predominant genus was *Escherichia* in both studies, but the distribution of serotypes and the blood group activity patterns were different. The serotypes recovered during the NIH study were more varied, and the predominant serotypes, O1, O4, and O6, correlated with the ones reported to be most commonly associated with bacteremia and urinary infection (20, 28-30; V. M. Kozij et al., Bacteriol. Proc., p. 64, 1963). In the Springer report, the serotypic distribution was more restricted, and the most prevalent serotypes isolated, O86, O127, and O128, are ones commonly associated with gastrointestinal distrubances (9). The unusually high percentage (47%) of active *E. coli* strains reported by Springer was undoubtedly influenced by multiple isolations of *E. coli* O86 which is known to exhibit high activity levels, in contrast to the active *E. coli* isolates (10.9%) of this study which did not include a single serotype that had been previously related to high activity. The difference in activity patterns was also apparent for *Klebsiella* and *Proteus* strains; the NIH study had appreciably lower numbers of active organisms, 11.0 and 5.8%, respectively, as compared with 52 and 45% in the other study. *Citrobacter, Enterobacter,* and *Serratia* strains from the NIH study were too few in number to adequately establish a clear pattern.

The incidence of blood active strains among the *Enterobacteriaceae* was 8.9% in the present study, and the only detectable blood group specificity was H(O), which occurred in three genera, *Escherichia, Klebsiella,* and *Proteus.* Consequently, in considering the effect of common antigenic determinants between host and pathogen upon host response, individuals of blood group O could theoretically be considered more susceptible to these blood group active organisms than the other blood groups, owing to the nonexistence of circulating H(O) isoagglutinins in the blood and theoretically to the impaired immunological response to a substance similar to the host's erythrocyte. As individuals of blood groups A and B also have small but variable quantities of H(O) substance and, therefore, do not have naturally occurring H(O) isoagglutinins, they would also be susceptible to the H(O) active organism. However, the data did not completely support these hypotheses. More individuals of blood group A (20%) were infected with the H(O) active organisms than were individuals of blood group O (10%) and of blood group B (0%). As the results were not explained by the theory of selective immunological advantage based on shared antigenic determinants, the increased occurrence of infection in blood group A individuals must have been due to other factors.

Indications of a unique mechanism in group A individuals have been cited by several authors (4-6, 17). Transient phenotypic isoagglutinogen alteration in group A individuals has been reported in the literature (4, 5, 16), and was believed to be caused by the adsorption of blood group substance elaborated by specific bacteria (4, 17, 18). The mechanism that permits this occurrence only in group A individuals has not been elucidated, and the existence of a blood group antigen in the presence of a specific antibody against it in only blood group A individuals can be interpreted as immunologically unique.

The increased susceptibility of group A individuals was reflected in the frequency distribution of the blood groups in the infected patients. Whereas the frequency of blood groups among the general population of the NIH hospital approximated that of a normal population, blood group A was the most prevalent among the infected patients. Thus, the group A individual was more susceptible to infection by the *Enterobacteriaceae,* irrespective of the bacterial blood group activity. Conversely, fewer group O individuals were in the infected group than in the general population; thus, they may be assumed to be more resistant to infection by these organisms. Although the data indicated that preferential susceptibilities were related to specific blood groups, the frequency of enterobacterial infections in the NIH patients studied was not influenced by the blood group activity of the infecting organism.

The number of patients studied to date is small, and only tentative conclusions may be drawn from the data obtained. The apparent susceptibility of individuals of blood group A to infections with *E. coli* must be corroborated by extended studies in larger numbers of individuals.

LITERATURE CITED

1. Austen, K. F., and Z. A. Cohn. 1963. Contributions of serum and cellular factors in host defense reactions. I. Serum factors in host resistance. N. Engl. J. Med. **268**:933-936.
2. Austen, K. F. and Z. A. Cohn. 1963. Contributions of serum and cellular factors in host defense reactions Ib. Serum factors in host resistance. N. Engl. J. Med. **268**:994-1000.
3. Austen, K. F., and Z. A. Cohn. 1963. Contributions of serum and cellular factors in host resistance. N. Engl. J. Med. **268**:1056-1064.
4. Burns, W., W. Friend, and J. Scudder. 1965. Development of an acquired blood group antigen in surgical patients with peritonitis due to *E. coli.* Surg. Gynecol. Obstet. **120**:757-760.
5. Cameron, C., F. Graham, I. Dunsford, G. Sickeles, and R. R. Race. 1959. Acquisition of a B-like antigen by red blood cells. Brit. Med. J. **2**:29-32.
6. Clofin, A. J., and H. H. Zimmerman, 1963. Anti-B isohemagglutinins in the serum of a patient with a weak red cell B antigen. Amer. J. Clin. Pathol. **39**:355-359.
7. Editorial. 1962. Lancet. **1**:626-627.
8. Edwards, P. R., and W. H. Ewing. 1962. Identification of *Enterobacteriaceae,* 2nd ed. Burgess Publishing Co., Minneapolis.
9. Ewing, W. H., and B. R. Davis. 1961. The O antigen groups of *E. coli* cultures from various sources. Communicable Disease Center Publications, Atlanta, Ga.
10. Eyquem, A., and L. LeMinor. 1965. Recherches sur les communautes antigeniques entre les substances de groupes sanguins et les enterobacteriés. Ann. Inst. Pasteur (Paris) **109**:85-93.
11. Fenton, J. W., II, C. R. Duggleby, C. Otten, and W. H. Stone. 1965. Isolation and fluorescent labeling of *Ulex europaeus* anti-H lectin. Vox Sang. **10**:208-211.
12. Finland, M., W. F. Jones, Jr., and M. W. Barnes. 1959. Occurrence of serious bacterial infections since introduction of antibacterial agents. J. Amer. Med. Ass. **170**:2188-2197.
13. Iseki, S., E. Onuki, and K. Kashiwagi. 1958. Relationship between somatic antigen and blood group substance, especially B substance of bacterium. Gunma J. Med. Sci. **7**:7-12.
14. Lee, M. R., N. S. Ikari, W. C. Branche, Jr., and V. M. Young. 1966. Microtiter bacterial hemagglutination technique for detection of *Shigella* antibodies. J. Bacteriol. **91**:463.
15. Mc Henry, M. C., W. J. Martin, M. M. Hargraves, and A. H. Baggenstoss. 1962. Bacteremia in patients with neoplastic or hematological disease. Proc. Staff. Meet. Mayo Clinic. **37**:43-55.
16. Majsky, A., J. Jakoubkova, and M. Machackova. 1967. Frequency and serological character of changes of group ABH-antigens in blood diseases and malignant tumours. Neoplasma (Bratislava) **14**:41-48.
17. Marsh, W. L. 1960. The pseudo B antigen; a study of its development. Vox Sang. **5**:387-397.
18. Marsh, W. L., W. J. Jenkins, and W. W. Walther. 1959. Pseudo B; an acquired group antigen. Brit. Med. J. **2**:63-66.
19. Moody, M. R., V. M. Young, and J. E. Faber. 1969. Effect of cultural environment on the blood group activity of microorganisms. Appl. Microbiol. **18**:262-267.
20. Rantz, L. A. 1962. Serological grouping of *Escherichia coli.* Study in urinary tract infection. Arch. Intern. Med. **109**:37-42.
21. Rogers, D. E. 1959. Changing pattern of life-threatening microbial disease. N. Engl. J. Med. **261**:677-683.
22. Rowley, D. and C. R. Jenkins. 1962. Antigenic cross reaction between host and parasite as a possible cause of pathogenicity. Nature (London) **198**:151-154.
23. Salmon, C., and D. Salmon. 1965. Deficit en antigene H chez certains sujets de groupe O atteints de leucemie aigue. Rev. Fr. Etud. Clin. Biol. **10**:212-214.
24. Shohl, J., J. L. Fahey, E. G. Morrison, and P. J. Schmidt. 1960. Studies on isohemagglutinins in a variety of dysproteinemias. Proc. 8th Int. Congr. Hematol., Tokyo, p. 1470-1473.

25. Springer, G. F., C. S. Rose, and P. Gyorgy. 1954. Blood group mucoids: their distribution and growth-promoting properties for *Lactobacillus bifidus* var. Penn. J. Lab. Clin. Med. **43**:532-542.

26. Springer, G. F., and P. Williamson. 1962. Genes affecting susceptibility to disease. Lancet **1**:1241.

27. Springer, G. F., P. Williamson, and W. C. Brandes. 1961. Blood group activity of gram negative bacteria. J. Exp. Med. **113**:1077-1093.

28. Turck, M., and R. G. Petersdorf. 1962. The epidemiology of non-enteric *Escherichia coli* infections: prevalence of serological groups. J. Clin. Invest. **41**:1760-1765.

29. Vosti, K. L., L. M. Goldberg, A. S. Monto, and L. A. Rantz. 1964. Host-parasite interaction in patients with infections due to *E. coli*: the sero grouping of *E. coli* from intestinal and extraintestinal sources. J. Clin. Invest. **43**:2377-2385.

30. Waisbren, B. A. 1951. Bacteremia due to gram negative bacilli other than Salmonella: clinical and therapeutic study. Arch. Intern. Med. 88:467-488.

31. Weiner, A. S., and E. B. Grodon. 1951. Repartition des facteurs de groupes sanguins dans une population de New York City, avec une étude speciale des agglutinogenes rares. Rev. Hematol. **6**:45-50.

Antimicrobial Agents and Chemotherapy—1969

Variable Results of Cephalothin Therapy for Meningococcal Meningitis

JOEL D. BROWN, ALLEN W. MATHIES, JR., DANIEL IVLER, W. STUART WARREN, and JOHN M. LEEDOM

Hastings Foundation Infectious Disease Laboratory and Departments of Medicine, Pediatrics, and Microbiology, University of Southern California School of Medicine, and the Communicable Disease Service, Los Angeles County–University of Southern California Medical Center, Los Angeles, California 90033

Twelve patients with meningococcal meningitis received cephalothin (100 to 250 mg per kg per day) because of penicillin allergy. Eight patients had prompt cures. Two other patients improved, but meningococci were cultured from their cerebrospinal fluids (CSF) for 72 hr; CSF cultures then became negative but were again positive on day 8 in one and day 13 in the other. A third patient responded favorably to cephalothin initially, but fever and CSF pleocytosis increased on day 15, although CSF cultures remained negative. These three patients had prompt cures with tetracycline. A fourth patient, deeply comatose on admission, did not improve clinically after 72 hr of treatment with cephalothin; gram-negative diplococci were visible in the CSF, but were apparently not viable, as cultures were negative. When tetracycline was substituted for cephalothin, the CSF improved, but the patient remained comatose and died 15 days after admission. These treatment failures did not seem to correlate with in vitro resistance to cephalothin. Furthermore, CSF cephalothin concentrations were generally within the therapeutic range. In 15 CSF specimens, from seven patients, the cephalothin concentrations ranged from 0.15 to 46.5 μg/ml. Two CSF specimens from two of these seven patients had no detectable cephalothin. It was concluded that cephalothin is not consistently effective in meningococcal meningitis and cannot be recommended as an alternative to benzyl penicillin or ampicillin.

Acute bacterial meningitis in persons 5 years of age or older is most often caused by *Neisseria meningitidis* or *Diplococcus pneumoniae.* Although *Haemophilus influenzae,* type B, often causes meningitis in younger children, it is seldom encountered in patients more than 5 years of age. Since 1963, it has been known that many cases of meningococcal disease are due to sulfadiazine-resistant meningococci. This knowledge led to the superannuation of sulfadiazine therapy (7), and either benzyl penicillin or ampicillin used alone has become the preferred treatment for pneumococcal or meningococcal meningitis (6, 7).

The best alternate antibiotic for patients allergic to penicillin is not well established. Such an antibiotic should be effective against both pneumococci and meningococci so that the clinician can initiate treatment prior to confirmed identification and antibiotic susceptibility testing of the infecting organism.

Cephalothin is a semisynthetic antibiotic structurally similar to penicillin, but it seldom causes allergic reactions when administered to patients who are allergic to penicillin (9). It has been effective in a variety of serious bacterial infections, but little experience with cephalothin in the treatment of meningococcal meningitis has been reported. In vitro, cephalothin inhibits meningococci and pneumococci in concentrations attainable in serum (2). Cephalothin diffuses poorly into the cerebrospinal fluids (CSF) of patients without meningitis (13), but adequate concentrations of this agent have been reported in the CSF of a few patients with bacterial meningitis (4, 9).

This information suggested that cephalothin might be effective therapy for meningococcal meningitis. Here we describe the results of cephalothin therapy in 12 penicillin-allergic patients with meningococcal meningitis.

MATERIALS AND METHODS

Patients studied. The Communicable Disease Service of the Los Angeles County–University of Southern California Medical Center serves as the major referral center in Los Angeles County for the management of patients with central nervous system infections. Patients of all ages, both sexes, and all socioeconomic levels are accepted for care.

Seventeen patients with meningococcal meningitis have been treated with cephalothin by the Communicable Disease Service. They were admitted between 16 March 1965 and 2 May 1969. Cephalothin therapy was chosen either because of a past history of penicillin allergy or because of the manifestation of such allergy shortly after admission and initial treatment with benzyl penicillin or ampicillin. Five patients developed skin rashes attributed to ampicillin or benzyl penicillin after 5 to 11 days of treatment. They recovered uneventfully, but, because they were treated with cephalothin only during the late, convalescent stages of their illnesses, they were omitted from this report.

Laboratory methods. The Communicable Disease Service Clinical Bacteriology Laboratory isolated and identified the bacteria by use of standard methods (*Bergey's Manual*). The isolates were transported to the Hastings Foundation Infectious Disease Laboratory, the identifications were reconfirmed, and the meningococcal serogroup of each strain was determined by the standard slide agglutination technique. Antibiotic susceptibility tests were done by the twofold dilution method with the use of Mueller-Hinton broth or GC medium fortified with 1% supplement B as described previously (3).

Blood and CSF specimens were promptly centrifuged, and the sera and the CSF supernatant fluids were stored at −20 C. After storage for 1 to 2 weeks, the specimens were packed in dry ice, and then were shipped to Eli Lilly & Co., Indianapolis, Ind., for cephalothin bioassays. The cephalothin bioassays were performed by the cylinder plate method with the use of a standard *Sarcina lutea* strain.

Clinical data. Clinical data were obtained from the hospital charts by use of a standardized form.

Severity of illness on admission was categorized according to the following scheme: 4+ for coma, semicoma, shock, or significant hypotension; 3+ for convulsions, but no hypotension or coma; 2+ for temperature ≥105 F (40.5 C; rectal), symptoms present >5 days, complications (e.g., arthritis) present on admission, marked lethargy, or petechiae; and 1+ for meningococcal meningitis with none of the above features.

Response to therapy was determined by routine physical examination and repeated CSF cell counts, chemical determinations, Gram stains, and cultures. Antibiotics were continued in each patient until: (i) the patient was afebrile for 5 days; (ii) the CSF cell count was ≤30 white blood cells (WBC) per mm^3 with few or no polymorphonuclear leukocytes; (iii) the CSF glucose concentration was normal; and (iv) the CSF protein concentration was normal or approaching normal.

RESULTS

Meningococcal meningitis. Twelve patients with meningococcal meningitis were treated with cephalothin during the acute stages of their illnesses. Cephalothin therapy was begun on admission in eight patients because of a history of penicillin allergy; cephalothin treatment was substituted for benzyl penicillin or ampicillin in four other patients who developed signs of penicillin allergy 4 to 48 hr after initiation of treatment. Clinical features and outcome for all 12 patients are shown in Table 1. Eight patients were ≥20 years of age, and the youngest patient was 10 years old. The size of the individual doses of cephalothin and the duration of drug administration varied among the different patients (Table 1). The drug was given, however, by rapid (30 min) intravenous (iv) infusion every 4 to 8 hr in total doses of 100 to 250 mg per kg of body weight per day.

Patients cured. Eight patients, including three who were severely ill, were cured after 6 to 18 days of cephalothin treatment (Table 1). Three of these eight patients received no other antibiotic, but the other five had received another antibiotic as initial therapy. Three of the latter group (O.J., G.G., and G.D.) had received single, large, parenteral doses of benzyl penicillin, of tetracycline, or of both before cephalothin was substituted. Two other patients, G.H. and J.F., had received large doses of ampicillin iv for 12 and 48 hr, respectively, before their treatment was changed to cephalothin. The mean duration of fever in these eight patients was 4.5 days (range, 1 to 10 days). Gram stain of the CSF sediment and culture of the CSF revealed no meningococci after the initial antibiotic therapy was started.

Patient G.D. (Table 1), who was cured with cephalothin, illustrates the courses of the eight patients with good responses. He was admitted with a 3-day history of headache and fever. Several hours prior to admission to the Communicable Disease Service, he became prostrate

Table 1. *Clinical data on 12 patients with meningococcal meningitis treated with cephalothin*

Patient, age, and sex	Method of diagnosis	Severity on admission[a]	Antibiotic therapy[b]		Total time treated (days)	Results of therapy and comments
			Initial	Second		
B. W. 67 years female	CSF and blood cultures positive	4+	Cephalothin, 1.75 g iv every 4 hr for 72 hr	Tetracycline, 500 mg iv, every 6 hr for 12 days	15	CSF cultures positive on admission and at 12 hr. CSF Gram stain positive at 72 hr, but culture negative. Change to tetracycline. Died.
L. W. 34 years female	CSF cultures positive	1+	Cephalothin, 1.75 g iv every 4 hr for 4 days; then 3 g iv every 4 hr for 8 days	Tetracycline, 500 mg iv every 6 hr for 2 days; then 400 mg iv every 6 hr for 6 days	20	Rapid initial clinical improvement, but CSF culture positive for 4 days on cephalothin. At 13 days after admission meningeal signs recurred and CSF cultures were again positive. Cured with tetracycline.
J. B. 15 years male	CSF and blood cultures positive	4+	Cephalothin, 1 g iv every 4 hr for 15 days	Tetracycline, 150 mg iv every 8 hr for 6 days	21	Initial improvement but fever persisted. CSF WBC increased on 13th and 15th days, but cultures were negative. Changed to tetracycline with eventual cure.
E. R. 46 years female	CSF cultures positive	4+	Cephalothin, 2 g iv every 4 hr for 4 days; then 2.5 g iv every 4 hr for 6 days	Tetracycline, 500 mg iv every 6 hr for 9 days	19	CSF cultures positive for *N. meningitidis* on days 1, 3, and 8 after beginning on cephalothin. Cephalothin discontinued and tetracycline begun on day 10. Cured with tetracycline.
G. H. 32 years male	Negative culture; typical petechiae present; CSF purulent	2+	Ampicillin, 1.5 g iv every 4 hr; discontinued after four doses	Cephalothin, 1 g iv every 4 hr	6	Recent history of hepatitis and acute glomerulonephritis. Uneventful cure of meningitis.
O. J. 65 years male	CSF and blood cultures positive	4+	Tetracycline, 500 mg iv for one dose	Cephalothin, 2 g iv every 4 hr	18	Uneventful cure.
R. P. 43 years male	CSF cultures positive	4+	Cephalothin, 2 g iv every 4 hr	None	16	Patient diabetic. Uneventful cure of meningitis.
V. T. 21 years female	CSF cultures positive	1+	Cepahlothin, 2.15 g iv every 4 hr	None	12	Patient pregnant. Uneventful cure of meningitis.
C. I. 41 years female	Blood cultures positive	2+	Cephalothin, 3.5 g iv every 4 hr	None	14	Uneventful cure.
C. G. 10 years male	CSF and blood cultures positive	1+	Benzyl penicillin and tetracycline im, one dose; dosages unknown	Cephalothin, 2 g iv every 8 hr	12	Uneventful cure.

(See footnotes at end of table)

Table 1. *(Continued)*

Patient, age, and sex	Method of diagnosis	Severity on admission[a]	Antibiotic therapy[b]		Total time treated (days)	Results of therapy and comments
			Initial	Second		
J. F. 14 years female	CSF cultures positive	1+	Ampicillin, 2 g iv every 4 hr for 48 hr → rash	Cephalothin, 2 g iv every 4 hr	8	Few bacteria seen in CSF Gram stain after 24 hr of ampicillin but all cultures taken after admission were negative. Cure.
G. D. 20 years male	CSF cultures positive	4+	Tetracycline, 500 mg im for one dose	Cephalothin, 2 g iv every 4 hr	18	Meningitis, arthritis, pericarditis. Uneventful cure.

[a] Severity code: 4+ = coma, semicoma, definite shock or significant hypotension; 3+ = convulsions, but no hypotension or coma; 2+ = any one of the following–temperature ⩾105 F (rectal) on admission, symptoms present more than 5 days, complication (e.g., arthritis) present on admission, marked lethargy, or petechiae; 1+ = none of the above.

[b] Each patient who was treated with cephalothin received an initial dose of 50 mg/kg by rapid intravenous infusion.

and delirious, and was admitted to a private hospital with a temperature of 100 F (37.8 C), normal blood pressure, and nuchal rigidity. At that time, the CSF specimen contained 10,200 WBC/mm^3 with 81% polymorphonuclear cells and 19% mononuclear cells. The CSF glucose was <10 mg/100 ml, and the protein was 184 mg/100 ml. Numerous gram-negative diplococci were seen on Gram stain of the CSF smear, and group C meningococci were recovered on culture. Because of a known severe penicillin allergy, G.D. was given 500 mg of tetracycline intramuscularly (im) and then transferred to the Communicable Disease Service. On arrival, 3 g of cephalothin was administered by rapid iv infusion followed by 2 g every 4 hr by the same route (150 mg per kg per day). The day after admission, septic arthritis of the left elbow was noted. Gram-negative diplococci were seen in the synovial fluid but did not grow in culture. At 36 hr after admission, G.D.'s delerium had cleared, and he was oriented but lethargic; the CSF white cell count had decreased to 1,400/mm^3, the CSF sugar had risen to 40 mg/100 ml, and no bacteria were seen on Gram stain of the CSF sediment nor recovered on culture. On the fifth hospital day, the patient was alert; however, a pericardial friction rub was heard for the first time, and an electrocardiogram was consistent with acute pericarditis. He was asymptomatic and had no signs of pericardial effusion; therefore, a pericardiocentesis was not done. The arthritis and pericarditis disappeared, and G.D. was afebrile by the seventh hospital day. On the 18th day, cephalothin was discontinued, and the patient has remained well. The minimal inhibitory concentration (MIC) and minimal bactericidal concentration (MBC) of cephalothin for the group C meningococcus isolated from the CSF were 0.2 and 0.4 μg/ml, respectively. Multiple cephalothin assays were performed on serum and CSF, with the results shown in Table 2.

Treatment failures. Four patients (B.W., L.W., J.B., and E.R., Table 1) had unsatisfactory responses. Their illnesses are discussed in some detail below.

B.W., a 67-year-old woman with a history of penicillin allergy, was admitted in a comatose state after a 1-day illness; CSF obtained on admission contained gram-negative diplococci, visible on direct examination of the CSF sediment, and cultures were positive for group C meningococci. An initial dose of 3.5 g of cephalothin was administered by rapid iv infusion in the admitting room. Subsequently, she received 150 mg of cephalothin per kg per day (10.5 g/day) by rapid iv infusion. The drug was divided into six equal doses and was given every 4 hr. No bacteria were seen in the Gram-stained sediment of a CSF sample obtained 12 hr after treatment was initiated, but *N. meningitidis* was again recovered upon culture. Furthermore, microscopic examination of a Gram stain of a CSF specimen obtained 72 hr after admission revealed abundant gram-negative diplococci, but cultures of this specimen were negative. Because the patient remained comatose and organisms were seen on Gram stain of a CSF smear, cephalothin therapy was discontinued after 72 hr, and tetracycline, 500 mg by rapid iv infusion every 6 hr, was begun. In spite of disappearance of the organism and improvement of the other CSF findings, B.W. remained comatose, developed hypotension and renal failure, and died 15 days after admission. Cephalothin assay of specimens obtained 2 hr after the rapid administration of 1.75 g of cephalothin iv during the first day of treatment revealed concentrations of 52.5 μg/ml in the serum and 46.5 μg/ml in the CSF. Broth-dilution susceptibility tests of the group C meningococcus isolated from B.W.'s CSF on admission demonstrated that the MIC and MBC of cephalothin were both 0.4 μg/ml.

Three other patients relapsed despite cephalothin therapy, or had suboptimal responses (Table 1), but were cured with tetracycline. Their clinical courses are described below.

Patient L.W., a 34-year-old woman, was admitted with fever, confusion, and neck stiffness. She responded clinically to 1.75 g of cephalothin by rapid infusion every 4 hr (150 mg per kg per day), but group B meningococci were eventually recovered in cultures of CSF samples obtained after the first, third, and fourth days of treatment. Cerebrospinal fluid obtained on the fifth day, 2 hr after administration of 1.75 g of cephalothin (given by rapid iv infusion), contained 0.24 μg of the antibiotic per ml. Later on the fifth day of therapy, the dose of cephalothin was increased to 3 g every 4 hr (250 mg per kg per day); CSF cultures became negative, and the patient continued to improve. However, on the 13th day of cephalothin therapy, clinical signs of meningeal irritation recurred; lumbar puncture showed CSF pleocytosis, and meningococci were again recovered in cultures of the CSF. L.W. was subsequently cured after 9 days of tetracycline therapy. The cephalothin susceptibility (MIC and MBC) of the original meningococcal strain recovered from the CSF was 0.4 μg/ml. The MIC and MBC for the organism recovered at the time of relapse were 0.2 and 0.4 μg/ml, respectively. On the 13th day, the day of relapse, the concentration of cephalothin in the CSF was 0.37 μg/ml 2 hr after the patient's regular dose of 3.0 g iv.

Patient E.R., a 46-year-old woman (Table 1), was comatose on admission, but became alert with cephalothin treatment at a dose of 150 mg per kg per day. Admission CSF cultures were positive for a group C meningococcus. However, despite the clinical improvement, CSF specimens obtained on days 1 and 3 after beginning cephalothin therapy eventually yielded group C meningococci. The dose of cephalothin was increased to 200 mg per kg per day, and she continued to improve. Cerebrospinal fluid obtained on the 7th day was sterile, but on the 10th day, the laboratory reported that a CSF culture, taken on the 8th day, was positive for a group C meningococcus. In spite of clinical well-being, cephalothin was discontinued, and the patient was cured after 9 days of tetracycline therapy. Both the MIC and the MBC for the group C meningococcus isolated at the time of admission and for that isolated from the day 8 CSF specimen were 0.4 μg of cephalothin per ml. Concentrations of cephalothin in this patient's serum and CSF on the 10th day of treatment, 2 hr after 2.5 g was infused rapidly iv, were 13.65 and 3.95 μg/ml, respectively.

A third patient, J.B., a 15-year-old boy, was admitted in coma. He was treated with cephalothin for 15 days and seemed to respond initially. By the third day of treatment he was responsive, and he was alert by the fifth day. Fever abated but never disappeared. All CSF cultures taken after initiation of therapy remained negative. By the 13th day of therapy, the CSF white cell count had increased slightly, but J.B.'s clinical condition was stable. However, on the 15th day, fever and CSF pleocytosis increased, and cephalothin was discontinued. He was cured after 6 days of tetracycline therapy. The MIC and MBC for the group C meningococcus isolated from the patient's admission CSF were 0.2 and 0.4 μg/ml, respectively. Cephalothin concentrations in blood and CSF were not determined in this patient.

Cephalothin concentrations in CSF and serum. Cephalothin concentrations were measured in CSF and serum samples obtained from five patients in this series and from two other patients not included in this series, J.D., who had been started on cephalothin after 10 days of ampicillin therapy for pneumococcal meningitis, and M.H., who was treated with cephalothin for a purulent meningitis of undetermined etiology. The data on the latter two patients have been included in Table 2 to expand the number of levels available for scrutiny.

The highest CSF levels were in patient B.W., who received 3.5 g of cephalothin rapidly iv on admission and then 1.75 g iv every 4 hr. At the end of the first day of treatment, B.W. had cephalothin concentrations of 52.5 μg/ml in her serum and 46.5 μg/ml in her CSF 2 hr after receiving 1.75 g of cephalothin iv. The patient's

Table 2. *Clinical correlates of cephalothin concentrations in CSF and serum among patients with acute bacterial meningitis*

Patient	Etiology	Day of therapy	CSF				Dose of cephalothin	Time after last dose (hr)	Cephalothin concn (μg/ml)			BUN (mg/100 ml)
			WBC /mm^3	Percent poly-morpho-nuclear	Sugar (mg/100 ml)	Protein (mg/100 ml)			Serum	CSF	CSF/serum	
B.W.	*Neisseria*	1	10,400	39	27	804	3.5 g iv; then	2	52.5	46.5	0.88	19
	menin-						1.75 g iv every	4		22.9		(shock)
	gitidis						4 hr					
L.W.	*N. menin-*	5	800	40	48	59	1.75 g iv every	2		0.24		9
	gitidis						4 hr	0		0.31		
							3 g iv every	2		0.37		
							4 hr					
E.R.	*N. menin-*	10	1,062	58	37	108	2.5 g iv every	2	13.65	3.95	0.29	10
	gitidis						4 hr					
J.F.	*N. menin-*	3	342	38	58	190	2 g iv every	2	3.2	0.54	0.17	15
	gitidis	7					4 hr	2	3.4	0.34	0.10	
G.D.	*N. menin-*	1	1,400	48	40	356	3 g iv; then	4	1.6	0.91	0.57	11
	gitidis	3	644	57	57	123	2 g iv every	2	12.0	1.88	0.16	
		7	183	21	73	40	4 hr	2	3.4	0.55	0.16	
		14	29	20	57	55		2	7.2	0		
J.D.[a]	*Diplo-*	15	62	21	33	199	2 g iv every	2	3.1	1.5	0.48	
	coccus						4 hr	4	0.88	0		
	pneu-											
	moniae											
M.H.[b]	*Unknown*	Adm.[c]	4,200	75	<10	250	2 g iv every					
		3	82	4	64	46	4 hr	2	2.1	0.15	0.07	12
		4	223	55	55	51		4		0.52		
		5	74	30	55	54		4		0.21		

[a] Cephalothin started on the 14th day of hospitalization; omitted from clinical study.
[b] Purulent meningitis with negative cultures, not included in series.
[c] Admission.

blood-urea nitrogen (BUN) at that time was 24 mg/100 ml, but she gradually became azotemic as her shock persisted. The lowest measurable CSF concentration, 0.15 μg/ml, was found in M.H. on the second day of therapy, but on the fourth day the CSF cephalothin content was 0.52 μg/ml. J.D., on the 15th day of treatment, had 1.5 μg of cephalothin per ml in his CSF 2 hr after 2.0 g had been given iv, but none was detectable at 4 hr. The ratio of cephalothin concentrations in CSF to those in serum was determined in nine instances in six different patients. The ratios ranged from a high of 0.88 to a low of 0.07. Too few samples were studied to permit generalizations, but it is of interest to note that the highest ratio, 0.88, was observed in patient B.W. when the CSF white cell count was 10,400 per mm^3 and the CSF protein was 804 mg/100 ml.

Summary of overall results of cephalothin treatment. Table 3 shows the overall results among the 12 patients treated with cephalothin for meningococcal meningitis. Eight recovered without sequelae after a course of cephalothin. Three other patients recovered without sequelae, but suboptimal bacteriological responses or clinical relapse dictated substitution of tetracycline for cephalothin. One patient (B.W.) died after 3 days of cephalothin followed by 12 days of tetracycline. Although organisms were slow to disappear from B.W.'s CSF during cephalothin treatment, it seems improbable that this slow bacteriological response caused her death. She was comatose and in shock on admission and

Table 3. *Results of cephalothin therapy for meningococcal meningitis*

Result	No. of patients
Cured without sequelae	8
Death	1[a]
Relapse with positive CSF cultures during therapy	2
Relapse clinically with negative CSF cultures during therapy	1
Total	12

[a] Patient B. W. CSF cultures positive 12 hr and CSF Gram stain positive 72 hr after initiating cephalothin therapy.

rapidly developed renal insufficiency. It is unlikely that initial treatment with any other antibiotic would have resulted in recovery.

DISCUSSION

There are few reports of cephalothin treatment for meningococcal meningitis.

Binns and Pankey (1) described a penicillin-allergic patient with meningococcal meningitis who was treated with cephalothin, 18 g per day, by continuous iv infusion. He recovered after 14 days of therapy and was discharged. However, 16 days later the patient developed a purulent meningitis from which no organism was cultured. This second attack was cured after penicillin desensitization and 17 days of penicillin therapy.

Southern and Sanford (11) reported two patients with meningococcal meningitis who had suboptimal responses to iv cephalothin at a dosage of 12 g/day. Cerebrospinal fluid white cell counts and glucose concentrations improved in both of these patients. However, one developed fever, obtundation, and an increase of CSF pleocytosis on the 10th day, although cultures were negative. Therapy was changed to penicillin after desensitization to this drug. Their second patient did not improve with cephalothin; meningococci were cultured from the CSF on the third day, and therapy was successfully completed with chloramphenicol. The first patient was infected with a group C meningococcus; the type recovered from the second patient was not given. The MIC of cephalothin for these two strains of meningococci was 0.78 μg/ml for the first and 3.125 μg/ml for the second. Concentrations of cephalothin in serum and CSF were not determined.

In our study, three patients who had not received even one dose of any other antibiotic were cured of meningococcal meningitis with cephalothin. Cephalothin was certainly responsible for curing four other patients who received minimal amounts of other antibiotics initially. An eighth patient (J.F.) probably was cured with cephalothin, but possibly her initial 48 hr of ampicillin was enough to eradicate her meningococci.

The one fatality occurred in a 67-year-old woman, B.W., who had severe, fulminant disease with coma and shock on admission. Her persistent coma and subsequent death cannot necessarily be attributed to antibiotic failure, but the positive CSF cultures after 12 hr of cephalothin therapy and the presence of abundant gram-negative diplococci in the CSF (which did not grow on culture) after 3 days of therapy could be deemed definitely unusual. Meningococci are seldom seen and rarely cultured after the first 12 to 24 hr of therapy with ampicillin or benzyl penicillin (6). It was also surprising that meningococci were recovered in culture of a CSF specimen with a high concentration of cephalothin. This CSF specimen, obtained after 12 hr of cephalothin therapy, contained 46.5μg of cephalothin per ml. It is tempting to ascribe this high level to decreased renal excretion of cephalothin, because the patient was oliguric and the simultaneous concentration in the serum was quite high, 52.5 μg/ml. However, it should be emphasized that the serum to CSF ratio was 0.88, and the CSF exhibited a very marked inflammatory response.

There are several possible explanations for the other three treatment failures. Patient L.W. had concentrations of cephalothin in the CSF of 0.24 and 0.34 μg/ml, which were less than the MIC for the infecting meningococcus. However, patient E.R. had cephalothin concentrations in the CSF greater than the MIC for her bacteria, and meningococci were still cultured from her CSF. Failure to sterilize the CSF in spite of apparently adequate concentrations of cephalothin in the CSF may have been due to sequestrations of bacteria in small abscesses or subdural effusions which cephalothin did not penetrate; however, persistence of meningococci or relapse of meningitis after treatment with other antibiotics is rare (6).

Like penicillin, cephalothin concentrations in the CSF tend to be highest when evidence of meningeal irritation is greatest, presumably as a consequence of increased permeability of meningeal vasculature. The concentrations found in the CSF and serum specimens of our patients were similar to those reported previously by others (4, 5, 9, 13).

Oppenheimer, Beaty, and Petersdorf (8) administered single cephalothin doses of 50 mg/kg iv on days 1, 4, and 7 to dogs with experimental pneumococcal meningitis. Serial CSF specimens were obtained from the animals after each dose of cephalothin. On day 1, peak CSF concentrations occurred 30 to 60 min after iv administration of 50 mg of the antibiotic per kg; after 120 min, CSF concentrations had dropped by approximately 50% or more. On the seventh day, during convalescence, CSF concentrations were about 25% of those measured on day 1. The results of these studies in dogs, if extrapolated to man, would suggest that CSF specimens obtained later than 30 to 60 min after iv administration, as was done in our studies, might contain less than the true maximum concentration.

The dynamics of antibiotic activity and host defenses in eradicating bacteria from the meninges are not well understood. Such information as MIC, MBC, bacterial growth rates, antibiotic killing rates, and concentrations of antibiotics in the CSF cannot be used to predict accurately the clinical efficacy of a given antimicrobial agent in patients with bacterial meningitis. For example, what concentration of a given antibiotic must be present in the CSF and how long must it be sustained to be effective? How important are antibiotic concentrations in the various central nervous system tissues? Thrupp et al. (12) demonstrated that some patients with bacterial meningitis treated with ampicillin had no detectable antibiotic in the CSF during the acute stage of disease, yet recovered uneventfully. However, in that study, a single lumbar puncture was performed at various intervals after iv administration of antibiotic, and it is likely that ampicillin had been present transiently in the CSF (12).

The phase of growth of bacteria in the CSF when antibiotic therapy is started is another variable of uncertain significance. Plorde, Garcia, and Petersdorf (10) demonstrated that in dogs with experimental pneumococcal meningitis, a single dose of penicillin given during the rapid bacterial growth phase promptly killed the bacteria. If therapy was delayed several hours, until the pneumococci were in the stationary phase of growth, the penicillin did not kill—viable organisms were present at 24 hr. This phenomenon was attributed to penicillin's mode of action on the cell wall of actively multiplying bacteria; organisms that were not dividing were not killed.

In our patients who were treated with cephalothin, success or failure in eradicating meningococci from the CSF could not necessarily be correlated with the concentration of cephalothin in the CSF or with the MIC of cephalothin for the infecting meningococci. Inadequate drug concentration in the CSF might possibly explain one treatment failure, but the reasons for three other treatment failures are obscure.

It should be emphasized that cephalothin is not a satisfactory substitute for penicillin in the treatment of meningococcal disease. The experience with cephalothin in meningococcal disease plainly illustrates that the physician should not be lulled into complacency by the results of in vitro susceptibility tests or by a favorable initial response to an antimicrobial agent whose efficacy has not been definitely proven by clinical experience.

ACKNOWLEDGMENTS

This investigation was supported by Public Health Service grants 5-TO1-AI00275 and 5-RO1-AI08011 from the National Institute of Allergy and Infectious Diseases, by contract DA-49-193-MD-2874 from the U.S. Army Research and Development Command, Commission on Acute Respiratory Diseases, Office of the Surgeon General, Department of the Army, by a grant-in-aid from Eli Lilly & Co., Indianapolis, Ind., and by the Hastings Foundation Fund.

LITERATURE CITED

1. Binns, J. O., and G. A. Pankey. 1966. Meningococcal meningitis treated with cephalothin: a case report. J. La. State Med. Soc. **118**:493–496.
2. Eickhoff, T. C., and M. Finland. 1963. Changing susceptibility of meningococci to antimicrobial agents. N. Engl. J. Med. **272**:395–398.
3. Ivler, D., J. M. Leedom, L. D. Thrupp, P. F. Wehrle, B. Portnoy, and A. W. Mathies, Jr. 1965. Naturally occurring sulfadiazine-resistant meningococci. Antimicrob. Agents Chemother.–1964, p. 444–450.
4. Klein, J. O., T. C. Eickhoff, J. G. Tilles, and M. Finland. 1964. Cephalothin: Activity *in vitro*, absorption and excretion in normal subjects and clinical observations in 40 patients. Amer. J. Med. Sci. **248**:640–656.
5. Lerner, P. I. 1969. Penetration of cephalothin and lincomycin into the cerebrospinal fluid. Amer. J. Med. Sci. **257**:125–131.
6. Mathies, A. W., Jr., J. M. Leedom, L. D. Thrupp, D. Ivler, B. Portnoy, and P. F. Wehrle. 1966. Experience with ampicillin in bacterial meningitis. Antimicrob. Agents Chemother.–1965, p. 610–617.
7. Millar, J. W., E. E. Siess, H. A. Feldman, C. Silverman, and P. Frank. 1963. *In vivo* and *in vitro* resistance to sulfadiazine in strains of *Neisseria meningitidis*. J. Amer. Med. Ass. **186**:139–141.
8. Oppenheimer, S., H. Beaty, and R. G. Petersdorf. 1969. Pathogenesis of meningitis. VIII. Cerebrospinal fluid and blood concentrations of methicillin, cephalothin, and cephaloridine in experimental pneumococcal meningitis. J. Lab. Clin. Med. **73**:535–543.
9. Perkins, R. L., and S. Saslow. 1966. Experiences with cephalothin. Ann. Intern. Med. **64**:13–24.
10. Plorde, J. J., M. Garcia, and R. G. Petersdorf. 1964. Studies on the pathogenesis of meningitis. IV. Penicillin levels in the cerebrospinal fluid in experimental meningitis. J. Lab. Clin. Med. **64**:960–969.

11. Southern, P. M., Jr., and J. P. Sanford. 1969. Meningococcal meningitis–Suboptimal response to cephalothin therapy. N. Engl. J. Med. **280**:1163–1165.
12. Thrupp, L. D., J. M. Leedom, D. Ivler, P. F. Wehrle, B. Portnoy, and A. W. Mathies. 1966. Ampicillin levels in the cerebrospinal fluid during treatment of bacterial meningitis. Antimicrob. Agents Chemother.–1965, p. 206–213.
13. Vianna, N. J., and D. Kaye. 1967. Penetration of cephalothin into the spinal fluid. Amer. J. Med. Sci. **254**:216–220.

Antimicrobial Agents and Chemotherapy—1969

Therapeutic Trial of Cephalexin in Meningococcal Carriers

WILLIAM B. DEAL and EUGENE SANDERS

Departments of Medicine and Microbiology, University of Florida College of Medicine, Gainesville, Florida 32601

Since the emergence of sulfadiazine-resistant meningococci, no antimicrobial agent has been significantly effective in decreasing the meningococcal carrier rate. Cephalexin, a new oral cephalosporin with demonstrated in vitro activity against meningococci, was evaluated in a double-blind placebo study of known meningococcal carriers. Administration of 500 mg every 8 hr for 4 days had reduced the carrier rate by only 6.7% at 5 days after initiation of therapy. Cephalexin thus appears ineffective in elimination of meningococci from known carriers.

No effective agent for the prophylaxis of meningococcal carriers is currently available. The usefulness of sulfadiazine has been limited by the widespread emergence of resistant strains of *Neisseria meningitidis* (7, 10, 11). Other antimicrobial drugs with in vitro activity and with demonstrable clinical activity against meningococci have failed to be effective in decreasing the meningococcal carrier rate (1, 3, 5, 6, 12). The availability of a new antimicrobial agent, cephalexin, with a high degree of activity against meningococci in vitro, plus the need for an effective prophylactic agent, prompted the present study.

Cephalexin is a relatively new cephalosporin with a spectrum of antibacterial activity virtually identical to that of other cephalosporins. It is well absorbed after oral administration. A single oral dose of 500 mg results in concentrations up to 18 μg per ml of serum within 1 hr, and detectable concentrations persist for 6 hr (8). Strains of meningococci tested to date are susceptible to 10 μg or less of cephalexin per ml. These characteristics suggested that a trial of cephalexin in meningococcal carriers was warranted.

MATERIALS AND METHODS

Culture and identification of organisms. Nasopharyngeal swabs were streaked directly onto Modified Thayer-Martin medium (Difco), which is highly selective for growth of pathogenic *Neisseria.* Plates were incubated in 10% carbon dioxide in air at 37 C for 48 hr. Colonies resembling *N. meningitidis* (meningococci) were tested for the production of oxidase and were confirmed as *Neisseria* by Gram stain. All meningococci isolated from subjects included in this study fermented dextrose and maltose but not sucrose or lactose. Serological typing (microagglutination method) was performed with the use of chicken antimeningococcal serum (National Communicable Disease Center, Atlanta, Ga.). Cultures were maintained on cysteine-Trypticase-agar with phenol red indicator (BBL) at 37 C in 10% CO_2 in air. For purposes of this study, a "positive culture" refers to the isolation of one or more colonies of meningococci from any one specimen in the post-treatment period.

Susceptibility of meningococci to cephalexin and sulfadiazine. Meningococci were tested for susceptibility to cephalexin by the agar-dilution technique (Mueller-Hinton agar, BBL). Cephalexin was dissolved in 0.9% saline to a concentration of 20 μg/ml and then was serially diluted to 10, 5.0, 2.5, and 1.25 μg/ml in duplicate test plates. Control plates, prepared in duplicate, contained only saline and Mueller-Hinton agar. Suspensions of meningococci were prepared in 0.9% sodium chloride. Each inoculum (0.01-ml milk-dilution loop), containing 2×10^4 to 6×10^4 colony-forming units of meningococci, was streaked onto an area of 1 to 2 cm^2 of the plate surface. Plates were incubated in 10% carbon dioxide in air at 37 C for 48 hr. The minimal inhibitory concentration (MIC) was accepted as the lowest concentration of drug that completely inhibited the growth of the organisms in duplicate plates. Susceptibility to sodium sulfadiazine was determined by the same technique. Sulfadiazine was dissolved in 0.9% sodium chloride, serially diluted, and added to Mueller-Hinton agar plates. Final concentrations of the drug in the test plates were 100 and 10 μg/ml. Technique, inoculum size, and method of determining MIC were similar to those used with cephalexin.

Therapeutic trial of cephalexin. Three hundred fifty-two healthy male and female students, 21 to 28 years of age, were cultured for meningococci in April 1969. Of these, 33 (9.4%) harbored meningococci on initial culture. The 30 subjects chosen for this study had positive cultures at the time of each of three subsequent examinations during the ensuing 2 weeks. The study was conducted by use of a double-blind technique with a placebo. Subjects were assigned numbers 1 to 30 by the investigator. An independent party numbered 30 vials, each containing 24 capsules, from a table of random numbers. Fifteen of the vials contained 250-mg capsules of cephalexin, and 15 contained identical capsules of placebo. Each subject was instructed to take two capsules three times a day for 4 days.

Previous double-blind studies involving this population have been conducted by the investigators. In these studies standard Food, Drug, and Cosmetic dyes have been included in both drug and placebo. This produced colored urine in both placebo and drug-treated groups. The population was reliable. In addition, the population is well known to the investigators, and the subjects were seen daily throughout the present study.

Nasopharyngeal cultures were obtained from all subjects on the first day of therapy. Subsequent cultures were taken on days 2 to 4, 7 to 11, and 14 to 18, and were numbered accordingly.

RESULTS

Susceptibility of meningococci to cephalexin and sulfadiazine in vitro. The susceptibility to cephalexin and sulfadiazine of the meningococci isolated from each subject was determined prior to treatment (Table 1). For 20 strains, the MIC of sulfadiazine was 10 μg/ml, and for one strain the MIC was 100 μg/ml. Nine strains were resistant to 100 μg of sulfadiazine per ml. The MIC of cephalexin was 2 μg/ml for 21 strains. Of the remaining nine strains, six were inhibited by 5 μg/ml, and three were inhibited by cephalexin in a concentration of 10 μg/ml. There was no correlation between sulfadiazine resistance and cephalexin resistance.

Results of therapeutic trial. All subjects completed the prescribed course of therapy (500 mg of cephalexin or placebo three times daily for 4 days) with no adverse reactions. Results of cultures obtained before, during, and after treatment are shown in Fig. 1. Only 5 of 15 subjects (33%) had a negative culture during therapy. In one subject (no. 30), the negative culture

Table 1. *Minimal inhibitory concentrations (MIC) of cephalexin and serological types of meningococci isolated from placebo and cephalexin-treated subjects*

Placebo group before therapy			Cephalexin group				
			Before therapy			After therapy	
Subject no.	MIC (μg/ml)	Serological type[a]	Subject no.	MIC (μg/ml)	Serological type	MIC (μg/ml)	Serological type of first positive culture after becoming negative
1	2.5	B	2	2.5	B	2.5	
3	5.0	B	5	2.5	C	2.5	C
4	10.0	NT	6	2.6	B	2.5	
7	2.5	B	8	2.5	B	2.5	
9	2.5	poly-ag	11	2.5	poly-ag	2.5	
10	2.5	B	14	2.5	C	2.5	
12	2.5	B	15	2.5	poly-ag	5.0	
13	2.5	B	17	2.5	poly-ag	2.5	
16	2.5	B	18	1.25	B	2.5	B
19	2.5	B	20	2.5	C	2.5	
22	2.5	B	21	2.5	B	2.5	NT
24	2.5	B	23	2.5	B	2.5	
25	2.5	C	27	2.5		2.5	
26	2.5	B	29	2.5	B	2.5	B
28	2.5	B	30	2.5	B	2.5	B

[a] NT, strains did not agglutinate in specific antisera; poly-ag, strains agglutinated equally in more than one specific antiserum.

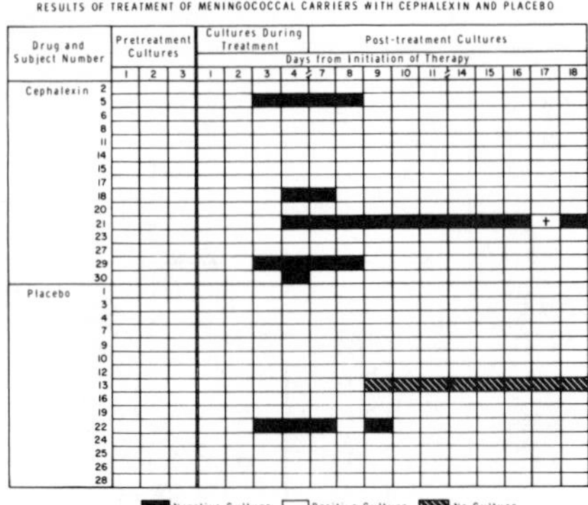

Fig. 1. *Results of treatment of meningococcal carriers with placebo and cephalexin. All patients harbored meningococci on each of three nasopharyngeal cultures during the 4 weeks preceding the study. Cephalexin (500 mg every 8 hr) and placebo were administered after an overnight fast, with use of a double-blind technique. A positive culture represented recovery of one or more colonies of N. meningitidis from any sample. Positive cultures are shown in white, and negative in black. Meningococci recovered from subjects indicated by + were of different serological reactivity from the strain originally carried.*

occurred only on the last day of treatment. Subject 18 had a negative culture on day 7 but was again positive thereafter. Subjects 5 and 29 became negative on the third day of treatment and remained negative through the eighth day. Subject 21 became negative on the fourth day of treatment and remained negative throughout the study, except for the 17th day, when a few colonies of a nontypable organism were isolated.

In the placebo group, one subject (no. 22) spontaneously became negative on the third, fourth, seventh, and ninth days. However, positive cultures were obtained on days 10, 11, and 14 to 18. Subject no. 13 abandoned the study on day 9.

DISCUSSION

At the dosage employed in this study, cephalexin clearly failed to cause a significant change in the meningococcal carrier rate among young adults. The reasons for this failure are not readily apparent. The dose administered probably produced drug concentrations in the serum that were equal to or in excess of the MIC for most of the strains carried, and there is a good reason to believe that all subjects took the medication as prescribed. It is possible that cephalexin failed to eliminate the carrier state for the same obscure reason(s) as other antimicrobial agents (such as penicillin, erythromycin, ampicillin, tetracycline, and ethoxzolamide) that possess high in vitro activity against meningococci and are efficacious in the treatment of established meningococcal disease (1, 5, 6, 12). Mechanisms postulated to explain these failures are as follows: (i) cell wall-active antimicrobials may induce spheroplast formation among strains carried, thus permitting survival of the microorganisms with reversion to the parent form after withdrawal of the drug; (ii) the drugs may not penetrate into the nasopharyngeal milieu in sufficient concentrations to permit bacterial killing; and (iii) the resident meningococci may be in a state similar to the stationary growth phase of microorganisms in vitro, wherein the cephalosporins and penicillins may be unable to exert a bactericidal effect.

Sulfadiazine is not predictably useful because of the increased prevalence of resistant organisms. As noted in Table 2, other antibiotics, with one exception, do not approach the former efficacy of sulfadiazine and are of no use in effectively decreasing the meningococcal carrier rate (1, 4, 5, 9, 12). Rifampin, on the other hand, has been demonstrated to possess a high degree of activity against meningococcal growth in vitro and in chronic meningococcal carriers. The lack of adverse reactions, the convenience of a single daily dose, and its effectiveness in the prophylaxis of meningococcal carriers make rifampin potentially useful. Further studies with rifampin in populations at greater risk to epidemic meningococcal disease are needed to confirm its efficacy (4).

In the present study, cephalexin in the dose used (500 mg every 8 hr for 4 days) failed to decrease significantly the meningococcal carrier rate in a selected student population. Although it is possible that larger doses or a longer duration of treatment might increase its effectiveness, the known failure of penicillin (which has a similar mechanism of antibacterial activity) makes this supposition doubtful. The efficacy of rifampin and the possible availability of effective antimeningococcal vaccines suggest that further studies with cephalexin for erradication of the meningococcal carrier state are not warranted.

Table 2. *Comparative efficacy of drugs in reduction of meningococcal carrier rate*[a]

Drug	Dose	Duration of therapy (days)	No. of subjects treated	Carrier rate (percentage of subjects with positive cultures)			
				Pretreatment	Post-treatment		
					1 week	2 weeks	3 weeks
Sulfadiazine (9)	3 g/day	3	100	30	0	2	–
	2 g/day	2	100	36	3	2	–
Oxytetracycline (5)	0.5 g twice daily	4	33	100	57.6	100	–
	0.5 g twice daily	8	49	100	37	90	–
Erythromycin (5)	1 g/day	4	12	100	63.6	100	–
	1 g/day	10	28	100	53.8	60	–
Penicillin G (5)	1 million units twice daily	4	23	100	61.5	75	–
	1 million units twice daily	10	37	100	31.5	66.7	–
Penicillin G (5)	1.5 million units	10	20	100	46	75	–
Ampicillin (5)	500 mg three times daily	10	26	100	32	38	–
Ethoxzolamide (12)	125–375 mg	3	8	100	100	100	–
Procaine penicillin (1)	1.2 million units/day	2	118	100	–	51	–
Erythromycin (1)	500 mg three times daily	2	7	100	–	100	–
Rifampin (4)	600 mg/day	4	15	100	6.7	6.7	6.7
Cephalexin	500 mg three times daily	4	15	100	93.3	93.3	–

[a] Data for drugs other than cephalexin were taken from the reference given after each drug name.

ACKNOWLEDGMENTS

This investigation was supported by grants-in-aid from Eli Lilly & Co., Indianapolis, Ind., and by Public Health Service grants AI-06514 and 5-T01-AI-00341 from the National Institute of Allergy and Infectious Diseases. Dr. Sanders is the recipient of Public Health Service research career-development award 1-K03-AI-38636 from the National Institutes of Health and is John and Mary R. Markle Scholar in Academic Medicine.

LITERATURE CITED

1. Artenstein, M. D., T. H. Lamson, and J. R. Evans. 1967. Attempted prophylaxis against meningococcal infection using intramuscular penicillin. Mil. Med. **132**:1009–1011.
2. Bristow, W. M., P. F. D. Van Peenan, and R. Volk. 1965. Epidemic meningitis in naval recruits. Amer. J. Public Health **55**:1039–1045.
3. Cheever, F. S., B. B. Breese, and H. C. Upham. 1943. The treatment of meningococcal carriers with sulfadiazine. Ann. Intern. Med. **19**:602–608.
4. Deal, W. B., and E. Sanders. 1969. Efficacy of rifampin in treatment of meningococcal carriers. N. Engl. J. Med. **261**:641–645.
5. Dowd, J. M., D. Blink, C. H. Miller, P. F. Frank, and W. E. Pierce. 1966. Antibiotic prophylaxis of carriers of sulfadiazine-resistant meningococci. J. Infec. Dis. **116**:473–380.
6. Eickhoff, T. C., and M. Finland. 1965. Changing susceptibility of meningococci to antimicrobial agents. N. Engl. J. Med. **272**:395–398.
7. Gauld, J. R., R. E. Nitz, D. H. Hunter, J. H. Rust, and R. L. Gauld. 1965. Epidemiology of meningococcal meningitis at Fort Ord. Amer. J. Epidemiol. **82**:56–72.
8. Kind, A. C., D. G. Kestle, H. C. Standiford, and W. M. M. Kirby. 1969. Laboratory and clinical experience with cephalexin. Antimicrob. Agents Chemother.–1968, p. 361–365.
9. Kuhns, D. M., C. T. Nelson, H. A. Feldman, and L. R. Kuhn. 1943. Prophylactic value of sulfadiazine in the control of meningococcal meningitis. J. Amer. Med. Ass. **123**:335–339.
10. Leedom, J. M., D. Ivler, A. W. Mathies, L. D. Thrupp, B. Portnoy, and P. F. Wehrle. 1965. Importance of sulfadiazine resistance in meningococcal disease in civilians. N. Engl. J. Med. **273**:1395–1401.
11. Millar, J. W., E. E. Siess, H. A. Feldman, C. Silverman, and P. Frank. 1963. In vivo and in vitro resistance to sulfadiazine in strains of *Neisseria meningitidis*. J. Amer. Med. Ass. **186**:139–141.
12. Sanders, W. E. 1967. Use of sulfonamide carbonic anhydrase inhibitors in treatment of meningococcal carriers: rationale and report of a clinical trial of ethoxzolamide. Amer. J. Med. Sci. **254**:709–716.

Antimicrobial Agents and Chemotherapy—1969

Printed in USA

Evaluation of the Bauer-Kirby-Sherris-Turck Single-Disc Diffusion Method of Antibiotic Susceptibility Testing

JOHN M. MATSEN, MARILYN J. H. KOEPCKE, and PAUL G. QUIE

Departments of Laboratory Medicine and Pediatrics, University of Minnesota Medical School, Minneapolis, Minnesota 55455

More and more clinical laboratories are using the single-, high-potency disc method of antibiotic susceptibility testing as advocated by Bauer et al. of the University of Washington. Several hundred bacterial strains, including most of the common species, were tested in our laboratory by this method in a controlled setting with comparison agar-dilution testing. Results of these comparative agar-dilution and disc-diffusion studies were plotted on regression graphs, and the line of regression was plotted by the formula of least squares and by computerized means. These regression curves were compared with regression curves obtained from John Sherris. The results of our studies were compared with the values outlined for the method as break-off points for reporting the susceptibility or resistance of an organism to a specific antibiotic. On the whole, regression values superimposed closely. However, certain problem areas were apparent. For example, existing values for penicillin relegate to a resistant classification many nonstaphylococcal organisms such as enterococci and *Proteus mirabilis* which may respond to penicillin therapy. Further, values given for colistin and polymyxin B do not appear to provide an accurate separation of susceptible and resistant organisms. For most antibiotics, the Bauer-Kirby-Sherris-Turck method appears to be a reproducible, accurate method for antibiotic susceptibility testing if guidelines are followed. Regression curves allow for quantitative interpretation from inhibition zone sizes over a range of minimal inhibitory concentrations for most antibiotics.

The single-, high-potency disc method of antibiotic susceptibility testing as advocated by Bauer et al. (1) appears to be gaining widespread use in clinical laboratories throughout the country. This method assumes that the results obtained should be reproducible if the recommended guidelines are employed.

This report details the results obtained at the University of Minnesota when bacterial strains, including most of the common species, were used to test this method in a controlled setting with comparison agar-dilution testing.

MATERIALS AND METHODS

Bacterial strains used in these studies were clinical isolates from the Clinical Microbiology Laboratory. For regression purposes, a single colony of each strain was inoculated in tryptose-phosphate broth (Difco) and incubated overnight at 35 C. This culture suspension was then visually standardized against an opacity standard prepared by adding 0.5 ml of 1% $BaCl_2$ to 99.5 ml of 1% H_2SO_4 (0.36 N).

Large (15-cm) petri plates filled with Mueller-Hinton agar (Difco) to a depth of 4 to 5 mm (requiring 70 to 75 ml of agar medium) were streaked evenly in three planes with a cotton swab, excess suspension having been removed from the swab by rotating it against the side of the tube containing the standardized bacterial suspension. In the case of beta-hemolytic streptococci, enterococci, pneumococci, and staphylococci, the Mueller-Hinton agar contained 5% sheep blood. After the inoculum had dried (about 5 min) discs were put in place on the agar surface, and the plates were incubated immediately. After 18 hr of incubation at 35 C, readings of zone sizes were made by two different individuals. Two plates were used for each strain tested. Thus, four values were recorded for each strain with each antibiotic disc used. These four values were then averaged to obtain the value used on the scatter graph and for the calculation of the regression line.

Agar-dilution testing with Mueller-Hinton agar was carried out by use of a Steers replicator (4). A 0.2-ml volume of a 2×10^2 dilution of the standardized or diluted suspension used for disc-diffusion testing was inoculated into the wells of the seed plate portion of the replicator. Serial dilutions of antibiotics from frozen stock solutions were added to Mueller-Hinton agar when it had cooled to 45 C after initial autoclaving. The combined antibiotic and Mueller-Hinton agar was then immediately poured into sterile 100-mm petri plates. Inoculation of agar plates with the replicator was carried out subsequent to the hardening of the agar. Each prong of the replicator delivers approximately 0.002 ml of inoculum. Readings of agar-dilution results were made after 18 hr of incubation at 35 C.

It should be noted that penicillinase-producing staphylococci were excluded when penicillin, ampicillin, and cephaloridine were tested.

Results of comparative agar-dilution and disc-diffusion studies were plotted on scatter graphs. The line of regression was calculated both by the formula of least squares and by computerized means which made use of the same mathematic principle.

RESULTS

Regression data are shown in Fig. 1-10. For purposes of comparison, regression data furnished by John C. Sherris of the University of Washington have been plotted along side our data on Fig. 1-5 and on Fig. 9. For the newer antibiotics, cephaloridine (Fig. 6) and gentamicin (Fig. 7), Minnesota data alone are shown, as is also the case with polymyxin B (Fig. 8) and penicillin (Fig. 10).

Organisms in the figures listed as nonfermenters included *Pseudomonas, Mima,* and *Herellea* strains. Coliforms included *Escherichia coli, Klebsiella,* and *Enterobacter.* Organisms included as other *Enterobacteriaceae* were *Proteus mirabilis, P. rettgeri, P. morganii, Providence, Serratia, Salmonella,* and *Shigella* species.

Table 1, kindly supplied by Dr. Sherris, is an updated, modified interpretive chart for the Bauer-Kirby-Sherris-Turck method.

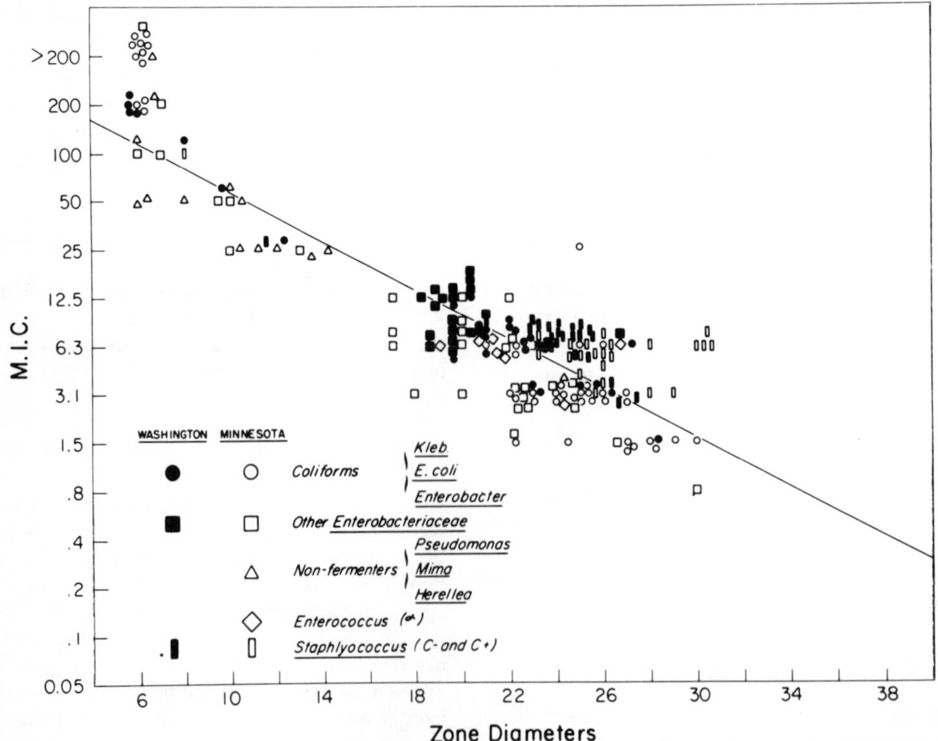

Fig. 1. *Regression graph for chloramphenicol (30 µg).*

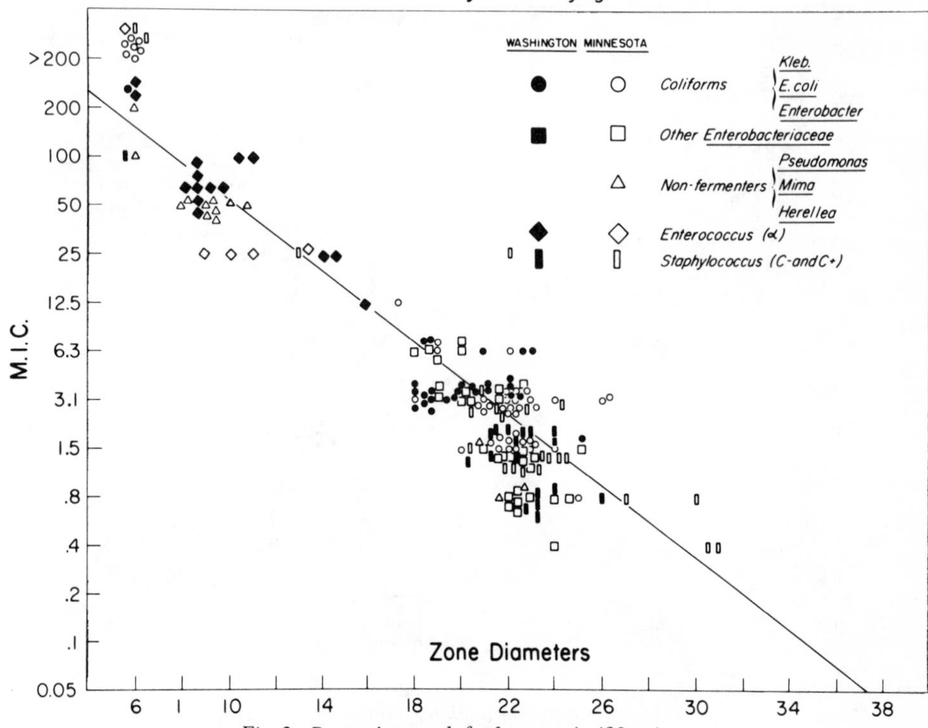

Fig. 2. *Regression graph for kanamycin (30 μg).*

Streptomycin (10μgm)

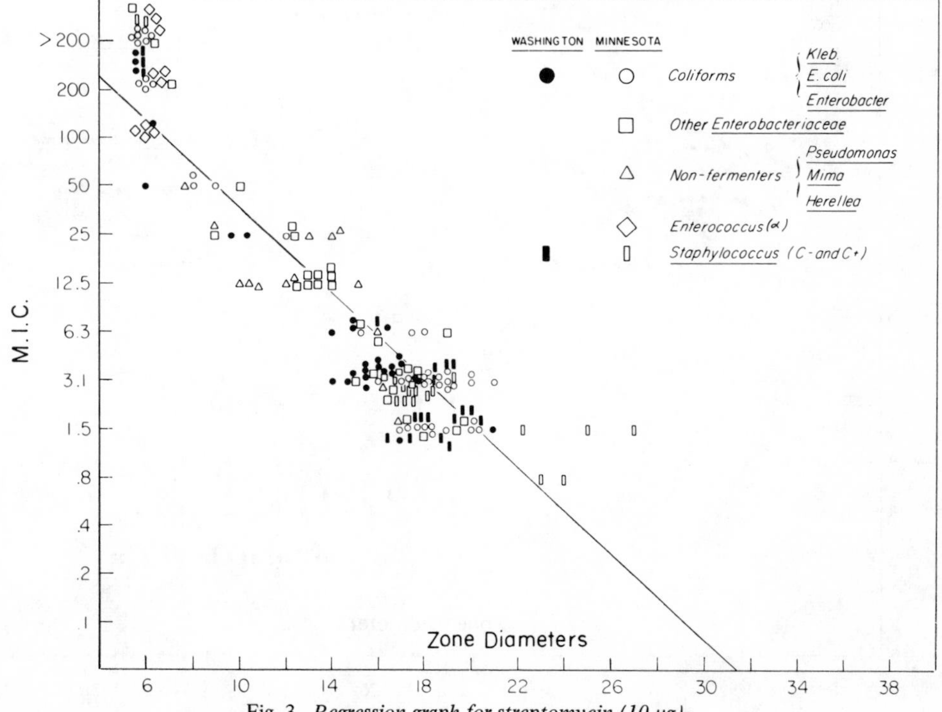

Fig. 3. *Regression graph for streptomycin (10 μg).*

Tetracycline (30 μgm)

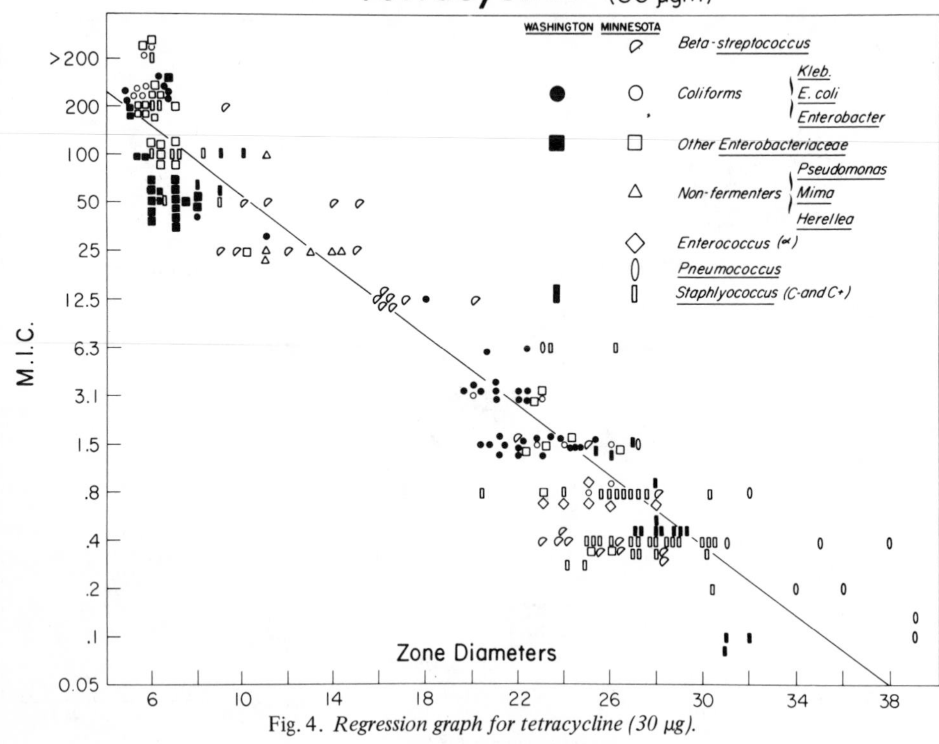

Fig. 4. *Regression graph for tetracycline (30 μg).*

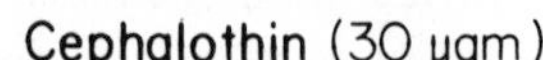

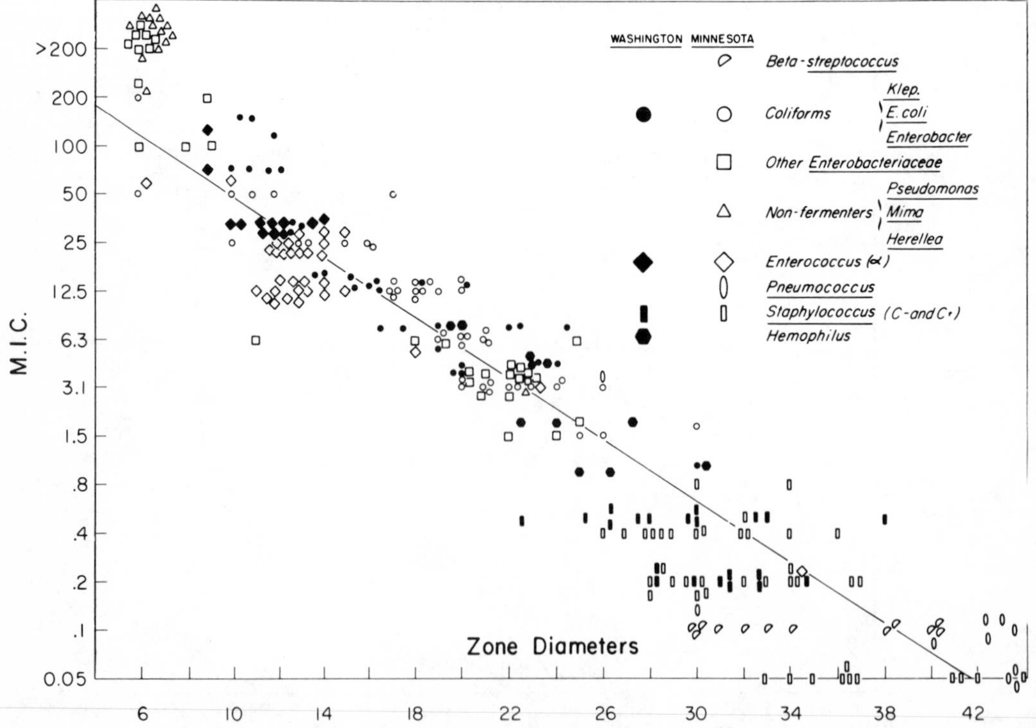

Fig. 5. *Regression graph for cephalothin (30 μg).*

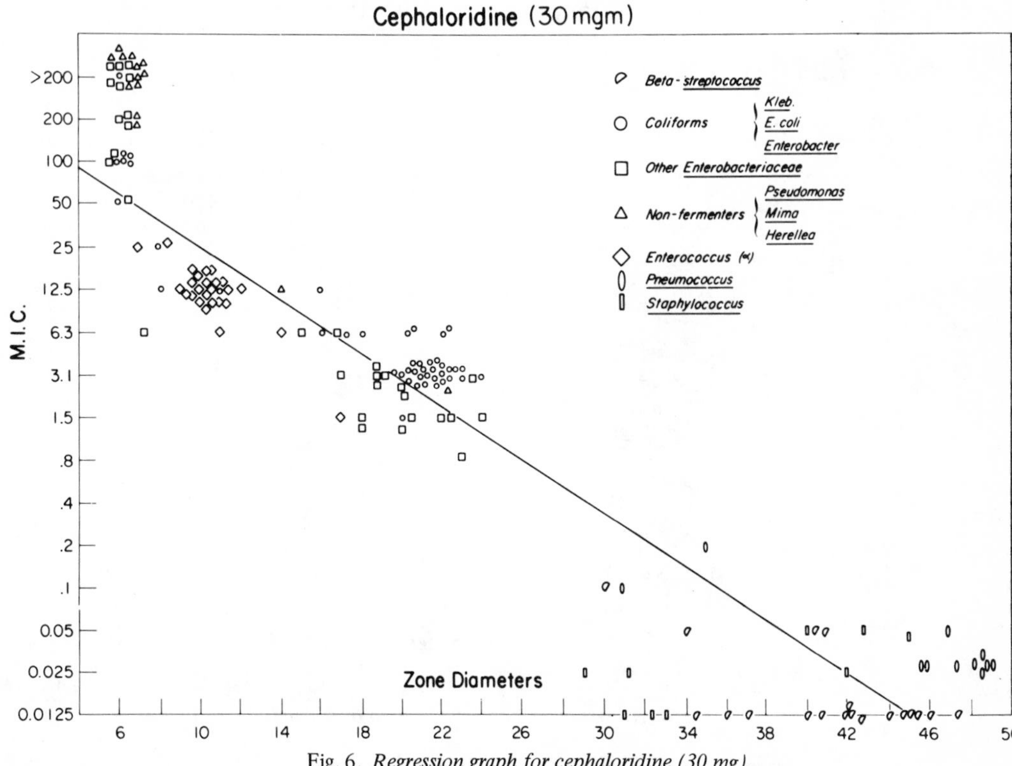

Fig. 6. *Regression graph for cephaloridine (30 mg).*

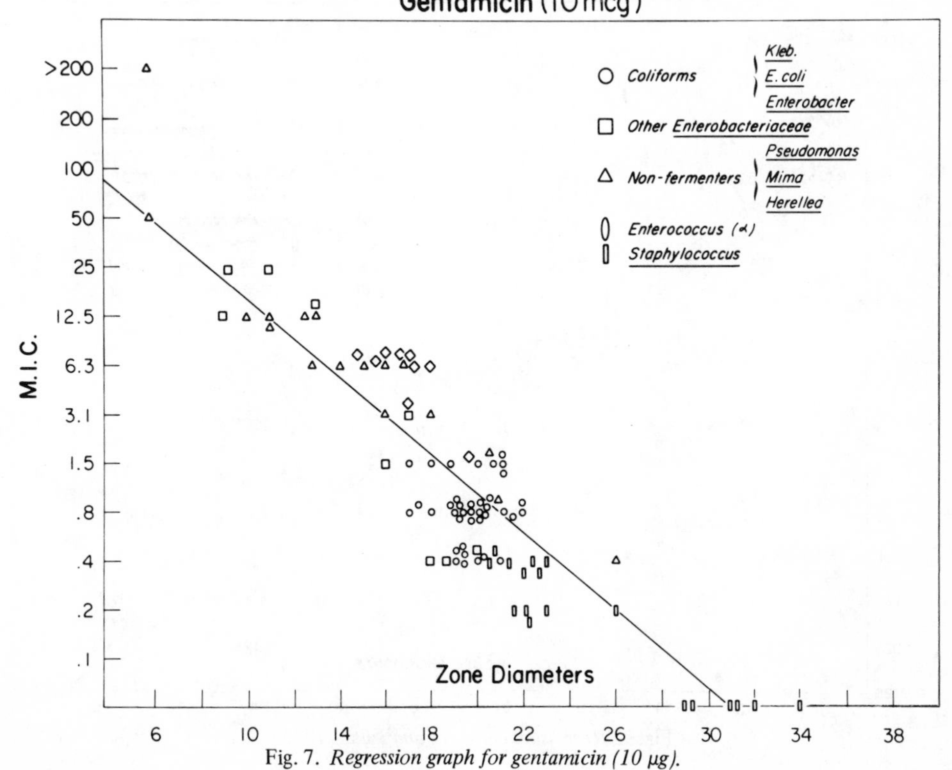

Fig. 7. *Regression graph for gentamicin (10 μg).*

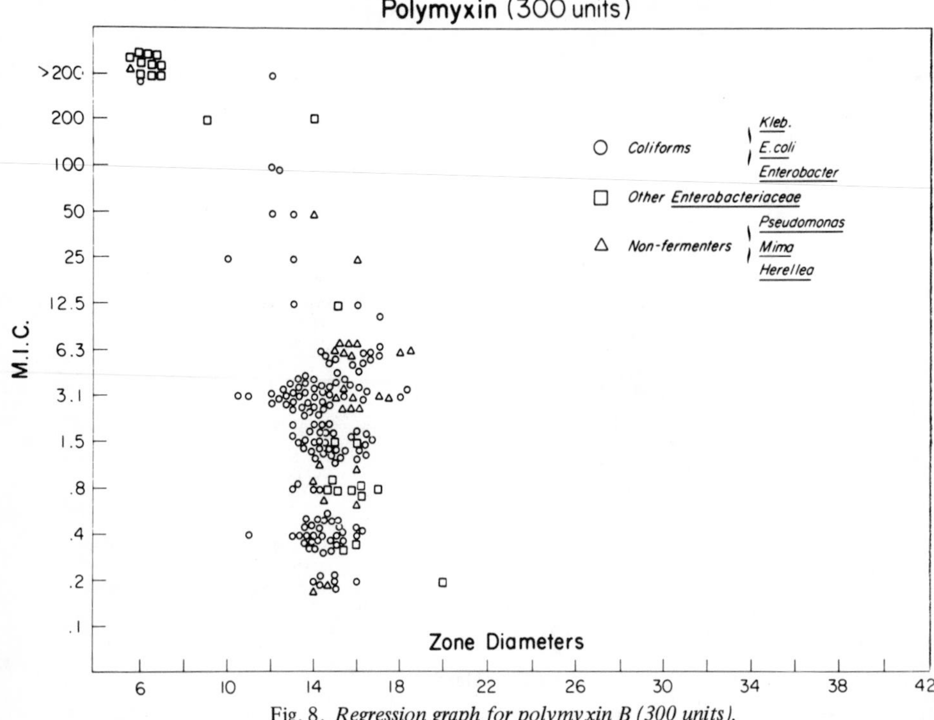

Fig. 8. *Regression graph for polymyxin B (300 units).*

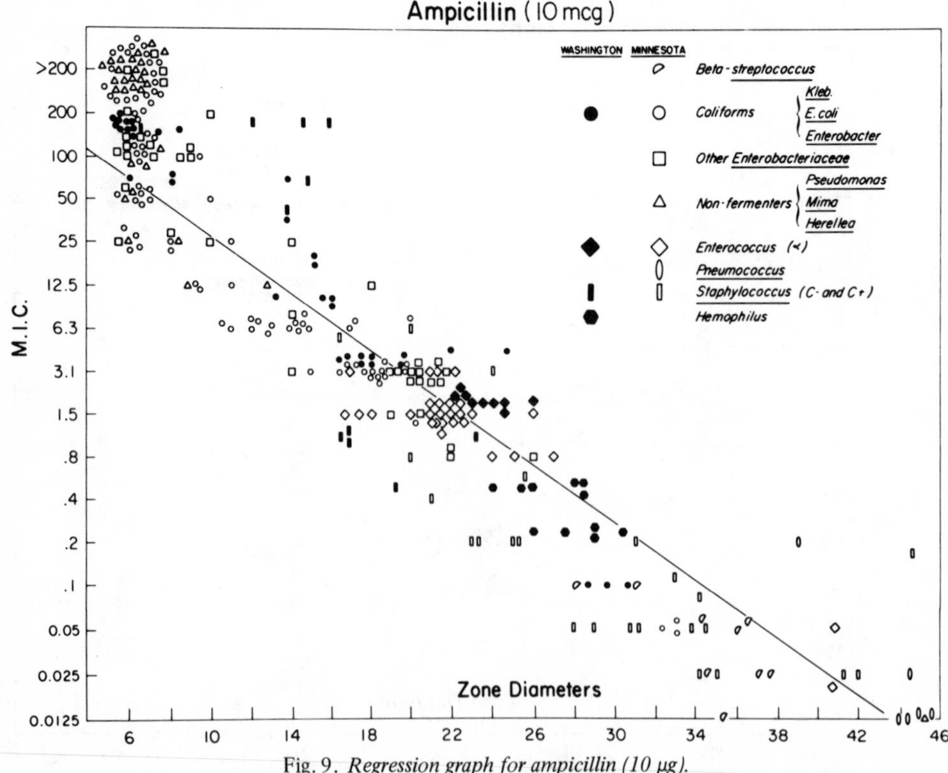

Fig. 9. *Regression graph for ampicillin (10 μg).*

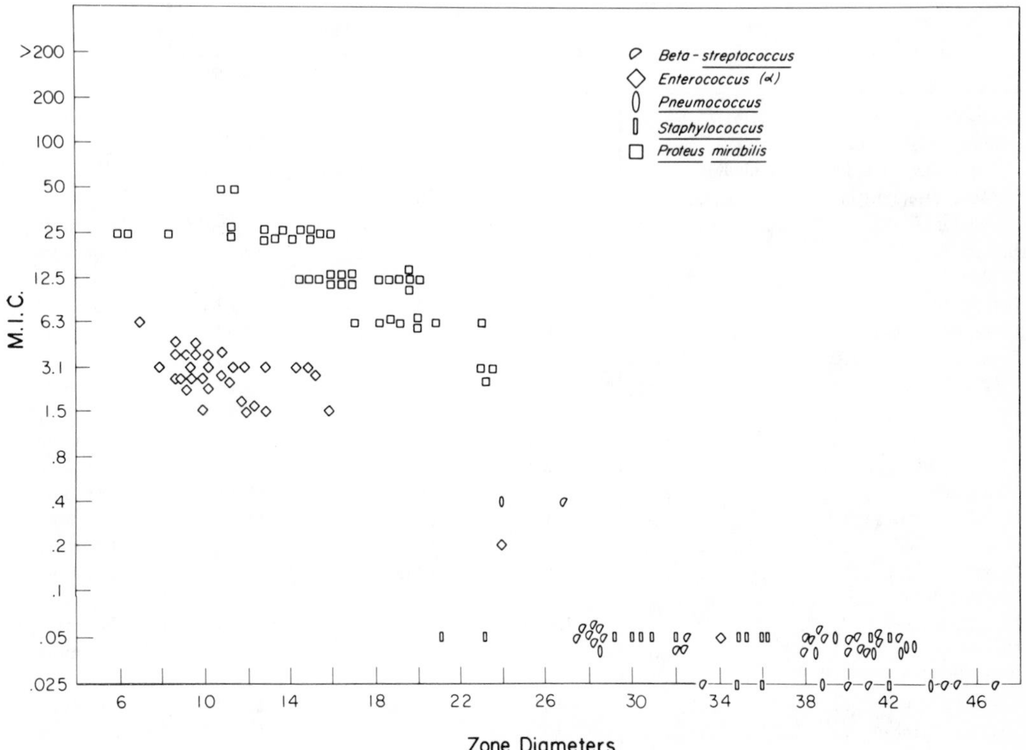

Fig. 10. *Regression graph for penicillin G (10 units).*

Table 2 is a tabulation of the comparison of disc zone size breakpoints, based on the interpretive values of Table 1, and the minimal inhibitory concentrations obtained on our regression curves for most of the common antibiotics.

DISCUSSION

Figures 1 through 5, representing the antibiotics chloramphenicol, kanamycin, streptomycin, tetracycline, and cephalothin, demonstrate the reproducibility of the Bauer-Kirby-Sherris-Turck method. Chloramphenicol, kanamycin, and tetracycline demonstrate a somewhat biphasic distribution of strains, with a group clearly susceptible, a group resistant, and relatively few strains in the intermediate range. Streptomycin (Fig. 3) shows more strains in the intermediate range, and cephalothin (Fig. 5) presents the situation of a continuous scattering of data plots. Cephalothin demonstrates the problem of the lack of clearly defined cut-off points for interpretive values caused by this continuing scatter of data. It also points out that the greatest utility of interpretation of the disc testing method occurs if one has a knowledge of the regression pattern of each antibiotic. A more sophisticated judgment of dosage and antibiotic administration is possible if one takes into account the variable nature of the different regression scatter graphs.

Our experience in doing repetitive testing of strains with both dilution and diffusion testing has led us to the conclusion that carefully done disc-diffusion testing is as valid and reproducible as dilution testing. Furthermore, we believe that, with these regression curves, it is possible to give a quantitative interpretation of the range of minimal inhibitory concentrations applicable for a given zone size with a specific antibiotic.

In our testing of the newer antibiotics for which the University of Washington group has provided interpretive values, cephaloridine (Fig. 6) seemed straightforward and the breakpoint

Table 1. *Zone size interpretative chart (1, 3)*[a]

Antibiotic or chemotherapeutic agent	Disc potency[b]	Inhibition zone diam to nearest mm		
		Resistant	Intermediate	Susceptible
Ampicillin				
Gram-negative and enterococci	10	11 or less	12-13	14 or more
Staphylococci and highly penicillin-susceptible organisms	10	20 or less	21-28	29 or more
Haemophilus[c]				20 or more
Bacitracin	10	8 or less	9-12	13 or more
Cephaloridine	30	11 or less	12-15	16 or more
Cephalothin	30	14 or less	15-17	18 or more
Chloramphenicol	30	12 or less	13-17	18 or more
Colistin	10	8 or less	9-10	11 or more
Erythromycin	15	13 or less	14-17	18 or more
Gentamicin[c]	10			13 or more
Kanamycin	30	13 or less	14-17	18 or more
Lincomycin	2	9 or less	10-14	15 or more
Methicillin	5	9 or less	10-13	14 or more
Nafcillin and oxacillin[c]	1	10 or less	11-12	13 or more
Nalidixic acid[d]	30	13 or less	14-18	19 or more
Neomycin	30	12 or less	13-16	17 or more
Novobiocin[e]	30	17 or less	18-21	22 or more
Nitrofurantoin[d]	300	14 or less	15-16	17 or more
Oleandomyxin	15	11 or less	12-16	17 or more
Penicillin G				
Staphylococci	10	20 or less	21-28	29 or more
Other organisms	10	11 or less	12-21[g]	22 or more
Polymyxin B	300	8 or less	9-11	12 or more
Streptomycin	10	11 or less	12-14	15 or more
Sulfonamides[d, f]	300	12 or less	13-16	17 or more
Tetracycline	30	14 or less	15-18	19 or more
Vancomycin	30	9 or less	10-11	12 or more

[a] Updated and modified July 1969.
[b] All given as micrograms except bacitracin, penicillin G, and polymyxin B, which are given in units.
[c] Tentative standards.
[d] Urinary-tract infections only.
[e] Not applicable to blood-containing media.
[f] Any of the commercially available 300- or 250-μgm sulfonamide discs can be used with the same standards of zone interpretation.
[g] This category includes some organisms such as enterococci which may cause systemic infections treatable by high doses of penicillin G.

values as listed seemed appropriate. Our results with gentamicin (Fig. 7) indicate that perhaps the tentative data (Table 1) recorded may be low. The reported tentative breakpoint (2) is 13 mm, and the data in Fig. 7 indicate that this value should be somewhat higher; 15 mm would be a more appropriate figure.

The polypeptide antibiotics, colistin and polymyxin B, provide examples (Fig. 8) of a real difficulty in differentiating between susceptible and resistant organisms by the disc method. At the present time, we use dilution testing with all organisms causing serious infections for which susceptibility testing with the polypeptide antibiotics is requested.

The Bauer-Kirby-Sherris-Turck method lists three separate interpretive values for ampicillin. Figure 9 demonstrates the complexity of the ampicillin regression graph. One set of interpretive values is for the gram-positive cocci, one for enterococci and the gram-negative organisms, and a third set for *Haemophilus.* In light of what is shown on Fig. 9, the need for these different criteria is evident.

Table 2. *Comparison of disc zone size breakpoints and minimal inhibitory concentrations (MIC) by the Kirby-Bauer-Sherris-Turck method*

Antibiotic	Disc content[a]	Resistant		Intermediate, Zone diam range	Susceptible	
		Zone diam	MIC correlate		Zone diam	MIC correlate
		mm	*μg/ml*	*mm*	*mm*	*μg/ml*
Cephaloridine	30	11	⩾12.5	12-15	16	6.3-12.5
Cephalothin	30	14	⩾25	15-17	18	6.3-12.5
Chloramphenicol	30	12	25	13-17	18	3.1-12.5
Colistin	10	8	–	9-10	11	–
Erythromycin	15	13	1.5	14-17	18	0.4-1.5
Gentamicin	10				13	12.5
Kanamycin	30	13	25	14-17	18	3.1-6.3
Lincomycin	2	9	⩾6.3	10-14	15	1.5-3.1
Methicillin	5	9		10-13	14	3.1-6.3
Naladixic acid	30	13	⩾12.5	14-18	19	3.1-12.5
Nitrofurantoin	300	14	50-200	15-16	17	25-100
Polymyxin B	300	8	–	9-11	12	–
Streptomycin	10	11	12.5-50	12-14	15	3.1-12.5
Tetracycline	30	14	25-50	15-18	19	6.3

[a] All given in micrograms except polymyxin B, which is given in units.

Penicillin (Fig. 10) also requires dual interpretive values. The sensitive cut-off point for staphylococci should be 0.1 unit/ml by minimal inhibitory concentration testing, and this plot is within the 29-mm disc-zone breakpoint advocated for susceptible strains. For other organisms, the value of 22 mm for a susceptible breakpoint excludes the majority of enterococci and relegates them to an intermediate zone or to a resistant classification. Occasionally physicians request penicillin susceptibilities for *P. mirabilis.* It will be noted that the *P. mirabilis* group does not fall in the same regression scatter pattern as do the other tested organisms. Use of the regression graph will allow for qualification of interpretation with both of these species.

Aside from the exceptions already noted, we believe that the breakpoints for the method are appropriate, and, indeed, that the method in general is a very practical, utilitarian method for use in the clinical microbiology laboratory.

ACKNOWLEDGMENTS

We most appreciatively acknowledge the contribution of John C. Sherris in supplying us with his regression data and the updated interpretation chart. We also acknowledge the help of the staff of the Diagnostic Microbiology Laboratory of the University of Minnesota Hospitals, who assisted in many ways.

LITERATURE CITED

1. Bauer, A. W., W. M. M. Kirby, J. C. Sherris, and M. Turck. 1966. Antibiotic susceptibility testing by a standardized single disk method. Amer. J. Clin. Pathol. **45**:493-496.
2. Kirby, W. M. M., and H. C. Standiford. 1969. Gentamicin: *In vitro* studied. J. Infec. Dis. **119**:361-363.
3. Sherris, J. C., A. L. Rashad, and G. A. Lighthart. 1967. Laboratory determination of antibiotic susceptibility to ampicillin and cephalothin. Ann. N.Y. Acad. Sci. **145**:248.
4. Steers, E., E. L. Foltz, and B. S. Graves. 1959. Inocula-replicating apparatus for routine testing of bacterial susceptibility to antibiotics. Antibiot. Chemother. 9:307-311.

Antimicrobial Agents and Chemotherapy—1969

Effect of Parenteral Iron Preparations on Renal Infection Due to *Escherichia coli* in Rats and Mice

JOHN FLETCHER[1] and ELLIOT GOLDSTEIN[2]

Thorndike Memorial Laboratory, Channing Laboratory, Harvard Medical Unit, Boston City and Mattapan Hospitals, Boston, Massachusetts 02118

Iron enhances bacterial virulence in vivo. Whether this effect is nonspecific or related to diminished defense mechanisms in particular organs is unknown. *Escherichia coli* was injected intravenously into mice and rats. Groups of animals then received daily intramuscular inoculations of equivalent amounts of organic iron (ferric ammonium citrate), iron bound as a small molecular complex (iron sorbitol citrate), or iron bound as a large molecular complex (iron dextran). Bacterial multiplication was studied up to 1 week. Multiplication occurred within the kidneys of rats and mice receiving ferric ammonium citrate or iron sorbitol citrate but not those receiving iron dextran. Rates of bacterial elimination from the lungs, liver, and spleen of rats was not affected by iron. Pathological study of the amounts of iron present in the kidney showed large deposits in animals receiving iron sorbitol citrate, less with ferric ammonium citrate, and almost none with iron dextran. The amounts seen histologically correlated with enhanced bacterial growth. It is concluded that, in this system, the kidney is the only organ susceptible to the effect of iron on bacterial virulence, and that this effect is due to iron present in small diffusible molecules.

Iron enhances bacterial growth in vivo (2, 5) and adversely influences experimental infection (9, 13). This in vivo effect is nonspecific and is related to the infecting organism, the route of infection, and the site of iron injection (9). Because iron bound to small molecular complexes is cleared through the kidneys, it appeared likely that it would also influence renal susceptibility to infection. We investigated this possibility by injecting rats and mice with *Escherichia coli* and then treating them with various iron-containing compounds. These studies showed that iron significantly alters host resistance to renal infection.

MATERIALS AND METHODS

Animals. Female Swiss strain rats (180 to 200 g) and male Swiss mice (20 to 30 g) from Charles River Laboratories were used in all experiments. Animals were housed in plastic cages and fed Purina Lab Chow and water *ad libitum.*

Microorganisms. The strain of *E. coli* used for intravenous injection was obtained from the urine of a patient with pyelonephritis. Cells were grown overnight in Trypticase Soy Broth and stored in 1-ml portions at −20 C. When required, a portion was incubated with 100 ml of fresh broth at 37 C for 4 hr. The bacteria were sedimented, washed with phosphate buffer (*p*H 7.5), centrifuged, and resuspended in buffer. Rats were injected intravenously with 0.5-ml amounts of the suspension containing approximately 4×10^8 organisms, and mice were injected intravenously with 0.2-ml amounts containing approximately 10^8 organisms.

Iron. Ferric ammonium citrate was dissolved in sterile saline (2.8 g/100 ml) and refrigerated at 4 C. The desired experimental iron concentrations were prepared daily by further dilution. Iron sorbitol citrate (Jectofer), iron dextran (Imferon), and iron dextrin (Astrafer) were also prepared daily by diluting the manufacturer's preparation with sterile saline. The animals were injected intramuscularly with 0.1- or 0.2-ml amounts of these preparations.

Infection schedules. Daily intramuscular injections of each iron preparation and a saline control were begun 18 hr after infection with *E. coli* and were continued for 4

[1] Present address: University College Hospital Medical School, London, England.

[2] Present address: School of Medicine, University of California, Davis, Calif.

days. On day 6, the animals were killed with ether and their kidneys were examined for abscesses. In some experiments, the lungs, liver, spleen, and kidneys were removed aseptically at intervals after bacterial injection, and population studies of the tissue homogenate were performed by pour plate techniques. Kidney specimens from animals receiving each of the iron preparations were fixed in Formol-saline and stained with Perl's iron stain; either hematoxylin and eosin or nuclear fast red (Kernichtrot) was used as a counterstain.

RESULTS

In rats infected with *E. coli* and injected daily for 4 days with various amounts of iron sorbitol citrate, macroscopic abscesses developed in one or both kidneys of 80% (24 of 30) of the animals receiving 5, 10, or 25 mg of iron/kg; no abscesses developed in the kidneys of 12 mice not receiving iron (Fig. 1). Iron sorbitol citrate injections did not cause abscesses or death in six control animals.

This experiment was repeated with ferric ammonium citrate (5 mg of iron/kg). Renal abscesses were found in 34% (6 of 17) of these animals and in none of 10 ammonium citrate-treated controls.

The effect of large molecular weight iron preparations (iron dextran and iron dextrin) was studied next. Doses of 5 mg of iron /kg were administered to 12 mice, and no abscesses occurred with either preparation. In contrast, abscesses developed in four of five iron sorbitol citrate-treated controls.

The significance of iron remaining within the kidney was investigated by injecting rats intramuscularly with iron sorbitol citrate (25 mg of iron/kg) for 4 days, and then challenging them 48 hr later with an intravenous injection of *E. coli.* None of these animals developed abscesses. Histological examination confirmed the presence of large deposits of iron within the renal parenchyma. To determine whether the observed effects applied to more than one animal species, the experiment was repeated with mice. Abscesses developed in 4 of 10 mice given daily injections of iron sorbitol citrate containing 10 mg of iron/kg. Abscesses were not found in 10 saline-treated controls.

Bacterial multiplication rates were studied in two sets of rats. In the first set, 20 rats were infected with 2×10^8 *E. coli* cells. After 24 hr, four animals were sacrificed, and daily intramuscular injections of iron sorbitol citrate (25 mg of iron/kg) were begun in half of the remainder. Four animals, two from the iron-treated and two from the control group, were sacrificed on days 2, 3, 4, and 6. The kidneys were removed individually and bacterial counts were made. Figure 2 shows the rapid increase in numbers of bacteria to levels above 10^6 organisms per kidney that was observed in treated animals. The numbers of bacteria within the kidneys of control animals did not change during the 6-day period from initial levels of 10^4 bacteria per kidney. In a similar experiment, bacteria were enumerated in the lungs, liver, and spleen of infected animals. The bacterial counts in each of these organs declined rapidly, and there was no difference between control and iron sorbitol citrate-treated animals.

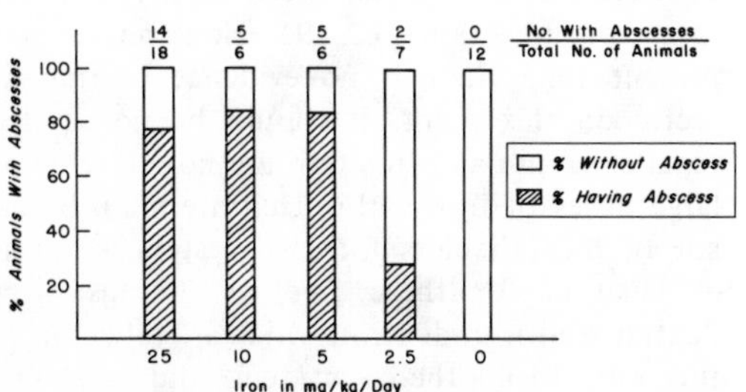

Fig. 1. *Percentage of rats developing renal abscesses due to Escherichia coli after daily injections of iron sorbitol citrate.*

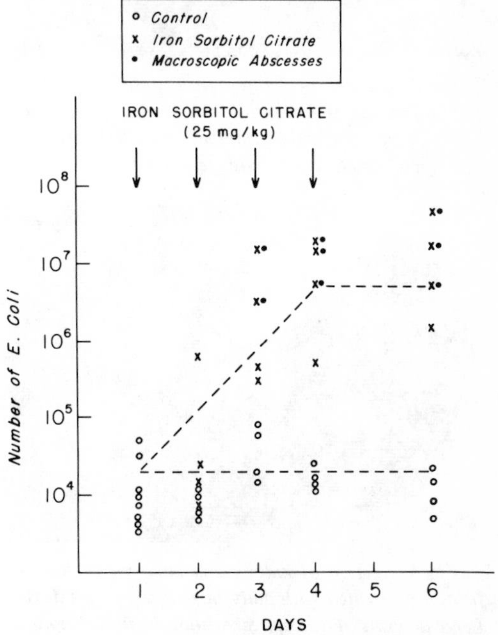

Fig. 2. *Number of bacteria cultured from individual kidneys of rats after injections of iron sorbitol citrate.*

Histological examination of kidneys from animals receiving iron sorbitol citrate showed large deposits of iron within cells of the proximal tubule and lesser amounts in the collecting ducts and distal tubules (Fig. 3). Much less iron was found in the kidneys of rats treated with ferric ammonium citrate, and none was found in those treated with iron dextran. Large deposits of iron were present in lymph glands of animals receiving iron dextran (Fig. 4), demonstrating the inability of iron bound to large molecular complexes to pass the renal glomerulus. The microscopic studies corroborated the gross findings by showing numerous micro-abscesses in the animals treated with the low molecular weight iron compounds and a lack of infection in iron dextran- and saline-injected controls.

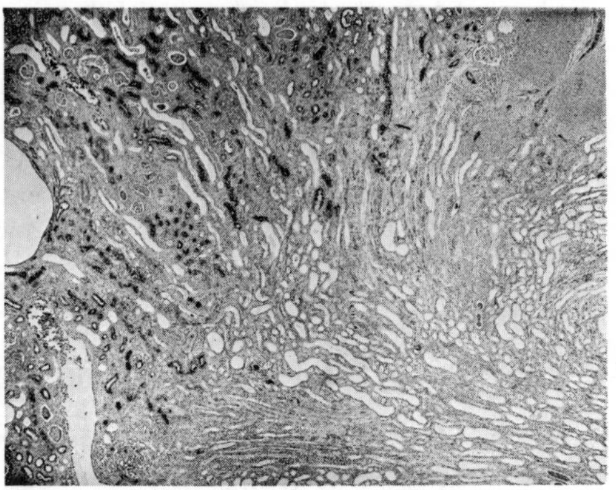

Fig. 3. *Section of kidney from a rat treated with daily injections of iron sorbitol citrate. Large deposits of iron can be seen within tubular cells. Perl's iron stain with a nuclear fast red counterstain* × *40.*

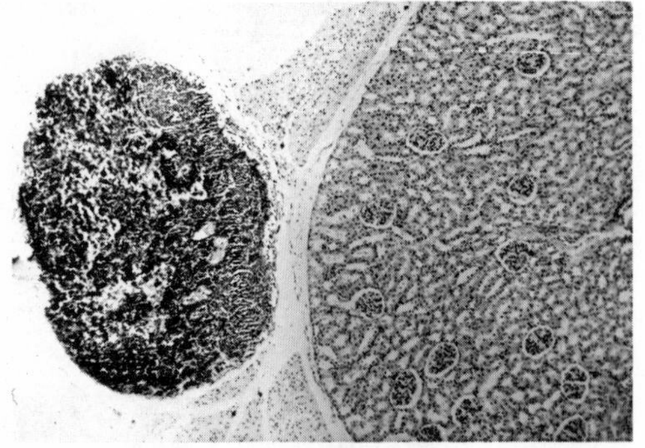

Fig. 4. *Section of kidney and adjacent lymph node from a rat treated with daily injections of iron dextran. Large deposits of iron appear within the lymph node and none within the kidney. Perl's iron stain with hemotoxylin and eosin counterstain* × *100.*

DISCUSSION

These experiments demonstrate an adverse effect of iron on renal resistance to infection. This deleterious action occurred in both rats and mice. The studies of bacterial multiplication showed that the effect of iron is limited to the kidney, and removal of the infecting bacteria from the lungs, liver, and spleen of rats occurs at the usual rate.

This effect of iron was most apparent when it was bound to small molecular weight complexes capable of traversing the glomerulus. Iron injected as iron sorbitol citrate, molecular weight ≈5,000 (5), enhanced bacterial infection and could be demonstrated in large amounts within the renal parenchyma by histological staining. Ferric ammonium citrate similarly enhanced the renal pathogenicity of *E. coli,* and, although much less iron was found in the kidneys of these animals, this compound undoubtedly reached the renal tubular regions since it readily crosses the glomerular membrane (6). Iron dextran and iron dextrin are large molecular weight complexes (7, 8) which do not pass the glomerulus, and in these experiments they did not enhance renal infection.

It also appears that iron must be in a diffusible form. In the experiments in which there was a 48 hr lapse of time between completion of the iron injections and inoculations of *E. coli,* abscesses did not develop even though large amounts of iron were present within tubular cells.

The mechanism of action of iron in these experiments is unknown. Iron may have acted as a bacterial growth-promoting factor, as it is well documented that the growth of several bacterial species in serum is enhanced by iron (10).

An alternative possibility is that iron depressed host resistance. In vivo inhibition of immune mechanisms has been reported to follow iron injections (2, 9). However, at the present time there is no evidence bearing directly on this point. It should be noted that renal structure and function are not affected by large doses of iron sorbitol citrate (11). Blockade of the reticuloendothelial system is not an explanation for these findings, because iron dextran and iron dextrin, which are taken up by the reticuloendothelial system, did not alter renal resistance, whereas ferric ammonium citrate, which is not known to affect the reticuloendothelial system, did. Furthermore, iron injections were not started until 18 hr after infection when the bacteria were already almost cleared from the circulation. The localization of impairment to the kidneys may be related to the microorganism chosen, because ordinarily only the kidneys are susceptible to infection with *E. coli* (12). Although it is difficult to extrapolate from animal models of infection to human disease, it is possible that iron-containing compounds such as iron sorbitol citrate may adversely influence renal infections in man. This hypothesis is supported by the findings of increased rates of urinary white cell excretion in patients with pyelonephritis treated with iron sorbitol citrate and by the suggested use of iron sorbitol citrate as a provocative test for pyelonephritis (13).

ACKNOWLEDGMENT

This investigation was supported by Public Health Service grants HD-02693 and T01-AI-00068 from the National Institutes of Health.

LITERATURE CITED

1. Briggs, J. D., A. C. Kennedy, and A. Goldberg. 1963. Urinary white-cell excretion after iron-sorbitol-citric-acid. Brit. Med. J. **2**:352-357.
2. Bullen, J. J., G. H. Cushnie, and H. J. Rogers. 1967. The abolition of the protective effect of *Clostridium welchii* type A antiserum by ferric iron. Immunology **12**:303–312.
3. Bullen, J. J., A. B. Wilson, G. H. Cushnie, and H. J. Rogers. 1968. The abolition of the protective effect of *Pasteurella septica* antiserum by iron compounds. Immunology **14**:889-898.
4. Guze, L. B., and P. B. Beeson. 1956. Experimental pyelonephritis. I. Effect of ureteral ligation on the course of bacterial infection in the kidney of the rat. J. Exp. Med. **104**:803-815.
5. Jackson, S., and T. W. Burrows. 1956. The virulence-enhancing effect of iron on non-pigmented mutants of virulent strains of *Pasteurella pestis*. Brit. J. Exp. Pathol. **37**:577-583.
6. Jackson, S., and B. C. Morris. 1961. Enhancement of growth of *Pasteurella pestis* and other bacteria in serum by the addition of iron. Brit. J. Exp. Pathol. **42**:363-368.
7. Lindvall, S., and N. S. E. Andersson. 1961. Studies on a new intramuscular haematinic, iron-sorbitol. Brit. J. Pharmacol. **17**:358-371.
8. Lucas, J. E., and A. B. Hagedorn. 1952. The intravenous use of high molecular ferric carbohydrate compound in the treatment of hyopchromic anaemia. Blood **7**:358-367.
9. Martin, C. M., J. H. Jandl, and M. Finland. 1963. Enhancement of acute bacterial infections in rats and mice by iron and their inhibition by human transferrin. J. Infer. Dis. **112**:158-163.
10. Martin, L. E., C. M. Bates, C. R. Beresford, J. D. Donaldson, F. F. McDonald, D. Dunlop, P. Sheard, E. London, and G. D. Twigg. 1955. The pharmacology of an iron-dextran intramuscular haematinic. Brit. J. Pharmacol. **10**:375-382.
11. Rubin, M. 1964. The significance of chelation for clinical problems of iron metabolism, p. 66–122. *In* A. Soffer (ed.), Chelation therapy. Charles C Thomas, Publisher, Springfield, Ill.
12. Schade, A. L. 1963. Significance of serum iron for growth, biological characteristics and metabolism of *Staphylococcus aureus*. Biochem. Z. **338**:140-148.
13. Sword, C. P. 1966. Mechanism of pathogenesis in *Listeria monocytogenes* infection. I. Influence of iron. J. Bacteriol. **92**:536-542.

Antimicrobial Agents and Chemotherapy—1969

Production and Therapy of *Proteus mirabilis* Pyelonephritis in Mice Undergoing Chronic Diuresis

GEORGE M. KALMANSON, EARL G. HUBERT, and LUCIEN B. GUZE

Medical and Research Services, Wadsworth Hospital, Veterans Administration Center, Los Angeles, California 90073, and Department of Medicine, UCLA School of Medicine, Los Angeles, California 90024

Diuresis in mice produced by voluntary ingestion of large amounts of glucose in water increases susceptibility of mice to ascending pyelonephritis due to *Proteus mirabilis*. The infection was more intense in animals with established diuresis than in other animals, as judged by the bacterial population in the kidney and the proportion of kidneys infected. The infection persisted for 11 weeks (duration of study). This persistence of infection permitted a clinical trial of ampicillin. The treatment of animals undergoing diuresis was delayed for 2 weeks, to allow the infection to become better established. In the dosage used, ampicillin did not cure the infection but it reduced the severity of infection and strikingly decreased the incidence of bladder stones.

Study of pyelonephritis has been handicapped by the absence of an entirely satisfactory experimental model. The hematogenous enterococcal experimental pyelonephritis in rats, described in many studies from this laboratory, produces acute, subacute, and chronic pyelonephritis without any manipulation of the host (9). Thus, effects of the infection are not complicated by the means used to facilitate production of pyelonephritis. Rat kidney streptococcal infection mimics human pyelonephritis both histologically and in its effect on impairment of kidney function. Although in many ways this is an ideal model, it is produced by an organism (*Streptococcus faecalis*) whose role in human pyelonephritis is not prominent. Until recently, studies with gram-negative bacteria, which represent the overwhelming majority of organisms isolated from humans with pyelonephritis, have been hampered by lack of a suitable animal model. Infections were produced only when manipulation was employed, such as ureteral ligation (7, 8, 12), direct kidney injury by cautery (13), or kidney massage (4), or by use of a foreign body in the bladder (5). Recently, Freedman (6) demonstrated that persistent bacteriuria could be produced in rats by installation of *Escherichia coli* in the bladder if the animals were undergoing chronic diuresis. This was accomplished by using 5% glucose in water as sole source of available fluid. The animals relished this 5% glucose to the extent that they drank several times the usual volume of water, thus producing a urine of low specific gravity and osmolality. Subsequent to intrabladder instillation of bacteria, although a persistant bacteriuria was established for several weeks, no evidence of kidney infection could be demonstrated. Rats undergoing diuresis did not have an increased susceptibility to intravenous inoculation of *E. coli*. Subsequently, Keane and Freedman (10) were able to show with similar studies in mice that not only was persistent bacteriuria produced but, in addition, in about half of the animals pyelonephritis occurred.

Present studies were designed to determine whether this model of experimental pyelonephritis would be useful for study with another gram-negative organism also important in human pyelonephritis, *Proteus mirabilis*.

MATERIALS AND METHODS

Bacteria. *P. mirabilis* 5, a laboratory strain originally isolated from urine of a patient, was used throughout the study. It was maintained on Brain Heart Infusion broth or agar (Difco). To maintain virulence, the organism was "animal-passed" as follows. An overnight broth culture was inoculated intravenously into an animal whose left ureter had been ligated on the previous day. The organism was recovered from agar plates prepared by streaking kidney homogenate obtained 1 day after inoculation. Several colonies were inoculated into one broth culture and the process was repeated two more times. After the third animal passage, the organism was grown in broth overnight, dispensed into 1-ml portions, and stored at −20 C. When a study was to be done, the frozen broth culture was thawed at room temperature, and a fresh overnight broth culture was made therefrom.

Animals. Random-bred Wistar male rats weighing about 125 g and Swiss-Webster mice weighing about 20 g were obtained from local commercial sources.

Production of pyelonephritis. Control animals were given tap water to drink, and animals undergoing diuresis were given 5% glucose in tap water beginning 1 week prior to infection; the glucose was continued throughout the experiment. The organism was washed three times with broth before inoculation to reduce the amount of preformed endotoxin. The bladder was surgically exposed, urine was withdrawn with a syringe fitted with a 26 needle, and the washed culture was then injected (0.5 ml in rats and 0.05 ml in mice). Overnight cultures usually contained 5×10^8 organisms per ml. The rats thus received about 2.5×10^8 cells and the mice received about 2.5×10^7 organisms intravesicularly. Rats were housed in groups of five in stainless steel cages; mice were housed individually in small plastic boxes. Urine collected by drop from each individual animal was tested for specific gravity (TS Meter, American Optical Co., Buffalo, N.Y.).

At time of sacrifice, the bacterial content of the kidney was determined quantitatively by methods previously described (9). Briefly, kidneys were removed aseptically and homogenized; serial dilutions were then made in broth and samples were plated in agar. When possible, urine was removed from the bladder, specific gravity was measured, and quantitative cultures were similarly made. If no urine was obtainable, the bladder mucosa was swabbed with a cotton applicator and streaked on agar to determine whether organisms were present. Several colonies from each plate were identified by standard techniques.

Treatment. Ampicillin (3 mg) was given to mice intramuscularly twice daily. The duration of therapy varied and is specified for each experiment.

RESULTS

An initial study was done comparing the outcome of intrabladder inoculation of *P. mirabilis* in mice and rats undergoing diuresis and in normal controls. Results at 1 and 4 weeks after infection are shown in Table 1. In rats, the proportion of kidneys showing bacteria markedly decreased at 4 weeks in both normal animals (2 of 10) and animals undergoing diuresis (1 of 12). On the other hand, in mice, although renal bacterial content decreased between 1 and 4 weeks, the majority of kidneys remained infected in both normal animals and animals undergoing diuresis. No difference in the proportion of kidneys infected was evident when test and control animals were compared (χ^2 test, $P > 0.5$). Although renal bacterial content at 4 weeks was greater in animals undergoing diuresis (log 3.81 organisms per g of kidney) than in controls (log 3.43 per g) , the difference was not statistically significant (t test, $P < 0.5$).

The fact that infection in mice persisted for 4 weeks suggested the possibility of using this model for studies of therapy. Persistence of infection past the acute stage would permit therapeutic studies more similar to those in man. The ascending route of infection also resembles that in man more closely.

Accordingly, therapy with ampicillin was studied in mice. Three groups of animals were examined; animals on glucose diuresis, treated or untreated, and untreated controls. The inclusion of untreated animals allowed additional evaluation of the effect of diuresis on infection. Therapy was started 2 weeks after infection and continued for 3 weeks. A few animals (indicated in Table 2) were given antibiotic for 6 weeks. Small numbers of animals at later harvests of control animals are due to greater mortality than anticipated, i.e., a smaller number of mice was originally in the tap water group than in the group undergoing diuresis and a greater proportion of them died than was expected. It may be seen that diuresis enhanced both intensity of infection as judged by renal content (t test, $P < 0.005$) and proportion of kidneys infected (χ^2 test, $P < 0.001$). Therapy with ampicillin

Table 1. *Effect of diuresis on kidney infection in rats and mice after intrabladder inoculation of Proteus mirabilis*

Animal	Time of sacrifice (weeks)	Animals undergoing diuresis	Tap water controls
Rat	1	4.34 (9/10)[a]	2.73 (5/10)
	4	7.38 (1/12)	4.41 (2/10)
Mouse	1	7.07 (18/18)	7.81 (16/18)
	4	3.81 (13/16)	3.43 (10/14)

[a] Log number of bacteria per gram of tissue and proportion of infected kidneys. Infected animals only.

decreased both average kidney content of bacteria (t test, $P<0.001$) and proportion of kidneys infected (χ^2 test, $P<0.001$) but did not eliminate the infection.

In treated mice with established diuresis, there were five instances of infected kidneys with no bacteria in the urine; no instances of the converse were observed. In untreated mice with established diuresis, there were no instances of infected kidneys with sterile urine, but two animals had bacteria in the bladder and none in the kidney. Among the untreated tap water controls, four had infected kidneys and sterile urine; none had the converse.

There was a rather frequent finding of unilateral kidney infection. In treated animals with diuresis, this occurred five times: three times it was the right kidney and twice, the left. Among untreated animals undergoing diuresis, it occurred nine times: twice on the right and seven times on the left. In the control animals, unilateral infection was noted five times: thrice on the right and twice on the left.

Table 2. *Effect of diuresis and ampicillin therapy on kidney infection after intrabladder inoculation of Proteus mirabilis*

Time of sacrifice (weeks)	Mice undergoing diuresis		Tap water controls (no treatment)
	No treatment	Ampicillin[a]	
2	5.09 (15/20)[b]	–	4.57 (7/20)
4	5.08 (16/20)	2.34 (4/10)	2.57 (7/20)
6	8.01 (2/10)	7.63 (1/10)	0.00 (0/2)
8	5.93 (10/10)	5.02 (2/10)	3.62 (1/4)
10	5.79 (4/10)	2.31 (4/34)	–
11	5.76 (10/14)	2.88 (4/16)[c]	3.55 (2/2)

[a] Ampicillin, 3 mg daily for 3 weeks beginning 2 weeks after infection.

[b] Log number of bacteria per gram of tissue and proportion of infected kidneys. Infected animals only.

[c] Ampicillin continued for 6 weeks.

In the study in Table 1, it was noted that some animals had bladder stones. Therefore, in the study presented in Table 2, animals found dead, as well as sacrificed animals, were examined whenever possible for bladder stones. The results are shown in Table 3. Lack of any dead animals in the treated animals undergoing diuresis is a reflection of the fact that practically all deaths occurred during the second week of infection, prior to institution of therapy. At 2 weeks, before the beginning of therapy, 28 of 101 animals undergoing diuresis had died as compared with 25 of 79 tap water controls. This difference is not significant (χ^2 test, $P<0.2$). The overall incidence of stones in untreated animals undergoing diuresis, 44 of 101, was not different than in untreated controls, 27 of 79 (χ^2 test, $P<0.3$). However, among animals which were sacrificed, i.e., had survived more than 2 weeks, 16 of 42 untreated animals undergoing diuresis had stones as compared with 2 of 24 untreated controls. This difference is significant (χ^2 test, $P<0.05$) and suggests greater intensity of infection in animals undergoing diuresis which survived the infection. It is striking that, although ampicillin treatment did not completely cure the infection (Table 2), it markedly reduced stone formation. There was only one of 35 treated animals undergoing diuresis with stones as compared with 16 of 42 untreated animals undergoing diuresis (χ^2 test, $P<0.001$).

Urine specific gravities in animals from which urine could be obtained were as follows. Animals undergoing diuresis but receiving no therapy (32 animals) had a preinfection mean specific gravity of 1.018 (range, 1.001 to 1.060); at sacrifice, the mean specific gravity was 1.018 (range, 1.001 to 1.080). Treated animals undergoing diuresis (31 animals) had a mean preinfection specific gravity of 1.018 (range, 1.001 to 1.090); at sacrifice, the mean specific gravity

Table 3. *Effect of diuresis and ampicillin therapy on incidence of bladder stones after intrabladder inoculation of Proteus mirabilis*

Group of animals	Mice undergoing diuresis		Tap water controls (no treatment)
	No treatment	Ampicillin[a]	
Animals sacrificed during study	16/42[b]	1/35[c]	2/24
Animals dead during study	28/59	–	25/55

[a] Ampicillin, 3 mg twice daily for 3 or 6 weeks beginning 2 weeks after infection.

[b] Proportion of animals having stones.

[c] Forty animals were sacrificed. Incidence of stones in five was not recorded.

was 1.018 (range, 1.002 to 1.060). Mice on water, no diuresis (17 animals), had a mean preinfection specific gravity of 1.071 (range, 1.007 to 1.110); at sacrifice, the mean specific gravity was 1.065 (range, 1.020 to 1.110). The difference in urine specific gravities between mice undergoing diuresis and controls at both preinfection and sacrifice times was significant (χ^2 test, $P<0.001$). No difference in urine specific gravities at sacrifice was apparent between infected and noninfected animals.

DISCUSSION

These studies have demonstrated that the model of ascending pyelonephritis described by Keane and Freedman (10) with *E. coli* in mice undergoing diuresis is applicable to another clinically important gram-negative organism, *P. mirabilis.* Mice undergoing diuresis secondary to voluntarily drinking large quantities of glucose water were more susceptible to infection than tap water controls. The infection in animals undergoing diuresis was greater both in regard to renal bacterial population and proportion of kidneys infected. (It should be noted that, whereas the initial pilot study reported in Table 1 did not show significant differences between mice undergoing diuresis and controls, subsequent studies noted in Table 2, with larger numbers of animals observed for longer periods of time, did reveal more infection in mice undergoing diuresis.) Greater severity of infection was also suggested by higher incidence of bladder stones in mice undergoing diuresis which had not died of the infection. The studies were *not* designed to evaluate ampicillin as a therapeutic agent, but rather to determine the utility of the model for therapy of subacute or chronic pyelonephritis. Nevertheless, it was shown that treatment reduced the severity of infection as judged both by kidney bacterial population and proportion of kidneys infected. Even more striking was the almost complete elimination of bladder stones by treatment. These results demonstrating increase of infection by diuresis, while in accord with those of Keane and Freedman (10), are contrary to those of Andriole, who found that diuresis cured pyelonephritis subsequent to intravenous inoculation of either staphylococci (2) or enterococci (1). It is not evident whether these differences are due to variation in organisms or the route of inoculation (ascending versus hematogenous).

The mechanism by which diuresis promotes ascending pyelonephritis in mice is not known. Among possibilities to be considered are: (i) ability of the organism to grow better in more dilute urine, (ii) some injurious effect of glucose on the kidney, and (iii) disturbance of a possible protective role of secretory gamma globulins. This last alternative might help explain the differences between ascending and hematogenous infection described above. There is evidence that secretory IgA may play a role in the resistance of mucous membranes to infection (14). Although the role of secretory IgA has not been defined in urinary-tract infection, it has been found in urine of man (3). In addition, Lehmann et al. (11) reported that, although the major antibody produced locally in pyelonephritic rabbit kidney is IgG, some IgA was also found.

ACKNOWLEDGMENTS

This investigation was supported by Public Health Service grants 02257 and 03310.

LITERATURE CITED

1. Andriole, V. T. 1968. Effect of water diuresis on chronic pyelonephritis. J. Lab. Clin. Med. **72**:1–16.
2. Andriole, V. T., and F. H. Epstein. 1965. Prevention of pyelonephritis by water diuresis: Evidence for the role of medullary hypertonicity in promoting renal infection. J. Clin. Invest. **44**:73–79.
3. Bienenstock, J., and T. B. Tomasi, Jr. 1968. Secretory γA in normal urine. J. Clin. Invest. **47**:1162–1171.
4. Braude, A. I., A. P. Shapiro, and J. Siemienski. 1955. Hematogenous pyelonephritis in rats. I. Its pathogenesis when produced by a simple new method. J. Clin. Invest. **34**:1489–1497.
5. Cotran, R. S., E. Vivaldi, D. P. Zangwell, and E. H. Kass. 1963. Retrograde Proteus pyelonephritis in the rat: Bacteriologic, pathologic and fluorescent-antibody studies. Amer. J. Pathol. **43**:1–31.
6. Freedman, L. R. 1967. Experimental pyelonephritis. XIII. On the ability of water diuresis to induce susceptibility to *E. Coli* bacteriuria in the normal rat. Yale J. Biol. Med. **39**:255–266.
7. Guze, L. B., and P. B. Beeson. 1956. Experimental pyelonephritis. I. Effect of ureteral ligation on the course of bacterial infection in the kidney of the rat. J. Exp. Med. **104**:803–815.
8. Guze, L. B., and P. B. Beeson. 1958. Experimental pyelonephritis. II. Effect of partial ureteral obstruction on the course of bacterial infection in the kidney of the rat and the rabbit. Yale J. Biol. Med. **30**:315–319.
9. Guze, L. B., B. H. Goldner, and G. M. Kalmanson. 1956. Pyelonephritis I. Observations on the course of chronic, nonobstructed enterococcal infection in the kidney of the rat. Yale J. Biol. Med. **33**:372–385.
10. Keane W. F., and L. R. Freedman. 1967. Experimental pyelonephritis. XIV. Pyelonephritis in normal mice produced by inoculation of *E. coli* into the bladder lumen during water diuresis. Yale J. Biol. Med. **40**:231–237.

11. Lehmann, J. D., J. W. Smith, T. E. Miller, J. A. Barnett, and J. P. Sanford. 1968. Local immune response in experimental pyelonephritis. J. Clin. Invest. **47**:2541–2550.
12. Lepper, E. H. 1921. The production of coliform infection in the urinary tract of rabbits. J. Pathol. Bacteriol. **24**:192–204.
13. Rocha, H., L. B. Guze, L. R. Freedman, and P. B. Beeson. 1958. Experimental pyelonephritis. III. The influence of localized injury in different parts of the kidney on susceptibility to bacillary infection. Yale J. Biol. Med. **30**:341–354.
14. Tomasi, T. B., Jr. 1969. On the mechanisms of transport and biological significance of antibodies in external secretions. Arthritis Rheum. **12**:45–50.

Antimicrobial Agents and Chemotherapy—1969

Microbiological and Pharmacological Study of a New Antibiotic, Coumermycin A_1

DAN MICHAELI, BURT R. MEYERS, and LOUIS WEINSTEIN

Infectious Disease Service, New England Medical Center Hospitals, and Department of Medicine, Tufts University School of Medicine, Boston, Massachusetts 02111

Coumermycin A_1, a new antibiotic different from all others in use today, is a *bis*-hydroxycoumarin derivative isolated from *Streptomyces rishiriensis.* Broth-dilution studies indicated a high degree of bacteriostatic and bactericidal activity against *Staphylococcus aureus* (including strains resistant to methicillin and to cephalothin), *Diplococcus pneumoniae,* and *Haemophilus influenzae* in concentrations up to 1 μg/ml. Enterococci, streptococci, and strains of *Serratia* and *Proteus* showed various degrees of susceptibility. Other gram-negative bacteria usually were not inhibited by concentrations lower than 6.25 μg/ml. Induction of resistance by repeated transfers of *S. aureus* in coumermycin was slow to develop. No change in activity was observed against enterococci when streptomycin was added. The effect of human serum on the in vitro activity of the drug was studied. When human volunteers were given 100-mg capsules of coumermycin A_1 as a single dose, concentrations in the blood averaged 0.8 μg/ml after 4 hr. With repeated doses (every 8 hr for 4 days), the drug concentrations in serum averaged 1.28 μg/ml on the fourth day. Gastrointestinal symptoms, including heartburn, abdominal cramps, and diarrhea, occurred in some subjects. These were relieved by antacids and disappeared promptly after medication was withdrawn.

Coumermycin A_1, an antibiotic elaborated by *Streptomyces rishiriensis,* was discovered independently in Japan (8) and in the U.S.A. (3). It is a *bis*-hydroxycoumarin derivative and is made up of a sugar, coumermose, and an aglycone, coumermic acid (7). A number of semisynthetic derivatives have been developed and are presently under study (6, 9). Coumermycin A_1 is related to novobiocin in chemical structure, products of degradation, and in vitro antimicrobial activity (7, 8). Nevertheless, it is essentially different from all other antibiotics presently in use. Preliminary studies have indicated that it suppresses the growth of staphylococci and other gram-positive organisms, *Neisseria meningitidis,* and, to a lesser extent, gram-negative bacilli (3, 5, 7, 8). It has been reported to be highly active against methicillin- and cephalothin-resistant strains of *S. aureus* (10).

MATERIALS AND METHODS

Studies of minimal inhibitory concentration (MIC) and minimal bactericidal concentration (MBC). The MIC and MBC of the drug were determined against strains of bacteria recovered from human infections. Each organism was maintained on an agar slant from which cultures were made in Trypticase Soy Broth. After incubation at 37 C overnight, 0.5 ml of a 10^{-4} dilution of each organism was employed as the inoculum for use in studies of antimicrobial activity.

Sterile coumermycin A_1 powder was dissolved in 10% dimethylsulfoxide (DMSO) to which four volumes of phosphate buffer (*p*H 6.3) were added. This stock solution was refrigerated until used; storage in the cold for as long as 3 months did not lead to loss of activity of the antibiotic. The desired concentrations of drug were made from the stock solution by serial twofold dilutions in 0.5 ml of Trypticase Soy Broth. These dilutions were inoculated with 0.5 ml of the standard inoculum, and the cultures were incubated at 37 C for 18 to 24 hr. The lowest concentration of drug inhibiting bacterial growth, as judged by turbidity, was considered to be the MIC. Subcultures of clear tubes were made on Trypticase Soy Agar and Broth. The smallest quantity of antibiotic found to inhibit growth in this situation was established as the MBC. It has been reported that 5 to 10% DMSO at *p*H 7.0 suppresses bacterial growth (2). However, the quantity of this agent used in the present study (less than 2% at pH 6.3) was not inhibitory for any of the bacterial species employed as the test organisms.

Paper-disc drug susceptibility studies. Trypticase Soy Agar plates were streaked with overnight cultures of the organisms under study. Paper discs containing 2, 10, 30, 60 and 100 μg of coumermycin were then placed on the agar surface. The zones of inhibition were measured at 18 hr and the sizes were recorded. (The paper discs were supplied by Hoffmann-La Roche, Inc., Nutley, N.J.)

Induced resistance. The MIC of coumermycin A_1 for 11 susceptible strains of *S. aureus* was determined in broth. The culture containing the highest concentration of drug exhibiting turbidity after incubation at 37 C for 18 hr served as the source of the inoculum for the next subculture. This procedure was repeated daily, and each MIC was recorded. A 10^{-4} dilution constituted the inoculum in most instances. However, when the degree of growth from the drug-containing tubes was slight, the inoculum size was increased to 10^{-2} or 10^{-1}. "Skip" tubes (suggestive of mutation) were subcultured on agar to check the possibility of contamination, and were then tested in parallel with the original strain.

Effect of serum. The MIC of coumermycin in a mixture of 50% serum in broth was compared with the MIC in broth alone.

Combination of coumermycin and streptomycin. Enterococci resistant to 50 μg of streptomycin per ml were used in this study. In one experiment, broth containing various quantities of coumermycin alone was employed; in another, a single concentration of streptomycin (25 μg/ml) was added to the coumermycin dilutions. Nine strains were exposed to these combinations and the MIC of each was determined.

In another study, we grew enterococci in (i) broth, (ii) broth with coumermycin (1.0 μg/ml) and streptomycin (20 μg/ml), (iii) broth with coumermycin (1.0 μg/ml), and (iv) broth with streptomycin (20 μg/ml). Bacterial counts were performed in pour-plates at appropriate intervals.

Assay of coumermycin in serum. The concentration of coumermycin in serum was determined by the cup-plate method with *S. aureus* (6538P) as the test organism. Coumermycin-methylglucamine powder was used for the standard solutions (without either DMSO or buffer). A new reference curve was made every day for the same agar and the same culture of test organism as that used to test the serum on that day. No assays of coumermycin in urine were performed. (Preliminary data indicated no detectable amounts in the urine of tested humans and animals.)

Pharmacological studies. Eight healthy young male adults were given capsules of 100 mg of coumermycin (in 400 mg of methylglucamine as a vehicle). In the first study, a single dose was given in the fasting state. Blood was drawn before and at 1, 2, 4, 6, 8, and 12 hr after medication, and serum levels were determined.

In the second study (3 to 4 weeks later), the subjects received capsules of 100 mg of coumermycin every 8 hr for 4 days. Drug concentrations in the blood were determined during that period and for 3 days after cessation of the drug.

RESULTS

The in vitro susceptibility to coumermycin of 169 clinical isolates is shown in Table 1. Coumermycin concentrations of 0.003 to 1.0 μg/ml inhibited 93% of strains of *S. aureus* (including methicillin- and cephalothin-resistant strains); for 3 of 32 strains (7%), concentrations

Table 1. *Minimal inhibitory concentrations (MIC) and minimal bactericidal concentrations (MBC) of coumermycin A_1*

Organism	No. of strains tested	MIC (μg/ml)		MBC (μg/ml)	
		Range	Mean	Range	Mean or remarks
Staphylococcus aureus	30	<0.003–5.0	0.26	0.003–>20.0	2.49
S. aureus (methicillin-resistant)	13	0.004–0.78	0.129	0.004–1.56	0.38
Diplococcus pneumoniae	2	0.047–1.0	–	0.047–2.0	–
Streptococcus pyogenes	17	0.03–25.0[a]	2.89	3.12–>25.0	6 strains >12.5
Enterococci	15	0.78–12.5	4.05	3.12–>25.0	2 strains >12.5
Serratia marscesens	8	0.78–12.5	10.64	0.78–>25.0	7 strains >12.5
Haemophilus influenzae	6	0.04–3.12	0.84	0.78–3.12	0.84
Escherichia coli	14	6.25–25.0	11.16	25.0–>50	10 strains >50
Paracolon bacilli	9	6.25–25.0	15.56	12.5–>25	7 strains >25
Shigella	2	25.0	–	>50	–
Proteus (not differentiated)	19	<1.56–6.25	<2.33	6.25–<25.0	(>20.0)
Salmonella	7	>25.0	–	>25	–
Klebsiella-Aerobacter	10	12.5–50	31.25	>50	–
Pseudomonas aeruginosa	17	6.25–25.0	13.2	6.25–>25	>22.9

[a] One strain over 6.25 μg/ml.

of 1.0 to 5.0 μg/ml were necessary for inhibition of growth. The MBC for 88% of these staphylococcal strains was less than 2.5 μg/ml; 47% (8 of 17) of strains of *S. pyogenes* were inhibited by less than 2.5 μg/ml. Only two strains of *D. pneumoniae* were tested, and these were inhibited by 0.047 to 1.0 μg/ml.

Enterococcal strains tested showed variable susceptibility. A concentration of 3.12 μg or less per ml inhibited 60% of the strains (9 of 15). However, the MBC for 13 strains was greater than 12.5 μg/ml. Most gram-negative organisms tested were not inhibited by concentrations lower than 6.25 μg/ml, with the exception of *Proteus* and *Haemophilus* strains. Seven of 19 (32%) strains of *Proteus* (nondifferentiated) were inhibited by 1.56 μg or less per ml, and 4 of 6 strains of *H. influenzae* were inhibited by less than 0.2 μg/ml.

Disc studies. Disc studies gave variable results. On different days, the same bacteria gave different zones of inhibition. A comparison with broth-dilution studies is shown in Table 2. Although it is not possible to derive the exact MIC from the zone of inhibition (or vice versa), there is good correlation, in general, between the "susceptibility" to the drug (MIC less than 3.1 μg/ml) and the zones of inhibition. There were little or no differences in the zones obtained with the discs containing 30, 60, or 100 μg.

Induction of resistance by repeated transfers in coumermycin. Eleven strains of *S. aureus* (five of which were methicillin-resistant) were transferred from 5 to 17 consecutive times (Table 3). Only three strains developed an MIC of 6.2 μg/ml, and this occurred after 8, 10, and 11 transfers. For four other strains, the MIC was 3.2 μg/ml after 6 to 9 transfers, and these strains did not acquire further resistance even after 12 transfers. One strain showed no increase in resistance after 10 transfers.

Effect of combination of coumermycin and streptomycin on enterococci. Growth curve determinations revealed a reduction of 10^4 or more bacteria per ml, in comparison with antibiotic-free controls, after 4 to 6 hr of incubation both with coumermycin alone and with the coumermycin-streptomycin combination. No difference from the controls was observed in tubes containing streptomycin alone.

Nine strains were studied by the broth-dilution method. There was no change in the

Table 2. *Diameters of zones of inhibition produced by 10- and 30-μg coumermycin A_1 discs*

Type of bacteria	Zone size (mm)	
	10 μg	30 μg
Susceptible[a]	10–22	25–45
Resistant[b]	–	<15

[a] MIC less than 3.1 μg/ml.
[b] MIC over 3.1 μg/ml.

Table 3. *Number of transfers of various strains of staphylococcus aureus required to achieve indicated MIC of coumermycin*

No. of strain	MIC (μg/ml)													Total no. of transfers
	0.0015	0.003	0.006	0.012	0.025	0.05	0.1	0.2	0.4	0.8	1.6	3.2	6.2	
968[a]	–	–	–	1	–	–	4	–	–	–	–	5	8	10
530[a]	1	–	–	2	–	–	4	5	–	–	–	9	–	11
966[a]	1	2	3	–	–	–	4	5	6	–	–	7	–	10
970[a]	1	3	5	–	–	–	–	–	–	–	–	8	–	9
6268[a]	–	–	1	12	–	–	–	–	–	–	–	–	–	17
302	–	1	2	3	–	–	–	–	–	–	–	6	–	7
007	–	–	–	1	–	–	–	–	2	3	5	6	10	10
525	–	–	1	–	–	–	5	–	–	–	–	–	–	9
365	–	–	1	–	–	3	–	–	–	–	–	–	–	7
967	–	–	1	3	–	–	–	–	–	–	–	–	–	5
935	–	–	1	10	–	–	–	–	–	–	–	–	–	10
935A[b]	–	–	1	–	–	–	–	–	10	–	–	–	11	15

[a] Methicillin-resistant strains.
[b] Strain 935A is a mutant which appeared as a "skip tube" on the 10th transfer of 935.

MIC of coumermycin when streptomycin was added.

Effect of human serum. When fresh human serum was used, a marked increase in the MIC was observed (from 0.02 to 5.0 μg/ml). When serum was prepared from old plasma, the results were variable and sometimes no effect was observed.

Drug concentrations in blood. A single dose of 100 mg gave a peak mean concentration of 0.88 μg/ml at 4 hr with a range of 0.77 to 0.98 μg/ml (Table 4).

Repeated doses of 100 mg given at 8-hr intervals for 4 days gave peak concentrations in two subjects of 2.1 μg/ml on the fourth day (4 hr after ingestion of the drug). At 8 hr after ingestion, on the fourth day, the mean concentration was 1.28 μg/ml (range of 1.07 to 1.53 μg/ml). At 56 hr after the last dose, all drug concentrations in blood were less than 0.15 μg/ml (Table 5).

Table 4. *Concentrations of coumermycin A_1 in the blood after a single oral dose of 100 mg*[a]

Patient no.	Concn (μg/ml)					
	1 hr	2 hr	4 hr	6 hr	8 hr	12 hr
1	0.65	0.79	0.95	0.6	0.34	0.15
2	0.52	0.80	0.76	0.58	0.41	0.15
3	0.65	0.76	0.98	0.62	0.48	0.14
4	0.60	0.77	0.91	0.67	0.39	0.14
5	0.45	0.74	0.94	0.58	0.45	0.16
6	0.72	0.67	0.77	0.73	0.48	0.15
7	0.58	0.69	0.86	0.6	0.39	0.15
8	0.65	0.85	0.84	0.59	0.45	0.15
Avg	0.61	0.76	0.88	0.63	0.45	0.15

[a] After 24 hr, no inhibition was observed.

Side effects. Only gastrointestinal symptoms were observed. One to two days after onset of medication, seven of the subjects complained of "heartburn," abdominal pains, nausea, and vomiting. This did not prevent them from continuing the experiment; symptoms were relieved by antacids and sedatives. Six of the eight volunteers had diarrhea (several watery stools a day). Symptoms cleared promptly upon discontinuation of medication. Laboratory tests were performed during and after the first and second studies and included blood-urea nitrogen, creatinine, serum glutamic oxalacetic and pyruvic transaminases, serum bilirubin, alkaline phosphatase, total protein and albumin to globulin ratio, urinalysis, hemoglobin, hematocrit, leukocytes and differential count, reticulocyte count, and prothrombin time. No abnormalities were found.

DISCUSSION

Coumermycin A_1 is highly active, in vitro, against strains of *S. aureus, D. pneumoniae, H. influenzae,* and *Proteus.* Methicillin- and cephalothin-resistant strains were as susceptible as other staphylococci.

Enterococci were less susceptible, and the addition of streptomycin had no apparent effect on the activity of coumermycin on these bacteria. Standard paper discs could be used for differentiation of "susceptible" from "resistant" bacteria. Both 10- and 30-μg discs were suitable

Table 5. *Drug concentrations in the blood after administration of multiple doses of coumermycin*[a]

Patient no.	Concn (μg/ml)										
	Day 1		Day 2		Day 3			Day 4		Day 5	Day 6
	4 hr	8 hr	4 hr	8 hr	4 hr	6 hr	8 hr	4 hr	8 hr		
1	0.925	–	1.04	–	1.08	–	–	2.1	–	0.24	0.48
2	1.025	–	1.20	–	–	0.84	–	2.1	–	0.24	0.47
3	–	0.97	–	1.04	–	–	0.74	–	1.07	0.25	0.43
4	–	1.03	–	1.02	–	–	0.93	–	1.53	0.20	0.34
5	–	1.10	–	1.45	–	–	1.03	–	1.35	0.18	0.55
6	–	1.05	–	1.24	–	–	0.91	–	1.25	0.26	0.43
7	–	1.18	–	1.04	–	–	1.04	–	1.25	0.26	0.43
8	–	1.08	–	1.13	–	–	0.78	–	1.25	0.22	0.51
Avg	0.972	1.07	1.12	1.12	1.08	0.84	0.97	2.1	1.28	0.22	0.46

[a] Concentrations were measured 4, 6, and 8 hr after the last midnight dose (except for the first day). Doses were 100 mg of coumermycin at 8 AM, 4 PM, and midnight, for four consecutive days. On the seventh day, all concentrations were $\leqslant$0.15 μg/ml.

for this purpose. No advantage was seen with the use of other discs, and only a rough estimate of the susceptibility of the bacteria to the drug could be achieved. Induction of resistance was slow in developing in vitro. If resistance develops as slowly in vivo, this may be an important antibiotic in the treatment of infections caused by methicillin- and cephalothin-resistant staphylococci (10).

The effect of serum on coumermycin activity in vitro should be further studied. Protein binding and the effect of *p*H are among the factors which may play a role in it. A direct effect of the serum itself cannot yet be ascertained.

The drug concentrations in the blood 4 hr after a single dose of 100 mg were higher than the MIC for all of the methicillin- and cephalothin-resistant *S. aureus* strains and for most other strains of *S. aureus.* With repeated doses, the highest concentration (2.1 μg/ml) exceeded the MIC for 47% of the enterococci, 37% of *Proteus* strains, and 60% of *Haemophilus* strains.

The fact that the structure of this compound is different from all others in use to date implies that it may have a role in the management of *S. aureus* infections in patients allergic to penicillins (and cephalosporins).

Subacute bacterial endocarditis due to the enterococci is still a difficult disease to treat. In patients allergic to penicillins, cephalosporin derivatives have not achieved bactericidal levels in serum (11). The in vitro activity of coumermycin against enterococci suggests that it may be useful in such cases.

The chemical relationship to warfarin should be noted. No disturbances in prothrombin time were observed. Yet such an effect may possibly be seen if larger groups are studied. *Bis*-hydroxycoumarin derivatives may become more active in the serum if the *p*H is changed or if other drugs are ingested at the same time (1, 11). Therefore, studies are needed to evaluate the activity of coumermycin A_1 when other drugs are taken by the patient. The effect of normal serum on the MIC should be studied in more detail.

This drug cannot yet be recommended for treatment of patients. The first problem is the relatively low concentrations obtained in serum after administration by the oral route. For the treatment of severe staphylococcal infections, and certainly for the treatment of other infections, higher concentrations are desirable. This oral route is even more hazardous in view of the relatively high frequency of gastrointestinal irritation observed. A parenteral preparation or one that will produce higher concentrations after oral administration is needed.

There is a possibility that concomitant administration of other drugs will alter its metabolism in general and may even produce a warfarin-like activity.

ACKNOWLEDGMENTS

These studies were supported by a grant from the Hoffmann-La Roche Laboratories, Nutley, N.J.

LITERATURE CITED

1. Aggler, P. M., R. A. O'Reilly, L. S. Leong, and P. E. Kowitz. 1967. Potentiation of the anticoagulant effect of warfarin by phenylbutazone. N. Engl. J. Med. **276**:496.
2. Basch, H., and H. H. Gadebusch. 1968. In vitro antimicrobial activity of dimethylsulfoxide. Appl. Microbiol. **16**:1953–1954.
3. Berger, J., A. J. Schocher, A. D. Batcho, B. Pecherer, O. Keller, J. Maricq, A. E. Karr, B. P. Vaterlaus, A. Furlenmeier, and H. Speigelberg. 1966. Production, isolation, and synthesis of the coumermycins (sugordomycins), a new streptomycete antibiotic complex. Antimicrob. Agents Chemother.–1965, p. 778–785.
4. Grunberg, E., and M. Bennett. 1966. Chemotherapeutic properties of coumermycin A_1. Antimicrob. Agents and Chemother.–1965. p. 786–788.
5. Grunberg, E., R. Cleeland, and E. Titsworth. 1967. Further observations on chemotherapeutic activity of coumermycin A_1. I. Activity against *Neisseria meningitidis* type A and meningopneumonitis. Antimicrob. Agents and Chemother.–1966, p. 397–398.
6. Ichikawa, M., and H. Ichibagase. 1968. Studies on coumarin derivatives. XX. Synthesis and antibacterial activity of derivatives of N-substituted 3-coumarincarboxamide. Chem. Pharm. Bull. (Tokyo) **16**:2093–2100.
7. Kawaguchi, H., T. Naito, and H. Tsukiura. 1965. Studies on coumermycin, *a new antibiotic.* II. Structure of coumermycin A_1 J. Antibiot. (Tokyo) Ser. A **18**:11–25.
8. Kawaguchi, H., H. Tsukiura, M. Okanishi, T. Miyaki, T. Ohmori, K. Fujisawa, and H. Koshiyama. 1965. Studies on coumermycin, *a new antibiotic.* I. Production, isolation and characterization of coumermycin A_1. J. Antibiot. (Tokyo) Ser. A **18**:1–10.
9. Keil, J. G., I. R. Hooper, M. J. Cron, H. Schmitz, D. E. Nettleton, and J. C. Godfrey. 1969. Preparation of semisynthetic coumermycin A_1 derivatives. III. Aromatic and heteroaromatic derivatives of 3-amino-4-hydroxy-8-methyl-7-[3-*O*-(5-methyl-2-pyrrolylcarbonyl)-noviosyloxy]-coumarin. Antimicrob. Agents Chemother.–1968, p. 120–127.
10. Michaeli, D., B. R. Meyers, and L. Weinstein. 1969. In vitro studies of the activity of coumermycin A_1 staphylococci resistant to methicillin and cephalothin. J. Infec. Dis. **120**:488–490.
11. O'Reilly, R. A. 1969. Interaction of the anticoagulant drug warfarin and its metabolites with human plasma albumin. J. Clin. Invest. **48**:193–202.
12. Rahal, J. J., Jr., B. R. Meyers, and L. Weinstein. 1968. Treatment of bacterial endocarditis with cephalothin. N. Engl. J. Med. **279**:1305–1309.

Antimicrobial Agents and Chemotherapy—1969

Alterations in the Bactericidal Capacity of the Rat Lung After Immunosuppression

ROBERT J. SHARBAUGH and JAMES B. GROGAN

Departments of Microbiology and Surgery, University of Mississippi Medical Center, Jackson, Mississippi 39216

The relationship between cyclophosphamide-induced immunosuppression and increased susceptibility to pulmonary infection was examined. Repeated administration of cyclophosphamide in doses of 25 mg/kg caused leukopenia and petechial hemorrhage of the lungs. In addition, higher doses (100 mg/kg) caused a severe hypogammaglobulinemia. The ingestion of *Staphylococcus aureus* and *Pseudomonas aeruginosa* by alveolar macrophages was not affected by treatment. In contrast, a significant decrease in the bactericidal ability of the lung was noted after immunosuppressive therapy. This decrease in cidal activity was manifested as a drastic increase in the number of bacteria detected within the lungs of treated animals. Enzymatic analysis showed that treatment with cyclophosphamide had no apparent effect on alveolar lysozyme activity. However, significant decreases in both acid phosphatase and myeloperoxidase activity were observed.

The numerous benefits provided by immunosuppressive agents have been accompanied by an increase in the incidence of infections in patients receiving immunosuppressive therapy (3). The microorganisms isolated from such infections have included bacteria of the genera *Staphylococcus* and *Pseudomonas* (10), fungi of the genera *Candida* and *Aspergillus* (4), and certain viruses (4).

Because the lungs appear to be the primary target organ of these infectious agents, the present study was undertaken in an effort to establish a cause and effect relationship between immunosuppressive therapy and increased susceptibility to pulmonary infection.

MATERIALS AND METHODS

Immunosuppressive therapy. Female rats of the Long-Evans strain, weighing 200 to 225 g, were used. Immunosuppressive therapy consisted of cyclophosphamide (Cytoxan, Mead Johnson Laboratories, Evansville, Ind.) administered in dosages of 25, 50, or 100 mg/kg on alternate days for a total of four injections. A minimum of six animals was included in each group.

Determination of total serum gamma globulin. Total serum gamma globulin was assayed by use of the immunodiffusion method described by Fahey and McKelvey (2). Reference samples were prepared with purified rat gamma globulin (Pentex, Inc., Kankakee, Ill.) in concentrations ranging from 0.25 to 4.0 mg/ml.

After overnight incubation at 4 C, the diameters of the rings of precipitation were measured with a magnified rule. Comparison of the unknown ring diameters with a logarithmic curve of the known standards afforded a quantitation of the level of gamma globulin in the unknown sera. Results are expressed in grams per 100 ml.

Preparation of rabbit anti-rat gamma globulin. Purified rat gamma globulin was dissolved in physiological saline, in a concentration of 6.75 mg/ml. After the addition of two parts Freund's complete adjuvant, 0.1 ml of the suspension of antigen was injected into each toe pad of the two forefeet of each of a group of adult rabbits. Three weeks later, the animals were challenged with a second dose consisting of 1,000 μg of purified antigen. Animals were bled 1 week later via cardiac puncture and the sera were stored at −20 C until used.

Radioassay for reticuloendothelial function of alveolar tissue. Measurements of the ingestive and digestive capabilities of the lung were performed by use of ^{32}P-labeled cells of *S. aureus* and *P. aeruginosa.* Animals were injected intravenously with 2×10^8 labeled bacteria, and 1 hr later the degree of bacterial uptake and kill was determined as described previously (12).

Infectivity studies. Animals were treated with 50 mg of cyclophosphamide per kg of body weight on alternate days for a total of four injections. After the last injection, the animals were subjected to an intravenous injection of 2×10^8 viable bacteria (*S. aureus* or *P. aeruginosa*). At various time intervals after infection, the number of viable organisms was determined by plate counts performed with Tryptic Soy agar.

Preparation of enzyme solutions. Anesthetized rats were exsanguinated via decapitation. Tissue specimens of known weight were obtained from the lungs, placed in 3.0 ml of cold 0.14 M KCl, and homogenized for 1 to 2 min. These preparations were centrifuged at $600 \times g$ for 10 min. The precipitate was discarded, and the supernatant fluid was centrifuged at $10{,}000 \times g$ for 10 min. The resulting lysosomal pellet was suspended in 9.0 ml of 0.15 M KCl and 1.0 ml of 1% Triton X-100. After incubation at 37 C for 10 min, the suspension was centrifuged at $100{,}000 \times g$ for 30 min. Enzymatic assays were carried out on the $10{,}000 \times g$ supernatant fluid (soluble enzyme fraction) as well as on the $100{,}000 \times g$ supernatant fluid (lysosomal or bound enzyme fraction). Results are expressed as the total enzymatic activity contained within these two fractions.

Enzymatic analysis. Lysozyme activity was determined according to the method of Smolelis and Hartsell (13), with *Micrococcus lysodeikticus* as the enzyme substrate. Enzyme concentrations were interpolated by use of a standard curve and are expressed as milligrams of lysozyme per gram (wet weight) of tissue.

Acid phosphatase activity was determined by use of a modification of the method described by Valentine and Beck (15), with sodium β-glycerophosphate as the substrate. Enzyme activity is expressed as milligrams of phosphorus liberated per hour per milligram (wet weight) of tissue.

Myeloperoxidase was measured by the method of Schultz et al. (11). To a standard 1-cm cuvette were added 2.0 ml of 0.22% quaicol, 0.1 ml of enzyme solution, and 0.01 M phosphate buffer to a total volume of 2.99 ml. This initial reaction mixture was set to an optical density (OD) of zero by use of a Beckman DU spectrophotometer. The spectrophotometer was then adjusted to read 50 OD divisions above this solution. The time after the addition of 0.01 ml of H_2O_2 (1 μmole) required for the galvanometer needle to reach zero was recorded. Enzyme activity is expressed in terms of a specific activity constant, *K*.

RESULTS

Side effects related to drug therapy. Some of the various side effects observed in animals receiving cyclophosphamide therapy are shown in Table 1. The lowest dose used, 25 mg/kg, caused petechial hemorrhage of the lungs in about 25% of the cases. Increasing the dosage led to an accompanying increase in the amount of pulmonary hemorrhage. Dosages of both 25 and 50 mg/kg had no apparent effect on the levels of total serum gamma globulin. However, dosages of 100 mg/kg were observed to cause a significant decrease in this serum fraction ($P < 0.001$). Treated animals exhibited levels of 0.64 g/100 ml compared with the normal average of 1.32 g/100 ml. As expected, drug therapy produced a severe leukopenia.

Effect of drug therapy on the ingestion and digestion of bacteria by the lung. The results of experiments designed to test the ability of the lungs of treated animals to ingest and subsequently destroy ^{32}P-labeled cells of *P. aeruginosa* and *S. aureus* are shown in Table 2. No significant change in the ability of the lung to ingest either organism was observed, regardless of treatment. Normal values of uptake in the range of 0.7×10^6 and 1.7×10^6 bacteria/g of tissue were obtained for *P. aeruginosa* and *S. aureus*, respectively.

Table 1. *Side effects produced by various dosages of cyclophosphamide*

Dosage[a]	Petechial hemorrhage	Gamma globulin	White blood cells per mm^3
mg/kg		*g/100 ml*	
Control	0/10[b]	1.32	10,965
25	5/16	1.10	880
50	13/15	1.18	78
100	14/16	0.64	0

[a] Administered on alternate days for a total of four injections.
[b] Number exhibiting side effect/number observed.

Table 2. *Number of bacteria ingested and killed per gram of lung tissue after treatment with cyclophosphamide*

Organisms	Drug dosage[a]	Avg. no. of bacteria ingested /g of tissue	Ingested bacteria killed in 1 hr	P
	mg/kg		%	
P. aeruginosa	Control	0.8×10^6	96	–
	25	0.6×10^6	85	<0.05
	50	0.7×10^6	84	<0.001
	100	0.7×10^6	65	<0.001
S. aureus	Control	1.8×10^6	62	–
	25	1.1×10^6	62	NS[b]
	50	1.2×10^6	35	<0.001
	100	2.7×10^6	20	<0.001

[a] Administered on alternate days for a total of four injections.
[b] Not significant.

In contrast, a significant decrease in the ability of the lung to destroy the bacteria once they had been ingested was noted. The lungs of untreated animals killed 96% of ingested pseudomonads; drug therapy of 50 and 100 mg/kg reduced this value to 84 and 65%, respectively. The staphylocidal effect was reduced from 62% in the lungs of untreated animals to 35 and 20% in the lungs of animals receiving 50 and 100 mg/kg, respectively.

Bacterial proliferation after drug therapy. Normal (control) animals were infected with either *S. aureus* or *P. aeruginosa*, and bacterial viability within the lungs and other tissues was determined. In animals infected with *P. aeruginosa,* plate counts showed that no significant decrease in the number of viable bacterial cells in the kidneys occurred within 24 hr after infection (Fig. 1). In contrast, the number of viable *P. aeruginosa* cells recovered from the liver and spleen continued to decline through the 24th hr. Blood cultures obtained from control animals showed a similar decline in bacterial numbers during the first 12 hr, but a gradual increase began at about the 12th hr.

In contrast to the control animals, rats treated with cyclophosphamide exhibited pronounced differences in the number of viable *P. aeruginosa* cells recovered from the various organs. There was a steady increase in bacterial numbers in the liver, whereas no change occurred through the 6th hr in the spleen, kidneys, and blood. None of the treated animals infected with this organism survived the 12- or 24-hr postinfective periods.

The most pronounced changes caused by experimental infection with either *P. aeruginosa* or *S. aureus* were observed in the lungs of treated animals. (Fig. 2). Viable counts revealed a gradual and continuous decline in staphylococcal viability through the 24th hr in untreated animals. In contrast, rats treated with 50 mg of cyclophosphamide per kg exhibited a marked increase in the number of viable staphylococci recovered from the lungs beginning 6 hr after infection. This rise in bacterial numbers continued, and by 24 hr after injection of the bacteria the number of viable staphylococci in the lungs of treated animals was nearly 10,000 times that in the control animals. Results with *P. aeruginosa* were similar.

Effect of drug therapy on intracellular enzyme activity within the lung. The results of experiments designed to assay the activity of various hydrolases within alveolar tissue are shown in Fig. 3. The lungs of untreated animals displayed lysozyme activity in the range of 1.5 mg/g. Treatment with cyclophosphamide had no apparent effect on this value.

In contrast, drug therapy produced a significant decrease in the levels of activity of alveolar acid phosphatase. Control animals exhibited values of approximately 0.004 mg of phos-

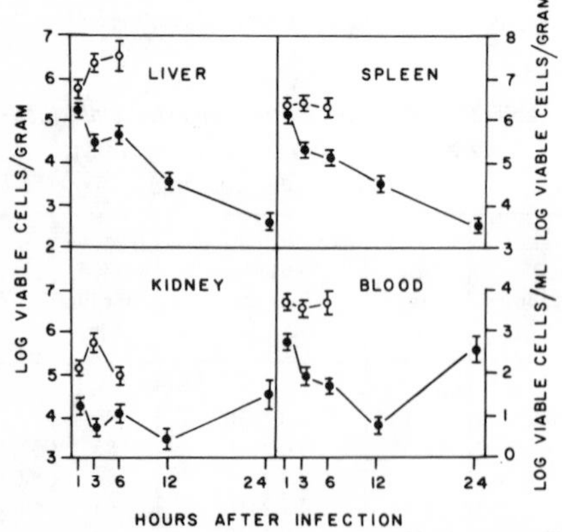

Fig. 1. *Viable P. aeruginosa cells recovered from various tissues of rats after treatment with cyclophosphamide. Symbols:* •, *controls;* ○, *treated with 50 mg/kg on alternate days for a total of four injections. Animals were experimentally infected 1 day after cessation of treatment.*

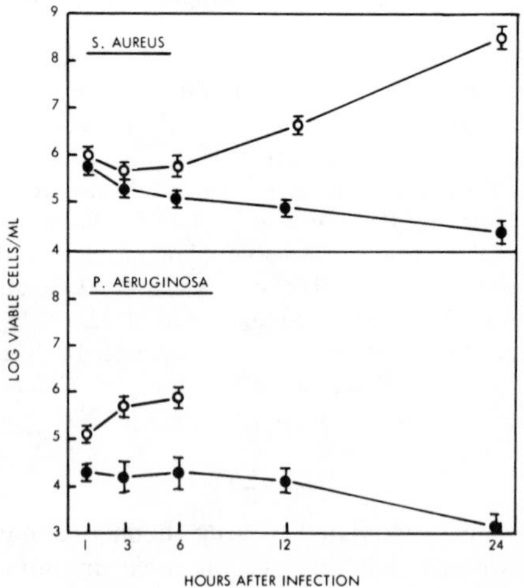

Fig. 2. *Viable bacteria recovered from the lungs of rats after treatment with cyclophosphamide. Symbols:* •, *control;* ○, *treated (50 mg/kg on alternate days for a total of four injections). Animals were experimentally infected 1 day after cessation of treatment.*

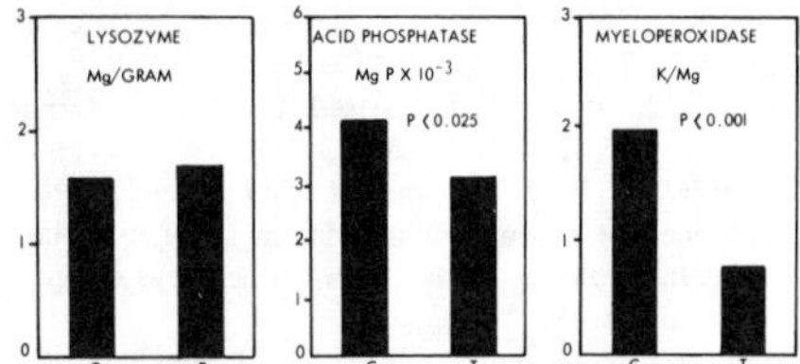

Fig. 3. *Effect of cyclophosphamide on the hydrolytic enzyme activity of alveolar tissue. C = controls; T = treated with 50 mg/kg on alternate days for a total of four injections.*

phorus, in comparison with 0.003 mg in treated animals.

Similarly, the activity of myeloperoxidase was significantly decreased after drug therapy. Treated animals displayed activity constants (*K* values) on the order of 0.80, whereas an average *K* value of approximately 2.0 was observed in the lungs of untreated control animals.

DISCUSSION

The treatment of rats with dosages of 25, 50, and 100 mg of cyclophosphamide per kg was accompanied by several side effects, including leukopenia and petechial hemorrhage in the lungs. Similar findings were reported by Wheeler et al. (16) and were attributed to drug toxicity. In addition, immunodiffusion analysis showed that serum gamma globulin levels decreased by more than 50% after treatment with 100 mg/kg dosages. A similar reduction in the gamma globulin fraction of cyclophosphamide-treated animals was reported by Mackiewicz (7).

The drug dosages used caused no deficiency in the ability of alveolar tissue to ingest either *P. aeruginosa* or *S. aureus*. This correlates with the finding that cyclophosphamide treatment has no apparent effect on the ingestive capabilities of the cells within the liver or spleen (12). However, a striking decrease in the ability of the alveolar phagocytes in the lung to kill ingested *Pseudomonas* cells was noted. Similar results were obtained with *S. aureus*, although this organism was apparently not as susceptible to degradation as was *P. aeruginosa*.

Alveolar macrophages are almost the only phagocytizing cells in lung tissue (5). We observed no significant change in the ingestive powers of alveolar tissue from treated animals. This defect, then, in the ability of the lungs to inactivate ingested bacteria apparently lies in the ability to kill the bacteria once they have been ingested.

The decrease in bactericidal activity of the lungs after drug therapy was further manifested as a rapid increase in the number of viable *P. aeruginosa* and *S. aureus* cells found in the lungs. A similar increase in bacterial numbers was observed in the liver, spleen, and kidney.

Cyclophosphamide was recently shown to inhibit the activity of various hydrolytic and proteolytic enzymes in leukocytes, liver, and kidney (9, 14). Analysis of the activity of various acid hydrolases found within alveolar tissue revealed no change in the levels of lysozyme present, regardless of treatment. However, drug therapy caused significant decreases in the activities of acid phosphatase and myeloperoxidase, both of which play dominant roles in the inactivation of phagocytosed bacteria (1, 6, 8). It is quite possible, then, that the cyclophosphamide-induced enhancement of bacterial susceptibility observed in these studies may be due to insufficient amounts or inefficient activity (or both) of these necessary hydrolytic enzymes. Such drug-induced enzyme inactivation may contribute to the high incidence of pulmonary infection in patients receiving immunosuppressive therapy.

ACKNOWLEDGMENTS

This investigation was supported by Public Health Service Training Grant AI 69 from the National Institute of Allergy and Infectious Diseases and by American Cancer Society grant T-416.

LITERATURE CITED

1. Cohn, Z. A., and J. G. Hirsch. 1960. The influence of phagocytosis on the intracellular distribution of granule-associated components of polymorphonuclear leucocytes. J. Exp. Med. **112**:1015–1022.
2. Fahey, J. L., and E. M. McKelvey. 1965. Quantitative determination of serum immunoglobulins in antibody-agar plates. J. Immunol. **94**:84–90.
3. Green, G. M. 1968. Pulmonary clearance of infectious agents. Ann. Rev. Med. **19**:315–336.
4. Hill, R. B., D. T. Towlands, and D. Rifkind. 1964. Infectious disease in patients receiving immunosuppressive therapy for organ transplantation. N. Engl. J. Med. **271**:1021–1027.
5. Karrer, H. E. 1960. Electron microscope study of the phagocytosis process in lung. J. Biophys. Biochem. Cytol. **7**:357–365.
6. Klebanoff, S. J. 1968. Myeloperoxidase-halide-hydrogen peroxide antibacterial system. J. Bacteriol. **95**:2131–2138.
7. Mackiewicz, U. 1967. Effect of cyclophosphamide on serum proteins in rats. Acta Pol. Pharm. (Transl.) **24**:551–555.
8. McRipley, R. J., and A. J. Sbarra. 1967. Role of the phagocyte in host-parasite interactions XII. Hydrogen

peroxide-myeloperoxidase bactericidal system in the phagocyte. J. Bacteriol. **94**:1425–1430.

9. Prokopowicz, J., L. Rejniak, and S. Niewiarowski. 1967. Influence of cytostatic agents on fibrinolytic and proteolytic enzymes and on phagocytosis of guinea pig leucocytes. Experientia **23**:813–814.
10. Rifkind, D., T. L. Marchioro, W. Waddell, and T. Starzl. 1964. Infectious diseases associated with renal homotransplantation. J. Amer. Med. Ass. **189**:397–407.
11. Schultz, J., H. Shay, and M. Gruenstein. 1954. The chemistry of experimental chloroma. I. Porphyrins and peroxidases. Cancer Res. **14**:157–162.
12. Sharbaugh, R. J., and J. B. Grogan. 1969. Suppression of reticuloendothelial function in the rat with cyclophosphamide. J. Bacteriol. **100**:117–122.
13. Smolelis, A. N., and S. E. Hartsell. 1949. The determination of lysozyme. J. Bacteriol. **58**:731–736.
14. Stachura, J., B. Papla, and M. Dubiel-Bigaj. 1968. The influence of cyclophosphamide on some hydrolases and oxidizing enzymes in the livers and kidneys of mice. Acta Med. Pol. **9**:319–328.
15. Valentine, W. N., and W. S. Beck. 1951. Biochemical studies on leucocytes. J. Lab. Clin. Med. **38**:39–55.
16. Wheeler, A. G., D. Dansby, H. C. Hawkins, H. G. Payne, and J. H. Weikel, Jr. 1962. A toxicologic and hematologic evaluation of cyclophosphamide (Cytoxan) in experimental animals. Toxicol. Appl. Pharmacol. **4**:324–343.

Antimicrobial Agents and Chemotherapy—1969

In Vitro Susceptibility of *Neisseria meningitidis* to Rifampin

DANIEL IVLER, JOHN M. LEEDOM, and ALLEN W. MATHIES, JR.

Hastings Foundation Infectious Disease Laboratory and Departments of Medicine, Pediatrics, and Microbiology, University of California School of Medicine, and the Communicable Disease Service, Los Angeles County-University of Southern California Medical Center, Los Angeles, California 90033

Since the advent of sulfadiazine-resistant strains of *Neisseria meningitidis,* no antimicrobial agent has proven effective in nasopharyngeal carriers of meningococci and in aborting epidemics in high-risk populations. Therefore, the in vitro antimeningococcal activity of rifampin was studied both by a standard two-fold broth-dilution method and by disc tests (2-, 5-, and 15-μg discs). Among the 50 strains of *N. meningitidis* tested, 38 were isolated from cerebrospinal fluid or blood of patients, and 12 were isolated from the pharynges of well persons. Of these 50 strains, 17 were highly resistant to sulfadiazine. Minimal inhibitory concentrations (MIC) of rifampin ranged from ≤0.1 to 0.8 μg/ml and were ≤0.1 μg/ml for 44 of the 50 strains (88%). Minimal bactericidal concentrations (MBC) were ≤0.1 to 1.6 μg/ml. For all but two strains, the MBC values were ≤0.4 μg/ml. In the disc tests, no correlation of convincing biological significance was found between the diameters of the zones of inhibition and disc strengths. Median diameters of zones of inhibition were 31.4, 33.7, and 36.4 mm, for 2-, 5-, and 15-μg discs, respectively. Furthermore, there was no clear correlation between the broth-dilution MIC and the diameter of zones of inhibition. It was found that meningococci highly resistant to rifampin can be selected by a single passage in the presence of the drug. This means that rifampin should not be used to treat meningococcal disease. Nevertheless, the in vitro activity of rifampin seems to justify its trial in meningococcal carriers.

The introduction of sulfonamides opened a new era of effective chemotherapy for meningococcal disease. Furthermore, during World War II, when group A meningococcal disease was epidemic, sulfonamides, particularly sulfadiazine, were shown to be effective as a mass prophylactic measure among military recruits (2). Mass administration of sulfadiazine to recruits stopped the occurrence of meningococcal disease in the treated groups, and usually eradicated meningococci from the pharynges of asymptomatic carriers (2).

For about 20 years, it seemed that the administration of sulfadiazine provided adequate prophylaxis against secondary cases among high-risk populations, such as military recruits or family contacts of cases. Then, in the spring of 1963, an outbreak of meningitis, due to group B meningococci, occurred among recruits at the San Diego Naval Training Center (3, 15). Mass administration of sulfadiazine failed to halt the outbreak, meningococcal pharyngeal carrier rates were not affected by sulfadiazine treatment, and group B meningococci highly resistant to sulfadiazine were isolated from both the cerebrospinal fluid (CSF) specimens of some of the patients and the pharynges of asymptomatic carriers (3, 15).

In May 1963, we began testing the sulfadiazine susceptibilities of meningococci from civilian patients admitted to the Communicable Disease Service, Los Angeles County-University of Southern California Medical Center, for the treatment of meningococcal disease. Sulfadiazine susceptibilities of meningococci from civilian almost immediately (6-9). Since then, group C sulfadiazine-resistant meningococci have become widespread in the United States (17), and resistant group A strains have been reported from North Africa.

Any one of several antibiotics, including benzyl penicillin, ampicillin, tetracycline, and chloramphenicol, yields excellent results in the treatment of meningococcal disease (5, 10, 11, 13, 14, 18). However, none of these drugs reliably eradicates pharyngeal carriage of *Neisseria meningitidis,* and none has been proven definitely effective in the prevention of secondary cases in families or in terminating epidemics among military recruits (3, 8, 15). Therefore, when rifampin, an antibiotic not related to any other antimicrobial in current use in the United States, became available to us in August 1967, we examined its activity against 50 strains of *N. meningitidis.*

MATERIALS AND METHODS

Bacteria tested. All but 1 of the 50 strains of *N. meningitidis* tested were isolated from patients with meningococcal disease or from asymptomatic carriers at the Los Angeles County-University of Southern California Medical Center. The single group A strain tested was isolated in Morocco and was kindly sent to us by Rene Faucon, Microbiological Research Laboratories, Military School of Tropical Medicine and Hygiene, Marseilles, France.

After receipt at the Hastings Foundation Infectious Disease Laboratory, the purity and identity of each meningococcal strain were verified by standard morphological and biochemical criteria (*Bergey's Manual*).

All isolates were serogrouped by the macroscopic slide agglutination test with the use of rabbit hyperimmune sera obtained from the National Communicable Disease Center, Atlanta, Ga., or produced in our own laboratory.

Sulfadiazine susceptibility testing. Sulfadiazine susceptibility testing was done by an agar-dilution method standardized in our laboratory and previously described (7). The most important features of our sulfadiazine susceptibility testing method are: (i) utilization of Mueller-Hinton agar, (ii) aerobic incubation in an atmosphere containing 5% CO_2, and (iii) use of an inoculum of $>10^5$ organisms in each test (7).

Rifampin disc susceptibility tests. All 50 strains of *N. meningitidis* were tested by the disc susceptibility test against 2-, 5-, and 15-μg rifampin discs (supplied by Dow Chemical Co., Human Health Research and Development Laboratories, Zionsville, Ind.). Mueller-Hinton agar plates were inoculated by swabbing their entire surfaces with cotton swabs which had been dipped in an 18-hr Mueller-Hinton broth culture of the strain to be tested and "wrung dry." After the inoculated plates had dried for 15 to 30 min, 2-, 5-, and 15-μg rifampin discs were placed firmly on the surface of each plate. The plates were then incubated for 24 hr at 37 C in a CO_2 incubator under 5% CO_2. Zones of inhibition were measured across the disc diameters and were recorded in millimeters.

Rifampin broth-dilution susceptibility tests. The rifampin standard was supplied as a powder (by Dow Chemical Co.). A 10-mg amount of rifampin standard was weighed out on an analytical balance. The rifampin powder was then dissolved in approximately 5.0 ml of distilled water, the *p*H was adjusted to 7.2 by the dropwise addition of 0.1 N NaOH, and distilled water was added to yield a stock solution with a volume of 10.0 ml and a rifampin concentration of 1,000 μg/ml. A fresh rifampin stock solution was prepared each day that the broth-dilution susceptibility tests were performed. In all further dilutions of the rifampin stock solutions, Mueller-Hinton broth was used as the diluent.

The inocula for the broth-dilution tests were 0.5-ml portions of 10^{-2} or 10^{-3} dilutions of 18-hr Mueller-Hinton broth cultures grown in a CO_2 incubator under 5% CO_2. Each 0.5-ml sample contained approximately 10^5 viable organisms. These 0.5-ml inocula were added to Wasserman tubes topped with loose metal caps, which contained either 0.5 ml of Mueller-Hinton broth or twofold serial dilutions of rifampin in 0.5 ml of Mueller-Hinton broth, so that the final volume in each tube was 1.0 ml. The final rifampin concentrations tested, after dilution to 1.0 ml by addition of the inocula, were 200, 100, 50, 25, 12.5, 6.3, 3.2, 1.6, 0.8, 0.4, 0.2, 0.1, and 0 μg/ml.

Tubes were incubated for 24 hr at 37 C under 5% CO_2 in a CO_2 incubator. At the end of that time, the tubes were removed, and the minimal inhibitory concentrations (MIC) were recorded as the lowest concentrations of rifampin completely inhibiting visible growth. To determine minimal bactericidal concentrations (MBC), a 3.0-mm standard bacteriological loop was used to plate samples from *all* tubes, clear and cloudy, on antibiotic-free Mueller-Hinton agar. After 18 to 24 hr of incubation at 37 C in a CO_2 incubator under 5% CO_2, the plates were examined. The MBC was recorded as the lowest concentrations of rifampin which failed to yield any viable organisms on subculture. Colonies which grew on these plates were verified as being *N. meningitidis.*

RESULTS

Serogroups, sulfadiazine susceptibilities, and anatomic origins of the meningococci tested. Table 1 shows the serogroups, anatomic origins, and sulfadiazine susceptibilities of the 50 meningococcal strains tested against rifampin. Most strains were isolated from blood or CSF of patients, but 12 pharyngeal isolates from carriers were included. Forty-eight strains belonged to serogroups B and C, the pathogenic groups most important recently in the United States. Of the 50 strains, 17 (34%) were highly resistant to sulfadiazine (MICs $\geqslant$10 mg/100 ml), 26 (52%) were very susceptible (MICs $\leqslant$0.5 mg/100 ml), and 7 (14%) were of intermediate susceptibility

Table 1. *Susceptibilities of 50 strains of N. meningitidis to sulfadiazine, classified by serogroup and anatomic site*

Serogroup	Anatomic site	No. of strains		
		Susceptible[a]	Intermediate[a]	Resistant[a]
A	CSF[b]	–	–	1
	Blood	–	–	–
	Throat	–	–	–
B	CSF	14	3	11
	Blood	2	–	2
	Throat	4	1	2
C	CSF	4	1	–
	Blood	–	–	–
	Throat	1	2	1
Y[c]	CSF	–	–	–
	Blood	–	–	–
	Throat	1	–	–

[a] Susceptible = MIC ⩾0.5 mg/100 ml; intermediate = MIC of 1, 2, or 5 mg/100 ml; resistant = MIC ⩾10 mg/100 ml.
[b] Cerebrospinal flud.
[c] Serogroup of Slaterus.

(MIC of 1, 2, or 5 mg/100 ml). None of these variables correlated with rifampin susceptibility, so they will not be discussed further.

Broth-dilution MICs and MBCs of rifampin. Table 2 shows the distribution of rifampin MICs and their corresponding MBCs for the 50 strains of *N. meningitidis* tested. The MICs for 44 of the 50 (88%) strains were ⩽0.1 μg/ml; for only one strain was the MIC as high as 0.8 μg/ml. For 40 of the 50 strains (80%), the MICs and MBCs were identical. For an additional eight strains (16%), the MBCs differed from the MICs by only one dilution. Certainly these differences, of only one doubling dilution between MICs and MBCs, cannot be regarded as significant. Only two strains had MBCs that were two or more tubes higher than the corresponding MICs. It is possible that, for these two strains, the observed differences between the MICs and their corresponding MBCs were significant. If so, the differences could have been due either to persistors or to the selection of a moderately resistant minority population.

Susceptibility to rifampin discs. All 50 strains of *N. meningitidis* were tested against 2-, 5-, and 15-μg rifampin discs. Figure 1 shows the distribution of the diameters of the zones of inhibition in millimeters for all 50 strains and all three

Table 2. *Rifampin susceptibilities of 50 strains of N. meningitidis as determined by the broth-dilution procedure–MICs with corresponding MBCs*

No. of strains	MIC (μg/ml)	MBC (μg/ml)				
		⩽0.1	0.2	0.4	0.8	1.6
44	⩽0.1	36[a]	6	1	1	–
5	0.2	–	4	1	–	–
1	0.8	–	–	–	–	1

[a] Number of strains.

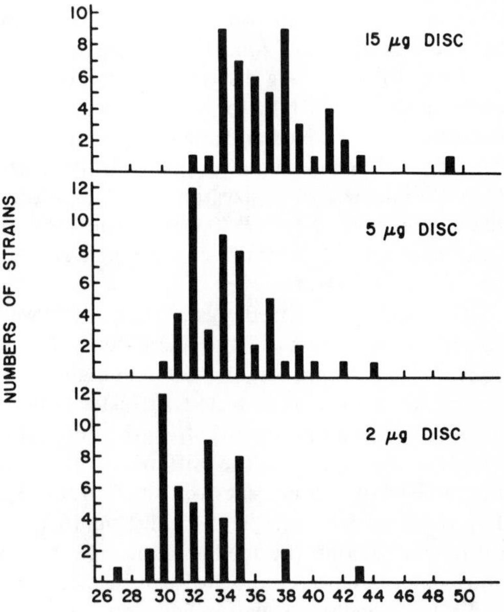

Fig. 1. *Lack of correlation between sizes of zones of inhibition and discs strengths for 50 strains of N. meningitidis.*

disc strengths. Although inspection of Fig. 1 seems to show a trend toward somewhat larger zone sizes with the discs containing the larger quantities of rifampin, considerable overlap is obvious.

The failure of the three disc strengths to segregate three distinct categories of zone diameters is perhaps even more apparent in Table 3. The overlapping of the ranges of the zone diameters for the three disc strengths was almost complete. Although other estimates of central tendency are shown in Table 3, the median was the most important statistic for comparative purposes, because the frequency distributions of

Table 3. *Diameters of zones of inhibition produced by three different strengths of rifampin discs tested against 50 strains of N. meningitidis*

Size of disc	Diam of zones of inhibition (mm)			
	Range	Mean	Mode	Median
μg				
2	27-43	32.5	30	31.4
5	30-44	35.3	32	33.7
15	32-49	35.2	34 and 38	36.4

the observed values were so clearly non-Gaussian. The median zone sizes were 31.4 mm for the 2-μg disc, 33.7 mm for the 5-μg disc, and 36.4 mm for the 15-μg disc. As determined by a nonparametric χ^2 test for the comparison of medians (16), the median zone size produced by the 15-μg rifampin disc was significantly larger than the median zone sizes produced by either the 2- or 5-μg discs ($P<0.001$). The median zone sizes produced by the 2- and 5-μg discs did not differ significantly ($P>0.05$).

It should be stressed again that there was considerable overlap in the diameters of the zones of inhibition of the 50 meningococcal strains when they were tested against rifampin discs of three different strength (Fig. 1). Furthermore, the absolute difference between the three median zones sizes was small (Table 3). For these reasons, the "statistically significant" differences among the median zone sizes noted above are of dubious biological significance.

Lack of evident correlation between zone sizes and broth-dilution MICs. Results of broth-dilution and disc-susceptibility tests did not correlate well, as can be seen in Fig. 2. However, Fig. 2 must be interpreted with caution because the lowest concentration of rifampin used in the broth-dilution tests was 0.1 μg/ml. However, the zone diameters, with all three disc sizes, for the six meningococcal strains for which the MICs were ⩾0.2 μg/ml, fell within the range of zone sizes exhibited by the meningococci for which the MICs were ⩽0.1 μg/ml.

"Skip tube" phenomenon. McCabe and Lorian (12) reported "skip tubes" when staphylococci were tested against rifampin, if the inoculum used in the test was 10^6 organisms or more. That is, when the MICs were read, McCabe and Lorian (12) observed several clear tubes at low rifampin concentrations with one or more cloudy tubes at higher rifampin concentrations. When the contents of McCabe and

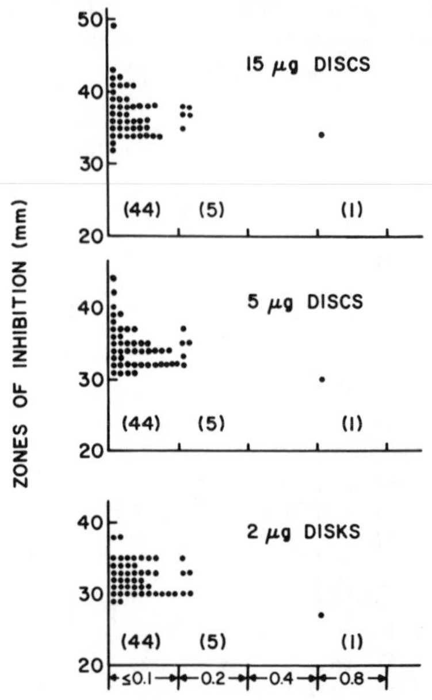

Fig. 2. *Lack of correlation between the results of disc and broth-dilution susceptibility tests for 50 strains of N. meningitidis tested against rifampin.*

Lorian's (12) "skip tubes" were subcultured, it was shown that a single passage in rifampin-containing medium had selected mutants of staphylococci which had a uniform high resistance to rifampin.

With the possible exception of two strains discussed in Table 2, this "skip tube" phenomenon was not observed in our determinations of bacteriostatic and bactericidal end points for 50 strains of *N. meningitidis* during routine susceptibility testing with a standard inoculum of approximately 10^5 organisms. *However, increasing the inoculum size did lead to the detection of "skip tubes" in the bactericidal test but not in the bacteriostatic test.*

The "skip tube" phenomenon in the bactericidal test is evident in Table 4, which shows the results of a representative experiment in which the inoculum size of a group C meningococcus was varied. With our standard inoculum, in this instance, 2.0×10^5 organisms, both the MIC and the MBC of rifampin were ⩽0.1 μg/ml. With an inoculum of 2.6×10^6 meningococci, the MIC was still ⩽0.1 μg/ml. *All antibiotic-containing tubes were clear.* However, upon streaking on antibiotic-free Mueller-Hinton agar,

Table 4. *Development of resistance to rifampin by N. meningitidis strain 67-4 (group C)*

Inoculum sizes (organisms/ml[a])	MBC of rifampin (μg/ml)
2.4×10^7	1.6 (skip 4 tubes to 25)
2.6×10^6	⩽0.1 (skip 5 tubes to 3.2)
2.0×10^5	⩽0.1 (no skips)

[a] Inoculum sizes determined by plate counts of further dilutions of 10^{-1}, 10^{-2}, and 10^{-3} dilutions of an 18-hr broth culture.

viable meningococci were recovered from a *single* antibiotic-containing tube–the tube containing 3.2 μg of rifampin per ml. Thus, the MBC for the inoculum containing 2.6×10^6 organisms might be read as ⩽0.1 μg/ml, with five clear tubes between the cloudy control tube containing no rifampin and the "skip tube" which contained 3.2 μg of rifampin per ml and yielded viable meningococci on subculture. When an inoculum of 2.4×10^7 organisms per tube was used, the MIC was impossible to read accurately, because the original inocula imparted a high degree of cloudiness to all of the tubes. However, the MBC would have been clearly 1.6 μg/ml except for recovery of meningococci from a *single* tube containing a higher concentration of rifampin, 25 μg/ml. This represented the occurrence of four tubes yielding no bacteria on subculture between the tube with 0.8 μg of rifampin per ml, which contained viable meningococci, and the "skip tube" with 25 μg of rifampin per ml, which also contained viable meningococci.

Study of colonies from "skip tubes". Colonies were picked from the MBC plates streaked from both "skip tubes." They were subcultured in Mueller-Hinton broth and reidentified as group C meningococci (*N. meningitidis* strain 67-4). Mueller-Hinton broth cultures of the two meningococcal strains derived from the colonies grown from the two "skip tubes" were employed as inocula in our standard rifampin broth-dilution system. The inocula actually used (Table 5) were 0.5-ml amounts of 10^{-3} dilutions of 18-hr broth cultures. These amounts gave an inoculum size of 3.2×10^4 viable organisms for the strain which had survived in a rifampin concentration of 25 μg/ml and 1.2×10^4 viable organisms for the strain which had survived in 3.2 μg/ml.

Table 5 compares the MICs and MBCs for the two meningococcal daughter strains derived from the "skip tubes" of *N. meningitidis,* strain

Table 5. *Development of resistance to rifampin (N. meningitidis, strain 67-4, group C)*

Concentrations of rifampin in which parent colonies survived	Rifampin susceptibilities of daughter strains	
(μg/ml)	MIC (μg/ml)	MBC (μg/ml)
25	25[a]	100
3.2	25[b]	⩾200

[a] Inoculum size = 3.2×10^4 viable organisms.
[b] Inoculum size = 1.2×10^4 viable organisms.

67-4. The MICs of both daughter strains were 25 μg/ml, and the corresponding MBCs were 100 and ⩾200 μg/ml, respectively. It should be recalled that the standard MIC and the standard MBC for the parent strain, 67-4, were both ⩽0.1 μg/ml. This experiment showed that meningococci highly resistant to rifampin can be rather easily selected by a single in vitro exposure of a susceptible strain to the drug. This marked increase in resistance seemed especially striking in view of the fact that the inoculum sizes employed in the broth-dilution tests were somewhat smaller than usual. That is, the inoculum sizes were approximately 10^4 viable organisms per tube.

DISCUSSION

Several aspects of our data deserve emphasis and discussion. Rifampin susceptibility among meningococci seemed independent of serogroup, anatomic origin, or sulfadiazine susceptibility. Upon disc susceptibility testing of the 50 meningococcal strains, the median diameter of the zones of inhibition produced by the 15-μg rifampin discs was significantly larger statistically than the median diameters of the zones of inhibition produced by the 2- and 5-μg discs. Nevertheless, the relationship between zone diameter and disc strength was not really clear-cut; the three disc strengths did not produce three distinct groupings of zone diameters, and the statistical difference was adjudged to be of dubious biological significance. Similar results in the correlation of zone diameters and rifampin disc strengths have been reported by McCabe and Lorian (12) with other bacterial species. Although failure to test our meningococcal strains against concentrations of rifampin lower than 0.1 μg/ml may have masked such correlations among the very susceptible strains, we found no clear-cut correlations between the diameters of the zones of inhibition in the disc tests and the MIC values determined by broth dilution. Again, similar results have been noted by others with other bacteria (1, 12). However, Atlas and Turck (1) observed better correlation with the disc test when the MICs were determined by the agar-dilution method than when they were determined by broth dilution.

The in vitro activity of rifampin seemed to warrant a trial of its efficacy in the eradication of pharyngeal carriage of meningococci. Recently, Deal and Sanders (4) compared rifampin and placebo in 30 chronic carriers of meningococci. They found that administration of 600 mg of rifampin daily for 4 days reduced the carrier rate by 93.3%, and this effect was sustained for 4 weeks (4). The results of Deal and Sanders (4) are highly encouraging, and it is hoped that rifampin will prove to be useful in the prevention of meningococcal disease in high-risk groups. The fact that none of the subjects studied by Deal and Sanders (4) acquired rifampin-resistant meningococci augurs well for the future. However, in view of the ease with which highly resistant mutants can be selected in vitro, rifampin should not be used to treat meningococcal disease. In addition, only a large experience, with careful monitoring, will teach us whether mass prophylaxis with rifampin will result in the widespread selection of resistant meningococci in vivo with resultant superannuation of the drug as a prophylactic measure.

ACKNOWLEDGMENTS

We thank the staff of the Diagnostic Bacteriology Laboratory, Communicable Disease Service, Los Angeles County-University of Southern California Medical Center for primary isolation of the meningococcal strains. Noemi Fiorentino furnished technical assistance.

This investigation was supported by Public Health Service grants 5-TO1-AI00275 and 5-RO1-AI08011 from the National Institute of Allergy and Infectious Diseases, by Contract DA-49-193-MD-2874 from the U.S. Army Research and Development Command, Commission on Acute Respiratory Diseases, Office of the Surgeon General, Department of the Army, by a Grant-in-Aid from the Dow Chemical Co., Zionsville, Ind., and by the Hastings Foundation Fund.

LITERATURE CITED

1. Atlas, E., and M. Turck. 1968. Laboratory and clinical evaluation of rifampicin. Amer. J. Med. Sci. **256**:247–254.
2. Aycock, W. L., and J. H. Mueller. 1950. Meningococcus carrier rates and meningitis incidence. Bacteriol. Rev. **14**:115–160.
3. Bristow, W. M., P. F. D. Van Peenen, and R. Volk. 1965. Epidemic meningitis in naval recruits. Amer. J. Public Health **55**:1039–1045.
4. Deal, W. D., and E. Sanders. 1969. Efficacy of rifampin in treatment of meningococcal carriers. N. Engl. J. Med. **273**:1395–1401.
5. Florey, M. E. 1957. Chloramphenicol and the tetracyclines, p. 80–81. *In* The clinical application of antibiotics, vol. 3. Oxford University Press, London.
6. Ivler, D., J. M. Leedom, A. W. Mathies, Jr., J. C. Fremont, L. D. Thrupp, B. Portnoy, and P. F. Wehrle. 1966. Correlates of sulfadiazine resistance in meningococci isolated from civilians. Antimicrob. Agents Chemother.–1965, p. 358–365.
7. Ivler, D., J. M. Leedom, L. D. Thrupp, P. F. Wehrle, B. Portnoy, and A. W. Mathies, Jr. 1965. Naturally occurring sulfadiazine-resistant meningcocci. Antimicrob. Agents Chemother.–1964, p. 444–450.
8. Leedom, J. M., D. Ivler, A. W. Mathies, Jr., L. D. Thrupp, J. C. Fremont, P. F. Wehrle, and B. Portnoy. 1967. The problem of sulfadiazine-resistant meningococci. Antimicrob. Agents Chemother.–1966, p. 281–292.
9. Leedom, J. M., D. Ivler, A. W. Mathies, L. D. Thrupp, B. Portnoy, and P. F. Wehrle. 1965. Importance of sulfadiazine resistance in meningococcal disease in civilians. N. Engl. J. Med. **273**:1395–1401.
10. Lepper, M. H., H. F. Dowling, P. F. Wehrle, N. H. Blatt, H. W. Spies, and M. Brown. 1952. Meningococcic meningitis: treatment with large doses of penicillin compared to treatment with gantrisin. J. Lab. Clin. Med. **40**:891–900.
11. Lepper, M. H., and H. W. Spies. 1962. Nontuberculous infections of the central nervous system. Gen. Practioner **25**:83–93.
12. McCabe, W. R., and V. Lorian. 1968. Comparison of the antibacterial activity of rifampicin and other antibiotics. Amer. J. Med. Sci. **256**:255–265.
13. Mathies, A. W., Jr., J. M. Leedom, D. Ivler, P. F. Wehrle, and B. Portnoy. 1968. Antibiotic antagonism in bacterial meningitis. Antimicrob. Agents Chemother.–1967, p. 218–224.
14. Mathies, A. W., Jr., J. M. Leedom, L. D. Thrupp, D. Ivler, B. Portnoy, and P. F. Wehrle. 1966. Experience with ampicillin in bacterial meningitis. Antimicrob. Agents Chemother.–1965, p. 610–617.
15. Millar, J. W., E. E. Siess, H. A. Feldman, C. Silverman, and P. Frank. 1963. *In vivo* and *in vitro* resistance to sulfadiazine in strains of *Neisseria meningitidis*. J. Amer. Med. Ass. **186**:139–141.
16. Moses, L. E. 1952. Non-parametric statistics for psychological research. Psychol. Bull. **49**:122–143.
17. National Communicable Disease Center. 1969. Meningococcal infections-United States. Morbidity and Mortality Weekly Rep. **18**:135 and 140.
18. Wehrle, P. F., A. W. Mathies, Jr., J. M. Leedom, and D. Ivler. 1967. Bacterial meningitis. Ann. N.Y. Acad. Sci. **145**:448–498.

Antimicrobial Agents and Chemotherapy—1969

Comparison of Antibiotic Susceptibility of Group D Streptococcus Strains Isolated at Boston City Hospital in 1953-54 and 1968-69

PUBLIO TOALA, ALICE McDONALD, CLARE WILCOX, and MAXWELL FINLAND

Thorndike Memorial Laboratory and Channing Laboratory, Harvard Medical Unit, Boston City Hospital, and Department of Medicine, Harvard Medical School, Boston, Massachusetts 02118

From August 1968 through May 1969, 382 enterococcal organisms isolated at Boston City Hospital were identified as group D streptococci. These organisms were classified according to species by their biochemical and cultural characteristics, and were tested for susceptibility to 21 antibiotics. The results were compared with those obtained with 187 strains from the same hospital in 1953-54. *Streptococcus liquefaciens*, currently the most frequent (56.8%), ranked third (17.6%) in 1953-54. *S. faecalis*, most frequent earlier (47%), ranked second (22%) among the recent isolates. *S. zymogenes* was more frequent (35.3%) in 1953–54 than in 1968–69. *S. faecium* and *S. durans*, not recognized earlier, contributed 4.5 and 1.0%, respectively. Ampicillin, penicillin G, and vancomycin, in that order, were the antibiotics most active against the recently isolated strains of all species. Penicillinase-resistant penicillins and cephalosporins were much less active. Gentamicin was the most active aminoglycoside. Doxycycline and minocycline were more active than demethylchlortetracycline and tetracycline. Novobiocin and the lincomycins resembled the tetracyclines in activity. Bacitracin, streptomycin, and cloxacillin were the least active. Erythromycin showed marked variation in activity against the 1968–69 strains, whereas the 1953–54 strains were nearly all highly susceptible. Recently isolated strains of each species were considerably less susceptible than earlier ones to the commonly used antibiotics, except penicillin G. Differences in susceptibility of individual species to some antibiotics were less striking in 1968–69 than in 1953–54.

Results of tests of the antibiotic susceptibility of several species of group D *Streptococcus* (enterococcus) were previously reported from Boston City Hospital (3). (The terms "group D streptococcus" and "enterococcus" are used interchangeably.) Since then, new antibiotics have been introduced and are currently in use. The present studies (6) concern in vitro observations on the antibiotic susceptibility of 382 enterococci isolated at Boston City Hospital from August 1968 through May 1969. The purpose of the study was to determine: the relative susceptibility of these isolates to currently available antibiotics, any differences in susceptibility among the species, and any changes in the incidence of strains resistant to the antibiotics tested in 1953–54 (3).

MATERIALS AND METHODS

The 382 strains used in this study were isolated and identified from routine cultures of infected materials sent to the diagnostic Bacteriology Laboratory. The strains selected for the study all satisfied the criteria for group D streptococci set forth by Topley and Wilson (7) and by Swift (5), and all reacted specifically with group D antiserum (Difco).

Solutions of antibiotics were freshly prepared in sterile distilled water; methanol was used first to effect the solution of erythromycin; and 3 N HCl was similarly used for bacitracin. Samples of each solution containing

2,000 μg of antibiotic per ml were stored at −20 C, and each was thawed only once prior to use. The antibiotics and their suppliers were as follows: sodium penicillin G and zinc bacitracin (Chas. Pfizer & Co., Inc., Brooklyn, N.Y.); ampicillin trihydrate, sodium methicillin, and sodium cloxacillin (Bristol Laboratories, Syracuse, N.Y.); sodium nafcillin (Wyeth Laboratories, Radnor, Pa.); lincomycin hydrochloride, clindimycin hydrochloride, and sodium novobiocin (The Upjohn Co., Kalamazoo, Mich.); sodium cephalothin, cephaloridine, erythromycin, and vancomycin hydrochloride (Eli Lilly & Co., Indianapolis, Ind.); chloramphenicol (Parke, Davis & Co., Detroit, Mich.); tetracycline hydrochloride, demethylchlortetracycline hydrochloride, and minocycline hydrochloride (Lederle Laboratories, Pearl River, N.Y.); doxycycline hyclate (Chas. Pfizer & Co., Inc.); streptomycin sulfate (Merck & Co., Inc., Rahway, N.J.); kanamycin sulfate (Bristol Laboratories); and gentamicin sulfate (Schering Corp., Bloomfield, N.J.)

The tests of in vitro susceptibility were carried out on Heart Infusion Agar (Difco), *p*H 7.2 to 7.4 (with 10% defibrinated sheep blood added), containing serial twofold dilutions of antibiotic. An undiluted inoculum from an overnight culture was applied by the inocula replicating method of Steers, Foltz, and Graves (4), and results were read after incubation for 18 to 20 hr at 37 C.

RESULTS

Table 1 shows the distribution of the isolates among the five species identified by biochemical tests in the present study and also in the previous study (3). *S. liquefaciens* [*S. faecalis* var. *liquefaciens* (1)] accounted for more than one-half of the strains in the present study, as compared with only 17.6% among the earlier strains. *S. faecalis* and *S. zymogenes* [*S. faecalis* var. *zymogenes* (1)] ranked second and third, and together accounted for 38% of the strains isolated in 1968–69; in 1953–54 *S. faecalis* represented 47.1% of the strains and *S. zymogenes* 35.3%. *S. faecium* ranked fourth with 4.5%, and four strains of *S. durans* were identified in 1968–69; no strains of either *S. durans* or *S. faecium* were recognized in 1953–54.

Table 1. *Distribution of enterococci by species isolated at Boston City Hospital*

Species	1953–54		1968–69	
	No. of isolates	Per cent	No. of isolates	Per cent
S. liquefaciens	33	17.6	217	56.8
S. faecalis	88	47.1	84	22.0
S. zymogenes	66	35.3	60	15.7
S. faecium	0		17	4.5
S. durans	0		4	1.0
Total	187	100	382	100

Table 2 summarizes the different sources of infected materials in the present study and in the earlier one. Infected urine was the most frequent source in both studies. Infections of the skin and subcutaneous tissue were the second most frequent source, representing 22 to 25% in both studies. About 14% of the strains were isolated from the sputum in 1968–69, but only 8% were isolated from that source in 1953–54. Only 7 strains (less than 2%) were isolated from blood cultures, whereas 15 strains (8%) were isolated from the same source in 1953–54. It is noteworthy that in the present study six strains were isolated from the tips of intravenous polyethylene catheters and five strains from the umbilical stumps of newborn infants.

The minimal inhibitory concentrations for the 382 strains tested are depicted in Figure 1. From Fig. 1, it is possible to compare directly the relative in vitro activity of each antibiotic against all of the strains tested. Ampicillin, penicillin G, and vancomycin, in that order, were the most active and were uniformly active against nearly all of the strains. The shape of the curve representing erythromycin is of interest. There is a wide and continuous range of minimal inhibitory concentrations of erythromycin; 46% of the strains were inhibited by 6.3 μg/ml or

Table 2. *Sources of group D streptococci isolated at Boston City Hospital*

Source	1953–54		1968–69	
	No. of isolates	Per cent	No. of isolates	Per cent
Urine	78	41.7	117	30.6
Skin and adnexa	47	25.1	85	22.3
Feces	18	9.6	75	19.6
Sputum	16	8.6	53	13.9
Blood	15	8.0	18[a]	4.7
Vagina and cervix	2	1.1	16	4.2
Peritoneum	3	1.6	6	1.6
Miscellaneous	8	4.3	12	3.1
Total	187	100	382	100

[a] Includes cultures of intravenous catheters (six) and umbilicus in newborns (five).

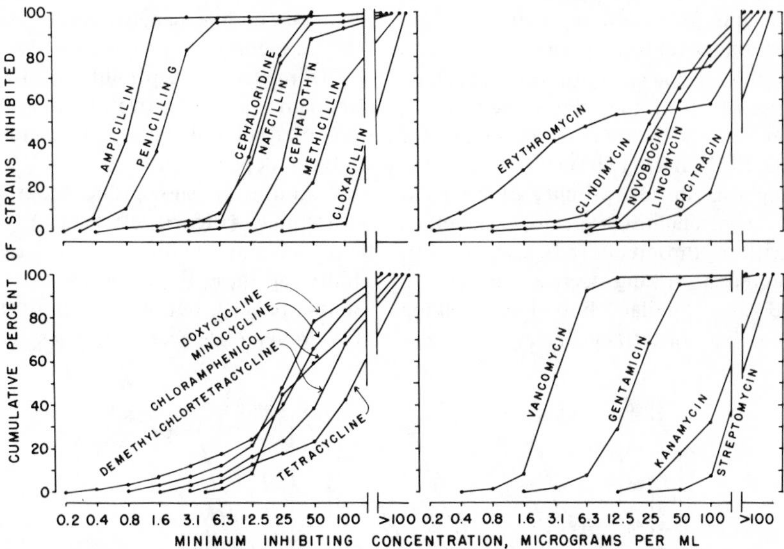

Fig. 1. *Susceptibility to 21 antibiotics of 382 strains of group D Streptococcus species isolated at Boston City Hospital, August 1968 through May 1969.*

less, whereas the remaining 54% required 50 to >100 μg/ml. Cephaloridine, nafcillin, and gentamicin were about equally active, and ranked next to vancomycin; cephalothin was only slightly less active. Methicillin and cloxacillin were the least active of the penicillins tested.

Among the four tetracyclines tested, doxycycline and minocycline were similar in activity and were more active than the others; tetracycline was the least active. The two lincomycins, novobiocin, and chloramphenicol were all similar in their activity. Bacitracin, kanamycin, streptomycin, and cloxacillin inhibited only small and decreasing proportions of strains and only in the highest concentrations used.

Strains belonging to four of the five species were tested for susceptibility to penicillins and cephalosporins (Fig. 2 and 3). Cloxacillin was essentially inactive against all species. The strains of *S. faecium* (Fig. 2) were the least susceptible to penicillins and cephalothin. Ampicillin, penicillin G, and nafcillin were the most active against *S. faecalis* and *S. zymogenes* (Fig. 3) and also against *S. liquefaciens* (Fig. 2). Cephalori-

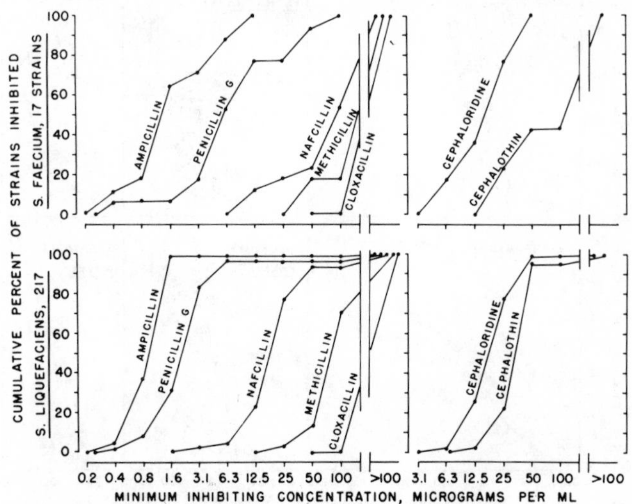

Fig. 2. *Susceptibility of strains of S. liquefaciens and S. faecium to penicillins and cephalosporins.*

dine (Fig. 2 and 3) was about equally active against the strains of all four species.

In Fig. 4, the relative susceptibility to each of six antibiotics of all of the strains used in this study is compared with the corresponding data based on the 1953–54 (3) strains. Of interest is the close similarity in susceptibility of strains in both studies to penicillin G (left upper panel) as compared with erythromycin (left lower panel), which exhibited a striking decrease in activity since 1953–54. Similar but less striking decreases in activity of tetracycline and chloramphenicol (middle panels), and of bacitracin and streptomycin (right panels), are also evident.

The relative susceptibility of the three predominant species to five of the antibiotics that were used in both the earlier and the present study is depicted in Fig. 5 and 6. All species were uniformly susceptible to penicillin G in both studies (Fig. 5, left panels). In 1953–54, there was no significant difference in susceptibility of these three species to erythromycin (middle panels), but in the current study, strains of *S. liquefaciens* were much less susceptible to

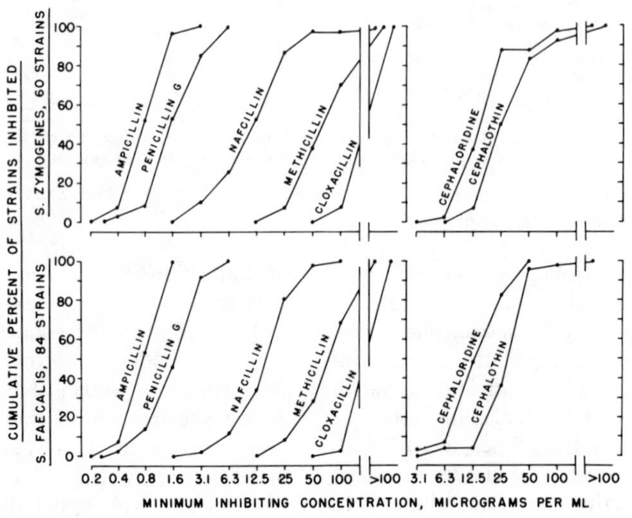

Fig. 3. *Susceptibility of strains of S. faecalis and S. zymogenes to penicillins and cephalosporins.*

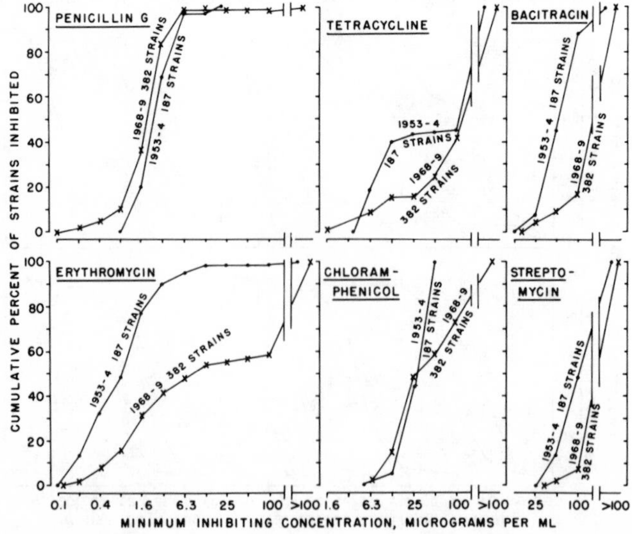

Fig. 4. *Comparison of antibiotic susceptibility of enterococci isolated in 1953–54 and 1968–69.*

this antibiotic than were those of *S. faecalis* and *S. zymogenes. S. faecalis* and *S. zymogenes* were very similar in susceptibility. All of the strains were also uniformly susceptible to chloramphenicol in 1953–54 (Fig. 5, right panels), whereas in 1968–69 there was a varying decrease in susceptibility of the three species. The difference in susceptibility was greatest among the strains of *S. liquefaciens* and only slightly less among those of *S. faecalis.*

In the present study, all three species were more or less uniformly resistant to tetracycline (Fig. 6, lower left panel); in 1953–54 (Fig. 6, upper left panel), there were marked differences. The strains of *S. liquefacies* were more susceptible and those of *S. zymogenes* much less susceptible than the strains of *S. faecalis*, about half of which were resistant. There were species differences also in the proportions of strains that were still susceptible to streptomycin in 1953–54 (Fig. 6, upper right panel), but nearly all recent strains of the three species were highly resistant to this antibiotic.

In summary, it is evident that considerable increases in the frequency and degree of resistance to erythromycin, tetracycline, streptomycin, and chloramphenicol have occurred among strains of the three predominant species. Resistance to penicillin G, however, has not increased to any appreciable extent.

DISCUSSION

During the 10 months of the present study, 382 separate cultures from infected materials obtained from patients at Boston City Hospital were identified as enterococci and classified within five species [or three species and two "varieties" or subspecies (1, 7)]. About 57% were classified as *S. liquefaciens*, 22% as *S. faecalis*, and 15% as *S. zymogenes*; the rest were distributed between *S. faecium* (5%) and *S. durans* (1%). In 1953–54, *S. faecalis* accounted for 47%, *S. zymogenes* for 35%, and *S. liquefaciens*, 18%; strains of *S. durans* were not encountered and *S. faecium* was not included in the classification.

In both studies, urine was the most frequent source, infected skin and subcutaneous tissues ranked second, and feces ranked third. Sputum contributed 14% of strains in the present study and 5% in the earlier one, along with 3% from throat cultures. Less than 2% were isolated from blood cultures in 1968–69 as compared with 8% in 1953–54; we have no explanation for this difference. However, colonization of the tips of intravenous catheters by enterococci in the current study is of some interest. Recently, Zinner and associates (8) cultured 436 indwelling polyethylene catheters removed from patients at Boston City Hospital and found five

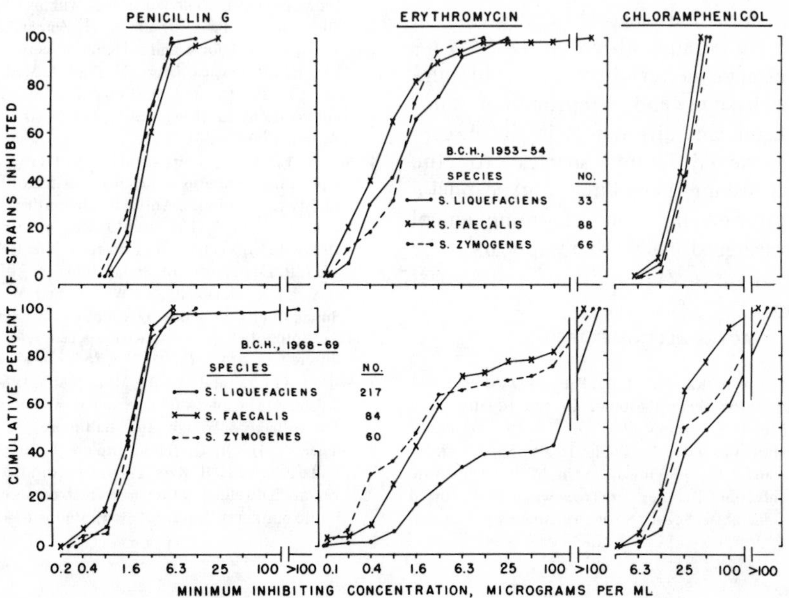

Fig. 5. *Comparison of susceptibility of strains of S. liquefaciens, S. faecalis, and S. zymogenes isolated in 1953–54 and 1968–69 to penicillin G, erythromycin, and chloramphenicol.*

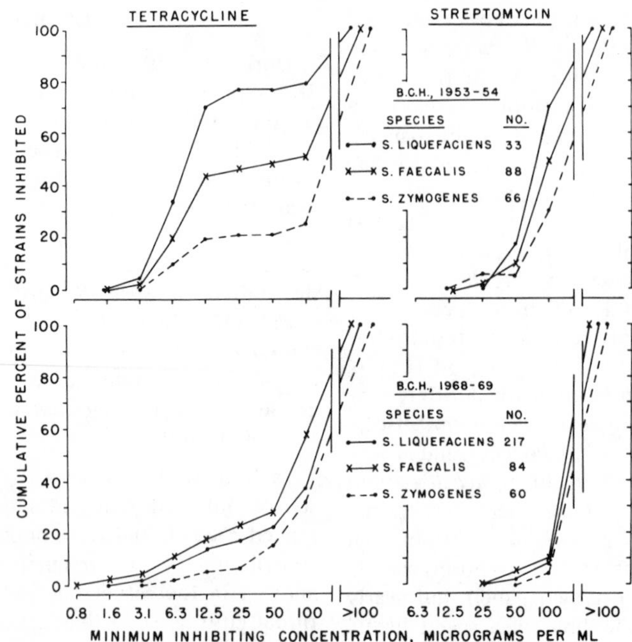

Fig. 6. *Comparison of susceptibility of strains of S. liquefaciens, S. faecalis, and S. zymogenes isolated in 1953–54 and 1968–69 to tetracycline and streptomycin.*

(1.1%) to be colonized by enterococci. In the present study, six strains (1.2%) were isolated from this source. The risk of potentially serious infections from prolonged retention of intravenous polyethylene catheters is obvious (2).

The data presented suggest a decrease in susceptibility of strains of group D *Streptococcus* to tetracycline, erythromycin, chloramphenicol, bacitracin, and streptomycin since 1953–54. Significant differences in the susceptibility of the different species to the penicillinase-resistant penicillins and cephalosporins, erythromycin, and chloramphenicol were demonstrated. Finally, there appears to be no decrease in the susceptibility of enterococci to penicillin G.

ACKNOWLEDGMENTS

We are indebted to A. Kathleen Daly, Patricia O'Connell, and Mary I. Kendrick for their assistance in the isolation and identification of the recent strains.

This investigation was aided by Public Health Service grants 5 ROI-AI-00023 and 2 TI-AI-00068 from the National Institute of Allergy and Infectious Diseases. Dr. Toala was also supported by El Hospital General Del Seguro Social, Panama City, Panama, contract 53-67, and by the Organization of American States Fellowship Program, contract 2-13,756.

LITERATURE CITED

1. Buchanan, R. E., J. G. Holt, and E. F. Lessel, Jr. (ed.). 1966. Index Bergeyana. The Williams & Wilkins Co., Baltimore.
2. Collins, R. N., P. A. Braun, S. H. Zinner, and E. H. Kass. 1968. Risk of local and systemic infection with polyethylene intravenous catheters. N. Engl. J. Med. **279**:340–343.
3. Jones, W. F., Jr., and M. Finland. 1957. Susceptibility of enterococcus to eleven antibiotics *in vitro*. Amer. J. Clin. Pathol. **27**:467–481.
4. Steers, E., E. L. Foltz, and B. S. Graves. 1959. Inocula replicating apparatus for routine testing of bacterial susceptibility to antibiotics. Antibiot. Chemother. **9**:307–311.
5. Swift, H. F. 1952. The streptococci, p. 265–323. *In* R. J. Dubos (ed.), Bacterial and mycotic infections of man, 2nd ed. J. B. Lippincott Co., Philadelphia.
6. Toala, P., A. McDonald, C. Wilcox, and M. Finland. 1969. Susceptibility of group D streptococcus (enterococcus) to 21 antibiotics *in vitro*, with special reference to species differences. Amer. J. Med. Sci. **258**:416–430.
7. Wilson, G. S., and A. A. Miles (ed.) 1964. Topley and Wilson's principles of bacteriology and immunity, 5th ed. The Williams & Williams Co., Baltimore.
8. Zinner, S. H., B. C. Denny-Brown, P. Braun, J. P. Burke, P. Toala, and E. H. Kass. 1969. Risk of infection with intravenous indwelling catheters: effect of application of antibiotic ointment. J. Infec. Dis. **120**:606–619.

Antimicrobial Agents and Chemotherapy—1969

In Vitro Susceptibility Patterns of Beta-Hemolytic Streptococci

JOHN M. MATSEN, DONNA J. BLAZEVIC, and S. STEPHEN CHAPMAN

Departments of Laboratory Medicine and Pediatrics, University of Minnesota, Minneapolis, Minnesota 55455

The susceptibility of 168 strains of beta-hemolytic streptococci of various Lancefield groups to bacitracin, erythromycin, penicillin, tetracycline, cephalothin, cephaloridine, cephaloglycine, and cephalexin was tested by agar-dilution and disc-diffusion methods. Clinical isolates from patients in Minnesota comprised 103 of the strains, and the remaining 65 strains were isolated from U.S. servicemen in Vietnam. All strains were grouped by the Lancefield method, and M and T typing was done on all group A streptococci. Susceptibility to bacitracin varied, depending upon the Lancefield group. For those strains which were very susceptible to penicillin, erythromycin, and the four cephalosporins, the inhibitory levels of these antibiotics were very uniform. However, there was a pronounced difference in the patterns of susceptibility to tetracycline; 73% of the Vietnam strains were inhibited only by concentrations of 12.5 μg/ml or higher, whereas the minimal inhibitory concentration for 94% of the U.S. strains was 1.6 μg or less per ml. This resistance to tetracycline did not relate to streptococcal group or M type.

As new antibiotics are discovered, there is a need to assess their value in the treatment of infections caused by a variety of microorganisms. Furthermore, there is a continuous necessity to evaluate the possible development of organisms' resistance to older, established antibiotics. Although infections caused by beta-hemolytic streptococci are successfully treated by a number of antibiotics now available, there is evidence that newer antibiotics of the cephalosporin group are effective against these strains (4, 8, 13, 14). At the same time, there is evidence of streptococci resistant to the tetracyclines (5, 7, 9, 10) and, rarely, to other antibiotics (11).

This report presents a comparison of the susceptibilities of various streptococcal strains to eight antibiotics. These strains are primarily group A and were isolated in Minnesota and from U.S. servicement in Vietnam. The latter strains had been sent to the University of Minnesota for grouping and typing.

MATERIALS AND METHODS

Included in the study were 76 strains of beta-hemolytic streptococci isolated from throats of patients in Minnesota, 65 strains isolated from skin lesions and wounds of U.S. servicemen in Vietnam, and an additional 27 strains of group A streptococci isolated from wounds and skin lesions in Minnesota.

Antibiotics used were bacitracin, erythromycin, penicillin, tetracycline, cephalothin, cephaloridine, cephaloglycine, and cephalexin. The cephaloridine, cephaloglycine, and cephalexin discs were kindly supplied by Eli Lilly & Co., and the other discs were purchased from BBL.

Mueller-Hinton broth or agar (BBL) was used for the susceptibility tests, which were done by both disc-diffusion and agar-dilution techniques. For disc testing, plates (150 × 15 mm) containing 75 ml of Mueller-Hinton agar with 5% sheep blood were used. These plates were dried by overnight incubation before use. Organisms were grown overnight at 37 C in Mueller-Hinton broth containing 5% sheep blood, and 1:10 dilution of the overnight culture was made in Mueller-Hinton broth. A sterile cotton swab was dipped into this dilution; the swab was squeezed against the side of the tube to remove excess fluid and then was used to inoculate the plates. The agar surface was swabbed in three directions, and after inoculation the plates were allowed to dry for 5 min. The antibiotic discs were then placed on the agar and pressed down to ensure good contact.

For agar-dilution testing, twofold dilutions of the

antibiotics were made in Mueller-Hinton agar containing 5% sheep blood. The plates were used on the same day they were prepared. The 1:10 dilution of overnight culture used for the disc tests was diluted in Mueller-Hinton broth to a final dilution of 1:1,000. For uniformity, each broth dilution was applied onto the antibiotic dilution plates by use of a replicator (12). A Mueller-Hinton plate with blood and no antibiotics was also inoculated with all test organisms as a growth control. Stock strains of *Escherichia coli* and *Staphylococcus aureus* were included in each experiment as controls to check on antibiotics, discs, media, and technique.

All plates were incubated at 37 C for 18 hr. The minimal inhibitory concentration (MIC) of each antibiotic was the least amount which inhibited growth of an organism on the agar-dilution plates. The diameters of inhibition zones around the discs were measured with calipers.

The streptococci were grouped by the method of Lancefield (6) as modified by Frank and Levenson (2). Typing of group A streptococci was done in two ways: the agglutination method of Griffith (3) was used to determine the T patterns, and the M type was determined by the capillary precipitin method of Lancefield (6).

RESULTS

The groups of the streptococcal strains are shown in Table 1. The majority of strains were group A. The Minnesota group A strains comprised 38 different serotypes, and there were 18 serotypes among the Vietnam group A organisms. There was no overlapping of serotypes in the two geographical groups.

Figures 1–3 show the MIC of each of the antibiotics for the two groups of organisms. The variation observed in susceptibility to bacitracin depended upon the Lancefield group. All strains of like Lancefield groups showed similar sus-

Table 1. *Lancefield groups of the Minnesota and Vietnam beta-hemolytic streptococci*

Group	No. of strains		
	Minnesota		Vietnam
	Respiratory	Skin and wound	
A	68	27	43
B	0	0	2
C	3	0	9
G	3	0	10
Other	2	0	1
Total	76	27	65

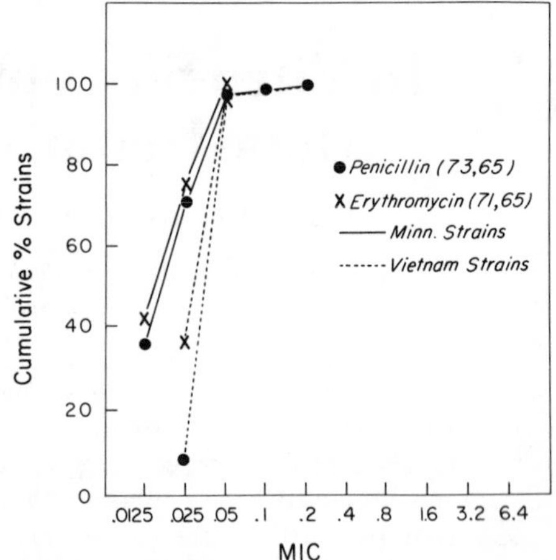

Fig. 1. *Minimal inhibitory concentration (MIC) of penicillin (units/ml) and erythromycin (µg/ml) for Minnesota and Vietnam streptococci of all groups. Numbers in parentheses indicate number of Minnesota and Vietnam strains tested.*

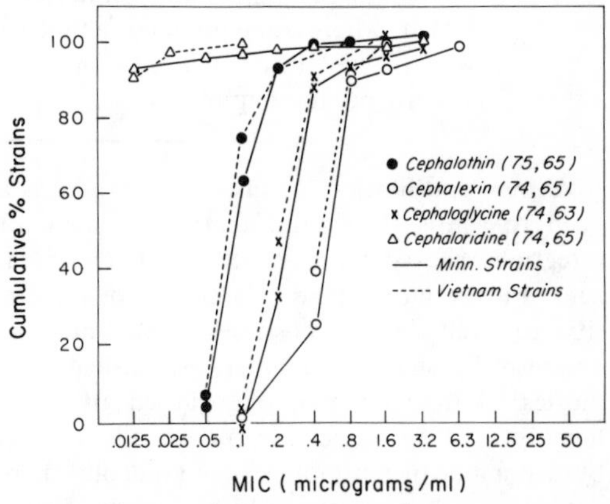

Fig. 2. *Minimal inhibitory concentration (MIC) of cephalosporins for Minnesota and Vietnam streptococci of all groups. Numbers in parentheses indicate number of Minnesota and Vietnam strains tested.*

ceptibility to all of the other antibiotics except tetracycline. The Vietnam strains showed much more resistance to this antibiotic than the Minnesota strains. A concentration of 12.5 µg/ml or higher was required for inhibition of 73% of the Vietnam strains, whereas the MIC for 94% of the U.S. strains was 1.6 µg or less per ml. This difference in resistance was not due to the smaller proportion of group A strains among the organisms from Vietnam, because the MIC for 81% of the group A Vietnam strains was 25 µg/ml or higher, whereas the MIC was that

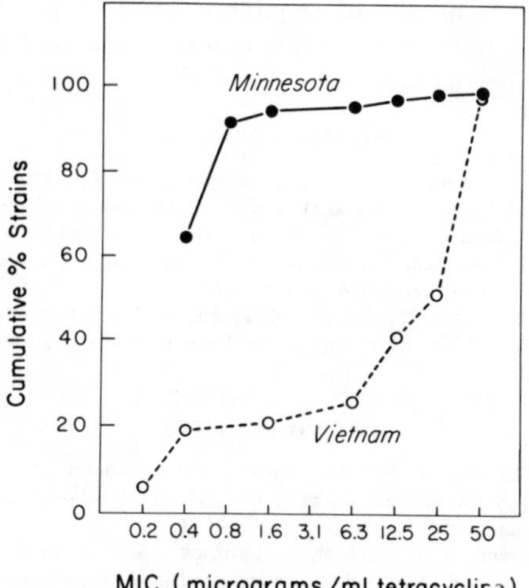

Fig. 3. *Minimal inhibitory concentration (MIC) of tetracycline for Minnesota (74 strains) and Vietnam (59 strains) streptococci of all groups.*

high for only 19% of the other groups. Neither was any specific serotype of group A streptococcus associated with the resistance to tetracycline.

Twenty-five of the Minnesota skin and wound organisms were inhibited by 0.1 μg of tetracycline per ml. For one strain, the MIC was 25 μg/ml, and for another, 50 μg/ml.

The susceptibility of streptococci to the four cephalosporin derivatives differed. The median MIC of cephaloridine was 10 to 20 times less than the median MIC of cephalothin, cephaloglycine, and cephalexin (Fig. 2).

The results obtained with tetracycline in agar-dilution studies and in the disc-diffusion test are compared in Fig. 4. Almost all of the Minnesota strains had zone diameters greater than 20 mm, whereas the zone diameters of the Vietnam strains ranged from 29 mm to no zone at all, with a preponderance of zones from 10 to 15 mm in diameter. Taken together, all of the streptococcal strains formed a continuous spectrum without a definite separation into a susceptible and a resistant group.

The zone sizes obtained with the other antibiotics for all of the strains are shown in Table 2. No regression curves could be calculated for these antibiotics because the organisms were a homogeneous group of susceptible strains.

DISCUSSION

Susceptibility testing is done less frequently with group A beta-hemolytic streptococci than with the other groups because it is usually assumed that the former group is uniformly susceptible to penicillin and erythromycin, the antibiotics commonly recommended for treatment. In fact, it was found that the beta-hemolytic streptococci tested in this study were similar in their in vitro susceptibility to penicillin, erythromycin, and the four cephalosporins.

Although increasing resistance of beta-

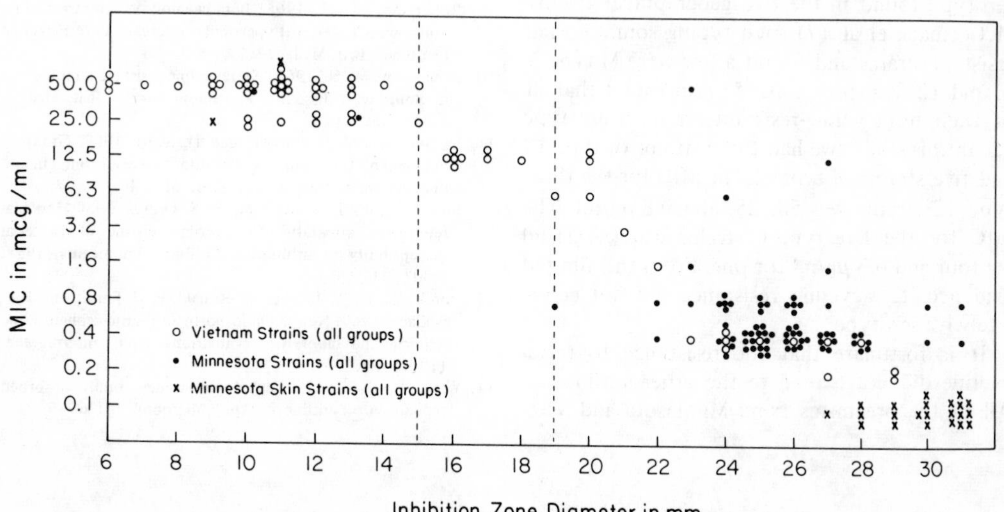

Fig. 4. *Comparison of disc and agar-dilution susceptibility results obtained with tetracycline with Minnesota and Vietnam streptococci of all groups.*

Table 2. *Inhibition zones obtained with seven antibiotics by use of the disc-diffusion technique with both Minnesota and Vietnam beta-hemolytic streptococci of all groups*

Antibiotic	Disc content	Highest MIC[a]	Zone size (range in mm)
Bacitracin	10 units	6.3 units	17–36
Cephalexin	30 μg	6.3 μg	20–38
Cephaloglycine....	30 μg	3.2 μg	22–39
Cephaloridine	30 μg	3.2 μg	30–54
Cephalothin	30 μg	3.2 μg	28–50
Erythromycin	15 μg	0.2 μg	23–44
Penicillin	10 units	0.4 units	27–48

[a] The largest amount (per milliliter) required to inhibit any of the strains when tested by the agar-dilution method.

hemolytic streptococci to tetracycline has been reported in Great Britain (9, 10) and the United States (5, 7), this did not appear to have occurred in the state of Minnesota. Since Robertson (9) reported that streptococci isolated from wounds tended to be more resistant to tetracycline than those isolated from the respiratory tract, it was thought that this might account for the differences between the Minnesota and Vietnam strains. However, the Minnesota skin and wound strains were as susceptible as those isolated from the respiratory tract.

It could be that the differences in serotypes account for the difference in susceptibility to tetracycline, because in no case was the same serotype found in the two geographical groups. McCormack et al. (7) tried typing some of their resistant strains and found a few were M-type 2, 6, and 12. Kuharic et al. (5) also found that 11 of their tetracycline-resistant strains were type 12. In this study, we had three strains of type 12 and five strains of type 6. The MIC for the three type 12 strains was 50, 25, and 0.8 μg/ml. The MIC for the five type 6 strains was 0.4 μg/ml for four and 6.3 μg/ml for one. From this limited evidence, tetracycline resistance did not correlate with serotype.

It is fortunate that the resistance to tetracycline did not extend to the other antibiotics. All of the organisms from Minnesota and Vietnam, from skin or respiratory tract, were very susceptible to penicillin, erythromycin, and the four cephalosporins.

ACKNOWLEDGMENTS

This investigation was under the sponsorship of the Commission on Streptococcal and Staphylococcal Diseases of the Armed Forces Epidemiological Board and of the U.S. Medical Research and Development Command under Research Contracts DADA 17-68-C-8040 and DADA 17-69-C-9124.

The technical assistance of Dwight R. Johnson, Margaret Ragan, Marilyn Klein, and Joyce Ryan is gratefully acknowledged.

LITERATURE CITED

1. Dadswell, J. V. 1967. Survey of the incidence of tetracycline-resistant haemolytic streptococci between 1958 and 1965. J. Clin. Pathol. **20**:641–642.
2. Frank, P. F., and M. L. Levinson. 1960. A laboratory manual of bacteriological and serological procedures used in the study of beta-hemolytic streptococcus infections, p. 13–20. Division of Bacteriology, Naval Medical Research Unit No. 4, U.S. Naval Training Center, Great Lakes, Ill.
3. Griffith, F. 1934. The serological classification of *Streptococcus pyogenes.* J. Hyg. **34**:542–584.
4. Johnson, W. D., J. M. Applestein, and D. Kaye. 1968. Cephaloglycin: clinical and laboratory experience with an orally administered cephalosporin. J. Amer. Med. Ass. **206**:2698–2702.
5. Kuharic, H. A., C. E. Roberts, Jr., and W. M. M. Kirby. 1960. Tetracycline resistance of streptococci. Arch. Intern. Med. **174**:1779–1782.
6. Lancefield, R. C. 1933. A serological differentiation of human and other groups of hemolytic streptococci. J. Exp. Med. **57**:571–595.
7. McCormack, R. C., D. Kaye, and E. W. Hook. 1962. Resistance of group A streptococci to tetracycline. N. Engl. J. Med. **267**:323–326.
8. Perkins, R. L., S. Saslaw, and J. Hackett. 1967. Cephaloridine and cephalothin: comparative *in vitro* evaluation. Amer. J. Med. Sci. **253**:293–299.
9. Robertson, M. H. 1965. Beta-haemolytic streptococci in South-west Essex, with particular reference to tetracycline resistance. Brit. Med. J. **2**:569–571.
10. Robertson, M. H. 1968. Tetracycline-resistant streptococci in South-west Essex: a continuing survey. Brit. Med. J. **3**:349–350.
11. Sanders, E., M. T. Foster, and D. Scott. 1968. Group A beta-hemolytic streptococci resistant to erythromycin and lincomycin. N. Engl. J. Med. **278**:538–540.
12. Steers, E., E. L. Foltz, and B. S. Graves. 1959. Inocula-replicating apparatus for routine testing of bacterial susceptibility to antibiotics. Antibiot. Chermother–1958. **9**:307–311.
13. Turck, M., D. W. Belcher, A. Ronald, R. H. Smith, and J. F. Wallace. 1967. New cephalosporin antibiotic-cephaloridine (clinical and laboratory evaluation). Arch. Intern. Med. **119**:50–59.
14. Wick, W. E. 1967. Cephalexin, a new orally absorbed cephalosporin antibiotic. Appl. Microbiol. **15**:765–769.

Antimicrobial Agents and Chemotherapy—1969

Antibiotic Susceptibility of *Klebsiella-Enterobacter* as Determined by a Single High-Concentration Disc Method

JAMES A. POUPARD, LINDA B. DEWEES, and HARRY E. MORTON

William Pepper Laboratory, Hospital of the University of Pennsylvania, Philadelphia, Pennsylvania 19104

In the present study, 509 strains of *Klebsiella* and *Enterobacter* isolated from clinical specimens were tested against 24 common antimicrobial agents by the single-disc method of Bauer et al. Ornithine decarboxylase and motility were used to differentiate between *Klebsiella* and *Enterobacter*. Strains of both organisms gave similar results with all drugs tested except cephalothin and cephaloridine. The susceptibilities of *Enterobacter* groups A and B were similar, but group C strains were more resistant. There was no correlation between the source of the strains and their susceptibility patterns. An effort is made to explain some of the discrepancies which exist in previously published reports. Critical tests are essential to differentiate *Klebsiella* and *Enterobacter*. Results with high-concentration antimicrobial discs and well-differentiated strains indicate that the susceptibility patterns are not adequate for taxonomic purposes.

The increased clinical importance of members of the *Klebsiella-Enterobacter-Serratia* division of the *Enterobacteriaceae* has been well documented in recent years. Several reports have indicated significant differences in the susceptibility patterns of *Klebsiella* and *Enterobacter* (2, 8, 9, 10), but there are many discrepancies among these reports. The purposes of this study were (i) to determine the susceptibility patterns of 509 strains of *Klebsiella-Enterobacter* to 24 common antimicrobial agents by use of the high-concentration disc method of Bauer et al. (1), (ii) to determine whether the susceptibility patterns are of taxonomic value to workers in a clinical laboratory, and (iii) to resolve some of the discrepancies which exist in reports on the drug susceptibility of these microorganisms.

MATERIALS AND METHODS

Microorganisms were collected over the period of January through August of 1969 from cultures isolated in the clinical microbiology laboratory of the Hospital of the University of Pennsylvania. Three isolated colonies were picked from a MacConkey agar plate, suspended in tryptose-phosphate broth, subcultured to a Heart Infusion Agar slant, and stored at 4 C. These stock cultures were tested to confirm classification as members of the *Klebsiella-Enterobacter-Serratia* division of the *Enterobacteriaceae* and to differentiate *Klebsiella* from *Enterobacter*. Further tests were performed to determine the groups of *Enterobacter* as A, B, or C, and the species of *Klebsiella*. All strains were tested for susceptibility to 24 antimicrobial agents.

Identification of *Klebsiella* and *Enterobacter* was based on the criteria of Edwards and Ewing (5): reactions on Triple Sugar Iron Agar, the indole, methyl red, Voges-Proskauer, citrate reactions, and fermentation of arabinose and sorbitol identified the *Klebsiella-Enterobacter* group; motility and ornithine decarboxylase differentiated *Klebsiella* from *Enterobacter;* lysine decarboxylase and rhamnose fermentation further identified *Enterobacter* as group A, B, or C. *Klebsiella* species were designated according to the biochemical reactions set forth by Cowan et al. (3). Strains not corresponding to the common *K. aerogenes* reactions were further tested for malonate utilization.

Antimicrobial susceptibility testing was performed according to the method of Bauer et al. (1) by use of high-concentration discs on Mueller-Hinton agar plates.

For the first 100 cultures, no significant distinguishing colony characteristics on MacConkey agar could be noted between *Klebsiella* and *Enterobacter*. Since consistently uniform results were obtained with the wet mounts and agar stab cultures for motility determination with the first 100 cultures, only agar stab cultures were employed thereafter unless there was a discrepancy between motility and ornithine results.

All 509 strains were tested against the following antimicrobial agents: sodium ampicillin, bacitracin, cephaloridine, cephalothin, chloramphenicol, colistin sulfate, erythromycin, kanamycin, lincomycin, methenamine mandelate, nalidixic acid, nitrofurantoin, sodium oxacillin, potassium penicillin G, polymyxin B, streptomycin, sulfadiazine, sulfamerazine, sulfamethoxypyridazine, sulfathiazole, sulfisoxazole, triple sulfa (trissulfapyrimidines), tetracycline, and vancomycin.

Minimal inhibitory concentrations (MIC) were determined by use of twofold serial dilutions of the drug in tryptose-phosphate broth. The seed cultures were prepared by diluting an overnight culture to 10^{-4} with tryptose-phosphate broth. The tests were incubated at 37 C and read after 18 hr.

RESULTS

A comparison of the susceptibility patterns of *Klebsiella*, *Enterobacter*, and the combined *Klebsiella-Enterobacter* group is shown in Table 1. Significant differences were noted with cephalothin and cephaloridine. Whereas 86 and 74% of the strains of *Klebsiella* were found to be susceptible to cephalothin and cephaloridine, respectively, only 15 and 13% of the strains of *Enterobacter* were susceptible to these two drugs. Most of the strains of *Klebsiella* were susceptible to colistin, methenamine mandelate, nalidixic acid, and polymyxin B, whereas most of the strains of *Enterobacter* were susceptible to chloramphenicol, colistin, kanamycin, and nalidixic acid. All strains of *Klebsiella* and *Enterobacter* were resistant to bacitracin, erythromycin, lincomycin, oxacillin, penicillin, and vancomycin. These strains were usually susceptible to the sulfa drugs, with the exception of sulfamerazine to which they were less susceptible.

Table 2 shows the susceptibility patterns of *Enterobacter* groups A, B, and C. Strains of *Enterobacter* C were resistant to more of the drugs tested than were strains of groups A and B. Both group A and B strains were predominantly susceptible to colistin, nitrofurantoin, polymyxin B, sulfisoxazole, and tetracycline; group C strains were predominantly resistant to these agents. Of the group A strains, 53% were susceptible to sulfamerazine, whereas only 24

Table 1. *Comparison of the susceptibility patterns of Klebsiella, Enterobacter, and the combined Klebsiella-Enterobacter group against 24 antimicrobial agents*

Antimicrobial agent	*Klebsiella* (367)[a]			*Enterobacter* (142)[a]			*Klebsiella-Enterobacter* (509)[a]		
	% S[b]	% R[b]	Pattern	% S	% R	Pattern	% S	% R	Pattern
Bacitracin, erythromycin, oxacillin, penicillin, lincomycin, vancomycin	0	100	R	0	100	R	0	100	R
Cephaloridine	74	20	S	13	85	R	57	38	S
Cephalothin	86	7	S	15	80	R	66	28	S
Ampicillin	7	90	R	14	82	R	9	88	R
Chloramphenicol	79	20	S	93	6	S	83	17	S
Colistin	97	2	S	90	10	S	95	4	S
Kanamycin	83	14	S	91	7	S	86	12	S
Methenamine mandelate	95	1	S	78	15	S	90	5	S
Nalidixic acid	93	5	S	95	4	S	94	5	S
Nitrofurantoin	90	3	S	82	8	S	87	4	S
Polymyxin B	99	1	S	89	11	S	97	3	S
Streptomycin	59	34	S	71	21	S	63	30	S
Sulfadiazine	44	36	S	62	19	S	49	31	S
Sulfamerazine	29	46	R	35	38	R	31	44	R
Sulfamethoxypyridazine	59	34	S	74	15	S	63	29	S
Sulfthiazole	62	32	S	81	11	S	67	26	S
Sulfisoxazole	68	29	S	86	9	S	73	23	S
Tetracycline	73	20	S	59	18	S	69	19	S
Triple sulfa	58	32	S	79	13	S	64	27	S

[a] Total number of strains tested.

[b] S = susceptible and R = resistant according to the diameter of the zone of inhibition (1); % S plus % R subtracted from 100 equals the percentage of strains of intermediate susceptibility.

Table 2. *Comparison of the susceptibility patterns of Enterobacter groups A, B, and C against 24 antimicrobial agents*

Antimicrobial agent	*Enterobacter* group A (45)[a]			*Enterobacter* group B (83)[a]			*Enterobacter* group C (14)[a]		
	% S[b]	% R[b]	Pattern	% S	% R	Pattern	% S	% R	Pattern
Bacitracin, erythromycin, oxacillin, penicillin, lincomycin, vancomycin	0	100	R	0	100	R	0	100	R
Cephaloridine	16	82	R	16	81	R	0	100	R
Cephalothin	9	91	R	22	69	R	0	100	R
Ampicillin	13	85	R	17	77	R	0	100	R
Chloramphenicol	98	2	S	92	7	S	86	14	S
Colistin	100	0	S	96	4	S	21	79	R
Kanamycin	91	7	S	93	7	S	79	21	S
Methenamine mandelate	64	29	S	87	8	S	71	7	S
Nalidixic acid	93	7	S	96	2	S	93	7	S
Nitrofurantoin	96	2	S	84	6	S	21	36	I
Polymyxin B	98	2	S	95	5	S	21	79	R
Streptomycin	73	16	S	71	17	S	79	21	S
Sulfadiazine	71	18	S	59	18	S	50	36	S
Sulfamerazine	53	25	S	24	46	R	36	43	R
Sulfamethoxypyridazine	76	9	S	77	15	S	50	36	S
Sulfathiazole	82	5	S	83	11	S	64	29	S
Sulfisoxazole	91	2	S	87	8	S	29	71	R
Tetracycline	62	2	S	63	17	S	14	71	R
Triple sulfa	87	11	S	80	11	S	57	36	S

[a] Total number of strains tested.
[b] S = susceptible and R = resistant according to the diameter of the zone of inhibition (1); % S plus % R subtracted from 100 equals the percentage of strains of intermediate (I) susceptibility.

and 36% of group B and C strains, respectively, were susceptible. More than 90% of group A and B strains of *Enterobacter* were susceptible to chloramphenicol, colistin, kanamycin, nalidixic acid, and polymyxin B. In addition, 90% of the group A strains were also susceptible to nitrofurantoin and sulfisoxazole. Nalidixic acid was the only drug to which 90% of the group C strains were susceptible.

Comparisons of *Klebsiella* and *Enterobacter* isolated from urine, respiratory-tract specimens, and other sources are shown in Tables 3 and 4. The antibiotic susceptibility of *Enterobacter* from the three sources showed similar patterns except for sulfamerazine. Strains from urine and the respiratory tract were predominantly resistant to sulfamerazine, but strains from other sources were predominantly susceptible. However, numerically, the differences between the three groups did not show a significant variation, partly because of the large number of strains which were intermediate between susceptible and resistant. Of the *Enterobacter* strains isolated from urine, 36% were resistant to sulfamerazine; 40% of the strains from the respiratory tract and 31% of the strains from all other sources were also resistant to sulfamerazine. *Klebsiella* cultures from comparable sources showed similar patterns of resistance except for sulfadiazine. Cultures from urine and other sources were predominantly susceptible, whereas those from the respiratory tract were predominantly resistant to sulfadiazine. Again, the numerical differences were not great.

Of the 509 isolates, 24 showed a discrepancy between results with ornithine and motility tests. Had these been classified as *Klebsiella* or *Enterobacter* with motility as the only differentiating criterion, 20 would have been designated *Klebsiella* and 4 would have been designated *Enterobacter*. (We called all 24 *Enterobacter* according to the specifications of Edwards and Ewing.) With the exception of susceptibility to cephalothin and cephaloridine, the susceptibility

Table 3. *Comparison of the susceptibility patterns of Enterobacter isolated from urine, respiratory tract, and other sources*

Antimicrobial agent	Urine (33)[a]			Respiratory (73)[a]			Other sources (36)[a]		
	% S[b]	% R[b]	Pattern	% S	% R	Pattern	% S	% R	Pattern
Bacitracin, erythromycin, oxacillin, penicillin, lincomycin, vancomycin	0	100	R	0	100	R	0	100	R
Cephaloridine	12	82	R	12	86	R	17	81	R
Cephalothin	18	76	R	14	79	R	6	92	R
Ampicillin	6	94	R	19	74	R	8	89	R
Chloramphenicol	94	6	S	93	6	S	92	8	S
Colistin	85	15	S	90	10	S	95	5	S
Kanamycin	88	12	S	99	1	S	78	19	S
Methenamine mandelate	79	12	S	81	14	S	72	20	S
Nalidixic acid	94	3	S	96	4	S	97	3	S
Nitrofurantoin	76	12	S	85	4	S	83	8	S
Polymyxin B	85	15	S	89	11	S	95	5	S
Streptomycin	70	21	S	78	15	S	58	22	S
Sulfadiazine	61	18	S	64	19	S	55	22	S
Sulfamerazine	33	36	R	33	40	R	42	31	S
Sulfamethoxypyridazine	73	12	S	78	15	S	69	17	S
Sulfathiazole	79	12	S	84	8	S	75	14	S
Sulfisoxazole	85	9	S	86	6	S	86	14	S
Tetracycline	58	21	S	56	18	S	64	14	S
Triple sulfa	76	18	S	82	11	S	75	14	S

[a] Total number of strains tested.
[b] S = susceptible and R = resistant according to the diameter of the zone of inhibition (1); % S plus % R subtracted from 100 equals the percentage of strains of intermediate susceptibility.

patterns of these strains did not differ from the patterns of *Klebsiella* or *Enterobacter.* Whereas the predominant pattern for *Klebsiella* is susceptibility to cephalothin and cephaloridine and the predominant pattern for *Enterobacter* is resistance to these drugs, the 24 strains in question were susceptible in nearly as many cases as they were resistant. Regardless of genus, their reactions were insignificant in affecting the overall susceptibility pattern of *Klebsiella* or *Enterobacter.*

Thirty-one of those *Klebsiella* strains not fitting the biochemical reactions for the species *K. aerogenes* [according to Cowan et al. (3)] were identified as *K. pneumoniae* (22 strains), *K. rhinoscleromatis* (3 strains), *K. ozaenae* (2 strains), *K. edwardsii* var. *edwardsii* (3 strains), or *K. edwardsii* var. *atlantsii* (1 strain). These, plus 12 unidentified strains, were found to have susceptibility patterns identical to those of the 324 *K. aerogenes* strains.

In the course of this study, 30 *Klebsiella* strains were tested for susceptibility by the disc method in conjunction with a standard broth-dilution method to determine the 18-hr MIC of cephalothin. An MIC of 25 μg or less per ml and a zone of inhibition of at least 18 mm were interpreted as susceptibility to cephalothin. A zone of inhibition 15 to 17 mm in diameter was interpreted as intermediate between susceptibility and resistance. Of the 30 strains, 25 yielded similar results by both methods. Of the five strains for which the MIC was 50 μg or more per ml, two were interpreted as susceptibile and three as intermediate by the disc method.

DISCUSSION

Of the 24 drugs tested, cephalothin and cephaloridine were the only ones to which there were significant differences in susceptibility between *Klebsiella* and *Enterobacter.* The possible use of the cephalosporin antibiotics for taxonomic purposes has been presented in several papers. Benner (2), using a broth-dilution test for determining the MIC, showed a distinct separation between *Klebsiella* and *Enterobacter*

Table 4. *Comparison of the susceptibility patterns of Klebsiella isolated from urine, respiratory tract, and other sources*

Antimicrobial agent	Urine (107)[a]			Respiratory (110)[a]			Other sources (90)[a]		
	% S[b]	% R[b]	Pattern	% S	% R	Pattern	% S	% R	Pattern
Bacitracin, erythromycin, oxacillin, penicillin, lincomycin, vancomycin	0	100	R	0	100	R	0	100	R
Cephaloridine	77	14	S	72	26	S	74	19	S
Cephalothin	89	5	S	85	9	S	84	8	S
Ampicillin	8	88	R	7	91	R	3	92	R
Chloramphenicol	76	23	S	78	22	S	81	18	S
Colistin	96	2	S	98	2	S	97	3	S
Kanamycin	84	12	S	83	17	S	84	13	S
Methenamine mandelate	96	0	S	94	4	S	96	0	S
Nalidixic acid	89	8	S	96	3	S	93	2	S
Nitrofurantoin	91	3	S	88	2	S	88	4	S
Polymyxin B	99	1	S	100	0	S	99	1	S
Streptomycin	61	33	S	59	34	S	58	34	S
Sulfadiazine	47	35	S	38	43	R	47	31	S
Sulfamerazine	28	46	R	31	50	R	29	41	R
Sulfamethoxypyridazine	61	32	S	56	40	S	61	30	S
Sulfathiazole	60	32	S	59	36	S	63	27	S
Sulfisoxazole	70	28	S	64	33	S	70	26	S
Tetracycline	74	20	S	76	17	S	68	25	S
Triple sulfa	59	31	S	55	36	S	61	26	S

[a] Total number of strains tested.

[b] S = susceptible and R = resistant according to the diameter of the zone of inhibition (1); % S plus % R subtracted from 100 equals the percentage of strains of intermediate susceptibility.

on the basis of susceptibility to these drugs, which suggested practical as well as taxonomic value. Lerner (8), also using a broth-dilution technique, and Ramirez (9), using an agar-diffusion method, noted the value of these drugs for differentiating *Klebsiella* and *Enterobacter.* Edmondson and Sanford (4), using an agar-dilution method, suggested that susceptibility to cephalothin was not as good as lack of motility for differentiating *Klebsiella* from *Enterobacter.* Benner (2) and others have noted the ability of *Klebsiella* to develop resistance to the cephalosporins. Furthermore, according to the results of Washington et al. (13), discrepancies exist between the broth-dilution and the agar-diffusion methods of testing *Klebsiella* and *Enterobacter* against cephalothin.

These results, in conjunction with the present study, indicate that when using the high-concentration disc method of susceptibility testing at least 14 to 20% error will be encountered if cephalothin is used to differentiate between the two genera, with the error increasing as more resistant strains become established. Therefore, motility and ornithine decarboxylase seem to be the most accurate and practical means of differentiating cultures of the two genera, the susceptibility pattern being useful to only a limited extent.

Our results indicate resistance of both *Klebsiella* and *Enterobacter* to bacitracin, erythromycin, lincomycin, oxacillin, penicillin G, and vancomycin. These findings disagree with those of Lerner (8). Using a broth MIC technique, he found *Klebsiella* to be susceptible to the amount of penicillin G obtained in urine and serum.

Both *Klebsiella* and *Enterobacter* appear to be less susceptible to sulfamerazine than to the other sulfa drugs tested.

Results of this study indicate that *Enterobacter* group C is more resistant to the drugs tested than groups A or B. However, this may be due to the proportionately smaller number of group C strains as compared with the other groups. No definite taxonomic value can be attributed to the different patterns.

A comparison of the susceptibility patterns of *Klebsiella* and *Enterobacter* isolated from the urinary and respiratory tracts and from other areas, by use of this method, did not show any significant variation attributable to the source. These observations are comparable to those of Sanford (11). Some variation exists in the susceptibility pattern of the sulfa drugs tested, but the differences in the percentage are not very significant, possibly because of the large number of isolates with intermediate susceptibility. Herrell et al. (7), using an agar-dilution technique, found *Klebsiella* isolated from the urinary tract to be significantly less susceptible to cephalothin than are those organisms from other sources (41% of the strains from urine as compared to 70% of the strains from other sources). Our studies did not detect these differences (84% of strains from urine and 87% of strains from other sources were susceptible). Eickhoff et al. (6), using the inocula-replicating method of Steers, noted that *Klebsiella* isolated from the respiratory tract was more susceptible to cephalothin, chloramphenicol, tetracycline, and particularly streptomycin than strains isolated from other sources. These differences were not detected to any significant extent in this study.

No significant differences in the susceptibility patterns of the species of *Klebsiella* were detected in this study. However, some species were represented by only a few strains and therefore no definite conclusion can be drawn.

The MIC in conjunction with disc susceptibility tests of cephalothin against *Klebsiella* indicated a difference in 17% of the strains tested. These findings are in agreement with those of Washington et al. (13). It should be kept in mind that the cephalosporins, which are the only drugs for which the above technique produces significantly different results in their reaction with *Klebsiella* and *Enterobacter*, have been reported by Turck et al. (12) and Washington et al. (13) to have the least correlation between disc and dilution methods.

There does not appear to be any specific taxonomic value to the susceptibility patterns of *Klebsiella* and *Enterobacter*. Motility and ornithine decarboxylase are well suited for this purpose. There are probably many reasons for the discrepancies that exist in some of the reports of the susceptibility of these two organisms. However, it is of interest to note that our results in general agree with those reports in which a disc- or agar-diffusion method was used, and in which a comparatively large number of isolates was used, such as the report of Russell (10). Differences in the clinical use of various antibiotics among institutions could account for some discrepancies; however, this would not account for high percentages of opposite results. Methodology and too few isolates seem to be the prime obstacle in comparing reports of various workers.

LITERATURE CITED

1. Bauer, A. W., W. M. M. Kirby, J. C. Sherris, and M. Turck. 1966. Antibiotic susceptibility testing by a standardized single disk method. Amer. J. Clin. Pathol. **43**:493–496.
2. Benner, E. J., J. S. Micklewait, J. L. Brodie, and W. M. M. Kirby. 1965. Natural and acquired resistance of *Klebsiella-Aerobacter* to cephalothin and cephaloridine. Proc. Soc. Exp. Biol. Med. **119**:536–543.
3. Cowan, S. T., K. J. Steel, C. Shaw, and J. P. Duguid. 1960. A classification of the *Klebsiella* group. J. Gen. Microbiol. **23**:601–612.
4. Edmondson, E. B., and J. P. Sanford. 1967. The *Klebsiella-Enterobacter (Aerobacter)-Serratia* group. A clinical and bacteriological evaluation. Medicine **46**:323–340.
5. Edwards, P. R., and W. H. Ewing. 1962. Identification of Enterobacteriacae. Burgess Publishing Co., Minneapolis, Minn.
6. Eickhoff, T. C., B. W. Steinhauer, and M. Finland. 1966. The *Klebsiella-Enterobacter-Serratia* division; biochemical and serologic characteristics and susceptibility to antibiotics. Ann. Intern. Med. **65**:1163–1179.
7. Herrell, W. E., A. Balows, and J. Becker. 1964. Antibiotic susceptibility studies on the *Klebsiella* group. Arch. Intern. Med. **114**:329–332.
8. Lerner, P. I., and L. Weinstein. 1967. The differentiation of *Klebsiella* from *Aerobacter* species by sensitivity to cephalothins and penicillins. Amer. J. Med. Sci. **254**:63–68.
9. Ramirez, M. J. 1968. Differentiation of *Klebsiella-Enterobacter (Aerobacter)-Serratia* by biochemical tests and antibiotic susceptibility. Appl. Microbiol. **16**:1548–1550.
10. Russell, J. P. 1968. Antibiotic sensitivity of *Klebsiella-Enterobacter*. Amer. J. Clin. Pathol. **51**:384–389.
11. Sanford, J. P. 1969. Sensitivity tests of *Klebsiella, Enterobacter,* and *Serratia*. J. Infec. Dis. **119**:388–390.
12. Turck, M., R. I. Lindemeyer, and R. G. Petersdorf. 1963. Comparison of single-disk and tube-dilution techniques in determining antibiotic sensitivities of gram-negative pathogens. Ann. Int. Med. **58**:56–65.
13. Washington, J. A., II, P. Yu, and W. J. Martin. 1969. Biochemical and clinical characteristics and antibiotic susceptibility of atypical *Enterobacter cloacae*. Minn. Med. **17**:843–845.

Antimicrobial Agents and Chemotherapy—1969

Pyocin Antibiosis in Chick Embryos

THOMAS J. BIRD and HANS G. GRIEBLE

Infectious Disease Research Laboratory and Section of Infectious Diseases and Immunology, Veterans Administration Hospital, Hines, Illinois 60141

Quantitative pyocin susceptibility tests were used to select a potent pyocin producer with highly specific activity against a susceptible strain of *Pseudomonas aeruginosa.* The pyocin thus chosen was used for in vivo neutralization tests. The *Pseudomonas* strain was lethal for chick embryos, even with an inoculum of only 10 to 30 viable organisms. A single dose of pyocin increased the survival of chick embryos from 3% (13 of 386) in the untreated to 46% (292 of 623) in the treated groups. Crude pyocin was toxic for 14% of 128 chick embryos receiving pyocin alone. Nutrient broth caused death of 6% of 106 chick embryos. In a series of 20 chick embryos per group, absorption of pyocin with heat-killed susceptible *Pseudomonas* cells, or challenge with a nonsusceptible *Pseudomonas* strain, gave no survivors; pyocin activity was lost on heating to 80 C and was markedly reduced by trypsin. Antibacterial activity of pyocin was not affected by ribonuclease or deoxyribonuclease treatment. The active substance was concentrated approximately 1,000 times. It could be partially purified by ultrafiltration and by ultracentrifugation followed by gel filtration in Sephadex G-200. It was estimated to be of high molecular weight (>200,000). The chromatographed fraction was biuret-reactive, and absorption spectrum analysis revealed a 280 to 260 nm ratio of 0.73.

Antibiotic activity in cultures of *Pseudomonas aeruginosa* was first described in 1889 by Bouchard (1). Subsequently, many papers described antibiotic preparations from *P. aeruginosa* in which pyocyanin or pyocyanase was considered to be the active principle. Schoental (18) in 1941 and Hays and co-workers (8) in 1945 reported extensive studies on antibiotic substances originating from *P. aeruginosa.*

Jacob discovered a new antibacterial principle produced by a strain of *Pseudomonas* and named it pyocin (12). Extensive studies on pyocins and other bacteriocins have since been recorded and were recently reviewed (2, 7, 15, 17). Pyocin has been successfully employed as an epidemiological tool for typing of hospital isolates; a battery of indicator strains is used for differentiation of the highly specific pyocins of the test strains (6; Grieble et al., N. Engl. J. Med. **282**:531–535, 1970).

The present study was designed to explore the potential use of pyocins as therapeutic bactericidal anti-*Pseudomonas* agents. Crucial to such use of pyocins is, of course, the relative absence of toxicity. Pilot studies on the toxic effect of pyocin were therefore made part of this investigation.

As a prelude to this study, a rapid quantitative pyocin susceptibility test was developed (Bird and Grieble, *unpublished results*) to screen clinical isolates of *Pseudomonas* for strains best suited to serve as infective challenge or as a source of pyocin in chick embryo neutralization experiments.

MATERIALS AND METHODS

Pyocin production and assay. Clinical isolates were grown in Nutrient Broth, and pyocin activity was assayed on Nutrient Agar. One-liter quantities of Nutrient Broth were inoculated with 1.0 ml of an overnight culture of *P. aeruginosa* strain #2 (Hines isolate) and incubated for 18 to 48 hr at 37 C. This culture was shaken with 100 ml of chloroform at room temperature (24 to 27 C) for 1 hr both to kill bacteria and to remove pyocyanin. After centrifugation at 600 × *g*, supernatant material was dialyzed for 24 hr against deionized water at 4 C and then lyophilized. The dried material was dissolved in 50 ml of deionized water. This crude preparation is hence referred to as pyocin and contained 3,000 units per ml. Further purification was sought by filtration (0.45 nm, Millipore Corp., Bedford, Mass.) and ultrafiltration (XM-100, Amicon Corp., Lexington, Mass.). Gel filtration (Sephadex G-200, Pharmacia Fine Chemicals, Inc., Piscataway, N.J.) was performed in a 2.5 × 35 cm column with the use of upward flow and a 0.1 M tris(hydroxyethyl)aminomethane (Tris)-hydrochloride, 1.0 M NaCl buffer (*p*H 8.0) for elution. Absorbancy of eluates was recorded at 260 and 280 nm in a Beckman model DUR spectrophotometer. Protein was estimated by the biuret method (20), with crystalline bovine albumin (Armour Pharmaceutical Co., Chicago, Ill.) as a standard.

Pyocin activity was assayed at all stages by a drop plate method (9) and was expressed in units, i.e., the reciprocal of the highest dilution showing a clear zone of inhibition.

Pyocin inactivation. Pyocin in Nutrient Broth, *p*H 7.0, was heated in a water bath for 1 hr at 40, 60, 80, and 100 C; activity was assayed as described above and also by plate count for survivors after exposure to pyocin in broth cultures (16). The pyocin-susceptible challenge strain (#21 Hines isolate) was heat-killed at 60 C for 1 hr for use in absorption experiments. Approximately 10^{10} organisms were added to 1 ml of pyocin (3,000 units) and incubated at room temperature for 1 hr. The mixture was stirred continuously. The bacteria were then removed by centrifugation, and the supernatant fluid was analyzed for residual pyocin activity.

Enzyme treatment with 1.0% trypsin (1:250, Difco), deoxyribonuclease, and ribonuclease (Nutritional Biochemicals Corp., Cleveland, Ohio) was performed by methods described by other investigators (14). Incubation was for 1 hr at 37 C. The activity of the pyocin after this treatment was assayed as described above.

In vivo neutralization. Viability of 8- to 10-day-old chick embryos was determined by candling. Approximately 10 to 30 organisms or 0.1 ml of a 10^{-5} dilution of a 2-hr broth culture of *P. aeruginosa* was inoculated into the allantoic cavity. This was immediately followed by injection of 0.1 ml of pyocin dilution (150 units) by the same route. Controls received pyocin alone or sterile broth. Deaths due to pyocin alone prompted dilution of the crude preparation; a 1:2 dilution of crude pyocin (3,000 units/ml) in Nutrient Broth was found to be less toxic and therefore was used throughout. Plate counts were always made to monitor the size of the inoculum. For convenience, 17, 24, and 48 hr were chosen for evaluation of survival.

RESULTS

Death of embryos was discernible as early as 12 hr after infective challenge, even with a dose of only 10 viable organisms. Protection by pyocin was evidenced by a typical experiment in which *P. aeruginosa* killed all of 10 challenged eggs and pyocin protected half of 20. Pyocin alone, and Nutrient Broth, allowed survival of six of eight and all of six of the embryos, respectively. (The odd number of eggs in the various groups was necessitated by the limited number of chick embryos available.)

On candling, eggs killed by *P. aeruginosa* showed floating engorged blood vessels with an abnormal distribution and also gross hemorrhagic lesions. Microscopic sections on representative embryos did not show the characteristic lesions described in *Pseudomonas*-infected humans and experimental animals. They showed, however, conspicuous congestion of blood vessels and hemorrhages in the kidney. Pyocin-protected embryos showed only minor inflammatory changes.

The sum of all experiments revealed that survival at 17 hr was increased from 3% in those receiving *Pseudomonas* alone to 55% in those embryos receiving a single dose of pyocin (Table 1). Pyocin was slightly toxic, producing a mortality of 11%, whereas Nutrient Broth, or trauma from injection alone, caused 6% mortality at both 17 and 24 hr.

Pyocin inactivated by various treatments was examined for protective effect by use of groups of 20 *Pseudomonas*-challenged chick embryos for each experiment. Heating at 40 and 60 C had no influence on pyocin activity, whereas heating to 80 C abolished all protective effect. Pyocin activity was absorbed by heat-killed strain #21 because none of the 20 challenged chick embryos was protected. This suggests specific receptor sites which removed pyocin from the mixture. Trypsin treatment of pyocin reduced its protective effect, since only 3 of 20 chick embryos survived. When strain #2, the pyocin producer in these experiments, was tested against its own pyocin, all of 20 chick embryos were dead at 17 hr. Loss of pyocin activity due to heating, absorption, and trypsinization was

Table 1. *Summary of pyocin antibiosis experiments*

Inoculum	No. of eggs in group	Survivors (%)	
		17 hr	⩾24 hr
P. aeruginosa #21[a]	386	3	3
P. aeruginosa #21 + pyocin #2[b]	623	55	46
Pyocin #2[b]	128	89	86
Nutrient Broth	106	94	94

[a] Challenge = 10 to 30 organisms in 0.1 ml.
[b] Pyocin 1:2 dilution containing 150 units in 0.1 ml.

confirmed by in vitro experiments. Deoxyribonuclease and ribonuclease treatment had no effect on the specific activity of pyocin as tested by in vitro assay.

Crude pyocin was passed through a 0.45-nm filter and was retained by an XM-100 ultrafiltration membrane. Crude pyocin was centrifuged at 41,000 rev/min for 1 hr (model B-60, A-211 head, International Equipment Co., Needham Heights, Mass.). Activity was recovered in the pellet. The resuspended sediment was fractionated by gel filtration. A 90-mg amount of biuret-reactive material was applied to the column in 10 ml of Tris buffer. Two peaks were eluted. Absorption of pools at 280 and 260 nm was as follows: fraction I, 0.42:0.57; fraction II, 1.09:1.15. Of the protein recovered, 10% was in the first and 90% in the second eluate. Pyocin activity was recovered exclusively in the first, sharply delineated fraction, as judged by in vitro assays. This fraction, concentrated 10 times by negative pressure dialysis, was also tested in neutralization experiments. Forty per cent of embryos receiving 0.1 ml of a 1:2 dilution survived *Pseudomonas* challenge. Survival dropped to 20% at a 1:4 dilution and to 0% at a 1:16 dilution. This partially purified material was much less stable than crude material; its activity declined sharply during 24 hr at 4 C. This lability of purified material agrees with the reports of others (10).

DISCUSSION

Although some pyocins can be induced by exposure to ultraviolet light or mitomycin C, we chose to work with a noninduced system. It is possible that this restriction contributed to the rather low toxicity observed in chick embryos. Other investigators have reported lack of toxicity with purified pyocins in rabbits and mice (9, 10). The estimate of toxicity in eggs is complicated by the fact that chick embryos protected by pyocin received two injections, doubling the possibility of death due to trauma of injection. This would explain the apparent increase of toxic effect when multiple doses of pyocin were administered to challenged eggs. When two injections of sterile broth alone were made, the percentage of deaths doubled. If one subtracts the estimated 12% of deaths from trauma, mortality due to pyocin alone would be decreased to 2%. Improved performance of pyocin in *Pseudomonas*-infected chick embryos could be expected if death from trauma per se were eliminated.

Higerd and co-workers achieved better yield of pyocin by the use of a medium richer than Nutrient Broth (9). Such a medium increased the yield of pyocin #2. However, production of pyocyanin was also increased and created some difficulty in chloroform extraction.

Investigations of the in vivo activity of bacteriocins and their possible role in pathogenicity and ecology have been few. One study concluded that colicin producers have a selective advantage in replacing nonproducers in the bladder (5). Others have reported that endotoxin interferes with the activity of colicin (3). Braude and Siemienski reported bactericidal activity of colicin in blood (4). Kelstrup and Gibbons (13) found that proteases in the oral cavity and the intestinal contents inactivated colicins. Gnotobiotic mice colonized with colicin-susceptible or colicin-resistant strains showed no appreciable difference in predominance after an appropriate colicin producer had been introduced. Further, both series of animals had the same percentage recovery of the colicin producer.

It is reasonable to ascribe partial inactivation of pyocin by trypsin to a proteolytic effect. An alternative explanation is that trypsin may have been carried over in quantity sufficient to act on the receptor sites of the susceptible bacteria. No experiments were conducted to differentiate these two possible mechanisms of action. The effect of trypsin and of trypsinized pyocin was not determined in this series of experiments.

The active material purified from crude pyocin by ultracentrifugation, gel filtration, and ultrafiltration was biuret-reactive, indicating the proteinaceous nature of the macromolecular pyocin. Definite proof of this awaits complete purification and further chemical analysis of the active substance. Absorption spectrum analysis of chromatographic fractions I and II revealed 280 to 260 nm ratios of 0.73 and 0.94, respectively. Estimates from these data, according to Warburg and Christian (19), indicate a nucleic acid content of 9% for fraction I and 4% for fraction II.

Preliminary attempts at partial purification of pyocin from the crude dialyzed preparation showed it to be sedimentable between 100,000 and 150,000 × *g*. This indicates a molecular size of >200,000. This estimate was confirmed by the fact that the active substance was not retained by Sephadex G-200 gel filtration. Differential ultrafiltration also pointed towards a molecular size of the active material in excess of 100,000.

Multiple types of pyocin were shown by others to originate in a single strain of *P. aeruginosa* (11). The results on neutralization of *Pseudomonas* in chick embryos by crude pyocin, reported here, do not rule out the participation of more than one pyocin. All of the in vivo and in vitro effects of purified high molecular weight protein were comparable, however, to the activity of the nonfractionated dialyzed crude pyocin preparation. Cell-bound pyocins were removed with the organisms, and induction of pyocin(s) was purposely avoided.

ACKNOWLEDGMENTS

We thank A. G. Hall, J. T. Hickerson and F. R. Colton for their expert assistance.

LITERATURE CITED

1. Bouchard, C. 1889. Influence qu'exerce sur la maladie charbonneuse l'inoculation du *bacille pyocyanique.* Compt. Rend. **108**:713–714.
2. Bradley, D. E. 1967. Ultrastructure of bacteriophages and bacteriocins. Bacteriol. Rev. **31**:230–314.
3. Branche, W. C., Jr., W. M. Young, H. G. Robinet, and E. D. Massey. 1963. Effect of colicine production on *Escherichia coli* in the normal human intestine. Proc. Soc. Exp. Biol. Med. **114**:198–201.
4. Braude, A. J., and J. S. Siemienski. 1965. The influence of bacteriocins on resistance to infection by gram-negative bacteria. I. The effect of colicin on bactericidal power of blood. J. Clin. Invest. **44**:849–859.
5. Braude, A. J., and J. S. Siemienski. 1968. The influence of bacteriocins on resistance to infection by gram-negative bacteria. II. Colicin action, transfer of colicinogency, and transfer of antibiotic resistance in urinary infections. J. Clin. Invest. **47**:1763–1773.
6. Gillies, R. R., and J. R. W. Govan. 1966. Typing of *Pseudomonas pyocyanea* by pyocine production. J. Pathol. Bacteriol. **91**:339–345.
7. Hamon, Y., M. Véron, and Y. Péron. 1961. Contribution a l'étude des propriétés lysogènes at bactériocinogènes dans le genre Pseudomonas. Ann. Inst. Pasteur (Paris) **101**:738–753.
8. Hays, E. E., I. C. Wells, P. A. Katzman, C. K. Cain, F. A. Jacobs, S. A. Thayer, E. A. Doisy, W. L. Gaby, E. C. Roberts, R. D. Muir, C. J. Carroll, L. R. Jones, and N. J. Wade. 1945. Antibiotic substances produced by *Pseudomonas aeruginosa.* J. Biol. Chem. **159**:725–750.
9. Higerd, T. B., C. A. Baechler, and R. S. Berk. 1967. In vitro and in vivo characterization of pyocin. J. Bacteriol. **93**:1976–1986.
10. Higerd, T. B., C. A. Baechler, and R. S. Berk. 1969. Morphological studies on relaxed and concentrated forms of purified pyocin particles. J. Bacteriol. **98**:1378–1389.
11. Homma, J. Y. and N. Suzuki. 1966. The protein moiety of the endotoxin of *Pseudomonas aeruginosa.* Ann. N.Y. Acad. Sci. Article 2, **133**:508–526.
12. Jacob, F. 1954. Biosynthese induit et mode d'action d'une pyocine antibiotique de *Pseudomonas pyocyanea.* Ann. Inst. Pasteur (Paris) **86**:149–160.
13. Kelstrup, J., and R. J. Gibbons. 1969. Inactivation of bacteriocins in the intestinal canal and oral cavity. J. Bacteriol. **99**:888–890.
14. Lin, T. H., and R. F. Maes. 1967. Methods of degrading nucleic acids and separating the components, p. 547–606. *In* K. Maramorosch and H. Koprowski (ed.), Methods in virology, vol. 2. Academic Press Inc., New York.
15. Nomura, M. 1967. Colicins and related bacteriocins. Ann. Rev. Microbiol. **21**:257–284.
16. Ozeki, H. 1968. Methods for the study of colicine and colicinogeny, p. 565–592. *In* K. Maramorosch and H. Koprowski (ed.), Methods in virology, vol. 4. Academic Press Inc., New York.
17. Reeves, P. 1965. The bacteriocins. Bacteriol. Rev. **29**:24–45.
18. Schoental, R. 1941. The nature of the antibacterial agents present in *Pseudomonas pyocyanea* cultures. Brit. J. Exp. Pathol. **22**:137–147.
19. Warburg, O., and W. Christian. 1941. Isolierung and Krystallisation des Gärungsferments Enolase. Biochem. Z. **310**:384–421.
20. Weichselbaum, T. E. 1946. Accurate and rapid method for determination of proteins in small amounts of blood serum and plasma. Amer. J. Clin. Pathol., Tech. Sect. **10**:40–49.

Antimicrobial Agents and Chemotherapy—1969

Survival of *Mima polymorpha* in the Liver and Spleen of Neonatally Thymectomized, Nonwasted Mice

RICHARD V. McCLOSKEY

The University of Texas Medical School at San Antonio, San Antonio, Texas 78229

Reticuloendothelial function, as reflected by the bactericidal capacity of the liver and spleen, was examined after an intravenous injection of viable or radioiodinated *M. polymorpha* (ATCC 14291) cells into neonatally thymectomized or neonatally sham-thymectomized HA/ICR conventionally reared mice. During the initial 4 hr after infection, fewer viable colony-forming units of *M. polymorpha* survived in the liver and spleen of thymectomized mice than in the same organs of control mice. The numbers of viable organisms surviving in the blood of thymectomized or control mice were not significantly different. Physical deposition of bacteria, as estimated by concentration of radioiodinated *M. polymorpha,* was similarly not significantly different. Therefore, the liver and spleen from thymectomized mice demonstrate increased killing of intravenously injected *M. polymorpha* in comparison with these organs in sham-operated animals. Chronic reticuloendothelial stimulation from the repeated infections thought to produce wasting syndrome is not an adequate explanation for these observations, because the pathophysiological characteristics of the wasting syndrome were not apparent in the mice when these experiments were performed.

There is a higher incidence of infection in neonatally thymectomized mice and rats than in sham-operated mice and rats (6). The wasting syndrome (post-thymectomy syndrome) associated with weight loss, lymphocytopenia, proliferation of the reticuloendothelial cellular elements, anemia, periorbital edema, diarrhea, and death is precipitated by infections diseases (4). When germ-free mice are removed to a conventional environment, the wasting syndrome will appear only in the thymectomized mice, not in control mice (11). Reticuloendothelial functional hyperactivity, which does occur after neonatal thymectomy, has been directly correlated with the severity of the wasting syndrome (5, 6, 8). The mechanism for reticuloendothelial hyperactivity is presumably chronic stimulation of the reticuloendothelial system by the frequent infections occurring in the thymectomized mouse (1).

In studies reported here, clearance (defined hereafter as the process by which intravenously deposited bacteria are killed in a given organ) was examined before the wasting syndrome developed to determine whether an altered capacity for bacterial clearance following thymectomy was a factor in promoting a state of heightened susceptibility to bacterial infections. The model, thought to represent opportunistic infection, uses *M. polymorpha,* which reliably infects the mice used in this study but does not produce morbidity or mortality.

MATERIALS AND METHODS

Mice. Neonatal HA/ICR mice were thymectomized by the method of Sjodin et al. within 12 hr after birth (9). Each litter was reduced to 10 mice. Thymectomized and sham-thymectomized mice were reared as litter mates under conventional conditions until 1 month of age. Completeness of thymectomy was established by inspection. Those animals which were not totally thymectomized were discarded.

Determination of viable colony-forming units in liver and spleen. Bacteria were grown in tryptic soy broth (Difco) for 18 hr at 37 C with constant agitation. Each mouse received an intravenous injection of 10^6 viable organisms contained in 0.1 ml of tryptic soy broth. The inoculum was standardized to contain 10^7 organisms/ml by the method of Kurokawa et al. (3). At 2 and 4 hr after intravenous injection, mice were exsanguinated. The liver and spleen were removed aseptically, weighed, and homogenized in *p*H 7.0 phosphate-buffered saline. A portion of the homogenate was mixed with 1.5% agar in Nutrient Broth (Difco). Duplicate plates were prepared from each homogenate. The numbers of colonies appearing after 48 hr of incubation at 37 C were counted by two independent observers. The results were expressed as numbers of colony-forming units per gram (wet weight) of organ. Blood obtained 2 and 4 hr after inoculation was diluted in nutrient agar. The numbers of colony-forming units per gram of blood were determined for each experimental animal (for thymectomized mice, $n = 71$; for control mice, $n = 65$).

Determination of distribution of radioiodinated M. polymorpha in liver and spleen. A culture preparation of *M. polymorpha* was labeled with $Na^{131}I$ (Abbot Laboratories, North Chicago, Ill.) according to a modification of the method described by Williams and Chase (10). At a concentration of 2.8×10^9 bacteria/ml, the radioactivity of the inoculum was 6×10^6 counts per min per ml. Each mouse received 6×10^7 organisms intravenously. The liver and spleen were removed 2 and 4 hr after inoculation and homogenized; a sample was assayed in a gamma spectrometer. Elemental iodine was added to the drinking water for 24 hr before mice were used for radioactivity experiments.

Serum bacterial agglutinating antibody determination. An 18-hr tryptic soy broth culture of *M. polymorpha* was held at 56 C for 30 min. The bacteria were suspended in *p*H 7.2 phosphate-buffered isotonic saline. This preparation was used as an antigen in a slide agglutination test (7) in which 0.1 ml of mouse serum and 0.1 ml of antigen were used. The agglutinating titer of the mouse serum was expressed as the reciprocal of the last dilution giving detectable agglutination.

RESULTS

A wasting syndrome had not appeared in the mice at 1 month of age. Rate of weight gain and carcass weight of the thymectomized animals were the same as those of control animals. No diarrhea, edema, or deaths occurred in the thymectomized group. There was no significant difference in mean liver or spleen weight at the time the experiments were performed. Total lymphocyte count was, however, significantly depressed in the thymectomized mice; the mean total lymphocyte count of the control mice was $2{,}830/mm^3$, whereas that of the thymectomized group was $1{,}410/mm^3$ ($P < 0.001$).

When examined 2 hr after intravenous injection, both the liver and the spleen of the thymectomized mice contained significantly fewer viable organisms than were found in these organs from control mice (Table 1). Table 1 also shows that the reduction in the numbers of viable organisms in the liver and spleen of thymectomized animals persisted for at least 4 hr after injection. There were no significant differences in the numbers of viable organisms persisting in the blood of the thymectomized and control animals; therefore, these data suggest that there was increased killing of *M. polymorpha* in the liver and spleen of the thymectomized animals.

However, the bactericidal capacity of a given organ is also determined in part by the extent of physical deposition of bacteria from the blood to the organ. The physical trapping of nonviable organisms was studied by use of radioiodinated heat-killed *M. polymorpha* cells to evaluate the possibility that the few surviving bacteria in the organs from thymectomized animals were simply a reflection of decreased physical deposition of bacteria in the liver and spleen of thymectomized animals. As shown in Table 2, the appearance of radioiodinated bacteria was nearly the same in the liver and spleen of both groups of mice, since there were no significant differences in the ratios of radioactivity per gram of organ to radioactivity per gram of blood. The data in Table 2 also indicate that the

Table 1. *Viable-colony counts of M. polymorpha per gram of organ 2 and 4 hr after intravenous injection of 10^6 organisms*

Time (hr)	Organ	Experimental group		P
		Sham-thymectomized	Thymectomized	
2	Liver	7,800 ± 2,110	4,600 ± 680	<.05
	Spleen	34,800 ± 5,450	16,700 ± 2,370	<.01
4	Liver	1,700 ± 402	800 ± 206	<.05
	Spleen	7,200 ± 1,400	3,800 ± 860	<.02

Table 2. *Ratio of counts per minute per gram of organ to counts per minute per gram of blood 2 and 4 hr after intravenous injection of radioiodinated M. polymorpha*

Time (hr)	Organ	Experimental group		P
		Sham-thymectomized	Thymectomized	
2	Liver	3.24 ± .24	2.70 ± .20	>.05
	Spleen	2.70 ± .22	2.02 ± .36	>.10
4	Liver	1.78 ± .18	1.56 ± .14	>.3
	Spleen	1.14 ± .18	1.32 ± .12	>.4

liver and spleen have approximately equal activity in removing *M. polymorpha* cells from the blood.

DISCUSSION

Smaller numbers of viable *M. polymorpha* cells persisted in the liver and spleen of thymectomized mice compared with controls for at least 4 hr after intravenous injection of 10^6 bacteria. This difference is not due to reduced physical trapping of the bacteria by the liver and spleen from thymectomized mice compared with controls, as was shown by studies with radioiodinated *M. polymorpha* cells. These findings suggest that there is increased killing of those bacteria which are cleared from the blood into the liver and spleen of the neonatally thymectomized mice. Both groups of mice were devoid of serum bacterial agglutinating antibody so that there was no effect of circulating antibody on the uptake and killing of bacteria by the liver and spleen of thymectomized animals. The data in Table 2 also indicate that the liver and spleen have approximately equal activity in removing *M. polymorpha* from the blood.

Neonatal thymectomy has been found not to affect the selective splenic uptake of intravenously injected *Brucella abortus* (2). In other studies, reticuloendothelial functional activity, as measured by the rate of disappearance of intravenously injected colloidal ^{198}Au, was the same in control and neonatally thymectomized mice, even though intravenously injected *Candida tropicalis* grew more rapidly in the spleen, liver, and kidneys of the thymectomized mice compared with control mice (11). On the other hand, the rate of disappearance of intravenously injected colloidal carbon from the blood has been shown to be significantly greater in neonatally thymectomized mice compared with control mice (5). The results of this study and those cited above indicate that the effect of neonatal thymectomy on host response to infection varies with the host species, the nature of the infecting organism, and the interval between thymectomy and exposure to the micoorganism.

Since a chronic post-thymectomy wasting syndrome was not present in those mice used in this study, chronic reticuloendothelial stimulation by repeated detected infection cannot be invoked as an explanation for the observed increased killing of *M. polymorpha* by the liver and spleen of neonatally thymectomized mice. One reasonable explanation is that *inapparent* infection may have been responsible for producing the hypertrophied bactericidal activity of these organs. If so, such inapparent infection accomplishes this phenomenon through mechanisms other than those involved in bacterial trapping in the liver and spleen.

ACKNOWLEDGMENTS

This research was supported by a grant from the Medical Research Foundation of Texas, Inc. I thank William Jackson for technical assistance.

LITERATURE CITED

1. Benveniste, J., and J. C. Salamon. 1968. Phagocytic activity after thymectomy in axenic mice. Proc. Soc. Exp. Biol. Med. **128**:1010–1012.
2. Duquesnoy, R. J., F. S. Juenet, H. J. Meuwissen, and R. A. Good. 1969. Fate of *Brucella abortus* in neonatally thymectomized rats. Int. Arch. Allergy Appl. Immunol. **35**:514–515.
3. Kurokowa, M., M. Hatano, N. Kashiwagi, T. Saito, S. Ishida, and R. Homma. 1967. A new method for the turbidimetric measurement of bacterial density. J. Bacteriol. **83**:14–19.
4. McIntire, K. R., S. Sell, and J. F. A. P. Miller. 1964. Pathogenesis of the post thymectomy wasting syndrome. Nature (London) **204**:151–155.
5. Miller, J. F. A. P., and J. G. Howard. 1964. Some similarities between the neonatal thymectomy syndrome and graft versus host disease. J. Reticuloendothel. Soc. **1**:369–392.
6. Miller, J. F. A. P., and D. Osaba. 1967. Current concepts of immunological function of the thymus. Physiol. Rev. **47**:437–520.
7. Nelson, J. D., and S. Shelton. 1965. Cultural, biochemical, and immunological properties of *Mima, Herellea,* and *Flavobacterium* species. Appl. Microbiol. **13**:801–807.
8. Schooley, J. C., L. S. Kelly, E. L. Dobson, C. R. Finney, H. W. Havens, and L. N. Cantor. 1965. Reticuloendothelial activity in neonatally thymectomized mice and irradiated mice thymectomized in adult life. J. Reticuloendothel. Soc. **2**:396–405.
9. Sjodin, K., A. P. Dolmasso, J. M. Smith, and C. Martinez. 1963. Thymectomy in newborn and adult mice. Transplanation **1**:521–525.
10. Williams, C. A., and M. W. Chase, 1967. Methods in immunology and immunochemistry, vol. 1, p. 391. Academic Press, Inc., New York.
11. Wilson, R., K. Sjodin, and M. Bealmer. 1964. Absence of wasting in thymectomized germ free (axenic) mice. Proc. Soc. Exp. Biol. Med. **117**:237–239.

AUTHOR INDEX

SUBJECT INDEX